THE OPEN UNIVERSITY GEOLOGI____ S____

366

25/4/17

# Magmatic Processes and Plate Tectonics

A VOLUME IN COMMEMORATION OF
THE WORK OF IAN GASS

GEOLOGICAL SOCIETY SPECIAL PUBLICATION NO 76

# Magmatic Processes and Plate Tectonics

EDITED BY

**H. M. PRICHARD**

University of Wales College of Cardiff
(previously at The Open University, Milton Keynes)

**T. ALABASTER**

Sunderland University

**N. B. W. HARRIS**

The Open University, Milton Keynes

**C. R. NEARY**

Natural Environment Research Council, Swindon

1993

Published by

The Geological Society

London

# Geological Society Special Publications
## *Series Editor* A. J. FLEET

## THE GEOLOGICAL SOCIETY

The Society was founded in 1807 as The Geological Society of London and is the oldest geological society in the world. It received its Royal Charter in 1825 for the purpose of 'investigating the mineral structure of the Earth'. The Society is Britain's national society for geology with a membership of 7500 (1992). It has countrywide coverage and approximately 1000 members reside overseas. The Society is responsible for all aspects of the geological sciences including professional matters. The Society has its own publishing house which produces the Society's international journals, books and maps, and which acts as the European distributor for publications of the American Association of Petroleum Geologists and the Geological Society of America.

Fellowship is open to those holding a recognized honours degree in geology or cognate subject and who have at least two years relevant postgraduate experience, or who have not less than six years relevant experience in geology or a cognate subject. A Fellow who has not less than five years relevant postgraduate experience in the practice of geology may apply for validation and, subject to approval, may be able to use the designatory letters C. Geol (Chartered Geologist).

Further information about the Society is available from the Membership Manager, The Geological Society, Burlington House, Piccadilly, London W1V 0JU, UK.

Published by The Geological Society from:
The Geological Society Publishing House
Unit 7
Brassmill Enterprise Centre
Brassmill Lane
Bath BA1 3JN
UK
(*Orders:* Tel. 0225 445046
Fax 0225 442836)

First published 1993

**Distributors**
USA
  AAPG Bookstore
  PO Box 979
  Tulsa
  Oklahoma 74101-0979
  USA
  (*Orders:* Tel. (918)584-2555
      Fax (918)584-0469)

Australia
  Australian Mineral Foundation
  63 Conyngham St
  Glenside
  South Australia 5065
  Australia
  (*Orders:* Tel. (08)379-0444
      Fax (08)379-4634)

India
  Affiliated East–West Press PVT Ltd
  G-1/16 Ansari Road
  New Delhi 110 002
  India
  (*Orders:* Tel. (11)327-9113
      Fax (11)326-0538)

Japan
  Kanda Book Trading Co.
  Tanikawa Building
  3-2 Kanda Surugadai
  Chiyoda-Ku
  Tokyo 101
  Japan
  (*Orders:* Tel. (03)3255-3497
      Fax (03)3255-3495)

**British Library Cataloguing in Publication Data**
A catalogue record for this book is available from the British Library
ISBN 0-903317-94-X

Typeset by Bath Typesetting Ltd
Bath, England

Printed in Great Britain by
Alden Press, Oxford

# Contents

# Preface

If this volume seems to have appeared swiftly it is because it started out as a Gass-schrift to commemorate, at the retirement of Ian Gass, his impact on the academic and geological world. The idea of compiling this publication was originally proposed by Tony and Sybil Richardson, two Open University students belonging to the OUGS, and reflecting the enormous respect for Ian in this group. Ian himself suggested the first list of authors to be approached and in many cases identified a research paper which he knew was waiting to be completed. Contributors here are his students, and in turn their students, as well as a wider circle of Ian's co-workers. Their admiration for Ian as a scientist and friend has made this volume as easy to complete as it could have been in the circumstances. In the tribute to Ian Gass we thought it appropriate to use much of a speech given at Ian's funeral by his friend Geoff Brown which emphasized Ian's life at the Open University. Had it not been for his own untimely death in January this year, Geoff might well have been writing the tribute himself. While still a retirement volume, Ian suggested that Professor Perce Allen should be asked to contribute to the preface and we are grateful for that insight into Ian's international commitments and administrative techniques. Lastly, it is noteworthy that both Geoff and Perce used the same phrases about Ian such as 'northern grit' and 'he called a spade a spade'.

### Tribute to Ian Gass

Ian's influence and forthright encouragement pervaded everything he touched: as a family man; as a first-class geologist, teacher, researcher and mentor; as a founder member of the Open University and as a respected member of the national and international geological community. Ian's northern grit and determination made him one of geology's memorable characters.

Born in Gateshead in March 1926, his early education was in Newcastle, Huddersfield and Oxford. His interest in geology was prompted by meeting a geologist in the Far East when he was on active duty in the armed forces. After the war, he went to the University of Leeds where, in time, he acquired no less than four degrees. An 8-year spell as a survey geologist, first in the Sudan and then in Cyprus, enabled him to establish links and research interests which he retained throughout his life. Indeed, he was

deeply involved in completing a geological memoir for southern Cyprus when he died. In 1960, he returned to England to become a lecturer at Leicester University and then a senior lecturer at Leeds University. In the UK, most will remember Ian Gass for 21 years of unswerving energy, enthusiasm and commitment to the Open University. Internationally, Ian Gass will be remembered for his contribution to the ophiolite story, and in particular to the geological understanding of the Cyprus and Oman ophiolites.

Ian was appointed in April 1969 as the Foundation Professor of Earth Sciences at the Open University. He led from the front in all academic pursuits. He did not suffer fools gladly; he called a spade a spade, especially when dealing with irritating administrative procedures. He never used his position to intimidate staff below him in the pecking order but did not hesitate to sort out what he saw as the misguided views of his peers. This was quite a different matter; they were big enough to look after themselves. For example, in the early days, when the new Earth Sciences department seemed never to be destined to have a permanent building, but to remain in temporary accommodation, Ian drafted a letter proposing that all Earth Sciences staff at the Open University move to the University of British Columbia, which had just advertised for staff to start a new department. He showed this to the Vice Chancellor and asked him if he could see any reason why it should not be sent. A few days later the Earth Sciences department was allocated a building.

By 1974, Ian had played a major role in developing both the first science foundation course and two popular second level courses for the Open University. He ensured that the Earth Sciences department was an agenda setter in curriculum development in higher education. Undoubtedly, the early success of Earth Sciences distance teaching owed much to the exciting 'plate tectonic' revolution of the late 1960s and this was soon to be translated by Ian and his colleagues into one of the most widely acclaimed text books in Earth Sciences: *Understanding the Earth*. Overnight this became the most widely used introductory Earth Sciences text, setting a new standard for a whole generation of geology students. One of his most recent accomplishments was to write the preface to the second edition published last year. Following his work on the foundation course he went on to lead teams that produced the first Open University courses in physical resources and oceanography, courses that broke away from the normal subject divisions of geology degrees. Ian's visionary approach has ensured that this highly practical subject continues to be accessible to thousands of home-based students. In all, Ian chaired 5 course teams, wrote innumerable teaching texts, and was the founding president of the ever-expanding student's geological society, the OUGS.

Perhaps Ian's most enduring legacy to the Open University is the policy he pursued in spite of his heavy duties during the university's formative years in establishing Earth Sciences as one of the leading research departments in the country. In less than 10 years he had secured a sound relationship with external funding agencies. He was quick to see, and take advantage of, new sources of funds and to integrate basic research with research that has application, provided the aim was greater understanding. Ian's own research in volcanology, ophiolites and Pan African crustal evolution involved 7 major projects with national and international collaboration. He supervised no less than 31 graduate students, authored and co-authored four books and about 100 research papers. Above all, his experience and wisdom have acted as a source of strength and encouragement to innumerable younger scientists.

Ian Gass was an ideas person who thought on a broad geological scale. His major contribution to plate tectonics was to suggest that the Troodos complex, in Cyprus, represents a section of oceanic crust and that its sheeted dyke complex uniquely indicates an oceanic spreading environment. He realized that the Troodos massif, forming what is now considered an ophiolite complex, was an oceanic part of the North African Plate. He applied his experience in Cyprus to many other ophiolite complexes and recently was influential in the International Drilling Project in Cyprus which sampled sections of the ophiolite stratigraphy and he was the head of the team which produced the first systematic geological maps of the Oman ophiolite. Keenly interested in magma genesis he suggested a relationship between stop-start plate motion and the eruption of flood basalts (with Professor Jim Briden) and linked geochemistry of oceanic volcanic islands to their distance from the present ridge axis (with Professor Alexander McBirney). Also, in the Middle East, he interpreted the petrology and geochemistry of the Quaternary Basalts in Western Saudi Arabia in terms of a magma-genetic model, proposed that the basic–ultrabasic bodies in the Saudi Arabian Shield are backarc ophiolites and was one of the first geologists to consider the geochemistry and magma genesis of the granitic rocks of the Northern Sudan using new analytical techniques.

Throughout his career Ian received many external accolades, measures of the esteem in which he was held by the academic community. For example, in the mid-1980s he was elected President of IAVCEI, the International Association for Volcanology and Chemistry of the Earth's Interior. He was awarded the Geological Society of London's Prestwich medal in 1979 and its Murchison medal in 1988. He was particularly proud of being asked in 1980 to act as President of Section C, Geology, for the British Association for the Advancement of Science. Most significantly, for his outstanding services and innovative research in the Earth Sciences, in 1983, he was elected to a Fellowship of the Royal Society, the first FRS for a member of staff while working at the Open University. Subsequently he was an influential member of the Society's Council and a Vice-President of the Royal Society. Within the Open University, since taking a personal chair, he was a respected member of several major committees, including the Council.

Always sceptical about committees, Ian never shirked serving when he felt the cause was justified. Around the table (and there were many of these) his interventions were to the point, impeccably timed, and delivered with a characteristic gruffness or dry sense of humour but never histrionics. He was a master of the pithy and earthy phrase, and *sotto voce* fragments such as '...through his hat'. This did wonders in the rarefied atmospheres of some councils and academies. As a committee chairman Ian would guide, persuade, coerce or cajole members to seemingly unachievable consensuses that left few grumbling and none late for their trains. He spared no effort in compiling committee reports and collaborated with bureaucrats on an equal man-to-man basis. One of the latter, returning from an overseas conference, lost the agreed draft on the train. Ian's response was merely to ask if he had 'gone off his trolly'. No heat, no repercussions, but a superb administrator was an even better one thereafter. Ian's insistence on doing what he had agreed to do was exemplified during the UGC and Royal Society–NERC Earth Science reviews. With selfless determination he spent a whole summer writing and rewriting one report during time which he had hoped to devote to his beloved ophiolites. Less known, perhaps, was Ian's pervasive influence in geopolitics outside the Open University or, as he put it, 'trying to get global geology done'. To this end he could, when tactics demanded, be ruthless with any 'established' geoscientist or administrator of whatever rank. Never kowtowing to received opinion he saw was wrong, he always probed deeply, especially into the administration of science. He had a healthy suspicion of administrators who had 'left the bench or field' and strove for action by people who he felt knew better what they were doing (where poss-, ible, active geoscientists). Hierarchies had no meaning for him. He pursued the things he believed in with zeal and energy. Many of his geopolitical activities have, indeed, proved globally important for the Earth Sciences but few are widely known. He successfully participated in gaining entry for the Geological Survey of Cyprus into the ISC and was involved in setting up a University of Cyprus.

With characteristic stubborness he came through a bypass operation 10 years ago, and over the last 5 years refused to allow the effects of a stroke to prevent him from accepting lecturing invitations that he felt were a part of his role or in which he had an interest. His skill and determination were especially evident at Vancouver in 1987 when he conducted the formal proceedings of IAVCEI while still recovering from his first stroke. We remember him at the retirement party which he enjoyed so much, and his enormous pleasure in receiving an Emeritus Professorship last year in Harrogate as the guest of honour at the Open University degree ceremony. He was particularly fond of a story he told as a reply to the Emeritus presentation: 'After I had accepted the offer of employment to be the Open University's first Professor of Earth Sciences in April 1969, I met one of my Leeds University academic colleagues on the road outside that University. With typical Yorkshire bluntness he said "Tha daft bugger" and referring to the Open University continued "twill be nowt but a flash int pan". All I can say is, some flash, some pan'. Many of those still associated with the Earth Sciences department at the Open University originally came to Milton Keynes wondering what sort of a place it was, but having met this man of charisma and presence, just wanted to work there. Ian created a department in which the professor, academics, technical staff, secretaries and students were all on first-name terms, and so all felt part of a team.

Ian was a generous man, always the first to buy a round of drinks, or to show concern for anyone in difficulties and always eager to offer professional advice and guidance. However busy he was, his door was always open. In personal relations, Ian had his *bêtes noires*, having no time for divided loyalties, subfuscation or double-dealing. Improper behaviour by top scientists who abused their position (e.g. by ignoring agreed committee rules) was anathema to him. Sometimes his habit of calling a spade a spade made things more difficult but he never departed from plain honesty and common sense. Ian was 'his own man' always, and his integrity was absolute.

Ian Gass lives on through the work of his students and through the lives of all of us who knew him. The world is a poorer place without him, but is so much richer for his influence and vitality.

# Mantle and magmatic processes

# Basaltic-volcano systems

GEORGE P. L. WALKER

*Hawaii Center for Volcanology, Department of Geology and Geophysics,*
*School of Ocean and Earth Science and Technology, University of Hawaii,*
*Honolulu, HI 96822, USA*

**Abstract:** This review and personal account of basaltic volcanism concentrates on the geological aspects and physical controls, unlike most others which concentrate on geochemistry. It serves as an update to reviews by Wentworth & Macdonald 20 to 40 years ago. The concept of volcanic systems is developed, a system including the plumbing, intrusions, and other accoutrements of volcanism, as well as the volcanic edifice. Five types of systems are described, namely lava-shield volcanoes, stratovolcanoes, flood-basalt fields, monogenetic-volcano fields, and central volcanoes (having silicic volcanics as well as basaltic). It is postulated that the system-type depends on (a) the magma-input rate and (b) the frequency with which magma-batches enter the system (or modulation frequency). These controls determine whether a hot pathway is maintained from the source to the high-level magma chamber, and hence if eruptions are concentrated in the central-vent system. Reviews are given on many aspects: the different kinds of rift zones that volcanoes exhibit, and their controls; the mostly small intrusions, including coherent-intrusion complexes, that occur in and under the volcanic edifices; the great sill swarms that are an alternative to flood basalts; the origin of the craters and calderas of basaltic volcanoes; high-level magma chambers, their locations, and cumulate prisms; the positive Bouguer gravity anomalies that are attributed to cumulates and intrusion complexes; the structures of basaltic lava flows; the characteristics of basaltic explosive volcanism and the consequences of participation by non-volcanic water; the products of underwater volcanism; the origin and significance of joints, formed either by contraction or expansion, in volcanic rocks; and the distribution of vesicles in basaltic rocks. A fairly extensive bibliography is included.

This is in part a review; it takes stock of changes in concepts since the publications by Wentworth & Macdonald (1953) and Macdonald (1967), which were models of clear description of basaltic volcanics, and since the publication 12 years ago of the landmark Basaltic Volcanism Study Project (1981). It also incorporates new ideas, new interpretations, and new ways of looking at the subject. The scope of basaltic volcanism is too broad to cover all aspects, and petrology and geochemistry are specifically omitted.

More than half of the world's volcanoes are basaltic or include basalt among their products; and about one third of known eruptions, involving about 20 volcanoes per year erupt basaltic magma. Basaltic volcanoes occur in all tectonic settings. Basaltic volcanism is associated with both divergent and convergent plate boundaries; it characterizes spreading ridges mostly concealed beneath the ocean; it characterizes hotspot volcanism which, in oceanic settings, is almost exclusively basaltic and, in continental settings, is commonly bimodal (basaltic plus rhyolitic); and it is widespread associated with andesitic and more silicic magmas in subduction-zone settings, particularly where oceanic lithosphere is subducted below oceanic or thin continental lithosphere, as in island arcs (e.g. the Mariana and Kurile arcs).

Basaltic magma is derived by incongruent partial melting of mantle peridotite, favoured in tectonic settings (e.g. hotspots and rifts) where mantle rock rises adiabatically to relatively shallow levels, or in subduction-zone settings where volatiles decrease the melting temperature of mantle rock.

Magma properties are basic parameters in volcanology:

- magma density relative to lithosphere density makes volcanism possible and helps determine the positions of magma chambers and intrusions;
- viscosity and yield strength determine the geometry and structures of lava flows and intrusions;
- gas content promotes eruptions and determines their explosivity; and
- gas content combined with viscosity and rheology controls the explosive violence of eruptions by determining the ease with which gases escape from magmas.

Little mention is made of these basic magma properties, because their values tend to be rather uniform amongst different basaltic volcanoes. They are, thus, the unifying features of basaltic volcanism. More attention is therefore directed at the influence of non-magmatic variables (e.g.

*From* Prichard, H. M., Alabaster, T., Harris, N. B. W. & Neary, C. R. (eds), 1993,
*Magmatic Processes and Plate Tectonics*, Geological Society Special Publication No. 76, 3–38.

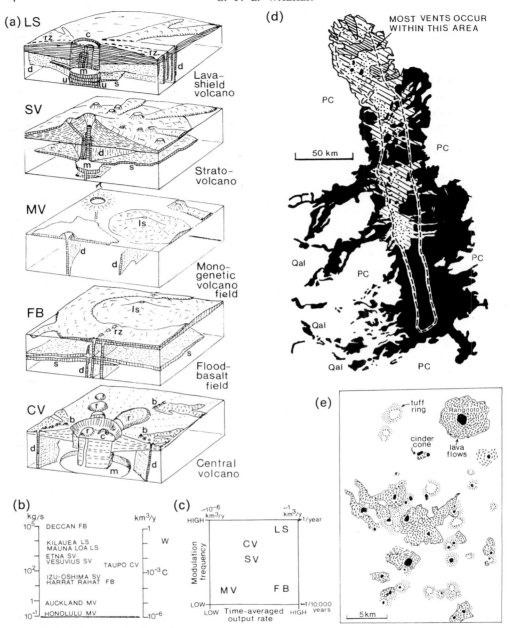

**Fig. 1.** Volcano types and volcano systems.

(**a**) The five types of basaltic-volcano systems, illustrated schematically by block diagrams. b: basaltic vents; c: caldera; d: dyke; ls: lava shield of scutulum type; m: magma chamber; rz: rift zone; r: rhyolitic lava dome; s: sill or intrusive sheet; u: cumulates. (**b**) Time-averaged output rates of selected volcanic systems. W: equivalent world energy consumption by man (excluding food); C: equivalent energy consumption (including food) by city having a population of 1 million. (**c**) Inferred fields for the five volcanic-system types on a plot of modulation frequency against time-averaged output rate. (**d**) Sketch map of a moderate-sized flood-basalt field: Harrat Rahat in Saudi Arabia (Camp & Roobol 1989). Solid black: lavas of 10–1.7 Ma old; open diagonal shading with dots: lavas of 1.7–0.6 Ma old and their cinder cones; close diagonal shading: lavas of <0.6 Ma old, including those of AD 641 and 1256; PC: Precambrian basement rocks; Qal: Quaternary sediments near Red Sea coast. (**e**) Sketch map of the Auckland monogenetic-volcano field, New Zealand, simplified by omitting the coastline (after Searle 1964).

magma-supply rate and involvement of non-magmatic water) in causing most of the diversity.

## Volcano types and volcanic systems

Five volcano types are distinguished (Fig. 1a): lava-shield volcanoes, stratovolcanoes, flood basalts, monogenetic volcanoes, and central volcanoes, this last having a significant proportion of silicic products in addition to basalt. Flood basalt vents, as well as monogenetic volcanoes, erupt once, and once only. Lava shields, stratovolcanoes and central volcanoes are polygenetic structures that erupt more than once.

There is much merit in regarding volcanoes as parts of magmatic or volcanic systems. A system may embrace the intrusions, magma chambers, conduits, magma source and accompanying geothermal fields as well as the volcano itself. The concept of volcanic systems acknowledges that the visible edifice of a volcano is only one part of a bigger entity.

A volcanic system may be compared with a system of civilization such as a city, with the extensive infra-structure of transportation, water and power supply, waste disposal and communications on which a city depends. Just as a volcanic system is sustained by a supply of energy (in the form of hot magma), so a city system is sustained by a supply of energy (in the form of fossil fuels, electric power, and food). Very roughly, a city of 1 million people requires about the same power input as a volcanic system having a magma input of 1 million $m^3$ per year.

Basaltic systems have a source in the mantle from which magma ascends, mainly because of its positive buoyancy but sometimes aided by tectonic forces, toward the surface. They have one or more conduits by which the magma ascends. Polygenetic volcano systems generally possess a high-level magma chamber, situated at a neutral buoyancy level, which stores magma and modulates its delivery to the volcano and to sub-volcanic intrusions. Deep storage reservoirs may also exist.

### Lava-shield volcanoes

These consist mainly of lava flows and have the form of low-angle shields. Slope angles tend to be small, mostly $4°-15°$ although steeper examples are known. Rift zones tend to be narrow and well-defined but grade into radial vent systems. The eruptive fissures are marked by spatter ramparts and mostly-small cinder cones.

Lava-shield volcanoes, as discussed here, are polygenetic structures commonly exceeding $1000 \, km^3$ in volume, and are not to be confused with small monogenetic lava shields categorized by Noe-Nygaard (1968) as of scutulum type (Latin: *scutulus*, diminutive of *scutus* – 'shield') which have volumes of $0.1-15 \, km^3$.

*Examples of lava-shield volcanoes* Mauna Loa in Hawaii is the largest. It has an estimated volume of $40\,000 \, km^3$, rises to 9–10 km above the surrounding ocean floor and has a keel that projects well below it. Subaerial slopes are mostly 3–6° except in the scars of old landslides. Pico in the Azores and Fogo in the Cape Verdes have steep ($>30°$) cones atop the shield. Shields in the Galapagos consist of an upwardly-convex dome with slopes as steep as 30° rising above the low-angle shield, and some of the eruptive fissures that occur on a narrow plateau around their large summit calderas are annular. Some lava shields, notably Kilauea and perhaps also Pico, consist mainly of pahoehoe. Others, such as Mauna Loa, consist of roughly equal proportions of pahoehoe and aa. Others again, for example Madeira, Tutuila (Samoa) and the Galapagos volcanoes are composed mainly of aa.

### Stratovolcanoes

These consist of a stratified succession of lava flows and interbedded pyroclastic deposits and tend to have a conical form with a slope that generally steepens upward until approximating the repose angle (about 33–36°) of loose debris. Most subduction-related basaltic volcanoes conform with this type. Commonly the cone is truncated by a caldera. Rift zones tend to be diffuse and ill-defined and grade into radial vent systems, and cinder cones tend to be conspicuous features on the volcano flanks. In many arc volcanoes basaltic andesite and more silicic types accompany basalt.

*Examples of stratovolcanoes* The Japanese island volcano of Izu-Oshima is representative of the arc-type basaltic cones. It has a basal diameter of 27 km, rises about 2200 m above the ocean floor to 758 m above sea-level, and has a volume of $415 \, km^3$ (Suga & Fujioka 1990) of which $23 \, km^3$ are above sea-level. It has subaerial slopes of up to about 20° but the cone is truncated by a caldera about 3 km in diameter. Pyroclastic rocks are more voluminous than lava flows. A broad and rather ill-defined rift zone parallels the long-axis of the island. It is marked by cinder cones and, near the coast, phreatomagmatic tuff-rings.

Izu-Oshima has displayed periodic activity through the past 10 000 years with on average about 100 years between larger eruptions (Tazawa 1984). From the careful volumetric study by Nakamura (1964) of eruptive products in the historic period, Izu-Oshima is a prime example of a 'steady-state' volcano, in which magma is fed at a uniform rate into the magma chamber and the output is modulated by the chamber characteristics.

Fuji, the highest volcano in Japan, rises to 3776 m above sea-level and about 3700 m above its base and has an estimated volume of 1400 km³. It is a fine example of a stratovolcano having the form of a typical andesite cone, but is exclusively basaltic apart from a minor volume of dacite pumice erupted explosively in the latest (1707) eruption (Tsuya 1955). The basal diameter is 25 km. The steep part of the cone above the 2000 m level has slopes exceeding 20°, but a broad apron sloping mostly <10° below the 1500 m level accounts for three-quarters of the total area.

## Monogenetic volcanoes

These consist of clusters of scattered and mostly small (>2 km³) volcanoes, each generated by a single eruption. Most commonly a volcano consists of a cinder cone associated with outflows of aa lava, but some are lava shields of scutulum-type (e.g. Rangitoto Island, Auckland, and Xitle in Mexico), and many that occur near the coast or close to lakes are phreatomagmatic tuff-rings or maars.

Some monogenetic fields (as Auckland) are exclusively basaltic whereas in others some of the volcanoes are more silicic. Thus the Kaikohe field north of Auckland includes a rhyolitic lava-dome. The Higasha-Izu field is bimodal; about 50 out of >70 volcanoes are basaltic, and the others are andesite, dacite or rhyolite (Aramaki & Hamuro 1977; Hayakawa & Koyama 1982). In some fields only a small proportion is basaltic. Xitle for example is the only basaltic volcano in the Chichinautzin field just south of Mexico City (Martin del Pozzo 1982).

*Examples of monogenetic-volcano fields* Two examples of young monogenetic fields are described from contrasted tectonic settings, namely Auckland, situated behind an active arc system on continental crust, and Honolulu in a hotspot setting on oceanic crust. Both are small-scale examples. In both fields, future eruptions may be expected, at long time intervals. The individual volcanoes may be considered as dead, but the volcanic systems are alive. ·

The Auckland field (Fig. 1e) is one of several in the northern part of New Zealand (Searle 1964; Heming & Barnet 1986). It coincides rather closely with the extent of Auckland City and consists of an apparently random scatter of about 50 basaltic vents spanning roughly the past 60 000 years. The setting is one of a drowned landscape in young eroded sedimentary rocks. Surface water or groundwater participated in many eruptions. More than half of the volcanoes are maars and the rest are cinder cones and lava flows. The latest (770 years BP) and largest eruption built Rangitoto Island, a low-angle shield of scutulum type, 6 km in diameter and 260 m high at the central cinder cone. The volume above sea-level is 1.2 km³.

The Honolulu Volcanics monogenetic field on Oahu, Hawaii, includes tuff-rings of Diamond Head and Hanauma Bay, and the Salt Lake and Aliamanu craters which contain lherzolite and garnet pyroxenite mantle-derived xenoliths. Some volcanoes are clearly distributed along fissures up to 4 km long.

The eroded vent systems including volcanic plugs of ancient polygenetic fields are known in many places, for example, in Fifeshire and the Edinburgh area in Scotland (Geikie 1897), and the Hopi Buttes in Arizona.

## Flood-basalt fields

These consist of monogenetic volcanoes erupted from widely scattered vents, but their lava flows cover wider areas than in monogenetic-volcano fields, overlap or are superposed to form parallel-stratified successions, and have much greater volumes.

Giant flood-basalt fields have volumes in the range 10⁵–10⁷ km³ (Yoder 1988; White 1992). They are distributed through geological time at average intervals of 32 Ma (Rampino & Stothers 1988), and each one formed at the time of inception of a hotspot, on arrival of an ascending mantle plume at the asthenosphere/lithosphere boundary (Richards *et al.* 1989).

*Examples of flood-basalt fields* Examples are the 16 Ma Columbia River Basalts in the northwestern USA (Tolan *et al.* 1989), and the 69–65 Ma Deccan Traps of peninsular India that may be implicated in the biological mass-extinction event at the Cretaceous/Tertiary boundary.

Moderate-sized flood-basalt fields related to the Ethiopian hotspot occur east of the Red Sea/Dead Sea rift system from Yemen to Syria. They include Harrat Rahat in Saudi Arabia (Camp & Roobol 1989; Fig. 1d). It spans the past 10 Ma and the youngest flow was erupted in AD 1256

(Camp *et al.* 1987). Future eruptions may be expected, at long time intervals. The field has a wide scatter of cinder cones marking the hundreds of vents, and the locus of activity tended to migrate northward with time. Several flows that travelled down valleys toward the Red Sea are about 100 km long. Lavas cover 20 000 km$^2$ and have an estimated total volume of 2000 km$^3$.

Other flood-basalt fields occur along the eastern part of Australia. In one, the McBride Province in Queensland (Stephenson *et al.* 1980), lava flows cover 6000 km$^2$ and came from a wide scatter of vents. The flows span 3 Ma and the youngest is the 190 ka Undara flow that is 170 km long and has a volume between 10 and 23 km$^3$. This flow is pahoehoe and has an exceptionally long system of lava tubes along its length (Atkinson *et al.* 1975; Atkinson 1991).

Many flood-basalt fields overlapping in time and space occur in Iceland. The basalts erupted from rift zones typically 10–20 km wide that can be traced 40 to > 100 km across country. Some systems have a central volcano on the rift zone and may be better characterized as central-volcano systems. The several en echelon rift zones of Reykjanes lack central volcanoes. Each rift zone is about 40 km long by 7–15 km wide and has eruptive fissures in the central part and non-eruptive fissures on the periphery.

### Central volcanoes

These are stratovolcanoes or shield volcanoes that have a significant proportion of silicic volcanic rocks in addition to basalt (usage of Johnson 1989), and generally have a bimodal composition in which rhyolite and basalt predominates and rocks intermediate in composition are scarce or absent. The silicic rocks form pumice and ashfall deposits, ignimbrites, and stubby lava flows or lava domes. Very commonly the volcanoes have one or more calderas resulting from subsidence consequent on large silicic eruptions.

*Examples of central volcanoes* Newberry volcano situated 60 km east of the Cascade Range in Oregon is a broad shield-like edifice with flanks inclined mostly under 4° capped by a steeper cone. The flanks are diversified by about 400 cinder cones and fissure vents arranged in several rift zones feeding extensive lava flows. Compositions include basalt although basaltic andesite predominates. The cone is truncated by a caldera 7 × 5 km in size, shallow because it is partially infilled by silicic flows, domes and pyroclastic deposits. Compositions include rhyolite, but rhyodacite predominates. Outflow sheets of ignimbrite occur on the flanks. Newberry has a shadow zone 12 km wide within which basaltic vents are absent but outside which they are abundant. The volcano has an estimated volume of 450 km$^3$ and erupted six times in the Holocene (Higgins 1973; Chitwood 1990).

Jebel Kariz in southern Arabia is a fine example of a central volcano the internal structure of which is revealed by deep erosion (Gass & Mallick 1968).

### Volcano morphology

The steeply conical form of many stratovolcanoes is due to several causes, notably the prevalence of low-intensity eruptions that tend to pile the erupted material close to the vent, and the magma viscosity which tends to be higher on stratovolcanoes than on shield volcanoes and increases the explosivity (Fig. 2).

The form of lava-shield volcanoes reflects the high proportion of output released on flank rift zones instead of at the summit, and the generally high discharge rate during eruptions which tends to produce lava flows that travel far. Caldera collapse and a general subsidence concentrated in the summit area also contribute to the morphology.

### Volcano collapse

Destructive processes have an important effect on volcano shape. Basaltic volcanoes can build to very large structures several kilometres high, and if they are built on sediments their foundations are weak. The dip of the layers outward from the centre and the presence of pyroclastic layers and hydrothermally altered zones produce inherent weakness in the volcanic edifice. Dyke injections that forcibly shoulder aside the rock to make space for themselves, local updoming of central volcanoes by the ascent of silicic-magma diapirs, and severe marine erosion on exposed coasts of island volcanoes all conspire to produce instability and cause major failure of parts of the volcanic edifice.

Most large basaltic volcanoes consequently suffer occasional volcano-collapse events. The cone of Stromboli, rising 3 km from the Mediterranean floor, is defaced on the NW side by the collapse scar of the Sciara del Fuoco. Tenerife is scalloped by several collapse scars; that of the Orotavo Valley has a volume exceeding 60 km$^3$. Las Canadas is possibly a landslide scar and not a caldera. The greatest volcanic landslides are those of Hawaii (Duffield *et al.* 1982; Moore *et al.* 1989). Some were catastrophic events; others not. Some involved 1000 km$^3$ of rock.

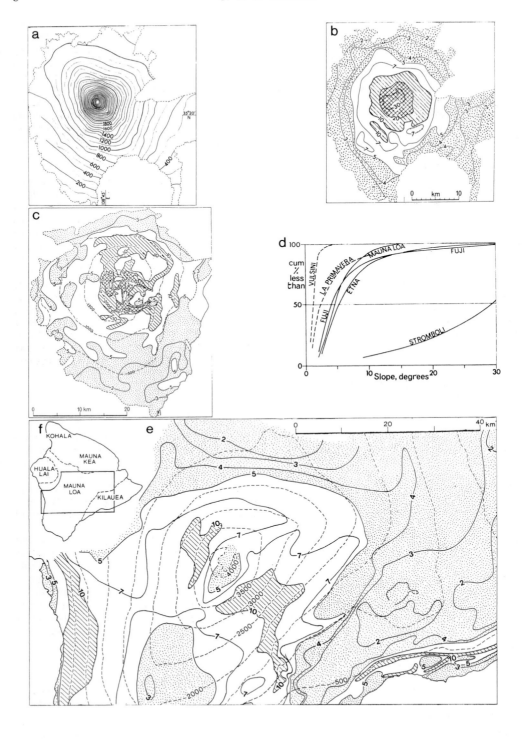

## Controls on system type

In the polygenetic volcano systems, magma batches ascend sufficiently frequently along the same conduit that the conduit walls are maintained in a hot condition and provide magma with a thermally and mechanically very favourable pathway toward the surface.

In the monogenetic and flood basalt systems magma batches ascend at such long time intervals that the pathway taken by one batch has effectively cooled by the time that the next batch is ready to ascend. In the absence of a thermally or mechanically favourable pathway, the new batch has to create a new pathway to the surface.

It is postulated here that two principal controls operate to determine the type of volcanic system that develops, namely the time-averaged magma-supply rate and the modulation frequency of the supply.

Consider the supply rate. Strictly it should include the magma that makes intrusions as well as that which erupts, but the former is generally not known and the volcanic output rate is then the best available measure of supply rate. In different volcanic systems the output rate varies over 5 orders of magnitude from $c.$ 1 kg s$^{-1}$ to $c.$ $10^5$ kg s$^{-1}$ (Fig. 1b). This rate may alternatively be expressed as an energy flux that varies from below 1 MW to nearly $10^5$ MW.

The highest output rates are achieved in the giant flood-basalt outpourings such as those of the Deccan and Columbia River Basalts. The most productive lava-shield volcanoes (as in Hawaii) at the peak of their activity, and some of the more productive flood-basalt fields in Iceland are about an order of magnitude lower. Most stratovolcanoes are one or two orders of magnitude lower still, although some such as Etna are highly productive. The lowest output rates are given by polygenetic-volcano fields.

Fedotov (1981) considered the question of the threshold magma-supply rate below which a hot pathway cannot be sustained and found it to be between 200 and 1600 kg s$^{-1}$ depending on whether the supply is continuous or intermittent, and whether the lithosphere section has a continental or oceanic geothermal gradient. This threshold agrees well with observed supply rates for monogenetic and polygenetic systems.

Consider now the modulation of the output. Strictly it occurs at a deep crustal or sub-crustal level, and for monogenetic-volcano and flood-basalt systems it is the frequency (commonly 1 per $10^3$ to $10^5$ years) with which magma batches rise to the surface. For polygenetic volcanoes little firm information exists, and the best that can be done is to take the frequency of eruptions, or of magma excursions from the shallow chamber (Fig. 1c).

The mechanism of modulation at a deep level can only be surmised. Magma that accumulates in or near the asthenosphere source-region exerts an upwardly-directed force because of its positive buoyancy. The magnitude of the force depends on the density contrast between magma and adjacent lithosphere, and the volume of magma that has segregated within a small area. When the force becomes sufficiently great the magma-batch ascends. Monogenetic volcanoes commonly have a volume of 0.1–1 km$^3$, and give an indication of the volume of magma that is required to create a pathway through the lithosphere. The availability of suitable fractures may also play an important part in aiding magma ascent.

### Storage of flood-basalt magma and underplating

A feature of flood-basalt systems is that individual erupted volumes are large so giving a moderate to high time-averaged output rate even though the eruption frequency is low. Because of the low frequency, conduits cool between eruptions and hence flood basalts erupt from a wide scatter of vents, and the individual flood-basalt lavas are monogenetic.

A problem of flood-basalt systems is how and where a large volume of magma is stored before an eruption. The volume that erupts can greatly exceed what is evidently needed to create a pathway to the surface in monogenetic fields. One possible mechanism is that magma accumulates at a deep level of neutral buoyancy (at or near the Moho?) where changes (crystal frac-

**Fig. 2.** Volcano types and volcano systems.
(**a**) Contour map of Fuji volcano. Contour interval 100 m. (**b**) Slope-angle map of Fuji volcano based on spacing of generalized contours; slope in degrees from the horizontal. (**c**) Slope-angle map of Etna on the same scale as (a). Dashed lines are contours at 500 m intervals. (**d**) Curves showing cumulative percentage of map area having less than the given slope angle, for selected volcanoes; La Primavera is a central volcano predominantly composed of silicic volcanics; Vulsini is an ignimbrite-shield volcano; Etna, Fuji and Stromboli are stratovolcanoes. (**e**) Slope-angle map of part of Mauna Loa on the same scale as (a) and (c); dashed lines are contours at 500 m intervals. (**f**) Index map of Island of Hawaii. (a)–(c) reproduced by permission of the Royal Society from Volcanological Research on Mount Etna 1975.

tionation; crustal assimilation; gas exsolution) take place that reduce the density of the magma until it becomes buoyant and rises. Alternatively the source region is laterally extensive and lateral connections are good so that, once buoyant ascent begins, magma drains laterally from a wide area into the newly created pathway.

The general absence of mantle xenoliths in flood basalts suggests that the magma resides sufficiently long at some level above the mantle for xenoliths to drop out (Clague 1987). Some continental flood basalts have assimilated crustal rocks, which would be favoured by residence in contact with the crust (Huppert & Sparks 1985). There is also evidence for underplating of the crust, which may be another consequence of deep storage.

Underplating is the formation of mafic intrusions at a deep crustal or sub-crustal level (Cox 1980; Fyfe 1992). Igneous underplating is evidenced by the presence in the lower crust of material having high seismic-wave velocities. Seismic refraction profiles point to the existence of thick underplating, for example, in the North Atlantic region under the sequence of submerged basalts recorded as seaward-dipping reflectors in the upper crust (White 1992). The basalts range in thickness up to 4 km; the intrusions are several times more voluminous.

Underplating may explain why continental crust that is uplifted by a hotspot (e.g. at 140 Ma in Brazil, near the Parana flood basalts; Cox 1989) remains uplifted long after plate motion has carried that crust far from the current hotspot position. Permanent surface uplift occurs provided that the underplating gabbroic rocks are less dense than underlying mantle.

Underplating could occur at a deep level of neutral buoyancy, or alternatively at a level where lithospheric layers having contrasted elastic or rheologic properties are juxtaposed (for example, at a deep crustal level where more rigid rock that tends to behave elastically overlies more ductile rock that tends to flow under stress).

Magnetotelluric surveys in Iceland indicate that a shallow (10 km) partial-melt zone over 100 km wide underlies and extends laterally beyond the active rift zone. This reservoir could store a large volume of magma. During the Krafla intrusive and eruptive events in 1978–1984, chronologically-matching changes took place at the Bardarbunga volcanic centre > 100 km away (Tryggvason 1989) suggesting that some form of lateral interconnection exists.

*Unmodulated long-sustained eruptions*

Under conditions of high thermal-energy supply rate, a more or less continuous magma pathway may become established between the mantle-source and the surface permitting a long-sustained and unmodulated eruption. In Hawaii such unmodulated activity gives rise to long-lived lava lakes, or generates scutulum-type pahoehoe shields exemplified by that of Mauna Ulu on Kilauea's east rift zone constructed 1969–1974 at a sustained delivery averaging about $5 \, m^3 \, s^{-1}$.

Compound pahoehoe shields of scutulum-type thought to have a similar origin are common in some flood-basalt fields such as the Deccan, and in the Snake River Plain give rise to what has been referred to as Plains-type volcanism (Greeley 1982; cf. Rutten 1964). Rangitoto Island and Xitle are other examples.

Many scutulum-type shields of relatively primitive basalt developed in Iceland in a short time period at about the end of the Ice Age when the widespread ice sheets rapidly declined. This was a period of greatly enhanced volcanic output, and could be attributed to the melting of the ice effectively reducing the lithosphere thickness by about 5–10% leading to an increase in the degree of partial melting in the upper mantle. Alternatively the redistribution of mass resulting from melting of the glaciers and rise of sea-level flexed the lithosphere and favoured creation of pathways to the surface (Sigvaldason *et al.* 1992).

*Fissure eruptions*

In older classifications of basaltic volcanoes great importance was placed on fissure eruptions as a distinctive type. It is now clear that most basaltic eruptions take place initially as a 'curtain of fire' from a fissure, whatever the volcano or system type, but, with time, eruption tends to become concentrated at one or several points. With concentration, local fissure-widening by wall-erosion may occur, enhancing concentration of discharge at that point. Effusion from a point tends to conceal the evidence that initially eruption was along a fissure.

## Changes in volcanic systems with time

The active life of most volcanic systems is between 0.1 and 10 Ma and if the magma-supply rate changes significantly during this time or if silicic magma becomes available the system may change from one type to another. These changes provide insights into significant features of the sub-surface plumbing systems of volcanoes.

Well-documented system changes occur in

Hawaii when a decline in magma-supply rate occurs as plate motion conveys a system away from the hotspot focus. Some changes are embodied in the concept that Hawaiian volcanoes pass through a characteristic sequence of life stages (Stearns 1946; details updated by Macdonald *et al.* 1983, Peterson & Moore 1987 and Walker 1990).

The peak of activity of an Hawaiian volcano is the shield-building stage, exemplified by Kilauea and Mauna Loa, when tholeiitic magma is voluminously produced. The declining 'postshield' or 'alkalic cap' stage, exemplified by Mauna Kea, marks a reduction in magma supply rate by one or two orders of magnitude. Magmas are transitional or alkalic basalt. Eruptions tend to be more explosive and build large cinder cones instead of the mostly small spatter deposits of the shield-building stage. Lavas are mostly aa.

Mauna Kea is a shield volcano capped by a stratovolcano, and the wide scatter of cinder cones suggests it may now have become a monogenetic field. The infilling of the summit caldera, the very low modulation frequency of about 1/ 10 000 years and the abundant inclusions of mafic and ultramafic cumulates indicate that the high-level magma chamber no longer exists, and the well-organized magma-distribution system that channelled magma into rift zones no longer functions.

Fractionation of alkali-cap magma to types such as mugearite and benmoreite undoubtedly takes place perhaps in a deep magma reservoir at the Moho or the base of the volcanic edifice.

Some Hawaiian volcanoes subsequently enter a rejuvenation ('post-erosional') stage in which a monogenetic-volcano field may develop, exemplified by the Honolulu Volcanics on Oahu about 1 Ma following cessation of shield-building activity on Koolau Volcano. Rejuvenation-stage lavas include highly alkalic types such as basanite, nephelinite and melilite-bearing types. Very similar rejuvenation-stage volcanism is seen for example on Lanzarote (Canary Islands) where vents and lava fields of the 1730–1736 and 1824 eruptions are scattered among the eroded stumps of an older volcano (Carracedo *et al.* 1993). Mantle xenoliths are common on Koolau and Lanzarote, indicating that no magma reservoir exists above the mantle-source.

A change of system-type from shield to central volcano is shown by Faial volcano in the Azores. Faial appears to be wholly made up of basalt apart from two trachytic lava domes and a covering up to about 20 m thick of trachytic pumice around the summit caldera. The rocks of Faial are up to 2 Ma old, and the latest eruption was in 1957–8. It is not known precisely when

silicic magma first appeared but it likely happened within the past 20 ka.

Volcanism in the Yellowstone hotspot trace exhibits the reverse sequence. The Yellowstone volcano has very infrequent large-volume rhyolitic eruptions (Christiansen 1984) and over the past 16 Ma the locus of rhyolitic activity migrated 700 km northeast into Yellowstone by plate motion (Pierce & Morgan 1992). Some mix-magma lava flows occur, showing that basaltic magma participated in the rhyolitic volcanism. Flood-basalt volcanism of the Snake River Plain, however, followed and lagged behind the rhyolitic activity.

## Rift zones, their orientation and intensity

Most basaltic eruptions occur from fissures, and virtually all basaltic volcano systems have eruptive fissures. Fissures are opened very easily by the hydraulic jacking action of magma, and are the 'natural' underground conveyance for low-viscosity magma (Emerman & Marrett 1990). They commonly extend for tens of kilometres and are typically concentrated into rift zones. Magma solidified in fissures forms dykes. Dykes have a high survival potential, and in deeply eroded areas may be virtually all that survives of the volcanic system.

### *Radial and fascicular fissure distribution*

Basaltic volcanoes that possess a magma chamber experience magma excursions which generate dykes or other intrusions and sometimes lead to volcanic eruption. A magma excursion occurs when the wall or roof of a magma chamber ruptures and some magma escapes. Rupture results when, because of magma input or vesiculation, a chamber swells. Magma excursions are critically important in volcano growth, contribute strongly to determining volcano morphology, and power active geothermal systems.

For a volcano that is not buttressed by a neighbouring volcano and occurs in a setting where there is no regional extensional deviatoric stress, the normal consequence of magma excursions is to generate radial fissures.

Radial fissures result from the pressure exercised by a swelling body of magma on its walls, in which extensional deviatoric stresses are set up tangential to the magma-chamber walls. Failure of wall rocks therefore occurs on fractures trending normal to the walls. In the ideal radial swarm the fissures would be straight, and their traces would radiate from a common point. The dyke intensity would be uniform in all directions at any given distance outward, but because of dyke divergence and restricted travel distance of narrow dykes the intensity would decrease radially outward.

Probably few basaltic volcanoes conform with this ideal; fissures tend to be more concentrated in some sectors than in others, and some fissures curve when traced outward to become approximately parallel. 'Fascicular' (Latin *fascia* – bundle or sheaf, as of sticks or wheat) is proposed for the case where the fissures are concentrated in two sectors 180° apart and tend toward parallelism when followed outward.

The classic example of a radial dyke swarm is that of eroded Spanish Peaks volcano (Colorado; Ode 1957), and Tristan da Cunha is an example of an active volcano having a radial swarm (Chevallier & Verwoerd 1987). Examples of fascicular fissure swarms occur in the Galapagos (Chadwick & Howard 1991), and subduction-related volcanoes that show them include Fuji (Nakamura 1977) Hakone (Kuno 1964), and Shitara (Takada 1988).

### Regional stress control

Most polygenetic volcanoes and flood-basalt fields possess rift zones, these being narrow extensional zones in which ground cracks, faults and eruptive fissures are concentrated. Rift zones are underlain by dyke swarms. They vary greatly in their orientation and the spacing of fissures in them.

The orientations of some rift zones are determined by a regional stress field. A good example is Iceland where the rifts are parallel with the spreading axis of the Mid-Atlantic Ridge.

In subduction-related volcanoes that have rift zones, the rifts are orientated normal to the subduction zone and parallel with the plate-convergence direction. Nakamura (1977) and Nakamura et al. (1977) regarded them as sensitive markers of regional stress trajectories. Lo Giudice et al. (1982) showed that two of Etna's several rift zones conform in orientation with conjugate shear fractures inclined at about 35° on either side of the plate-convergence direction.

The rift zones in that part of the Azores southwest of the Mid-Atlantic spreading ridge are arranged, unlike in Iceland, approximately normal to the spreading axis, and are parallel with horsts and grabens in a major zone of faulting (the East Azores fracture zone) that extends toward the Straits of Gibraltar. This extensional zone, described as a leaky transform fault by Krause & Watkins (1970), is seismically very active and volcanic eruptions tend to be temporally closely related to major earthquakes.

The latest eruption, that of 1957 at Capelinhos off the western tip of Faial, was accompanied by earthquakes and up to 1 m of subsidence along a graben crossing the island (Machado et al. 1962).

On Sao Miguel, basaltic eruptive fissures of Holocene age trending northwest as elsewhere in the Azores have an en echelon distribution and occur in a broad and nearly west-trending band of country parallel with the length of the island. These fissures were postulated by Booth et al. (1978) to be shear fractures developed by right-lateral transcurrent movement on an underlying west-trending fault.

### Gravitational stress control

In Hawaii, eruptive fissures and dykes are tightly concentrated in narrow rift zones some of which are traceable for 50 km on land and up to 70 km more under water. Fiske & Jackson (1973) postulated that they are shallow features, found little evidence for a regional stress or structural control, and attributed these rift zones to gravitational stresses acting on high volcanoes and causing rifting along the elongation-axis of the edifice.

On Etna the edifice effect explains well the orientation of some fissures close to, but outside and parallel with, the edge of the deep Valle del Bove landslide scar (Guest et al. 1984; McGuire & Pullen 1989). The marked increase in the rate of fissure formation in recent years possibly has dangerous implications (McGuire et al. 1990). Sao Jorge in the Azores also illustrates well the edifice effect. This island is a narrow horst and the precipitous bounding fault scarp along the north is up to 800 m high. Eruptions tend to occur from fissures localized near the crest of the horst and trending parallel with its length.

Note that the extensional stress regime resulting from the edifice effect is likely to be pronounced only at shallow, superficial levels in volcanoes; other controls such as operation of a regional stress field are likely to operate at deeper levels.

### Neutral buoyancy control

Impressed by the great number and non-Gaussian intensity distribution of sub-parallel dykes in the Koolau dyke complex, Oahu, Walker (1986, 1992a) proposed a mechanism by which concentrations of weakly- or non-vesicular dykes constitute a zone of high density situated in a zone of lower-density vesicular lava flows. Positions of neutral buoyancy exist on both sides and over the top of the high-density zone, and intrusions tend to be channelled into these positions so accentuating the density zonation. Some earlier dykes moreover have planes of weakness at or parallel with their margins that are commonly exploited by later dykes, so providing an additional reason for localization in a narrow zone.

'Coherent-intrusion complex' was proposed for high-intensity complexes of small intrusions (Walker, 1992a), and two kinds were recognized – namely dyke complexes and intrusive-sheet complexes. Roughly half of documented major basaltic volcanoes possess the latter. Formation of a dyke complex requires that a volcano be capable of widening sufficiently to accommodate the dykes; otherwise an intrusive-sheet (cone-sheet) complex that is accommodated by thickening of the volcano develops instead. Recent studies (Gautneb & Gudmundsson 1992; Walker, this volume) show that cone-sheets are closely similar to dykes in width and in having their dilation vector normal to the intrusion-plane.

### Other controls

Walker (1990) observed that along the Hawaiian Islands, rift zones tend to be aligned alternately parallel with the direction of motion of the Pacific Plate over the Hawaiian hotspot, and parallel with major transform faults such as those of the Molokai fracture zone. The faults were planes of weakness exploited by the hotspot magma. Rift zones in Samoa are aligned WNW parallel with the plate-motion direction except on Tutuila where they are aligned ENE, roughly parallel with the North Fiji transform fault. It is thought that an extension on this fault was activated when, by plate motion, the hotspot focus came into alignment with it (Walker & Eyre, in prep.).

### Rift propagation rate

In the 1984 eruption of Mauna Loa, rifting began near the summit and fissures quickly propagated some 15 km down the northeast rift zone at an average of 1.2 km h$^{-1}$ (Lockwood et al. 1987). The 1959–60 summit eruption of Kilauea was followed 24 days later by activity 47 km downrift (Macdonald 1962). In its latest eruption (in 1983) a flank fissure on the strato-volcano of Miyakejima extended 4.5 km laterally at 1.5–2.4 km h$^{-1}$ (Aramaki et al. 1986).

From time to time earthquake swarms occur in rift zones in which foci and epicentres migrate progressively down-rift and are thought to mark the lateral propagation of bladed dykes. Epicentres in one such swarm in Iceland in July 1978, extended to 27 km from Krafla volcano migrating on average at 1.6 km h$^{-1}$ (Einarsson & Brandsdottir 1980). In another in Kilauea's southwest rift zone in August 1981 (one of many in the 1980s), foci migrated 12 km downrift at 2.6 km h$^{-1}$ (Klein et al. 1987). No eruption occurred in either.

Such seismic swarms are clear, but indirect, evidence for lateral magma excursions. The basaltic eruption of 1874–75 in Sveinagja, Iceland some 50–70 km north of Askja and the simultaneous caldera subsidence in Askja (Sigurdsson & Sparks 1978) is more tangible evidence that magma migrated laterally.

### Small intrusions

Volcanic systems characteristically include small intrusions, often in such large numbers as to rival the volume of the volcano (Fig. 3). Intrusions having a narrow sheet-like form predominate and propagation of a sheet-like intrusion by hydraulic fracturing at the advancing tip occurs very readily.

Small intrusions are commonly called hypabyssal, implying a shallow level of emplacement, or subvolcanic, implying that they form beneath where volcanic activity occurs. They are also commonly called minor intrusions, bearing in mind that although individually small, collectively they may be major components of a volcanic system.

The nomenclature of sheet-like intrusions is slightly confused, because it is based on two different criteria, namely dip and whether the intrusions are concordant or discordant to the countryrock bedding. Discordant intrusions that are vertical, or nearly so, are called dykes. Concordant intrusions that are horizontal, or nearly so, are called sills. Most sills, however, locally transgress the countryrock layers at a small angle, typically in step-like fashion. Intrusions that are inclined at a moderate angle either to the horizontal or to the countryrock layers may be called intrusive sheets or inclined sheets.

Individual intrusions are often highly irregular in form. This results from their strong propensity to follow pre-existing planes of weakness such as joints, faults and bedding planes. Sidesteps are common where, having followed one joint or plane of weakness, an intrusion steps sideways to follow another.

An important aspect of small intrusions is the attitude of their dilation vector, namely the direction in which the rocks on either side moved apart to accommodate the intrusion. Generally the vector is normal to the intrusion plane or, if

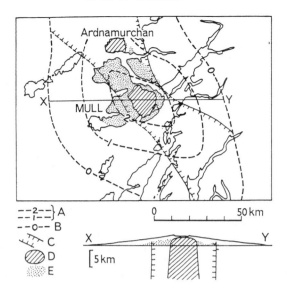

### Estimation of original volumes of lavas and intrusions in the Mull Volcano system

(a) Above base of volcano
    Total volume inside B
        9000 km² × 0.9 km (average thickness)             = 8100 km³
    Central intrusive complex (D)
        300 km² × 2 km × 50% of this volume            =   300 km³ ⎫ intrusions
    Dyke swarm outside limits of D                             ⎬ 500 km³
        4000 km² × 1 km × 5% of this volume            =   200 km³ ⎭
    Total lavas = 8100 − 500                        = 7600 km³
(b) Extra, to an arbitrary depth of 10 km below base of volcano:
    Intrusives (D), mainly cumulate prism
    inferred from gravity anomaly                     = 3500 km³
    Dyke swarm (C) outside D
        4000 km² × 10 km × 5% of this volume       = 2000 km³
    Therefore total extra intrusions               = 5500 km³
(c) Total (a) plus (b):
    Lavas       7600 km³ (56% of total)
    Intrusions  6000 km³ (44% of total)
    Total       13600 km³

**Fig. 3.** Map and section of the Tertiary central-volcano system of Mull, Scotland, and a volume estimate to illustrate the importance of intrusions in such a system. A: 1 and 2 km isopachs for the volcano; reconstruction based on amygdale-mineral zonation; B: inferred original extent of the Mull Volcano – extrapolated line of zero thickness; C: approximate limits of intense dyke swarm; D: central intrusive complexes; E: present extent of lavas of the Mull Volcano.

the intrusion is irregular, to the plane that approximates the average strike and dip of the intrusion (Walker 1987). The dilation vector plunges at a small angle in dykes and at a steep angle in sills.

Some intrusive sheets occur in swarms, the members of which dip toward a common focus, and have been widely termed cone-sheets. A particular mode of origin, namely injection along inverted-conical shear fractures propagated above a magma chamber by upwardly directed magma pressure, tends to be implicit in the definition and the original term 'centrally-inclined sheets' which lacks a genetic connotation is to be preferred.

Most small intrusions are inferred to record magma excursions from a magma chamber that was sufficiently swollen (by incursions of fresh magma or gas expansion) to suffer chamber-wall rupture. Some excursions lead to volcanic eruptions and the intrusion then marks the pathway to the surface. On Kilauea, however, fewer than half of magma excursions lead to eruption and many other volcanoes experience seismic swarms, with foci ascending with time toward the surface (suggestive of magma ascent in dykes) but without eruption; examples of such 'abortive eruptions' include the Long Valley seismic event of 1983 (Savage & Cockerman 1984).

Bruce & Huppert (1990) showed that narrow dykes can travel only a short distance before they are blocked by rapid cooling. The number and total width of dykes injected in a given time-interval therefore decreases strongly with distance outward from a volcanic centre (Walker 1988). Dykes injected within a given time-interval therefore constitute a wedge tapering down-rift. Their injection sets up localized stresses in the central region that are relieved by the formation of intrusions approximately orthogonal to the general trend. Asymmetric addition of dykes to one side of a rift zone moreover can cause originally collinear rift zones to become non-collinear.

## Propagation of bladed dykes

The conditions for lateral propagation of bladed dykes were comprehensively reviewed by Rubin & Pollard (1987). Lister & Kerr (1990) studied the fluid-mechanical aspects including effects of injection along the level of neutral buoyancy, and concluded that the resistance to dyke propagation by fracturing of crustal rocks is negligible in relation to that due to viscous pressure drop.

Lateral dyke-injection from a high-level magma chamber is thought to be important near volcanic centres, but further away dykes may commonly be injected vertically upward from a deep reservoir (Gautneb & Gudmundsson, 1992).

## Magma-flow direction

In eroded volcanoes, the magma-flow direction in dykes can be inferred from the orientation of various structural features: shallow grooves on the dyke walls (Walker 1987), the elongation direction of dyke segments and 'fingers' at the leading edge of dykes (Pollard *et al.* 1975; Baer & Reches 1987), the crystal fabric of the dyke-rock (Shelley 1985), the deformation pattern of vesicles (Coward 1980), and the direction of pipe vesicles in dyke margins. Some, such as the last-mentioned feature, permit the absolute direction (azimuth) of flow to be inferred.

A powerful technique for inferring the flow direction is based on the magnetic fabric. Magnetic susceptibility, a measure of the ease with which a rock may be magnetized when exposed to a magnetic field, has an anisotropy that is thought to be related to a preferred orientation of elongated magnetic crystals. The maximum-susceptibility direction marks the magma-flow direction. Near dyke margins the maximum-anisotropy axis is not parallel with the dyke walls but has an imbricate-like orientation from which the flow azimuth can be inferred.

Knight & Walker (1988) found a wide scatter of flow azimuths in dykes of the Koolau complex, with an average azimuth upward at about 30° from the horizontal. Staudigel *et al.* (1992) found a similar variability in the Troodos sheeted-dyke complex. Ernst & Baragar (1992) found in dykes of the continent-ranging Mackenzie swarm in the Canadian Shield, that the magma-flow direction is vertical within about 500 km of the focus and horizontal farther out. Wada (1992) found in the 1983 dyke on Miyakejima that lateral magma flow was followed by near-vertical flow.

## Re-injection intrusions

Back-draining often occurs in lava eruptions in Hawaii. Up to 2.2 million $m^3 h^{-1}$ of lava drained back into the Kilauea Iki vent during pauses in the 1959 eruption, for example (Macdonald 1962). Re-injection is easily explained because the neutral-buoyancy level for non-vesicular magma is well below the surface (about 1 km deep?) and if newly erupted vesicular lava loses bubbles its effective density rises and it may then descend to a neutral-buoyancy level. Note that this re-injection is not the same as water draining down into a volcano. The water in doing so passively percolates down into any available voids whereas the re-injected lava has the power actively to open old fissures or create new ones.

Generally re-injection generates dykes; they look like normal dykes but have glassy margins that are depleted in sulphur, lost in the 1-atmosphere conditions of surface eruption (Easton & Lockwood 1983). Anisotropy of magnetic susceptibility or other flow-direction indicators would demonstrate that downward magma-movement has occurred.

A class of small intrusion recently recognized in Hawaii is a kind of sill that transgresses downward at about 10° across the countryrock lavas in an outward direction extending as far as 10 km from the volcanic or rift zone centre. Mostly these intrusions are non-vesicular and rich in olivine, giving them a high density of around $3.1\,\mathrm{Mg\,m^{-3}}$ about $0.8\,\mathrm{Mg\,m^{-3}}$ greater than average basaltic lava. From what is known of the fracture toughness of lavas, gravity is perfectly capable of propagating such intrusions. On the island of Kauai these intrusions locally comprise a swarm having an intensity of about 10%.

## Craters, calderas and pit craters

Craters and calderas are depressions, commonly deep and precipitous, that mark the eruptive vents of volcanoes. Those at or near the volcano summit may directly overlie the magma chamber, and for those such as Stromboli (Giberti *et al.* 1992) that are persistently active a direct connection exists from the chamber to the conduit and vent. The most noteworthy are those few volcanoes that sustain a long-lived lake of molten lava in their summit crater or caldera.

The craters of basaltic stratovolcanoes are in no way different from the craters of more silicic volcanoes. They have elevated rims largely of pyroclastic deposits and can have an impressive depth exceeding 500 m. Not all basaltic craters are circular. The explosively generated Chasm of the Tarawera 1886 fissure eruption in New Zealand is a nearly straight trench 8 km long and 300 m wide by, on average, 100 m deep.

Calderas are subsidence features bigger than craters (Fig. 4) and by convention exceed about one mile in diameter. Those in subduction-related settings originated in explosive eruptions that emitted large volumes of pyroclastic material. Collapse of part of the volcano then took place into the magma chamber. Masaya caldera (Nicaragua) is related to an extensive basaltic ignimbrite (Williams 1982) and appears to have this origin. Williams & Stoiber (1983) proposed 'Masaya-type' for this the mafic analogue of 'Krakatau-type' calderas. The impressive calderas of Ambrym (Vanuatu; 12 km in diameter; Monzier *et al.* 1991) and Niuafo'ou (near Tonga; Macdonald 1948) also appear to have this origin.

Opinions differ whether caldera width in general is comparable to the magma-chamber width. In examples where cauldron subsidence of a cylinder of rock within a ring fracture occurred, the widths must be comparable; in other examples subsidence occurred in a localized funnel-like central area and the caldera then widened by scarp retreat. The scarcity of mafic ring dykes in eroded volcanoes (Chapman 1966) suggests that the second alternative may be more generally applicable to basaltic volcanoes.

Calderas of hotspot or rift-related volcanoes are generally not accompanied by a significant amount of pyroclastic deposits and appear thus to be due to subsidence with little explosive activity.

Two basaltic caldera-collapse events are known to have occurred in historic time: the $2\,\mathrm{km^3}$ Oskjuvatn caldera on Askja volcano in Iceland formed by subsidence in 1874–1875, and part of the floor of Fernandino caldera in the Galapagos subsided in 1968 to increase the caldera volume by $1$–$2\,\mathrm{km^3}$.

The Oskjuvatn event accompanied rifting in which lateral flow of basalt magma evidently took place to Sveinagja, some 50–70 km north of Askja, where lava erupted. A short plinian eruption of rhyolitic pumice also occurred from a vent in Oskujuvatn. The $0.3\,\mathrm{km^3}$ of erupted basalt plus the $0.2\,\mathrm{km^3}$ (dense-rock equivalent volume) of rhyolitic pumice was only a fraction of the caldera volume, and the balance may be contained in the dyke that solidified in the fissure (Sigurdsson & Sparks 1978).

In the Fernandino event (Simkin & Howard 1970) a large part of the $7\,\mathrm{km^2}$ floor of the already-existing caldera subsided within an elliptical area by as much as 300 m. The subsided block sagged slightly in the middle suggesting that the bounding faults had an inward dip. Explosions also occurred and a large ash plume rose, but the ash volume was minor compared with the subsided volume. A lava eruption occurred on the volcano flank but the lava-volume was also minor. Possibly a larger eruption took place unseen on the submerged flank.

Caldera collapse on basaltic volcanoes is not necessarily related to magma discharge: Walker (1988) proposed that Hawaiian calderas are funnel-like structures caused by downsagging, due to the weight of intrusions, into thermally weakened lithosphere. The inward dip shown by many layered gabbros may be symptomatic of central sagging.

Pit craters are similar to, but smaller than, calderas. Fine examples occur along the active rift zones on Kilauea and are ephemeral structures that appear, widen by wall collapse, grow by coalescing with other pit craters, and are destined eventually to be infilled with lava. The largest, Makaopuhi, is 1.6 km long by 1.0 km wide, and prior to partial infilling in 1965–74 was 300 m deep. The youngest is Devil's Throat, formed in about 1921. The caldera of Mauna Loa (called Mokuaweoweo; Macdonald 1965) and also that of Grand Comore (Strong & Jacquot 1971) originated in part by coalescing pit craters.

Walker (1988) proposed that pit craters of

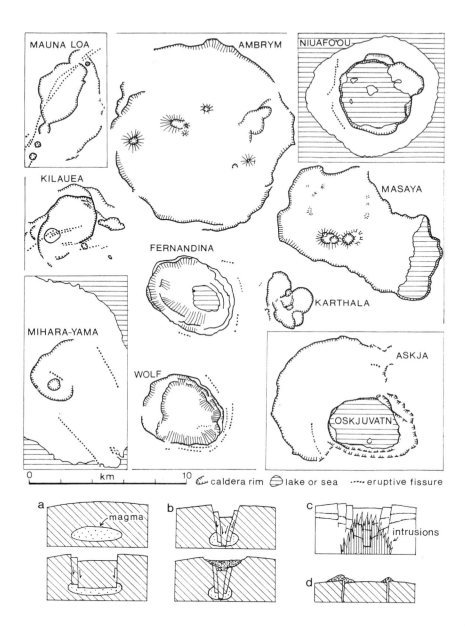

**Fig. 4.** Craters, calderas and pit craters. (Above) Maps on the same scale of basaltic calderas; north is up; Mauna Loa and Kilauea in Hawaii, after Walker (1988); Mihara-Yama in Izo-Oshima, Japan; Ambrym in Vanuatu after Monzier *et al.* (1991); Niuafo'ou near Tonga, after Macdonald (1948); Fernandina and Wolf in the Galapagos, after Munro (1992); Karthala in Grande Comore, after Strong & Jacquot (1971); Askja and Oskjuvatn in Iceland.

(Below) Schematic sections showing proposed caldera-forming mechanisms – (**a**): subsided cylinder – cauldron subsidence into magma chamber; (**b**): narrow pit caused by subsidence into magma chamber, widened by mass wasting; (**c**): funnel-like downsag caused by load of intrusions (Walker 1988); (**d**): ring mountains generated by eruptions on annular fissures (Brown *et al.* 1991).

Kilauea are surface manifestations of a deep sub-horizontal duct that conveys magma intermittently from the summit chamber into a rift zone. In an active duct, localized roof collapse may generate vaults that extend upward by roof collapse, some of the debris being carried away by lava, and eventually the vault breaks surface.

Some pit craters contain long-lived lava lakes, notably those of Erta'ale (Ethiopia; Le Guern *et al.* 1978), Nyiragongo (Zaire; Tazieff 1977, 1984) and Kilauea prior to 1924 (Macdonald *et al.* 1983). Their depth varies as periods of infilling by lava alternate with subsidence or drainback events.

Particularly deep drainback allows hot groundwater to escape and permits groundwater to enter the hot conduit, leading to violent phreatic steam explosions such as those of 1790 and 1924 on Kilauea (Decker & Christiansen 1984). A catastrophic escape of lava from the Nyiragongo lake in 1977 produced an exceptionally fast-moving lava flow on the volcano flanks that overwhelmed many people and elephants (Tazieff 1977).

## Magma chambers, neutral buoyancy, and cumulate prisms

Probably all polygenetic volcanoes at or near the peak of their activity possess a magma chamber. This chamber is more than simply an underground pool of magma: it occupies a central position in the volcano, it serves as a storage container in which magma newly arrived from the mantle accumulates, and it modulates the supply of magma to intrusions and to the surface. Fractionation occurs in it to generate on the one hand more evolved magmas and on the other great masses of mafic to ultramafic cumulate rocks. Processes that operate in magma chambers are reviewed by Marsh (1989).

The depth of Kilauea's magma chamber, as inferred from ground-deformation data and the position of an aseismic zone thought to be occupied by magma, is between 0.6 and 9 km (Ryan 1987; Ryan *et al.* 1981). Seismic probing is more favourable under water and reflection techniques have identified reflectors, regarded as magma, at a depth of 2–3 km below sea-bottom in the East Pacific Rise (Detrick *et al.* 1987). These chambers appear to be strongly elongated parallel with the ridge axis, are several kilometres wide, and are thin.

Long-lived magma chambers occur in neutral buoyancy positions where, in a vertical sense, they are in gravitational equilibrium. A level of neutral buoyancy is normally, however, a laterally extensive surface, and gravitational forces tend to cause the chamber to expand laterally along this surface. Expansion is opposed by the strength of wall-rocks and cooling of magma as it extends into cold rocks.

For these reasons a magma chamber is in only a partial state of gravitational equilibrium. As it inflates due to the input of newly arrived magma or the formation of gas bubbles, so rupture of the chamber walls or roof eventually occurs and a magma excursion results.

Little is known about the sizes or shapes of magma chambers of subaerial basaltic volcanoes. Some, but not necessarily all, gabbro intrusions seen in eroded volcanoes are solidified magma chambers, but it is generally unlikely that the whole volume of the intrusion was fluid at one time. An example of a large intrusion that apparently is a solidified chamber is the Kap Edvard Holm gabbro in East Greenland, the minerals of which show that it behaved as an open system (Bernstein *et al.* 1992), whereas nearby Skaergaard intrusion that shows extreme fractionation behaved as a closed system (McBirney & Noyes 1979).

Fedotov (1982) investigated the growth and extinction conditions for magma chambers. He showed that they grow and reach a maximum and stable diameter of several kilometres, at which heat influx balances heat losses, within a few thousand years. In a similar study Hardee (1982) found that a narrow sill may become a confluent intrusion or magma chamber at a magma influx rate of $> 10^{-3}$ km$^3$ a$^{-1}$.

Gudmundsson (1987) assumed that magma exhibits poroelastic behaviour (i.e. melt occurs in pore spaces of a brittle crystalline framework), and from compressibility considerations calculated from the size of Icelandic magma excursions, assumed that the volume of magma chambers is typically in the range 100–1000 km$^3$, about 2000 times the excursion-volume.

If a magma chamber is enclosed by rocks that are elastic, when the chamber swells elastic strain energy is then stored in the magma. When an excursion occurs the magma-flux should decay exponentially. Records of some actual eruptions (Wadge 1981) conform poorly with an exponential decay. A possible explanation is that while eruption occurs, so a partial replenishment occurs from the deep magma-source.

Little is known of magma-chamber shape. A complex of interconnected dykes and sheets is envisaged by some (e.g. Fiske & Kinoshita 1969) but this is not a stable configuration. Incoming magma would likely enter the hottest and most fluid part of the chamber, and heating of reentrants and cooling of salients would tend to round the outlines. The most likely shape would be that of a triaxial ellipsoid with the longest and intermediate axes lying in the neutral buoyancy plane, and the longest axis extending into rift zones. The ellipsoid might be deformed into a funnel-like shape by floor subsidence, reaching a maximum in the centre. A shape something like this is not unusual among gabbro intrusions: the hypersthene gabbro of centre 3 at Ardnamurchan (Wells 1954) and the Ben Buie gabbro in Mull (Lobjoit 1959) are examples. In some volcanoes the chamber may simply consist of the cylinder of magma underlying the summit crater.

## Cumulate prisms

Magma chambers of large basaltic volcanoes are underlain by mafic and ultramafic plutonic rocks, such as gabbro, dunite and harzburgite. Many of these rocks are cumulates and originated by the sedimentation of pyrogenetic minerals from the magma. Various lines of evidence point to the existence of such prisms.

(1) Great cumulate prisms are exposed in the cores of some deeply eroded volcanoes notably those of Rhum (Emeleus 1987) and the Cuillin Hills of Skye (Wadsworth 1982).

(2) Inclusions of cumulate rocks are commonly brought to the surface by magma eruptions, particularly during declining phases in the life of the volcano when the high-level magma chamber has solidified (e.g. Hualalai volcano; Chen *et al.* 1992; Lesser Antilles volcanoes: Arculus & Wills 1980).

(3) Large positive Bouguer gravity anomalies are centred on the volcanoes (Fig. 5) and are greatest in the central area (e.g. in Hawaii; Strange *et al.* 1965; Kinoshito 1965).

(4) A 3 km deep drillhole into the positive gravity anomaly on Piton de la Fournaise (Reunion: Rancon *et al.* 1989) passed through gabbros and then cumulate rocks from 1.92 km to the bottom of the hole at 3 km depth.

(5) Seismic refraction lines across the centre of Koolau volcano revealed the existence of rocks with a P-wave velocity of $7.7 \, km \, s^{-1}$ (near that of upper mantle rocks) at a shallow (1 km) depth (Furumoto *et al.* 1965).

It is envisaged that as a volcano is built up, so the prism of cumulate rocks grows and the neutral buoyancy level and magma chamber are displaced upward. The high-level chamber, which initially may have developed at the base of, or below, the volcano, migrates upward into the volcano, while the dense cumulate rocks accentuate the zonation that governs neutral buoyancy positions.

The excess of mass indicated by each of the Rhum, Cuillins and Mull gravity anomalies is $3–7 \times 10^{11}$ tonnes and can be modelled by prisms of mafic and ultramafic rocks $0.2–0.3 \, Mg \, m^{-3}$ denser than crystalline basement rocks, having volumes of $1100–3500 \, km^3$ (McQuillin & Tuson 1963; Bott & Tuson 1973). The well-exposed prism of Rhum is 10 km in diameter at the top and might thus extend downward some 15 km. The diameter of the prism should be related to that of the chamber.

## Ultramafic inclusions

Magmas very commonly bring inclusions (xenoliths) of coarsely crystalline mafic or ultramafic rock to the surface. These inclusions because of their high density (commonly $3.0–3.3 \, Mg \, m^{-3}$) relative to basaltic magma (about $2.75 \, Mg \, m^{-3}$) and common large size ($>0.1$ m) have high settling rates through Newtonian magma ($>1 \, cm \, s^{-1}$) for a viscosity of $10^3 \, Pa \, s$; their appearance at the surface indicates either ascent velocities higher than this, or possession by the magma of a yield strength (Sparks *et al.* 1977a).

More importantly, as pointed out by Clague (1987), such inclusions drop out if the magma pauses or resides at a level above their source; the transport to the surface of dunite cumulates from below the high-level magma chamber indicates that the high-level chamber has solidified, and the transport of mantle lherzolites and garnet pyroxenites to the surface indicates that no crustal magma chamber or reservoir exists at any level above the mantle.

## Confluent intrusions

These are intrusions that grow incrementally. If a dyke or intrusive sheet is injected into an earlier dyke or sheet while the middle of the earlier intrusion is still partially molten, one is not chilled significantly against and merges into the other, and an intrusion of confluent type results. By successive increments, the intrusion widens and cools more slowly to produce a more coarsely crystalline rock. A succession of small intrusions may, thus, build a gabbro intrusion, the incremental origin of which may be difficult to detect. The gabbro may, however, be seen to pass at its lateral extremities into a cluster of dykes or sheets. Some time constraints for the increments are considered by Hardee (1982).

## Shadow zones in central volcanoes

A significant feature of large central volcanoes is that each possesses a 'shadow zone' within which

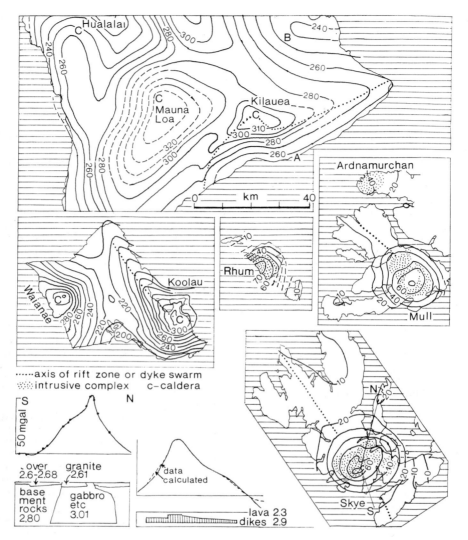

**Fig. 5.** Magma chambers, neutral buoyancy, and cumulate prisms. (Main picture) Bouguer gravity anomaly maps, on the same scale, contour interval 10 mgals, of Mauna Loa and Kilauea volcanoes, Hawaii (Kinoshito 1965); Koolau and Waianae volcanoes in Oahu (Strange *et al.* 1965); and intrusive volcanic centres of Rhum (McQuillin & Tuson 1963), Mull (Bott & Tuson 1973) and Skye (Bott & Tuson 1973). (Below left) gravity profiles across Skye and Kilauea, and density structure in the upper crust that is capable of producing the observed anomaly (Kilauea: after Furumoto 1978). Rock-density values in Mg m$^{-3}$.

basaltic vents are rare or absent. The shadow zone is interpreted to overlie a body of silicic magma through which ascending basaltic magmas are normally unable to pass (Hildreth 1981). Examples are Newberry, Pantelleria, and Torfajokull (Iceland; Walker 1989*a*).

Silicic vents are concentrated in the shadow zone. It is thought that basaltic magma incursions heat the silicic body, promote convection by reducing its viscosity and density and cause

vesiculation (the solubility of gas in magma decreases as the temperature increases). In effect, the basaltic magma 'stokes' the silicic magma and causes changes that favour or trigger its eruption (Sparks *et al.* 1977*b*).

Some basaltic magma batches may succeed in rising through the silicic magma body if their ascent rate is high or if the silicic magma has a high yield strength. They locally heat and mobilize the silicic magma, provide a hot pathway for it toward the surface and thus play an active role in promoting silicic eruptions. This is thought to have happened in the composite dykes having basaltic margins and a silicic centre, and composite lava flows having a basaltic base overlain by rhyolite, that occur in Iceland and the Hebridean Province.

It has evidently also happened in the case of some silicic eruptions that were immediately preceded by a basaltic eruption. A fine example is the great Rotoehu Ash/Rotoiti Ignimbrite eruption from Okataina volcano, New Zealand, about 50 000 years ago which released some 100 km³ of rhyolitic magma and was immediately preceded by eruption of the volumetrically insignificant Matahi basalt.

Paradoxically, the more efficient the heat-exchanger system of a central volcano, the less clear is the evidence that basaltic magma participated. Thus, in the Taupo Zone a great volume of silicic volcanic rocks occurs but basaltic rocks comprise only about 1% of the total eruptive volume (Cole 1973). A few silicic units were erupted as mixed magmas (Blake et al. 1992), but generally contain only a very minor amount of basaltic material.

Net-veined intrusive complexes that are exposed in many deeply eroded central volcanoes (e.g. Southeast Iceland; Blake 1966; Mattson et al. 1986) provide some of the clearest evidence for injection of basaltic magma into silicic magma.

## Major sill swarms

Sills underlie many flood-basalt fields. They can have large individual volumes, comparable with flood-basalt lava flows, and sill swarms can rival flood basalts in total volume (Walker & Poldervaart 1949). The sills mostly intrude thick sedimentary rock sequences that at the time of sill injection were young and poorly consolidated. One can infer that levels of neutral buoyancy existed between well- and less well-consolidated sediments, or alternatively the sill magma simply flowed under loose sediment. Bradley (1965) recognized that if a magma is denser than the rock it intrudes, the roof may effectively float on the magma. This, however, is an oversimplification of the situation since the magma has the capability of reaching the surface and building a volcano there (sills normally underlie volcanoes).

A swarm of Jurassic dolerite sills up to 300 m thick occurs in Tasmania and outcrops over 25% of the 65 000 km² surface area of the island. Parts of the same sill swarm are found on disrupted portions of Gondwanaland in Antarctica and South Africa (Frankel 1967). The Palisades and Gettysburg sills are of early Jurassic age and cut Triassic sediments under the Newark volcanics that extend from New Jersey to Newfoundland. Major sills including those of the Shiant Isles underlie the Tertiary flood basalts of Skye (Gibson & Jones 1991; Gibb & Henderson 1989).

Sills characteristically transgress across the countryrock bedding. Carey (1958) investigated this transgression in a Tasmanian sill by constructing isostrats – lines on a map connecting points where the sill is in contact with the same stratigraphic horizon – and demonstrated that the sill has the overall form of a saucer or low-angle inverted cone relative to the stratigraphy. He inferred that magma was injected at the low point of the cone. Francis (1982) found a similar pattern of isostrats in the Whin Sill and observed that the sill systematically thickens toward the low-point (Fig. 6a).

The Whin Sill, of late Carboniferous age, extends over at least 5 000 km² and has an average thickness of about 40 m. The aspect ratio is about 1/2000 and the volume is over 200 km³ (Francis 1982). The question arises, as with major flood-basalt flows, whether large-volume sills are emplaced rapidly or slowly. Gibb & Henderson (1992) and Husch (1990) present evidence that some sills form incrementally from successive magma incursions.

The injection of sills into poorly consolidated sediments commonly generates soft-sediment deformation structures in the countryrocks (Fig. 6g). Fine examples are described by Duffield et al. (1986). Einsele et al. (1980) pointed out that the volume contraction in baked and dewatered sediments may be sufficient to make space for a sill.

Peperites are rocks that are formed by mixing of magma with wet sediment, commonly in a weakly explosive manner. Peperites formed at margins of sills are described by Busby-Spera & White (1987) and Walker & Francis (1987), and very similar examples related to lava flows are described by Schmincke (1967). Yagi (1969) described a sill emplaced in wet sediment that partly subdivided into pillows.

Miocene flows and associated intrusions that outcrop along the coast of Washington and Oregon have been identified as distal portions of the Columbia River basalts that invaded, and locally flowed as shallow sills under, soft estuarine and deltaic sediments (Beeson et al. 1979; Pfaff & Beeson 1989).

It is probable that sills can form without surface volcanism. A possible example may be the sills penetrated by drillholes in the Fastnet

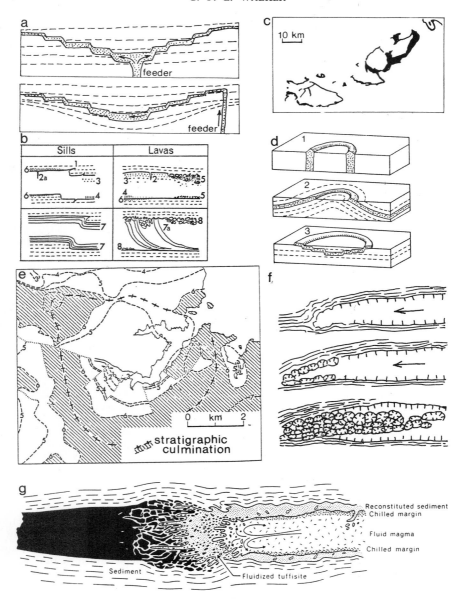

**Fig. 6.** Major sill swarms.

(a) Saucer-shaped sills; dashed lines are countryrock stratigraphic horizons; (upper) magma injected at the low-point (Carey 1958); (lower) magma injected at a high level and accumulating at bottom of sedimentary basin (Francis 1982). (b) Distinction between sills and lava flows: (above) more fluid magmas; (below) less fluid magmas. 1: cross-cutting of roof rocks; 2: infilled cracks; 3: vesicles; 4: pipe vesicles; 5: plant molds; 6: baked rocks; 7: flow planes; 7a: ramp structure of flow planes. (c) Ring-shaped outcrop pattern of the Gettysburg sill in the Triassic Newark Basin in Pennsylvania (Hotz 1952). (d) Intrusions that can give ring-like outcrops include: 1: ring dykes; 2: folded sills; 3: saucer-shaped transgressive sills. (e) Isostrat map of a sill in Tasmania (Carey 1958). Dashed lines are isostrats for successively higher stratigraphic horizons 1 to 6. Shaded areas: sill in contact with rocks above horizon 6. (f) Inferred mechanism of formation of a pillowed sill (Yagi 1969). (g) Interaction of magma with coal (black) and unconsolidated sediments. (Walker & Francis 1987); reproduced by permission of the Royal Society of Edinburgh and authors from *Transactions of the Royal Society of Edinburgh: Earth Sciences*, **77** (1986), 295–307.

Basin (Caston *et al.* 1981) where coeval volcanism appears to be absent. The extensive sills in Tasmania are not accompanied by volcanism on that island although the Stormberg Series flood basalts are coeval with them.

## Eruptions and eruption products

### Basaltic lava flows

Lava flows are generated in most basaltic eruptions and form on about 20 volcanoes per year. They range over more than six orders of magnitude in volume and three in length, and generally have a low aspect ratio of <0.01. Many are of clastogenetic origin: the lava passes briefly through a fragmental stage in 'fire fountains' before the fragments coalesce and flow away. All gradations are found between such lavas and welded tuffs or agglutinate in which the distance flowed was insufficient to destroy the fragmental texture.

Close-proximal lava flows tend to be highly vesicular. In shelly pahoehoe coalescence and expansion of bubbles under the chilled skin generates hollow lava flows like gas bags with a roof crust commonly <0.1 m thick (Swanson 1973). Walking across a field of shelly pahoehoe can be quite hazardous where the crust is too weak to support a person's weight.

### Pahoehoe and aa

Basaltic lava flows form two main structural types, one smooth-surfaced and called pahoehoe and the other rough-surfaced and called aa, which are fundamentally different in their structures and flow dynamics. As lava flows away from the source vents, the volumetric flow rate determines whether it becomes pahoehoe or aa (Rowland & Walker 1990).

At a low volumetric rate ($<20 \, m^3 \, s^{-1}$ in Hawaii) restriction of flow by rapid growth of a chilled crust causes the lava to be subdivided into small flow units averaging a few cubic metres in volume. In consequence the lava inside each unit (except for that which continues to flow under the crust) becomes static before cooling significantly.

In contrast, lava erupted at a high volumetric rate ($> 20 \, m^3 \, s^{-1}$ in Hawaii), destined to become aa, travels fast in open channels, and continues to flow after it has cooled significantly. Then, if the surface crust is torn by differential flow, the viscosity and yield strength of underlying lava are too high for it to well up and repair the tear. So by repeatedly tearing the lava comes to have a surface layer of spinose clinkery rubble fragments and has become aa. 'Fingers' of lava that rise into the rubble carapace break on cooling joints and contribute debris to it. Morphometric features of aa flow-fields are described by Guest *et al.* (1987), Kilburn & Lopez (1991) and Wadge & Lopez (1991).

Aa flows invariably have an internal portion consisting of coherent basalt that underlies the surface rubble, and the coherent part averages about 60 per cent of the total flow thickness. Flowage has sometimes been likened to the advance of a caterpillar-track vehicle but this is a poor analogy since the rubble layer at the base is almost invariably much thinner than that at the top and is not simply the top rubble layer translated over the flowfront to the base. Over much of their travel distance aa flows possess a yield strength and move by plug flow. They effectively bulldoze obstacles in their path.

Traced from proximal to distal end, aa flows become progressively thicker and flowfronts commonly exceed 10 m high, while vesicles are strongly deformed and progressively eliminated until the lava becomes almost totally non-vesicular (except for new voids that are generated by shearing).

Pahoehoe flows advance slowly and the flow front consists of a multitude of small flow units which surge forward, become static, and spawn new flow units. Jones (1968) referred to this manner of advance as digital, referring to the numerous finger-like units. The flow units are fed through a system of lava tubes. In tubes the lava flows freely and without cooling significantly so enabling it to travel great distances (the Undara pahoehoe flow in Queensland is 160 km long; Stephenson & Griffin 1975) despite the low discharge-rate conditions.

Pahoehoe on slopes exceeding about 4° in Hawaii resides for only a short time in tubes and is highly vesicular (spongy or S-type pahoehoe; Walker 1989*b*). Pahoehoe on shallower slopes, as on the coastal terrace of an island volcano, resides longer in tubes, emerges with fewer but larger vesicles, and develops the highly distinctive pipe vesicles along the flow base (pipe-bearing or P-type pahoehoe; Wilmoth & Walker 1993). Pipe vesicles may be attributed to bubbles rising at the same rate as a rheology front. Behind this front the lava possesses a yield strength which prevents closure of lava behind the ascending bubbles.

An important aspect of pahoehoe flows particularly on shallow (<4°) slopes is the injection of lava under a surface crust, so jacking up this crust to produce lava rises or the localized whaleback-shaped uplifts, gashed by deep clefts, called tumuli. By this lava-rise mechanism a lava flow initially < 1 m thick can thicken to > 5 m (Walker 1991; Hon *et al.* in press). Evidence is accumulating that some of the lava flows in flood basalt fields that were formerly thought to be erupted at extremely high discharge rates (Swanson *et al.* 1975) may in fact be lava rises formed by long-sustained and relatively low-discharge rate activity.

Pahoehoe lava shows a strong propensity to construct localized lava shields of scutulum type. A small-scale example is 110 m high Mauna Ulu, formed in the 1969–1974 eruption of Kilauea volcano. Much larger examples, exemplified by the 600 m high shield of Skjaldbreidur, occur in Iceland.

Some basaltic lava flows in subduction-related settings have a distinctly higher viscosity than those of other settings. This is inferred, for example, from the great flow-thickness, up to 30 m, of the flows erupted in 1759–1774 on El Jorullo (Mexico; Segerstrom 1950). Such lava may possess a yield strength at the time of eruption. This is inferred from the vesicle distribution pattern and occurrence of megavesicles in the Xitle basalt (Mexico City; Walker in press). Jorullo and Xitle lavas both erupted with a high content of crystals consistent with possession of a yield strength.

The surface aspect of these flows may be that of a block lava such as is more characteristic of andesite and silicic lavas than aa. The blocks are on the whole larger than the rubble fragments of aa and are bounded mostly by smooth cooling-crack surfaces.

## Explosive eruptions and their products

Shield volcanoes produce a minimum of explosive products and have an explosivity index (i.e. percentage of pyroclastic deposits among their total products) as low as 10%. In contrast, stratovolcanoes in subduction-related settings typically have an explosivity index exceeding 50%.

On shield volcanoes at the peak of activity the eruptions are predominantly of hawaiian style, in which 'fire-fountains' play to a height of mostly tens of metres. Because of the large size of most lava fragments, nearly complete phase separation occurs so that only the lightest particles enter the soaring gas plume. Spatter ramparts are built along eruptive fissures, and cones or rings of spatter and cinders are built at points where effusion is concentrated. Most of the spatter lumps thrown up in eruptions of this style weld together when they land to form agglutinate or coalesce and flow away as lava flows.

Strombolian-style activity predominates on stratovolcanoes and monogenetic volcanoes.

The typical products are cinder cones. Cones occur in great numbers on the flanks of large stratovolcanoes; 200 occur on Etna and 60 on Fuji, and 132 occur on Mauna Kea shield volcano as products of its declining phases of activity. Cinder cones built in single eruptions range up to about 400 m high. They commonly include welded layers and contain variable proportions of spatter. The morphology of cinder cones is described by Wood (1980), and the dynamics of hawaiian- and strombolian-style activity are analysed by Wilson & Head (1981) and Head & Wilson (1989).

Cinder cones > 400 m high are known but are not called cinder cones. Usually they are stratovolcanoes buttressed by lava flows. An example is Izalco in El Salvador which was born 1769–1770 and has since grown to > 650 m high.

Strombolian cones often contain volcanic bombs. Some bombs are cored (Brady & Webb 1943). The core may be a piece of scoria or a mantle xenolith and is coated with basalt. Other bombs are fusiform (spindle shaped) and made of very dense material that evidently resided sufficiently long in the vent to lose most of its gas bubbles. It was formerly thought that the spindle shape is due to aerodynamic drag while spinning through the air, but Tsuya (1941) showed that it is produced by stretching, leading to necking and disruption of lava strands as they rose from the vent. Francis (1973) described cannonball bombs rounded by attrition as they bounded down the side of a cone, and Walker (in prep.) found potato-shaped lapilli and bombs 2–200 m in size on Tantalus, Oahu, rounded by tossing of still-plastic lava among loose ash in the vent.

Cinder-cone slopes are at the angle of repose of loose cinders (33–35° from the horizontal). Extensive redistribution of cinders by grain-flow occurs as the cone becomes oversteepened by excessive deposition immediately around the crater. The grain-flow deposits are recognized by their inverse size-grading and laterally-discontinuous lenticular bedforms. Many of the larger cinder fragments fall apart along cooling joints while in the grain flows. After ejection, the scoria vesiculates and develops a concentric vesicle zonation, and this zonation is truncated by the cooling joints.

In the most powerful strombolian activity, fire-fountains exceed 1 km high. They were up to 1600 m in the November 1986 eruption of Izu-Oshima (Aramaki *et al.* 1988). The brief October 1983 eruption of Miyakejima was particularly intense: the eruption lasted under 15 h at an average discharge of 1300 $m^3 s^{-1}$ (Aramaki *et al.* 1986). In such intense activity, phase separation is incomplete, much of the ejecta enters the convective plume, and an extensive blanket of fall deposits extends around the cinder cone.

Much of the explosive activity in subduction zone settings is better characterized as violent strombolian or vulcanian. The Paricutin eruption of 1943–1952 is a good example (of basaltic andesite, not basalt). The ejecta are highly fragmented and eruptive columns are dark coloured because of the abundance of ash. The ejecta tend to be dense and poorly vesiculated, and rich in lithics. It is inferred that the erupted magma had a yield strength that inhibited escape of gases and enhanced explosive violence; the generally crystal-rich condition of the magma is consistent with this inference.

The high degree of fragmentation and high density of violent strombolian or vulcanian ejecta favour the generation of pyroclastic flows. An extensive basaltic ignimbrite occurs at Masaya volcano (Williams 1982), basaltic pyroclastic flows were observed on Lopevi, Vanuatu, in 1960 (Williams & Curtis 1964) and Ulawun, Papua New Guinea, in 1978 (McKee et al. 1981), and pyroclastic flow deposits are found among the 1759–1774 ejecta in El Jorullo.

## Phreatomagmatic eruptions

When copious amounts of water enter an erupting vent to mingle with the upjetting lava, a great column of steam is generated and the lava is quenched and highly fragmented (Wohletz 1986). Fall-out of ash builds an ash ring that within a few years may become lithified to a tuffring. The crater rim diameter of 0.5–1.5 km is significantly larger than that of strombolian-style cinder cones.

The resulting eruptive style is called surtseyan (after the Surtsey eruption in the ocean off Iceland, 1963–1965; Thorarinsson et al. 1964). Surtseyan eruptions occur frequently near the coast in shallow seas (140 m deep at Surtsey) or lakes. They belong to a class of volcanic eruptions known generally as phreatomagmatic or hydrovolcanic. Kokelaar (1983, 1986) and Sohn & Chough (1989) discuss significant features of such activity and its products.

When an eruption occurs on low-lying land where the rocks are permeable and the water table is high, the explosions excavate a crater extending well below the general land surface. A lake accumulates in the crater. If the erupted volume is small and the crater is surrounded by a low pyroclastic ring, the depression may be a more striking topographic feature than the pyroclastic ring. The resulting structure is called a maar (Lorenz, 1985, 1986).

Phreatomagmatic activity generates base surges, recorded by the dune-bedded structures of their deposits. The type examples of base surges formed in the 1965 eruption of Taal volcano (Philippines; Moore 1967). These surges swept outward to 4 or 5 km from the eruption crater. Trees that remained standing were coated with mud and ash on their up-vent side. The deposits on the ground had a wavy surface consisting of ring dunes tangential to the crater, showing internal dune bedding (Fisher & Waters 1970). Great numbers – scores to hundreds – of base surges are recorded in some tuff-rings.

Some eruptions are comparatively wet: their ash deposits contain accretionary and ash-coated lapilli, show intra-formational gullying and slumping, and pitting of some bedding planes by rain-drop impressions. Others are relatively dry, have a lower content of fine ash, and mark a transition to strombolian-style activity (Verwoerd & Chevallier 1987).

Phreatomagmatic vents quarry down often some hundreds of metres into the underlying rocks, and pieces of these rocks are abundant as included lithics in the pyroclastic deposits. Blocks also occur deeper than the level from which they originated. In ancient examples where the surface deposits have been eroded away the vent survives as a diatreme, a more or less cylindrical neck or pipe infilled with pyroclastic material.

## Rootless vents

Steam explosions commonly form craters and pyroclastic accumulations where lava flows from land into water. These structures were referred to by Thorarinsson (1953) as 'pseudocraters', but the craters are real and are better referred to as rootless vents. At the type locality in Iceland where a lava invaded the shallow Lake Myvatn, many hundreds of pyroclastic structures occur ranging from hornitos little more than 1 m across to ash-rings of 0.5 km rim diameter.

Littoral cones are common in Hawaii at the point of entry of lava into the sea. The most common type consists of a pair of half-cones on either side of the lava (pyroclasts that fell onto the lava were carried away), exemplified by Puu Hou (Fisher 1968). These pyroclastic accumulations appear identical to those at primary vents except that the density of the pyroclasts is commonly higher (reflecting gas losses from the flowing lava; Walker 1992b). A newly recognized type of littoral cone, exemplified by Puu Ki, that occurs on some pahoehoe flows of Mauna Loa, consists of complete and nested craters about a central rootless vent apparently fed from a lava tube (Jurado et al. in prep.).

## Phreatic eruptions

These are steam explosions in which no juvenile magma is erupted. Some kind of heat-exchange mechanism operates in which magmatic heat is transferred to water of external origin to power the explosions.

## Underwater basaltic volcanism

A large proportion, probably amounting to $3.5 \, km^3 \, a^{-1}$, of the world's basalt is erupted under water, mostly at divergent plate boundaries (spreading ridges). Knowledge of this underwater volcanism is derived from bottom studies (including observations from submersibles), sea-floor drilling, and investigation of ophiolites that appear to be tectonically uplifted portions of oceanic crust. Valuable supplementary information is supplied from places such as Iceland, where widespread volcanism occurred under the extensive ice sheets (now largely melted) of the Ice Age.

The principal difference between underwater and subaerial volcanism is that explosive volcanism is suppressed under water. The deeper the water, the more strongly it is suppressed. This is because, under the confining pressure of water, less volatiles are exsolved from magma than at the surface, and also because a given mass of exsolved gas has a much smaller volume. Under a confining pressure of 0.1 kb appropriate to a water depth of 1 km, for example, the solubility of water in basalt is 1.2 wt% (cf. <0.1% at 1 atmosphere pressure), and 1 g of exsolved water vapour at 1150°C has a volume of only 0.06 l (cf. 6 l at 1 atmosphere). Explosive fragmentation of magma requires that the volume fraction of gas bubbles should exceed about 0.7, likely to be rare except in water less than about 200 m deep.

## Pillowed lava

Many of the lava flows erupted under water are compound and subdivided into small rounded flow units called pillows. Pillows are very similar in size and shape to pahoehoe flow units but tend to be narrower, have a larger aspect ratio (vertical dimension/horizontal dimension), and have continuous glassy rims. Pillow lava seen in cross-section has an appearance like that of a pile of sandbags, and formerly it was considered that each pillow is a discrete sack-like lava body. It is now thought that generally pillows are connected by narrow tubes that are intertwined rather like spaghetti (Jones 1968).

Conceptions of pillow-lava growth were strongly influenced by direct observations made by diving on the 1969–71 lava delta of Kilauea volcano (Moore 1975). In this instance the pillows flowed down an underwater slope of 20° or more and were strongly elongate downslope. Pillows have not yet been observed forming on shallow slopes.

Pillow lavas are remarkably similar to pahoehoe, but are on average less vesicular. Pipe vesicles are common in pillows on small-angle slopes. Tumuli and tumulus-like features from which many pillows have issued have been described by Appelgate & Embley (1992) and Ballard & Moore (1977). Sheet lavas also occur (Ballard et al. 1979) and form at a higher discharge rate (cf. Griffiths & Fink 1992). Commonly sheet lava has a pillowed base or top. Tribble (1991) observed lava flowing in open channels, and the ultrathin lava layers described by Moore & Charlton (1984) may be similar, formed in channels or as multiple crusts in lava tubes. Even where vesicles are scarce, large voids can occur in pillows at all depths due to drainage of lava from tubes (Fornari 1986).

## Hyaloclastite lava

Another kind of lava flow that forms under water may be designated a hyaloclastite lava: like aa it has a fragmental carapace and a coherent core. The fragmented top layer tends to be thicker and finer grained than in aa, and the fragments tend to be less vesicular and more glassy, smooth surfaced and angular in shape, due to their fragmentation by the shattering and crumbling of lava in contact with water.

Rittmann (1962) introduced 'Hyaloclastite' for rocks fragmented by the quenching and granulation of hot lava in water, and 'hyaloclastic' for the process of producing a hyaloclastite (Greek hyalos = glass, klastos = broken). Not all 'broken glass' rocks are included: only those broken in contact with water. Note that the products of surtseyan eruptions are also glassy but some at least of the juvenile ejecta are highly vesicular. They are strictly pyroclastic and are better called 'hyalotuffs' (Honnorez & Kirst 1975).

A hyaloclastite lava occupying a glacial valley was described by Walker & Blake (1966) in southeastern Iceland. By inversion of topography it now constitutes a ridge (called Dalsheidi). The valley was occupied by a glacier when Dalsheidi erupted. A highly irregular body of coherent basalt that occurs near the bottom of the palaeovalley marks the master conduit through which lava flowed down-valley. It shows conspicuous prismatic jointing everywhere.

The hyaloclastite carapace of Dalsheidi, up to

300 m deep, is envisaged to have grown endogenously as lava escaped from the conduit, and a system of irregular dykes and intrusive sheets that branch off from the main conduit represent the pathways taken by this lava. Such dykes that occur within and are a part of a lava flow are called lava dykes (Silvestri 1962). Lava dykes commonly occur also in pahoehoe compound flows. The most important features of Dalsheidi were the evidence it provided that lava is capable of flowing for tens of kilometres below ice (and by implication under water) and that a hyaloclastite carapace may grow endogenously.

Much more extensive hyaloclastite lavas are described from southern Iceland by Bergh & Sigvaldason (1991). They form sheets up to 200 m thick, and individual flows cover up to 280 km$^2$. Traced laterally a number of distinct facies are observed including mass-flow hyaloclastites.

A particularly favourable environment for hyaloclastite formation is the littoral zone where lava enters water from land, and where the repeated dashing of waves against freshly exposed incandescent lava causes rapid and voluminous fragmentation. Generally the lava and hence the hyaloclastic fragments have a low to moderate content of vesicles.

## Lava deltas and tuyas

Pahoehoe lava that flows into the sea extends the shoreline outward as a lava delta (Jones 1969; Moore et al. 1973). An abrupt passage zone separates subaerial lava of the delta from the underlying flow-foot deposits formed underwater. Flow-foot rocks are mainly hyaloclastic breccias containing pillows. Commonly they dip at 20–25° like the foreset beds of a river delta, and the pillows are strongly elongated in the dip direction. Furnes & Fridleifsson (1974) described regular fluctuations in level of the passage zone in an Icelandic lava delta and attributed them to the tidal variations in water level; since each tidal cycle is about 13 hours, this provides a means of calculating the rate of advance of the delta.

Certain table mountains called tuyas, common in Iceland and known also in British Columbia, Alaska and Antarctica, are distinctively-shaped volcanoes formed by eruptions under former ice-sheets. Each tuya has a core and pedestal of pillow lava and hyaloclastite overlain by hyalotuff. This is capped by a lava-delta that formed in an intraglacial meltwater lake, and the relatively flat top consists of subaerial lavas of the delta (Mathews 1947).

Tuyas in Iceland are mostly monogenetic

structures and are the intraglacial equivalent of scutulum-type shields. They commonly have a volume of between 1 and 10 km$^3$. Tuya-like structures also form by eruptions in the sea: Surtsey, which consists of hyalotuffs capped by a lava delta, is an example. Overlapping tuyas may have passage zones at widely different levels related to different thicknesses of ice sheet or levels of the sea (Jones & Nelson 1970).

Aa lava that flows into the sea tends to proceed as though the water is not there, and may have an underwater flow width and flow thickness little different from those on land. The extension of the coastline is minimal (Moore et al. 1973). One can infer that distal-type aa exhibits this behaviour because it possesses a yield strength.

## Palagonite and palagonitization

Glassy basalt readily hydrates to palagonite, an orange-coloured hydrogel and its fibro-crystalline derivative. Chemical constituents that are leached out crystallize commonly as zeolites in void spaces and effectively lithify the loose deposits (Furnes 1974). Palagonite forms rapidly under hydrothermal conditions, and its rate of formation doubles with every 12°C temperature increase. When a drillhole passed through the Surtsey hyalotuff 12 years after the eruption virtually the entire deposit was well lithified (Jakobsson & Moore 1986).

## Jointing in basaltic rocks

Cracks (joints) are ubiquitous in basaltic rocks but few systematic studies of them have hitherto been attempted. They have not been employed to any significant extent as a tool from which to infer processes and conditions, and no review exists.

## Contraction joints

When a volcanic rock body such as a lava flow or dyke cools from magmatic to atmospheric temperature it undergoes a volume contraction by several percent. This contraction is accommodated in part by the formation of contraction joints which develop at right angles to the cooling surfaces and subdivide the rock body into crude prisms. Contraction joints are more closely spaced near the cooling surface and the spacing widens further where the cooling rate is lower. Commonly a parting occurs in or near the middle of the body where joints that propagated inward from one cooling-surface of the body meet joints that propagated inward from

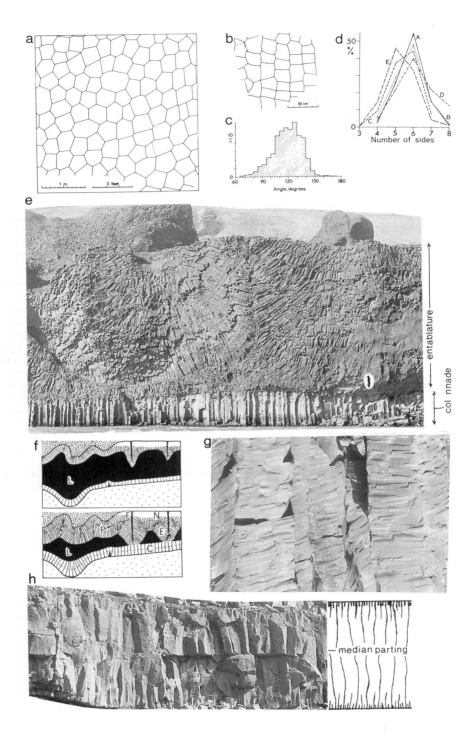

the opposite cooling surface. The pattern of jointing is one of the basic criteria for delineating cooling units within volcanic rock-bodies (Fig. 7h).

Prismatic joints commonly have band-like markings (called chisel structure by James 1920) on their surface. The bands are typically a few centimetres wide and approximately parallel with the cooling surface. Ryan & Sammis (1978) showed that chisel marks are due to incremental crack-propagation into the cooling rock body. They called them 'striations' (Fig. 7).

De Graff et al. (1989) showed how the joint-propagation direction can be inferred from surface markings on joint surfaces. Peck & Minakami (1968) observed that the incremental joint propagation can be detected in a cooling lava-lake by seismometer.

Jointing that subdivides the rock into prisms that are unusually regular in form and uniform in size is called columnar. In lava flows it is best developed where the lava occurs in valleys and topographic depressions. From this it is inferred to be favoured by cooling in static conditions, so that stresses resulting from volume contraction are uniformly distributed. Where a lava flow overlies water-rich sediment such as lignite, dewatering is accompanied by a volume contraction of the sediment that helps generate the topographic depression occupied by the lava.

Columnar-jointed lava flows commonly show a multi-tiered structure in which broad and regular columns form a lower part (called the colonnade; Tomkeieff 1940) and a zone of narrow and irregular curvicolumnar prisms forms an upper part called the entablature. Typically there is a very abrupt transition from colonnade to entablature. Sometimes the entablature is capped by an upper colonnade (Fig. 7e).

Saemundsson (1970) proposed that the entablature is caused by water cooling, particularly where it is much thicker than the colonnade. Supporting evidence for water cooling is that the glassy mesostasis is more abundant in the entablature-lava than in the colonnade-lava (Long & Wood 1986). Lava flows occupying river valleys are particularly liable to be water-cooled because

the displaced river flows over the top surface of the lava. The upper colonnade formed before water cooling began.

Not all contraction joints in volcanic rocks are related to cooling. Palagonite-rich tuffs commonly exhibit prisms several millimetres to several centimetres wide, attributed to a volume reduction due to a partial desiccation of the palagonite when exposed to the air. The prisms are orientated normal to today's land surface showing that they are not palaeostructures but are due to drying out in today's atmosphere.

## Expansion (inflation) joints

An important class of joint in volcanic rocks has a significant gape and results from an expansion of a volcanic rock body causing disruption of the chilled crust. Familiar examples are the distinctively jointed breadcrust blocks so often thrown out by explosive eruptions of andesitic volcanoes and the distinctive whaleback hillocks called tumuli in pahoehoe flow-fields.

The gaping cracks in breadcrust blocks form as the centre of a block expands due to continued vesiculation (Walker 1968). Tumuli grow by the injection of lava under a solid crust, jacking up the crust (Walker 1991). They are deeply gashed by V-shaped lava-inflation clefts that grew at the same time as the lava crust, their tip projecting into red-hot lava. Tumuli are localized uplifts. Lava rises are more extensive uplifts and similar clefts occur around their margins.

Lava-inflation cracks form also in the underwater environment. Thus, tumuli occur in underwater flowfields (Appelgate & Embley 1992) and many pillows have gaping expansion cracks adjacent to which partial springing-off of the chilled selvage allows water to penetrate and generate multiple selvages. Alternatively multiple selvages are due to implosion (Yamagishi 1985).

The opening of cracks enables water to penetrate deeply into a cooling lava; when secondary joints then develop normal to these new cooling surfaces they generate the highly distinctive joint system of 'pseudo-pillow lava' (Watanabe &

**Fig. 7.** Jointing in basaltic rocks.
(**a**) Plan view of columnar joints in the Giant's Causeway basalt. (**b**) Plan view of a less regular pattern of cooling joints. (**c**) Histogram of angle in degrees between column sides at the Giant's Causeway (O'Reilly 1879). (**d**) Percentage of columns having a given number of sides, at the Giant's Causeway (A; measured by Walker) and several other columnar lavas (Beard 1959). (**e**) Two-tiered columnar jointing in the basalt at Hloduklettur, NE Iceland. The lava is ponded in a river valley, and the irregular top is due to emplacement below its own cinder accumulation. (**f**) Stages in the growth of (**e**). L: liquid lava; F: master joint allowing ingress of water coolant; C: colonnade; E: entablature. (**g**) Chisel structures several centimetres wide on column surfaces, Iceland. (**h**) Lava flow about 5 m thick cut through by the Dettifoss canyon in NE Iceland, showing distribution of cooling joints. The overlying and underlying flows have been cut off the photograph for clarity.

Katsui 1976). The same joint pattern commonly occurs in the entablature of columnar basalts. Such cobble-jointed rock is called 'kuppaberg' in Iceland.

Not all expansion joints in volcanic rocks form during cooling. Many basalts contain a glassy mesostasis, and this is particularly liable to hydrate to palagonite. Hydration accompanied by expansion may then cause additional joint systems to develop. The ball and socket joints that subdivide the columns of the Giant's Causeway (Preston 1930) may be such a system. Column rinds that form by weathering (Smedes & Lang 1955) cause tensional stresses in each column that are relieved by the formation of cross-joints.

### Flow jointing

During flowage of lava flows or magmatic intrusions, shearing occurs that may cause platy crystals (e.g. of plagioclase feldspar) to be orientated into near-parallelism with one another (this parallelism is called a trachytic texture), or cause gas bubbles to be deformed and their planes of flattening or elongation to be similarly orientated. This gives the rock a foliation along which it may split readily into platy fragments, particularly when accentuated by weathering.

Commonly the foliation/flow jointing exhibits ramp structure, being mostly inclined inward and up-flow along planes that curve across the flow and in plan view are concave in the up-flow direction. In longitudinal section these planes are steep at the flow-top and curve down to asymptote against the flow-base in the up-flow direction.

## Vesicularity of basaltic rocks

Gas bubbles or vesicles are ubiquitous in basaltic flows. They form mainly by exsolution of dissolved magmatic gases in the volcanic conduit under the vent where, by their expansion and the positive buoyancy that they confer on the magma, they are a powerful driving force for eruption. Water of external origin that enters the magmatic system may contribute to the gas budget at any stage. A massive loss of gas occurs at the vent, and as lava flows away it steadily becomes degassed. The final gas loss occurs as the lava crystallizes.

The pattern of degassing, and features of the vesicles that remain in lava flows, can yield important information on flow mechanisms and lava rheology. This brief chapter concentrates attention on this aspect of magmatic gases. It is brief because few studies have yet pursued this topic (Fig. 8).

A general relationship is that gas bubbles tend to rise and grow by coalescence (Sahagian et al. 1989) so increasing their ascent velocity. The lower and middle parts of a flow thus become depleted in vesicles, while vesicles become concentrated near the flow top (Aubele et al. 1988). In general, the thicker the lava flow and hence the longer it takes to solidify, the more nearly complete is the loss of bubbles from the lower and middle parts of the flow.

Vesicle shapes, sizes and distribution patterns are very sensitive to lava rheology. Deformed bubbles stay deformed if the combined effect of surface tension and gas pressure fails to overcome the yield strength. Possession by lava of a yield strength can prohibit the ascent of all bubbles smaller than a threshold size.

If a lava flow is initially Newtonian but a rheology front ascends into it from the flow-base, bubbles that ascend at the same rate as the front become pipe vesicles because their lower end fails to close. Pipe bubbles grow as they ascend by scavenging smaller bubbles, and may become megavesicles (exceptionally as much as 1 m in size) that ascend diapirically and tend to accumulate under the surface crust (Walker in press).

At a late stage, a residual low-melting-temperature fraction of melt and gases expelled by crystallization escape from the crystal mush leaving microscopic angular voids ('diktitaxitic' texture; Dickinson & Vigrass 1965). This fluid segregates, ascends in vesicle cylinders commonly 5–10 cm wide, and injects as near-horizontal and highly vesicular segregation veins near the middle of the lava flow where viscosity and yield strength begin to increase upward. Segregation veins propagate laterally by hydraulic fracturing. Partial separation of gas bubbles from the segregation melt generates segregation vesicles (Smith 1967) floored by segregation melt. The segregated rock is characteristically not chilled against the host basalt.

Thin (<2 m) flow units of spongy ('S-type') pahoehoe that occur in Hawaii on groundslopes >4° are initially Newtonian, permitting larger mafic crystals to settle toward the base giving an S-shaped profile, but they cooled and acquired a yield strength before the initially small vesicles ascended or grew significantly. The vesicle-size and concentration curves therefore tend to be bilaterally symmetrical about the median plane giving a D-shaped profile (Walker 1989b). The vesicle concentration near the middle may be so high that a median parting has developed, the roof of it upbowed to form a gas blister. Gas

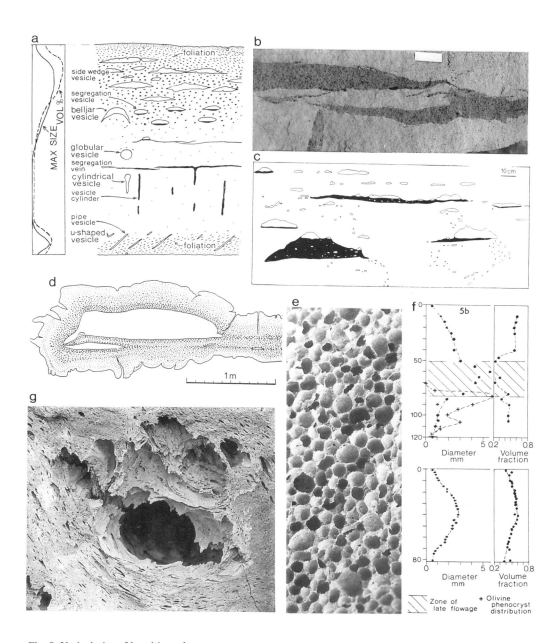

**Fig. 8.** Vesicularity of basaltic rocks.

(**a**) Generalized section across a pahoehoe flow unit about 5 m thick of Xitle volcano in Mexico, showing varieties of megavesicles and their zonal distribution (Walker 1993); profiles of vesicle size and abundance left. (**b**) Segregation vein (dark) in basalt flow, E Iceland; scale is 15 cm long. (**c**) Segregation vesicles with zeolite-infilled amygdales, Ballintoy, Antrim. (**d**) Gas blister in a pahoehoe flow unit, Reykjanes, Iceland. (**e**) Spongy pahoehoe, La Palma, Canary Islands; vesicles up to 5 mm in size. (**f**) Profiles across two spongy-pahoehoe flow units, Hawaii, showing variations in size and volume fraction of vesicles; depth scale in cm; olivine crystals are strongly concentrated in the lower part of one unit (Walker 1989*b*). (**g**) A type of vesicle that grew dynamically in a fast-moving aa flow (Xitle volcano, Mexico).

blisters are distinguished from drained lava tubes because they have bubble-wall texture on roof and floor, and the floor lacks flow structures.

Thick flow units of pipe-vesicle bearing ('P-type') pahoehoe that occur in Hawaii on slopes $< 4°$ have fewer and larger vesicles due to longer residence of the lava in tubes (Wilmoth & Walker 1993). Significant bubble loss has occurred. A banding of vesicles often occurs due to growth of the lava by continued injection under a surface crust ('lava-rise' mechanism).

Aa flows have considerably different vesicle distribution patterns because active flowage persists until considerable cooling has occurred. Shearing progressively eliminates vesicles, and distal-type aa tends to be non-vesicular apart from new planar crevices that are caused by shearing.

This paper began as an invited talk ('Modern Volcanic concepts – basalt volcanic systems') at Pacific Rim Congress 90, organized by the Australasian Institute of Mining and Metallurgy and held at Gold Coast, Queensland, 6–12 May 1990. A first draft was written during the week of the Congress and I thank the organizers for offering me the opportunity and stimulus for its inception. I thank reviewers Stephen Blake and Bill McGuire for their helpful comments. This paper is dedicated to the memory of Ian Gass, a fine scientist and a good friend.

SOEST contribution number 3281.

# References

APPELGATE, B. & EMBLEY, R. W. 1992. Submarine tumuli and inflated tube-fed lava flows on Axial Volcano, Juan de Fuca Ridge. *Bulletin of Volcanology*, **54**, 447–458.

ARAMAKI, S. & HAMURO, K. 1977. Geology of the Higashi-Izu monogenetic volcano group. *University of Tokyo, Earthquake Research Institute Bulletin*, **52**, 235–278.

——, HAYAKAWA, Y., FUJII, T., NAKAMURA, K. & FUKUOKA, T. 1986. The October 1983 eruption of Miyakejima Volcano. *Journal of Volcanology and Geothermal Research*, **29**, 203–229.

——, WATANABE, H., IDA, Y., YUKTAKE, T., NOTSU, K. & SHIMOZURU, D. 1988. The 1986–1987 eruption of Izu-Oshima volcano. *University of Tokyo Earthquake Research Institute*.

ARCULUS, R. J. & WILLS, J. K. A. 1980. The petrology of plutonic blocks and inclusions from the Lesser Antilles Island Arc. *Journal of Petrology*, **21**, 743–799.

ATKINSON, A. 1991. The Undara lava tubes, North Queensland, Australia. *6th International Symposium on Vulcanospeleology, Hawaii, August 1991*.

——, GRIFFIN, T. J. & STEPHENSON, P. J. 1975. A major lava tube system from Undara Volcano, North Queensland. *Bulletin Volcanologique*, **39**, 266–293.

AUBELE, J. C., CRUMPLER, L. S. & ELSTON, W. 1988. Vesicle zonation and vertical structure of basalt flows. *Journal of Volcanology and Geothermal Research*, **35**, 349–374.

BAER, G. & RECHES, Z. 1987. Flow patterns of magma in dikes. Makhtesh Ramon, Israel. *Geology*, **15**, 569–572.

BALLARD, R. D. & MOORE, J. G. 1977. *Photographic atlas of the Mid-Atlantic Ridge rift valley.* Springer-Verlag, New York.

——, HOLCOMB, R. T. & VAN ANDEL, T. H. 1979. The Galapagos Rift at 86°W: 3. Sheet flows, collapse pits, and lava lakes in the rift valley. *Journal of Geophysical Research*, **84**, 5407–5422.

BASALTIC VOLCANISM STUDY PROJECT. 1981. *Basaltic volcanism on the terrestrial planets.* Pergamon Press Inc, New York.

BEARD, C. N. 1959. Quantitative study of columnar jointing. *Geological Society of America Bulletin*, **70**, 379–381.

BEESON, M. H., PERTTU, R. & PERTTU, J. 1979. The origin of the Miocene basalts of coastal Oregon and Washington: an alternative hypothesis. *Oregon Geology*, **41**, 159–166.

BERGH, S. G. & SIGVALDASON, G. E. 1991. Pleistocene mass-flow deposits of basaltic hyaloclastite on a shallow submarine shelf, South Iceland. *Bulletin of Volcanology*, **52**, 597–611.

BERNSTEIN, S., ROSING, M. T., BROOKS, C. K. & BIRD, D. K. 1992. An ocean-ridge type magma chamber at a passive volcanic, continental margin: the Kap Edvard Holm layered gabbro complex, East Greenland. *Geological Magazine*, **129**, 437–456.

BLAKE, D. H. 1966. The net-veined complex of the Austurhorn intrusion, Southeastern Iceland. *Journal of Geology*, **74**, 891–907.

BLAKE, S., WILSON, C. J. N., SMITH, I. E. M. & WALKER, G. P. L. 1992. Petrology and dynamics of the Waimihia mixed magma eruption, Taupo Volcano, New Zealand. *Journal of the Geological Society, London*, **149**, 193–207.

BOOTH, B., CROASDALE, R. & WALKER, G. P. L. 1978. A quantitative study of five thousand years of volcanism on Sao Miguel, Azores. *Philosophical Transactions of the Royal Society of London*, **A288**, 271–319.

BOTT, M. H. P. & TUSON, J. 1973. Deep structure beneath the Tertiary volcanic regions of Skye, Mull and Ardnamurchan, North-west Scotland. *Nature Physical Science*, **242**, 114–116.

BRADLEY, J. 1965. Intrusion of major dolerite sills. *Royal Society of New Zealand Transactions*, **3**, 27–55.

BRADY, L. F. & WEBB, R. W. 1943. Cored bombs from Arizona and California volcanic cones. *Journal of Geology*, **51**, 398–410.

BROWN, G. C., EVERETT, S. P., RYMER, H., McGARVIE, D. W. & FOSTER, I. 1991. New light on caldera evolution – Askja, Iceland. *Geology*, **19**, 352–355.

BRUCE, P. M. & HUPPERT, H. E. 1990. Solidification and melting along dykes by the laminar flow of basaltic magma. In: RYAN, M. P. (ed.) *Magma transport and storage.* Wiley & Sons, Chichester, 87–101.

BUSBY-SPERA, C. J. & WHITE, J. D. L. 1987. Variation in peperite textures associated with differing host-sediment properties. *Bulletin of Volcanology*, **49**, 765–775.

CAMP, V. E. & ROOBOL, M. J. 1989. The Arabian continental alkali basalt province. Part I. Evolution of Harrat Rahat, Kingdom of Saudi Arabia. *Geological Society of America Bulletin*, **101**, 71–95.

——, HOOPER, P. R., ROOBOL, M. J. & WHITE, D. L. 1987. The Madinah eruption, Saudi Arabia: magma mixing and simultaneous extrusion of three basaltic chemical types. *Bulletin of Volcanology*, **49**, 489–508.

CAREY, S. W. 1958. The isostrat: a new technique for the analysis of structure of the Tasmanian dolerite. In: *Dolerite: a symposium*. University of Hobart, Tasmania, 130–164.

CARRACEDO, J. C., BADIOLA, E. R. & SOLER, V. 1993. The 1730–1736 eruption of Lanzarote, Canary Islands: a long, high-magnitude basaltic fissure eruption. *Journal of Volcanology and Geothermal Research*, **53**, 239–250.

CASTON, V. N. D., DEARNLEY, R., HARRISON, R. K., RUNDLE, C. C. & STYLES, M. T. 1981. Olivine-dolerite intrusions in the Fastnet Basin. *Journal of the Geological Society, London*, **138**, 31–46.

CHADWICK, W. W. & HOWARD, K. A. 1991. The pattern of circumferential and radial eruptive fissures on the volcanoes of Fernandina and Isabela islands, Galapagos. *Bulletin of Volcanology*, **53**, 259–275.

CHAPMAN, C. A. 1966. Paucity of mafic ring-dikes – evidence for floored polymagmatic chambers. *American Journal of Science*, **264**, 66–77.

CHEN, C.-H., PRESNALL, D. C. & STERN, R. J. 1992. Petrogenesis of ultramafic xenoliths from the 1800 Kaupulehu Flow, Hualalai volcano, Hawaii. *Journal of Petrology*, **33**, 163–202.

CHEVALLIER, L. & VERWOERD, W. J. 1987. A dynamic interpretation of Tristan da Cunha Volcano, South Atlantic Ocean. *Journal of Volcanology and Geothermal Research*, **34**, 35–49.

CHITWOOD, L. A. 1990. Newberry, Oregon. In: WOOD, C. A. & KIENLE, J. (eds) *Volcanoes of North America*. Cambridge University Press, 200–202.

CHRISTIANSEN, R. L. 1984. Yellowstone magmatic evolution: its bearing on understanding large-volume explosive volcanism. In: *Explosive Volcanism, inception, evolution, and hazards*. National Research Council, Washington, D.C., 84–95.

CLAGUE, D. A. 1987. Hawaiian xenolith populations, magma supply rates, and development of magma chambers. *Bulletin of Volcanology*, **49**, 577–587.

COLE, J. W. 1973. High-alumina basalts of Taupo Volcanic Zone, New Zealand. *Lithos*, **6**, 53–64.

COWARD, M. P. 1980. The analysis of flow profiles in a basaltic dyke using strained vesicles. *Journal of the Geological Society, London*, **137**, 605–615.

COX, K. G. 1980. A model for flood basalt vulcanism. *Journal of Petrology*, **21**, 629–650.

—— 1989. The role of mantle plumes in the development of continental drainage patterns. *Nature*, **342**, 873–876.

DE GRAFF, J. M., LONG, P. E. & AYDIN, A. 1989. Use of joint-growth directions and rock textures to infer thermal regimes during solidification of basaltic lava flows. *Journal of Volcanology and Geothermal Research*, **38**, 309–324.

DECKER, R. W. & CHRISTIANSEN, R. L. 1984. Explosive eruptions of Kilauea Volcano, Hawaii. In: *Studies in Geophysics. Explosive volcanism: inception, evolution and hazards*. National Academy Press, Washington D.C., 122–132.

DETRICK, R. S., BUHL, P., VERA, E., MUTTER, J., ORCUTT, J., MADSEN, J. & BROCHER, T. 1987. Multi-channel seismic imaging of a crustal magma chamber along the East Pacific Rise. *Nature*, **326**, 35–41.

DICKINSON, W. R. & VIGRASS, L. W. 1965. Geology of the Suplee-Izee area, Crook, Grant, and Harney Counties. *Oregon Department of Geology and Mineral Resources, Bulletin*, **58**.

DUFFIELD, W. A., BACON, C. R. & DELANEY, P. T. 1986. Deformation of poorly consolidated sediment during shallow emplacement of a basalt sill, Caso Range, California. *Bulletin of Volcanology*, **48**, 97–107.

——, STIELTJES L. & VARET, J. 1982. Huge landslide blocks in the growth of Piton de la Fournaise, La Reunion, and Kilauea volcano, Hawaii. *Journal of Volcanology and Geothermal Research*, **12**, 147–160.

EASTON, R. M. & LOCKWOOD, J. P. 1983. 'Surface-fed dikes' – the origin of some unusual dikes along the Hilina fault zone, Kilauea Volcano, Hawaii. *Bulletin Volcanologique*, **44**, 45–53.

EINARSSON, P. & BRANDSDOTTIR, B. 1980. Seismological evidence for lateral magma intrusion during the July 1978 deflation of the Krafla volcano in NE Iceland. *Journal of Geophysics*, **47**, 160–165.

EINSELE, G. & 18 others, 1980. Intrusion of basaltic sills into highly porous sediments, and resulting hydrothermal activity. *Nature*, **283**, 442–445.

EMELEUS, C. H. 1987. The Rhum layered complex, Inner Hebrides, Scotland. In: PARSONS, I. (ed.) *Origins of igneous layering*. D. Reidel Publishing Company, Dordrecht, 263–286.

EMERMAN, S. H. & MARRETT, R. 1990. Why dikes? *Geology*, **18**, 231–233.

ERNST, R. E. & BARAGAR, W. R. A. 1992. Evidence from magnetic fabric for the flow pattern of magma in the Mackenzie giant radiating dyke swarm. *Nature*, **356**, 511–513.

FEDOTOV, S. A. 1981. Magma rates in feeding conduits of different volcanic centers. *Journal of Volcanology and Geothermal Research*, **9**, 379–394.

—— 1982. Temperatures of entering magma, formation and dimensions of magma chambers of volcanoes. *Bulletin of Volcanology*, **45**, 333–347.

FISHER, R. V. 1968. Puu Hou littoral cones, Hawaii. *Geologisch Rundschau*. **57**, 837–864.

—— & WATERS, A. C. 1970. Base surge bedforms in maar volcanoes. *American Journal of Science*, **268**, 157–180.

FISKE, R. S. & JACKSON, E. D. 1973. Orientation and growth of Hawaiian volcanic rifts. The effect of regional structure and gravitational stress. *Royal Society of London Proceedings*, **A329**, 299–326.

—— & KINOSHITA, W. T. 1969. Inflation of Kilauea volcano prior to its 1967–1968 eruption. *Science*, **165**, 341–349.

FORNARI, D. J. 1986. Submarine lava tubes and channels. *Bulletin of Volcanology*, **48**, 291–298.

FRANCIS, E. H. 1982. Magma and sediment. I. Emplacement mechanism of Late Carboniferous tholeiite sills in northern Britain. *Journal of the Geological Society, London*, **139**, 1–20.

FRANCIS, P. W. 1973. Cannonball bombs, a new kind of volcanic bomb from the Pacaya volcano, Guatamala. *Geological Society of America Bulletin*, **84**, 2791–2794.

FRANKEL, J. J. 1967. Forms and structures of intrusive basaltic rocks. In: HESS, H. H. & POLDERVAART, A. (eds) *Basalts: the Poldervaart treatise on rocks of basaltic composition*. Interscience Publishers, New York, N.Y., 63–102.

FURNES, H. 1974. Volume relations between palagonite and authigenic minerals hyaloclastites, and its bearing on the rate of palagonitization. *Bulletin Volcanologique*, **38**, 173–186.

—— & FRIDLEIFSSON, I. B. 1974. Tidal effects on the formation of pillow lava/hyaloclastite deltas. *Geology*, **2**, 381–384.

FURUMOTO, A. S. 1978. Nature of the magma conduit under the East Rift Zone of Kilauea volcano, Hawaii. *Bulletin Volcanologique*, **41**, 435–453.

——, THOMPSON, N. J. & WOOLLARD, G. P. 1965. The structure of Koolau Volcano from seismic refraction studies. *Pacific Science*, **19**, 296–305.

FYFE, W. S. 1992. Magma underplating of continental crust. *Journal of Volcanology and Geothermal Research*, **50**, 33–40.

GASS, I. G. & MALLICK, D. I. J. 1968. Jebel Khariz: an Upper Miocene stratovolcano of comenditic affinity on the south Arabian coast. *Bulletin Volcanologique*, **32**, 33–88.

GAUTNEB, H. & GUDMUNDSSON, A. 1992. Effect of local and regional stress fields on sheet emplacement in West Iceland. *Journal of Volcanology and Geothermal Research*, **51**, 339–356.

GEIKIE, Sir A. 1897. *Ancient volcanoes of Great Britain*. Macmillan, London.

GIBB, F. G. H. & HENDERSON, C. M. B. 1989. Discontinuities between picritic and crinanitic units in the Shiant Isles sill: evidence of multiple intrusion. *Geological Magazine*, **126**, 127–137.

—— & —— 1992. Convection and crystal settling in sills. *Contributions to Mineralogy and Petrology*, **109**, 538–545.

GIBERTI, G., JAUPART, C. & SARTORIS, G. 1992. Steady-state operation of Stromboli volcano, Italy: constraints on the feeding system. *Bulletin of Volcanology*, **54**, 535–541.

GIBSON, S. A. & JONES, A. P. 1991. Igneous stratigraphy and internal structure of the Little-Minch sill complex, Trotternish Peninsula, northern Skye, Scotland. *Geological Magazine*, **128**, 51–66.

GREELEY, R. 1982. The Snake River Plain, Idaho: representative of a new category of volcanism. *Journal of Geophysical Research*, **87**, 2705–2712.

GRIFFITHS, R. W. & FINK, J. H. 1992. Solidification and morphology of submarine lavas: a dependence on extrusion rate. *Journal of Geophysical Research*, **97**, 19729–19738.

GUDMUNDSSON, A. 1987. Formation and mechanics of magma reservoirs in Iceland. *Royal Astronomical Society Geophysical Journal*, **91**, 27–41.

GUEST, J. E., CHESTER, D. K. & DUNCAN, A. M. 1984. The Valle de Bove, Mount Etna: its origin and relation to the stratigraphy and structure of the volcano. *Journal of Volcanology and Geothermal Research*, **21**, 1–23.

——, KILBURN, C. R. J., PINKERTON, H. & DUNCAN, A. M. 1987. The evolution of lava flow-fields: observations of the 1981 and 1989 eruptions of Mount Etna, Sicily. *Bulletin of Volcanology*, **49**, 527–540.

HARDEE, H. C. 1982. Incipient magma chamber formation as a result of repetitive intrusions. *Bulletin of Volcanology*, **45**, 41–49.

HAYAKAWA, Y. & KOYAMA, M. 1992. Eruptive history of the Higashi-Izu monogenetic volcano field 1: 0–32 ka. *Volcanological Society of Japan Bulletin*, **37**, 167–181.

HEAD, J. W. & WILSON, L. 1989. Basaltic pyroclastic eruptions. *Journal of Volcanology and Geothermal Research*, **37**, 261–271.

HEMING, R. F. & BARNET, P. R. 1986. The petrology and petrochemistry of the Auckland volcanic field. *In*: SMITH, I. E. M. (ed.) *Late Cenozoic Volcanism in New Zealand*. Royal Society of New Zealand Bulletin, **23**, 64–75.

HIGGINS, M. W. 1973. Petrology of Newberry volcanoes, Central Oregon. *Geological Society of America Bulletin*, **84**, 455–488.

HILDRETH, W. 1981. Gradients in silicic magma chambers: implications for lithospheric magmatism. *Journal of Geophysical Research*, **86**, 10153–10192.

HON, K., KAUAHIKAUA, J., DENLINGER, R. & MCKAY, K. in press. Emplacement and inflation of pahoehoe sheet flows – observations and measurements of active lava flows on Kilauea volcano, Hawaii. *Geological Society of America Bulletin*.

HONNOREZ, J & KIRST, P. 1975. Submarine basaltic volcanism: morphometric parameters for discriminating hyaloclastites from hyalotuffs. *Bulletin Volcanologique*, **39**, 441–465.

HOTZ, P. E. 1952. Form of diabase sheets in southeastern Pennsylvania. *American Journal of Science*, **250**, 375–388.

HUPPERT, H. & SPARKS, R. S. J. 1985. Cooling and contamination of mafic and ultramafic magmas during ascent through continental crust. *Earth and Planetary Science Letters*, **74**, 371–386.

HUSCH, J. M. 1990. Palisades sill: origin of the olivine zone by separate magmatic injection rather than gravity settling. *Geology*, **18**, 699–702.

JAKOBSSON, S. P. & MOORE, J. G. 1986. Hydrothermal minerals and alteration rates at Surtsey volcano, Iceland. *Geological Society of America Bulletin*, **97**, 648–659.

JAMES, A. V. G. 1920. Factors producing columnar jointing in lavas and its occurrence near Melbourne, Australia. *Journal of Geology*, **28**, 458–469.

JOHNSON, R. W. 1989. Volcano distribution and classification In: JOHNSON R. W. (ed.) *Intraplate volcanism in eastern Australia and New Zealand*. Cambridge University Press, Cambridge.

JONES, J. G. 1968. Pillow lava and pahoehoe. *Journal of Geology*, **76**, 485–488.

—— 1969. Intraglacial volcanoes of the Laugarvatn region, south-west Iceland – I. *Quarterly Journal of the Geological Society of London*, **124**, 197–211.

—— & NELSON, P. H. H. 1970. The flow of basalt lava from air into water – its structural expression and stratigraphic significance. *Geological Magazine*, **107**, 13–19.

KILBURN, C. R. J. & LOPEZ, R. M. C. 1991. General patterns of flow field growth: aa and blocky lavas. *Journal of Geophysical Research*, **96**, 19721–19732.

KINOSHITO, W. T. 1965. A gravity survey of the Island of Hawaii. *Pacific Science*, **19**, 339–340.

KLEIN, F. W., KOYANAGI, R. Y., NAKATA, J. S. & TANIGAWA, W. R. 1987. The seismicity of Kilauea's magma system. *United States Geological Survey Professional Paper*, **1350**, 1019–1185.

KNIGHT, M. D. & WALKER, G. P. L. 1988. Magma flow direction in dikes of the Koolau Complex, Oahu, from magnetic fabric lineations direction. *Journal of Geophysical Research*, **93**, 4301–4319.

KOKELAAR, B. P. 1983. The mechanism of Surtseyan volcanism. *Journal of the Geological Society, London*, **140**, 939–944.

—— 1986. Magma–water interactions in subaqueous and emergent basaltic volcanism. *Bulletin of Volcanology*, **48**, 275–289.

KRAUSE, D. C. & WATKINS, N. D. 1970. North Atlantic crustal genesis in the vicinity of the Azores. *Royal Astronomical Society Geophysical Journal*, **19**, 261–283.

KUNO, H. 1964. Dike swarm in Hakone Volcano. *Bulletin Volcanologique*, **27**, 53–59.

LE GUERN, F., CARBONNELLE, J. & TAZIEFF, H. 1978. Erta'ale lava lake: heat and gas transfer to the atmosphere. *Journal of Volcanology and Geothermal Research*, **6**, 27–48.

LISTER, J. R. & KERR, R. C. 1990. Fluid-mechanical models of crack propagation and their application to magma-transport in dykes. *Journal of Geophysical Research*, **96**, 10049–10077.

LO GUIDICE, A., PATANE, G., RASA, R. & ROMANO, R. 1982. The structural framework of Mount Etna. In: ROMANO, R. (ed.) *Mount Etna Volcano*. Memoir Society Geological Italy, **23**, 125–158.

LOBJOIT, W. M. 1959. On the form and mode of emplacement of the Ben Buie intrusion, Isle of Mull, Argyllshire. *Geological Magazine*, **96**, 393–402.

LOCKWOOD, J. P., DVORAK, J. J., ENGLISH, T. T., KOYANAGI, Y., OKAMURA, A. T., SUMMERS, M. L. & TANIGAWA, W. R. 1987. Mauna Loa 1974–1984: A decade of extrusive and intrusive activity. *United States Geological Survey, Professional Paper*, **1350**, 537–570.

—— & LIPMAN, P. W. 1987. Holocene eruptive history of Mauna Loa volcano. *United States Geological Survey, Professional Paper*, **1350**, 509–535.

LONG, P. E. & WOOD, B. J., 1986. Structures, textures, and cooling histories of Columbia River basalt flow. *Geological Society of America Bulletin*, **97**, 1144–1155.

LORENZ, V. 1985. Maars and diatremes of phreatomagmatic origin: a review. *Transactions of the Geological Society of South Africa*, **88**, 459–470.

—— 1986. On the growth of maars and diatremes and its relevance to the formation of tuff rings. *Bulletin of Volcanology*, **48**, 265–274.

MACDONALD, G. A. 1948. Notes on Niuafo'ou. *American Journal of Science*, **246**, 65–77.

—— 1962. The 1959 and 1960 eruptions of Kilauea volcano, Hawaii, and the construction of walls to restrict the spread of the lava flows. *Bulletin Volcanologique*, **24**, 249–294.

—— 1965. Hawaiian calderas. *Pacific Science*, **19**, 320–334.

—— 1967. Forms and structures of extrusive basaltic rocks. In: HESS, H. H. & POLDERVAART, A. (eds) *Basalts. The Poldervaart treatise on rocks of basaltic composition*. Interscience Publishers, New York, N.Y, 1861.

——, ABBOTT, A. T. & PETERSON, F. L. 1983. *Volcanoes in the sea* (2nd edn). University of Hawaii Press, Honolulu.

MACHADO, F., PARSONS, W. H., RICHARDS, A. F. & MULFORD, J. W. 1962. Capelinhos eruption of Fayal Volcano, Azores, 1957–1958. *Journal of Geophysical Research*, **67**, 3519–3529.

MARSH, B. D. 1989. Magma chambers. *Annual Reviews of Earth and Planetary Science*, **17**, 439–474.

MARTIN DEL POZZO, A. L. 1982. Monogenetic volcanism in Sierra Chichinautzin, Mexico. *Bulletin of Volcanology*, **45**, 9–24.

MATHEWS, W. H. 1947. 'Tuyas'. Flat-topped volcanoes in northern British Columbia. *American Journal of Science*, **245**, 560–570.

MATTSON, S. R., VOGEL, T. A. WILBAND, J. T. 1986. Petrochemistry of the silicic-mafic complexes at Vesturhorn and Austurhorn, Iceland: evidence for zoned/stratified magma. *Journal of Volcanology and Geothermal Research*, **28**, 197–223.

MCBIRNEY, A. R. & NOYES, R. M. 1979. Crystallization and layering of the Skaergaard intrusion. *Journal of Petrology*, **20**, 487–554.

MCGUIRE, W. J. & PULLEN, A. D. 1989. Location and orientation of eruptive fissures and feeder-dykes at Mount Etna: influence of gravitational and regional stress regimes. *Journal of Volcanology and Geothermal Research*, **38**, 325–344.

——, —— & SAUNDERS, S. J. 1990. Recent dyke-induced large-scale block movement at Mount Etna and potential slope failure. *Nature*, **343**, 357–359.

MCKEE, C. O., ALMOND, R. A. COOKE, R. J. S. & TALAI, B. 1981. Basaltic pyroclastic avalanches and flank effusion from Ulawun volcano in 1978. *In*: JOHNSON, R. W. (ed.) *Cooke-Ravian Volume of volcanological papers*. Geological Survey of Papua New Guinea, Memoir **10**, 153–165.

MCQUILLIN, R. & TUSON, J. 1963. Gravity measurements over the Rhum Tertiary plutonic complex. *Nature*, **199**, 1276–1277.

MONZIER, M., ROBIN, C., EISSEN, J-P. & PICARD, C. 1991. Découverte d'un large anneau de tufs basaltiques associé à la formation de la caldera d'Ambrym (Vanuatu, SW Pacifique). *Compte Rendus of the Academy of Science, Paris*, **313**, 1319–1326.

MOORE, J. G. 1967. Base surge in recent volcanic eruptions. *Bulletin Volcanologique*, **30**, 337–363.

—— 1975. Mechanism of formation of pillow lava. *American Scientist*, **63**, 269–277.

—— & CHARLTON, D. W. 1984. Ultrathin lava layers exposed near San Luis Obispo Bay, California. *Geology*, **12**, 542–545.

——, CLAGUE, D. A., HOLCOMBE, R. T., LIPMAN, P. W., NORMARK, W. R. & TORRESAN, M. E. 1989. Prodigious submarine landslides on the Hawaiian Ridge. *Journal of Geophysical Research*, **94**, 17465–17484.

——, PHILLIPS, R. L., GRIGG, R. W., PETERSON, D. W. & SWANSON, D. A. 1973. Flow of lava into the sea, 1969–1971, Kilauea volcano, Hawaii. *Geological Society of America Bulletin*, **84**, 537–546.

MUNRO, D. C. 1992. *The application of remotely sensed data to studies of volcanism in the Galapagos Islands*. PhD thesis, University of Hawaii at Manoa.

NAKAMURA, K. 1964. Volcano-stratigraphic study of Oshima volcano, Izu. *University of Tokyo Earthquake Research Institute Bulletin*, **42**, 649–728.

—— 1977. Volcanoes as possible indicators of tectonic stress orientation – principle and practice. *Journal of Volcanology and Geothermal Research*, **2**, 1–16.

——, JACOB, K. H. & DAVIES, J. N. 1977. Volcanoes as possible indicators of tectonic stress orientation – Aleutians and Alaska. *Pure and Applied Geophysics*, **115**, 87–112.

NOE-NYGAARD, A. 1968. On extrusion forms in plateau basalts. Shield volcanoes of 'Scutulum' type. *Science in Iceland Anniversary Volume*, 10–13. Societas Scientiarum Islandica, Rekjavik.

ODE, H. 1957. Mechanical analysis of the dike pattern of the Spanish Peaks area, Colorado. *Geological Society of America Bulletin*, **68**, 567–576.

O'REILLY, J. P. 1879. Explanatory notes, Giant's Causeway. *Transactions of the Royal Irish Academy*, **26**, 641–734.

PECK, D. L. & MINAKAMI, T. 1968. The formation of columnar joints in the upper part of Kilauean lava lakes. *Geological Society of America Bulletin*, **79**, 1151–1166.

PETERSON, D. W. & MOORE, J. G. 1987. Geologic history and evolution of geologic concepts, Island of Hawaii. *United States Geological Society Professional Paper*, **1350**, 149–189.

PFAFF, V. J. & BEESON, M. H. 1989. Miocene basalt near Astoria, Oregon: geophysical evidence for Columbia Plateau origin. *In*: REIDAL, S. P. & HOOPER, P. R. (eds) *Volcanism and tectonism in the Columbia River flood-basalt province*. Geological Society of America Special Paper **239**, 143–156.

PIERCE, K. L. & MORGAN, L. A. 1992. The track of the Yellowstone Hot Spot: volcanism, faulting, and uplift. *In*: LINK, P. P. K., KUNTZ, M. A. & PLATT, L. B. (eds) *Regional Geology of eastern Idaho and western Wyoming*. Geological Society of America, Memoir **179**, 1–53.

POLLARD, D. D., MULLER, O. H. & DOCKSTADER, D. R. 1975. The form and growth of fingered sheet intrusions. *Geological Society of America Bulletin*, **86**, 351–363.

PRESTON, F. W. 1930. Ball and socket jointing in basalt prisms. *Proceedings of the Royal Society of London*, **B106**, 87–93.

RAMPINO, M. R. & STOTHERS, R. B. 1988. Flood basalt volcanism during the past 250 million years. *Science*, **241**, 663–668.

RANCON, J. P., LEREBOUR, P. & AUGE, T. 1989. The Grand Brule exploration drilling: new data on the deep framework of the Piton de la Fournaise volcano. Part 1: lithostratigraphic units of and volcanostructural implications. *Journal of Volcanology and Geothermal Research*, **36**, 113–127.

RICHARDS, M. A., DUNCAN, R. A. & COURTILLOT, V. E. 1989. Flood basalts and hotspot tracks: plume heads and tails. *Science*, **246**, 103–107.

RITTMANN, A. 1962. *Volcanoes and their activity*. Wiley, New York, N.Y.

ROWLAND, S. K. & WALKER, G. P. L. 1990. Pahoehoe and aa in Hawaii: volumetric flow rate controls the lava structure. *Bulletin of Volcanology*, **52**, 615–628.

RUBIN, A. M. & POLLARD, D. D. 1987. Origins of blade-like dikes in volcanic rift zones. *United States Geological Survey Professional Paper*, **1350**, 1449–1470.

RUTTEN, M. G. 1964. Formation of a plateaubasalt series (from the example of Iceland). *Bulletin Volcanologique*, **27**.

RYAN, M. P. 1987. Neutral buoyancy and the mechanical evolution of magmatic systems. *In*: MYSEN, B. O. (ed.) *Magmatic processes: physicochemical principles*. Geochemistry Society Special Publication, **1**, 259–287.

——, KOYANAGI, R. Y. & FISKE, R. S. 1981. Modeling the three-dimensional structure of macroscopic magma transport systems: applications to Kilauea volcano, Hawaii. *Journal of Geophysical Research*, **86**, 7111–7129.

—— & SAMMIS, C. G. 1978. Cyclic fracture mechanisms in cooling basalt. *Geological Society of America Bulletin*, **89**, 1295–1308.

SAEMUNDSSON, K. 1970. Interglacial lava flow in the lowlands of southern Iceland and the problem of two-tiered columnar jointing. *Jokull*, **20**, 62–77.

SAHAGIAN, D. L., ANDERSON, A. T. & WARD, B. 1989. Bubble coalescence in basalt flows: comparison of a numerical model with natural examples. *Bulletin of Volcanology*, **52**, 49–56.

SAVAGE, J. C. & COCKERMAN, R. S. 1984. Earthquake swarm in Long Valley, California, January 1983: evidence for dike inflation. *Journal of Geophysical Research*, **89**, 8315–8374.

SCHMINCKE, H-U, 1967. Fused tuff and peperites in south-central Washington. *Geological Society of America Bulletin*, **78**, 319–330.

SEARLE, E. J. 1964. *City of Volcanoes: a geology of Auckland*. Paul's Book Arcade, Auckland.

SEGERSTROM, K. 1950. Erosion studies at Paricutin, State of Michoacan, Mexico. *United States Geological Survey Bulletin*, **965-A**

SEN, G. & JONES, R. E. 1990. Cumulate xenoliths in Oahu, Hawaii: Implications for deep magma chambers and Hawaiian volcanism. *Science*, **249**, 1154–1157.

SHELLEY, D. 1985. Determining paleo-flow directions from groundmass fabrics in the Lyttleton radial dykes, New Zealand. *Journal of Volcanology and Geothermal Research*, **25**, 69–80.

SIGURDSSON, H. & SPARKS, R. S. J. 1978. Rifting episode in North Iceland in 1874–1875 and the eruptions of Askja and Sveinagja. *Bulletin Volcanologique*, **41**, 149–167.

SIGVALDASON, G. E., ANNERTZ, K. & NILSSON, M. 1992. Effect of glacier loading/deloading on volcanism: postglacial volcanic production rate of the Dyngjufjoll area, central Iceland. *Bulletin of Volcanology*, **54**, 385–392

SILVESTRI, S. C. 1962. Lava-dikes in hyaloclastites at Cape Passero (Sicily). *Bulletin Volcanologique*, **25**, 271–275.

SIMKIN, T. & HOWARD, K. A.. 1970. Caldera collapse in the Galapagos Islands 1968. *Science*, **169**, 429–437.

SMEDES, H. W. & LANG, A. J. 1955. Basalt column rinds caused by deuteric alteration. *American Journal of Science*, **253**, 173–181.

SMITH, R. E. 1967. Segregation vesicles in basaltic lava. *American Journal of Science*, **265**, 696–713.

SOHN, Y. K. & CHOUGH, S. K. 1989. Depositional processes of the Suwolbong tuff-ring, Cheju Island (Korea). *Sedimentology*, **36**, 837–855.

SPARKS, R. S. J., PINKERTON, H. & MACDONALD, R. 1977a. The transport of xenoliths in magmas. *Earth and Planetary Science Letters*, **35**, 234–238.

——, SIGURDSSON, H. & WILSON, L. 1977b. Magma mixing: a mechanism for triggering acid explosive eruptions. *Nature*, **267**, 315–318.

STAUDIGEL, H. GEE, J., TAUXE, L. & VARGA, R. J. 1992. Shallow intrusive directions of sheeted dikes in the Troodos ophiolite: anisotropy of magmatic susceptibility and structural data. *Geology*, **20**, 841–844.

STEARNS, H. T. 1946. Geology of the Hawaiian Islands. *Hawaii Division of Hydrography, Bulletin* **8**.

STEPHENSON, P. J. & GRIFFIN, T. J. 1975. Some long basaltic lava flows in North Queensland. *In*: JOHNSON, R. W. (ed.) *Volcanism in Australia*. Elsevier Science Publishing Company, Amsterdam, 41–50.

——, —— & SUTHERLAND, F. L. 1980. Cainozoic volcanism in northeastern Australia. *In*: HENDERSON, R. A. & STEPHENSON, P. J. (eds) *The geology and geophysics of northeastern Australia*. Geological Society of Australia, 349–374.

STRANGE, W. E., MACHESKY, L. F. & WOOLLARD, G. P. 1965. A gravity survey of the Island of Oahu, Hawaii. *Pacific Science*, **19**, 354–358.

STRONG, D. F. & JACQUOT, C. 1971. The Karthala Caldera, Grande Comore. *Bulletin Volcanologique*, **34**, 663–680.

SUGA, K. & FUJIOKA, H. 1990. Volume of volcanic materials along northern Izu-Bonin Arc. *Volcanological Society of Japan Bulletin*, **35**, 359–374.

SWANSON, D. A. 1973. Pahoehoe flows from the 1969–1971 Mauna Ulu eruption Kilauea volcano, Hawaii. *Geological Society of America Bulletin*, **84**, 615–626.

——, WRIGHT, T. L. W. & HELZ, R. T. 1975. Linear vent systems and estimated rates of magma production and eruption for the Yokima basalt of the Columbia Plateau. *American Journal of Science*, **275**, 877–905.

TAKADA, A. 1988. Subvolcanic structures of the central dike swarm associated with the ring complexes in the Shitara district, Central Japan. *Bulletin of Volcanology*, **29**, 106–118.

TAZAWA K. 1984. Coastal deposits of Izu-Oshima Island: their implications in the volcanic activity and sea level change. *Volcanological Society of Japan Bulletin*, **29**, 1–15.

TAZIEFF, H. 1977. An exceptional eruption: Mt. Niragongo, Jan. 10th, 1977. *Bulletin Volcanologique*, **40**, 189–200.

—— 1984. Mt. Niragongo: renewed activity of the lava lake. *Journal of Volcanology and Geothermal Research*, **20**, 267–280.

THORARINSSON, S. 1953 The crater groups in Iceland. *Bulletin Volcanologique*, **14**, 3–44.

——, EINARSSON, Th., SIGVALDASON, G. & ELISSON, G. 1964. The submarine eruption off the Vestmann Islands 1963–64. A preliminary report. *Bulletin Volcanologique*, **27**, 435–446.

TOLAN, T. L., REIDEL, S. P., BEESON, M. H., ANDERSON, J. L., FECHT, K. R. & SWANSON, D. A. 1989. Revisions to the estimates of the areal extent and volume of the Columbia River Basalt Group. *In*: REIDEL, S. P. & HOOPER, P. R. (eds) *Volcanism and Tectonism in the Columbia River flood-basalt province*. Geological Society of America, Special Paper, **239**, 1–20.

TOMKEIEFF, S. I. 1940. Basalt lavas of the Giant's Causeway. *Bulletin Volcanologique*, ser 2, **18**, 89–143.

TRIBBLE, G. W. 1991. Underwater observation of active lava flows from Kilauea Volcano, Hawaii. *Geology*, **19**, 633–636.

TRYGGVASON, E. 1989. Ground deformation in Askja, Iceland: its source and possible relation to flow in the mantle plume. *Journal of Volcanology and Geothermal Research*, **39**, 61–71.

TSUYA, H. 1941. On the form and structure of volcanic bombs from Volcano Miyakeshima. *University of Tokyo Earthquake Research Institute, Bulletin*, **19**, 597–611.

—— 1955. Geological and petrological studies of Volcano Fuji. 5. On the 1707 eruption of Volcano Fuji. *University of Tokyo Earthquake Research Institute Bulletin*, **33**, 341–384.

VERWOERD, W. J. & CHEVALLIER, L. 1987. Contrasting types of Surtseyan tuff rings on Marion and Prince Islands, southwest Indian Ocean. *Bulletin of Volcanology*, **49**, 399–417.

WADA, J. 1992. Magma flow directions inferred from preferred orientations of phenocrysts in a composite feeder dike, Miyake-Jima, Japan. *Journal of Volcanology and Geothermal Research.* **49**, 119–126.

WADGE, G. 1977. The storage and release of magma on Mount Etna. *Journal of Volcanology and Geothermal Research*, **2**, 361–384.

—— 1981. The variation of magma discharge during basaltic eruptions. *Journal of Volcanology and Geothermal Research*, **11**, 139–168.

—— 1982. Steady state volcanism: evidence from eruption histories of polygenetic volcanoes. *Journal of Geophysical Research*, **87**, 4035–4049.

—— & LOPES, R. M. C. 1991. The lobes of lava flows on Earth and Olympus Mons, Mars. *Bulletin of Volcanology*, **54**, 10–24.

WADSWORTH, W. J. 1982. The major basic intrusions. *In:* SUTHERLAND, D. S. (ed.) *Igneous rocks of the British Isles.* Wiley, Chichester, 416–425.

WALKER, B. H. & FRANCIS, E. H. 1987. High-level emplacement of an olivine-dolerite sill into Namurian sediments near Cardenden, Fife. *Royal Society of Edinburgh Transactions, Earth Sciences*, **77**, 295–307.

WALKER, F. & POLDERVAART, A. 1949. Karroo dolerites of the Union of South Africa. *Geological Society of America Bulletin*, **60**, 591–706.

WALKER, G. P. L. & BLAKE, D. H. 1966. The formation of a palagonite breccia mass beneath a valley glacier in Iceland. *Quarterly Journal of the Geological Society of London*, **122**, 45–61.

—— 1968. The breaking of magma. *Geological Magazine*, **106**, 166–173.

—— 1986. Koolau dike complex, Oahu: intensity and origin of a sheeted-dike complex high in a Hawaiian volcanic edifice. *Geology*, **14**, 310–313.

—— 1987. The dike complex of Koolau volcano, Oahu: internal structure of a Hawaiian rift zone. *United States Geological Survey Professional Paper*, **1350**, 961–993.

—— 1988. Three Hawaiian calderas: an origin through loading by shallow intrusions? *Journal of Geophysical Research*, **93**, 14,773–14,784.

—— 1989a. Gravitation (density) controls on volcanism, magma chambers and intrusions. *Australian Journal of Earth Sciences*, **36**, 149–165.

—— 1989b. Spongy pahoehoe in Hawaii: a study of vesicle-distribution patterns in basalt and their significance. *Bulletin of Volcanology*, **51**, 199–209.

—— 1990. Geology and volcanology of the Hawaiian Islands. *Pacific Science*, **44**, 315–347.

—— 1991. Structure, and origin by injection of lava under surface crust, of tumuli, 'lava rises', 'lava-rise pits', and 'lava-inflation clefts' in Hawaii. *Bulletin of Volcanology*, **53**, 546–558.

—— 1992a. 'Coherent intrusion complexes' in large basaltic volcanoes – a structural model. *Journal of Volcanology and Geothermal Research*, **50**, 41–54.

—— 1992b. Puu Mahana near South Point in Hawaii is a primary Surtseyan ash ring, not a Sandhills-type littoral cone. *Pacific Science*, **46**, 1–10

—— in press. Origin of vesicle types and distribution patterns in the Xitle pahoehoe basalt, in Mexico City. *Bulletin of Volcanology*.

WATANABE, K. & KATSUI, Y. 1976. Pseudo-pillow lavas in the Aso caldera, Kyusyu, Japan. *Journal of the Japanese Association of Mining, Petroleum, and Economic Geologists*, **71**, 44–49.

WATERS, A. C. & FISHER, R. V. 1971. Base surges and their deposits: Capelinos and Taal volcanoes. *Journal of Geophysical Research*, **76**, 5596–5614.

WELLS, M. K. 1954. The structure and petrology of the hypersthene-gabbro intrusion, Ardnamurchan, Argyllshire. *Quarterly Journal of the Geological Society of London*, **103**, 346–397.

WENTWORTH, C. K. & MACDONALD, G. A. 1953. Structures and forms of basaltic rocks in Hawaii. *United States Geological Survey Bulletin*, **944**.

WHITE, R. S. 1992. Crustal structure and magmatism of North Atlantic continental margins. *Journal of the Geological Society, London*, **149**, 841–854.

WILLIAMS, C. E. & CURTIS, R. 1964. The eruption of Lopevi, New Hebrides, July 1960. *Bulletin Volcanologique*, **27**, 423–433.

WILLIAMS, S. N. 1982. Basaltic ignimbrite erupted from Masaya caldera complex, Nicaragua. *EOS, Transactions of the American Geophysical Union*, **63**, 1155.

—— & STOIBER, R. E. 1983. 'Masaya-type caldera' redefined as the mafic analogue of the 'Krakatau-type caldera' (abstr). *EOS, Transactions of the American Geophysical Union*, **64**, 877.

WILMOTH, R. A. & WALKER, G. P. L. 1993. P-type and S-type pahoehoe: a study of vesicle distribution patterns in Hawaiian lava flows. *Journal of Volcanology and Geothermal Research*, **55**, 129–142.

WILSON, L. & HEAD, J. W. 1981. Ascent and eruption of basaltic magma on the Earth and Moon. *Journal of Geophysical Research*, **86**, 2971–3001.

WOHLETZ, K. H. 1986. Explosive magma–water interactions: thermodynamics, explosive mechanisms, and field studies. *Bulletin of Volcanology*, **48**, 254–264.

WOOD, C. A. 1980. Morphometric evolution of cinder cones. *Journal of Volcanology and Geothermal Research*, **7**, 387–413.

YAGI, K. 1969. Petrology of the alkali dolerite of the Nemuro Peninsula, Japan. *Geological Society of America, Memoir*, **115**, 103–147.

YAMAGISHI, H. 1985. Growth of pillow lobes – evidence from pillow lavas of Hokkaido, Japan, and North Island, New Zealand. *Geology*, **13**, 499–502.

YODER, H. S. 1988. The great basaltic 'floods'. *South African Journal of Geology*, **91**, 139–156.

# Trace element geochemical effects of imperfect crystal–liquid separation

## M. J. O'HARA

*Institute of Earth Studies, University of Wales, Aberystwyth, Dyfed SY23 3DB, UK*

**Abstract**: The strongly contrasted effects of melting or crystallization under perfect equilibrium conditions; of perfect fractional partial melting; and of perfect fractional crystallization upon the relative concentrations of the highly incompatible and highly compatible elements are well known and are surveyed briefly at the start. A major role for either of the two latter processes in the genesis of natural basaltic magmas and peridotitic residues is apparently excluded provided that the liquids or crystals are removed in infinitesimally small batches, the crystals and melts are perfectly separated and there is no flux of source material or residue in or out of the greater system during the process (either liquid or crystals must be removed from the immediate, or lesser, system if it is undergoing perfect fractional melting or perfect fractional crystallization).

The consequences of small departures from (i) infinitesimal size of the batches of liquid or crystals removed, (ii) perfect separation of the crystal and liquid phases, or (iii) perfect closure of the greater system to fluxes of the source material and the residue are explored. These departures can very substantially reduce the differences between the trace element concentrations generated in the products and those expected in a perfect equilibrium process.

These effects are illustrated here by means of 3D plots of the logarithm of relative concentration in the liquid phase as a function of the logarithm of the distribution coefficient and the logarithm of the mass fraction of liquid involved in each process. There are also significant complementary effects on the compositions of the residues or precipitates from these processes which are not illustrated in this paper, although the necessary equations and some worked examples are provided. With the values of parameters chosen in these examples, the fluxing of liquid or solid through a 'box' in which fractional crystallization or fractional melting is taking place proves to be by far the most important factor in modifying the results towards those of the equilibrium processes.

Although much trace element behaviour in basalts can be quite successfully modelled using the perfect equilibrium melting relationships, it is unsafe to exclude on these grounds a major role for physical processes of fractional melting and fractional crystallization in the genesis of these magmas or to conclude that equilibrium partial melting is the principal physical process involved in their genesis.

Many attempts have been made to interpret the major and trace element geochemistry of erupted basalt liquids and hence, to use them as probes into the sub-surface materials and processes of the Earth (e.g. Carmichael *et al.* 1974; Ringwood 1975), Moon (e.g. Taylor 1975) and Achondrite Parent Planet (e.g. Stolper 1977; Stolper *et al.* 1979), with the prospect that such applications might eventually be extended to samples from Mars, Venus and even Mercury.

This paper explores one small facet of a very complex problem. Field evidence, major element geochemistry and phase equilibria studies suggest that fractional crystallization is an important factor in the evolution of basic magmas within the crust at least (O'Hara 1982); while theoretical and experimental studies suggest that the processes of magma formation in and removal from the source regions will be closer in character to fractional melting than to the per-

fect equilibrium process (McKenzie 1984, 1985).

The equations which describe the evolution of the pattern of absolute and relative concentrations of trace elements in the liquids and the solids during both perfect fractional melting and perfect fractional crystallization make specific predictions about those patterns in natural basalts and peridotites; predictions which are, in general, not satisfied. Rather, these trace element patterns can be better interpreted in terms of the processes of equilibrium partial melting or crystallization (Gast 1968).

Attention has shifted to the possible effects of imperfections in the fractional processes upon the patterns of trace element concentrations which would be generated in natural basalts and peridotites under real geological conditions. This investigation has been approached both through the interpretation of natural data sets (e.g. Cox & Hawkesworth 1985; Langmuir *et al.* 1977)

*From* Prichard, H. M., Alabaster, T., Harris, N. B. W. & Neary, C. R. (eds), 1993, *Magmatic Processes and Plate Tectonics*, Geological Society Special Publication No. 76, 39–59.

and through simplified models (e.g. O'Hara &
Mathews 1981; Cann 1982; Dobson & Cann
1982).

This contribution reviews much existing
knowledge about these effects in the form of
computer-generated 3D graphic images of the
surfaces of relative concentration which are developed as functions of the mass fraction of melt
in the system and the crystal–liquid distribution
coefficient. Some new conclusions are uncovered
and two worked examples are provided at the
end of the paper.

## Perfect equilibrium processes

In this model, perfect chemical equilibrium is
maintained between the solid phases and the
changing mass fraction of melt at all stages
during the heating (equilibrium partial melting,
or hereafter EPM) process or the cooling (equilibrium partial crystallization, or hereafter EPC)
process. During these processes the greater and
lesser systems are closed to addition or subtraction of the parent solid or liquid, or to any
exchange of material to the country rock. It is
necessary to distinguish between the greater system, which includes all material which may take
part in a process at any stage, and the lesser
system, which is that involved in the immediate
process and that for which the mass balances
are considered. In the case of the equilibrium
process greater and lesser systems are identical,
but this is not generally the case in the models
considered in this paper.

The following symbols will be used in this
section:

$d$ = crystal–liquid distribution coefficient =
concentration in solid/concentration in liquid;
$f$ = mass fraction of the system which is liquid;
$C_O$ = concentration of element in the source
material (all solid or all liquid);
$C_M$ = concentration of element in the melt
phase;
$C_C$ = concentration of the element in the crystalline phase.

It is assumed that the distribution coefficient, $d$,
remains constant throughout all stages of the
melting process and at all concentrations of the
trace element concerned. More realistic assumptions would complicate the presentation without
altering the general conclusions – except perhaps
in the case of trace elements which become
markedly more incompatible as partial melting
proceeds or markedly less incompatible as crystallization proceeds, due to changes in the solid
phase assemblage present (as might be the case
for heavy rare earth elements if garnet were

eliminated from the residue at an early stage, or
for chromium if spinel were eliminated from the
residue at an early stage).

The familiar relationships (Gast 1968; Shaw
1970) for the relative concentration in the liquid
and solid phases respectively can be derived by
simple mass balance:

$$C_M/C_O = 1/\{f + d(1-f)\} \ldots \qquad (1)$$

$$C_C/C_O = d/\{f + d(1-f)\} \ldots \qquad (2)$$

Analysis shows that as $f$ tends to 0, these ratios
for the relative concentrations in the liquid (1)
and the solid (2) tend to $1/d$ and to unity,
respectively, while as $f$ tends to 1, these tend to 1
and $d$ respectively. In other words, the relative
concentration is unity in the appropriate phase
when the system is all liquid or all solid; the first
drop of liquid to form or last to solidify has the
relative concentration, $1/d$, which is the value
most different from unity achievable in the process. In an analogous way, the first crystal to
form, or last to melt, has the relative concentration, $d$, which is also the value most different
from unity achievable in the process. As $d$ tends
to 0, relative concentration in the melt tends to
$1/f$; in the residue it tends to $d/f$.

The EPM and EPC processes produce very
high concentrations of highly incompatible elements (those with $d$ less than 0.01 and log $d$ less
than −2) in the liquid phase (Figs 1 and 2), with
good discrimination as a function of small differences in $d$ between such elements (steep slope of
the surface as a function of log $d$), at low values
of $f$ (small mass fractions of melt in the system).
Relative concentrations and discrimination decline as $f$ increases.

The EPM and EPC processes produce
uniformly low, but not dramatically low, relative
concentrations of the highly compatible elements (those with $d$ greater than 10 or log $d$
greater than 1) over most of the range of $f$, but
there is rapid variation of the relative concentration of these elements when $f$ is close to 1, i.e.
when the system is largely molten. Discrimination between compatible elements of different
$d$ is good, but again not dramatic (compared to
what is achieved in other processes) over most of
the range of $f$.

These features are illustrated in Figs 1 and 2.
The surface in Fig. 1 can be viewed as an eccen-
tric roof. This roof has four prominent morphological features which recur in modified form in
later figures. There is a ridge (fold) on the
surface where the numerical values of $f$ and $d$ are
approximately equal; this ridge falls from high
values of the relative concentration at low values

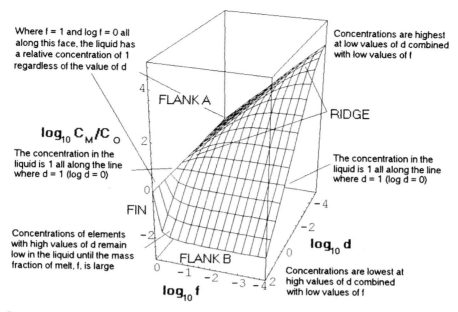

**Fig. 1.** Concentration of a trace element in the liquid phase developed during equilibrium partial melting or equilibrium partial crystallization of a source solid or source liquid respectively, relative to its initial concentration in that source material. The plot shows the logarithm of this relative concentration as a function of the logarithm of the mass fraction of melt developed in the system and of the distribution coefficient. Mass fractions of melt range from tiny at 0.0001 (0.01%, $\log f = -4$) to total at 1.0 (100%, $\log f = 0$). Distribution coefficients range from highly incompatible at 0.00001 ($\log d = -5$) to highly compatible at $d = 100$ ($\log d = 2$). The incompatible rare earth elements, for example, behave as though they had distribution coefficients close to 0.01 ($\log d$ close to $-2$) in most igneous processes while compatible nickel behaves as though it had a distribution coefficient close to 10 ($\log d = 1$). Model and assumptions as stated in this section.

of $f$ and $d$ towards a relative concentration of 1 ($\log C_M/C_O = 0$) when $f = d = 1$ ($\log f = \log d = 0$).

This ridge is the junction between two flanks. Flank A inclines downwards towards high values of $f$ and $\log f$ and **in this particular case** has almost no inclination in the direction of high values of $d$ and $\log d$. Cross-sections of the roof which show the inclination of flank A towards high values of $\log f$ are displayed in the upper part of Fig. 2A. Flank B inclines downwards towards high values of $d$ and $\log d$ and **in this particular case** has almost no inclination in the direction of high values of $d$ and $\log d$ except as discussed below. Cross-sections of the roof which show the inclination of flank B towards high values of $\log d$ are displayed in the upper part of Fig. 2B.

In the high $f$, high $d$ region, flank B is folded up into a fin. **In the particular case** of the EPM and EPC processes this fin terminates in a line at relative concentration 1 ($\log C_M/C_O = 0$). The fin appears in the cross-sections displayed in the lower part of Fig. 2A but does not appear in Fig. 2B.

At any point on the roof shown in Fig. 1 its inclination can be resolved into two components parallel to the $\log f$ and $\log d$ axes, respectively. The magnitude and sign of the (mathematical) slope in the direction of the $\log f$ axis is a measure of the sensitivity of relative concentration of an element to small variations in the mass fraction of liquid. The magnitude and sign of the (mathematical) slope in the direction of the $\log d$ axis is a measure of the discrimination of relative concentration of an element in response to small variations in the distribution coefficient of elements of otherwise similar behaviour.

*Note*:

1. This is log-log-log space; convex curvatures in this space can represent concave curvatures in linear space; linear relationships in this space can represent curves in linear space – and vice versa!

2. This and other figures in the paper show results to very low numerical values of $f$ and $d$ (1 part in 10 000 and 1 part in 100 000, respectively). Although very small, these are

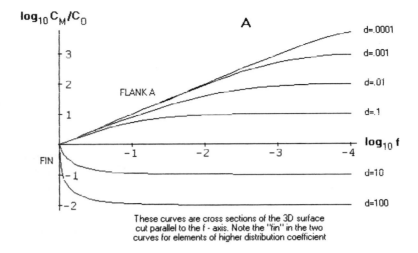

These curves are cross sections of the 3D surface
cut parallel to the f - axis. Note the "fin" in the two
curves for elements of higher distribution coefficient

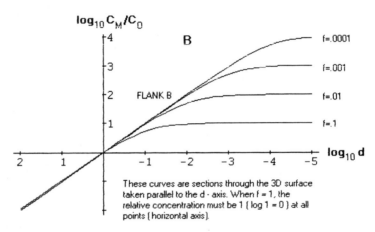

These curves are sections through the 3D surface
taken parallel to the d - axis. When f = 1, the
relative concentration must be 1 ( log 1 = 0 ) at all
points ( horizontal axis).

**Fig. 2.** Cross-sections of the surface shown in Fig. 1: (**A**) at constant values of the distribution coefficient, superimposed on the log relative concentration–log mass fraction of melt plane; and (**B**) at constant values of the mass fraction of melt, superimposed on the log relative concentration–log distribution coefficient plane. The reader may readily develop similar cross-section figures from each of the equations in this paper using little more than a good pocket calculator – the 3D images presented throughout this paper take more computing power but summarize a wealth of qualitative information in a readily recalled form.

not the same thing as zero. Even at these low values there are differences, which would decrease to nothing when the value of $f$ or $d$ is truly zero, to be seen between the relative concentrations yielded by different processes.

## Perfect fractional melting and accumulated perfect fractional melting

During a heating (partial melting) process each newly formed infinitesimal mass fraction of melt is formed under EPM rules, but is instantly and perfectly withdrawn from the (lesser) system

before any further melt is formed (perfect fractional melting, hereafter PFM). An infinite number of events is required to remove any given mass fraction of the original lesser system as melt. The melt droplets may be accumulated elsewhere to yield an average liquid composition (accumulated perfect fractional melting, hereafter APFM).

The following additional or altered symbols and definitions are used in this section:

$f$ = mass fraction of the original (lesser) system which has been extracted as melt. The drop of liquid currently being formed and extracted is, of course, infinitesimally small;

$x = (1 - f)$ = mass fraction of the original (lesser) system which remains as participating solid;

$C_O$ = concentration of element in the original solid source material;

$C_R$ = concentration of element in the residual source material after melt extraction;

$C_M$ = concentration of element in the next drop of melt phase;

$C_M^{av}$ = average concentration in the accumulated melt phase extracted;

$C_C$ = concentration of the element in the residual crystalline phase.

The familiar relationships (Gast 1968; Shaw 1970) are:

$$C_M/C_O = (1-f)^{(1-d)/d}/d \ldots \quad (3)$$

or $x^{(1-d)/d}/d \ldots \quad (4)$,

$$C_M^{av}/C_O = \{1-(1-f)^{1/d}\}/f \ldots \quad (5)$$

or $(1-x^{1/d})/(1-x) \ldots \quad (6)$

and $C_R/C_O = (1-f)^{(1-d)/d} \ldots \quad (7)$

or $x^{(1-d)/d} \ldots \quad (8)$.

The second pair of relationships is readily obtained from the first pair by simple mass balance or by integration of the composition of the instantaneous liquid compositions. The instantaneous solid composition is always given by multiplying the instantaneous liquid composition by the distribution coefficient.

PFM produces instantaneous liquids which, in the region of flank B, are almost indistinguishable from those produced by EPM or EPC provided that the numerical value of $f$ is less than that of $d$ (Figs 3 and 4).

At any value of $d < 1$, as $f$ increases PFM eventually produces liquids and solids showing a precipitous decline in the relative concentration $C_M/C_O$ because the element concerned has all been extracted into earlier portions of liquid. Flank A is almost vertical and the onset of this steep slope is in approximately the same position as the ridge in Fig. 1.

The fin is again present, and theoretically extends to infinite concentrations as $f$

Key features are flank B where relative concentrations are very similar to those produced in "batch" melting, the precipitous decline of concentrations on flank A at low d, high f (where the elements concerned have been almost wholly extracted in previously formed liquids) and the "fin" at high f, high d, where compatible elements finally enter the liquid in large amounts.

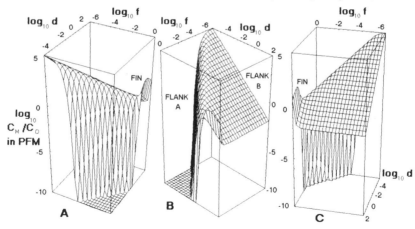

**Fig. 3.** Concentration of a trace element in the next drop of the liquid phase developed during perfect fractional partial melting of a source solid relative to its initial concentration in that source solid. The plot shows the logarithm of this relative concentration as a function of the logarithm of the mass fraction of the system previously developed and extracted as melt and of the distribution coefficient. Three orientations (A,B,C) are shown to display all the features of the surface. Model and assumptions as stated in this section.

The surface of the logarithm of the relative concentration of a trace element in the liquid produced by accumulating and perfectly mixing each miniscule drop of the liquid phase developed during perfect fractional partial melting is so similar to Fig. 1 that there is no merit in reproducing it here.

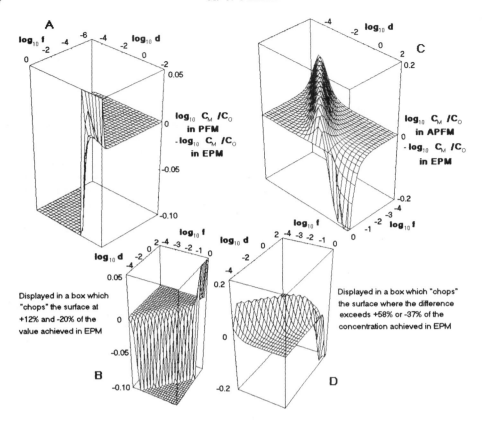

**Fig. 4.** Differences between the surface depicted in Fig. 1, taken as a reference surface, and (**A,B**) the surface shown in Fig. 3; and (**C,D**) that which might have been drawn for the relative concentrations in the accumulated perfect fractional partial melt, shown as functions of the logarithm of the mass fraction of melt involved and of the distribution coefficient. Two orientations of each figure are shown to display all the features of the surfaces. The logarithms of relative concentrations have been subtracted, hence what is shown is the logarithm of the factor by which the relative concentration generated in perfect fractional melting processes is greater or less than that generated in the perfect equilibrium process.

approaches 1 (but the physical model, particularly the assumption of constant $d$, becomes increasingly unrealistic).

The APFM liquid compositions are so similar to those produced in EPM (Fig. 1) that there is no point in presenting a figure analogous to Figs 1 and 3, but there is a small enhancement of relative concentrations in the moderately incompatible elements (i.e. a loss of discrimination among the more incompatible elements relative to the EPM process at low $f$) a little to the high $d$ side of the ridge in Fig. 1 which is obvious in Figs 4C and 4D. There is also a depletion among the compatible elements at very high values of $f$ (which is of little significance because very high values of $f$ have little geological relevance and, moreover, the assumption that $d$ is constant is most vulnerable at high $f$).

Neither erupted basaltic liquids nor residual peridotites display the characteristics of extreme depletion of highly incompatible elements that would be expected in either the instantaneous liquids or the residues produced by PFM according to the model developed above. However, there is much field evidence to suggest that mass fractions as high as 0.3 (O'Hara *et al.* 1975) have been removed from some peridotites by partial melting (which should guarantee massive depletion of highly incompatible elements if the process were PFM) and other arguments suggesting that the process of melting and extraction should approximate to PFM (McKenzie 1985).

Where $f$ is numerically somewhat greater than $d$, discrimination between incompatible elements of similar $d$ is extreme in PFM (the inclination of flank A is extremely steep parallel to both log *f* and log *d* axes in Fig. 3), but is reversed relative to that obtaining throughout in EPM (i.e. in PFM, the more incompatible element is depleted relative to the less incompatible element).

At any given value of *f* there is a very narrow region of values of *d* (in the range less than 0.1 associated with incompatible elements) within which the more incompatible element of a pair will achieve a lower relative concentration than the element with higher *d* (reverse discrimination), but in which the relative concentrations of both are also still higher than in the original source solid. This is the region extending just onto the top of flank A from the crest of the ridge in Fig. 3. If really high relative concentrations are to be combined with reverse discrimination in an erupted lava, then the value of *f* must be low and is very tightly constrained by the values of *d* for the elements concerned (Thompson *et al.* 1984); furthermore, the liquid extracts must be erupted with minimal mixing with any previous extracts because such mixing obliterates the effect. This is, moreover, the only simple physical model so far investigated which produces this effect.

*Warning*

Two extreme situations arise in the interpretation of natural basalt trace element geochemistry. At the one extreme, it is perceived that the combined uncertainties relating to (i) the actual values of the crystal–liquid distribution coefficients, (ii) the phase assemblages involved and hence the bulk distribution coefficient to be applied, (iii) sampling and analytical errors, and (iv) the assumptions which have to be made about either the source composition or the mass fraction of melting, are so great that there can be little chance of distinguishing between alternative physical processes on the basis of the trace element chemistry of the liquids. At the other extreme it is believed that these uncertainties are sufficiently tightly constrained, in which case it is necessary to consider carefully what misinterpretation might result if the incorrect physical process is chosen for modelling purposes.

For example, if one were satisfied as to accuracy and precision, and attempted to interpret the APFM liquids using the EPM model (see Fig. 4 C,D) there will be a positive discrepancy among the moderate to highly incompatible elements which does not extend to the most incompatible elements. This discrepancy might be wrongly ascribed to the source rock composition, and thence to processes of mantle metasomatism, or to prior very small-scale fractional melting of an

'enriched source' (to selectively rid the system of the most incompatible elements which are deficient relative to the moderately incompatible elements – all things are relative).

## Perfect fractional crystallization

During a cooling (partial crystallization) process each newly formed infinitesimal mass fraction of solid is formed under EPM rules, but is instantly and perfectly withdrawn or isolated from the lesser system before any further solid is formed (perfect fractional crystallization, hereafter PFC). An infinite number of events is required to remove any given mass fraction of the original lesser system as solid.

Symbols used or redefined in this section are:

*f* = mass fraction of the original lesser system which remains as participating melt. The crystal currently being formed and extracted is, of course, infinitesimally small;

*x* = mass fraction of the original lesser system which has been extracted as solid ($x = (1 - f)$ provided there is no trapped or escaped liquid which is no longer participating and no suspended crystals which do participate in later stages);

$C_O$ = concentration of element in the original liquid source material;

$C_M$ = concentration of element in the remaining melt phase;

$C_C^{av}$ = average concentration in the accumulated solid phase extracted.

The familiar relationships (Gast 1968; Shaw 1970) are:

$$C_M/C_O = f^{(d-1)} \ldots \tag{9}$$

$$\text{or } (1-x)^{d-1} \ldots \tag{10}$$

$$\text{and } C_C^{av}/C_O = (1-f^d)/(1-f) \ldots \tag{11}$$

$$\text{or } \{1-(1-x)^d\}/x \ldots \tag{12}$$

The second pair of relationships is readily obtained from the first pair by simple mass balance or by integration of the composition of the instantaneous solid compositions. The instantaneous solid composition is always given by multiplying the instantaneous liquid composition (Equations 9, 10) by the distribution coefficient.

PFC produces high relative concentrations ($C_M/C_O$) of highly incompatible elements only when *f* is extremely low (original system almost entirely crystalline) but it simultaneously produces comparably high concentrations of less

Key features are the extended surface of flank A falling from low towards high log f at low values of log d, the modified ridge which now runs approximately where d is numerically c. 1000 f, and the precipitous fall of flank B (compare with figure 1). All sections of the surface at constant d are straight lines (a simple power function is being plotted).

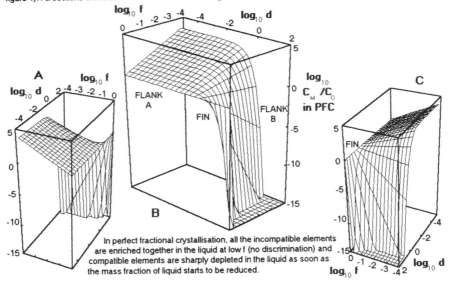

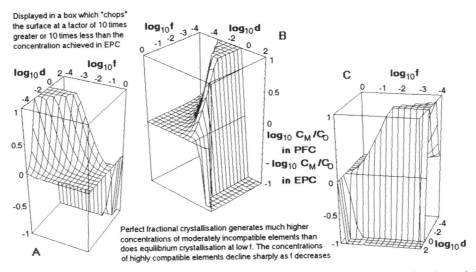

**Fig. 5.** Concentration of a trace element in the liquid phase developed during perfect fractional partial crystallization of a source liquid relative to its initial concentration in the source liquid. The plot shows the logarithm of this relative concentration as a function of the logarithm of the mass fraction of the system previously developed and extracted as solid, and of the distribution coefficient. Three views are shown to illustrate all the features of the surface. Model and assumptions as stated in this section.

**Fig. 6.** Differences between the surface depicted in Fig. 1 and that shown in Fig. 5, shown as functions of the logarithm of the mass fraction of melt involved and the distribution coefficient. The logarithms of relative concentration have been subtracted, hence what is shown is the logarithm of the factor by which the relative concentration generated in perfect fractional crystallization is greater or less than that generated in the perfect equilibrium process. Three views are shown to illustrate all aspects of this difference surface.

incompatible elements (Figs 5 and 6). This results in very poor discrimination between highly incompatible elements. Sections of the surface in Fig. 5 at constant $f$ are almost flat in the region of very low $d$. Unlike EPM and EPC, PFC (or any process involving a PFC component) has the potential to yield relative concentrations of incompatible elements which exceed the limit of $1/d$ imposed by the form of the EPM, EPC equations. This effect may be very large and routinely affects all incompatible elements for which $d$ is numerically larger than $f$. At low values of $f$, the concentrations on the EPC surface tend to $1/d$ and any excess over this appears as a 'hill' on the difference surface (Fig. 6).

High concentrations of highly compatible elements in natural basalts are, in general, associated with good discrimination of their relative concentrations when compared with likely mantle source materials. The liquids produced in PFC thus show marked enhancement in the relative concentrations of the moderately incompatible elements when compared with concentrations in liquids produced in EPC, an effect similar to that shown by APFM-generated liquids relative to EPM products. A component of PFC in the evolution of a liquid will reinforce the effects of APFM in this respect.

The liquids produced in PFC show precipitous decline in relative concentrations of the highly compatible elements early in the process (when $f$ is still high), a decline which rapidly becomes catastrophic as crystallization proceeds. Such extreme depletions of compatible elements such as nickel and chromium are not observed in common terrestrial basalts, implying that they have not undergone a significant amount of PFC as modelled in this section.

## Three types of imperfect crystal–liquid fractionation

### (A) Finite increment size in melting and crystallization

During a heating (partial melting) or cooling (partial crystallization) process, melt or solid is formed under EPM or EPC rules respectively until a small but finite amount of melt or solid has been created. After this small batch of melt or solid has been removed or perfectly isolated from the system, the event is repeated. It requires a finite but possibly very large number of extraction events to remove a given mass fraction of the original system as melt or solid by this imperfect fractional melting (hereafter IFM) or imperfect fractional crystallization (hereafter IFC) process.

Symbols used or redefined in this section are:

$F$ = mass fraction of the original solid extracted eventually as liquid;
$f$ = mass fraction of the original solid extracted as liquid in each event;
$X$ = mass fraction of the original liquid extracted eventually as solid;
$x$ = mass fraction of the original liquid extracted as solid in each event;
$q$ = number of events required to extract $F$ or $X$, i.e. $f = F/q$ and $x = X/q$;
$C_S$ = concentration of an element in the source solid or liquid for these processes;
$C_R^n$ = concentration of an element in the residue after $n$ events;
$C_{LM}^n$ = concentration of an element in the liquid formed in the $n$th melt removal event;
$C_{LC}^n$ = concentration of an element in the liquid formed in the $n$th crystal removal event;
$d$ = crystal–liquid distribution coefficient.

It is assumed that the small mass fractions of melt removed have the same size throughout the process and that $d$ is constant throughout the process.

The first step of melting yields a mass fraction $(1-f)$ of residual solid by EPM, whose composition is given by

$$C_R^1 = \frac{C_S.d}{d+f(1-d)}.$$

The second step of melting yields a mass fraction $(1-2f)$ of residual solid, whose composition (by simple mass balance) must be

$$C_R^2 = \frac{C_S.d(1-f)}{\{d+f(1-d)\}} \cdot \frac{d}{\{d+f(1-2d)\}}$$

and after $n$ repetitions a mass fraction $(1-nf)$ of residual solid has a composition

$$C_R^n/C_S = \prod_{n=1}^{n=n} \frac{d\{1-(n-1)f\}}{\{d+f(1-nd)\}} \cdots \quad (13)$$

and the liquid formed in the same step has the composition $C_R^n/d$. After $q$ such steps, therefore

$$C_{LM}^q/C_s = \frac{1}{d} \cdot \prod_{n=1}^{n=q} \frac{d\{1-(n-1)f\}}{\{d+f(1-nd)\}} =$$

$$\frac{1}{d} \cdot \prod_{n=1}^{n=q} \frac{\{1-(n-1)(F/q)\}}{\{1-(n-1/d)(F/q)\}} \cdots \quad (14)$$

By similar argument the relationship for the

composition of the residual liquid after multiple small mass fractions of crystals have been extracted is:

$$C_{LC}^{q}/C_{S} = \prod_{n=1}^{n=q} \frac{\{1-(n-1)x\}}{1-x(n-d)\}} =$$

$$\prod_{n=1}^{n=q} \frac{\{1-(n-1)(X/q)\}}{\{1-(n-d)(X/q)\}} \cdots \quad (15)$$

Note that $X$ in this last relationship can be replaced by a $(1-F)$ for this process, but this $F$ should be distinguished from that in the relationship for repeated melting.

As $q$ becomes very large, these relationships approach the equations given above for the liquid composition in PFM and PFC, respectively. It is not, however, simple to demonstrate this fact analytically. Figures 7 and 8 demonstrate this truth graphically. As $q$ tends to unity, the relationships in IFM, IFC obviously tend to the EPM, EPC relationship.

Imperfect fractional melting and crystallization still produce the characteristic depletions of trace elements with $d$ very different from unity. But when the physical model assumes extraction of liquid or crystals in a finite number, even a very large finite number of events (Figs 7–10) the scale of the effects is rapidly reduced, and by many factors of ten. Note, for example, the case of IFM with $F = 0.1$ and $d = 0.001$ (log $d = -3$) in Figs 7A, 9A. When $q$ is $c.$ 100 the concentration is a million times greater in IFM than PFM. It is only when $q$ becomes greater than $c.$ 5000 that the concentration comes within a factor of 2 of the PFM result and $q$ must be greater than $c.$ 100 000 before the concentration closely approximates that in PFM. Figure 10A, however, shows that the concentration achieved in IFM has already fallen by a factor of greater than a million relative to the EPM result when $q$ is barely 10.

Similarly for the case of IFC with $F = 0.1$ and $d = 100$ (log $d = 2$) in Figs 8A, 9B. When $q$ is $c.$ 1000 the concentration in IFC is a million times greater than in PFC. It is only when $q$ is greater than 100 000 that the concentration comes within a factor of 2 of the PFC result and $q$ must be greater than 1 000 000 before the concentration closely approximates that in PFC. Figure 10B, however, shows that the concentration achieved in IFC has already fallen by a factor of a million relative to that in EPC when $q$ is barely 10.

## (B) Incomplete separation of liquid and crystals

During a fractional melting or fractional crystallization process conducted by infinitesimal steps (i.e. under PFM or PFC rules) solid-melt separation may not be perfect. A small mass fraction of liquid may remain trapped in the solids and re-equilibrate in the next infinitesimal step (e.g. Langmuir et al. 1977) and/or a small mass fraction of solid may remain suspended in the liquid and re-equilibrate either in the next infinitesimal step or soon after the liquid is extracted. This is incomplete (phase) separation fractional melting (hereafter ISFM) and incomplete (phase) separation fractional crystallization (hereafter ISFC).

The following symbols and new definitions are used in this section:

$t$ = mass fraction of the residual or precipitated 'solid' which is trapped liquid available for re-equilibration with the crystals;
$u$ = mass fraction of the separated 'liquid' which is suspended solid available for re-melting or re-equilibration with that liquid.

Note that $t, u$ are expressed as mass fractions of parts of the lesser system, NOT as parts of the whole, original or greater system. This can produce some entertaining results, visible in some of the figures at very high $f$, where a model may require there to be (absolutely) more crystal material suspended in the 'liquid' than is present in the 'solid'.

The effective distribution coefficient, $D^*$, is (concentration in 'solid'/concentration in 'liquid') or,

$$D^* = d(1-t) + t/1 + u(d-1) \cdots \quad (16)$$

The trapped liquid has been treated as an additional phase whose individual distribution coefficient happens to be 1.

In most geologically relevant situations (other than, perhaps, a very rapidly ascending diapir) the magnitudes of $t$ and $u$ are both going to be small (e.g. <0.1).

By inspection, when $d$ is very small (the highly incompatible elements) $D^*$ will be significantly larger than $d$ if $t$ is large relative to $d$ (Fig. 11A), and the result will not be very sensitive to the value of $u$. When $d$ is large (the compatible elements) $D^*$ will be significantly smaller than $d$ if $u$ is non-zero (Fig. 11B), but will not be very sensitive to the value of $t$.

Two principal cases are considered here: that of highly incompatible elements in a fractional melting process with the assumption that $u = 0$ because the presence of some suspended crystals

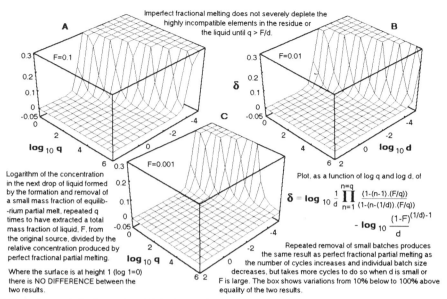

**Fig. 7.** Logarithm of the factor by which the relative concentration of a trace element in the liquid phase, developed by extracting a given mass fraction of melt in $q$ small increments, differs from its relative concentration in the liquid developed during perfect fractional partial melting to yield the same mass fraction of melt. Results are shown as a function of the logarithm of the number of cycles taken ($q$) and the logarithm of the distribution coefficient ($d$) for 3 values of the mass fraction of liquid involved. The plots show differences of up to a factor of 2 from the PFM result. Model and assumptions as stated in this section.

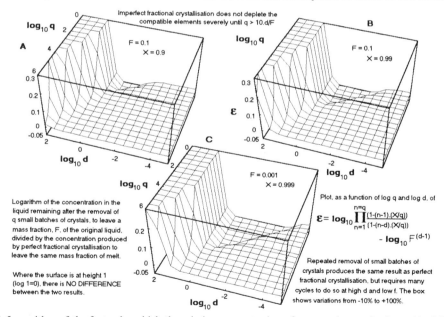

**Fig. 8.** Logarithm of the factor by which the relative concentration of a trace element in the residual liquid phase, developed by extracting a given mass fraction of solid in $q$ small increments, differs from its relative concentration in the liquid developed during perfect fractional crystallization to yield the same mass fraction of residual melt. Results are shown as a function of the logarithm of the number of cycles taken and the logarithm of the distribution coefficient for 3 values of the mass fraction of liquid remaining. The plots show differences of up to a factor of 2 from the PFC result. Model and assumptions as stated in this section.

Concentrations of highly incompatible elements may be more than a million times greater in imperfect fractional melting than in perfect fractionalmelting, and the concentration of highly compatible elements more than ten thousand times greater in imperfect fractional crystallisation than in perfect fractional crystallisation when, in the case illustrated, the size of the mass fractions removed is 0.001 rather than infinitesimal (i.e. q is of the order of 100).

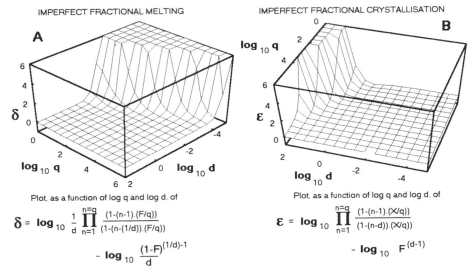

IMPERFECT FRACTIONAL MELTING

**A**

IMPERFECT FRACTIONAL CRYSTALLISATION

**B**

Plot, as a function of log q and log d, of

$$\delta = \log_{10} \frac{1}{d} \prod_{n=1}^{n=q} \frac{(1-(n-1).(F/q))}{(1-(n-(1/d)).(F/q))}$$
$$- \log_{10} \frac{(1-F)^{(1/d)-1}}{d}$$

$$\varepsilon = \log_{10} \prod_{n=1}^{n=q} \frac{(1-(n-1).(X/q))}{(1-(n-d)).(X/q))}$$
$$- \log_{10} F^{(d-1)}$$

**Fig. 9.** The surfaces shown for IFM and IFC in Figs 7A and 8A respectively, for the cases where the mass fraction of melt involved is 0.1, but plotted with a vertical scale showing differences, relative to the PFM or PFC surfaces of Figs 3 and 5 respectively, of up to a factor of 1 000 000 rather than the factor of 2 portrayed in the previous figures.

Concentrations of highly incompatible elements in imperfect fractional melting and those of highly compatible elements in imperfect fractional crystallisation are nevertheless rapidly reduced to a factor of one millionth of those expected from the equilibrium process, even when the increments are as large (in this particular case) as mass fraction 0.01 and q = 10.

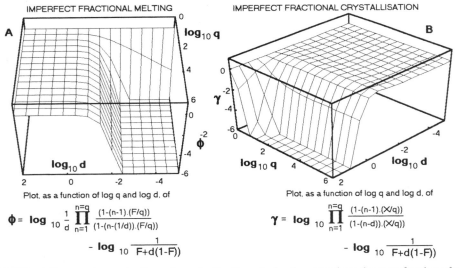

IMPERFECT FRACTIONAL MELTING

**A**

IMPERFECT FRACTIONAL CRYSTALLISATION

**B**

Plot, as a function of log q and log d, of

$$\phi = \log_{10} \frac{1}{d} \prod_{n=1}^{n=q} \frac{(1-(n-1).(F/q))}{(1-(n-(1/d)).(F/q))}$$
$$- \log_{10} \frac{1}{F+d(1-F)}$$

$$\gamma = \log_{10} \prod_{n=1}^{n=q} \frac{(1-(n-1).(X/q))}{(1-(n-d)).(X/q))}$$
$$- \log_{10} \frac{1}{F+d(1-F)}$$

**Fig. 10.** The surfaces analogous to those shown in Fig. 9, again for the case where the mass fraction of melt involved is 0.1, and plotted with a vertical scale showing differences of up to a factor of 1 000 000. These surfaces, however, show differences with respect to the reference surface for EPM/EPC liquids shown in Fig.1.

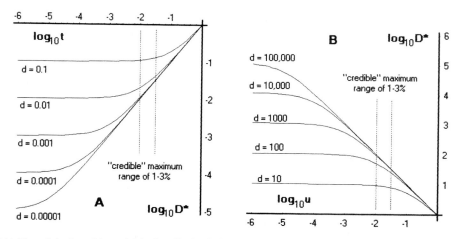

**Fig. 11.** (**A**) Plot of the logarithm of $D^*$, the effective bulk distribution coefficient, as a function of the logarithm of the mass fraction of trapped liquid, $t$, when $u = 0$. Model and assumptions as stated in this section. (**B**) Plot of the logarithm of $D^*$, the effective bulk distribution coefficient, as a function of the logarithm of the mass fraction of suspended crystals, $u$, when $t = 0$. Model and assumptions as stated in this section.

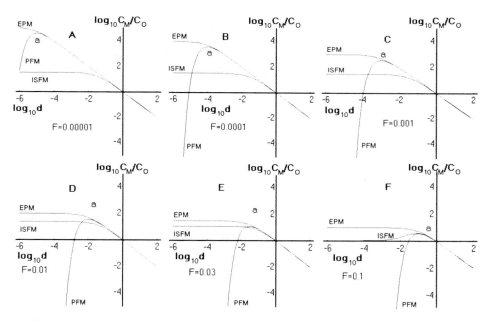

The ISFM surface lies below the EPM and above the PFM surface at low d and the three surfaces are almost identical at higher d. In the intermediate range, best displayed in the figure for F=0.001, as d decreases the difference ISFM-PFM is first negative, passes through a maximum at d=a in each figure, then decreases to zero and becomes positive and eventually very large as the PFM surface falls away.

The difference ISFM-EPM increases as d decreases but tends to a constant value at low d. This constant difference at any one value of F passes through a minimum value when F is approximately equal to t (0.03).

**Fig. 12.** Logarithms of the relative concentrations generated by ISFM ($t = 0.03$ or 3% trapped melt; $u = 0$), EPM and PFM as a function of log $d$ at 6 values of $f$, the mass fraction of the original system which has been melted and extracted. These curves are sections of three surfaces, the differences between which are shown in Fig. 14.

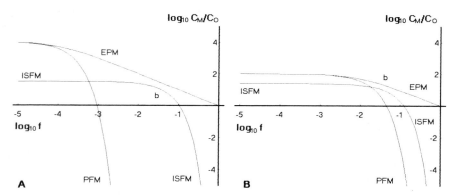

At high values of the melt fraction, f, ISFM yields results between EPM and PFM and the latter are extremely low, especially at very low d. The difference ISFM-PFM is huge and positive at high f but becomes negative at low f. The difference ISFM-EPM is everywhere negative, at a minimum at b and increases rapidly towards high f, more slowly towards low f.

**Fig. 13.** Logarithms of the relative concentrations generated by ISFM ($t = 0.03$ or 3% trapped melt; $u = 0$), EPM and PFM as a function of log $f$ at two values of $d$, the crystal–liquid distribution coefficient. These curves are sections of three surfaces, the differences between which are shown in Fig. 14.

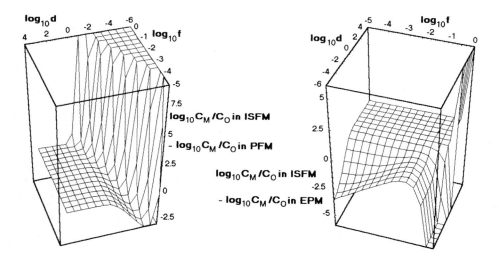

**Fig. 14.** Differences between the surface of relative concentrations developed in the liquid by ISFM when there is 3% trapped melt in the residue and (**A**) that developed by PFM (Fig. 3), and (**B**) that developed in EPM (Fig. 1), shown as functions of the logarithm of the mass fraction of melt involved and of the distribution coefficient. The logarithms of relative concentration have been subtracted, hence what is shown is the logarithm of the factor by which the relative concentration generated in ISFM is greater or less than that generated in the PFM or EPM process.

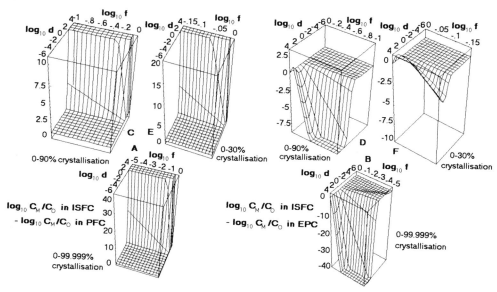

**Fig. 15.** Differences between the surface of relative concentrations developed in the liquid by ISFC when 3% of the residual liquid is suspended and eventually re-equilibrated crystals and (**A,C,E**) that developed by PFC (Fig. 5); and (**B,D,F**) that developed by EPC (Fig.1), shown as functions of the logarithm of the mass fraction of melt involved and of the distribution coefficient. The logarithms of relative concentration have been subtracted, hence what is shown is the logarithm of the factor by which the relative concentration generated in ISFC is greater or less than that generated in the EPC process. The figures are each drawn with a variety of scales of $\log f$ and log of the ratio of the relative concentrations – greatest interest attaches to Figs E and F which show what happens during the first 30% of crystallization ($f$ ranges from 1 to 0.7, $\log f$ from 0 to $-0.155$) but the other figures place these results in context.

in the extracted melt is not going to influence the result greatly; and that of highly compatible elements in a fractional crystallization process with the assumption that $t = 0$ because the presence of a small amount of trapped liquid in the crystal extract is not going to affect the result greatly.

The difference surfaces for ISFM (Fig. 14) are surprisingly complex considering the simplicity of the relationship involved, hence cross-sections (Figs 12 and 13) are provided to illustrate how the features arise.

Even tiny amounts of trapped liquid in the solid residue will rapidly suppress the depletion of highly incompatible trace elements in both residual solid and new liquid increments during fractional melting processes and when $t = 0.3$ the effects are dramatic. This is illustrated in Figs 12 and 14A where the concentration achieved in ISFM of an element with $d = 0.001$ becomes more than a hundred million times greater than the result in PFM as the mass fraction of melt extracted increases to $c.\,0.03$. Figs 12, 13 and 14B show that the ISFM concentration will be only a little lower than that achieved in EPM.

On the other hand, small amounts of e.g. olivine or chromite crystals which remain suspended in the liquid and re-equilibrate with it during ISFC will rapidly suppress the spectacular depletion of the compatible trace elements (Fig. 15) during such processes. Consider for example an element with a distribution coefficient of 100 ($\log d = 2$) when fractional crystallization is taking place with $u = 0.03$. After $c.$ 35 per cent crystal extraction ($f = 0.63$, $\log f = -0.2$) the concentration in the residual liquid is more than a $10^{10}$ greater than it would be in PFC (Fig. 15C) and the result is only 1000 times lower than would have been obtained in EPC (Fig. 15D) – observe carefully the different orientations of these two figures (and the different scales in the other pairs of figures) which have been chosen to display the important features of the two difference surfaces.

The effects are most marked when the crystal–liquid partition coefficient is either very small or very large – the effect of ISFM and ISFC is to selectively and rapidly eliminate the 'characteristic' discriminatory effects of perfect fractional processes on such trace elements.

*(C) Imperfect closure of the system: solid and liquid fluxes*

The lesser system undergoing partial melting is periodically or continuously replenished with source material, e.g. (1) by flow of fertile source material into the region undergoing melt extraction, which triggers the extraction of a melt fraction from the solids and the displacement of some solid residue from the lesser system. A new increment of partial melt is then formed. This is replenished–extracted–mixed melting (hereafter REXM), or (2) the lesser system undergoing partial crystallization is periodically replenished with new parental magma which triggers the eruption of some of the residual liquid from the chamber prior to mixing of the new liquid with the remaining residual liquid (O'Hara & Mathews 1981). Partial crystallization follows and the solids formed are extracted from the lesser system. This is refilled–tapped–mixed–fractionated crystallization (hereafter RTXC).

Details of the applicable partial melting or partial crystallization rules are specific to individual models. The extent and timing of mixing of the new and old solid materials are also variables within specific models (Albarede 1982). However, it can be shown or appreciated intuitively that as the mass fraction of the lesser system which is changed (added or subtracted) in each cycle decreases (i.e. the process moves from episodic towards continuous operation) then those differences between the compositions of the liquid products which are dependent upon the precise timing of mixing relative to melting or crystallization must diminish to zero.

Furthermore, it ceases to matter which of the many models of the melting or crystallization process which have been discussed above is assumed in these circumstances. Each ultimately depends on the assumption of EPM or EPC rules in the production of some small mass fraction of melt or crystals, and consequently the results of the REXM and RTXC processes must approach the results of EPM or EPC processes acting on the steady-state composition of the lesser system as the mass fraction of liquid produced in each event decreases.

Separately, it can be argued that in most geologically relevant situations, the mass fraction of the lesser system which is changed in each cycle will be small ($<0.1$, probably $\ll 0.1$). Deeper complications to the process, such as EPC of added magma batches before mixing of the residual liquid, may have dramatic effects (O'Hara & Mathews 1981). They need to be kept in mind but are not dealt with further here.

The following new or redefined symbols are used in this section:

$f$ = mass fraction of melt extracted in partial melting in each cycle;
$x$ = mass fraction of crystals extracted in partial crystallization in each cycle;
$y$ = mass fraction of solid residue or crystal extract which is removed from the system under consideration in each cycle;
$C_O$ = concentration of element in the source solid for the REXM process;
$C_P$ = concentration of element in the parental liquid for the RTXC process;
$C_S$ = concentration in the steady-state (mixed) system which undergoes melting or crystallization;
$C_R$ = concentration in the residue outflowing residue from the REXM process;
$C_E$ = concentration in the liquid extract from the REXM process;
$C_L$ = concentration in the residual and erupted liquid composition for RTXC process;
$C_X$ = concentration in the average crystal extract formed in the RTXC process.

It is assumed that a steady state, in which output from the lesser system is matched exactly in mass and composition by the input in each cycle, has been achieved. In REXM it is assumed that the liquid extracted from the different parts of the lesser system is well mixed as also must be the new source rock and the residues. This is useful as a limiting case, if not very plausible. Another extreme is dealt with at the end of this section (see below).

For each element in the steady state situation, the following equations express the mass balance in each cycle:

mass in source solid added + mass in solid residue = mass in steady state =
mass in solid residue + mass in outflowing residue + mass in extracted melt

mass in parental liquid added + mass in liquid residue = mass in steady state =
mass in liquid residue + mass in escaping lava + mass in extracted crystals

or,

$$C_O.(f+y)+C_R.(1-f-y) = C_S.1 = C_R.(1-f-y)+C_R.y+C_E.f$$
$$C_P.(x+y)+C_L.(1-x-y) = C_S.1 = C_L.(1-x-y)+C_L.y+C_X.x$$

and given that the melting or crystallization process is quantifiable and can be expressed as a function of the steady-state composition, then $C_S = C_R \cdot g_1(f)$; $C_S = C_L \cdot g_2(x)$.

Then by substituting and rearranging, the following general relationships are obtained:

$$C_R/C_O = (f+y)/\{g_1(f)-(1-f-y)\} \ldots \quad (17)$$

$$C_L/C_P = (x+y)/\{g_2(x)-(1-x-y)\} \ldots \quad (18)$$

$$C_E/C_O = (f+y) \cdot \{g_1(f)-(1-f)\}/$$
$$f \cdot \{g_1(f) - (1-f-y)\} \ldots \quad (19)$$

$$C_X/C_P = (x+y) \cdot \{g_2(x)-(1-x)\}/$$
$$x \cdot \{g_2(x)-(1-x-y)\} \ldots \quad (20)$$

If $g_1(f) = 1/(1-f)^{(1-d)/d}$; $g_2(x)-1/(1-x) = 1/(1-x)^{d-1}$ (from the relationships for PFM residue and PFC liquid respectively) then by substituting for the steady-state composition in (17), (19), (18) and (20) respectively and rearranging:

$$C_R/C_O = \frac{(f+y) \cdot (1-f)^{(1-d)/d}}{\{1-(1-f-y)(1-f)^{(1-d)/d}\}} \ldots \quad (21)$$

which, when $(f+y) = 1$, reduces to $(1-f)^{(1-d)/d}$, the equation for residue composition in PFM, and

$$C_E/C_O = \frac{(f+y) \cdot \{1-(1-f)^{1/d}\}}{f \cdot \{1-(1-f-y)(1-f)^{(1-d)/d}\}} \ldots \quad (22)$$

which, when $(f+y) = 1$, reduces to $(1-(1-f)^{1/d})/f$, the equation for the liquid composition in APFM, and

$$C_L/C_P = \frac{(x+y) \cdot (1-x)^{d-1}}{\{1-(1-x-y)(1-x)^{d-1}\}} \ldots \quad (23)$$

which, when $(x+y) = 1$, reduces to $(1-x)^{d-1}$, the equation for liquid composition in PFC, and

$$C_X/C_P = \frac{(x+y) \cdot \{1-(1-x)^{d}\}}{x \cdot \{1-(1-x-y)(1-x)^{d-1}\}} \ldots \quad (24)$$

which, when $(x+y) = 1$, reduces to $(1-(1-x)^d)/x$, the equation for accumulated cumulus composition in PFC.

It may be shown that when $(f+y)$ and $(x+y)$ are small (and $f,x$ necessarily are also small) then the above equations reduce to the form of the EPM or EPC equations $C_R/C_O = d/F + d(1-F)$

and $C_L/C_P = 1/\{F + d(1-F)\}$ respectively, where $F = $ either $f/(f+y)$ or $y/(x+y)$. In this form, the equations become subject to the same limiting restriction on the maximum possible relative concentration as the EPM and EPC equations (i.e. $1/d$) but when $(x+y)$ is large and $y$ is small in Equation (23) then relative concentrations achieved can exceed the $1/d$ limit for all incompatible elements having $d$ numerically greater than $F$, just as they do in PFC – this effect is, for example, clearly displayed by the 'hill' on the surface for $(x+y) = 0.7$ in Fig. 17.

Substituting a symbol $S$ for $(f+y)$ and $(x+y)$ and either $S.F$ for $f$ or $S.(1-F)$ for $x$ in Equations (22) and (23) above yields the forms shown in Equations (25) and (26) which are much more convenient for plotting and comparison with results portrayed in Figs 1, 3–7, 14 and 15 above (because the parameter $F$ used here is identical to the mass fraction of melt present in the equivalent EPM or EPC equation when $S$ becomes small):

$$C_E/C_O = \frac{\{1-(1-SF)^{1/d}\}}{F \cdot \{1-(1-S)(1-SF)^{(1-d)/d}\}} \ldots \quad (25)$$

and

$$C_L/C_P = \frac{S \cdot (1-S(1-F))^{d-1}}{\{1-(1-S)(1-S(1-F))^{d-1}\}} \ldots \quad (26)$$

These equations have been evaluated for selected values of $S$ (the mass fraction of the lesser system which is changed in each cycle) and allowing $F$ (the 'equivalent' mass fraction of melt involved in the process) to vary. When $S$ is small enough, $F$ closely approximates the mass fraction of melt in the EPM and EPC processes.

If the REXM model is modified to exclude mixing of the residue (see assumptions in this section), the other extreme case is generated, in which a rod of source material is passed through the processing zone, fully fertile at entry, depleted by the removal of mass fraction $F = f/(f+y)$ by PFM or IFM. The equations then become analogous to Equations (5) and (7) above with $F$ as defined here replacing $f$ as defined there – i.e. the result in this case is independent of the value of $S$ and identical to those displayed in Fig 4 C and D and Fig. 16 A.

When either process approaches a continuous-flow steady state, with $(f+y)$ or $(x+y)$ small (Figs 16 and 17), the liquids produced are not distinguishable from those produced by EPM or EPC of the feedstock to the system – in the RTXC case, this is the input parental magma, already a product of partial melting. Moreover,

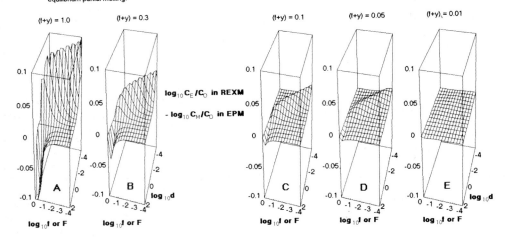

Results are displayed in a box which "chops" the surface at +25% and -20% of the relative concentration which would be achieved in equilibrium partial melting.

**Fig. 16.** Difference between the logarithm of the relative concentration of a trace element in the liquid phase developed during REXM of a steady-state mantle flow and the logarithm of the relative concentration in the liquid developed in an equilibrium partial melting process (EPM). Results are shown as a function of the logarithm of $f$ or of $F$, the 'equivalent' mass fraction of melt removed from the system in the REXM process, and of the distribution coeffficient for each element. They are displayed for 5 values of $S$, the mass fraction of the lesser system which is removed and replaced in each cycle. Model and assumptions as stated in this section.

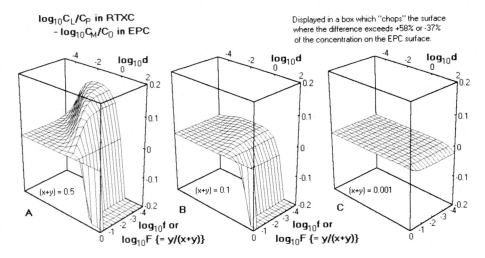

**Fig. 17.** Difference between the logarithm of the relative concentration of a trace element in the liquid phase developed during RTXC evolution of a steady-state magma chamber from a source liquid and the logarithm of the relative concentration in the liquid developed in an equilibrium partial crystallization process (EPC). Results are shown as a function of the logarithm of $f$ or of $F$, the 'equivalent' mass fraction of melt remaining in the system in the RTXC process, and of the distribution coeffficient for each element. They are displayed for 3 values of $S$, the mass fraction of the lesser system which is removed and replaced in each cycle. Model and assumptions as stated in this section.

once the mass fraction of the lesser system, $S$, which is changed in each cycle has fallen below 0.1 (10%) the absolute and relative concentrations of the highly incompatible trace elements differ very little from those attained in EPM or EPC.

The concentrations of highly compatible elements achieved in RTXC do not closely match the products of EPM or EPC until the mass fraction of the system which changes in each cycle becomes very small (< 0.01 or 1%). This is not a useful discriminant in the natural situation, both because there are grounds for thinking that the mass fraction, $S$, is indeed very small in many cases and because there are great uncertainties about the magnitude and the constancy of the distribution coefficients to be used for the highly compatible elements.

## Leaky fractionation

Leaky fractionation (Cann 1982) may be regarded as ISFC with $t$ finite and $u = 0$, provided that leakage is continuous and that the explorer's eye is kept firmly on the fact that the relationship in Equation (9) is written in terms of $f$, the mass fraction of the original lesser system which remains AND participates in the ongoing fractional crystallization process. When the leakage is episodic but fractionation is continuous, leaky fractionation can be viewed as a case of a non-steady state, deflating RTXC magma chamber – supply has dwindled or ceased, crystallization and escape continues; at the other extreme is the inflating magma chamber closed to lava escape (O'Hara & Mathews 1981).

## Turbulent crystallization before mixing, boundary layer crystallization and other possible departures from simple crystal–liquid separation models

A further class of departure from simple models has been considered by some workers, principally in relation to crystallization in magma chambers, in which only part of the system is involved in the crystallization process and the residual liquid is mixed with the uninvolved liquid before repetition of the process.

These departures have been envisaged as leading to EPC of a batch of hot dense liquid prior to the mixing of the residual melt with the melt already in the magma chamber (O'Hara & Mathews 1981) and as formation of a boundary layer in which a packet of magma undergoes EPC or PFC prior to release of its residual liquid to mix with the uninvolved liquid (Langmuir 1989).

Space does not permit the portrayal here of the effects of these processes. The overwhelming effect is, however, to massively reduce the depletion of the highly compatible elements predicted by PFC while leaving the effects of PFC on incompatible element concentrations relatively untouched. Crystallization of a large body of liquid in a stack of rapidly convecting double-diffusive layers, within each of which there may be a close approximation to EPC, is a further process which demands consideration but presents great difficulties because of the diffusive chemical transfers taking place across the interfaces between the double-diffusive cells.

An extension of these thoughts to partial melting processes, in which the packet of source region which undergoes PFM is small and its residue is rapidly mixed with a much larger body of potential source region (e.g. in an ascending diapir) is a logical development and will probably act to greatly subdue the extreme depletions of highly incompatible elements associated with simple PFM.

## Examples: scale of the possible effects

As illustrations of the possible effects of imperfect fractional processes, two cases of arguable geological relevance have been explored with arbitrary sets of parameters which will not be defended further here – dissenters are free to do their own evaluations.

The first case is that of the residue composition achieved in a steady-state but 'jerky' mantle convection in which 1% of the 'partial melting box' is replaced by fresh source material in each cycle, the box contents well mixed and then subjected to 0.1% partial melt extraction in 100 equal equilibrium events, each withdrawing 0.001% of the original mass, before the next replenishment occurs. Throughout the process, 0.1% of the mass of the residue is composed of trapped liquid. The equivalent value of $F$ in Equation (25) is then 0.1.

The second case is that of a steady-state magma chamber, 1% of whose mass is extruded or crystallized in each cycle, and which is then replenished. The mixed magma is subjected to 0.3% crystallization in a series of 100 equal equilibrium events each involving the removal of 0.003% of the mass of the magma chamber. Some 3% of the largely liquid material which re-equilibrates in each event is assumed to be suspended crystals. The equivalent value of $F$ in Equation (26) is then 0.7.

Table 1 lists at its foot the parameters used and the results for relative concentration yielded by the above equations for two values of the

**Table 1.** Relative concentrations achieved in the residue and extracted liquid for two specific cases using different models of the melting and crystallization processes

| | Residues from partial melting | | | Liquids in partial crystallization | |
|---|---|---|---|---|---|
| Process | $d = 0.0001$ | $d = 0.001$ | Process | $d = 10$ | $d = 100$ |
| EPM using $D^*$ | $1.09 \times 10^{-2}$ | $1.96 \times 10^{-2}$ | EPC using $D^*$ | $3.26 \times 10^{-1}$ | $1.22 \times 10^{-1}$ |
| General ($D^*$) | $6.75 \times 10^{-3}$ | $1.52 \times 10^{-2}$ | General ($D^*$) | $3.24 \times 10^{-1}$ | $1.17 \times 10^{-1}$ |
| EPM using $d$ | $1.00 \times 10^{-3}$ | $9.9 \times 10^{-3}$ | EPC using $d$ | $2.70 \times 10^{-1}$ | $3.26 \times 10^{-2}$ |
| General ($d$) | $7.23 \times 10^{-7}$ | $5.84 \times 10^{-3}$ | General ($d$) | $2.67 \times 10^{-1}$ | $2.810 \times 10^{-2}$ |
| REXM | $4.52 \times 10^{-7}$ | $5.8 \times 10^{-3}$ | RTFC | $2.67 \times 10^{-1}$ | $2.806 \times 10^{-2}$ |
| ISFM | $2.78 \times 10^{-42}$ | $1.43 \times 10^{-23}$ | ISFC | $8.6 \times 10^{-2}$ | $1.8 \times 10^{-4}$ |
| IFM | $6.85 \times 10^{-107}$ | $6.13 \times 10^{-32}$ | IFC | $4.3 \times 10^{-2}$ | $8.0 \times 10^{-14}$ |
| PFM | $2.96 \times 10^{-458}$ | $1.94 \times 10^{-46}$ | PFC | $4.0 \times 10^{-2}$ | $4.6 \times 10^{-16}$ |
| $F$ | | 0.1 | | 0.7 | |
| $f$ | | 0.001 | | 0.997 | |
| $x$ | | 0.999 | | 0.003 | |
| $y$ | | 0.009 | | 0.007 | |
| $d$ | 0.0001 | | 0.001 | 10 | 100 |
| $q$ | | 100 | | 100 | |
| $t$ | | 0.001 | | 0 | |
| $u$ | | 0 | | 0.03 | |

distribution coefficient in each case. In descending sequence, the rows show the results for the:

- equilibrium partial melting or crystallization in which trapped melt contributes to residue composition and suspended crystals to the liquid composition;
- a general equation in which all three types of imperfection can be combined, but in which imperfect separation of crystals and liquid has been assumed with $t$ and $u$ as indicated;
- equilibrium partial melting or crystallization with perfect crystal–liquid separation;
- a general equation in which all three types of imperfection can be combined, but in which separation of crystals and liquid has been assumed to be perfect (i.e. $D^* = d$);
- replenished fractional melting or crystallization to achieve respective equivalent $F$ using $f$, $x$ and $y$ as indicated;
- imperfect separation fractional melting or crystallization to achieve respective $F$ with $t$ or $u$ as indicated;
- imperfect fractional melting or crystallization processes to achieve the respective $F$ in 100 cycles;
- perfect fractional melting or crystallization processes using $F = 0.1$ and 0.7 respectively;

The general equations used to obtain the relative concentrations in the 'general' residue and the 'general' liquid were obtained by combining relevant equations above to yield:

$$C_{GR}/C_S = \frac{(f+y).(\text{IFM}_{\text{residue}}(F,D^*,q))}{(1-(1-f-y).(\text{IFM}_{\text{residue}}(F,D^*,q)))} \quad \dots \quad (27),$$

and

$$C_{GL}/C_S = \frac{(x+y).(\text{IFC}_{\text{Liquid}}(X,D^*,q))}{(1-(1-x-y).(\text{IFC}_{\text{Liquid}}(X,D^*,q)))} \quad \dots \quad (28).$$

The effects are most marked when the distribution coefficient departs most from unity. Given the choice of parameters, imperfect separation of the phases and replenishment of the system with new stock are the more influential processes in modifying the drastic effects of the perfect fractional processes and the scale of the modifications can be enormous.

## Summary and conclusions

Specific conclusions and observations are listed in the commentary at the end of each section and are not repeated here. All models of possible imperfections in the fractional processes which have been considered here lead, independently, to the often rapid and dramatic reduction of the contrasts between the predicted liquid (and solid) compositions and those produced in equilibrium processes.

The EPM, EPC equations may, therefore, be more useful than one has any right to expect when exploring first-order models of the type 'Is lava A a possible liquid product derived from material B?', provided that if an apparent good fit is found, then no deeper physical significance is assumed and no attempt is made to interpret small departures from the expected fit without full consideration of the alternative processes available.

Real processes are likely to involve imperfections of all of the types considered, which will reinforce each other – the exploration of these effects beyond what is displayed in the final section is left to the reader.

## Further information

The Mathematica code used to generate the relationships and each of the 3D graphics images may be obtained from the author (Tel: UK 970 832460; Fax: 970 622659) or at the address given at the start of this paper. This code can easily be modified to explore the effect of combining two or more of the imperfections discussed here and it enables production of the figures with colour shading and to much larger scales.

This work was supported by NERC grant between 1986 and 1990. I wish to express my sincere and heartfelt thanks to Dr Paul Abbott of Wolfram Research Inc. for his assistance and support – but any errors are all my own work. Thanks are also due to J. R. Cann, K. G. Cox, R. K. O'Nions, R. S. J. Sparks, M. Wilson, and B. J. Wood for their suggestions and comments leading to improvement of the first draft.

## References

ALBAREDE, F. 1982. Regime and trace element evolution in open magma chambers. *Nature*, **318**, 356–358.

CANN, J. R. 1982. Rayleigh fractionation with continuous removal of liquid. *Earth and Planetary Science Letters*, **60**, 114–116.

CARMICHAEL, I. S. E., TURNER, F. J. & VERHOOGEN, J. 1974. *Igneous Petrology*. McGraw–Hill, New York.

COX, K. G. & HAWKESWORTH, C. J. 1985. Geochemical stratigraphy of the Deccan Traps at Mahabaleshwar, Western Ghats, India, with implications for open system magmatic processes. *Journal of Petrology*, **26**, 355–377.

DOBSON, D. & CANN, J. R. 1982. A geochemical model of mid-ocean ridge magma chambers. *Earth and Planetary Science Letters*, **60**, 93–104.

GAST, P. W. 1968. Trace element fractionation and the origin of tholeiitic and alkaline magma types. *Geochimica et Cosmochimica Acta*, **32**, 1057–1086.

LANGMUIR, C. H. 1989. Geochemical consequences of in situ crystallisation. *Nature*, **340**, 199–205.

——, BENDER, J. F., BENCE, A. E., HANSON, G. N. & TAYLOR, S. R. 1977. Petrogenesis of basalts from the FAMOUS area: Mid-Atlantic Ridge. *Earth and Planetary Science Letters*, **36**, 133–156.

MCKENZIE, D. P. 1984. The generation and compaction of partially molten rock. *Journal of Petrology*, **25**, 713–765.

—— 1985. The extraction of magma from the crust and mantle. *Earth and Planetary Science Letters*, **74**, 81–91.

O'HARA, M. J. 1982. MORB – a mohole misbegotten? *EOS*, **63**, 537.

—— & MATHEWS, R. E. 1981. Geochemical evolution in an advancing, periodically replenished, periodically tapped, continuously fractionated magma chamber. *Journal of the Geological Society, London*, **138**, 237–277.

——, SAUNDERS, M. J. & MERCY, E. L. P. 1975. Garnet-peridotite, primary ultrabasic magma and eclogite: Interpretation of upper mantle processes in kimberlite. *Physics and Chemistry of the Earth*, **9**, 571–604.

RINGWOOD, A. E. 1975. *Composition and Petrology of the Earth's Mantle*. McGraw-Hill, New York.

SHAW, D. M. 1970. Trace element fractionation during anatexis. *Geochimica et Cosmochimica Acta*, **34**, 237–243.

STOLPER, E. M. 1977. Experimental petrology of eucritic meteorites. *Geochimica et Cosmochimica Acta*, **41**, 587–611.

——, MCSWEEN, H. Y. & HAYS, J. F. 1979. A petrogenetic model of the relationships among achondritic meteorites. *Geochimica et Cosmochimica Acta*, **43**, 589–602.

TAYLOR, S. R. 1975. *Lunar Science: A post-Apollo view*. Pergamon, New York.

THOMPSON, R. N., MORRISON, A. M., HENDRY, G. L. & PARRY, S. J. 1984. An assessment of the relative roles of crust and mantle in magma genesis: an elemental approach. *Philosophical Transactions of the Royal Society*, **A310**, 549–590.

# Differentiated rocks of the Galapagos hotspot

ALEXANDER R. McBIRNEY

*Center for Volcanology, University of Oregon, Eugene, Oregon, 97403 USA*

**Abstract**: Virtually all the MORB-like tholeiites and differentiated rocks of the Galapagos Islands are concentrated along the central axis of the archipelago within 100 km of its leading island. Both have a remarkable symmetry. Those close to the centre are strongly tholeiitic, but towards the north and south they become increasingly alkaline.

Most of the differentiated suites are readily explained by crystal fractionation at shallow depths, but voluminous, aphyric rhyolites erupted from a large active volcano immediately downstream from the hotspot are more difficult to explain. Although the geochemical criteria are consistent with crystal fractionation, these extreme differentiates are not accompanied by expected amounts of intermediate compositions, such as those found on older islands; instead, they have been erupted concurrently with basalts that have undergone only minor amounts of differentiation.

The central region in which tholeiitic rocks and their differentiates have been erupted lies west of a transform fault that separates 10 million-year-old lithosphere on the west from thinner 5 million-year-old lithosphere on the east. It is also the region of thickest crust: the MOHO reaches a maximum depth of about 18 km below sea-level directly underneath the same region.

Three possible mechanisms of differentiation have been considered for the voluminous rhyolites: (a) inward crystallization of a large reservoir; (b) side-wall crystallization with convective segregation of a light felsic liquid; and (c) melting of the base of the crust. Although the first two are consistent with the geochemical nature of the rhyolites, they are not compatible with the geological relations. Moreover, they do not explain why such rocks are found only in very restricted settings. In the case of the Galapagos, these extreme differentiates are found only in the region where the crust reaches a maximum thickness near the centre of the Galapagos Platform and directly downstream from the hotspot. On a global scale, oceanic rhyolites are found close to spreading ridges and nowhere else.

These relations indicate that oceanic rhyolites are generated only where the lithospheric mantle is thin enough to permit the thermal effect of hotspots to reach the base of unusually thick crust. Remelting of pockets of felsic differentiates produced by earlier differentiation when the gabbroic layer was close to the ridge would result in trace element compositions consistent with crystal fractionation.

Twenty-five years ago, during the exuberant days when theories of plate tectonics were just beginning to fall into place, Ian Gass and I put together a short paper (McBirney & Gass 1967) pointing out the curious spatial relationships of the rocks of oceanic islands to mid-oceanic ridges. Although a variety of basalts can be found on most islands, tholeiites and their differentiates tend to be concentrated close to ridges and other regions of high heat flow, whereas alkaline rocks are found at greater distances where the lithosphere is thicker. Rhyolites occur only on islands close to ridges – Iceland, Ascension, and Bouvet Islands in the Atlantic, Easter and the Galapagos in the Pacific – never on islands, such as Hawaii and the Marquesas, where the basalts may be tholeiitic, but the lithosphere is older and thicker. We had a vague idea that these relationships had something to do with thermal gradients. On digging out this paper a few months ago, I wondered how we would write it today, particularly in the light of the extraordinary relations since found in the Galapagos Islands.

The Galapagos hotspot is remarkable in many ways, but especially for the diversity and regular spatial patterns of its igneous rocks. The compositions of both basalts and differentiated rocks have a consistent pattern of zoning with respect to the geometry of the hotspot trail and seem to reflect the manner in which mantle plumes interact with the oceanic lithosphere.

## Tectonic and structural setting

The Galapagos hotspot and platform (Fig. 1) are situated only a short distance south of the Galapagos Spreading Centre where they form the youngest, shallowest part of the Carnegie Ridge. The spreading ridge has a 600 km long offset,

*From* Prichard, H. M., Alabaster, T., Harris, N. B. W. & Neary, C. R. (eds), 1993, *Magmatic Processes and Plate Tectonics*, Geological Society Special Publication No. 76, 61–69.

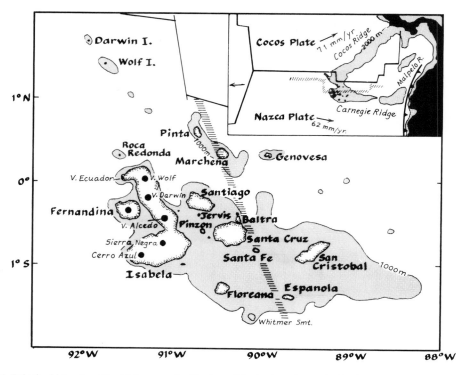

**Fig. 1.** Principal islands of the Galapagos Archipelago. The hashured zone indicating a possible projection of the main transform fault corresponds to a belt of block faulting where the oldest exposed rocks of the archipelago are found. Inset shows the regional tectonic setting of the Galapagos Spreading Centre, Platform, and the Carnegie Ridge and Cocos Ridge. The hashured line in the inset map indicates the approximate position of the spreading ridge before it moved north about 5 Ma ago.

which appears to have lagged behind the rest of the ridge when it moved northwards off the hotspot about 5 Ma ago (Hey 1977; Hey *et al.* 1977). The transform fault marking the western end of this offset segment projects through the Galapagos Platform, so that the western islands stand on lithosphere that is older and thicker than that under islands to the east. The exact position of this boundary is poorly defined, owing to the thick cover of the platform and, for this reason, no two maps show it in exactly the same place. As drawn in Fig. 1, it coincides with

a belt of recent block-faulting and uplifted submarine lavas on the islands close to the southern end of its inferred trace. In addition to the effect of differing ages, geophysical studies (Feighner & Richards in revision) have shown that the thickness of the crust varies as a result of the accumulation of basalts forming the platform.

Volcanic centres are scattered over the platform in a seemingly random fashion. Each island has its own distinctive form and compositional character. The volcanoes of the two westernmost islands, Fernandina and Isabela, are the largest

**Fig. 2. (a)** When components of the most primitive, aphyric analysed samples from each eruptive centre and age group are contoured, they reveal a concentration of MORB-like basalts in and around the central islands. These lavas have $K_2O$ contents of less than 0.15 wt % and $^{87}Sr/^{86}Sr$ less than about 0.703. Age-corrected locations of samples are indicated by crosses. Contour interval 0.1% $K_2O$. Data from the Galapagos Spreading Centre are taken from Schilling *et al.* (1976, 1982) and Verma & Schilling (1982). **(b)** When the minimum ratios of $MgO/(MgO + FeO)$ of aphyric basalts of each volcanic centre are contoured in the same way, they reveal a strong minimum in the same central area. Thus the degree of differentiation tends to be greatest in the same region as that in which MORB-like tholeiites are concentrated. **(c)** The thickness of the crust forming the Galapagos Platform reaches a maximum in the same region immediately downstream from the hotspot. (After Feighner & Richards, in revision.)

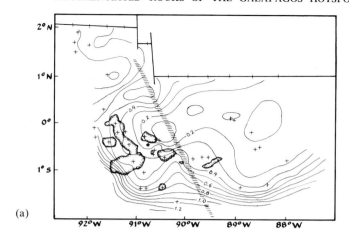

(a)

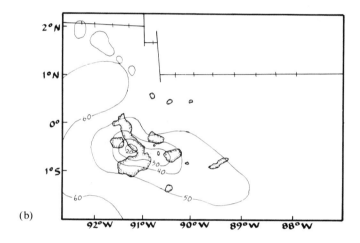

(b)

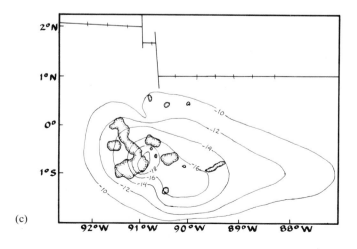

(c)

and have had the most recent activity. The older islands are smaller, and although they have had very recent eruptions, they are much less active.

## Petrologic relations

### Compositional and spatial variations

Unlike Hawaii, the islands have no consistent pattern of temporal evolution. Some of the youngest lavas erupted far downstream are essentially identical to those erupted when the same island was close to the hotspot. A factor more important than age is the relationship of the islands to the axis of the hotspot trail (Fig. 2; White et al., in press). Basalts erupted near the centre of the axis have a distinctly MORB-like character with $K_2O$ contents of less than 0.15 wt % and $^{87}Sr/^{86}Sr$ less than 0.703. Those appearing outside this central zone tend to be more mafic and are progressively more enriched in incompatible elements and radiogenic strontium, particularly toward the southern margin of the platform. The gradients of composition are especially steep between the central axis and the southern margin of the platform. The island of Santa Cruz, for example, has MORB-like tholeiites and ferrobasalts along its north coast and on the smaller adjacent islands but only olivine-rich alkaline basalts on its summit area and southern slope.

Very few primitive basalts are found along the main central axis west of the projection of the transform fault. Basalts with more than 8% MgO are rare, if not totally absent in the central region but are more common toward the north and south. Conversely, MORB-like tholeiites and lavas more differentiated than ferrobasalt have yet to be found outside the central region. Notable amounts of differentiated rocks have been reported from all the central islands (Santiago, Jervis, Pinzon, and Santa Cruz) and on the large shield volcano of Alcedo on the islands of Isabela. Without exception, all the centres with well-developed differentiated series lie close to the central axis of the archipelago; they also appear to be confined to the west side of the transform fault.

## Differentiated rocks

### The central islands

Taken as a group, these islands are distinguished by the diversity of their forms. Santiago is an east–west elongated shield built mainly of mildly alkaline lavas erupted from fissures parallel to its east–west axis. The small island of Jervis is a complex of domes composed of ferrobasalts, icelandites, and siliceous trachyte. Santa Cruz is a broad shield with numerous small cones scattered about its summit and northern slope. The small island of Pinzon has two coalescing calderas and the most complete suite of differentiated lavas in the archipelago. Only Santiago has had historic activity.

The differentiated series of Pinzon and Jervis have pronounced tholeiitic trends with strong iron enrichment in the early and middle stages followed by a sharp increase of silica. The trend of differentiation is similar to that of rocks and glasses dredged from nearby sections of the Galapagos Spreading Centre (Munz 1985). The most differentiated compositions are quartz trachyte and dacite (Baitis & Lindstrom 1980). Major element and trace element variations (Fig. 3) are consistent with fractionation of plagioclase, augite, olivine, and iron-titanium oxides – all minerals that are stable at shallow depths. Clear evidence of shallow intrusions is found in coarse-grained xenoliths found in a few lavas and among the ejecta of a small cinder cone on the north shore of Jervis. Ranging from olivine gabbros through quartz syenites, the rocks define a trend roughly parallel to that of the tholeiitic lavas.

The trends of differentiation on islands immediately to the north and south are more alkaline (Fig. 4), but differentiation of the alkaline series is much less pronounced than that of the tholeiites. The minerals fractionated to form the alkaline series are essentially the same as those of the tholeiitic series, olivine, plagioclase, Ca-rich pyroxene, and Fe-Ti oxides, but the depth of differentiation seems to have been greater. Bow (1979) found that the trace element variations in the lavas of Santa Cruz and other islands near the centre of the platform show the effect of fractionation of plagioclase, whereas those of the southernmost island, Floreana, reflected fractionation of spinel. This interpretation is consistent with the fact that spinel-bearing ultramafic xenoliths are found in the tuffs and lavas of Floreana, whereas only plagioclase-bearing xenoliths are found on the other islands.

### Alcedo

Lying immediately downstream from the presumed core of the hotspot under Fernandina, Alcedo is the central member of a chain of six large shield volcanoes making up the island of Isabela. Like its neighbours, it has a broad summit caldera, but it differs from all others in having an extensive flow of rhyolitic lava on the caldera floor and a blanket of rhyolitic pumice

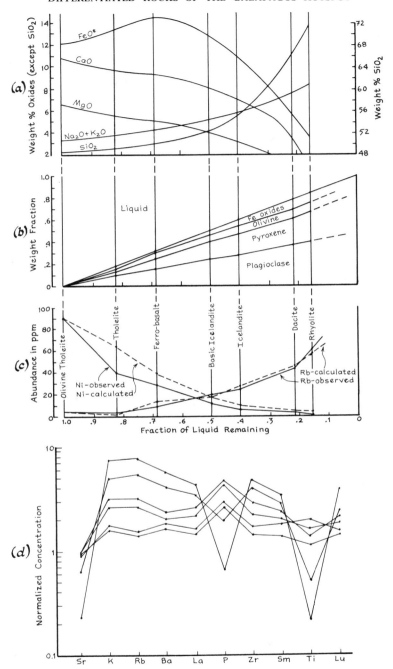

**Fig. 3.** The compositional variations of the tholeiitic differentiated rocks of the island of Pinzon and the volcano Alcedo on Isabela show smooth variations (**a**) consistent with crystal fractionation of the minerals found as phenocrysts and components of plutonic xenoliths (**b**). Each member of the series could result from fractionation of the observed phenocrysts from the previous, less-differentiated composition. (**c**) The observed abundances of Ni and Rb in the rocks are compared with those predicted by the mass-balance calculations. (**d**) Spider diagram in which the members of this series have been normalized to the most primitive basalt on Pinzon. The six curves correspond to the succession of liquids in the other diagrams. (Based on data of Baitis & Lindstrom (1980) with corrections and additions.)

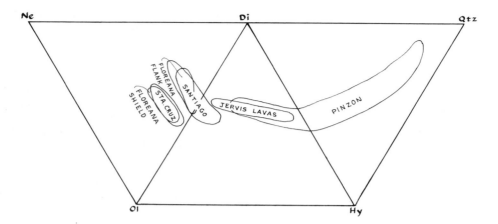

**Fig. 4.** Normative Di–Ne–Ol–Hy–Qtz diagram for the differentiated rocks of the Galapagos Platform. The two small islands of Jervis and Pinzon near the centre of the archipelago follow a tholeiitic trend with strong enrichment, first of iron and then of silica, whereas the lavas of Santiago, immediately to the north, and Santa Cruz and Floreana, closer to the southern margin, become increasingly alkaline with differentiation. Compiled from various sources including Baitis & Lindstrom (1980), Swanson *et al.* (1974) and Bow & Geist (1992).

on its flanks (McBirney *et al.* 1985). The total volume of this rhyolite is of the order of 1 km³. The caldera does not seem to have resulted from subsidence following a large outpouring of siliceous magma, for the caldera was already close to its present size when the rhyolite was erupted. Like that of similar calderas on the neighbouring volcanoes of Isabela and Fernandina, its collapse seems to have been the result of lateral injection of sills (Cullen *et al.* 1987).

The rocks of Alcedo are strongly bimodal. Intermediate compositions are distinctly subordinate, and many, if not most, appear to result from mingling of the two end members, basalt and rhyolite, which in some cases have erupted simultaneously from the same fissure. Most compositional features of the rhyolites, including trace elements and isotopic ratios, fall close to the trends defined by the differentiated series of older islands, such as Pinzon (Fig. 3).

Active fumaroles on the floor of the caldera are remarkable for their extraordinarily large concentrations of $CO_2$. (Table 1, Nordlie & Colony 1973).

## Origins of extreme felsic differentiates

Although the differentiated rocks of the central islands are readily explained as the products of progressive differentiation by crystal fractionation, the voluminous rhyolites of Alcedo are more difficult to account for. It is unclear why the most differentiated magma in the entire archipelago should be erupted in large amounts concurrently with basalts immediately downstream from the hotspot. In a more general sense, the bimodal Alcedo suite poses the same problem of basalt–rhyolite associations that petrologists have been debating since the time of Bunsen (1851): how are such extreme differentiates produced in such volumes without comparable amounts of intermediate compositions, and why are the differentiates erupted together with the basic lavas from which they are thought to be derived by cooling and crystal fractionation? If crystal fractionation produces rhyolites, why do we not find them on islands where the evidence for that mechanism is more apparent?

**Table 1.** *Semi-quantitative gas analyses of Alcedo fumaroles (Nordlie & Colony 1973). Constituents are reported in parts per million. The bulk of the remainder is $H_2O$*

| Gas | Vent 1 | Vent 2 |
| --- | --- | --- |
| HCl | 3 | 2 |
| $CO_2$ | 95 000 | 45 000 |
| CO | 135 | 75 |
| $CS_2$ | 400 | 150 |
| $SO_2$ | 200 | 100 |
| $H_2S$ | 250 | 100 |
| HF | <0.5 | tr. |

## Crystal fractionation

Viewed abstractly as numbers in a data table, nothing in the geochemical relations is inconsistent with differentiation by inward crystallization or crystal settling in a large, slowly cooled intrusion. Viewed in terms of the geological relations, however, this seems to be the least plausible of the possible mechanisms. As Marsh and his co-workers (1991) have recently emphasized, 'highly differentiated, residual melts normally reside within inward advancing solidification fronts and are generally inaccessible to eruptive processes.' Even if there were a suitable means of segregating such liquids, the observed volume of rhyolite erupted from Alcedo (at least 1 km$^3$) would require efficient differentiation of at least 100 km$^3$ of basaltic magma and a period of slow cooling of the order of several centuries. The size and nature of the volcano and its record of frequent recent activity make this unlikely.

Some of the limitations of progressive crystallization are surmounted if cooling at the walls of an intrusion results in gravitational segregation of a buoyant differentiated liquid. Few lavas of intermediate compositions would be expected in this case, because the strong enrichment of iron during much of the middle course of differentiation would cause a dense liquid to descend and pond in the lower levels of the reservoir. Unlike static crystallization that must be very slow to effect efficient fractionation, convective liquid fraction during side-wall crystallization functions best when the rate of heat loss to the walls is relatively rapid (McBirney et al. 1985). The chemical effects are broadly similar to those of other types of crystal fractionation, but minor differences may result from the different diffusivities of individual elements through the compositional boundary layer (Baker & McBirney 1985).

In these respects, convective liquid fractionation seems to offer a satisfactory explanation for the compositions of Galapagos rhyolites and their close association with more basic magmas. In fact, it was proposed as such in 1985 (McBirney et al. 1985). But such a mechanism, as Morse (1986) has emphasized, still requires crystallization of a volume of magma at least as great as that of any other style of crystal fractionation. Moreover, one might justifiably ask why no rhyolites have been produced elsewhere in the Galapagos and why they seem to be confined to settings close to mid-oceanic ridges. In looking for some aspect of Alcedo that might explain its unique character, the most conspicuous feature is its position immediately downstream from the hotspot where the lithosphere is being heated by the mantle plume. Under such conditions, anatexis may offer a reasonable alternative to crystal fractionation.

## Melting of the lithosphere

Marsh and his co-workers (1991) have recently addressed the marked contrast between Iceland with its disproportionate amounts of rhyolite and Hawaii where felsic tholeiitic differentiates are found only in trivial amounts. They conclude that, while crystal fractionation is an effective mechanism of differentiation in Hawaii, it rarely if ever produces significant volumes of magmas more differentiated than basalt. They find it difficult, however, to attribute the bimodal basalt–rhyolite associations of Iceland to such a process and conclude that melting of the basaltic crust offers a more satisfactory explanation. In support of this interpretation they point to geochemical evidence, particularly differences in the isotopic compositions of the basic and felsic rocks, that rules out a direct genetic link between the rhyolites and their associated basalts (e.g. Gunnarsson et al. 1988; Sigmarsson et al. 1991).

In addition to these geochemical factors, they set out two criteria for recognition of anatectic rhyolites: (1) they contain disequilibrium mineral assemblages derived from a period of earlier solidification; and (2) they have inclusions of solid or partly melted fragments of their source rocks. Although the Icelandic rhyolites meet these criteria, those of the Galapagos do not. The latter contain scattered crystals, but the phases appear to be in equilibrium with their host liquid. This may not, of course, rule out an anatectic origin for the Galapagos rhyolites, for the absence of inclusions could have other explanations. Basalts rarely contain relict mantle minerals from their ultramafic source rocks, and yet few petrologists doubt that they are products of partial melting of the mantle. Nevertheless, no essential difference has yet been found between the isotopic ratios of strontium, neodymium, or oxygen in the Alcedo basalts and rhyolites (White et al. in press; D. J. Geist, pers. comm.); both have typical mantle ratios.

While the geochemical evidence may point to a close genetic link of the rhyolite to a basaltic parent, the parent need not be an Alcedo Basalt, and the site of differentiation need not be a subvolcanic reservoir. Similar, if not identical, compositions could be produced by melting residual pockets of felsic differentiates within a gabbroic layer produced at the spreading axis. Such a source would be more likely to yield extractable quantities of melt than would basaltic rocks in which the melt would be distributed in amounts that are too small and too dispersed to be segregated.

Geophysical evidence cited in an earlier section indicates that the crust reaches its maximum thickness under the western part of the Galapagos Platform in an area that corresponds closely with a zone where primitive basalts are least abundant, and differentiated rocks are most common (Fig. 2c). If the interpretations of Feighner & Richards (in revision) are correct, conditions under Alcedo are consistent with partial melting at a depth of 17–18 km, close to the base of the crust.

The amount of melting that is possible under these conditions is severely constrained by the amount of heat that can be supplied by a plume impinging on the base of the lithosphere. Most of the heat added to the lithosphere must be introduced by basic magmas rising from the plume, for the amount that can be added by conduction in the short period that elapsed before the first rhyolites appear must be very small. The thermal requirements for producing rhyolitic melts are much less severe than those for producing basalt. Because the solidus temperature of a rhyolitic melt is much lower than the liquidus temperature of basalt, the latter can supply heat by crystallizing only a few percent without being immobilized or undergoing extensive compositional changes. The rarity of primitive basalts in the central part of the Galapagos Platform may be due to this effect. In addition, volatile, low-melting components mobilized when the plume first begins to heat the mantle passing over it may rise to shallower levels and act as a flux to lower the temperature of the solidus and further increase the thermal leverage of basalt relative to a rhyolite. Thus the thermal requirements for producing rhyolitic melts can probably be met by crystallization of only a small fraction of the liquidus phases from basaltic magmas rising through the lithosphere.

Much must depend, of course, on the thickness and initial thermal gradient of the lithosphere. The fact that oceanic rhyolites are found only on islands close to spreading ridges indicates that outside this zone, the heat contributed by a hotspot is insufficient to raise temperatures to the requisite levels for partial melting.

## Conclusions

Extensive differentiation has been confined to volcanic centres near the central axis of the Galapagos Platform, with tholeiitic rocks close to the centre giving way to more alkaline trends toward the margins. The magmas of the central islands appear to have evolved by crystal frac-tionation in shallow, crustal reservoirs as the centres migrate eastward away from a hotspot under Fernandina.

Although the compositions of rhyolites erupted from the large shield volcano of Alcedo fall on the same trend as the differentiated tholeiites of older islands, geological relations rule out differentiation of a large sub-volcanic reservoir. Although side wall crystallization and convective liquid fractionation could produce the observed assemblages, a large mass of magma would have to crystallize and differentiate with extreme efficiency over long periods of time.

A clue to the origin of these rhyolites, as well as those on other oceanic islands, is found in their regional settings. In all cases, they are found where hotspots are close to spreading ridges and the combination of thick crust and thin lithosphere favour remelting of residual pockets of felsic differentiates in the gabbroic layer near the base of the crust.

Ian Gass and I exchanged letters on this topic not long before he passed away. Had he lived to contribute his keen insight and broad perspective of oceanic igneous rocks to this discussion, I am sure this paper would have been much better.

I am grateful to Derek Bostok, Mark Richards, Mark Feighner, William M. White, and Dennis Geist for sharing their information on the Galapagos and for lively discussions of views that they do not necessarily share. The paper benefited greatly from the thoughtful comments of Bruce Marsh, Dean Presnall, and an anonymous reviewer.

## References

BAITIS, H. & LINDSTROM, M. M. 1980. Geology, petrography, and petrology of Pinzon Island, Galapagos Archipelago. *Contributions to Mineralogy and Petrology*, **72**, 367.

BAKER, B. H. & McBIRNEY, A. R. 1985. Liquid fractionation. Part III: Geochemistry of zoned magmas and the compositional effects of liquid fractionation. *Journal of Volcanology and Geothermal Research*, **24**, 55–81.

BOW, C. S. 1979. *The geology and petrogenesis of the lavas of Floreana and Santa Cruz Islands, Galapagos Archipelago*. PhD thesis, University of Oregon.

—— & GEIST, D. J. 1992. Geology and petrology of Floreana Island, Galapagos Archipelago, Ecuador. *Journal of Volcanology and Geothermal Research*, **52**, 83–106.

BUNSEN, R. 1851. Ueber die Prozesse der vulkanischen Gesteinbildungen Islands. *Pogg. Ann.*, **83**, 197–272.

CULLEN, A. B., McBIRNEY, A. R. & RODGERS, R. D. 1987. Structural controls on the morphology of Galapagos shields. *Journal of Volcanology and Geothermal Research*, **34**, 143–151.

FEIGHNER, M. A. & RICHARDS, M. A. in revision. Lithospheric structure and compensation mechanisms of the Galapagos Archipelago. *Journal of Geophysical Research*

GUNNARSSON, B., TAYLOR, H. P. Jr & MARSH, B. D. 1988. Origin of oxygen isotope anomalies in Icelandic lavas: Part I – Flank zone volcanoes. *Geological Society of America Abstract with Programs*, **20**, A158.

HEY, R. 1977. Tectonic evolution of the Cocos–Nazca spreading center. *Geological Society of America Bulletin*. **88**, 1404–1420.

——, JOHNSON, G. L. & LOWRIE, A. 1977. Recent plate motions in the Galapagos area. *Geological Society of America Bulletin*. **88**, 1395–1403.

MARSH, B. D., GUNNARSSON, B., CONGDON, R. & CARMODY, R. 1991. Hawaiian basalts and Icelandic rhyolite: indicators of differentiation and partial melting. *Geologische Rundschau* **80**, 481–510.

MCBIRNEY, A. R., CULLEN, A. B., GEIST, D. J., VICENZI, E. P., DUNCAN, R. A., HALL, M. L. & ESTRELLA, M. 1985. The Galapagos volcano Alcedo: a unique oceanic caldera. *Journal of Volcanology and Geothermal Research*, **26**, 173–177.

—— & GASS, I. G. 1967. Relations of oceanic volcanic rocks to midoceanic rises and heat flow. *Earth and Planetary Science Letters*, **2**, 265–276.

MORSE, S. A. 1986. Liquid collection in side-wall crystallization of magma: a comment on 'Liquid Fractionation. Part I' by A. R. McBirney, B. H. Baker, and R. H. Nilson. *Journal of Volcanology and Geothermal Research*, **30**, 163–168.

MUNZ, A. E. 1985. *Comparing volcanic rocks of the Galapagos Islands with those from the Galapagos Spreading Center: Chemical differences and what they may indicate about magmatic evolution.* Bachelors thesis, University of Oregon.

NORDLIE, B. E. & COLONY, W. E. 1973. Fumarole with periodic water fountaining, Volcan Alcedo, Galapagos Islands. *Geological Society of America Bulletin*, **84**, 1709–1720.

SCHILLING, J. G., ANDERSON, R. N. & VOGT, P. R. 1976. Rare earth, Fe and Ti variations along the Galapagos mantle plume. *Nature*, **261**, 108–113.

——, KINGSLEY, R. & DEVINE, J. 1982. Galapagos hot spot – spreading center system 1. Spatial petrological and geochemical variations (83°–101°W), *Journal of Geophysical Research*, **87**, 5593–5610.

SIGMARSSON, O., HEMOND, C., CONDOMINES, M., FOURCADE, S. & OSKARSSON, N. 1991. Origin of silicic magma in Iceland revealed by Th isotopes. *Geology*, **19**, 621–624.

SWANSON, F. J., BAITIS, H. W., LEXA, J. & DYMOND, J. 1974. Geology of Santiago, Rabida, and Pinzon Islands, Galapagos. *Geological Society of America Bulletin*, **85**, 1803–1810.

VERMA, S. P. & SCHILLING, J. G. 1982. Galapagos hot spot – spreading center system 2. $^{87}Sr/^{86}Sr$ and Large Ion lithophile element variations (85°–101°W). *Journal of Geophysical Research*, **87**, 838–856.

WHITE, W. M., MCBIRNEY, A. R. & DUNCAN, A. R., in press, Petrology and geochemistry of the Galapagos Islands: portrait of a pathological mantle plume. *Journal of Geophysical Research*.

# Palaeozoic and Cenozoic lithoprobes and the loss of > 120 km of Archaean lithosphere, Sino-Korean craton, China

MARTIN A. MENZIES,[1] WEIMING FAN[2] & MING ZHANG[3]

[1] *University of Montpellier II, CNRS-CGG, 34095 Montpellier, Cedex 5, France and Royal Holloway, University of London, Egham, Surrey, TW20 0EX, UK*
[2] *Changsha Institute of Geotectonics, Changsha, Hunan, People's Republic of China*
[3] *Department of Geological Sciences, College of Liberal Arts and Science, Box 4398, Chicago, Illinois 60680, USA*

**Abstract**: In eastern China Palaeozoic kimberlites and Cenozoic basalts have been erupted through the same Archaean crust, thus providing deep probes of the cratonic lower lithosphere over a period of 400 Ma. While Palaeozoic diamondiferous kimberlites point to the existence of thick, refractory lower lithosphere in the east, Cenozoic basalt-borne xenoliths reveal the presence of hot, thin, less refractory lower lithosphere. Remnants of the Archaean lithosphere may have survived as harzburgites which are chemically similar to those from the Kaapvaal craton but very different from recently accreted lherzolites. In the absence of convincing evidence for supra-subduction or intraplate processes it is believed that the dramatic change of lithosphere architecture in the Phanerozoic was caused by indentor tectonics resulting from the collision of India and Eurasia. Passive reactivation and remobilization of the Archaean lower lithosphere, in particular metasome horizons, contributed to Cenozoic magmatism aligned along major lithospheric faults.

Traditionally the oldest Archaean cratonic nuclei are thought of as the most stable, inert parts of the Earth's surface. In the case of South Africa, Canada and Western Australia, Archaean cratons (Liu *et al.* 1992) lie atop a thick mechanical boundary layer characterized by high velocity anomalies (Anderson *et al.* 1992). In addition, the occurrence of Archaean P-type diamonds in on-craton kimberlites confirms the presence of an ancient thick lithospheric keel that, in some cases, was stabilized to depths of 200 km in the first billion years of Earth's history (Boyd & Gurney 1986). However, not all cratons have retained their structural integrity. In the case of the Greenland–Hebridean craton, elevated mantle temperatures associated with the Iceland plume and tectonic forces related to the opening of the North Atlantic, may have been responsible for erosion of the craton margin. This would account for the existence of thinned Archaean crust (< 30 km) on the eastern Atlantic margin (i.e. Hebridean craton) and the survival of a thick cratonic nucleus in Greenland (Scott-Smith 1987). Similarly a thick cratonic keel does not underlie the Sino-Korean Archaean craton, eastern China. Detailed seismic tomography (Chen *et al.* 1991; Liu 1992) indicates that the 'present-day' lithosphere is < 80 km thick (see Fig. 4) with greatly thinned lithosphere around the Bohai Sea (Ma & Wu 1981). The presence of thin lithosphere with a low velocity structure similar to an ocean ridge is substantiated by heat flow studies in eastern China (Teng *et al.* 1983) which reveal a region of very high heat flow on the craton in the vicinity of the Bohai Sea and Beijing (Fig. 1). The measured heat flow (1.2–2.53 HFU) corresponds to geotherms observed in tectonically active continents or ocean basins (50–105 mW m$^{-2}$).

The aim of this paper is to review the temporal evolution of the lower lithosphere beneath the Sino-Korean craton, a crustal province known to contain some of the oldest crustal rocks on Earth (Jahn *et al.* 1987). In this review we will:

(a) present petrological and geochemical evidence for the character of the Palaeozoic and Cenozoic lithosphere;
(b) review the available geological and geochemical data on eastern China pertinent to lithosphere evolution,
(c) outline a model to explain the temporal changes in lithosphere architecture.

## Palaeozoic kimberlite-borne xenoliths

Palaeozic (400 Ma) kimberlites entrain a variety of xenoliths and megacrysts including diamonds (Lu *et al.* 1991; Zhang *et al.* 1991; Chi *et al.* 1992) (Fig. 1). While the petrology, mineralogy and thermal history of peridotite xenoliths and heavy mineral concentrates have been determined across the Sino-Korean craton, very little geochemical data are available for these xeno-

*From* Prichard, H. M., Alabaster, T., Harris, N. B. W. & Neary, C. R. (eds), 1993, *Magmatic Processes and Plate Tectonics*, Geological Society Special Publication No. 76, 71–81.

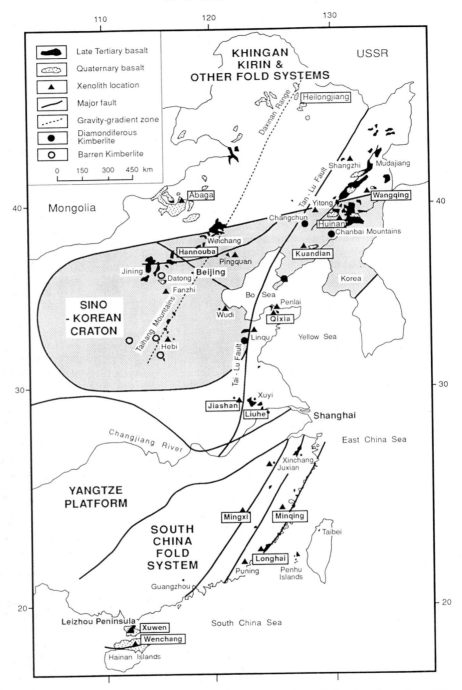

**Fig. 1.** Map of crustal age provinces and volcanic fields of eastern China. Volcanic rocks and xenolith localities are widespread across the Sino-Korean craton (Fan & Hooper 1989) as are the location of diamondiferous (closed circles) and barren on-craton kimberlites (open circles) (Zhang *et al.* 1991). The age of the Sino-Korean craton is well defined on the basis of multi-isotopic analyses (Jahn *et al.* 1987; Liu *et al.* 1992) with remnants of <3500 Ma crust being reported east of Beijing. Note the presence of major fault zones (Tan–Lu) which traverse the craton and are associated with regions of extremely thin lithosphere (Chen *et al.* 1991).

liths, so discussion will concentrate on the elemental geochemistry and thermal history. He (1987) noted that dunites/harzburgites are widespread in the Palaeozoic kimberlites of eastern China in association with spinel and garnet lherzolites or harzburgites, mica peridotites and eclogites. Zhang *et al.* (1991) reported a similarity in the chemistry of diamond inclusions from the Chinese kimberlite pipes and those from the Yakatia and Kaapvaal kimberlites. In addition, they noted that the lithosphere is dominated by harzburgite, dunite, lherzolite and wehrlite. Zhou *et al.* (1991, 1993) studied indicator minerals from the diamondiferous and barren kimberlites of eastern China. The diamondiferous kimberlites tended to contain abundant high Cr pyrope garnets while the barren kimberlites have higher proportions of low Cr pyropes. Also the elemental geochemistry of the indicator minerals pointed to hydrous metasomatism in the lower lithosphere and the presence of a high temperature group, perhaps related to megacryst formation (i.e. magma movement). In contrast the barren kimberlites are dominated by low temperature garnets with a minor amount of high temperature garnets. Elemental data are characteristic of low temperature, low pressure garnets and any high temperature garnets are believed to reflect short-lived events. The presence of high Cr, moderate Mg chromite (with a chemistry similar to diamond-hosted spinels) is indicative of derivation from harzburgite or lherzolite wall rock. In contrast, low Cr, high Mg spinels represent disrupted lherzolites. On the basis of such data Griffin *et al.* (1992a,b) produced lithostratigraphic profiles for the Sino-Korean craton, at Liaoning and Shandong. Griffin *et al.* (1992a,b) defined shield geotherms of $<40 \text{ mW m}^{-2}$ ($<1$ HFU), at the time of kimberlite emplacement, vertical variability in the petrology of the lithosphere and a change in the thermal structure on either side of the Tan–Lu fault. These authors demonstrated that the Palaeozoic lithosphere was thick and varied from 150–220 km from west to east, thus accounting for the predominance of diamondiferous (180–220 km) kimberlites in the eastern part of the craton (Zhang & Hu 1991). In addition, cratonic lithosphere was found to be more lherzolitic in the west and more harzburgitic in the east, and a metasome level (mica, apatite, carbonate and oxides) was defined around 80–100 km (F. Lu, pers. comm., 1992). Using indicator minerals, Zhou *et al.* (1993) demonstrated the presence of hydrous metasomatism and melt metasomatism in the Liaoning and Shandong pipes. Overall the thermal, petrological and diamondiferous character of the Palaeozoic lower lithosphere of eastern China is consistent with the existence of thick, cold Archaean lithosphere in the eastern part of the Sino-Korean craton.

## Cenozoic basalt-borne xenoliths

Basalt-borne xenoliths, from thirty on- and off-craton localities of eastern China (Fig.1), have been studied in much more detail than the kimberlite xenoliths (Cao & Zhu 1987; Lu & Luo 1992). The paucity of garnet peridotite (high pressure) xenoliths from on-craton locations (Fan & Hooper 1989), and the ubiquity of spinel peridotites, indicates that on-craton volcanism has not sampled the thickness of craton that existed in the Palaeozoic. This is either because the cratonic lithosphere had already undergone considerable thinning by the Cenozoic, or that the level of entrainment of xenoliths had changed from deep (Palaeozoic) to shallow (Cenozoic). The presence of garnet lherzolites at Mingxi, a region of high heat flow, may reflect sub-lithospheric processes (i.e. asthenosphere). In general, basalt-borne xenoliths display high temperature dislocations (Jin *et al.* 1989; Xu, Y. G. *et al.* 1992) and most xenoliths, from widespread localities across the craton, conform to an oceanic ridge geotherm ($>2.0$ HFU) (Fan & Hooper 1989).

On-craton harzburgites of eastern China have high modal percentage of orthopyroxene (20–35% which makes them comparable to the Kaapvaal harzburgites. Clinopyroxenes in harzburgites, from eastern China, are chemically identical to those from Kaapvaal particularly in their Ti/Zr and Sr/Zr ratios and their light rare earth enriched character (Zhang *et al.* 1993). In contrast, clinopyroxenes in lherzolites from eastern China are distinct from the bulk of cratonic harzburgites, and have chemical affinities with mantle lherzolites from tectonically active continental regions (e.g. western USA; eastern Australia; western Europe). Overall, the Chinese (MgO $> 44\%$ and SiO$_2$ = 42–48) and Kaapvaal harzburgites define overlapping trends on element–element plots (Fig. 2) (Zhang *et al.* 1990a). Consideration of the possible difference between cratonic, circum-cratonic and oceanic peridotites indicates that the lower lithosphere beneath eastern China is a complex hybrid containing old cratonic nuclei (Archaean harzburgites) and more recently accreted peridotites (post-Archaean lherzolites). However, preliminary ICP-MS data (Menzies & Dupuy, unpublished data) indicate that on-craton and off-craton lherzolites may have experienced different processes. Clinopyroxenes from on-craton

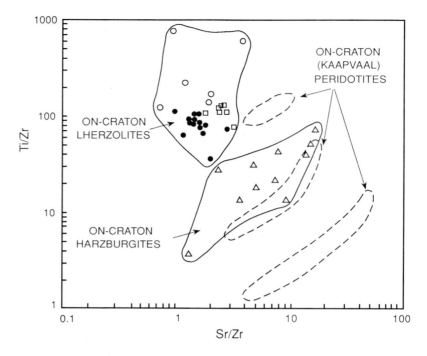

**Fig. 2.** Elemental variations in clinopyroxenes from harzburgites and lherzolites from eastern China in relation to the Kaapvaal harzburgites (Zhang *et al.* 1993). In eastern China the on-craton lherzolites are compositionally different from the on-craton harzburgites.

lherzolites tend to be U and LREE enriched relative to clinopyroxenes from recently accreted lithosphere (i.e. Hainan Island). Taken in conjunction with elevated Zr/Sm and Zr/Hf ratios this may indicate that the on-craton lherzolites have experienced influx of carbonatitic melts while the off-craton lherzolites (Hainan Island) have evolved in a high Pb and Th environment (sediment subduction).

$^{87}Sr/^{86}Sr$ and $^{143}Nd/^{144}Nd$ data for clinopyroxenes in peridotites, from on- and off-craton locations, reveal that spinel lherzolites (i.e. shallow mantle) are isotopically depleted and similar to mid-ocean ridge and ocean island basalts (Song & Frey 1989; Tatsumoto *et al.* 1992b; Menzies *et al.* 1992) (Fig. 3). MORB-like on-craton lithosphere appears to predominate in the east, around the Bohai Sea and Yellow Sea, a region of thin Archaean–Proterozoic crust. While the widespread occurrence of depleted reservoirs must be stressed, on-craton and off-craton provinciality is also evident with mantle domains ranging in composition from depleted (peridotites) to enriched (pyroxenites). Indeed, the existence of on-craton heterogeneous lower lithosphere at Hannuoba may point to the pres-

ence of deeper older, enriched reservoirs (garnet-facies) and chemically stratified lithosphere (Song & Frey 1989; Tatsumoto *et al.* 1992b; Menzies *et al.* 1992; Fan & Menzies 1992). While Rb–Sr, U–Pb and Sm–Nd isotope data support the presence of Archaean lithosphere (Song & Frey 1989; Tatsumoto *et al.* 1992b; Menzies *et al.* 1992), Re–Os data from Hannuoba may indicate the presence of more recently accreted lithosphere (R. Walker, pers. comm. 1992).

These elemental and isotopic data support a hybrid, complex origin for the lower lithosphere beneath the Sino-Korean craton. While some of the elemental and isotopic data are similar to those found beneath other circum-cratonic (tectonically active) continental regions, the existence of older cratonic remnants is also indicated by elemental and isotopic data. Presumably lower lithosphere evolved in a manner similar to the overlying crust, such that relics of Archaean cratonic lithosphere are surrounded by accreted Proterozoic or Phanerozoic lithosphere. Overall, the thermal, petrological, chemical and isotopic character of the Cenozoic subcrustal mantle is consistent with the presence of thin, hot (oceanic) lithosphere that contrasts markedly with the

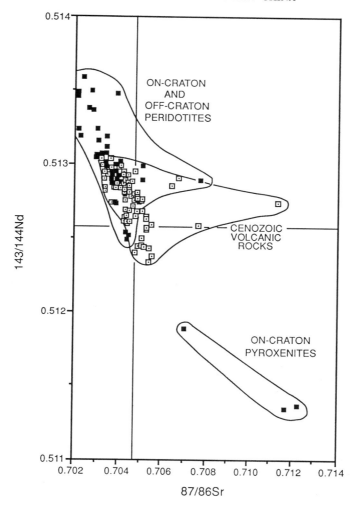

**Fig. 3.** Variation in Nd and Sr isotopes in Tertiary to Quaternary volcanic rocks (open symbols) and Chinese mantle xenoliths (filled symbols). While Chinese volcanic rocks do not sample the most enriched (high $^{87}Sr/$ $^{86}Sr$ and low $^{143}Nd/^{144}Nd$ ratio) or the most depleted (low $^{87}Sr/^{86}Sr$ and high $^{143}Nd/^{144}Nd$ ratio) reservoirs, as represented by xenoliths, the isotopic data are dispersed in a manner suggestive of possible involvement of lithospheric reservoirs in the genesis of late Phanerozoic volcanic rocks. Data sources: (a) volcanic rocks – Basu *et al.* (1991); Chung *et al.* (1992); Song *et al.* (1990); Tu *et al.* (1991); Fan & Menzies (1992); Zartman *et al.* (1992); (b) xenoliths – Song & Frey (1989); Menzies *et al.* (1992); Tatsumoto *et al.* (1992b)

widespread occurrence of thick, cold (shield) lithosphere across the craton 400 Ma earlier. Greater isotopic heterogeneity exists in western regions of thick (≫ 100 km), cold? lithosphere, than eastern regions of thin (≪ 100 km), hot? lithosphere. This can be interpreted in several ways. In areas of greatest lithospheric thinning (e.g. Bohai Sea), on the craton, the pre-existent cold Archaean lithosphere was totally replaced by the accretion of (homogeneous) hot Cenozoic oceanic lithosphere. However, this is inconsis-

tent with the presence of Archaean remnants in the Cenozoic lower lithosphere (Tatsumoto *et al.* 1992*a,b*) or the presence of old enriched pyroxenites (Menzies *et al.* 1992). Alternatively isotopic heterogeneity was most prevalent in the lower-most Archaean lithosphere (> 80 km) and was remobilized during Tertiary–Quaternary volcanism leaving remnants of a depleted shallower lithosphere to be sampled during Quaternary volcanism. Accretion of younger lithosphere associated with late Phanerozoic magmatism produced a hybrid lower lithosphere. Several geological facts are consistent with the later hypothesis. These include kimberlite-borne xenolith data that indicate the presence of an 80–120 km metasome horizon; elemental and isotopic data (Zhang *et al.* 1990*a*, 1993) indicating the existence of a mixed population of cratonic and oceanic peridotites; and Sr and Nd isotopic data indicating a vertical isotopic variation from depleted (shallow) to enriched (deep) lithospheric mantle.

## Cenozoic volcanism – key to the missing lithosphere?

The aforementioned xenolith suites bracket a period of basaltic volcanism in eastern China, which may have been produced, in part, by reactivation and remobilization of the Archaean lower lithosphere. Volcanism began in the early Tertiary and has continued until the present day. Pioneering work on volcanic rocks from eastern China suggested that the Cenozoic cratonic lithosphere of eastern China, was laterally and vertically heterogeneous and that such lithosphere participated in magma genesis (Zhou & Armstrong 1980). Recent studies have concluded that oceanic-type reservoirs predominated in eastern China, but that other enriched reservoirs also existed, either in the deep or shallow (i.e. crust) lithosphere (Peng *et al.* 1986; Basu *et al.* 1991). While we accept that crustal contamination may be an important factor in basalt genesis, in the case of xenolith-bearing alkaline and potassic magmas we believe that crustal contamination has played a somewhat minor role. Because of the intrinsically high levels of Sr, LREE, U in these alkaline and potassic volcanic rocks, one would have to invoke assimilation of large amounts of crust to register a change in the Sr, Nd and Pb isotopic composition. Assimilation of large amounts of crust would most probably have been associated with fractionation, and together such processes would not have resulted in the survival of broadly basaltic compositions in the surface eruptives. Comparison of the isotopic composition of Cenozoic volcanic rock and xenoliths indicates the presence of common enriched source components in the lower lithosphere (Fig. 3). Most workers now accept that the depleted oceanic reservoir is probably sub-lithospheric in origin and that the enriched reservoir is a lower lithospheric reservoir (Tu *et al.* 1991; Tatsumoto *et al.* 1992*b*; Menzies *et al.* 1992; Zartman *et al.* 1992; Chung *et al.* 1993). Finally, a subduction influence in the late Cenozoic magmatism of eastern China is not supported by geological and geochemical data (Kimura *et al.*

1990; Zartman *et al.* 1992). This has important implications when, in a later section, we consider the mechanisms responsible for thinning of the cratonic lithosphere. Spatial changes in volcanic rock geochemistry in relation to lateral changes in lithosphere thickness are important in any consideration of the role of lithosphere in magma-magenesis. Early Tertiary basalts from Beijing and Bohai (40–70 Ma) display changes in elemental and isotopic geochemistry from west to east. Sub-alkalic basalts (west) have $^{87}Sr/^{86}Sr$ > 0.704 and $^{206}Pb/^{204}Pb$ < 17.93 and alkalic basalts (east) have $^{87}Sr/^{86}Sr$ < 0.704 and $^{206}Pb/^{204}Pb$ > 18.179. In addition, temporal changes in basalt geochemistry are apparent from Tertiary to Quaternary times due to temporal changes in lithosphere thickness and possible changes in reservoir chemistry.

## Lithosphere evolution

Integration of the available data gives us some insight into the evolution of the lower lithosphere of eastern China during the Phanerozoic. Lithostratigraphic studies (Griffin *et al.* 1992*a,b*) and the occurrence of diamonds (Zhang *et al.* 1991) indicate that Palaeozoic lithosphere was 150–220 km thick (west–east) and, as such, may have retained its structural integrity since the Archaean. By the Tertiary the lithosphere was thinner ($\ll$ 150 km), in that no young diamondiferous alkaline rocks are known, but some Tertiary alkaline volcanic rocks still appear to have a contribution from enriched (garnet-bearing) sources (lower lithosphere) (Fig. 4). The participation of enriched lithospheric sources in Tertiary volcanism may indicate that the metasome level (80–120 km) in the lithosphere was tapped/consumed in the Tertiary. Indeed the sudden surge in magmatism in the late Phanerozoic may have been triggered by the interception of upwelling isotherms with a low melting metasome layer (40 km thick). If we can interpret the presence of spinel peridotite xenoliths and the widespread lack of garnet peridotite xenoliths as an indicator of lithosphere thickness (and not depth of entrainment) then we can speculate that by the late Cenozoic the lithosphere was around 75–80 km thick. Fortunately such an inference is supported by seismic tomographic data (Chen *et al.* 1991).

Lithosphere thinning could have been brought about by several factors including Pacific plate subduction; enhanced mantle temperatures associated with plumes or extrusion tectonics resulting from the India–Eurasia collision. We will evaluate each of these in turn.

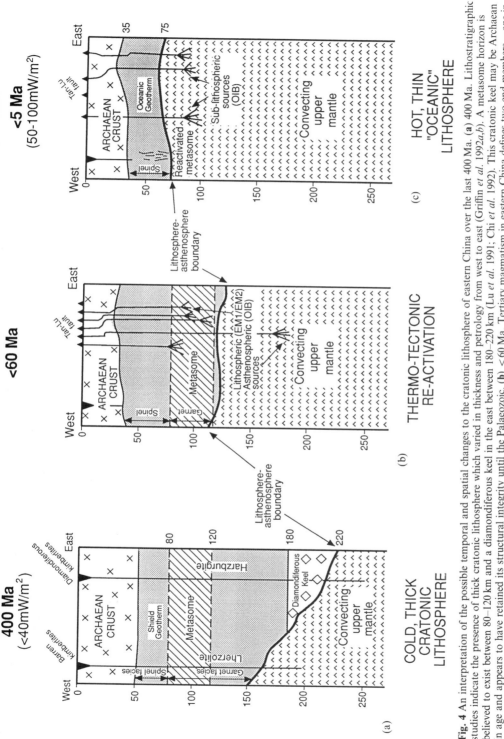

**Fig. 4** An interpretation of the possible temporal and spatial changes to the cratonic lithosphere of eastern China over the last 400 Ma. (**a**) 400 Ma. Lithostratigraphic studies indicate the presence of thick cratonic lithosphere which varied in thickness and petrology from west to east (Griffin *et al.* 1992*a,b*). A metasome horizon is believed to exist between 80–120 km and a diamondiferous keel in the east between 180–220 km (Lu *et al.* 1991; Chi *et al.* 1992). This cratonic keel may be Archaean in age and appears to have retained its structural integrity until the Palaeozoic. (**b**) <60 Ma. Tertiary magmatism in eastern China defines two end-members — one in the convecting upper mantle (PREMA/OIB) and one/two in the lower lithosphere (EM1/EM2). One can speculate that thermo-tectonic processes in the vicinity of the Tan–Lu Fault may have caused thermal/mechanical erosion of the lower lithosphere. (**c**) <5 Ma. Seismic tomography reveals the presence of <80 km of lithosphere and a low velocity structure between 80–180 km, very similar to modern ocean ridges. High pressure xenoliths point to spinel facies peridotites (<75 km) and an apparent lack of an ancient metasome horizon. However, the past existence of such metasomes is indicated by the presence of pyroxenite veins at Hannuoba. These pyroxenites have $^{87}Sr/^{86}Sr > 0.707$ and $^{143}Nd/^{144}Nd < 0.5120$ (Tatsumoto *et al.* 1992*b*; Menzies *et al.* 1992) similar to the enriched (shallow) reservoir (i.e. EM1) tapped by Tertiary magmatism. Quaternary magmas have isotopic ratios similar to oceanic basalts and as such are believed to originate in sub-lithospheric reservoirs, perhaps due to the thinned nature of the lithosphere.

## (a) Supra-subduction processes

During the Mesozoic, a northwestward-dipping subduction zone affected parts of southeastern China to the east of the Tan-Lu Fault. Tian *et al.* (1992) argued that episodes of rifting in the Jurassic–early Cretaceous; late Cretaceous and Eocene–Neogene were related to subduction of the Pacific Plate. However, the lack of any evidence for a subduction zone influence in the geochemistry of early Tertiary to Recent volcanic rocks argues against a dominant influence from modern subduction in late Phanerozoic lithospheric processes (Zartman *et al.* 1992). Despite this, some recent models for the evolution of the lithosphere beneath eastern China, have invoked subduction as a major mechanism in lithospheric growth (Jin *et al.* 1989; Basu *et al.* 1991).

## (b) Intraplate processes

The degree to which plumes can or cannot affect cratonic keels and the role of plumes in late Phanerozoic magmatism, in eastern China, have been debated recently (Hill 1991; Chung & Sun 1992). The general consensus amongst workers in the field of volcanology (Zartman *et al.* 1992; Chung *et al.* 1992, 1993; Chung & Sun 1992) is that Cenozoic magmatism in eastern China was not related to plume structures. This is consistent with seismic tomography (Anderson *et al.* 1992) which does not support the present-day existence of major plumes beneath eastern China. The presence of plumes in the Palaeozoic or Mesozoic is difficult to evaluate, but the lack of surface volcanism with a plume derived geochemical signature during the early to mid-Phanerozoic makes their presence rather doubtful.

## (c) Passive processes

Destabilization of thick cratonic lithosphere requires enhanced mantle temperatures, tectonic thinning due to plate tectonics and/or breakup of the craton due to major faults (Tapponier & Molnar 1977; Ma & Wu 1981). Tapponier & Molnar (1977) argued that all the Cenozoic tectonics of eastern China are related to the convergence of India and Eurasia. Recently it has been demonstrated that a radial stress orientation exists throughout China (Xu, Z. *et al.* 1992) which is believed to be related to indentor collision models (India–Eurasia) and not to local phenomena. The Tancheng–Lujiang (Tan–Lu) Fault (>2400 km long) in eastern China is a major sinistral strike-slip fault active during late

Jurassic to early Cretaceous times. It cross-cuts the craton and is associated with major displacements of several hundred kilometres in the crust, and more importantly, the shallow mantle. In the past it has been related to oblique subduction but, for several reasons, it is now believed to have formed due to extrusion tectonics (Kimura *et al.* 1990; Tian *et al.* 1992). Extrusion tectonics may provide an important mechanism for lithosphere destabilization as a result of deep lithosphere faults/shear zones and tectonic thinning of otherwise stable cratonic lithosphere. Major faults like the Tan–Lu may have focused thermotectonic change within the craton with eventual alignment of Cenozoic volcanism along the strike-slip systems. Late Phanerozoic basaltic magmatism could be related to passive crustal extension, since much of the volcanism appears to relate to major shear zones and deep lithospheric faults. Such a passive model is consistent with the isotopic geochemistry of basaltic rocks (Fig. 3), which can be explained by the involvement of depleted sub-lithospheric source regions (MORB or OIB) and enriched reservoirs (EM1/EM2) within the shallow lithosphere. If one can demonstrate the juxtaposition of isotopically distinct provinces in the lower lithosphere, on either side of a major fault, this may indicate that faults like Tan–Lu constitute major deep lithospheric fractures. Griffin *et al.* (1992*a,b*) and Zhou *et al.* (1993) reported differences in the thermal character of the lower lithosphere, across the Tan–Lu Fault in the Palaeozoic. East of the Tan–Lu Fault (e.g. Liaoning) the lithosphere was cooler and less metasomatized than lithosphere to the west of the fault (e.g. Shandong–Guizhou) at the time of the kimberlite emplacement (400–500 Ma ago) (Zhou *et al.* 1993). Our preliminary data (Menzies *et al.* 1992) indicate that, to the west of the Tan–Lu Fault, the continental interior is characterized by shallow mantle with $^{87}Sr/^{86}Sr$ <0.7075, whereas to the east the Pacific margin is characterized by shallow mantle with $^{87}Sr/^{86}Sr$ <0.7038. This may point to relatively recent (<60 Ma ago) emplacement of hotter, more oceanic, lower lithosphere (east) against older, cratonic lower lithosphere preserved to the west of the Tan–Lu Fault zone. From these data, it is apparent that to the east of the Tan–Lu Fault the old continental lithosphere has been greatly thinned.

The observed lithosphere thickness change in the Sino-Korean craton (Fig. 4) can be accounted for with different thinning rates. (1) A slow rate of 0.25–0.35 cm a$^{-1}$ assuming uniform thinning since the Palaeozoic associated with Cretaceous–Tertiary–Quaternary volcanism. (2) A fast rate of 1.6–2.3 cm a$^{-1}$ assuming that all the lithosphere thinning post-dated the collision of India with Eurasia (50–55 Ma). Essentially this would mean that the Archaean keel remained intact until the Palaeozoic and survived volcanic episodes in the Permo-Triassic. (3) A variable rate of 0.24 cm a$^{-1}$ until the Tertiary and 0.73 cm a$^{-1}$ until the present day. Here we assume that by the Tertiary the lithosphere had been thinned to the base of the metasome layer (120–80 km). The presence of an Archaean metasome horizon (80–120 km) would have facilitated participation of the cold, thick Palaeozoic (Archaean?) lower lithosphere (150–220 km) in magmatism (Figs 4a–c). A possible derivative of this ancient enriched horizon in the Cenozoic xenolith record takes the form of pyroxenite veins which infiltrate spinel peridotites at Hannuoba (Song & Frey 1989; Tatsumoto et al. 1992a; Menzies et al. 1992). Tertiary to Quaternary magmatism may have reactivated, and largely consumed, Archaean metasomes, thus accounting for the temporal and spatial change in isotopic composition of volcanic rocks. Tertiary magmas have a mixed asthenosphere–lithosphere signature and Quaternary magmas have a more dominant asthenospheric signature. Alkaline and potassic magmatism erupted through thick lithosphere (Peng et al. 1986) have a greater lower lithospheric contribution than magmas erupted through thin lithosphere. Such systematics in basalt geochemistry in relation to lithosphere parameters are also apparent off the craton, where potassic magmas erupted through thick lithosphere (Wudalianchi) are compositionally distinct to those erupted through thin lithosphere in the Songliao Basin (Peng et al. 1986; Zhang et al. 1990b, 1993).

## Summary

A review of the geology and geochemistry of kimberlite and basalt xenoliths allows a number of points to be made.

(1) Kimberlite-borne xenoliths point to the existence of thick, cold lithosphere in the Precambrian, particularly in the eastern part of the Sino-Korean craton.

(2) Basalt-borne peridotite xenoliths reveal the presence of thin, hot lithosphere in the Cenozoic and composite peridotite–pyroxenite xenoliths reveal the existence of deeper (garnet facies) reservoirs, with a distinct isotopic signature. Seismic tomography indicates that the lithosphere is 80 km thick (i.e. spinel facies only), so one can speculate that garnet facies mantle must have been consumed in the past.

(3) The involvement of enriched (possibly ancient) lithospheric reservoirs in the genesis of Tertiary to Recent volcanic rocks is indicated by their Sr, Nd and Pb isotopic geochemistry. Since similar enriched reservoirs exist as composite xenoliths one can speculate that thermo-tectonic reactivation and consumption of an ancient metasome layer (80–120 km) may have played a major role in Tertiary to Recent volcanism.

(4) Mantle plumes and Pacific margin subduction are not believed to have been responsible for the dramatic change in the thermal, petrological and chemical character of the cratonic lithosphere. The stress field associated with the collision of India and Eurasia is believed to have destroyed the physical integrity of the craton, with the provision of major shear zones/strike-slip faults that penetrated the crust–mantle boundary; facilitated fluid ingress; reactivated the Archaean metasome horizon and ultimately caused passive continental volcanism in the late Phanerozoic.

The Royal Society is thanked for support for Weiming Fan as a post-doctoral fellow at Royal Holloway (1990–1991) and for supporting MM in China (1989–1992). This work was completed while the senior author was an invited Professor at the University of Montpellier (UMII), Centre Géologique et Géophysique (CNRS), Montpellier, France. Claude Dupuy and Guy Vasseur are thanked for their valuable feedback. Chris Hawkesworth and Peter Nixon are thanked for their comments on an earlier version of this paper.

## References

ANDERSON, D. L., TANIMOTO, T. & ZHANG, Y 1992. Plate tectonics and hotspots: the third dimension. Science, 256, 1645–1650.

BASU, A. R., WANG, J. W., HUANG, W. K., XE, G. H. & TATSUMOTO, M. 1991. Major element, REE and Pb, Sr and Nd isotopic geochemistry of Cenozoic volcanic rocks of eastern China: implications for their origin from sub-oceanic type mantle reservoir. Earth and Planetary Science Letters, 105, 149–169.

BOYD, F. R. & GURNEY, J. 1986. Diamonds and the African lithosphere. Science, 239, 472–477.

CAO, R. L. & ZHU, S-H. 1987. Mantle xenoliths and alkali-rich host rocks in eastern China. In: NIXON, P. N. (ed.) Mantle Xenoliths. J. Wiley & Sons, Chichester, 167–180.

CHENG, G. Y., SONG, Z-H., AN, C-Q., CHENG, L-H., ZHUANG, Z., FU, Z-W., LU, Z-L. & HU, J-F. 1991. Three dimensional crust and upper mantle structure of the North China region. Acta Geophysica Sinica, 34, 172–181.

CHI, J., LU, F., ZHAO, L., ZHAO, C., ZHENG, J. & DENG, F. 1992. A study of primary diamond deposits North China Platform – genesis and pros-

*pects*. China University of Geosciences, Beijing.

CHUNG, S-L. & SUN, S-S. 1992. Cenozoic magmatism in southern China and its implications for origin of DUPAL domains in the northwestern Pacific. *International Symposium on Cenozoic Volcanic rocks and deep-seated xenoliths of China and its Environs*, Institute of Geology, Chinese Academy of Sciences, Beijing, 20.

——, ——, TU, K., CHEN, C-H. & LEE, C-Y. 1992. Generation of the Late Cenozoic basalts in SE China: consequences of continental extension and asthenosphere upwelling in response to India–Eurasia collision. *International Geological Congress*, Tokyo, **2**, 545.

——, ——, ——, & ——. 1993. Late Cenozoic basaltic volcanism around the Taiwan Strait, SE China: product of lithosphere–asthenosphere interaction. *Chemical Geology* (submitted).

FAN, Q. C. & HOOPER, P. R. 1989. The mineral chemistry of ultramafic xenoliths of eastern China: implications for upper mantle composition and the palaeo-geotherms. *Journal of Petrology*, **30**, 1117–1158.

FAN, W. & MENZIES, M. A. 1992. Contribution of the lithospheric mantle to extension-related volcanics – geochemical evidence from Cenozoic basaltic rocks in Hainan Island and Leizhou Peninsula, southern China. *In*: RUOXIN, L. (ed.) *Chronology and Geochemistry of Cenozoic Volcanic Rocks in China*. Seismology Press, China, 320–329.

GRIFFIN, W. L., RYAN, C. G., GURNEY, J. J. & SOBOLEV, N. V. 1992*a*. Comparative geochemical evolution of the southern African, Siberian, and Australian cratonic lithospheres. *International Geological Congress*, Tokyo, **1**, 175.

——, O'REILLY, S. Y. & RYAN, C. G. 1992*b*. Composition and thermal structure of the lithosphere beneath South Africa, Siberia and China: proton microprobe studies. *International Symposium on Cenozoic Volcanic rocks and deep-seated xenoliths of China and its Environs*, Institute of Geology, Chinese Academy of Sciences, Beijing, 20.

HE, G-Z. 1987. Mantle xenoliths from kimberlites in China. *In*: NIXON, P. N. (ed.) *Mantle Xenoliths*. J. Wiley & Sons, Chichester, 182–185.

HILL, R. I. 1991. Starting plumes and continental break-up. *Earth and Planetary Science Letters*, **104**, 398–416.

JAHN, B. M., AUVRAY, B., CORNICHET, J., BAI, Y. L., SHEN, Q. H. & LIU, D. Y. 1987. 3.5 Ga old amphibolites from eastern Hebei province, China: field occurrence, petrography, Sm–Nd isochron age and REE geochemistry. *Precambrian Research*, **34**, 311–346.

JIN, Z-M., GREEN, H. W. & BORCH, R. S. 1989. Microstructures of olivine and stress in the upper mantle beneath eastern China. *Tectonophysics*, **169**, 23–50.

KIMURA, G., TAKASHI, M. & KONO, M. 1990. Mesozoic collision extrusion tectonics in eastern Asia. *Tectonophysics*, **181**, 15–23.

LIU, D. Y. 1992. Seismic tomography in China. *International Geological Congress*, Tokyo, **3**, 668.

——, NUTMAN, A. P., COMPSTON, W., WU, J. S. & SHEN, Q. H. 1992. Remnants of 3800 Ma crust in the Chinese part of the Sino-Korean craton. *Geology*, **20**, 339–342.

LU, F., HUAN, Z., ZHENG, J. & REN, Y. 1991. Characteristics of Palaeozoic mantle lithosphere in Fuxian, Liaoning province. *Geological Science and Technology Information*, **10**, 1–20. China University of Geosciences, Beijing.

—— & LUO, Z. 1992. Eastern China – 4000 kilometres of mantle samples. *International Symposium on Cenozoic volcanic rocks and deep-seated xenoliths from China and its Environs*, Institute of Geology, Chinese Academy of Sciences, Beijing, 81–84.

MA, X. & WU, D. 1981. Early tectonic evolution of China. *Precambrian Research*, **14**, 185–202.

MENZIES, M. A., THIRLWALL, M. F., WEIMING, F. & ZHANG, M. 1992. Depleted and enriched lithosphere beneath eastern China – evidence from Quaternary alkaline volcanic rocks and their xenoliths. *Transactions of the American Geophysical Union*, **73**, 1717.

PENG, Z. C., ZARTMAN, R. E., FUTA, K. & CHEN, D. 1986. Pb, Sr and Nd isotopic systematics and chemical characteristics of Cenozoic basalts eastern China. *Chemical Geology*, **59**, 3–33.

SCOTT-SMITH, B. 1987. Greenland. *In*: NIXON, P. H. (ed.) *Mantle Xenoliths*. J. Wiley & Sons, Chichester, 23–32.

SONG, Y. & FREY, F. A. 1989. Geochemistry of peridotite xenoliths in basalt from Hannuoba eastern China: implications for subcontinental mantle heterogeneity. *Geochimica et Cosmochimica Acta*, **53**, 97–113.

——, —— & ZHI, X. C. 1990. Isotopic characteristics of Hannuoba basalts, eastern China: implications for their petrogenesis and the composition of subcontinental mantle. *Chemical Geology*, **85**, 35–52.

TAPPONIER, P. & MOLNAR, P. 1977. Active faulting and tectonics of China. *Journal of Geophysical Research*, **82**, 2905–2930.

TATSUMOTO, M., NAKAMURA, Y. & BASU, A. R. 1992*a*. Enriched mantle lithosphere at the eastern Eurasian continental margin. *International Geological Congress*, Tokyo, **2**, 545.

——, BASU, A. R., WANKANG, H., JUNWEN, W. & GUANGHONG, X. 1992*b*. Sr, Nd, and Pb isotopes in ultramafic xenoliths in volcanic rocks of eastern China: enriched components EM1 and EMII in subcontinental lithosphere. *Earth and Planetary Science Letters*, **113**, 107–128.

TENG, J. W., WANG, Q. S., LIU, Y. C. & WEI, S. Y. 1983. Geophysical field characteristics, distribution and formation of hydrocarbon bearing basins of eastern China. *Journal of Geophysics*, **26**, 319–330.

TIAN, Z-Y., HAN, P. & XU, K-D. 1992. The Mesozoic–Cenozoic East China rift system. *Earth and Planetary Science Letters*, **208**, 341–363.

TU, K., FLOWER, F. J., CARLSON, R. W., ZHANG, M. & XIE, G. H. 1991. Sr, Nd and Pb isotopic compositions of Hainan basalts (South China): implications for a subcontinental lithosphere Dupal source. *Geology*, **19**, 567–569.

XU, Y. G., MERCIER, J. C. C., ROSS, J. V., LIN, C. Y. & SHI, L. B. 1992. A first insight into the upper mantle beneath a lithospheric fault zone: the spinel lherzolite xenoliths from Yitong Basalts, north-eastern China. *International Symposium on Cenozoic volcanic rocks and deep-seated xenoliths from China and its Environs*, Institute of Geology, Chinese Academy of Sciences, Beijing, 102.

XU, Z., WANG, S., HUAN, Y. & GAO, A. 1992. Tectonic stress field of China inferred from a large number of small earthquakes. *Journal of Geophysical Research*, **97**, 11867–11877.

ZARTMAN, R. E., FUTA, K. & PENG, Z. C. 1992. A comparison of Sr–Nd–Pb isotopes in young and old continental lithospheric mantle: Patagonia and eastern China. *Australian Journal of Earth Sciences*, **38**, 545–557.

ZHANG, A., XU, D., XIE, X., GUO, L., ZHOU, J. & WANG, W. 1991. The status and future of diamond exploration in China. CPRM Special Publication, **92**, 10–11.
cation, **92**, 10–11.

ZHANG, M., FLOWER, M. F. J. & SHIMIZU, N. 1990*a* Major and trace element heterogeneities of sub-continental mantle lithosphere in eastern China and its significance. *Transactions of the American Geophysical Union*, **43**, 1559.

——, —— & ——. 1993 Diversification of continental lithospheric mantle: a study of mantle xenoliths and clinopyroxenes. *Geochimica et Cosmochimica Acta* (in prep).

——, MENZIES, M. A., SUDDABY, P. & THIRLWALL, M. F. 1990. EM1 signature from within post-Archaean subcontinental lithospheric mantle: isotopic evidence from the potassic volcanic rocks in NE China. *Geochemical Journal*, **25**, 329–340.

——, SUDDABY, P., THOMPSON, R. N., MENZIES, M. A. & THIRLWALL, M. F. 1993. Potassic volcanic rocks in NE China: 1 Geochemical constraints in mantle sources and magma genesis. *Journal of Petrology* (in revision).

ZHANG, P. & HU, S. 1991. Metallogenic model of kimberlite in North China Craton, China. *Proceedings of the fifth Kimberlite Conference*. CPRM

ZHOU, J., GRIFFIN, W. L., JAQUES, A. L., RYAN, C. G. & WIN, T. T. 1991. Geochemistry of indicator minerals from Chinese kimberlites and lamproites. CPRM Special Publication, **92**, 475–477.

——, ——, —— & ——. 1993. Geochemistry of diamond indicator minerals from China. *Proceedings of the Fifth Kimberlite Conference* (in press).

ZHOU, X. H. & ARMSTRONG, R. L. 1982. Cenozoic volcanic rocks of eastern China – secular and geographic trends in chemistry and strontium isotopic composition. *Earth and Planetary Science Letters*, **58**, 301–329.

# Ophiolites and oceanic crust

# Development of concepts concerning the Troodos ophiolite and adjacent units in Cyprus

ALASTAIR ROBERTSON[1] & COSTAS XENOPHONTOS[2]

[1] *Department of Geology and Geophysics, University of Edinburgh, Edinburgh EH9 3JW, UK*
[2] *Geological Survey Department, Nicosia, Cyprus*

**Abstract**: The foundations for study of the Troodos ophiolite and adjacent units in Cyprus were laid down by systematic mapping by the Cyprus Geological Survey Department (1952–1970). Prior to the late 1950s, Cyprus geology was interpreted in classic geosynclinal terms. The first, integrated description of the Troodos was given by Gass & Masson Smith in 1963. Publication of the Vine & Matthew's (1963) sea-floor spreading hypothesis was followed by Ian Gass's key interpretation in 1968 of the Troodos as oceanic lithosphere formed by sea-floor spreading. During the early 1970s, the dominant view of the Troodos was of a mid-ocean ridge, formed by spreading at a narrow, linear spreading zone, fed by a single, axial magma chamber. However, early geochemical studies suggested that genesis could have taken place above a subduction zone. During the 1980s, drilling related to the International Cyprus Crustal Study Project stimulated much new field work. By 1990 a popular view of the Troodos was that it had formed above a northward-dipping subduction zone during the earlier stages of convergence within an oceanic basin, similar in some respects to the origin of SW Pacific forearcs. Others favoured an origin as a marginal basin formed by spreading above a southward-dipping subduction zone, either in the vicinity of Cyprus, or located in central Turkey. In whatever scenario, it is generally accepted that the spreading fabric was unstable and was fed by small, multiple magma chambers. The extension outpaced magma supply and this favoured extensional detachment faulting, mainly near the base of the sheeted dykes. The Troodos lithosphere was also bounded by an oceanic fracture zone to the present south. Studies of the Late Cretaceous–Recent sediment cover have documented deep-sea sedimentation and later uplift, related to Africa–Eurasia convergence. In W Cyprus, the adjacent Mamonia Complex was pieced together as a Mesozoic passive margin bordering a small ocean basin, although whether this was a Red Sea-type basin, or a backarc marginal basin is still debated. The Mamonia lavas and sediments were juxtaposed with the Troodos ophiolite by processes, variously interpreted as subduction/accretion, oceanic transform faulting, strike-slip, collision and/or palaeorotation of a Troodos microplate. The Kyrenia Range in N Cyprus also includes remnants of Mesozoic passive margin; it was emplaced in stages apparently by a combination of strike-slip and thrusting. On a regional scale, the Troodos ophiolite preserves part of one of a number of inferred small oceanic basins within the Mesozoic Tethyan area of the Eastern Mediterranean.

The Troodos ophiolite and related units in Cyprus have played a crucial role in testing and development of plate tectonics theory, following Ian Gass's far-sighted suggestion in 1968 that the Troodos formed at a spreading ocean ridge. How our present knowledge has come about is a fascinating story, involving the interrelated studies over several decades of several hundred geologists from a large number of countries, working within many earth science disciplines. Our objective here is to trace the development of concepts concerning the genesis of the Troodos ophiolite and related units in Cyprus. We will see how some early ideas have continued to be accepted and have evolved, while others, although initially 'consensus views', were later abandoned as new data became available. More recent results highlight the success of coordinated international research. Cyprus has been a magnificent training ground for several generations of PhD students, who have contributed tremendously to our present knowledge. Despite all these efforts, we are forced to conclude that critical problems still remain in relating processes of modern ocean crust formation and deformation to ophiolite genesis and emplacement, in even this, the best-documented ophiolite. To this extent, the 'ophiolite problem' can still be considered as unsolved.

## Setting of the Troodos ophiolite in the Eastern Mediterranean

We begin by outlining basic aspects of the geology that need to be grasped by any reader unfamiliar with Cyprus. The island encompasses three tectonic units (Fig. 1). The first is the Troodos ophiolite (Troodos Massif), comprising a relatively undeformed, complete ophiolite succession, following the 1972 Penrose Conference

*From* Prichard, H. M., Alabaster, T., Harris, N. B. W. & Neary, C. R. (eds), 1993,
*Magmatic Processes and Plate Tectonics*, Geological Society Special Publication No. 76, 85–119.

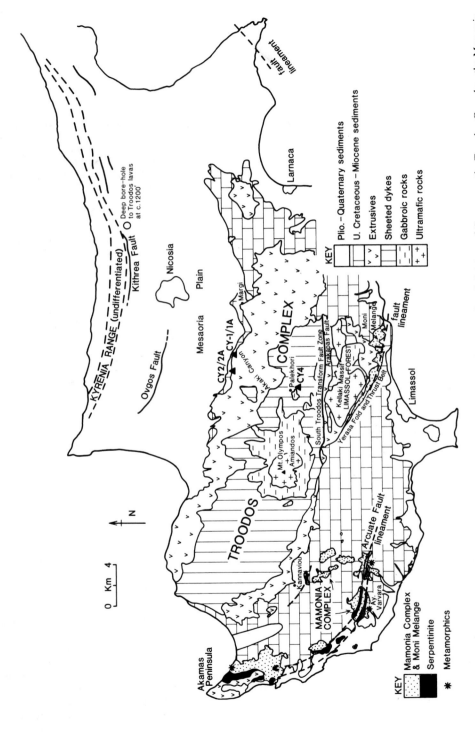

**Fig. 1.** Outline tectonic map of Cyprus showing places mentioned in the text. The three tectonic subdivisions of Cyprus are the Troodos Complex, the Mamonia Complex, and the Kyrenia Range.

definition. It has been updomed, producing a sequence of ultrabasic rocks in the centre, surrounded by gabbros, sheeted dykes, lavas and deep-sea sediments. The ophiolite is mineralized, with podiform chromite in the ultrabasic part of the sequence and volcanogenic massive sulphides in the lava sequence. The complex is marked by strong positive gravity and magnetic anomalies. The ophiolite is Late Cretaceous in age, and was not subaerially exposed and deeply eroded until Plio-Quaternary time. Unlike most other ophiolites there is no exposed metamorphic sole (except possibly locally in SW Cyprus; see later). The second unit, in SW Cyprus, is the Mamonia Complex, which is separated from the Troodos ophiolite by high-angle faults. This is mainly Triassic lavas and Mesozoic sedimentary rocks, with subordinate ophiolitic rocks, largely serpentinite, extrusives and minor metamorphics, located along fault zones. The third unit, the Kyrenia Range, in N

Cyprus, has the structure of a small Alpine-type fold-and-thrust belt. It has a core of Mesozoic shallow-water carbonates, and an envelope of younger volcanics and sediments. The Kyrenia Range was emplaced in stages from latest Cretaceous to mid-Tertiary. The Mamonia Complex will figure in the following discussion. The Kyrenia Range is, however, not discussed in any detail here, mainly because of more limited study and its complexity. The present-day tectonic setting of Cyprus in the Eastern Mediterranean is shown in Fig. 2.

Much of the interest in Cyprus stems from the microcosm of Tethyan geology that is exposed there. The Late Cretaceous Troodos ophiolite has counterparts in Turkey, Syria, Iran and Oman, for example. Rocks similar to the Mamonia Complex are also exposed on a much larger scale in other areas, including Greece, SW Turkey, Syria and Oman.

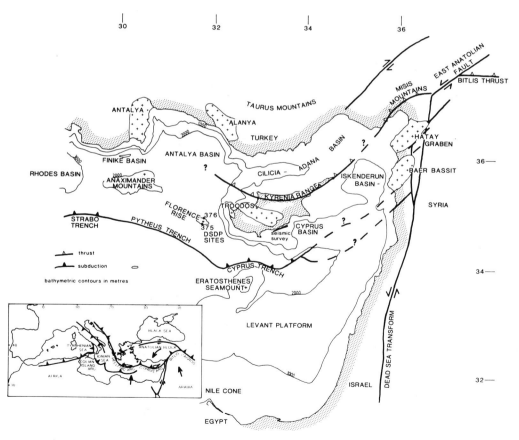

**Fig. 2.** Present-day tectonic setting of Cyprus in the Eastern Mediterranean Sea. Inset: the trends of active margins in the Mediterranean. From Robertson *et al.* 1991*b*.

## Importance of ophiolites in plate tectonic theory

From the early days, discoveries in the oceans enabled ophiolites and related sediments to be interpreted. For example, Peach & Horne (1899) interpreted radiolarian cherts of the Ballantrae Igneous Complex in SW Scotland as oceanic sediments, following the discoveries of the Challenger Expedition (1872–1876). Ophiolites were found in the central ('axial') parts of many orogenic belts, associated with deep-water 'geosynclinal' sediments. From work in the northern Apennines as early as 1821, Brongniart noted an association of ultrabasics, gabbros, diabase-spilite and chert. This was more complete in fact than the well-known 'Steinmann Trinity', which excluded cherts (Steinmann 1927), as discussed by Amstutz (1980). How these rocks formed later became known as the 'ophiolite problem'. Following classic field work, mainly in the Pindos Mountains of northern Greece, J. H. Brunn (1980) was of the opinion that ophiolites formed as massive outpourings of magmas within deep-water geosynclines. During the 1940s and 1950s ocean ridges were being systematically surveyed, followed, in 1963 by the discovery of sea-floor spreading, made possible by the correlation of oceanic magnetic anomalies (Vine & Matthews 1963). At a stroke, the 'ophiolite problem' seemed to have been solved: ophiolites were simply remnants of ocean ridges exposed on land. Mapping was already in progress in Cyprus, leading to the early identification by Ian Gass (1968) of the Troodos Massif as an ophiolite formed at a spreading ridge. Cyprus was thus, early on, established as an ideal location to test and refine plate tectonics concepts, within the Tethyan context (Sylvester-Bradley 1968).

## Nature of the problems posed

How then was the model of the Troodos as an ancient spreading ocean ridge to be tested? Clearly the anatomy of the ophiolite needed to be documented by basic petrological and geophysical work. If the Troodos was a spreading ridge, how did it operate? Was there evidence of a magma chamber beneath the ridge crest and how was it fed? Could a linear deformed ophiolite zone in S Cyprus preserve remnants of an oceanic fracture zone? What could be inferred from overlying sediments about the oceanic setting? How did the Troodos ophiolite relate to the rest of Cyprus geology? Attempts to answer these questions occupied much of the 1970s (e.g. Coleman 1977). The Troodos also became a testing ground for the application of new geo-chemical analytical techniques that offered the prospect of determining past tectonic environments from chemical compositions of extrusive rocks.

During the 1980s, international research on the island increased greatly, stimulated and focused by the Cyprus Crustal Study Project. This succeeded in documenting an almost complete ophiolite crustal succession, by drilling sections in different parts of the ophiolite, a process known as 'offset drilling'. Questions posed became more sophisticated, commonly involving advanced instrumentation. Was there one or more magma chambers? How did spreading operate – smoothly, or with erratic ridge jumps? Did podiform chromites represent mantle residues or cumulates, or both? What role did faulting play in constructing the oceanic crust? How similar were the massive sulphides to the newly discovered black smokers of spreading ridges? Was alteration of the crust pervasive and layered, or patchy? What processes operated in an oceanic fracture zone? What could be learned about uplift of Troodos from facies and biostratigraphic studies of the overlying sediments; what was the present-day crustal structure around Cyprus?

As confidence grew that many of these questions were well on the way to being answered, more effort was directed to determine how the Troodos ophiolite related to adjacent units of Cyprus and the Eastern Mediterranean, generally. A raft of new questions was posed, many of which are still largely unanswered.

In the following discussion, we begin by outlining the main findings in Cyprus up to the discovery of plate tectonics in the mid-1960s. We chart the pioneering work of the 1970s, see how it was amplified and tested by new work in the 1980s, focused on the Cyprus Crustal Study Project. Lastly, we discuss a number of questions concerning the regional tectonic setting of Troodos.

## Pre-plate tectonic research in Cyprus

The classical geological interpretation of Cyprus was summarized by Henson et al. in 1949. By then, the basic geological units of Cyprus were already quite well known. Mesozoic sedimentary rocks in SW Cyprus, known as the 'Trypa Group', were thought to overlie the 'Troodos Igneous Complex' depositionally, which was, thus, Palaeozoic or older. The sedimentary and igneous 'series' were interpreted in classical geosynclinal terms. Early geophysical work revealed gravity anomalies in Cyprus (Mace 1939).

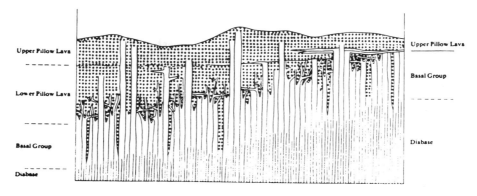

**Fig. 3.** Pattern of dyke intrusion inferred by Wilson in 1959 (from Wilson 1959).

Comprehensive mapping at 1:5000 scale by the Cyprus Geological Survey was begun in 1952. The maps published subsequently, at 1:25 000 scale, and accompanying memoirs, by Wilson (1959), Bagnall (1960), Bear (1960a), Carr & Bear (1960), Gass (1960), Morel (1960) and Pantazis (1967) provided a firm basis for research on the island. During the 1950s most Survey geologists envisaged Troodos as having a 'layer-cake' volcanic stratigraphy. The extrusives were mapped as a pillow lava series, divided into the Basal Group, Lower Pillow Lavas and the Upper Pillow Lavas. Much of the Troodos Massif beneath these lavas consisted of basic–intermediate composition, fine–medium–grained igneous rocks, altered to zeolite and/or greenschist facies mineralogy. Bishopp, the first director of the Cyprus Geological Survey (1952–1954), termed these rocks the Sheeted Diabase and interpreted them as isoclinally folded lava flows (Bishopp 1952).

On the other hand, Wilson clearly understood that 'the diabase is a series of intrusive sheets which over a long period of time were successively injected and acted as feeders to the overlying flows' (Wilson 1959; Fig. 3), a view that rapidly gained acceptance (e.g. Bear 1960b). Soon afterwards, in 1963, Ian Gass & David Masson Smith gave the first fully integrated account of the geology and geophysical setting of the Troodos, concluding that it formed as a volcanic pile affected by extensional stresses within an oceanic setting, located between Africa and Eurasia. Cyprus was seen as having been uplifted as a consequence of northward underthrusting of the African continental margin (Fig. 4a,b). At this stage, interpretation of Cyprus geology was greatly influenced by the discovery of sea-floor spreading by Fred Vine & Drum-

mond Matthews (1963). In 1968, Ian Gass proposed that the Troodos was a fragment of ocean floor generated by sea-floor spreading at a mid-ocean ridge. This conclusion was a milestone that was to influence much of the later research on Cyprus.

The massive sulphides within the Troodos Massif have figured greatly in the Cyprus story. Much of the groundwork, including studies of field relations, mineralogy and ore genesis, was established following a number of early studies (e.g. Cullis & Edge 1922; Searle 1968; Hutchinson & Searle 1970; Johnson 1972; Constantinou & Govett 1972) and a 'volcanic exhalative origin' was generally accepted.

The stratigraphy of the Troodos sedimentary cover unfolded as maps and memoirs were published. Early dating of radiolarites close to the lava–sediment contact (Perapedhi Fm.; Mantis 1970) suggested that no long time break need have separated the genesis of the Troodos (Cenomanian) and its in situ sedimentary cover (early Campanian). Bagnall (1960) was the first to use modern facies analysis, to infer the palaeoenvironments of the Miocene in SE Cyprus, while de Vauma (1961–1962) investigated the geomorphology and its relationship to regional uplift. Henriette Lapierre (1968b, 1975) reported the existence of unusual volcaniclastic sediments depositionally overlying the Troodos ophiolite in SW Cyprus.

Mapping in SW Cyprus by Lapierre (1968a) also led to the important discovery that the Mesozoic 'Trypa Group' was allochthonous relative to the Troodos, and a Cretaceous rather than Palaeozoic age became accepted for the ophiolite after Michael Mantis (1971) reported Late Cretaceous benthic foraminifera within the Troodos lavas. The complex geology of SW

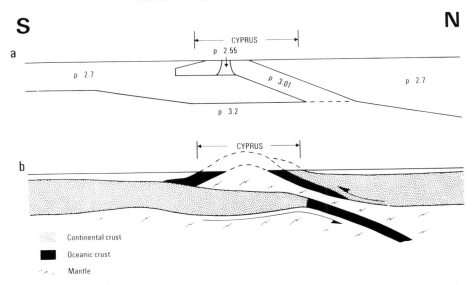

**Fig. 4.** Early evidence of the present-day tectonic setting of Cyprus. (**a**) Geometry of a high-density slab beneath Cyprus. (**b**) Uplift of the Troodos Massif in response to northward subduction, then underthrusting of the African plate (from Gass & Masson Smith 1963).

Cyprus was interpreted by Lapierre in terms of Alpine-type 'thrusts and nappes' (Lapierre 1972). She drew cross-sections indicating two major Mesozoic nappes, a lower, volcanic one and an upper, sedimentary one that were thrust, together, from the NE, over the Troodos ophiolite, during the Late Cretaceous. Similar emplacement of a 'Cyprian gravity nappe' was inferred by Turner (1973). Where present, deformation structures of the Troodos were also explained by some geologists in terms of compressional thrusting, as in the Kellaki Massif (Limassol Forest) (Lapierre & Rocci 1967) and the southern slopes of Mt. Olympus (Bortolotti et al. 1976), More recently, these structures were to be reinterpreted as mainly ocean floor in origin (see later).

Mapping of the Kyrenia Range of N Cyprus revealed that it, too, was allochthonous. The United Nations geologist, Ducloz (1972) believed that the Mesozoic shallow-water core of the western part of the Kyrenia Range was formed of giant carbonate olistoliths. Sir Frank Dixey (1972) envisaged gravity sliding as the main mode of emplacement. However, François Baroz (1979) preferred an origin as large thrust sheets, emplaced from the north during Late Cretaceous and Eocene time. Geophysical data indicated a fundamental crustal contrast between the Troodos Massif and the Kyrenia Range (Aubert & Baroz 1974). Also, deep boreholes in the foothills of the Kyrenia Range encountered Troodos-type pillow lavas. Specifi-

cally, one borehole, located 20 km E of Nicosia encountered lavas at a depth of 650 m, while another, 25 km ENE of Nicosia, intersected lavas at 2700 m (Cyprus Geological Survey, unpublished data). Troodos-type basement was, thus, inferred to extend northwards beneath the Mesaoria Plain to near the southern margin of the Kyrenia Range (Fig. 5).

By the early 1970s much work, mainly by French geologists, had also been completed on the adjacent 'Isparta angle' of SW Turkey, an area with a similar geology to Cyprus. One school of thought (Brunn et al. 1971; Dumont et al. 1972) viewed the Cyprus and Antalya units as fragments of a deep-marine basin (Pamphylian Basin), formed along the northern margin of Gondwana, while another (Ricou et al. 1975) held that all these units were grossly allochthonous and had been thrust from a single Tethyan suture zone located far to the north, in Northern Turkey. In both models, the Troodos was envisaged as a wholly allochthonous nappe, thrust onto the Arabian continental margin in the latest Cretaceous. This view was integrated into some early attempts at tectonic synthesis (Biju-Duval et al. 1976).

## Plate tectonics inspired developments

Cyprus geology then entered the first of several phases of more focused research designed to test and develop plate tectonics concepts.

Fred Vine and Eldridge Moores hoped to test

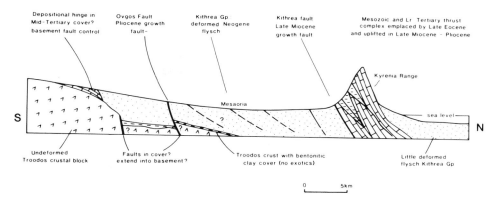

**Fig. 5.** Simplified cross-section of the Kyrenia Range (from Clube & Robertson 1986).

the sea-floor spreading hypothesis in Cyprus. The presence of linear magnetic anomalies in the Troodos would confirm an ocean ridge origin for the Troodos, as in the oceans. Palaeomagnetism was the key. An aeromagnetic survey had already been flown by Hunting Geophysics in 1967–1968, funded jointly by a grant to Ian Gass and Fred Vine. The survey revealed a linear anomaly, running N from Larnaca, that was interpreted as a structural graben filled with sediments (Vine *et al.* 1973), rather than as a magnetic reversal. Palaeomagnetic sampling of the ophiolite did not reveal the hoped for systematic linear magnetic anomalies either. By this time, it was realized that magnetic anomalies were absent from oceanic crust of Late Cretaceous age within the oceans, in what became known as the Late Cretaceous Uniform Polarity Interval; the available radiometric and microfossil age evidence suggested the Troodos formed during this time (Poster 1973). A totally unexpected by-product of the palaeomagnetic work was the discovery that magnetic declinations were directed westward throughout the Troodos, implying that 90° anticlockwise rotation had taken place since formation. The tectonic puzzle thus posed has continued to occupy tectonic geologists until the present time. More relevant to the sea-floor spreading question, much additional petrological, geophysical and other information was amassed, greatly strenthening the hypothesis that the Troodos formed at a Late Cretaceous ocean ridge within the present Eastern Mediterranean Sea area (Moores & Vine 1971). A model of Troodos petrogenesis involving small multiple magma chambers was proposed, one that has recently found renewed favour. The Bouguer gravity anomaly associated with the core of Mt Olympus (Gass & Masson Smith 1963) was interpreted as a deeply rooted

serpentinite diapiric structure. It was also suggested that a prominent zone of E–W faulting (Arakapas fault belt) in south Troodos might be an oceanic transform fault: much research on this was to follow.

## Anatomy of the ophiolite as a spreading ridge

In 1972 the ophiolite concept was formalized during a Penrose Conference of the Geological Society of America. During the 1970s the anatomy of the ophiolite was investigated as a guide to spreading processes (Fig. 6). This work was undertaken by a new generation of Earth Science graduates, the first to be trained in the New Global Tectonics. The outline of their main findings which follows is organized moving upwards through the ophiolite succession.

### Magmatic sequence

An initial objective was to clarify the tectonostratigraphy and origin of the ultramafic rocks. Seismic refraction data from the oceans led to the inference that the 'geophysical Moho' was located at the contact between more dense, ultramafic and less dense, mafic rocks, whereas in ophiolites the 'petrological Moho' was located between ultramafic tectonites and overlying cumulates.

Pioneering work was carried out by David Greenbaum (1972*a*), Dick George (1975, 1978) and Cameron Allen (1975). Greenbaum (1972*b*) established that tectonized harzburgites represented refractory mantle, while Allen (1975) proposed that dunite bodies within the harzburgites were emplaced as mantle diapirs, produced by partial melting of the underlying mantle. Plagioclase lherzolites were interpreted as fertile mantle, rather than refractory residues,

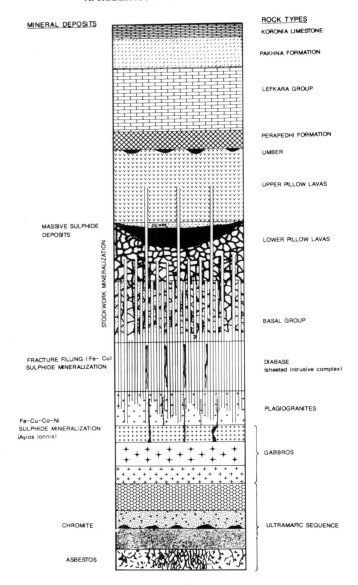

**Fig. 6.** Generalized lithological column of the Troodos ophiolite showing the relationship between sulphide mineralization and the Upper and Lower Pillow Lavas (from Constantinou 1980). The importance of extensional detachment faulting in the ophiolite was not then apparent.

like the harzburgites (Menzies & Allen 1974). Podiform chromites in the Troodos were established to be of cumulate origin (Greenbaum 1972b, 1977). High-level plagiogranites were identified below the sheeted dykes (Allen 1975) and small trondjemite bodies within the gabbros were interpreted by Don Aldis (1978) as siliceous residues from fractional crystallization.

Cameron Allen (1975) also argued, based on detailed mapping, that the dykes had tapped off magmas from near the top of the gabbros. Greenbaum (1972b) initially proposed a single magma chamber model (Fig. 7), but this could not be reconciled with field relationships (e.g. high-level intrusions) and was soon replaced by multiple magma chamber models (Gass 1980).

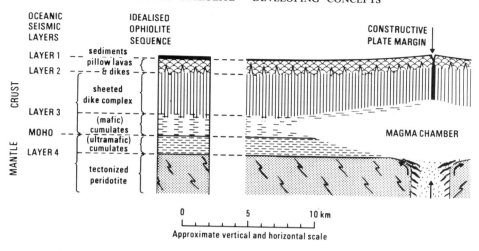

**Fig. 7.** Greenbaum's model of a single magma chamber (from Gass 1980). Multiple magma chamber models were favoured later.

## Dyke structures

A novel test for the spreading ridge mechanism, devised by Joe Cann (Cann 1974), was that if dykes were successively injected along the axis of a spreading ridge, then at least some dykes should be split and end up in opposing oceanic plates. The task of measuring chill directions in myriads of sheeted dykes fell to Rupert Kidd (1976). Kidd & Cann (1974) proposed that statistically valid evidence existed of one-way chilling and this, in turn, implied that the oceanic crust was generated at a narrow, linear spreading axis, located to the west of Cyprus. Conversely, Alain Desmet (1977) argued that several stages of dyke injection could be recognized in many outcrops, implying a more complicated intrusion history (Desmet *et al.* 1978), in keeping with the earlier suggestion by Bear (1960*b*) that as many as five phases of intrusion could be recognized in the Sheeted Dyke Complex.

## Hydrothermal alteration

John Smewing (1975) was the first to study systematically, alteration and metamorphism of the extrusives, concluding that the Upper Pillow Lavas showed evidence of only low-grade, zeolite facies metamorphism, whereas the Lower Pillow Lavas experienced slightly higher temperature metamorphism, although still mainly in the zeolite facies. The Basal Group lavas had undergone higher-grade, greenschist facies metamorphism. The Upper Pillow Lavas were, thus, envisaged as having been erupted onto the surface of the Lower Pillow Lavas when already cold. These later lavas apparently were erupted in a different tectonic setting, some distance off-axis (Gass & Smewing 1973). On the other hand, geochemical studies suggested that the entire Troodos suite was co-magmatic (Smewing *et al.* 1975; Desmet 1976, 1977) and, thus, eruption of different parts of the extrusive succession in different tectonic settings was not easily envisaged. A very different view of the hydrothermal metamorphism of the Troodos extrusives was to emerge in the 1980s, as discussed below.

## Massive sulphides

George Constantinou (1972) gave the first systematic description of the field relations, mineralogy and chemistry of the Cyprus massive sulphide orebodies. He also interpreted the overlying ferruginous ochres as 'submarine gossans' (Constantinou & Govett 1972, 1973; Constantinou 1980). Exploration for new sulphides peaked in the early 1970s with, for example, George Maliotis's (1978) work on induced polarization (Maliotis & Khan 1980). Nick Adamides (1984) demonstrated that massive sulphides and stockworks were generated in sea-floor half-grabens (Adamides 1980, 1990; Fig. 8), a forerunner of similar discoveries at modern spreading ridges. Simon Sheppard was amongst the first to appreciate the importance of isotopic studies as a guide to hydrothermal metamorphism. Oxygen and hydrogen isotopic studies of the altered crustal sequences and of the sulphides by Tim Heaton (1977) confirmed

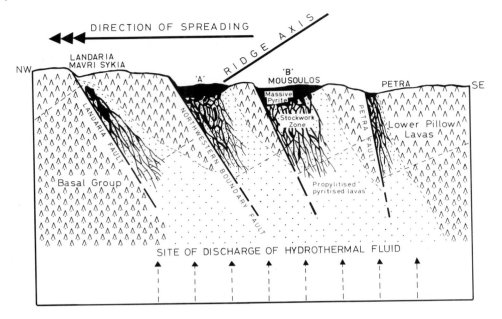

**Fig. 8.** Adamides's (1980) model of massive sulphide genesis related to spreading, as applicable to the Kalavasos ore body, S Troodos (from Adamides 1980).

the importance of circulating sea-water in mineralization (Heaton & Sheppard 1976). Ed Spooner modelled hydrothermal processes in terms of pervasive alteration, as sea water passed downwards through the crust where it was heated, chemically altered, and expelled upwards in narrow zones, followed by metal precipitation in contact with the sea water above (e.g. Spooner 1976; Fig. 9). More recently collaboration between George Constantinou and Elizabette Oudin led to the conclusion that the Cyprus massive sulphides are similar in origin to oceanic black-smokers, following the discovery of the remains of pyritic smoker vents (Oudin & Constantinou 1984).

### Oceanic fracture zone processes

Kapo Simonian (1975) followed up the earlier suggestion by Moores & Vine of the existence of a transform fault within the Troodos Massif in southern Cyprus. His mapping established the presence of an ophiolitic basement, overlain by thick volcaniclastic sediments and basalt lava flows, which he interpreted as the fill of a 'leaky' transform fault. In addition, Andreas Panayiotou (1977, 1980) documented the occurrence of a plutonic complex within the fossil transform and its associated Cu–Ni–Co–Fe sulphide and chromite deposits.

### Sedimentation

Alastair Robertson (1975a) studied the sedimentary cover of the Troodos Massif throughout southern Cyprus (Fig. 10). Based on field and geochemical work, initially with John Hudson, the basal metalliferous umbers were interpreted as primary chemical precipitates formed at a spreading ocean ridge (Robertson & Hudson 1973), whereas the ferruginous ochres were seen as being spatially and genetically related to the massive sulphides (Robertson 1976a). Field relations revealed sea-floor topographic features (talus etc.) similar to modern ocean ridges (Robertson 1975b). Overlying siliceous and pelagic carbonates were compared with modern and ancient oceanic sediments. The Troodos was noted to be anomalous, as non-calcareous, rather than calcareous, sediments were the first to accumulate on the oceanic crust (Robertson & Hudson 1974). The origin and diagenesis of cherts, both within the Late Cretaceous radiolarites and the overlying Early Tertiary carbonates, were documented (Robertson 1977d). The Moni Melange, part of the sedimentary cover of S Cyprus (Fig. 1), was explained in terms of a model involving gravity sliding of detached blocks (olistoliths) of Mesozoic continental margin lithologies at a destructive plate margin (Robertson 1977a). Late Cretaceous volcaniclas-

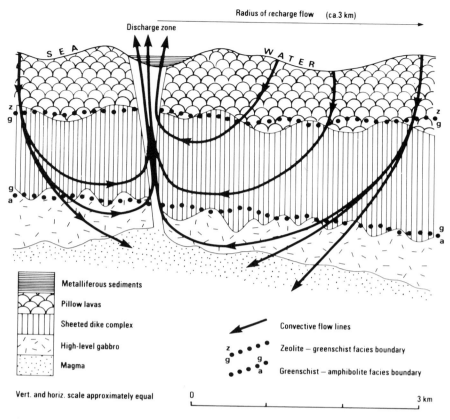

**Fig. 9.** 1970s model of ophiolite metamorphism showing pervasive alteration related to hydrothermal recharge, as envisaged by Spooner (1976) and Smewing 1975 (from Gass 1980). 1980s work revealed much more patchy alteration.

tic sediments of the Kannaviou Formation in SW Cyprus were shown to have been derived from arc-type volcanism, located somewhere to the present W or NW of Cyprus, with an incoming of terrigenous sediment towards the top of the succession (Robertson 1977*b*). Deep-water carbonates of Early Tertiary age in southern Cyprus were found to be largely calciturbidites (Robertson 1976*b*). Synthesis of the available information revealed that Cyprus was progressively uplifted from mid-Tertiary onwards (Robertson, 1977*c*; Fig. 11).

### Subduction-related genesis?

Geochemical evidence from the Troodos lavas increasingly called into question formation at a simple ocean ridge. It was found, empirically, that basalt compositions varied according to plate tectonic setting. Certain elements (e.g. Ti, Y, Cr) were relatively immobile during weather-ing and low-grade metamorphism and were suitable for chemical discrimination (Pearce & Cann 1973). On this basis, some of the Troodos extrusives were more similar to basalts from above subduction zones than from ocean ridge settings (Pearce 1975, 1980). The Troodos could, thus, have formed at a spreading axis above a subduction zone, as a 'marginal basin' (Smewing *et al.* 1975).

Miyashiro (1973) went much further and rejected the ocean ridge model, proposing instead an oceanic volcanic arc setting for Troodos. In a vigorous debate that followed (e.g. Gass *et al.* 1975), apparent misconceptions in Miyashiro's analysis were discussed and, eventually, the ocean ridge model emerged largely unscathed, albeit as spreading above a subduction zone, rather than at a mid-ocean ridge. However, some geologists preferred to discount the geochemical evidence of a subduction setting and have continued to support the ocean ridge model. The ocean ridge model has continued to be applied, for example to the Turkish ophiolites (Whitechurch *et al.* 1984) and the Semail ophiolite, Oman (Nicolas 1989). More definitive geochemical evidence on the Troodos, at least, was to be forthcoming in the 1980s.

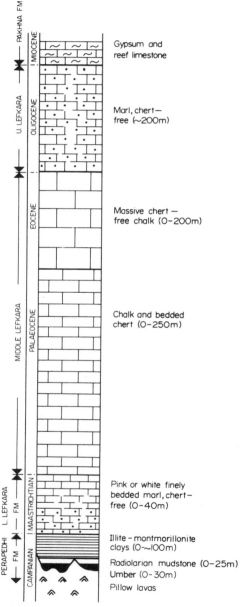

**Fig. 10.** Composite column of the Upper Cretaceous, Lower Tertiary sediments of Cyprus (from Robertson & Hudson 1974). Recent work has indicated the umbers may be as old as Cenomanian (Blome & Irwin (1985)).

## Units adjacent to the Troodos

During the 1970s, units bordering the Troodos ophiolite began to be re-examined, in part to assess their hydrocarbon potential (Ealey & Knox 1975; Cleintaur *et al.* 1977). Based on sedimentological and structural studies, Alastair Robertson and Nigel Woodcock argued that the Mesozoic deep-sea sediments and volcanics (Lapierre & Rocci 1976) of the Mamonia Complex formed at the passive continental margin of a rifted small ocean basin (Robertson & Woodcock 1979). High-angle, rather than low-angle, structures dominated arcuate lineaments within the Mamonia Complex. Derivation of the Mamonia Complex from the NE, over the Troodos Massif, as envisaged by Lapierre (1972, 1975), was ruled out, in view of the intact Late Cretaceous to Neogene sedimentary cover preserved around the northern and eastern margins of the ophiolite. Fold geometry also indicated displacement generally northeastwards, towards the Troodos ophiolite, mainly by inferred gravity sliding.

Dick Swarbrick (1979) remapped the entire Mamonia outcrop and showed that SW Cyprus could be interpreted in terms of the juxtaposition of contrasting tectonic blocks of Late Cretaceous 'Troodos-type' basement on the one hand, and composite units of both Triassic 'Mamonia-type' volcanic basement (Dhiarizos Group) and structurally overlying Mesozoic deep-water sedimentary thrust sheets (Ayios Photios Group), on the other. These different basement blocks were envisaged as being brought together by strike-slip faulting, marked by arcuate, high-angle fault lineaments, largely filled with serpentinite (Swarbrick 1980; Fig. 1). In this model, pure sinistral strike-slip dominated in the south, in contrast to transpressional strike-slip further north. Slivers of amphibolite facies metamorphic rocks within the serpentinite lineaments (at Ayia Varvara) were mapped and dated and an oceanic transform setting was proposed (Spray & Roddick 1981). Localized 'melange units' were interpreted mainly as sedimentary debris flows (Swarbrick & Naylor 1980). The stratigraphy of the Mamonia Complex and related units was also formally redefined at this time (Swarbrick & Robertson 1980); this continues to be used by most workers.

## 1980s: era of the Cyprus crustal study project

The 1970s research phase culminated with the Cyprus Geological Survey hosting an important international meeting 'Ophiolites and Oceanic

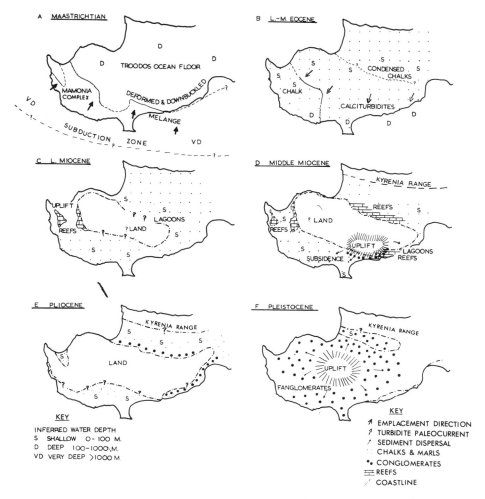

**Fig. 11.** Summary of the palaeogeographic evolution of Cyprus, as envisaged in the 1970s (from Robertson 1977*b*). More recent work suggests the uplift took place above a N-dipping subduction/collision zone.

Crust' in Nicosia during April 1979, interspersed with field excursions. Judging by the attendance, international interest in ophiolites was then at its peak. The conference was followed in 1980 by publication of 'the ophiolite volume', edited by Andreas Panayiotou. This summarized all the important results so far and included several synthesis articles (Gass 1980; Robertson & Woodcock 1980). By this time, much work had already been published on other Tethyan ophiolites, notably Oman (later summarized in Lippard *et al.* 1986), allowing useful comparisons. Also, research on the Eastern Mediterranean area as a whole was steadily advancing, both on land and at sea (e.g. Makris *et al.* 1983), providing an improved tectonic framework in which to

interpret the Troodos (e.g. Sengör *et al.* 1984; Robertson & Dixon 1984).

During the early 1980s, an ever increasing number of geologists were attracted to work in Cyprus. Costas Xenophontos interacted with many visiting geologists, assisted with supervision of a number of PhD projects and also helped formulate new ideas on the Troodos ophiolite in its Eastern Mediterranean context. Improved radiometric (Mukasa & Ludden 1987; Staudigel *et al.* 1986) and radiolarian microfossil evidence (Blome & Irwin 1985) indicated a Cenomanian–Turonian age (92–90 Ma ago) for Troodos, up to 8 Ma older than previously believed.

The decision to drill the Troodos ophiolite

followed directly on from similar work in Iceland and resulted in formation of the International Crustal Research Drilling Group for work in Cyprus. The proposal was to drill the ocean crust, or crust that was similar to it, at a much lower cost and with much higher core-recovery than was possible by drilling in the oceans (i.e. DSDP/ODP). Drilling was also aimed at stimulating related field studies. International funding was obtained and field work began in selected areas in 1980. Canadian drillers provided the technical expertise, while the Cyprus Geological Survey underpinned the logistics. The drilling took place between April 1982 and March 1985.

## Offset-drilling objectives

The main objective was to obtain a complete section of oceanic crust by 'offset drilling'. Holes were sited on different parts of the (dipping) surface outcrop and overlapping sections were recovered and then correlated. Eventually, the project was a great success. The drilling finally confirmed that the Troodos ophiolite preserved an intact stratigraphy and was not a stack of thrust sheets, as in some 1970s tectonic models (Fig. 12).

Highlights of the drilling results, summarized by Paul Robinson and John Malpas (1990), included the piecing together of a composite

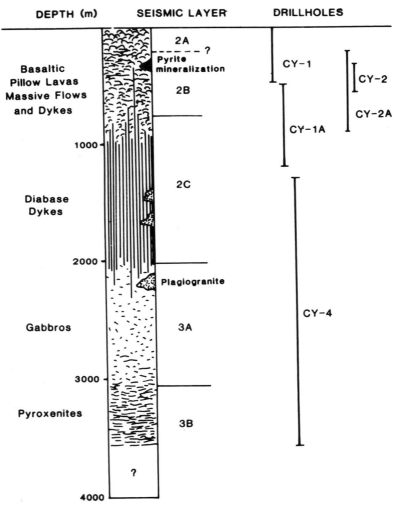

**Fig. 12.** Summary lithological section of the Troodos crust showing the suggested stratigraphic positions of the deep holes drilled in the Troodos Massif. Note the almost complete succession drilled (from Vine & Smith 1990).

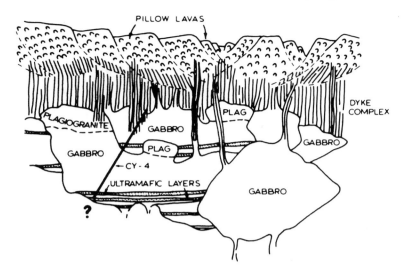

**Fig. 13.** Multiple magma chamber model. This contrasts with the popular 1970s single magma chamber, but was not dissimilar to the interpretation of Moores & Vine (1971) (from Robinson & Malpas 1990).

section, as far down as the cumulate ultramafics. The evidence of small-scale intrusive relationships supported a multiple, rather than a single, magma chamber model (Benn 1986; Benn & Laurent 1987; Browning et al. 1989; Herbert & Laurent 1990; Laurent 1990, 1992). However, Thy et al. (1988) interpreted borehole relationships differently, believing that the available evidence favoured a relatively closed magma chamber system for the lower cumulates, in contrast to the upper cumulates (see discussion in MacLeod et al. 1992 and Dilek et al. 1992). A stockwork zone was also drilled beneath a massive sulphide orebody. Full details of the two sites drilled in the Agrokipia ore deposits are given in Robinson et al. (1987), encompassing information on the sulphide mineralogy, alteration of the associated extrusives, palaeomagnetic and rock magnetic properties and geophysical data, including physical properties. New information on lava geochemistry, hydrothermal alteration and metallogenesis was permitted by the availability of fresh rock (away from sulphide mineralized zones) for the first time (e.g. Cann et al. 1987). Logging also provided the geophysical database necessary for valid comparison with oceanic crust (i.e. Hole 504B) (Smith 1986; Smith & Vine 1989; Vine & Smith 1990). In addition, a number of geologists from developing countries underwent training in Cyprus under the direction of Jim Hall.

### Recent field results on the ophiolite sequence

The drilling also stimulated a range of associated field studies. Indeed study of the cores and outcrops went hand in hand. John Malpas initiated comprehensive remapping of the Troodos plutonic core with the help of MSc students, culminating in publication of two coloured map sheets (Pano Amiandos and Palekhori; Malpas & Brace 1987). The cumulates were reinvestigated, as were the chromites (Malpas & Robinson 1987). Intrusive relations confirmed the former existence of multiple magma chambers, rather than a single magma chamber (Fig. 13).

The Cyprus Crustal Study Project also gave a major boost to knowledge of the Troodos extrusives. The threefold division of the extrusives onto the Basal Group, Lower Pillow Lavas and the Upper Pillow Lavas, mapped by the Cyprus Geological Survey, was replaced by Hans-Ulrich Schmincke and associates with the concept of volcano-tectonic units (Fig. 14). Pillow Lavas, sheet flows and breccia flows developed during volcanic–tectonic–hydrothermal cycles, active near spreading centres (Schmincke 1987; Schmincke & Bednarz 1990).

It was not previously appreciated that volcanic glasses in the Troodos extrusive sequence were commonly unaltered and could yield useful petrogenetic information (Robinson et al. 1983; Thy et al. 1985; Thy & Xenophontos 1991). In

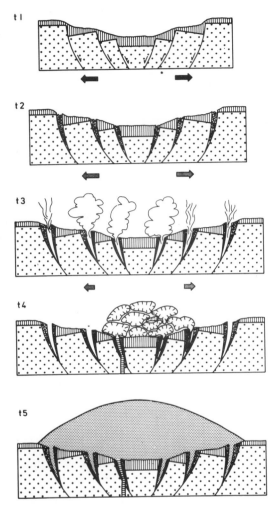

**Fig. 14.** Concept of a volcano-tectonic-hydrothermal cycle: (t1) graben formation and sheet flow extrusion; (t2) continued crustal extension, (t3) hydrothermal activity, possibly driven by rise of new magma; (t4) upbuilding of a pillow lava volcano; (t5) completed pillow lava volcano smothering the original graben. Graben width is less than 500 m. (from Schmincke & Bednarz 1980).

addition, an enormous amount of whole-rock geochemical data on the lavas of the North Troodos margin was amassed, mainly by Jim Mehegan (1988), Martina Rautenschlein (1987; Rautenschlein et al. 1985, 1987) and Rex Taylor (1988, 1990; Taylor & Nesbitt 1988). Trends in the Akaki River section, the best documented area, are shown in Fig. 15.

In addition, earlier reports of 'layered ultra-mafic pillow lavas' at Margi, E Troodos by Searle & Vokes (1969) were followed up by detailed petrogenetic analysis that revealed the importance of high-Mg andesite (boninite-type lavas; Malpas & Langdon 1984). Similarities between the high-magnesian Troodos extrusives (e.g. at Margi, the Arakapas and, locally in SW Cyprus (see later)), were first noted by Warrington Cameron (1985) and helped to convince many geologists of the probable genesis of Troodos above a subduction zone (Pearce 1980; Moores et al. 1984; Robertson & Dixon 1984).

## Revised view of hydrothermal metamorphism

The main discovery here was that the alteration that was previously assumed to be pervasive (Smewing 1975) was, in fact, found to be much more restricted (Fig. 16). Kathy Gillis noted that fresh glass was particularly abundant beneath the metalliferous umbers, at the top of the Troodos lava succession. Beneath this, zones of pervasive, oxidative sea-floor weathering extended from the sediment–lava boundary downwards into the lava pile, for tens to a few hundred metres. Non-pervasive, low-temperature alteration, with fresh glass locally preserved, underlies this zone (Robinson et al. 1983; Gillis 1987, 1990; Gillis & Robinson 1990). A sharp boundary between the low- and high-temperature alteration zone was then observed, which generally coincided with the transition from the lavas to the sheeted dykes (Staudigel & Gillis 1990; Gillis & Robinson 1990). In addition, Debbie Kelly (1990) evaluated the role of magmatic fluids in the formation of epidotized plagio-granites and their contribution to the overlying hydrothermal system (Kelley & Robinson 1990; Kelley et al. 1992).

Companion studies of lava alteration were carried out by Schmincke and his colleagues and by 'the Davis group' (Schiffman & Smith 1988; Schiffman et al. 1987, 1990). This work provided further evidence that the alteration of the lavas was similar to that of the modern oceanic crust, being restricted to what were interpreted as hydrothermal pathways. This left much of the crust fresh, with pristine glass preserved to the base of the volcanic pile in places (Schmincke et al. 1983; Rautenschlein 1987).

Very detailed structural, volcanological and mineralogical mapping of the Akaki River section, mainly by Martina Rautenschlein (Rautenschlein 1987; Fig. 16) and of the Pediaeous river system by Ulrich Bednarz (1988; Bednarz & Schmincke 1987, in press a, b; Schmincke & Bednarz 1990) provided very

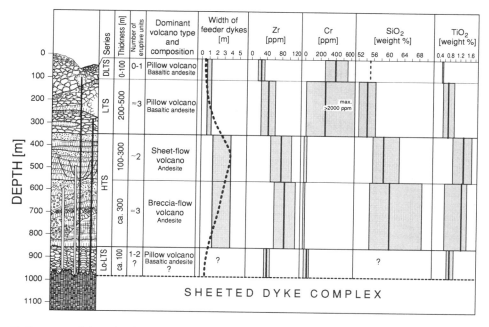

**Fig. 15.** Summary of the volcanic succession and geochemical trends in the Akaki River section, N Troodos (kindly supplied by H.-U. Schmincke).

detailed reference sections for comparison with DSDP/ODP drill cores. Martina Rautenschlein carried out a detailed isotope and trace-element study on separated samples (Rautenschlein *et al.* 1985), while Bednarz compared glass compositions, mainly from the Pediaeous river section, with similar material in drill holes through the volcanic crust. This work allowed a quantitative estimate of mass transfer between sea water and 'oceanic crust' (Bednarz & Schmincke 1989, 1990). The highly volatile nature of the glasses (Muenow *et al.* 1990) was in keeping with geophysical data, acquired by Fred Vine and Carl Poster, that indicated that the extrusive sequence was of relatively low density compared to MOR-type oceanic crust (Vine & Smith 1990).

### Role of extensional faulting

Starting in the early 1980s, Eldridge Moores initiated an integrated study of the structure of the Troodos crustal sequence. Major extensional detachment faults (e.g. the 'Kakopetria Detachment') were identified within, and particularly near the base of, the Sheeted Dyke Complex (Verosub & Moores 1981); this highlighted the role of extensional faulting in oceanic crust genesis (Fig. 17). Mapping and palaeomagnetic

work by Bob Varga and Todd Ramsden (1987) indicated the existence of a number of discrete sea-floor grabens (e.g. Solea graben; Varga & Moores 1985, 1990), hypothesized as being extinct spreading axes, fossilized by progressive ridge jumps eastwards. Companion studies were also carried out by Laurie Bettison (pers. comm., 1990) and Carol Eddy (pers. comm., 1990). Eldridge Moores and his colleagues stressed the relationship between extensional faulting, high temperature alteration and massive sulphide genesis (Schiffman & Smith 1988; Schiffman *et al.* 1987).

Fred Vine and Simon Allerton devised a sophisticated palaeomagnetic technique that could be used to infer past rotations of the Troodos sheeted dykes and extrusives about horizontal, as well as vertical, axes. This led to an explanation of the Troodos spreading fabric in terms of discrete half-grabens and grabens that developed off-axis, in response to amagmatic stretching (Allerton 1988; Allerton & Vine 1987, 1990; Allerton 1989).

Joe Cann initiated new research on hydrothermal processes during this time, mainly directed towards understanding the role of epidosites in massive sulphide genesis. It was argued that epidosites in the sheeted dykes represent alteration pipes that record the deep

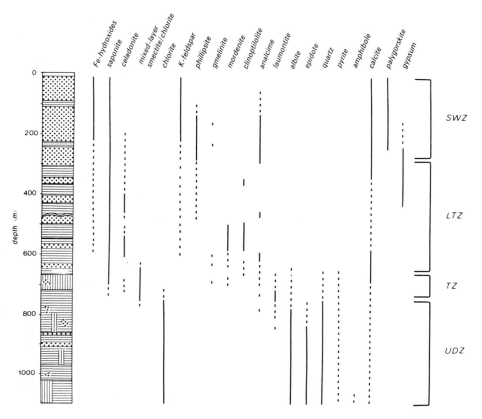

**Fig. 16.** Revised hydrothermal mineral zonation in the N Troodos. Note that low temperature mineralogy persists in many places to the base of the extrusives (from Gillis & Robinson 1990).

high-temperature root zones of black smoker sulphide systems (Richards 1987; Richardson *et al.* 1987; Richards & Cann 1989).

A group led by Bob Baragar investigated the geochemistry of the sheeted dykes in relation to the extrusives (Baragar *et al.* 1989, 1990). Both depleted and less-depleted magma types are present, as in the extrusives, but without systematic cross-cutting relationships; this suggested repeated injections of magmas of differing composition from multiple magma chambers. Incidentally, this did not confirm the earlier reported preferential one-way chilling of dykes (Kidd & Cann 1974).

### New data on the Arakapas transform

During this period Ian Gass initiated further study of what became known as the Southern Troodos Transform Fault Zone. Bramley Murton (1986*b*) mapped and reconstructed the Western Limassol Forest, concentrating on

magmatism within the transform (Murton 1986*a*; Murton & Gass 1986; Fig. 18). Chris MacLeod (1988) mapped the Eastern Limassol Forest, focusing on the structure of dismembered crustal blocks within the transform domain, combined with palaeomagnetic analysis (MacLeod 1990). A separate crustal fragment, termed the Anti-Troodos plate, was inferred in the Limassol Forest to the south of the southern margin of the transform zone (MacLeod 1988; 1990). MacLeod also identified an important extensional fault, the Akapnou Forest Detachment, which post-dated transform tectonism, and could have been related to palaeorotation of the Troodos microplate (see later). This work, in turn, led to modelling of processes operating near an inferred ridge/transform intersection (MacLeod *et al.* 1990). Specifically, Allerton & Vine (1992) developed a model for the structural processes operative at ridge–transform intersections, based on palaeomagnetic work in the southeastern part of the Troodos ophiolite. All the

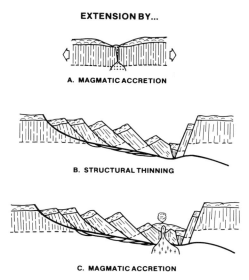

**EXTENSION BY...**

**A. MAGMATIC ACCRETION**

**B. STRUCTURAL THINNING**

**C. MAGMATIC ACCRETION**

**Fig. 17.** Non-steady state model for magmatism and tectonic extension, supported by studies of the Troodos Sheeted Dyke Complex: (**a**) magma injection keeps pace with extension; (**b**) extension continuing but with low magma supply, giving rise to extensional detachment faulting; (**c**) magma injection is renewed. Such graben structures could be abandoned when the spreading centre was relocated. Contrast with the 1970s model of steady state spreading (Kidd & Cann 1974) (from Varga & Moores 1990).

available information was subsequently synthesized by Ian Gass and Costas Xenophontos and associates into two 1:25 000 map sheets, published by the Cyprus Geological Survey (Gass *et al.* 1991*a,b*). The accompanying memoir No. 9 is in press (Gass *et al.* 1992). A comprehensive review of all the relevant information and interpretations of the South Troodoos Transform Fault Zone is given by MacLeod & Murton (1993) in this volume.

## Summary of revised ophiolite model

The main conclusions from the new work on the ophiolite in the 1980s were that the Troodos formed above a subduction zone, possibly during the earlier stages of the convergence of two oceanic plates in the Late Cretaceous (prior to development of any mature oceanic arc). Dyke swarms below the level of the plagiogranites emanated from magma chambers at different depths and, thus, indicated the existence of multiple magma chambers. These dykes, in turn, fed unstable, shifting ridge axial grabens, offset by an oceanic fracture zone to the south. Alteration processes were variable in space and time, rather than pervasive. The Arakapas was established as by far the most documented fracture zone within an ophiolite. The tectonic setting of the Troodos, however, remained controversial.

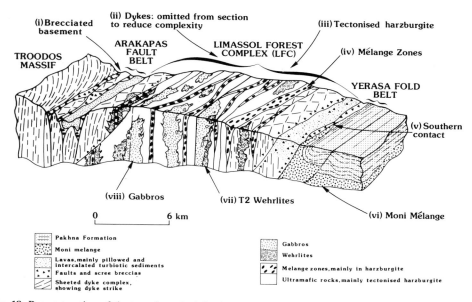

(i) Brecciated basement

(ii) Dykes: omitted from section to reduce complexity

(iii) Tectonised harzburgite

**TROODOS MASSIF**

**ARAKAPAS FAULT BELT**

**LIMASSOL FOREST COMPLEX (LFC)**

(iv) Mélange Zones

**YERASA FOLD BELT**

(v) Southern contact

(viii) Gabbros

(vii) T2 Wehrlites

(vi) Moni Mélange

0     6 km

Pakhna Formation
Moni melange
Lavas, mainly pillowed and intercalated turbiotic sediments
Faults and scree breccias
Sheeted dyke complex, showing dyke strike

Gabbros
Wehrlites
Melange zones, mainly in harzburgite
Ultramafic rocks, mainly tectonised harzburgite

**Fig. 18.** Reconstruction of the transform fault in the S of the Troodos Massif, in the Western Limassol Forest. Note particularly the serpentinite shear zones, the high-level intrusions and the swing of dyke trends into the transform (from Murton 1990).

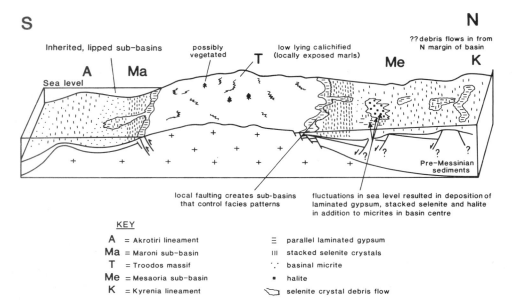

**Fig. 19.** Inferred setting of the Troodos as it was in the Late Miocene, following partial uplift. The evaporites formed in small basins, that were tectonically active, especially in N and SW Cyprus (based on McCallum 1989).

## Progress on the sedimentary cover

During the 1980s Alastair Robertson initiated further research on the sedimentary cover of the Troodos ophiolite (Robertson *et al.* 1991*b*). Based on detailed mapping, John Boyle (1984) showed that the metalliferous umbers accumulated in small, elongate half-grabens, similar in morphology, for example, to those of the modern Galapagos spreading axis (Boyle & Robertson 1984; Boyle 1990). Simon Eaton (1987; Eaton & Robertson 1993) found that mixed calcareous/clastic sediments of the Miocene Pakhna Formation of S Cyprus accumulated in tectonically active small basins. Channels, previously mapped as being within the Miocene Pakhna Formation, were found to be Pliocene, based on calcareous nannofossil dating (Haughton *et al.* 1990). Uplift of the Troodos was progressive, with exposure during the Messinian salinity crisis (Fig. 19). Jean McCallum (1989), combined surface and sub-surface data to show that the Pliocene sediments N of Troodos, in the Mesaoria, accumulated in response to active extensional faulting (McCallum & Robertson 1990). Ed Follows (1990) found that active faulting exerted the dominant control of the development of Miocene reefs and related carbonate facies around the margins of the Troodos Massif. Specifically, patch reefs were constructed on rotated, extensional fault blocks along the N Troodos margin (Follows & Robertson 1990; Follows *et al.* in press). Detailed information on reef diagenesis was also published (Follows 1992). Andy Poole (1992) used the U-Series dating method to date coastal marine terraces (Poole *et al.* 1990), which could be lithologically correlated with fluvial/deltaic clastic sediments around Troodos. Uplift of the Troodos peaked in the Early to Mid-Quaternary (Poole & Robertson 1991). The main cause of uplift was envisaged as the combined effects of tectonic underthrusting of continental crust of the African plate **and** serpentinite diapirism (Robertson 1990), in essence supporting the original model of Gass & Masson Smith (1963). The area uplifted is much greater than that of the Troodos alone and includes the Kyrenia Range and a basement ridge linking with the Misis Mountains in southern Turkey. However, earthquake data imply that subduction under SW Cyprus is still active and, thus, that collision is not yet complete in the Cyprus area (e.g. Kempler & Ben-Avraham 1987).

During the same period, F. Orszag-Sperber initiated a study of the Messinian of southern Cyprus (Elion 1983; Orszag-Sperber & Rouchy 1983; Orszag-Sperber *et al.* 1980, 1989) and particularly documented a range of palaeoenvironments during the Late Miocene and the facies changes during Early Pliocene time.

## Towards a plate tectonic model

In early October 1987 a further international conference, with field excursions, was held in Cyprus. Many of the data accrued during the 1980s were published in the resulting volume: *Ophiolites: Oceanic Crustal Analogues*, edited by John Malpas, Eldridge Moores, Andreas Panayiotou & Costas Xenophontos. A comprehensive volume of field guides was edited by Costas Xenophontos & John Malpas (1987). By this stage an origin of the Troodos above a subduction zone had been widely accepted (e.g. Gass 1990; Robinson & Malpas 1990) and much active debate centred on the regional setting of Troodos.

Evidence from adjacent areas, including Greece and Turkey suggested that the Troodos represents one of a number of small ocean basins, formed by rifting of the north margin of Gondwana, initially during the Triassic. The continental fragments were later reassembled by collision during Late Mesozoic–Early Tertiary time (Robertson *et al.* 1991*a*). Indeed, the history of Cyprus can be divided into three main phases:

(1) Triassic–Jurassic rifting and spreading to form a small ocean basin in the Cyprus area, bordered by passive margins. This history is documented by evidence in the Mamonia Complex and the better exposed Antalya Complex in SW Turkey (e.g. Robertson & Woodcock 1982). However, it is still debated as to whether these small ocean basins were of Red-Sea type, as argued by Robertson & Dixon (1984), or were instead backarc basins, developed above (one or several) southward-dipping subduction zones (Sengör *et al.* 1984; Dilek & Moores 1990);

(2) during the Late Cretaceous–Early Tertiary period the Troodos ophiolite was formed and then deformed and tectonically juxtaposed with the Mamonia Complex in SW Cyprus. The Kyrenia Range was emplaced to near its present position in the Late Eocene (Baroz 1980; Robertson & Woodcock 1986). Events during this second phase are contentious and are discussed further below;

(3) finally, there is the third, essentially neotectonic phase, dominated by northward underthrusting of the Africa plate beneath Cyprus.

A number of important questions are currently being vigorously debated, as follows:

### (1) What was the tectonic setting of the Troodos ophiolite?

As noted above, the Troodos is believed by many to have formed at a spreading axis above a subduction zone in the Late Cretaceous. There is no direct evidence of the orientation, or location of this subduction zone. Genesis above an originally essentially northward-dipping subduction zone is inferred for other Late Cretaceous ophiolites, including Oman (Lippard *et al.* 1986; Fig. 20). Indeed, it is generally assumed that the thrusts along which the ophiolites were emplaced started off as subduction zones above which the ophiolites were initially created. However, there is no proof that this was necessarily so. As an alternative, Yildirin Dilek *et al.* (1990, 1992) infer S-dipping subduction within a remnant of 'Palaeotethys' further N in central Turkey, such that the Troodos formed as a marginal basin to the south. This marginal basin is thought by them to have developed within pre-existing Triassic rifts. MacLeod *et al.* (1992),

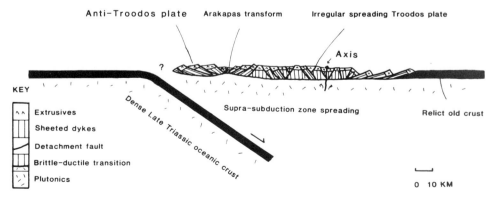

**Fig. 20.** View of the Troodos as formed by spreading above a N-dipping subduction zone, cut by a transform fault (from Robertson 1990).

however, favour genesis of the Troodos above a northward-dipping subduction zone, within the same small ocean basin as the Troodos. For them, the subduction zone dipped northwards, but for Taylor (1988, 1990) it was more likely to have been S-dipping (original coordinates), based on geochemical comparison with the modern Mariana forearc.

## (2) What was the sense of motion on the South Troodos transform?

This influences the geometry of plate reconstruction. Bramley Murton argued that the trend of the dykes and the structural fabrics, mainly in serpentinites, indicates left-lateral (sinistral) slip (Murton 1986a). However, palaeomagnetic studies, in particular suggested the opposite, right-lateral sense of displacement.

Palaeomagnetic study, in principle, could determine if the more E–W-, rather than N–S-trending dykes in the fracture zone were intruded into a 'leaky' fracture zone (Simonian & Gass 1978), or were, instead, physically bulk rotated? Tristan Clube (1985) palaeomagnetically sampled sediments within the transform and identified evidence of large-scale relative clockwise rotation, suggestive of right-lateral (dextral) shear (Clube & Robertson 1986). Palaeomagnetic study of dykes north of the Arakapas Fault gave a similar result (Bonhommet et al. 1988). Simon Allerton (1988), Chris MacLeod (1988) and Tony Morris (1990) also found evidence of dominantly clockwise rotation of dykes, lavas and sediments within the transform domain and adjacent areas, especially E Troodos. Based on re-evaluation of the structural and palaeomagnetic evidence, Chris MacLeod and Bramley Murton (this volume) now conclude in favour of the dextral strike-slip model.

## (3) When was the Troodos rotated?

Earlier work by Moores & Vine indicated that the Troodos Massif, as a whole, underwent a 90° tectonic rotation. The only obvious way to determine when this took place was to sample palaeomagnetically the sedimentary cover of the Troodos Massif.

With this in mind, Tristan Clube sampled sediments around the Troodos and confirmed that the whole unit had undergone essentially the same 90° anticlockwise rotation (Clube 1985). It was also established that the rotation had taken place after eruption of the Troodos extrusives in the Upper Cretaceous and was complete by Early Eocene (Clube et al. 1985). (An earlier, pilot palaeomagnetic study by Shel-

ton & Gass (1985) had suggested rotation in the Miocene.) Other, less extensive, palaeomagnetic studies (Abrahamsen & Schonharting 1987) were in agreement. Tony Morris later sampled Upper Cretaceous successions in more detail (e.g. at Margi) and inferred that rotation began in the upper levels of the Perapedhi Formation (Upper Campanian) (Morris et al. 1990) and that at least 60° of the rotation had taken place by the Maastrichtian.

## (4) How large was the rotated unit?

This question could best be answered by locating adjacent areas that did not undergo palaeomagnetic rotation similar to the Troodos. A second, less definitive approach would be to identify the strike-slip boundaries of the rotated area in the field.

A near consensus has emerged that the rotated area was relatively small: i.e. a microplate (see Fig. 24). Mainland Turkey to the north and Africa to the south have not been similarly rotated (see for example, Kissel & Laj 1988). Sheeted dykes in Baer-Bassit (60 km to the east) are orientated E–W (Parrot 1977) which, assuming that they were originally part of the same spreading axis as the Troodos, suggests that this ophiolite did not undergo rotation. There are no palaeomagnetic data on the Kyrenia Range in N Cyprus, but it retains the E–W structural trends of southern Turkey. Thus, the microplate was located in the environs of Cyprus.

## (5) What was the tectonic setting of the Mamonia Complex?

The sediments, at least the more proximal facies, are now generally accepted as remnants of a passive margin (Robertson & Woodcock 1979), probably of a microcontinent within Tethys (see Figs 21, 23). The Triassic extrusives can be viewed as remnants of a small ocean basin, similar in scale to the modern Southern Red Sea. The Triassic 'reef limestone olistoliths' within the Mamonia Complex are seen as carbonate build-ups on ocean islands (Clube & Robertson 1986; Malpas et al. 1987, 1992). The thinner-bedded, deeper-water facies accumulated more distally on the abyssal plain of the small ocean basin. The view of the Triassic Mamonia lavas as having formed in a small ocean basin, rather than merely an intra-continental rift, as favoured by Dilek et al (1992), gains support from the discovery of MOR-type tholeiites, in addition to alkaline, within-plate-type lavas in SW Cyprus (Malpas et al. 1992; this volume).

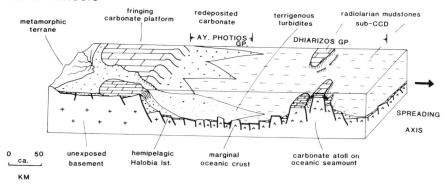

**Fig. 21.** Reconstruction of the Mamonia Complex (Ayios Photios and Dhiarizos Gps) as a passive margin of a Red Sea-type small ocean basin (from Robertson 1990).

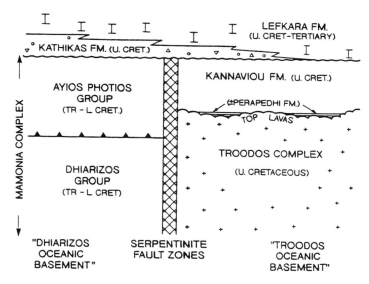

**Fig. 22.** Schematic diagram of units in SW Cyprus. Troodos and 'Mamonia' units are separated by steep serpentinite fault zones (from Swarbrick 1993).

## (6) How were the Mamonia and Troodos complexes juxtaposed?

Field relations indicate that the Southern Troodos Transform Fault Zone can be traced into SW Cyprus within the coherent Troodos ophiolite (i.e. as far as Kannaviou; Robertson 1977b). Beyond this, no link can be proved, as the ophiolitic units in the Mamonia Complex are separated from the Troodos by structural lineaments of unknown displacement. However, field, petrological and geochemical studies show that the ophiolitic slivers in the Mamonia Com-

plex include lithologies that are very similar to those within the South Troodos Transform Fault Zone in S Cyprus, including the presence of strongly depleted boninite-type extrusives (Swarbrick 1980; Afrodisis & Xenophontos 1983; Malpas et al. 1992; this volume). It is, therefore, likely that these ophiolitic slivers represent the disrupted former westward continuation of the transform into SW Cyprus. On the other hand, Dick Swarbrick (1993) notes that some of the serpentinite protoliths are dissimilar to those in the S Cyprus transform and were probably derived from MOR-type units, sug-

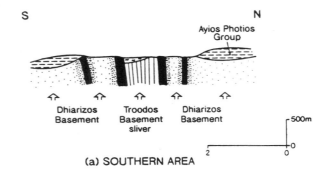

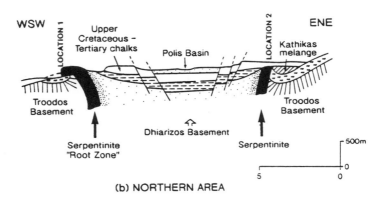

**Fig. 23.** Interpretative cross-sections of the Mamonia Complex, contrasting south and north areas. Transpression and uplift are inferred in the north area. The neotectonic Polis graben inverted this structure in the Neogene (from Swarbrick 1993).

gesting that more than one type of oceanic crust and mantle are present within the ophiolitic lineaments in SW Cyprus.

Slivers of amphibolite (with meta-cherts) and greenschist facies metamorphic rocks (with igneous and deep-sea sedimentary protoliths) are found within the ophiolitic lineaments in SW Cyprus (e.g. at Ayia Varvara and Baths of Aphrodite). The amphibolites were radiometrically dated as of similar age to the Troodos (Spray & Roddic 1981), but are more MORB-like in composition (Malpas et al. 1992). These metamorphics are in some respects similar to the metamorphic soles beneath other Tethyan ophiolites (e.g. Woodcock & Robertson 1977) as in Oman (e.g. see Lippard et al. 1986). However, no large-scale overriding ophiolitic thrust sheet is present in SW Cyprus. Plate convergence has been inferred to explain the existence of the metamorphics, involving subduction and accretion of

Tethyan MORB-type igneous rocks and deep-sea sediments to the base of Troodos-type ophiolitic lithosphere, exposed within the ophiolitic lineaments (Moores et al. 1984; Clube & Robertson 1986; Murton, 1990, Malpas et al. 1987, 1992). Deformation of the metamorphic slivers within the high-angle fault zones was reported to indicate dextral shear (Spray & Roddick 1981), raising the possibility that the inferred accretion took place in an oblique-slip setting, rather than one of orthogonal subduction.

Based on mapping the relevant outcrop areas in SW Cyprus, Dick Swarbrick (1979, 1980) had earlier argued that the Mamonia Complex and Troodos Complex were juxtaposed by strike-slip faulting along high-angle fault lineaments (Fig. 22). This was complete by Early Tertiary, when the fault zones were transgressed by deep-water carbonates. Pure strike-slip was inferred in the

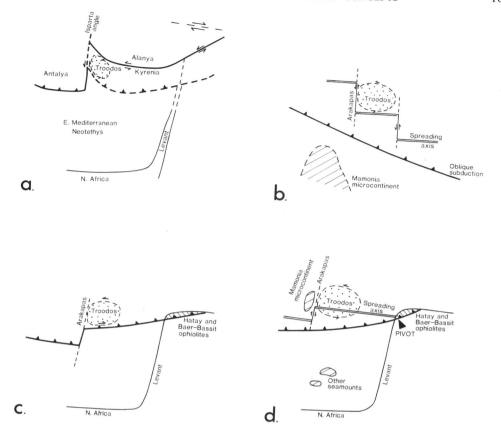

**Fig. 24.** Alternative tectonic models of the rotation of the Troodos microplate. (**a**) Expulsion from the Isparta angle, modified after Robertson & Woodcock 1980. (**b**) Collision, subduction erosion and underthrusting of a 'Mamonia microcontinent', essentially as envisaged by Moores *et al.* (1984), Murton (1990), Robinson & Malpas (1990) and Malpas *et al.* (1992). (**c**) Rotation related to collision of a trench with the Arabian continental margin to the east, as in Clube & Robertson (1986). (**d**) As modified by Robertson (1990). MacLeod (1988) adopted a similar model, but placed the Mamonia unit on the lower (subducting plate).

south (Fig. 23a), with transpression (i.e. strike-slip with compression) in the north with a central plug of Triassic volcanic basement (Dhiarizos Group) being uplifted by transpressive faulting, bounded by ophiolitic units to the east and west (Swarbrick 1980, 1993; Fig. 23b). Transpression was also inferred by Bramley Murton during mapping of the Akamas Peninsula (Murton 1990). Recently, Swarbrick (1993) has reported new preliminary findings of sinistral strike-slip within unmetamorphosed lithologies in the ophiolitic lineaments, contrasting with dextral displacement in the metamorphic slivers (Fig. 25b).

Most recently, Malpas *et al.* (this volume) present new structural data which they interpret as indicating that thrust tectonics, rather than

strike-slip was possibly the main mode of 'docking' of the Mamonia and Troodos complexes (Fig. 25a). In their view, the Mamonia lavas and sediments were initially delaminated from their substrate upon arrival at a subduction zone, and then emplaced onto a highly extended forearc region of the Troodos microplate (Fig. 25a). However, further structural data are still needed to decide the relative roles of strike-slip, and/or compression in juxtaposing the Troodos and Mamonia units.

*(7) Was the Mamonia/Troodos juxtaposition related to Troodos rotation?*

Clube & Robertson (1986) noted that the timing of Troodos rotation and juxtaposition with the

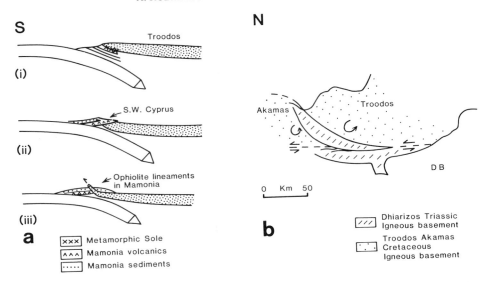

**Fig. 25.** Most recent models. (**a**) Thrust model of juxtaposing Troodos and Mamonia units (based on Malpas *et al.*, this volume): (i) subduction to the north under Troodos at starved trench; (ii) Mamonia lavas, then sediments thrust onto inferred Troodos ophiolitic basement; (iii) back-thrusting event producing ophiolitic lineaments, followed by 90° anticlockwise rotation. (**b**) Model of Swarbrick (1993) placing the Troodos within a large-scale sinistral shear zone, within which anticlockwise rotation takes place at restraining bends, as in the California Transverse Ranges. The true tectonic history is, however, more complex than either of these interpretations would imply.

Mamonia Complex were broadly coeval. They hypothesized that the arcuate ophiolitic lineaments in SW Cyprus marked boundaries of the rotated 'microplate'. Sheared serpentinites in the Moni Melange of S Cyprus were located near the southern boundary of the microplate. Indirect evidence suggested that strike-slip also influenced deformation of the Kyrenia Range during latest Cretaceous–Early Tertiary time (Robertson & Woodcock 1986). The rotated microplate could, thus, have been more or less the size of the present Troodos Massif, although additional palaeomagnetic data are still needed from adjacent areas (e.g. Kyrenia Range, S Turkey, Syria) to test this hypothesis. The question as to whether the ophiolitic lineaments reflect strike-slip, rather than merely compressional tectonics also needs more work.

## (8) What caused the rotation?

Suggestions include the following:

(1) Robertson & Woodock (1980) originally proposed tectonic expulsion from the Isparta angle (Fig. 24a);

(2) Clube *et al.* (1985) suggested simple oblique subduction as the driving mechanism;

(3) Moores *et al.* (1984), Murton (1990) and

Malpas *et al.* (1992) invoked collision with a 'Mamonia seamount' to the SW of Cyprus (Fig. 24b). Problems with this model include the absence of coeval collisional deformation, the lack of any obvious mechanism to drive the Troodos anticlockwise and the fact that the Mamonia rocks were not thrust beneath Troodos during the inferred collision;

(4) Clube & Robertson (1986; Fig. 24c) proposed passive rotation, in response to collision elsewhere, a view supported by MacLeod (1988). In this case, the Troodos ophiolite formed above a northward-dipping subduction zone. The trench then collided with the Arabian promontory to the east, emplacing the Hatay and Bear-Bassit ophiolites. The Troodos remained within a remnant ocean basin to the west. Within continuing Africa–Eurasia convergence, the Troodos microplate then pivoted anticlockwise, motion being complete by Early Eocene time (Robertson 1990).

(5) More recently Dick Swarbrick (1993) has attempted to reconcile his inferred sinistral strike-slip in SW Cyprus with anticlockwise palaeorotation of a Troodos microplate, by suggesting that the Troodos as a whole was displaced anticlockwise, within a large-scale

sinistral shear zone, comparable to the rotations along restraining bends of the San Andreas fault in the Transverse Ranges of S California (Fig. 25b). How this model would fit in with the regional geology, however, remains unclear.

## Conclusions

Cyprus is now internationally accepted as the type ophiolite and has been studied in more detail that any other. Perhaps the most important reasons for this are that, uniquely, the Troodos has suffered minimal deformation related to tectonic emplacement, thus, original sea-floor relationships can be studied with confidence. Added to this are the accessibility of the island, the excellent framework provided by early geological survey mapping, a fine climate and the delightful hospitality of the Cypriot people.

With new discoveries in the oceans (e.g. sulphides; ridge processes), researchers soon arrived in Cyprus to test and develop conceptual models. A good example is extensional faulting, recently recognized as critical to ocean crust genesis. Extensional faults in the Troodos Sheeted Dyke Complex have, in consequence, been subject to recent careful study (Dietrich & Spencer, this volume). Also, the Troodos has come to be seen as an excellent example of an ophiolite actually in the process of emplacement, so the neotectonic geology, both onshore and offshore has assumed considerable importance.

Studies continue: the crescendo of research in the 1980s is unlikely to be repeated, but results from Cyprus will continue to excite worldwide interest. Indeed, many detailed studies remain to be undertaken, or are already in progress: e.g. relating local patterns of faulting to larger-scale, inferred graben structures in the Troodos; extending study of the regional geochemical variation of the extrusives; more quantitative and model-orientated studies of hydrothermal processes; more detailed structural studies in SW Cyprus (T. Morse, pers. comm., 1992); improving the biostratigraphy of the Mesozoic (Bragin & Krylov 1991; Urquhart 1992; Urquhart & Banner, in press) and Tertiary (G. Kahler, pers. comm., 1992) sedimentary cover; and facies analysis (e.g. in the Polis graben, Payne & Robertson 1993). Also, there is need for new work on the Kyrenia Range (e.g. palaeomagnetic studies).

We conclude that no consensus as to the tectonic setting of Troodos has yet emerged. This is likely to remain the case until such time as a definite counterpart is found, actually forming today within the oceans. The depleted, boninite-type lavas of Troodos are widely compared with those of SW Pacific forearcs, and a forearc origin is the most widely favoured hypothesis at present. However, big surprises about the origin of Troodos could yet be in store!

We would like to acknowledge helpful input from Ian Gass, Kathy Gillis, Roger Laurent, Chris MacLeod, Eldridge Moores, Hazel Prichard, Hans-Ulrich Schmincke, Dick Swarbrick and Fred Vine in preparing this summary of research developments in Cyprus.

## References

ABRAHAMSEN N. & SCHONHARTING, G. 1987. Palaeomagnetic timing of the rotation and translation of Cyprus. *Earth and Planetary Science Letters*, **81**, 409–418.

ADAMIDES, N. G. 1980. The form and environment of formation of the Kalavasos ore deposits, Cyprus. *In*: PANAYIOTOU, A. (ed.) *Ophiolites: Proceedings of the International Symposium, Cyprus, 1979*. Cyprus Geological Survey Department, 117–128.

—— 1984. *Cyprus volcanogenic sulphide deposits in relation to their environment of formation*. PhD thesis, University of Leicester.

—— 1990. Hydrothermal circulation and ore deposition in the Troodos ophiolite, Cyprus. *In*: MALPAS, J., MOORES, E. M., PANAYIOTOU, A. & XENOPHONTOS, C. (eds) *Ophiolites: Oceanic Crustal Analogues*. Cyprus Geological Survey Department, 685–704.

AFRODISIS, S. & XENOPHONTOS, C. 1983. *The Mamonia Complex and its relationship to the Troodos Massif*. Geological Survey Department, unpublished Report.

ALDIS, D. 1978. *Plagiogranites and associated plutonic rocks of various ophiolite complexes*. PhD thesis, Open University, Milton Keynes.

ALLEN, C. R. 1975. *The petrology of a portion of the Troodos plutonic complex, Cyprus*. PhD thesis, University of Cambridge.

ALLERTON, S. 1988. *Palaeomagnetic and structural studies of the Troodos ophiolite, Cyprus*. PhD thesis, University of East Anglia.

—— 1989. Fault block rotations in ophiolites: results of palaeomagnetic studies in the Troodos Complex, Cyprus. *In*: KISSEL, C. & LAJ, C. (eds) *Palaeomagnetic Rotations and Continental Deformation*. NATO ARI Series C, Volume 254, 393–410.

—— & VINE, F. J. 1987. Spreading structure of the Troodos ophiolite Cyprus: Some palaeomagnetic constraints. *Geology*, **15**, 593–597.

—— & —— 1990. Palaeomagnetic and structural studies of the southeastern part of the Troodos complex. *In*: MALPAS, J., MOORES, E. M., PANAYIOTOU, A. & XENOPHONTOS, C. (eds) *Ophiolites: Oceanic Crustal Analogues*. Cyprus Geological Survey Department, 99–111.

—— & —— 1992. Deformation styles adjacent to transform faults: evidence from the Troodos ophiolite, Cyprus. *In*: PARSON, L. M. & MURTON, B. J. (eds) *Ophiolites and their Modern Oceanic*

*Analogues.* Geological Society, London, Special Publication, **60**, 251–262.

AMSTUTZ, G. C. 1980. The early history of the term ophiolites and its evolution until 1945. *In*: PANAYIOTOU, A. (ed.) *Ophiolites: Proceedings of the International Symposium, Cyprus, 1979.* Cyprus Geological Survey Department, 149–152.

AUBERT, M. & BAROZ, F. 1974. Structure profonde de la chaîne du Pentadaktylos et de la Mesaoria (Chypre). *Révue Institut Français de Pétrole*, **29**, 361–373.

BAGNALL, P. S. 1960. *The geology and mineral resources of the Pano Lefkara area.* Cyprus Geological Survey Department Memoir, **5**.

BARAGAR, W. R. A., LAMBERT, M. B., BAGLOW, N. & GIBSON, I. L. 1989. Sheeted dikes of the Troodos ophiolite, Cyprus. *In*: HALLS, H. C. & FAHRIG, W. C. (eds) *Mafic Dike Swarms.* Geological Society of Canada Paper **88–9**.

——, ——, —— & —— 1990. The sheeted dyke zone in the Troodos ophiolite. *In*: MALPAS, J., MOORES, E. M., PANAYIOTOU, A., XENOPHONTOS, C. (eds) *Ophiolites: Oceanic Crustal Analogues.* Cyprus Geological Survey Department, 37–52.

BAROZ, F. 1979. *Étude géologique dans le Pentadactylos et de la Mesaoria (Chypre septentrionale)*, 2 volumes. PhD thesis, University of Nancy, France.

—— 1980. Volcanism and continent–island arc collision in the Pentadactylos Range, Cyprus. *In*: PANAYIOTOU, A. (ed.) *Ophiolites: Proceedings of the International Symposium, Cyprus, 1979.* Cyprus Geological Survey Department, 73–86.

BEAR, L. M. 1960a. *The geology and mineral resources of the Akaki-Lythrondonda area.* Cyprus Geological Survey Department Memoir, **3**.

—— 1960b *The Sheeted Intrusive Complex.* Cyprus Geological Survey Department Annual Report for 1959.

BEDNARZ, U. 1988. *Volcanological, geochemical and petrological evolution, and sub-seafloor alteration in the northeastern Troodos ophiolite (Cyprus).* Disertation Ruhr-Universitat Bochum.

—— & SCHMINCKE, H.-U. 1987. Volcanology of the Pediaeos, Onouphrios, Kokkinivrisi and Mazovounos River system. *In*: XENOPHONTOS, C. & MALPAS, J. G. (eds) *Field Excursion Guidebook. Troodos 87 – Ophiolites and Oceanic Lithosphere.* Cyprus Geological Survey Department, 260–285.

—— & —— 1989. Chemical patterns of sub-seafloor alteration and budget of mass transfer in the upper Troodos crust, Cyprus. *Contributions to Mineralogy and Petrology*, **102**, 93–101.

—— & —— 1990. Chemical patterns of seawater and hydrothermal alternation in the northeastern Troodos extrusive series and sheeted dyke complex, Cyprus. *In*: MALPAS, J., MOORES, E. M., PANAYIOTOU, A. & XENOPHONTOS, C. (eds) *Ophiolites: Oceanic Crustal Analogues.* Cyprus Geological Survey Department, 639–654.

—— & —— Petrological and chemical evolution of the northeastern Troodos Extrusive Series (Cyprus, Eastern Mediterranean), *Journal of Petrology*, in press a.

—— & —— Basaltic andesite to rhyodacitic submarine volcanoes in the Troodos Extrusive Series (Cyprus, Eastern Mediterranean), *Geologisch Rundschau*, in press b.

BENN, K. 1986. Petrology of the Troodos plutonic complex in the Caledonian Falls area, Cyprus. MSc thesis, University of Laval, Quebec.

—— & LAURENT, R. 1987. Intrusive suite documented in the Troodos ophiolite plutonic complex, Cyprus. *Geology*, **15**, 821–824.

BIJU-DUVAL, B., DERCOURT, J. & LE PICHON, X. 1976. From the Tethys Ocean to the Mediterranean Sea: A plate tectonic model of the evolution of the western Alpine system. *In*: BIJU-DUVAL, B. & MONTADERT, L. (eds) *Structural history of the Mediterranean basins.* Editions Technip Paris, 143–164.

BISHOPP, D. W. 1952. Some new features of the geology of Cyprus. *19th International Geological Congress*, **17**, 13–18.

BLOME, C. D. & IRWIN, W. P. 1985. Equivalent radiolarian ages from the ophiolite terrains of Cyprus and Oman. *Geology*, **13**, 401–404.

BONHOMMET, N., ROPERCH, P. & CAZA, F. 1988. Palaeomagnetic arguments from block rotations along the Arakpas fault (Cyprus). *Geology*, **16**, 422–425.

BORTOLOTTI, V., LAPIERRE, H. & PICCARDO, G. B. 1976. Tectonics of the Troodos Massif (Cyprus): preliminary results. *Tectonophysics*, **35**, T1–T5.

BOYLE, J. F. 1984. *The origin and geochemistry of the metalliferous sediments of the Troodos Massif, Cyprus.* PhD thesis, University of Edinburgh.

—— 1990. The composition and origin of oxide metalliferous sediments from the Troodos ophiolite, Cyprus. *In*: MALPAS, J., MOORES, E. M., PANAYIOTOU, A. & XENOPHONTOS, C. (eds) *Ophiolites: Oceanic Crustal Analogues.* Cyprus Geological Survey Department, 705–717.

—— & ROBERTSON, A. H. F. 1984. Evolving metallogenesis at the Troodos spreading axis. *In*: GASS, I. G., LIPPARD, S. J. & SHELTON, A. W. (eds) *Ophiolites and Oceanic Lithosphere.* Geological Society, London, Special Publication, **13**, 169–181.

BRAGIN, N. YU & KRYLOV, K. A. 1991. Radiolarian biostratigraphy of the Agios Photios Group (Mamonia Complex, Cyprus). *Interrad*, **6**, Firenze, p. 18.

BRONGNIART, A. 1821. Sur le gisement ou position relative des ophiolites, euphotides, jaspes etc. dans quelques parties des Apennins. *Annales des Mines ou Recueil de Memoites sur l'Exploitation des Mines*, **6**, 177–238.

BROWNING, P., ROBERTS, S. & ALABASTER, T. 1989. Fine scale modal layering and cyclic units in ultramafic cumulates from the CY-4 borehole, Troodos ophiolite: evidence for an open system magma chamber. *In*: GIBSON, I. L. *et al.* (eds) *Cyprus Crustal Study Project: Initial Report, Hole CY 4.* Geological Survey of Canada Special Paper, **88–9**, 193–220.

BRUNN, J. H. 1980. Ophiolites, origins of orogens and oceanisation. *In*: PANAYIOTOU, A. (ed.) *Ophiolites:*

*Proceedings of the International Symposium, Cyprus, 1979.* Cyprus Geological Survey Department, 169–171.

——, DUMONT, J. F., DE GRACIANSKY, P. C., GUTNIC, M., JUTEAU, T., MARCOUX, J., MONOD, O. & POISSON, A. 1971. Outline of the geology of the western Taurides. *In:* CAMPBELL, A. S. (ed.) *Geology and history of Turkey.* Petroleum Exploration Society of Libya, Tripoli, 225–255.

CAMERON, W. E. 1985. Petrology and origin of primitive lavas from the Troodos ophiolite, Cyprus. *Contributions to Mineralogy and Petrology,* **89,** 239–255.

CANN, J. R. 1974. A model for oceanic crustal structure development. *Geophysics Journal of the Royal Astronomical Society,* **39,** 169–187.

——, OAKELY, R. J., RICHARDS, H. G. & RICHARDSON, C. J. 1987. Geochemistry of hydrothermally altered rocks from Cyprus Drill Holes, Cy-2 and Cy-2a compared with other Cyprus stockworks. *In:* ROBINSON, P. T., GIBSON, I. L. & PANAYIOTOU, A. (eds) *Cyprus Crustal Study Project: Initial Report, Holes Cy-2 and 2a.* Geological Survey of Canada Special *Paper,* **85–29,** 87–102.

CARR, J. M. & BEAR, L. M. 1960. *The Geology and Mineral Resources of the Peristerona-Lagoudhera area.* Cyprus Geological Survey Department Memoir **2.**

CLEINTAUR, M. R., KNOX, G. J. & EALEY, P. J. 1977. The geology of Cyprus and its place in the East Mediterranean framework. *Geologie en Mijnbouw,* **56,** 66–82.

CLUBE, T. M. M. 1985. *The palaeorotation of the Troodos microplate.* PhD thesis, University of Edinburgh.

——, CREER, K. M. & ROBERTSON, A. H. F. 1985. The palaeorotation of the Troodos microplate. *Nature,* **317,** 522–525.

—— & ROBERTSON, A. H. F. 1986. The palaeorotation of the Troodos microplate, Cyprus, in the Late Mesozoic–Early Cenozoic plate tectonic framework of the Eastern Mediterranean. *Surveys in Geophysics,* **8,** 375–434.

COLEMAN, R. G. 1977. *Ophiolites Ancient oceanic lithosphere?* Springer-Verlag.

CONSTANTINOU, G. 1972. *The geology and genesis of the sulphide ores of Cyprus.* PhD thesis, University of London.

—— 1980. Metallogenesis associated with the Troodos ophiolite *In:* PANAYIOTOU, A. (ed.) *Ophiolites: Proceedings of the International Symposium, Cyprus, 1979.* Cyprus Geological Survey Department, 663–674.

—— & GOVETT, G. J. S. 1972. Genesis of sulphide deposits ochre and umber of Cyprus. *Transactions of the Institution of Mining and Metallurgy,* **81,** B34–36 and discussion **82,** B68–75, B125–130.

—— & —— 1973. Geology, geochemistry and genesis of Cyprus sulphide deposits. *Economic Geology,* **68,** 843–858.

CULLIS, C. G. & EDGE, A. B. 1922. *Report on the cupriferous deposits of Cyprus.* Crown Agents for Overseas Governments and Administrations, London.

DESMET, 1976. Evidence for co-genesis of the Troodos lavas, Cyprus. *Geological Magazine,* **113,** 165–168.

—— 1977. *Contribution a l'étude de la croute oceanique mésozoique de Mediterranée orientale: Les Pillow-lavas de Troodos (Chypre).* PhD thesis, University of Nancy.

——, LAPIERRE, H., ROCCI, G., GAGNY, Cl., PARROT, J.-F. & DELALOYE, M. 1978. Constitution and significance of the Troodos Sheeted Dyke Complex. *Nature,* **273,** 527–530.

DIETRICH, D. & SPENCER, S. 1993. Spreading-induced faulting and fracturing of oceanic crust: examples from the sheeted Dyke complex of the Troodos ophiolite, Cyprus. This volume.

DILEK, Y. & MOORES, E. M. 1990. Regional tectonics of the eastern Mediterranean ophiolites *In:* MALPAS, J., MOORES, E. M., PANAYIOTOU, A. & XENOPHONTOS, C. (eds) *Ophiolites: Oceanic Crustal Analogues.* Cyprus Geological Survey Department, 295–309.

——, THY, P, MOORES, E. M. & RAMSDEN, T. W. 1990. Tectonic evolution of the Troodos ophiolite within the Tethyan framework. *Tectonics,* **9,** 811–823.

——, ——, —— & —— 1992. Reply to comment by MacLeod *et al.* on 'Tectonic evolution of the Troodos ophiolite within the Tethyan framework.' *Tectonics,* **11,** 916–923.

DIXEY, F. 1972. The geology of the Kyrenia range. *In: Cyprus geological tour.* Unpublished report, Department of Geology, University of Leicester.

DUCLOZ, C. 1972. The geology of the Bellapais–Kythrea area of the central Kyrenia Range. *Cyprus Geological Survey Department Bulletin,* **6.**

DUMONT, J. F., GUTNIC, M., MARCOUX, J., MONOD, O. & POISSON, A. 1972. Le Trias des Taurides occidentales (Turquie). Definition du basssin pamphylien: Un nouveau domain a ophiolites a la marge externe de la chaine taurique. *Z. Dtsch. Geol. Ges.* **123,** 385–409.

EALEY, P. J. & KNOX, G. D. 1975. The pre-Tertiary rocks of S W Cyprus. *Geologie en Mijnbouw,* **54,** 85–100.

EATON, S. 1987. *The sedimentology of mid to Late Miocene carbonates and evaporites in Southern Cyprus.* PhD thesis, University of Edinburgh.

—— & ROBERTSON, A. H. F. 1993. The Miocene Pakhna Formation and its relation to the Neogene tectonic evolution of the Eastern Mediterrean, *Sedimentary Geology,* **86,** 273–296.

ELION, P. 1983. *Étude Structurale et Sédimentologique du bassin Neogène de Pissouri (Chypre).* Thesis Docteur 3ème. Cycle, Université de Paris-Sud.

FOLLOWS, E. J. 1990. *Sedimentology and tectonic setting of Miocene reefs and related sediments in Cyprus.* PhD thesis, University of Edinburgh.

—— 1992. Patterns of reef sedimentation and diagenesis in the Miocene of Cyprus. *Sedimentary Geology,* **79,** 225–253.

—— & ROBERTSON, A. H. F. 1990. Sedimentology and structural setting of Miocene reefal limestones in Cyprus. *In:* MALPAS, J., MOORES, E. M., PANAYIOTOU, A. & XENOPHONTOS, C. (eds) *Ophiolites:*

*Oceanic Crustal Analogues.* Cyprus Geological Survey Department, 207–216.

——, —— & Scoffin, T. P. Miocene reefs and related carbonate facies in Cyprus. *In*: Jordan, C., Colgan, M. & Esteban, M. (eds) *Miocene Reefs: a global comparison,* in press.

Gass, I. G. 1960. *The geology and mineral resources of the Dhali area.* Cyprus Geological Survey Department Memoir, **4**.

—— 1968. Is the Troodos massif of Cyprus a fragment of Mesozoic ocean floor? *Nature,* **220,** 39–42.

—— 1980. The Troodos massif: Its role in the unravelling of the ophiolite problem and its significance in the understanding of constructive margin processes. *In*: Panayiotou, A. (ed.) *Ophiolites: Proceedings of the International Symposium, Cyprus, 1979.* Cyprus Geological Survey Department, 23–35.

—— 1990. Ophiolites and Oceanic Lithosphere. *In*: Malpas, J., Moores E. M., Panayiotou, A. & Xenophontos, C. (eds) *Ophiolites: Oceanic Crustal Analogues.* Cyprus Geological Survey Department, 1–12.

——, MacLeod, C. J., Panayiotou, A., Simonian, K. O. & Xenophontos, C. 1991a. *Geological map of the southern Troodos Transform Zone, Cyprus at 1:25,000 scale: Sheet 1 (west).* Cyprus Geological Survey Department.

——, ——, ——, —— & —— 1991b. *Geological map of the southern Troodos Transform Zone, Cyprus at 1:25,000 scale: Sheet 2 (east).* Cyprus Geological Survey Department.

——, ——, ——, —— & ——, 1992. *Geology of the Southern Troodos Transform fault zone, Cyprus.* Cyprus Geological Survey Department Memoir **9,** in press.

—— & Masson Smith, D. 1963. The geology and gravity anomalies of the Troodos Massif, Cyprus. *Philosophical Transactions of the Royal Society of London,* **A255,** 417–467.

——, Neary, C, R., Plant, J., Robertson, A. H. F., Simonian, K. O., Smewing, J. D., Spooner, E. T. C. & Wilson, R. A. M. 1975. Comments on 'The Troodos ophiolite complex was probably formed in an island arc' by A. Miyashiro. *Earth and Planetary Science Letters,* **25,** 236–238.

—— & Smewing, J. D. 1973. Intrusion and metamorphism at constructive margins: evidence from the Troodos massif, Cyprus. *Nature,* **242,** 26–29.

George, R. P. Jr. 1975. *The internal structure of the Troodos ultramafic complex, Cyprus.* PhD thesis, University of Stony Brook.

—— 1978. Structural petrology of the Olympos ultramafic complex in the Troodos ophiolite. *Geological Society of America Bulletin,* **89,** 845–865.

Gillis, K. M. 1987. *Multistage alteration of the extrusive sequence, Troodos ophiolite* PhD thesis, University of Dalhousie, Halifax.

—— 1990 Patterns and processes of alteration of the lavas and dykes of the Troodos ophiolite, Cyprus. *Journal of Geophysical Research,* **95** (21), 532–548.

—— & Robinson, P. T. 1990. Multistage alteration in the extrusive sequence of the Troodos ophiolite,

Cyprus. *In*: Malpas, J., Moores, E. M., Panayiotou, A. & Xenophontos, C. (eds) *Ophiolites: Oceanic Crustal Analogues.* Cyprus Geological Survey Department, 655–664.

Greenbaum, D. 1972a. *The geology and evolution of the Troodos Plutonic Complex and associated chromite deposits, Cyprus.* PhD thesis, University of Leeds.

—— 1972b. Magmatic processes at oceanic ridges: evidence from the Troodos Massif, Cyprus. *Nature,* **242,** 26–29.

—— 1977. The chromitiferous rocks of the Troodos ophiolite complex, Cyprus. *Economic Geology,* **72,** 1175–1194.

Haughton, S. D., Jenkins, D. G., Xenophontos, C. & Gass, I. G. 1990. Microfossil evidence for a latest Pliocene age for the Amathus and Khirokitia channel deposits, southern Cyprus and thereby the unroofing of the Troodos massif. *In*: Malpas, J., Moores, E. M., Panayiotou, A. & Xenophontos, C. (eds) *Ophiolites: Oceanic Crustal Analogues.* Cyprus Geological Survey Department, 231–234.

Heaton, T. 1976. *A hydrogen and oxygen isotope study of the metamorphism and mineralisation of the Troodos Complex.* PhD thesis, University of Edinburgh.

—— & Sheppard, S. M. F. 1976. Hydrogen and oxygen isotope evidence for sea-water hydrothermal alteration and ore deposition, Troodos Complex, Cyprus. *In: Volcanic processes in ore genesis.* Institution of Mining and Metallurgy and Geological Society, London, Special Publication, **7,** 42–57.

Henson, F. R. S., Browne, R. V. & McGinty, J. 1949. A synopsis of the stratigraphy and geological history of Cyprus. *Quarterly Journal of the Geological Society of London,* **105,** 1–41.

Herbert, R. & Laurent, R. 1990. Mineral chemistry of the plutonic section of the Troodos ophiolite: new constraints for genesis of arc-related ophiolites. *In*: Malpas, J., Moores, E. M., Panayiotou, A. & Xenophontos, C. (eds) *Ophiolites: Oceanic Crustal Analogues.* Cyprus Geological Survey Department, 149–164.

Hutchinson, R. W. & Searle, D. L. 1970. Stratabound pyrite deposits in Cyprus and relations to other sulphide ores. *In: Symposium on stratabound sulphide ore deposits, IMA-IAGOD Meetings, Tokyo, Japan.*

Johnson, A. E. 1972. Origin of Cyprus pyrite deposits. *In: 24th International Congress, Montreal, Section 4,* 291–298.

Kelley, D. S. & Robinson, P. T. 1990. Development of a brine dominated hydrothermal system at temperatures of 400–500° C in the upper plutonic sequence of the Troodos ophiolite, Cyprus. *Geochimica et Cosmochmica Acta,* **54,** 653–661.

—— & Malpas, J. G. 1992. Processes of brine generation and circulation in the oceanic crust: fluid inclusion evidence from the Troodos ophiolite, Cyprus. *Journal of Geophysical Research,* **97**(9), 307–9, 322.

KEMPLER, D. & BEN-AVRAHAM, Z. 1987. The tectonic evolution of the Cyprean arc. *Annales Tectonicae*, **1**, 58–71.

KIDD, R. G. W. 1976. *Modelling of processes at spreading plate boundaries*. PhD thesis, University of East Anglia.

—— & CANN, J. R. 1974. Chilling statistics indicate an ocean spreading origin for the Troodos Complex, Cyprus. *Earth and Planetary Science Letters*, **24**, 151–156.

KISSEL, C. & LAJ, C. 1988. The Tertiary geodynamical evolution of the Aegean arc: a palaeomagnetic reconstruction. *Tectonophysics*, **146**, 183–201.

LAPIERRE, H. 1968*a*. Nouvelles observations sur la série sédimentaire de Mamonia (Chypre). *Comptes Rendus de l'Académie des Sciences, Paris*, **D267**, 32–35.

—— 1968*b*. Découverte d'une série volcano-sédimentaire probablement d'age Crétacé supérieur au SW de l'île de Chypre. *Comptes Rendus de l'Académie des Sciences, Paris*, **D267**, 1817–1820.

—— 1972. *Les formations sédimentaire et éruptive des nappes de Mamonia et leurs rélations avec le massif de Troodos (Chypre occidentale)*. Doctoral thesis, University of Nancy, France.

—— 1975. Les formations sédimentaire et éruptive des nappes de Mamonia et leurs rélations avec le massif de Troodos (Chypre occidentale). *Mémoir de la Société Géologique de France*, **123**.

—— & ROCCI, G. 1967. Le massif de Kellaki (Chypre). Étude pétrographique et structurale. *Scïence de la Terre*, **12**, 145–181.

—— & —— 1976. Le volcanisme du sud-ouest de Chypre et le problème de l'ouverture des régions Téthsiennes au Trias. *Tectonophysics*, **30**, 299–313.

LAURENT, R. 1990. Parental magma and crystal fractionation modeling of the CY4 plutonic rocks, Troodos ophiolite, Cyprus. *In*: MALPAS, J., MOORES, E. M., PANAYIOTOU, A. & XENOPHONTOS, C. (eds) *Ophiolites: Oceanic Crustal Analogues*. Cyprus Geological Survey Department, 139–148.

——, 1992. Peridotite intrusions emplaced in the fossil suprasubduction zone environment of Cyprus. *In*: PARSON, L. M. & MURTON, B. J. (eds) *Ophiolites and their Modern Oceanic Analogues*. Geological Society, London, Special Publication, **60**, 233–240.

LIPPARD, S. J., SHELTON, A. W. & GASS, I. G. 1986. *The Ophiolite of Northern Oman*. Geological Society, London, Memoir, **11**.

MACE, C. 1939. Gravity Measurements. In Royal Astronomical Society (Geophysics Supplement).

MCCALLUM, J. E. 1989. *Sedimentology and tectonics of the Plio-Pleistocene of Cyprus*. PhD thesis, University of Edinburgh.

—— & ROBERTSON, A. H. F. 1990. Pulsed uplift of the Troodos massif-evidence from the Plio-Pleistocene Mesaoria basin. *In*: MALPAS, J., MOORES, E. M., PANAYIOTOU, A. & XENOPHONTOS, C. (eds) *Ophiolites: Oceanic Crustal Analogues*. Cyprus Geological Survey Department, 217–230.

MACLEOD, C. J. 1988. *The tectonic evolution of the Eastern Limassol Forest Complex, Cyprus*. PhD thesis, Open University, Milton Keynes.

—— 1990. Role of the Southern Troodos Transform Fault in the rotation of the Cyprus microplate: evidence from the Eastern Limassol Forest. *In*: MALPAS, J., MOORES, E. M., PANAYIOTOU, A. & XENOPHONTOS, C. (eds) *Ophiolites: Oceanic Crustal Analogues*. Cyprus Geological Survey Department, 75–85.

——, ALLERTON, S., GASS, I. G. & XENOPHONTOS, C. 1990. Structure of a fossil ridge-transform intersection in the Troodos ophiolite. *Nature*, **348**, 717–720.

—— & MURTON, B. J. 1993. Structure and tectonic evolution of the Southern Troodos Transform Fault Zone, Cyprus. This volume.

——, ROBERTSON, A. H. F., ALLERTON, S., BROWNING, P., GASS, I. G., TAYLOR, R. N., VINE, F. J. & XENOPHONTOS, C. 1992. Comments on 'Tectonic evolution of the Troodos ophiolite within the Tethyan framework' by Dilek, Y., Thy, P., Moores, E. M. & Ramsden, T. W. (*Tectonics*, **9**, 811–823.). *Tectonics*, **11**, 910–915.

MAKRIS, J., BEN-AVRAHAM, Z., BEHLE, A., GINSBURG, A., GIESE, P., STEINMETZ, L., WHITMARSH, R. B. & ELEFTHERIOUS, S. 1983. Seismic refraction profiles between Cyprus and Israel and their interpretation. *Journal of the Royal Astronomical Society*, **75**, 575–591.

MALIOTIS, G. 1978. *The applicability and limitations of the Induced Polarisation Method in the search for sulphide mineralisation in the Troodos Igneous complex, Cyprus*. PhD thesis, University of Leicester.

—— & KHAN, M. A. 1980. The applicability of the induced polarisation method of geophysical exploration in the search for sulphide mineralisation within the Troodos ophiolite complex of Cyprus. *In*: PANAYIOTOU, A. (ed.) *Ophiolites: Proceedings of the International Symposium, Cyprus, 1979*. Cyprus Geological Survey Department, 129–138.

MALPAS, J. & BRACE, T. 1987. *The geology of the Pano Amiandos-Palekhori area, Cyprus, 1:12,500 map with marginal notes*. Cyprus Geological Survey Department.

——, CALON, T. & SQUIRES, G. 1993. The development of a late Cretaceous microplate suture zone in SW Cyprus. This volume.

—— & LANGDON, G. 1984. Petrology of the upper pillow lava suite, Troodos ophiolite, Cyprus. *In*: GASS, I. G., LIPPARD, S. J. & SHELTON, A. W. (eds) *Ophiolites and Oceanic Lithosphere*, Geological Society, London, Special Publication, **13**, 155–167.

——, MOORES, E. M., PANAYIOTOU, A. & XENOPHONTOS, C. (eds) 1990. *Ophiolites: Oceanic Crustal Analogues*. Cyprus Geological Survey Department.

—— & ROBINSON, P. T. 1987. Chromite mineralisation in the Troodos ophiolite, Cyprus. *In*: STOWE, C. W. (ed.) *Evolution of Chromium Orefilelds*. Van Nostrand-Reinhold, 220–237.

——, XENOPHONTOS, C. & ROBERTSON, A. H. F. 1987. Mamania Complex and its relationship to the

Troodos Complex. *In*: XENOPHONTOS, C. & MALPAS, J. G. (eds) *Field Excursion Guidebook. Troodos 87 – Ophiolites and Oceanic Lithosphere.* Cyprus Geological Survey Department, 234–259.

——, —— & WILLIAMS, D. 1992 The Ayia Varvara Formation of S. W. Cyprus: a product of complex collisional tectonics. *Tectonphysics*, **212**, 193–241.

MANTIS, M. 1970. Upper Cretaceous–Tertiary foraminiferal zones in Cyprus. *Epetiris*, **3**, 227–241.

—— 1971. Palaeontological evidence defining the age of the Troodos Pillow Lava series in Cyprus. *Kypriakos Logos*, **3**, 202–208.

MEHEGAN, J. 1988. *Temporal, spatial, and chemical evolution of the Troodos ophiolite lavas, Cyprus.* PhD thesis, University of Dalhousie, Halifax.

MENZIES, M. & ALLEN, C. A. 1974. Plagioclase lherzolite. Residual mantle within two eastern Mediterranean ophiolites. *Contributions to Mineralogy and Petrology*, **45**, 197–213.

MIYASHIRO, A. 1973. The Troodos ophiolite complex was probably formed in an island arc. *Earth and Planetary Science Letters*, **19**, 218–224.

MOORES, E. M., ROBINSON, P. T., MALPAS, J. & XENOPHONTOS, C. 1984. A model for the origin of the Troodos Massif, Cyprus and other mideast ophiolites. *Geology*, **12**, 500–503.

—— & VINE, F. J. 1971. The Troodos Massif, Cyprus and other ophiolites as oceanic crust: evaluation and implications. *Philosophical Transactions Royal Society of London*, **A268**, 433–466.

MOREL, S. W. 1960. *The geology and mineral resources of the Apsiou–Akrotiri area.* Cyprus Geological Survey Department Memoir, **7**.

MORRIS, A. 1990. *Palaeomagnetic studies in Cyprus, Turkey and Greece.* PhD thesis, University of Edinburgh.

——, CREER, K. M. & ROBERTSON, A. H. F. 1990. Palaeomagnetic evidence for clockwise rotations related to dextral shear along the Southern Troodos Transform Fault. *Earth and Planetary Science Letters*, **99**, 250–262.

MUENOW, D. W., GARCIA, M. O., AGGREY, K. E., BEDNARZ, U. & SCHMINCKE, H.-U. 1990. Volatiles in submarine glasses as a discriminant of tectonic origin: application to the Troodos ophiolite. *Nature*, **343**, 159–161.

MUKASA, S. B. & LUDDEN, J. N. 1987. Uranium–lead ages of plagiogranites from the Troodos ophiolite, Cyprus, and their tectonic significance. *Geology*, **15**, 825–828.

MURTON, B. J. 1986a. Anomalous oceanic lithosphere formed in a leaky transform fault: evidence from the western Limassol Forest Complex, Cyprus: evidence from the western Limassol Forest Complex, Cyprus. *Journal of the Geological Society, London*, **143**, 845–854.

—— 1986b. *The tectonic evolution of the Western Limassol Forest Complex, Cyprus.* PhD thesis, Open University, Milton Keynes.

—— 1990. Was the Southern Troodos Transform Fault a victim of microplate rotation. *In*: MALPAS, J., MOORES, E. M., PANAYIOTOU, A. & XENOPHONTOS, C. (eds) *Ophiolites: Oceanic Crustal Analogues.* Cyprus Geological Survey Department, 87–98.

—— & GASS, I. G. 1986. Western Limassol Forest Complex, Cyprus: part of an Upper Cretaceous leaky transform fault. *Geology*, **14**, 255–258.

NICOLAS, A. 1989. *Structures of ophiolites and dynamics of oceanic lithosphere*, Kluwer Academic Publishers.

ORSZAG-SPERBER, F. & ROUCHY, J.-M. 1983. Un jalon dans la connaissance de l'évolution paléo-climatique à la limite Miocène–Pliocène en Mediterranée orientale: l'example du bassin de Pissouri (Chypre). *Paléobiologie Continentale (Montpellier)*, **14**, 377–383.

——, ——, BIZON, G., BIZON, J.-J., CRAVATTE, J. & MULLER, C. 1980. La sédimentation messinienne dans le bassin de Polemi (Chypre). *Géologie Méditerranéenne*, **7**, 91–102.

——, —— & ELION, P. 1989. The sedimentary expression of regional tectonic events during the Miocene–Pliocene transition in the southern Cyprus basins. *Geological Magazine*, **136**, 291–299.

OUDIN, E. & CONSTANTINOU, G. 1984. Black smoker chimney fragments in Cyprus sulphide deposits. *Nature*, **308**, 349–353.

PANAYIOTOU, A. 1977. *Geology and geochemistry of the Limassol Forest plutonic complex and the associated Cu–Ni–Co–Fe sulphide and chromite deposits, Cyprus.* PhD thesis, University of New Brunswick.

—— 1980. Cu–Ni–Co–Fe sulphide mineralisation, Limassol Forest, Cyprus. *In*: PANAYIOTOU, A. (ed.) *Ophiolites: Proceedings of the International Symposium, Cyprus, 1979.* Cyprus Geological Survey Department, 102–116.

PANTAZIS, Th. M. 1967. *The geology and mineral resources of the Pharmakas-Kalavasos area.* Cyprus Geological Survey Department Memoir, **9**.

PARROT, J.-F. 1997. Assemblage ophiolitique du Bäer-Bassit et termes éffusives du volcano-sédimentaire. *Travaux et Documents de L'ORSTROM*, **72**.

PAYNE, A. S. & ROBERTSON, A. H. F. 1993. Stages in the development of the Neotectonic Polis Graben, west Cyprus. *Terra Abstracts*, **5**, 281–282.

PEACH, B. N. & HORNE, J. 1899. *The Silurian rocks of Britain, 1: Scotland.* Memoir of the Geological Survey of the United Kingdom.

PEARCE, J. A. 1975. Basalt geochemistry used to investigate past tectonic environments in Cyprus. *Tectonophysics*, **25**, 41–67.

—— 1980. Geochemical evidence for the genesis and setting of lavas from Tethyan ophiolites. *In*: PANAYIOTOU, A. (ed.) *Ophiolites: Proceedings of the International Symposium, Cyprus, 1979.* Cyprus Geological Survey Department, 261–272.

—— & CANN, J. R. 1973 Tectonic setting of basic volcanic rocks determined using trace element analysis. *Earth and Planetary Science Letters*, **11**, 290–300.

POOLE, A. 1992. *Quaternary of Cyprus.* PhD thesis, University of Edinburgh.

—— & ROBERTSON, A. H. F. 1991. Quaternary uplift and sea-level change at an active plate boundary, Cyprus. *Journal of the Geological Society, London*, **148**, 909–921.

——, SMIMMIELD, G. B. & ROBERTSON, A. H. F. 1990. Late Quaternary uplift of the Troodos ophiolite, Cyprus: uranium-series dating of Pleistocene coral. *Geology*, **18**, 894–897.

POSTER, C. K. 1973. *A geophysical study of the Troodos Igneous Massif, Cyprus*. PhD thesis, University of East Anglia.

RAMSDEN T. W. 1987. *The structural geology and palaeomagnetism of the sheeted dyke complex in Mitsero–Arakapas area, Troodos ophiolite, Cyprus*. MSc thesis, University of California at Davis.

RAUTENSCHLEIN, M. 1987. *Geology and geochemistry of Akaki volcanics*. Doctoral thesis, Ruhr-Universitat Bochum.

——, JENNER, G. A., HERTOGEN, J., HOFMANN, A. W., KERRICH, R., SCHMINCKE, H.-U. & WHITE, W. M. 1985. Isotopic and trace element compositions of volcanic glasses from the Akaki Canyon, Cyprus: implications for the origin of the Troodos ophiolite, Cyprus. *Earth and Planetary Science Letters*, **75**, 369–383.

——, HOFFMAN, A. W. & SCHMINCKE, H.-U. 1987. Troodos Upper Pillow Lavas – a division still justified? Evidence from the Akaki River. *In: Troodos 87, Ophiolites and Oceanic Lithosphere* (Abstracts). Cyprus Geological Survey Department.

RICHARDS, H. G. 1987. *Petrology and geochemistry of hydrothermal alteration pipes in the Troodos ophiolite, Cyprus*. PhD thesis, University of Newcastle-upon-Tyne.

—— & CANN, J. R. 1989. Mineralogical and metasomatic zonation of alteration pipes of Cyprus sulphide deposits. *Economic Geology*, **84**, 91–115.

RICHARDSON, C. J., CANN, J. R., RICHARDS, H. G. & COWAN, J. G. 1987. Metal enriched root zones of the Troodos ore-forming hydrothermal systems, Cyprus. *Earth and Planetary Science Letters*, **84**, 243–253.

RICOU, L.-E., ARGYIADIS, I. & MARCOUX, J. 1975. L'axe calcaire de Taurus, un alignment de fenêtres arabo-africaines sous des nappes radiolitique, ophiolitique et métamorphiques. *Bulletin de la Société géologique de France*, **17**, 1024–1044.

ROBERTSON, A. H. F. 1975a. *Studies of the pre-Miocene sedimentary cover of the Troodos Massif, Cyprus*. PhD thesis, University of Leicester.

—— 1975b. Cyprus umbers: basalt-sediment relationships on a Mesozoic ocean ridge. *Journal of the Geological Society, London*, **131**, 511–531.

—— 1976a. Origins of ochres and umbers: evidence from Skouriotissa, Troodos Massif, Cyprus. *Transactions of the Institution of Mining and Metallurgy*, **85**, B245–251.

—— 1976b. Pelagic chalks and calciturbidites from the Lower Tertiary of the Troodos Massif. *Journal of Sedimentary Petrology*, **46**, 1007–1016.

—— 1977a. The Moni Melange, Cyprus: an olistostrome formed at a destructive plate margin. *Journal of the Geological Society, London*, **133**, 447–466.

—— 1977b. The Kannaviou Formation, Cyprus: volcaniclastic sedimentation of a probable Late Cretaceous volcanic arc. *Journal of the Geological Society, London*, **134**, 269–292.

—— 1977c. Tertiary uplift history of the Troodos Massif, Cyprus. *Geological Society of America Bulletin*, **88**, 1763–1772.

—— 1977d. The origin and diagensis of cherts from Cyprus. *Sedimentology*, **24**, 11–30.

—— 1990. Tectonic evolution of Cyprus. *In*: MALPAS, J., MOORES, E. M., PANAYIOTOU, A., XENOPHONTOS, C. (eds) *Ophiolites: Oceanic Crustal Analogues*. Cyprus Geological Survey Department, 235–252.

——, CLIFT, P. D., DEGNAN, P. J. & JONES, G. 1991a. Palaeoceanographic and palaeotectonic evolution of the Eastern Mediterranean Neotethys. *Palaeogeography, Palaeoclimatology, Palaeoecology*, **87**, 289–343.

—— & DIXON, J. E. 1984. Introduction: Aspects of the geological evolution of the Eastern Mediterranean, *In*: DIXON, J. E. & ROBERTSON, A. H. F. (eds) *The Geological Evolution of the Eastern Mediterranean*. Geological Society, London, Special Publication, **17**, 1–74.

——, EATON, S., FOLLOWS, E. J. & McCALLUM, J. E. 1991b. The role of local tectonics versus gobal sea-level change in the Neogene evolution of the Cyprus active margin. *In*: MACDONALD, D. I. M. (ed.) *Sedimentation, Tectonics and Eustasy – sea level changes at Active Margins*. International Association of Sedimentologists, Special Publication, **12**, 331–369.

—— & HUDSON, J. D. 1973. Cyprus umbers: chemical precipiates on a Tethyan ocean ridge. *Earth and Planetary Science Letters*, **18**, 93–101.

—— & —— 1974. Pelagic sediments in the Cretaceous and Tertiary history of the Troodos Massif, Cyprus. *In*: HSÜ, K. J. & JENKYNS, H. C. (eds). *Pelagic Sediments on Land and under the Sea*. International Association of Sedimentologists, Special Publication, **1**, 403–436.

—— & WOODCOCK, N. H. 1979. The Mamonia Complex, southwest Cyprus: the evolution and emplacement of a Mesozoic continental margin. *Geological Society of America Bulletin*, **90**, 651–665.

—— & —— 1980. Tectonic setting of the Troodos Massif in the East Mediterranean. *In*: PANAYIOTOU, A. (ed.) *Ophiolites: Proceedings of the International Symposium, Cyprus, 1979*. Cyprus Geological Survey Department, 261–272.

—— & —— 1982. Sedimentary history of the south-western segment of the Mesozoic–Tertiary Antalya continental margin, south-western Turkey. *Eclogae Geologicae Helvetiae*, **75**, 517–562.

—— & —— 1986. The geological evolution of the Kyrenia Range: a critical lineament in the Eastern Mediterranean: *In*: READING, H. G., WATTERSON, J. & WHITE, S. H. (eds) Major crustal lineaments and their influence on the geological history of the continental lithosphere. *Philosophical Transactions of the Royal Society of London*, **A317**, 141–171.

ROBINSON, P. T., GIBSON, I. L. & PANAYIOTOU, A. (eds) 1987. *Cyprus Crustal Study Project: Initial Report, Holes CY-2 and 2a*. Geological Survey of Canada,

Special Paper **85–29**.

—— & MALPAS, J. 1990. The Troodos ophiolite of Cyprus: new perspectives on its origin and emplacement. *In*: MALPAS, J., MOORES, E. M., PANAYIOTOU, A. & XENOPHONTOS, C. (eds) *Ophiolites: Oceanic Crustal Analogues.* Cyprus Geological Survey Department, 13–36.

——, MELSON, W. G., O'HEARN, T. & SCHMINCKE, H-U. 1983. Volcanic glass compositions of the Troodos ophiolite, Cyprus. *Geology*, **11**, 400–404.

SCHIFFMAN, P., BETTISNON, L. A. & SMITH, B. M. 1990. Mineralogy and geochemistry of epidosites from the Solea graben, Troodos ophiolite, Cyprus. *In*: MALPAS, J., MOORES, E. M., PANAYIOTOU, A. & XENOPHONTOS, C. (eds) *Ophiolites: Oceanic Crustal Analogues.* Cyprus Geological Survey Department, 673–684.

—— & SMITH, B. M. 1987. Petrology and oxygen isotope geochemistry of a fossil seawater hydrothermal system within the Solea graben, Northern Troodos ophiolite. *Journal of Geophysical Research*, **93** 4616–4624.

——, ——, VARGA, R. J. & MOORES, E. M. 1987. Geometry, conditions and timing of the off-axis hydrothermal metamorphism and ore deposition in the Solea graben, N Troodos ophiolite, Cyprus. *Nature*, **325**, 423–425.

SCHMINCKE, H-U. 1987. Volcanology of the Akaki River Canyon. *In*: XENOPHONTOS, C. & MALPAS, J. G. (eds) *Field excursion Guidebook – Troodos 87 – Ophiolites and Oceanic Lithosphere.* Cyprus Geological Survey Department.

—— & BEDNARZ, U. 1990. Pillow, sheet flows and breccia flow volcanoes and volcano-tectonic hydrothermal cycles in the extrusive series of the northeastern Troodos ophiolite, Cyprus. *In*: MALPAS, J., MOORES, E. M., PANAYIOTOU, A. & XENOPHONTOS, C. (eds) *Ophiolites: Oceanic Crustal Analogues.* Cyprus Geological Survey Department, 207–216.

——, RAUTENSCHLEIN, M., ROBINSON, P. T. & MEGEHAN, J. M. 1983. Troodos extrusive series of Cyprus: A comparison with oceanic crust. *Geology*, **11**, 405–409.

SEARLE, D. L. 1968. Summary of the geology of the Troodos cupriferous sulphite deposits and notes on their mineralogy and origin. Unpublished Report of the Cyprus Geological Survey Department.

—— & VOKES, F. M. 1969. Layered ultrabasic lavas from Cyprus. *Geological Magazine*, **106**, 515–530.

SENGÖR, A. M. C., YILMAZ, Y. & SUNGURLU, O. 1984. Tectonics of the Western Mediterranean Cimmerides: nature and evolution of the termination of Palaeo-Tethys. *In*: DIXON, J. E. & ROBERTSON, A. H. F. (eds) *The geological evolution of the Eastern Mediterranean.* Geological Society, London, Special Publication, **17**, 77–112.

SHELTON, A. W. & GASS, I. G. 1980. Rotation of the Troodos microplate. *In*: PANAYIOTOU, A. (ed.) *Ophiolites: Proceedings of the International Symposium, Cyprus, 1979.* Cyprus Geological Survey Department, 61–65.

SIMONIAN, K. O. 1975. *The geology of the Arakapas Fault Belt, Troodos Massif, Cyprus.* PhD thesis,

Open University, Milton Keynes.

—— & GASS, I. G. 1978. Arakapas fault belt, Cyprus: a fossil transform belt. *Geological Society of America Bulletin*, **89**, 1220–1230.

SMEWING, J. D. 1975. *Metabasalts of the Troodos massif, Cyprus.* PhD thesis, Open University, Milton Keynes.

——, SIMONIAN, K. O. & GASS, I. G. 1975. Metabasalts from the Troodos Massif, Cyprus: genetic implications deduced from petrology and trace element compositions. *Contributions to Mineralogy and Petrology*, **51**, 49–64.

SMITH, G. C. 1986. Physical properties of the Deep Drill core, Troodos ophiolite, Cyprus. PhD thesis, University of East Anglia.

—— & VINE, F. J. 1989. The physical properties of diabases, gabbros and ultramafic rocks from C. C. S. P. Drill Hole CY-4 at Palekhori, Cyprus. *In*: GIBSON I. L. *et al.* (eds) *Cyprus Crustal Study Project, Initial Report, CY-4.* Geological Survey of Canada, Special Paper **88–9**, 295–314.

SPOONER, E. T. C. 1976. Hydrothermal model for the origin of the ophiolitic cupriferous pyrite ore deposits of Cyprus. *In*: *Volcanic processes in ore genesis.* Institute of Mining and Metallury/Geological Society, London, Special Publication 7, 58–71.

SPRAY, J. G. & RODDICK, J. C. 1981. Evidence for Upper Cretaceous transform metamorphism in West Cyprus. *Earth and Planetary Science Letters*, **55**, 273–291.

STAUDIGEL, H. & GILLIS, K. M. 1990. The timing of hydrothermal alteration in the Troodos ophiolite. *In*: MOORES, E. M. & PANAYIOTOU, A. (eds) *Troodos '87, Ophiolites and Oceanic Lithosphere.* Cyprus Geological Survey Department, Nicosia.

——, —— & DUNCAN, R. 1986. K/Ar and Rb/Sr ages of celadonites from the Troodos ophiolite, Cyprus. *Geology*, **14**, 72–75.

STEINMANN, G. 1927. Die ophiolithischen Zonen in den mediterranen Kettebgebirger. *Congrès de Géologie Internationale, 14th Session, Madrid, 1929*, 637–677.

SWARBRICK, R. E., 1979. *The sedimentology and structure of SW Cyprus and its relationship to the Troodos Complex.* PhD. thesis, University of Cambridge.

—— 1980. The Mamonia Complex of SW Cyprus and its relationship with the Troodos Complex. *In*: PANAYIOTOU, A. (ed.) *Ophiolites: Proceedings of the International Symposium, Cyprus, 1979.* Cyprus Geological Survey Department, 86–92.

—— 1993 Sinistral strike-slip and transpressional tectonics in an ancient oceanic setting: Mamonia Complex. *Journal of the Geological Society, London*, **150**, 381–392.

—— & NAYLOR, M. A. 1980. The Kathikas Melange southwest Cyprus: late Cretaceous submarine debris flows. *Sedimentology*, **27**, 63–78.

—— & ROBERTSON, A. H. F. 1980. Revised stratigraphy of the Mesozoic rocks of southern Cyprus. *Geological Magazine*, **117**, 547–563.

SYLVESTER-BRADLEY, P. C. 1968. Tethys: the lost ocean, *Science Journal*, **4**, 47–52.

TAYLOR, R. N. 1988. *The stratigraphy, geochemistry and petrogenesis of the Troodos extrusive sequences, Cyprus.* PhD thesis, Univeristy of Southampton.

—— 1990. Geochemical stratigraphy of the Troodos extrusive sequence: temporal development of a spreading centre magma chamber. *In*: MALPAS, J., MOORES, E. M., PANAYIOTOU, A. & XENOPHONTOS, C. (eds) *Ophiolites: Oceanic Crustal Analogues.* Cyprus Geological Survey Department, 173–184.

—— & NESBITT, J. C. 1988. Light rare-earth enrichment of supra-subduction zone mantle: evidence from the Troodos ophiolite, Cyprus. *Geology*, **16**, 448–451.

THY, P., BROOKS, C. K. & WALSH, J. N. 1985. Tectonic and petrogenetic implications of major and rare earth element chemistry of Troodos glasses, Cyprus. *Lithos*, **18**, 165–178.

——, SCHIFFMAN, P. & MOORES, E. M. 1988. Igneous mineral stratigraphy and chemistry of the Cyprus Crustal Study Project drill core in the plutonic sequence of the Troodos ophiolite. *In*: GIBSON, I. L., MALPAS, J., ROBINSON, P. T. & XENOPHONTOS, C. (eds) *Cyprus Crustal Study Project: Initial Report, Hole CY-4*, Geological Survey of Canada, Special Paper, **88–9**.

—— & XENOPHONTOS, C. 1991. Crystallisation orders and phase chemistry of the glassy lavas from the pillow sequence, Troodos ophiolite. *Journal of Petrology*, **32**, 403–428.

TURNER, W. M. 1973. The Cyprian gravity nappe and the autochthonous basement of Cyprus. *In*: DE JONG, K. A. & SCHOLTEN, R. (eds) *Gravity and Tectonics*. Wiley, New York, 287–307.

URQUHART, E. 1992. *Biostratigraphy of supra-ophiolite sediments of the Troodos Massif, Cyprus.* PhD thesis, University College, London.

—— & BANNER, F. T. Biostratigraphy of the supra-ophiolite sediments of the Troodos Massif, Cyprus: the Mesozoic Cretaceous Perapedhi, Kannaviou, Moni and Kathikas formations. *Geological Magazine*, in press.

VARGA, R. J. & MOORES, E. M. 1985. Spreading structure of the Troodos ophiolite, Cyprus; *Geo-logy*, **13**, 846–850.

—— & —— 1990. Intermittent magmatic spreading and tectonic extension in the Troodos Ophiolite: implications for exploration for black smoker-type ore deposits. *In*: MALPAS, J., MOORES, E. M., PANAYIOTOU, A. & XENOPHONTOS, C. 1990. (eds) *Ophiolites: Oceanic Crustal Analogues.* Cyprus Geological Survey Department, 53–64.

VAUMA, E. DE, 1961–1962. *Further contributions to the geomorphology of Cyprus.* Annual Report of the Cyprus Geological Survey for 1960–1961, 24–34.

VEROSUB, K. L. & MOORES, E. M. 1981. Tectonic rotations in extensional regimes and their paleomagnetic consequences for oceanic basalts. *Journal of Geophysical Research*, **86**, 6335–6349.

VINE, F. J. & MATTHEWS, D. H. 1963. Magnetic anomalies over oceanic ridges. *Nature*, **199**, 947–949.

——, POSTER, C. K. & GASS, I. G. 1973. Aeromagnetic surveys of the Troodos Igneous Massif, Cyprus. *Nature* (Physical Sciences), **244**, 34–38.

—— & SMITH, G. C. 1990. Structural and physical properties of the Troodos crustal section at ICRDG drillholes CY1, 1a and 4. *In*: MALPAS, J., MOORES, E. M., PANAYIOTOU, A. & XENOPHONTOS, C. (eds) *Ophiolites: Oceanic Crustal Analogues.* Cyprus Geological Survey Department, 113–124.

WILSON, R. A. M. 1959. *The geology of the Xeros–Troodos area, Cyprus.* Cyprus Geological Survey Department Memoir, **1**, 1–136.

WHITECHURCH, H., JUTEAU, T. & MONTIGNY, R. 1984. Role of the Eastern Mediterranan ophiolites (Turkey, Syria, Cyprus, in the history of the Neo-Tethys. *In*: DIXON, J. E. & ROBERTSON, A. H. F. (eds) *The Geological Evolution of the Eastern Mediterranean.* Geological Society, London, Special Publication, **17**, 301–318.

WOODCOCK, N. H. & ROBERTSON, A. H. F. 1992. Origins of some ophiolite-related metamorphic rocks of the 'Tethyan' belt. *Geology*, **5**, 373–376.

XENOPHONTOS, C. & MALPAS, J. G. (eds) 1987. *Field Excursion Guidebook. Troodos 87 – Ophiolites and Oceanic Lithosphere.* Cyprus Geological Survey Department.

# Spreading-induced faulting and fracturing of oceanic crust: examples from the Sheeted Dyke Complex of the Troodos ophiolite, Cyprus

DOROTHEE DIETRICH & SARA SPENCER

*Geologisches Institut, ETH Zentrum, CH-8092 Zürich, Switzerland*

**Abstract**: Detailed mapping and structural analysis of the Sheeted Dyke Complex of the Troodos ophiolite, Cyprus, has provided valuable insight into the extensional processes active during the formation of oceanic crust. Oceanic extension is essentially accommodated by: (1) a dense network of small-scale normal faults (metric to several metres spacing of the fault planes) which migrate upwards in time and space through the Sheeted Dyke Complex; and (2) larger-scale normal faults (decametric spacing of the fault planes) which detach into sub-horizontal shear zones and which cause rotation of overlying dyke packets. Geometric models are derived from these structures which differ markedly from the known models of continental extension. In particular, a new ramp/flat model of normal faulting is proposed for the most frequently occurring type of small-scale faults.

The Troodos massif of Cyprus represents a well-exposed slice of oceanic crust and upper mantle (Gass & Masson-Smith 1963; Gass 1968) which extends 30 km north–south and 110 km east–west. Formed during the Cenomanian–Turonian (91.6 ± 1.4 Ma ago) (Blome & Irwin 1985; Mukasa and Ludden 1987), this ophiolite has an internal structure (Moores & Vine 1971) and geochemistry (Pearce *et al.* 1984) compatible with formation within a marginal basin, supra-subduction setting (Miyashiro 1973; Pearce 1975; Moores *et al.* 1984).

In the Late Cretaceous, Troodos was juxtaposed against a remnant of the Mesozoic southern continental margin of Neo-Tethys, through subduction, strike-slip and palaeo-rotation of the Troodos microplate (e.g. Swarbrick 1980; Moores *et al.* 1984; Clube *et al.* 1985; Clube & Robertson 1986; Murton & Gass 1986; Malpas & Robinson 1987; Gass 1990; MacLeod 1988; 1990; Murton 1990; Robertson 1990; Malpas *et al.* 1992). The exact nature of the interplay of these mechanisms remains controversial (e.g. Dilek *et al.* 1990; MacLeod *et al.* 1992).

Strong late Tertiary to Recent uplift of the ophiolite was driven by the progressive convergence of the African and Eurasian plates (Kempler & Ben Avraham 1987; Robertson 1990). This uplift, presently centred on Mount Olympus, has resulted in an annular map pattern with the deepest structural level cropping out at the centre in an updome (Wilson 1959; Fig. 1). The centre exhibits a core of peridotite tectonite underlain by a serpentinite diapir which is stratigraphically overlain by a mafic–ultramafic plutonic complex. This is, in turn, overlain by the Sheeted Dyke Complex which crops out below a rim of lavas and Upper Cretaceous–Tertiary sediments. Upper Pliocene to Pleistocene uplift tilted the summit erosional level and hence the sediments and the ophiolite by approximately 6° to the south (Gass, pers. comm.), leading to the development of normal faults which cut through the overall rock sequence.

## Aims

Over recent decades a wealth of geophysical and borehole data from oceanic cruises (e.g. Harrison & Stieltjes 1977; Macdonald & Atwater 1978; Macdonald 1982; 1986; Anderson *et al.* 1982; White 1984; McClain *et al.* 1985; Mutter *et al.* 1985; Vogt & Tucholke 1986; Leg 109 shipboard scientific party 1986; Karson *et al.* 1987; Karson & Winters 1987; Karson & Rona 1990; Leg 118 shipboard scientific party 1988; McAllister *et al.* 1992) and subsequent modelling (Tapponier & Francheteau 1978; Sleep & Rosendahl 1979; Chen & Morgan 1990*a,b*) have allowed us to begin to understand the role of extensional faulting in slow–medium spreading centre tectonics. Despite this, our understanding is limited since it is largely linked to a three-dimensional interpretation of two-dimensional data sets. In particular, there is little evidence as to the nature of faults at depth. For the present paper our preliminary aim was, therefore, to undertake a detailed analysis of similar extensional faults within the Troodos ophiolite induced as a direct consequence of the generation of oceanic crust.

Extensional models have previously been applied to the oceanic crust by Verosub & Moores (1981), Harper (1982), Varga & Moores (1985), Karson (1987), Allerton (1989), Moores *et al.* 1990, Gass *et al.* (1991*a,b*) and Varga (1991). Here we wish to further this work through

*From* Prichard, H. M., Alabaster, T., Harris, N. B. W. & Neary, C. R. (eds), 1993,
*Magmatic Processes and Plate Tectonics,* Geological Society Special Publication No. 76, 121–139.

121

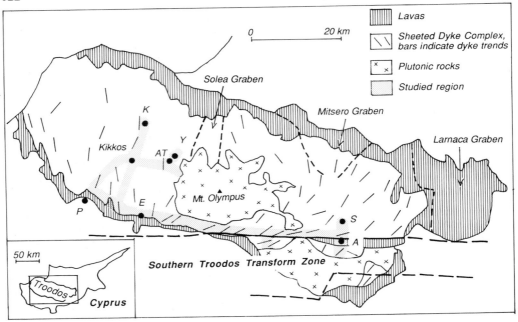

**Fig. 1.** Simplified geological map of the Troodos ophiolite. Major Cretaceous oceanic structures such as the Southern Troodos Transform Fault (Simonian & Gass 1978) and fossil ridge axes (the Solea, Mitsero and Larnaca grabens, Allerton & Vine 1991), are indicated. The dyke trend data from the Sheeted Dyke Complex are taken from MacLeod *et al.* (1990). A: Arakapas; AT: Ayia Triadha; E: Elea bridge; K: Kambos; P: Pano Panayia; S: Sykopetra; Y: Yerakies.

detailed analysis of particular structural geometries within the Sheeted Dyke Complex of the Troodos ophiolite, enabling us not only to determine the mechanisms and amounts of tectonic extension on any single fault or fault zone, but also allowing us to obtain a three-dimensional picture of ridge tectonics.

## Why Troodos?

Although we realize that Troodos, or indeed any ophiolite, cannot be a true analogue of a mid-oceanic spreading ridge, the similarities in internal structure (e.g. Gass 1968; Moores & Vine 1971) do allow comparisons to be made. The Troodos ophiolite offers a unique study area in that since it was uplifted above a rising serpentinite diapir (Gass & Masson-Smith 1963) it lacks the later overprinting compressional structures identified in other ophiolites of the Alpine chain (Coward & Dietrich 1989, and references therein). The ophiolite stratigraphy and, in particular, the Sheeted Dyke Complex is, therefore, well preserved. Furthermore, the recognition of large-scale oceanic structures within the Troodos ophiolite such as the Solea graben, a fossil ridge axis according to Varga & Moores (1985), and the Southern Troodos Transform Fault Zone

(STTFZ) (Moores & Vine 1971; Simonian & Gass 1978; Murton & Gass 1986; Murton 1986a; MacLeod 1990) allows for the identification of not only those structures related directly to the ridge axis but also of those at ridge transform intersections (MacLeod *et al.* 1990).

Important small-scale oceanic structures in the Sheeted Dyke Complex of Cyprus have also been observed. In outcrop scale an extremely dense network of metric-scale faulting and fracturing is visible (Allerton 1988, 1989; MacLeod *et al.* 1990; Varga & Moores 1990). As noted colloquially by Ian Gass (pers. comm.), 'two out of three contacts between sheeted dykes are tectonic'. We show in the following that this deformation originated in the crustal accretion zone.

According to field observation, the dykes which make up the sheeted complex occur over a 1–1.5 km depth interval (e.g. Baragar *et al.* 1987). From top to bottom of the Cyprus oceanic crust, the lavas pass downwards into sheeted dykes through a mixed zone of dykes and pillow lava screens into a zone of 100% dykes (Baragar *et al.* 1987). The mixed zone or 'Basal Group' is only a few tens of metres thick with an abrupt transition to 100% dykes over a stratigraphic interval of 25–50 m (Gass 1980). The contact at the base of the dykes is more complex, with plagiogranites and gabbros of the underlying plutonic complex cutting and being cut by the dykes (Moores & Vine 1971; Baragar *et al.* 1990). Some dykes are thought to be 'rooted' in the gabbro (Allan 1975).

An orthogonal relationship between dykes and the bedding of overlying sediments and volcanics along the north flank of the Troodos massif has been described by Verosub & Moores (1981), Schmincke *et al.* (1983) and Varga (1991). The sheeted dykes can, therefore, be assumed to represent originally vertical or subvertical intrusions.

The dykes vary in width from a few centimetres to several metres, the average width at outcrop being approximately 1.5 m (Baragar *et al.* 1987; 1990). Today, the dykes show a wide range of dip and dip direction (e.g. Allerton & Vine 1987; Moores *et al.* 1990). Typically, dykes trend N–S to NNW–SSE (e.g. Gass *et al.* 1991*a,b*), although in the vicinity of Palekhori close to the STTFZ, Baragar *et al.* (1987) noted that most of the dykes trend with azimuths between 050–060° and have an average dip of 50°. New data (see Fig. 2a) show a similar trend with a mean dip of 65° towards the southeast. The smallest dykes (1–10 cm) display greater variation in orientation, often displaying pinch and swell structures or branching prior to tapering out (Baragar *et al.* 1987). The dykes are predominantly of andesitic composition (Baragar *et al.* 1990) and are commonly altered to greenschist facies by sea-floor hydrothermal metamorphism (Gass & Smewing 1973). The mineral components are secondary albite (after a more calcic plagioclase), chlorite, epidote, actinolite, sphene, quartz and pyrite. Clinopyroxene and amphiboles are also common. The dykes often show an extremely fine-grained or cryptocrystalline chilled margin one to several centimetres wide. We follow both Cann (1974) and Kidd & Cann (1974) and assume that they were injected along sub-vertical fissures at, or near, the ridge axis, and that their planar structure results from intrusion into a host rock consisting entirely of older subvertical dykes (Gass & Smewing 1973). Early statistics of the chilling relations in the dykes (Kidd & Cann 1974; Kidd 1977) gave evidence for an apparent regional asymmetry of the chilled margins, interpreted as being the result of the intrusion of new dykes through the centres of older dykes. However, Baragar *et al.* (1987) suggest that new dykes tend to intrude along the margins of older dykes, the dykes with symmetrically chilled margins being in fact the most common.

Structural work within the Sheeted Dyke Complex has emphasized the importance of rotational deformation in association with the STTFZ (Moores & Vine 1971; Simonian & Gass 1978; Murton 1986*a,b*, 1990; MacLeod 1988, 1990; MacLeod *et al.* 1990; Allerton 1989; Allerton & Vine 1990, 1991, 1992; Gass *et al.* 1991*a,b*) and the Solea graben (e.g. Varga & Moores 1985; Allerton & Vine 1987; Varga 1991). Field observations together with palaeomagnetic data (Bonhommet *et al.* 1988; Allerton 1988; Allerton & Vine 1990, 1991, 1992, MacLeod *et al.* 1990; Morris *et al* 1990) from dykes in, and adjacent to, the STTFZ have demonstrated rotations about vertical axes. Dykes in the northern Troodos have a north/south trend and show a progressive clockwise rotation to east/west as they approach the fault zone (e.g. Simonian & Gass 1978; see also Fig. 1). Similar field observations of dykes and faults in the Solea graben (Varga & Moores 1985; Allerton & Vine 1987, 1990) suggest dyke rotations of more than 100° about horizontal/sub-horizontal axes accommodated by listric faults (e.g. Verosub & Moores 1981; Varga 1991). Here, originally vertical dykes dip towards each other to define the axis of a graben. Indeed identification of similar patterns of opposing dyke dips led Varga & Moores (1985) and Moores *et al.* (1990) to propose the existence of two further axes along the Mitsero and Larnaca grabens (Fig. 1) which they interpreted as fossil ridge axes forming part of an easterly system of ridge jumps. This interpretation is disputed by Allerton & Vine (1991) and MacLeod *et al.* (1992) who argue that the intrusive relationships do not support the existence of ridge axes but rather off-axis grabens formed by crustal stretching.

## Data collection and analysis

The Sheeted Dyke Complex of the Troodos ophiolite has excellent exposure along many of the road-cuts that traverse the mountains. Individual dykes within this complex represent mappable units in which cross-cutting relationships can be readily identified.

Two types of survey were adopted. The first involved regional reconnaissance, measuring dyke orientations across a wide area in an attempt to supplement the existing data (e.g. Wilson 1959; Varga & Moores 1985; Gass *et al.* 1991 *a,b*). This was particularly useful in determining any variations in the regional pattern. The second, more fruitful, technique was to produce vertical cliff maps on a scale of 1:100. A similar approach had been taken by Baragar *et al.* (1987, 1990), although their emphasis was on geochemical variation between dykes rather than

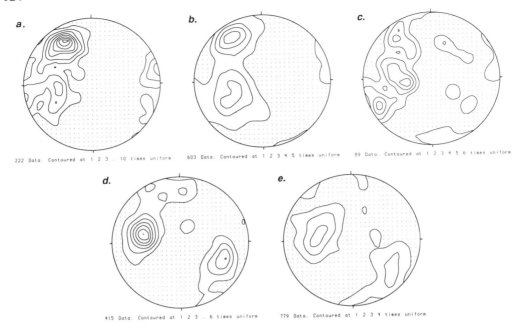

Fig. 2. The orientation of the structures in the Sheeted Dyke Complex of the Troodos ophiolite; lower hemisphere equal area projections. (a) The dyke orientation from northern and western Troodos. (b) The orientation of the dyke-parallel and dyke-cross-cutting normal faults from northern and western Troodos. (c) The orientation of the dyke-cross-cutting normal fault segments only, northern and western Troodos. Note that the faults form two statistically equally developed maxima in the SW quadrant, at 60° and 102° relative to the mean dyke orientation shown in (a). The two sets of faults dip, therefore, to opposite sides relative to the mean dyke orientation. (d) The dyke orientation from the Southern Troodos Transform Fault Zone (STTFZ). (e) The fault orientation from the STTFZ. The dykes and the faults have been rotated by transtensive movements along the Upper Cretaceous transform zone, indicating formation of the rotated faults in the plate accretion zone.

structural geometry. Individual outcrops were chosen at intervals throughout the ophiolite in order to study the small-scale tectonic structures and to discover any regional variations in fault style or geometry. All of the outcrops chosen for detailed analysis shared the following criteria: (1) they comprised 100% Sheeted Dyke Complex; (2) they were generally large (>3 × 20 m) road-cuts perpendicular to the dykes in which it was possible to trace both dykes and faults across substantial distances. This approach not only allowed individual dykes and faults to be mapped, but also enabled us to record minor changes in orientation and aspect over short distances and thereby obtain a detailed picture of the fault/dyke geometry.

## Results

### The orientation analysis of the Sheeted Dyke Complex

Figure 2 shows a series of stereograms which comprise all of our orientation data collected in the Sheeted Dyke Complex with respect to both the dykes and the faults. The localities from which these data were collected are shown in Fig. 1. The data have been split in order to separate out those orientations that result from structures in proximity to the STTFZ (Figs 2d–e) from those orientations not affected by the transtensive movements along this fault (Figs 2a–c).

Figure 2a shows the orientation of dykes measured over a wide area in western Troodos (see Fig. 1). The measurements refer to dykes with intrusive contacts and, in 90 per cent of cases, clearly visible chilled margins; measurements from dykes indicating tectonization as shown by lateral fault gouges, cross-cutting faults, etc. are not included in this figure. This stereogram shows a clear point maximum indicating a mean dip of 65° towards 150°. It is important, however, to note that NE- and W-dipping dyke packets also occur. These latter orientations have been interpreted as represen-

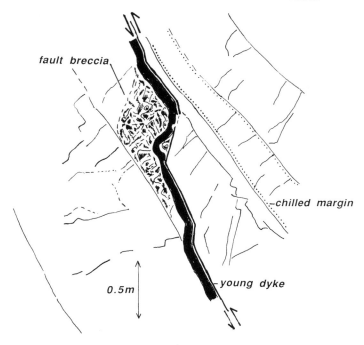

**Fig. 3.** Evidence for deformation of the Sheeted Dyke Complex in an oceanic environment I: a young dyke (black) intrudes parallel to a normal fault which cross-cuts the earlier dykes. The fault breccia has also been intruded. Note the sharply pointed termination of the dyke beneath the fault step. Sketch from field photograph. Road Pano Panayia–Kykkos, 12.4 km after beginning of dirt track.

ting later cross-cutting dykes (e.g. MacLeod *et al.* 1990) or as indicating rotations of groups or packets of dykes on major low-angle faults.

Figure 2b shows all the normal faults measured in the same area of western Troodos as were the dykes in Fig. 2a. The measurements include both those fault segments which parallel the dyke margins and those which cross-cut the dykes. The dyke-parallel fault segments are the most common. In outcrop, the faults can consist of knife-sharp tectonic contacts, or gouge/breccia zones, ranging in size from a centimetre- up to a metre-wide. The overall orientation distribution of the faults is similar to that of the dykes shown in Fig. 2a, and the two stereograms show overlapping maxima in the NW quadrant. In Fig. 2b, the second maximum in the SW quadrant of the stereogram is much wider than in Fig. 2a and comprises both dyke-parallel and dyke-cross-cutting fault segments. The cross-cutting fault segments show a range of possible orientations.

In Fig. 2c those segments of the faults which cross-cut the dykes are shown separately. The two pronounced maxima in the SW quadrant of the stereogram indicate two sets of cross-cutting

faults. The angles between the mean dyke orientation (Fig. 2a) and the two sets are 60° and 102°, respectively; i.e. the two sets have opposite dip directions. Both cross-cutting fault sets occur with the same overall regional frequency. This pattern can also be seen from the overall fault orientation (Fig. 2b). The maximum in the NW quadrant of Fig. 2b corresponds to dyke-parallel fault segments, whereas the large double maximum in the SW quadrant comprises the two separate maxima of Fig. 2c.

Figures 2d and e show the dyke and fault orientations in the zone affected by the movements along the northern side of the STTFZ. Both dykes and faults are rotated relative to the dykes and faults far from the transform zone and show lower dip values. The dykes (Fig. 2d) strike generally NE–SW, but can change orientation to an E–W strike, in accordance with the clockwise sense of rotation along the dextral transform segment mapped and described by Gass *et al.* (1991*a*,*b*).

Perhaps the most interesting results, however, come from the detailed analysis of the metric scale fault/dyke geometries, discussed in the following section.

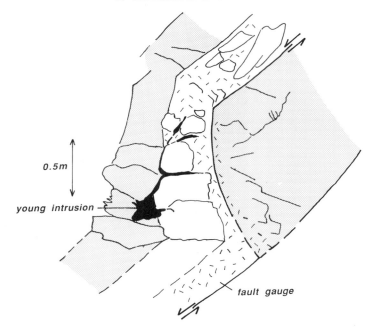

**Fig. 4.** Evidence for deformation of the Sheeted Dyke Complex in an oceanic environment II: the bending of dykes, induced by normal faulting, has led to brecciation: younger basalt intrudes the breccia. Note the wedge-shaped termination of the large dyke below the fault. Sketch from field photograph. Kaminaria valley, near Elea bridge.

## Extensional fault mechanisms and geometries within the Sheeted Dyke Complex

We are of the opinion that most of the faults described below, both small and meso-scale extensional structures, were created on the ocean floor, prior to the obduction and recent uplift of the ophiolite. The main arguments are as follows.

(1) Later dykes intrude and cross-cut earlier dykes, faults and fault breccias (e.g. Moores *et al.* 1990; Gass *et al.* 1991*a,b*). Figure 3, for example, clearly shows a young dyke intruding a normal fault. The dyke also intrudes the fault breccia, indicating that faulting had occurred whilst the Sheeted Dyke Complex was still being formed. Figure 4 shows dykes which were brecciated in response to the bending strain about a normal fault step. The fault gouge shows a small basalt intrusion, indicating once more that magmatic activity postdated faulting. Figure 5 shows three dyke generations intruding each other consecutively. If the dykes are assumed to intrude vertically, then the earlier formed dykes had to rotate to lead to the observed

geometry shown in Fig. 5b. Tectonically rotated dykes can be seen in the hanging wall of low-angle normal faults. The low-angle normal fault responsible for the rotation of the dykes shown in Fig. 5b must have been active in the plate accretion zone, where subsequent dyke intrusion was possible.

(2) The movements along the STTFZ, an oceanic transform zone according to Moores & Vine (1971), Simonian & Gass (1978), Murton (1986a), Allerton & Vine (1990) and MacLeod (1990) induced tectonic rotation of dykes and earlier formed metric-scale faults (Figs 2d and e), relative to the dyke and fault orientations far from the transform zone.

The geometry of deformation of a Sheeted Dyke Complex differs in five essential ways from the models proposed for continental crustal extension. These are discussed in detail below.

(1) Vertical fissures in the plate accretion zone giving rise to dykes were created entirely by an unlimited amount of uniaxial extension, a mode of deformation not seen in continents.

(2) The oceanic system is not closed since new dykes intrude into the extending dyke complex. The basic rule of geometric models

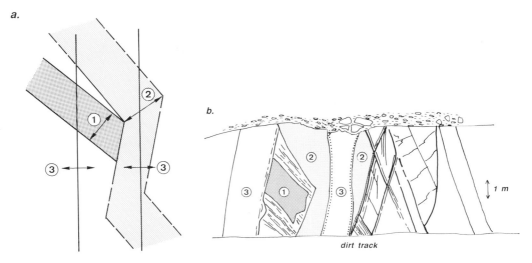

**Fig. 5.** Evidence for deformation of the Sheeted Dyke Complex in an oceanic environment III: dykes cross-cut earlier rotated dykes. (**a**) Cross-cutting relationships between three generations of dykes in a profile view. The oldest dyke system, 1, has been rotated and intruded by dyke system 2. Dyke system 2 itself rotated and will be intruded by dyke system 3 (shown as vertical fractures which will develop into a dyke). The extension directions associated with the three systems (arrows) rotated progressively in a clockwise sense. Such a progressive rotation could be expected to occur in the hanging wall of a listric normal fault. (**b**) The geometry of the three systems discussed in (a), after the intrusion of dyke system 3. The central dyke of system 3 has chilled margins, indicated with points. Sketch from field photographs and a cliff map. Road Pano Panayia–Kykkos, 11.1 km after beginning of dirt track.

of continental deformation, 'source = sink' (i.e. mass is not added or lost during deformation), is therefore invalid.

(3) The main anisotropy is not horizontal, as normally assumed in modelling extensional structures, but vertical. The dykes are thin relative to the thickness of the overall dyke layer and the closely spaced dyke boundaries confer a strong mechanical anisotropy to the Sheeted Dyke Complex. These anisotropy surfaces, emphasized by the chilled margins, are parallel to the dyke sheets, and perpendicular to the extension at the ridge axis. The resulting geometry of deformation is very different from extensional geometries seen, for example, in sediments where extension direction and mechanical anisotropy are generally parallel. The shear strength parallel to dyke boundaries is much lower than the shear strength on any other surface within the sheeted complex, allowing for easy dyke-parallel gliding.

(4) In the sheeted complex the normal fault geometry shows two sets of fault segments which cross-cut the dykes with opposing dip directions relative to the dyke orientation (Fig. 2c). From models of continental extension it would be expected that one of the two

sets would develop into the locally dominant fault system, creating domino domains (e.g. Vendeville *et al.* 1987).

(5) The dyke emplacement during continuous uniaxial extension is intermittent, originating from multiple, discrete centres below the spreading ridge and leading to the interleaving of dyke sheets as shown in Fig. 6. As a consequence, the deformation within the Sheeted Dyke Complex is extremely heterogeneous. The growth of an ellipsoidal-shaped fracture for dyke C in Fig. 6 will require deformation of the previously adjacent dykes B and D. In the case of dyke into dyke intrusion, the two halves B and D of the former dyke B–D will progressively separate. The stress concentration at the tip of the opening fracture will induce instabilities in the dyke(s) adjacent to the fracture. In an environment of unlimited extension and therefore of poor deformation constraint, these instabilities lead to an extremely heterogeneous deformation. Normal faults and fault-related kink folds in the hanging wall will rapidly die out in a lateral direction. Many of the structures observed appear to be the result of local gravity collapse rather than of a homogeneous deformation.

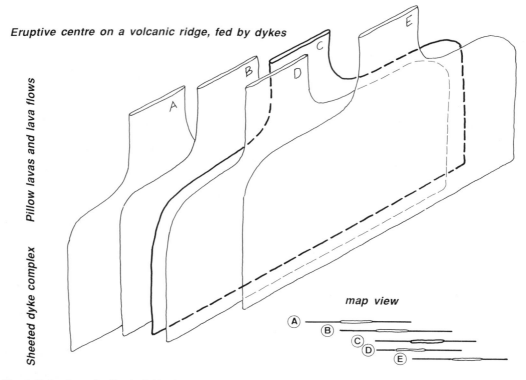

*Eruptive centre on a volcanic ridge, fed by dykes*

**Pillow lavas and lava flows**

**Sheeted dyke complex**

*map view*

**Fig. 6.** Dyke sheets feeding individual eruptive centres on an oceanic ridge. Uniaxial extension leads to intrusion of dyke C into the older interleaving dykes A–E. The stress concentration at the tip of the opening fracture will induce extremely heterogeneous deformation in the adjacent dykes. Adapted from Baragar *et al.* (1987, 1990) and Gudmundsson (1990).

The theoretical geometry for a normal fault formed within vertical sheeted dykes is shown in Fig. 7. It comprises segments parallel to the chilled dyke margins and segments which cross-cut the dykes at an angle of approximately 60° (Fig. 2c). The overall geometry is thus similar to that seen in thrust belts with the existence of ramps and flats (Boyer & Elliott 1982). Movement on these faults leads to the creation of two potentially open spaces, one in the hanging wall and the other in the footwall of the fault. These open spaces represent instabilities which subsequently induce either new normal faulting or some other form of accommodation structure, the nature of which is related to the amount of extension on the fault. Given extension upon a fault with an initial geometry similar to that shown in Fig. 7, we identify two categories of structural accommodation mechanism. These are accommodation of the instability by second, third, etc. order faulting, or local accommodation, through brecciation, folding or new dyke intrusion.

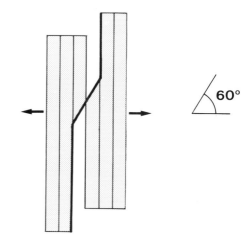

**Fig. 7.** Theoretical geometry of a normal fault formed within vertical sheeted dykes. The open space in the footwall will be filled by the downfaulted dykes. The open space in the hanging wall represents an instability which will induce renewal of normal faulting.

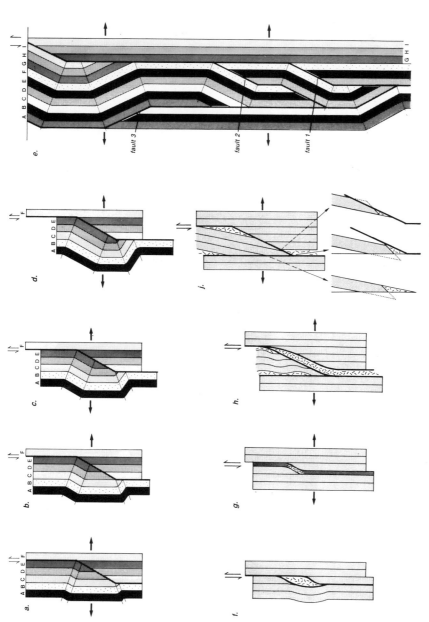

**Fig. 8.** Sequence of diagrams showing accommodation structures related to normal faulting as observed in the Sheeted Dyke Complex. The arrows indicate the direction of oceanic extension. (**a**)–(**d**) show the progressive movement of dykes A–E down the fault step. The bending of the dyke packet is realized through widening kink folds. Fault-related kinking is only locally developed and affects only dykes A–E. An open space has to exist between dyke A and the undeformed adjacent dykes on the left-hand side (not shown). (**a**)–(**d**), therefore, represent unstable geometric configurations, preceding stage (**e**). (**e**) Final and stable dyke geometry after second- and third-order faulting. Note the ramp/flat geometry, which, if the sequence is tilted, could easily be misinterpreted as thrusting. Note as well that the dip direction of the 'ramps' of faults 1 and 2 is opposite to the dip direction of the 'ramp' of fault 3. (**f**)–(**j**) Accommodation structures related to normal faults extending only by a small amount, up to one dyke width. (**f**) A fault gouge fills the open space, removing material from the fault step. (**g**) A dyke intrudes the open space and also penetrates the fault gouge. (**h**) Poorly constrained dykes in the hanging wall of a normal fault expand laterally into the open space through folding. (**j**) Poorly constrained dykes in the hanging wall of a normal fault slide into the open space. The inserts show geometric solutions for area conservation by brecciation of the dyke terminations.

**Fig. 9.** Dykes delimited by faults, showing upward and downward sharply pointed terminations. Compare with Fig. 8(e). Road to Cedar Valley, 1.7 km N of turn-off from road Kambos–Kykkos.

*Accommodation of faulting instability (open space) by second, third etc. order faulting: down 'thrusting' of dykes and upward migration of faulting instabilities*

This is probably the most frequently occurring extensional structural geometry observed within the Sheeted Dyke Complex. It is associated with faults which extend by an amount greater than the width of one dyke. Figures 8a–d show progressive extension on a normal fault increasing up to the amount of two dykes' width. The step in the fault plane acts as a ramp deflecting the dykes in the hanging wall. Dyke C in Fig. 8a and b is being downfaulted into an opening space created by progressive extension. A kink structure develops in the hanging wall of the fault and widens as the amount of extension increases. Unlike the model by Suppe (1983), where the resulting ramp anticline propagates through the overall rock sequence up to the surface, we observed only local development of fault-induced kink folding. The amount of energy expended in kinking adjacent dykes is clearly limited in such an environment of general extension. We are, therefore, left with an open space at the left side of models a–d in Fig. 8, which increases as the amount of extension increases. This instability is accommodated in Fig. 8e,

where the final and stable dyke geometry is shown. The space that opens as a result of the kinking (Fig. 8d) induces a renewal of faulting: fault 1 thus induces fault 2, which in turn induces fault 3, and so on (Fig. 8e). Note that, as a consequence of the model, the cross-cutting fault segments of faults 1 and 2 in Fig. 8e dip towards the left, but the one of fault 3 dips towards the right-hand side, relative to the dyke orientation. Such opposite dip directions have been observed (Fig. 2c). Faults 1 and 2 delimit a group of three dykes which display sharply pointed terminations in both up and down directions. Sharply pointed terminations of dykes or groups of dykes are in fact commonly observed (Figs 3, 4 and 9) and are interpreted as representing the end result of a sequence of normal faulting. The resulting overall deformation geometry indicates vertical shortening of the Sheeted Dyke Complex.

The dyke segments which pass through the kink bends have to deform. Dykes can simply brecciate, but two other accommodation structures for bending exist. The dykes can fracture and break, and the spaces between the fragments have been observed to be intruded by new basic dykelets (e.g. Fig. 4). Such an intrusion has to result in a dramatic lowering of the bending

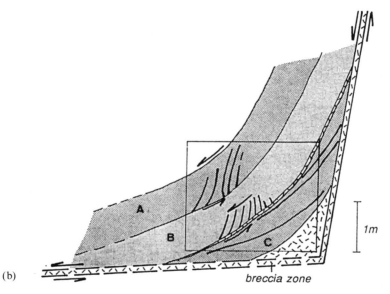

**Fig. 10(a).** The bending of dykes being accommodated by jointing. Kaminaria valley, near Elea Bridge. (**b**) Model, explaining the jointing pattern in (a). Dykes A and B show sigmoidal joints, dyke C shows radial joints. The joint pattern in A and B is the result of superposition of a stress field related to shearing upon the bending stress.

resistance. Alternatively the dykes can show only jointing as shown in Fig. 10a. The position of the joints in the outer arc of the folded dykes can be related to a stress field induced by bending (outer arc tension, inner arc compression). The sigmoidal form of the joint pattern, as well as the fact that the joints are located slightly off the region of greatest curvature of the fold indicates superposition of a second stress field induced by shearing parallel to the dyke boundaries (Fig. 10b).

*Local accommodation of faulting instability through brecciation, folding or new dyke intrusion*

These structures are generally associated with faults extending by a small amount of less than,

**Fig. 11.** Folded dykes in the hanging wall of a normal fault. The fault is overturned. Compare with Fig. 8h. Road Yerakies–Ayia Triadha, near Yerakies.

**Fig. 12.** Dykes slid into and filling the open space in the hanging wall of a normal fault. Compare with Fig. 8j. Road Pano Panayia–Kikkos, 15.7 km after beginning of dirt track.

**Fig. 13.** Dyke geometry above a low-angle normal fault. (**a**) The fault appears to be listric, but upon close observation, as shown in (**b**), it consists of steep planar faults which detach into a sub-horizontal shear zone. Note the apparent reverse sense of faulting through the dislocation of dyke A to A'. The small dykes above the shear zone form extensional horses. Road Pano Panaya–Kykkos, *c.* 10 km N of Pano Panayia.

or the equivalent of, one dyke width. Four different geometric solutions for the open space problem have been observed.

(a) Open space filled by fault gouge. Figure 8f shows the development of a gouge parallel to the fault planes. The open space is filled with material removed from the fault step and redeposited along the fault/dyke margin. This situation is ubiquitous occurring throughout the dyke complex.

(b) Open space filled by intruding dyke. Figures 3 and 8g show how a small dyke can intrude into the open space created by faulting. The small dyke has been observed to penetrate the region of fault gouge formed at the fault step.

(c) Open space filled by folded dykes. Figures 8h and 11 show the development of a gouge filling the open space in the footwall of the normal fault, whilst the poorly constrained dykes in the hanging wall are expanded laterally through the development of folds.

(d) Open space filled by sliding dykes. Figures 8j and 12 show how the dykes slipped down the fault step. The three inserts indicate geometric solutions for area conservation by brecciation of the dyke terminations.

*Low-angle normal faults*

The steep planar extensional faults described above are by far the most commonly observed

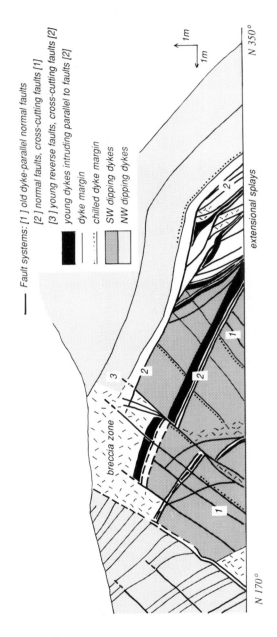

**Fig. 14.** Cliff map showing the reorientation of dykes on normal faults. Intrusions of new dykes (black) parallel to the normal faults are part of the oceanic transform environment. Road Arakapas–Sykopetra, 2.15 km N of Arakapas.

structures seen within the Sheeted Dyke Complex. These structures alone, however, cannot accommodate the rotation of the dykes about horizontal/sub-horizontal axes (Figs 2a–e), thus implying the existence of major low-angle extensional structures at depth. Such structures have been observed at outcrop both within the Sheeted Dyke Complex and within the underlying gabbros (Verosub & Moores 1981; Varga & Moores 1985; Baragar *et al.* 1987, 1990; Varga 1991). The classic detachment is seen at Lemithou (e.g. Varga *et al.* 1987) where subhorizontal dykes are found in juxtaposition with sheared gabbro. Some of these structures appear to be listric (Fig. 13a) but most, upon close observation (Fig. 13b), are seen to comprise a series of both dykes and steep planar extensional faults or individual large steep planar faults (with gouges several metres wide and throws of tens of metres) which detach upon planar low-angle structures. A group of dykes in the hanging wall of the sub-horizontal shear zone in Fig. 13b exhibit the geometry of extensional horses (nomenclature according to Boyer & Elliott 1982). The planar low-angle structures may be either discrete fault planes or wider zones of brittle/ductile shear. The pattern is thus one of simple domino block rotation (Emmons & Garrey 1910) in which the basal keels of the rotated blocks are deformed through a combination of brecciation and/or brittle/ductile flow (e.g. Wernicke & Burchfiel 1982). A similar architecture has been described from the strata above the Arakapas fault decollement (MacLeod 1988).

## Low-angle and dyke-parallel normal faults which accommodate transtension in the Southern Troodos Transform Fault Zone

Impressive normal faulting is associated with the transtensive movements along the STTFZ. Packets of dykes were rotated more than 150° on normal faults (MacLeod 1988; Allerton 1988). Figure 14 shows SW-dipping dykes, with chilled margins and dyke-parallel faults, cut by a NW-dipping system of low-angle faults. The dykes in the hanging wall of the low-angle faults dip also towards NW. The movement on these faults was towards present-day NE, in agreement with dextral E–W-directed transtension (Figs 15a and b).

## Discussion

Extensional faulting is ubiquitous within the Sheeted Dyke Complex. Most of these faults are planar, they parallel the dyke margins and locally they display a ramp/flat geometry (Boyer

& Elliott 1982). The ramp segments of the faults can dip on opposite sides, relative to the dyke orientation. Opposite dip directions of the ramps are observed on a local as well as on a regional scale, although in any one area one orientation occurs more frequently. This can be interpreted in terms of Fig. 8e, assuming that the formation of ramps of one orientation is favoured as opposed to the other set. The controlling factors could be a combination of the effects of local topography induced by proximity to ridge axis, the presence of local magma chambers at different stages in their life cycle, or large controlling faults in the footwall. The amount of extension accommodated on individual steep planar faults is generally limited to a few metres; however, the fact that there are so many of them suggests that their overall contribution to tectonic extension is significant. This is particularly important to remember when estimating extension on oceanic ridges since the very scale of these structures precludes their recognition by most geophysical techniques (Vogt & Tucholke 1986).

Tectonic extension within the upper crustal levels is also accommodated by a combination of large dyke-parallel/sub-parallel faults (geometrically similar but an order of magnitude greater than those described above) and sub-horizontal shear zones (Fig. 13). These structures, though not observed as frequently as the metric-scale faults, are considered to be first-order structures responsible for the overall rotation of the dyke complex from the vertical. Similar geometries have been described by Karson & Rona (1990) from the TAG area, Mid-Atlantic Ridge at 26°N. In the Troodos some of these structures are formed demonstrably within the plate accretion zone, as supported by the presence of epidote in the fault gouges and by cross-cutting dykes. Others are late structures, which cross-cut dykes/faults within the ophiolite and the overlying sedimentary sequence. These latter faults are thought to have formed as a direct consequence of either the uplift of the ophiolite, the upcoming of which induced both tilting and a renewal of extensional faulting or the rotation of the Troodos microplate.

Oceanic listric faults were also identified, and though they account for only a small percentage of all the faults mapped, the amount of extension that they can accommodate through rotations is greater than that of planar faults. Again, similar faults have been described by Karson & Rona (1990) from the ridge axis of the TAG area. Listric faults, however, only allow extension in the hanging wall of the fault. Sequences below the fault remain undisturbed. This locally leads to an imbalance except in cases

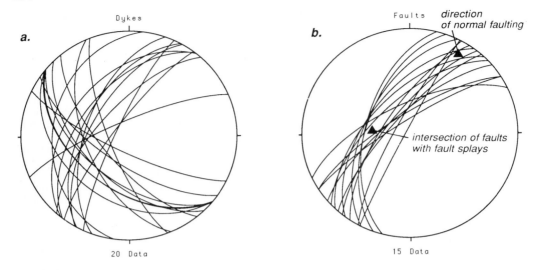

**Fig. 15(a).** The orientation of the dykes in Fig. 14. Some dykes retain the original SW dip direction, others have been reorientated to a NW dip direction. (**b**) Direction of the transtensional movements in the Southern Troodos Transform Fault zone, calculated from the intersection of the major low-angle faults with the extensional splays (Fig. 14). The resulting NE-direction for the movements on the faults agrees with E–W dextral transtension. Both stereograms are lower hemisphere equal area projections.

where magmatism adds material at lower crustal levels but is of insufficient intensity to promote extrusion. Here listric faults provide an important accommodation mechanism whereby overall crustal extension can be maintained.

The rotation of dykes/planar faults through listric faulting or through a combination of faults parallel and at a high angle to the dykes (i.e. sub-horizontal shear zones) leads to a geometry apparently associated with reverse faulting (A–A' in Fig. 13b). Dykes and cross-cutting normal fault steps (Fig. 8e), rotated into a sub-horizontal orientation, exhibit a ramp/flat geometry as would be seen in a thrust belt. In such cases this geometry is purely a consequence of rotation and should not be considered to be representative of compression on the ridge axis. It does also not necessarily infer later compression associated with the uplift of the ophiolite, although this possibility cannot be ruled out wherever supporting evidence for sea-floor genesis is absent.

The variety of geometries observed in the Troodos ophiolite has regional implications for the interpretation of larger-scale structures. However, where outcrops are insufficient to observe directly the larger-scale structure, it is unwise to use observations of local dyke orientations to define the nature of the controlling large-scale structure; there are too many possible

deformation geometries which could explain local dyke orientations.

## Conclusions

(1) The Troodos ophiolite of Cyprus offers a unique opportunity to study faults generated within the zone of crustal accretion. Many faults are observed which were demonstrably formed on or in proximity to the ridge axis. Furthermore the nature of the uplift of the ophiolite has left minimal late cross-cutting structures.

(2) The Sheeted Dyke Complex contains a network of small-scale normal faults with metric to several metres spacing of the fault planes. These faults are considered to make a significant contribution to overall tectonic extension at upper crustal levels. The geometry of faulting consists of extensional ramps and flats propagating upwards through the Sheeted Dyke Complex.

(3) True listric faults are rare. Rotational geometries are often controlled by a combination of steep and low-angle planar faults the perturbations of which lead to local variations in dyke orientation.

(4) Detailed structural and palaeomagnetic analysis is an invaluable tool in understanding ophiolite/ocean tectonics.

We were very lucky to have been introduced to the geology of Cyprus by Professors Ian Gass, John Malpas, Eldridge Moores and by Dr Costas Xenophontos; the excursion in October 1991 is unforgotten. Professors J. R. Cann, Ian Gass and J. G. Ramsay are thanked for critically reading an earlier version of this article. We are indebted to the editor, Dr Hazel Prichard, for encouragement, and to the reviewers R. Baragar, Ian Gass, C. J. MacLeod and to an anonymous reviewer for their comments. Financial support from Schweizerischer Nationalfonds, project 20-27462.89 (D.D.), and from the Royal Society, London (S.S.), is gratefully acknowledged.

# References

ALLAN, C. R. 1975. *The petrology of a portion of the Troodos Plutonic Complex, Cyprus*. PhD thesis, Cambridge University.

ALLERTON, S. 1988. *Palaeomagnetic and structural studies of the Troodos ophiolite, Cyprus*. PhD thesis, University of East Anglia.

—— 1989. Fault block rotations in ophiolites: results of palaeomagnetic studies in the Troodos Complex, Cyprus. *In*: KISSEL, C. & LAJ, C. (eds) *Palaeomagnetic Rotations and Continental Deformation*. NATO ARI Series C, **254**, 393–410.

—— & VINE, F. J. 1987. Spreading evolution of the Troodos ophiolite, Cyprus: Some palaeomagnetic constraints. *Geology*, **15**, 593–597.

—— & —— 1990. Palaeomagnetic and structural studies of the southeastern part of the Troodos complex. *In*: MALPAS, J., MOORES, E. M., PANAYIOTOU, A. & XENOPHONTOS, C. (eds) *Ophiolites: Oceanic Crustal Analogues*. Geological Survey Department, Nicosia, Cyprus, 99–111.

—— & —— 1991. Spreading evolution of the Troodos ophiolite, Cyprus. *Geology*, **19**. 637–640.

—— & —— 1992. Deformation styles adjacent to transform faults: evidence from the Troodos ophiolite, Cyprus. *In*: PARSON, L. M., MURTON, B. J. & BROWNING, P. (eds) *Ophiolites and their Modern Oceanic Analogues*. Geological Society, London, Special Publication, **60**, 251–261.

ANDERSON, R. N., HONNOREZ, J., BECKER, K., ADAMSON, A., ALT, J., EMMERMANN, R., KEMPTON, P., KINOSHITA, H., LAVERN, C., MOTTL, M. & NEWMARK, R. 1982. DSDP Hole 504B, the first reference section over 1 km through layer 2 of the oceanic crust. *Nature*, **300**, 589–594.

BARAGAR, W. R. A., LAMBERT, M. B., BAGLOW, N. & GIBSON, I. L. 1987. Sheeted dykes of the Troodos ophiolite, Cyprus. *In*: HALLS, H. C. & FAHRIG, W. F. (eds) *Mafic Dyke Swarms*. Geological Association of Canada Special Paper, **34**, 257–272.

——, ——, & —— 1990. The sheeted dyke zone in the Troodos ophiolite. *In*: MALPAS, J., MOORES, E. M., PANAYIOTOU, A. & XENOPHONTOS, C. (eds) *Ophiolites: Oceanic Crustal Analogues*. Geological Survey Department, Nicosia, Cyprus, 37–51.

BONHOMMET, N., ROPERCH, P. & CALZA, F. 1988. Paleomagnetic arguments for block rotations along the Arakapas fault (Cyprus). *Geology*, **16**, 422–425.

BOYER, S. E. & ELLIOTT, D. 1982. Thrust systems. *American Association of Petroleum Geologists Bulletin*, **66**, 1196–1230.

BLOME, C. D. & IRWIN, W. P. 1985. Equivalent radiolarian ages from ophiolitic terranes of Cyprus and Oman. *Geology*, **13**, 401–404.

CANN, J. R. 1974. A model for oceanic crustal structure developed. *Geophysical Journal of the Royal Astronomical Society*, **39**, 169–187.

CHEN, Y. & MORGAN, W. J. 1990a. Rift valley/no rift valley transition at mid-ocean ridges. *Journal of Geophysical Research*, **95** (**B11**), 17571–17581.

—— 1990b A non-linear rheology model for mid-ocean ridge axis topography. *Journal of Geophysical Research*, **95** (**B11**), 17583–17604.

CLUBE, T. M. M., CREER, K. M. & ROBERTSON, A. H. F. 1985. The palaeorotation of the Troodos microplate. *Nature*, **317**, 522–525.

—— & ROBERTSON, A. H. F. 1986. The palaeorotation of the Troodos microplate, Cyprus in the Late Mesozoic–Early Cenozoic plate tectonic framework of the eastern Mediterranean. *Surveys in Geophysics*, **8**, 375–437.

COWARD, M. P. & DIETRICH, D. 1989. Alpine Tectonics – an overview. *In*: COWARD, M. P., DIETRICH, D. & PARK, R. G. (eds) *Alpine Tectonics*. Geological Society, London, Special Publication, **45**, 1–29.

DILEK, Y., THY, P., MOORES, E. M. & RAMSDEN, T. W. 1990. Tectonic evolution of the Troodos ophiolite within the Tethyan framework. *Tectonics*, **9**, 811–823.

EMMONS, W. H. & GARREY, G. H. 1910. General Geology. *In*: RANSOME, F. L. *et al*. (eds) *Geology and Ore deposits of the Bullfrog District*. Bulletin of the US Geological Survey, **407**, 19–89.

GASS, I. G. 1968. Is the Troodos massif of Cyprus a fragment of oceanic floor? *Nature*, **220**, 39–42.

—— 1980. The Troodos Massif: Its role in the unravelling of the ophiolite problem and its significance in the understanding of constructive plate margin processes. *In*: PANAYIOTOU, A. (ed.) *Ophiolites*. Proceedings of the International Ophiolite Symposium, 1979. Geological Survey Department, Ministry of Agriculture and Natural Resources, Nicosia, Cyprus, 23–35.

—— 1990. Ophiolites and Oceanic Lithosphere. *In*: MALPAS, J., MOORES, E. M., PANAYIOTOU, A., XENOPHONTOS, C. (eds) *Ophiolites: Oceanic crustal Analogues*. Geological Survey Department, Nicosia, Cyprus, 1–12

—— & MASSON-SMITH, D. 1963. The geology and gravity anomalies of the Troodos massif, Cyprus. *Philosophical Transactions of the Royal Society of London*, A **255**, 417–467.

——, MACLEOD, C. J., MURTON, B. J., PANAYIOTOU, A., SIMONIAN, K.O. & XENOPHONTOS, C. 1991 (a&b) *Geological map of the Southern Troodos Transform Fault Zone* (two sheets). Geological Survey Department, Nicosia, Cyprus.

—— & SMEWING, J. D. 1973. Intrusion, extrusion and metamorphism at constructive margins: evidence from the Troodos massif, Cyprus. *Nature*, **242**, 26–29.

GUDMUNDSSON, A. 1990. Emplacement of dikes, sills and crustal magma chambers at divergent plate boundaries. *Tectonophysics*, **176**, 257–275.

HARPER, G. D. 1982. Evidence for large scale rotations at spreading centres from the Josephine ophiolite. *Tectonophysics*, **82**, 25–44.

HARRISON, C. G. A. & STIELTJES, L. 1977. Faulting within the median valley. *Tectonophysics*, **38**, 137–144

KARSON, J. A. 1987. Factors controlling the orientation of dykes in ophiolites and oceanic crust. *In*: HALLS, H. C. & FAHRIG, W. F. (eds) *Mafic Dyke Swarms*. Geological Society of Canada Special Paper, **34**, 229–241.

—— & RONA, P. A. 1990. Block-tilting, transfer faults, and structural control of magmatic and hydrothermal processes in the TAG area, Mid Atlantic Ridge 26°N. *Geological Society of America Bulletin*, **102**, 1635–1645.

——, THOMPSON, G., HUMPHRIS, S. E., EDMOND J. M., BRYAN W. B., BROWN J. R., WINTERS A. T., POCKALNY, R. A., CASEY, J. F., CAMPBELL, A. C., KLINKHAMMER G., PALMAR M. R., KINZLER, R. J. & SULANOWSKA, M. M. 1987. Along axis variations in seafloor spreading in the MARK area. *Nature*, **328**, 681–685.

—— & WINTERS, A. T. 1987. Tectonic extension on the Mid-Atlantic Ridge. *EOS*, **68**, 1508.

KEMPLER, D. & BEN AVRAHAM, Z. 1987. The tectonic evolution of the Cyprean arc. *Annales Tectonicae*, **1**, 58–71.

KIDD, R. G. W. 1977. A model for the process of formation of the Upper Oceanic Crust. *Geophysical Journal of the Royal Astronomical Society*, **50**, 149–183.

—— & CANN, J. R. 1974. Chilling statistics indicate an ocean-floor spreading origin for the Troodos complex, Cyprus. *Earth and Planetary Science Letters*, **24**, 151–155.

LEG 109 SHIPBOARD SCIENTIFIC PARTY 1986. Coring the crust & mantle. *Nature*, **323**, 492–493.

LEG 118 SHIPBOARD SCIENTIFIC PARTY 1988. Plutonic rocks in fracture zones. *Nature*, **333**, 115–116.

MACDONALD K. C. 1982 Mid-ocean ridges fine scale tectonic, volcanic and hydrothermal processes within the plate boundary zone. *Annual Review of Earth and Planetary Science*, **10**, 155–190.

—— 1986. The crest of the Mid-Atlantic Ridge. *In*: VOGT, P. R. & TUCHOLKE B. E (eds) *Geology of North America volume M: The Western North Atlantic Region*. Geology Society of America, 51–68.

—— & ATWATER T. M. 1978. Evolution of rifted ocean ridges. *Earth & Planetary Science Letters*, **39**, 319–327.

MACLEOD, C. J. 1988. *The tectonic evolution of the Eastern Limassol Forest Complex, Cyprus*. PhD thesis, Open University.

—— 1990. Role of the Southern Troodos Transform Fault in the rotation of the Cyprus microplate: evidence from the Eastern Limassol Forest Complex. *In*: MALPAS J., MOORES E. M., PANAYIOTOU,

A. & XENOPHONTOS, C. (eds) *Ophiolites: Oceanic Crustal Analogues*. Geological Survey Department, Nicosia, Cyprus, 75–85.

——, ALLERTON, S., GASS, I. G. & XENOPHONTOS, C. 1990. Structure of a fossil ridge transform intersection in the Troodos ophiolite. *Nature*, **348**, 717–720.

—— ROBERTSON, A. H. F., ALLERTON, S., BROWNING, P., GASS, I. G., TAYLOR, R. N., VINE, F. J. & XENOPHONTOS, C. 1992. Comments on 'Tectonic evolution of the Troodos ophiolite within the Tethyan framework' by Dilek, Y., Thy, P., Moores, E. M. & Ramsden, T. W. (*Tectonics*, **9**, 811–823). *Tectonics*, **11**, 910–915.

MALPAS, J. & ROBINSON, P. T. 1987. Chromite mineralisation in the Troodos ophiolite, Cyprus. *In*: STOWE, C. W. (ed.) *Evolution of Chromium Orefields*, Van Nostrand Reinhold, 220–237.

——, XENOPHONTOS, C. & WILLIAMS, D. 1992. The Ayia Varvara Formation of SW Cyprus: a product of complex collisional tectonics. *Tectonophysics*, **212**, 193–211.

McALLISTER, E., SPENCER, S. & CANN, J. R. 1992. Fault patterns along the spreading axis of the Reykjanes Ridge, south-west Iceland. *Earth and Planetary Science Letters*, submitted.

McCLAIN, J. S., ORCUTT, J. A. & BURNETT, M. 1985. The East Pacific Rise in cross-section: A seismic model. *Journal of Geophysical Research*, **90**, 8627–8639.

MIYASHIRO, A. 1973. The Troodos ophiolite complex was probably formed in an island arc. *Earth and Planetary Science Letters*, **19**, 218–224.

MOORES, E. M. & VINE, F. J. 1971. The Troodos massif, Cyprus, and other ophiolites as oceanic crust. Evaluation and implications. *Royal Society of London Philosophical Transactions*, **A268**, 443–466.

——, ROBINSON, P. T., MALPAS, J. & XENOPHONTOS, C. 1984. Model for the origin of the Troodos massif, Cyprus and other mideast ophiolites. *Geology*, **12**, 500–503.

——, VARGA, R. J., VEROSUB, K. L. & RAMSDEN, T. 1990 Regional structure of the Troodos dyke complex. *In*: MALPAS J., MOORES, E. M., PANAYIOTOU, A. & XENOPHONTOS, C. (eds) *Ophiolites: Oceanic Crustal Analogues*. Geological Survey Department, Nicosia, Cyprus, 27–35.

MORRIS, A., CREER, K. M. & ROBERTSON, A. H. F. 1990. Palaeomagnetic evidence for clockwise rotations related to dextral shear along the Southern Troodos Transform Fault. *Earth and Planetary Science Letters*, **99**, 250–262.

MUKASA, S. B. & LUDDEN, J. N. 1987. Uranium–lead ages of plagiogranites from the Troodos ophiolite, and their tectonic significance. *Geology*, **15**, 825–828.

MURTON, B. J. 1986a. Anomalous oceanic lithosphere formed in a leaky transform fault. Evidence from the Western Limassol Forest Complex, Cyprus. *Journal of the Geological Society. London*, **143**, 845–854.

—— 1986b *The tectonic evolution of the Western Limassol Forest Complex, Cyprus*. PhD thesis,

Open University.

—— 1990. Was the Southern Troodos Transform fault a victim of microplate rotation? *In*: MALPAS J., MOORES, E. M., PANAYIOTOU, A. & XENOPHONTOS, C. (eds) *Ophiolites: Oceanic Crustal Analogues*. Geological Survey Department, Nicosia, Cyprus, 87–98.

—— & GASS, I. G. 1986. Western Limassol Forest Complex, Cyprus: part of an upper Cretaceous leaky transform fault. *Geology*, **14**, 255–258.

MUTTER, J. C. & NORTH ATLANTIC TRANSECT (NAT) STUDY GROUP 1985. Multichannel seismic images of the oceanic crust's internal structure: Evidence for a magma chamber beneath the Mesozoic Mid-Atlantic Ridge. *Geology*, **13**, 629–632.

PEARCE, J. A. 1975. Basalt geochemistry used to investigate past tectonic environment of Cyprus. *Tectonophysics*, **25**, 41–67.

——, LIPPARD, S. J. & ROBERTS, S. 1984. Characteristics and tectonic significance of supra-subduction zone ophiolites. *In*: KOKELAAR, B. P. & HOWELLS, M. F. (eds) *Marginal Basin Geology*, 77–94.

ROBERTSON, A. H. F. 1990. Tectonic evolution of Cyprus. *In*: MALPAS, J., MOORES, E. M., PANAYIOTOU, A. & XENOPHONTOS, C. (eds) *Ophiolites: Oceanic Crustal Analogues*. Geological Survey Department, Nicosia, Cyprus, 235–252.

SCHMINCKE, H.-U., RAUTENSCHLEIN, M., ROBINSON, P. T. & MEGEHAN, J. M. 1983. Troodos extrusive series of Cyprus: A comparison with oceanic crust, *Geology*, **11**, 405–409.

SIMONIAN, K. O. & GASS, I. G. 1978. Arakapas fault belt, Cyprus: a fossil transform fault. *Geological Society of America Bulletin*, **89**, 1220–1230.

SLEEP, N. H. & ROSENDAHL, B. R. 1979. Topography and tectonics of mid-ocean ridge axis. *Journal of Geophysical Research*, **84(B12)**, 6831–6839.

SUPPE, J. 1983. Geometry and kinematics of fault-bend folding. *American Journal of Science*, **283**, 684–721.

SWARBRICK, R. E. 1980. The Mammonia Complex of SW Cyprus and its relationship with the Troodos complex. *In*: PANAYIOTOU, A. (ed.) *Ophiolites*. Proceedings of the International Ophiolite Symposium, 1979. Geological Survey Department, Ministry of Agriculture and Natural Resources, Nicosia, Cyprus, 86–92.

TAPPONIER, P. & FRANCHETEAU, J. 1978. Necking of the lithosphere and the mechanics of slowly accreting plate boundaries. *Journal of Geophysical Research*, **83**, 3955–3970.

VARGA, R. J. 1991. Modes of extension at oceanic spreading centers: evidence from the Solea graben, Troodos ophiolite, Cyprus. *Journal of Structural Geology*, **13**, 517–537.

—— & MOORES, E. M. 1985. Spreading structure of the Troodos ophiolite, Cyprus. *Geology*, **13**, 846–850.

—— & —— 1990. Intermittent magmatic spreading and tectonic extension in the Troodos Ophiolite: implications for exploration for black smoker-type ore deposits. *In*: MALPAS, J., MOORES, E. M., PANAYIOTOU. A. & XENOPHONTOS, C. (eds). *Ophiolites: Oceanic Crustal Analogues*. Geological Survey Department, Nicosia, Cyprus, 53–64.

——, SCHIFFMAN, P., SMITH, B. M., MOORES, E. M. & HURST, S. 1987. Structure and Hydrothermal metamorphism of the Solea Graben, Troodos Ophiolite. *In*: *Troodos 87 Ophiolites and Oceanic Lithosphere Symposium*. Field Excursion Guidebook. Geological Survey Department, Nicosia, Cyprus.

VENDEVILLE, B., COBBOLD, P. R., DAVY, P., BRUN, J. P. & CHOUKROUNE, P. 1987. Physical models of extensional tectonics at various scales. *In*: COWARD, M. P., DEWEY, J. F. & HANCOCK, P. L. (eds) *Continental Extensional Tectonics*. Geological Society, London, Special Publication, **28**, 95–107.

VEROSUB, K. L. & MOORES, E. M. 1981. Tectonic rotations in extensional regimes and their paleomagnetic consequences for oceanic basalts. *Journal of Geophysical Research*, **86**, 6335–6349.

VOGT, P. R. & TUCHOLKE, B. E. 1986. Imaging the ocean floor: History and state of the art. *In*: VOGT P. R. & TUCHOLKE B. E. (eds) *Geology of North America volume M: The Western North Atlantic Region*. Geological Society of America, 19–44.

WERNICKE, B. & BURCHFIEL, B. C. 1982. Modes of extensional tectonics. *Journal of Structural Geology*, **4**, 105–115.

WHITE, R. S. 1984. Atlantic oceanic crust: Seismic structure of a slow spreading ridge. *In*: GASS I. G., LIPPARD S. J. & SHELTON A. W (eds) *Ophiolites and Oceanic Crust*. Geological Society, London, Special Publication, **13**, 101–111.

WILSON, R. A. M. 1959. *The geology of the Xeros–Troodos area. Geological Survey Department, Nicosia, Cyprus*, Memoir **1**.

# Structure and tectonic evolution of the Southern Troodos Transform Fault Zone, Cyprus

C. J. MacLEOD & B. J. MURTON

*Institute of Oceanographic Sciences, Brook Road, Wormley, Godalming, Surrey GU8 5UB, UK*

**Abstract**: A major strike-slip fault zone, at least 5 km in width, trends E–W along the southern margin of the Troodos ophiolite. It is an ocean-floor feature, overlain by undeformed pelagic sediments, and is orientated perpendicular to the mean strike of the sheeted dyke complex of the main ophiolite massif. It has long been recognized as probably the foremost example of a fossil transform fault within an ophiolite.

We present here detailed description of the structure and tectonic evolution of this so-called 'Southern Troodos Transform Fault Zone' (STTFZ), based upon 1:5000 scale mapping of the whole of the southern margin of the Troodos ophiolite. The styles of strike-slip deformation at all levels of the oceanic crust and upper mantle, and the variations in deformation style with time, are documented and the role of vertical-axis rotations within and adjacent to the transform zone is discussed. Evidence for the kinematics of deformation is reviewed; previous studies have been unable to agree even on such fundamentals as the sense of slip of the STTFZ. In an attempt to resolve the controversy we have made a systematic re-examination of the evidence for the direction of motion along the transform, supplemented by new field observations where necessary. We conclude that, although there is incontrovertible evidence for both sinistral *and* dextral shear along the STTFZ whilst it was in an oceanic environment, the overwhelming indications are for dextral slip. We show that sinistral indicators are restricted to a few small mylonite shears that are probably related to local geometrical complexities associated with the intrusion of gabbroic plutons into the transform; there is no need to invoke wholesale reversal of slip sense along the STTFZ as a whole.

The E–W-trending valley that separates the Limassol Forest Complex, the most southerly portion of the Troodos ophiolite, from the rest of the Troodos massif, had long been identified as an important fault zone by early workers (Bear 1958; Wilson 1959; Bear 1960; Bagnall 1960, 1964; Lapierre & Rocci 1967; Pantazis 1967). Its strike-slip character had been recognized (Bear 1958), but it was only in 1971 that Moores & Vine made the suggestion that the fault zone might represent a fossil oceanic transform fault. This fault zone, termed the 'Arakapas fault belt' (Figs 1 & 2), together with the adjacent Limassol Forest Complex, became the subject of a detailed research programme at the Open University under the direction of Ian Gass. He supervised three PhD theses: initially by Simonian (1975) on the Arakapas fault belt (AFB), and later Murton (1986b) on the western and MacLeod (1988) on the eastern parts of the Limassol Forest Complex (LFC). These detailed studies, which were based upon 1:5000 scale field mapping (now published at 1:25 000 scale: Gass *et al.* 1991a,b), essentially verified the transform fault hypothesis.

Simonian (1975) and Simonian & Gass (1978) showed that the AFB is an elongate zone of intense E–W transcurrent faulting, within which wholesale fault brecciation of the Sheeted Dyke Complex is common. Erupted unconformably onto this brecciated dyke complex 'basement', and infilling small basins between upstanding fault blocks, are irregular sequences of lava flows intercalated with volcaniclastic sediments (Fig. 3). These sediments, derived by the submarine erosion of fault scarps within and on the flanks of the fault belt, are evidence for considerable bathymetric relief across the area at the time. The nature of the lava sequence in the AFB contrasts markedly with the orderly lava successions from the north flank of Troodos, in which volcaniclastic sediments are rare; the present Arakapas valley, therefore, appears to reflect, albeit in a subdued manner, the bathymetry of the original sea floor. In this, a clear analogy can be drawn with modern-day oceanic fracture zones, in which a broad fault zone several kilometres in width is associated with a marked bathymetric depression (e.g. Menard & Atwater 1969; Bonatti & Honnorez 1976).

Simonian & Gass (1978) envisaged the AFB to be only the northern wall of the transform fault zone, and suggested that the entire LFC was also part of the structure. In the western LFC large

*From* Prichard, H. M., Alabaster, T., Harris, N. B. W. & Neary, C. R. (eds), 1993, *Magmatic Processes and Plate Tectonics*, Geological Society Special Publication No. 76, 141–176.

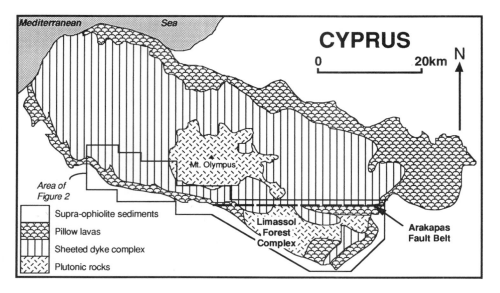

**Fig. 1.** Cartoon map of the Troodos ophiolite, Cyprus. The Limassol Forest Complex is separated from the main Troodos massif by the E–W-trending Arakapas Fault Belt. The area of Fig. 2 is marked in outline.

areas of serpentinite are exposed, with isolated blocks of peridotites and gabbros (Bear & Morel 1960). The serpentinites were considered to have been intruded diapirically into the transform, as proposed for some modern oceanic transforms (Bonatti 1976), and the plutonic rocks ridge axis-generated material that had been entrained within the rising serpentinite diapir (Bear & Morel 1960; Panayiotou 1977; Simonian & Gass 1978). That the western LFC was part of the transform zone was verified by Murton (1986a,b; Murton & Gass 1986), who documented E–W serpentinite shear zones and mylonites (described herein), both indicating transcurrent movement, across the entire width of the western LFC serpentinite outcrop. He also showed that the serpentinite outcrops, supposedly diapiric, were in fact passively serpentinized tectonized harzburgites and dunites of mantle origin, and that the peridotite and gabbro blocks were multiple plutons intruded into the lithospheric mantle whilst strike-slip deformation was continuing. Abundant dyke swarms associated with, and emanating from, these 'Transform Sequence' intrusives fed the unusually primitive and depleted boninitic lavas that occur only within the transform zone (Murton 1986a,b; 1989). As much as 22% extension may have been accommodated by the magmatism in the western LFC, leading Murton to conclude that the western LFC represented part of a 'leaky' transform fault zone.

The eastern part of the LFC preserves higher erosion levels than to the west, being characterized for the most part by disrupted blocks of a c. 4 km thick axis-generated oceanic crustal sequence (MacLeod 1988, 1990). The structural style there is quite distinct, with the strong E–W fabric of the AFB and western LFC much less apparent, and low-angle normal faulting instead predominating. MacLeod showed that the area had been subjected to a significant degree of extension, oblique to the trend of the transform, in the Late Cretaceous, soon after the cessation of magmatism in that area. He was able to demonstrate that this extensional deformation was founded upon, and reused, earlier transform-related structures in the northeastern LFC, but that such structures were notably absent in the southeast. The most southerly identifiably transform-related structure was the Mavridhia Fault (Adamides 1980; and see below) in the Kalavasos Mines. This structure coincides with the southerly disappearance of interlava volcaniclastic sediments, implying that a southern boundary to the transform existed at that latitude (MacLeod 1988, 1990). This indicates an original width for the transform fault zone of approximately 5 km in the eastern LFC, comparable to many modern oceanic fracture zones. The 50 km$^2$ of crust to the south of this boundary he considered to have been created at an 'Anti-Troodos' ridge axis.

With the completion of mapping of the LFC it

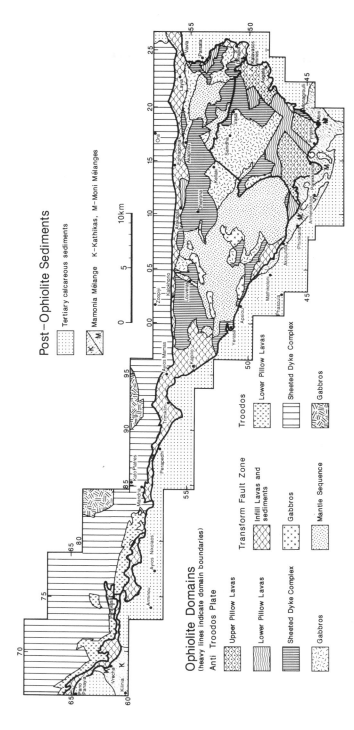

**Fig. 2.** Simplified geological map of the southern margin of the Troodos ophiolite. Heavy lines delimit approximate boundaries between the domains of the Troodos Plate, Southern Troodos Transform Fault Zone and Anti-Troodos Plate.

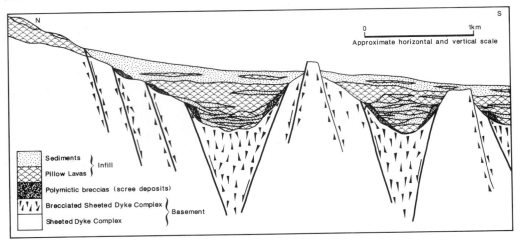

**Fig. 3.** Cartoon cross-section across the STTFZ, showing the relationship between the basement, composed of variably brecciated Sheeted Dyke Complex, and overlying lavas and volcaniclastic sediments. The sediments are derived from the mass wasting of fault scarps within and from the flanks of the transform valley; clasts are of lava, dyke-rock and (very rarely) microgabbroic origin. Modified from Simonian & Gass (1978).

became apparent that the transform-tectonized zone in southern Cyprus spanned the AFB and part, but not all of the LFC. With inconsistencies developing in terminology by some authors, MacLeod (1990) suggested introducing the term 'Southern Troodos Transform Fault Zone' (STTFZ) to describe the oceanic entity of the transform zone, to contrast with the geographical entities of the AFB and LFC.

## Structures in the transform fault zone

### High-temperature tectonite fabric in the Mantle Sequence

The harzburgites and dunites that constitute the Mantle Sequence of the LFC have penetrative tectonite fabrics, identical in character to those reported from other ophiolitic and abyssal peridotites. In hand specimen, harzburgite usually displays a foliation and sometimes lineation defined by the orientation of flattened orthopyroxene grains; in many cases (and in the dunites) the lineation may be recognized more readily by the elongation of chrome spinel grains or clusters of grains. In harzburgites the foliation may be accompanied by a (usually sub-parallel) diffuse, compositional or 'segregation' layering, defined by variations in the modal proportions of olivine to orthopyroxene on a centimetre to decimetre scale. This segregation layering is a dynamic metamorphic effect, analogous to gneissic layering (Dick & Sinton 1979), and thus

contrasts with the phase-layered 'cumulate' fabrics observed in many layered plutonic sequences (e.g. Nicolas & Poirier 1976; Nicolas 1989).

In thin section the harzburgites display a mosaic porphyroclastic texture (Harte 1976) with, in sections cut perpendicular to the foliation plane and parallel to the lineation, a pronounced elongation of orthopyroxene and spinel grains. Kink bands parallel to (100), with a spacing in the order of 0.2–1.0 mm, are visible within the larger olivine porphyroclasts in both harzburgites and dunites. Alignment of these kink band boundaries demonstrates a strong lattice-preferred fabric in addition to the mineral shape-preferred fabric.

It is well established, following experimental work and crystallographic studies (e.g. Carter & Avé Lallemant 1970; Nicolas & Poirier 1976), that olivine deforms plastically at elevated temperatures ($>1000°C$) by slip along $\{0k1\}[100]$ planes, resulting in the formation of kink band boundaries parallel to (100). Continued deformation under such conditions is accommodated by dislocation slip and climb with variable degrees of grain boundary migration and syntectonic recrystallization (Nicolas & Poirier 1976). Obliquity between the shape-preferred fabric that defines the foliation and lineation and the lattice-preferred orientation of crystals is taken to indicate deformation under conditions approaching a simple shear regime (e.g. Mercier et al. 1977; Bartholemew 1983; Nicolas 1989). Such olivine fabrics occur pervasively through-

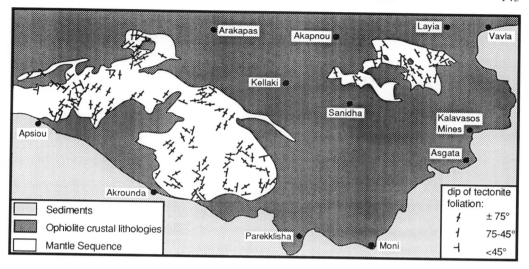

**Fig. 4.** Map of high temperature tectonite fabrics in Mantle Sequence harzburgites from the Limassol Forest Complex. Symbol bars indicate the strike of the foliation; ticks the dip direction and magnitude.

out the peridotite sections of the Troodos and other ophiolites, and their presence is taken by most authors to indicate that these peridotites have suffered deformation due to solid-state flow under high-temperature (up to 1200–1250°C), low deviatoric stress conditions (0.2–0.8 MPa: Karato 1984; Ceuleneer *et al.* 1988) in the convecting asthenospheric mantle. The orientation of the fabric on a regional scale can therefore be taken to represent a fossilized record of the trajectory of asthenospheric flow (e.g. Nicolas & Violette 1982).

In the STTFZ, Mantle Sequence lithologies crop out in two principal areas (Figs 2 & 4). The larger area, of some 60 km², forms the central and western parts of the LFC, and was studied in detail by Murton (1986*b*). The smaller area of Mantle Sequence crops out in the Akapnou Forest, in the northeast corner of the LFC, over an area of approximately 12 km². The latter area was studied by MacLeod (1988) and Georgiou & Xenophontos (1990). Harzburgites form *c.* 90 per cent of the Mantle Sequence outcrop, although in the southwestern part of the Akapnou Forest substantial areas (5 km²) of massive dunite, forming a stratigraphic unit up to 200 m thick, overlie the harzburgites. The harzburgites display a more or less well-developed tectonite fabric, as described above; variations of its apparent intensity having been noted by Murton (1986*b*). Widespread serpentinization and/or shearing, however, often make measurement of this fabric difficult, for which reason lineations have rarely been recorded on a routine basis in

the STTFZ. Any fabric that might have been visible in dunites has been destroyed with their pervasive serpentinization.

The orientations of foliations from the western LFC and Akapnou Forest Mantle Sequence outcrops are shown in Fig. 4. Substantial brittle deformation, which has locally disrupted and obliterated the penetrative fabric orientations, is particularly important in the southern part of the western LFC, which has been affected by Miocene deformation in the Yerasa fold and thrust belt (Bear & Morel 1960; Robertson 1977; Murton 1986*b*). Elsewhere foliations tend to show only gradual changes in trend on a regional scale, as has been reported from the main Troodos massif (George 1978; Nicolas & Violette 1982) and other ophiolite complexes (e.g. Oman: Bartholemew 1983; Ceuleneer 1986; Ceuleneer *et al.* 1988; Nicolas 1989). We think it probable that the gradual difference in strike between the northeastern and western sub-areas of the western LFC mantle sequence outcrops, and between these and the Akapnou Forest outcrops, are original features; therefore, that they record the changing trajectory of asthenospheric flow.

With the lack of lineation data and sense of shear determinations our knowledge of the kinematics of mantle flow in the STTFZ is necessarily limited, and the significance of the changing orientation of tectonite fabrics across the LFC cannot be addressed in any detail. Nevertheless, Murton (1986*b*) speculated that the swing in mantle flow fabric from NE–SW to E–W across

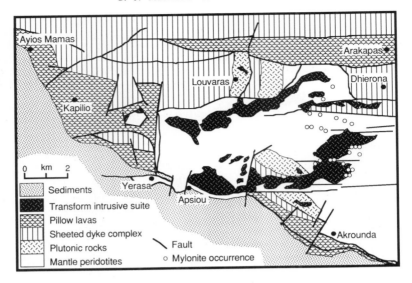

**Fig. 5.** Highly simplified geological map of the western LFC, showing the location of the principal Transform Sequence intrusions and the occurrences of mylonite shear zones.

the west to northeastern LFC sub-areas (Fig. 4) might either represent part of a fossilized mantle diapir uprising into a transtensional transform setting, or alternatively be due to drag in a dextral transcurrent transform system. The latter scenario has geological precedent, from descriptions of mantle flow fabrics from transform faults preserved in other ophiolites: in the Bogota peninsula, New Caledonia (Prinzhofer & Nicolas 1980); in Antalya, Turkey (Reuber 1985); and in the possible transform structure of Wadi Tayin in the Oman ophiolite (Nicolas *et al.* 1988*a, b*; Nicolas 1989). The significance of the average trending NW–SE foliation of the Akapnou Forest, however, is not clear in either of these scenarios, and both must be considered speculative.

*Mylonites*

Multifarious definitions exist for the term 'mylonite' (Lapworth 1885; White 1976, 1982; Sibson 1977; White *et al.* 1980, 1986); here we use the term to describe those cohesive, foliated shear zones within which substantial plastic deformation and/or dynamic recrystallization can be inferred, from either field or petrographic criteria. Although it could be argued that some of the schistose serpentinite shear zones that traverse the lower stratigraphic levels of the STTFZ might also fit this definition (cf. Norrell *et al.* 1989), the serpentinite shears are sufficiently distinct in their appearance and deformation

style to warrant separate description (see below).

Mylonite shear zones are rare in the STTFZ, having been recognized only in the core of the western LFC (Murton 1986*a,b*). They are always spatially associated with Transform Sequence gabbroic intrusions, in some cases bounding parts of the plutons (Fig. 5). In other instances protomylonitic inclusions occur within undeformed gabbros close to the margins of the intrusions (Murton 1986*b*). Most of the mylonite shear zones cut the surrounding Mantle Sequence peridotites (and therefore post-date the high-temperature foliation in the harzburgite tectonites) but, significantly, have mafic mineralogies themselves. Low strain remnants within a mylonite shear zone at map reference (5)0705 (38)5278 show the protolith to be a dolerite identical to the abundant Transform Sequence mafic dykes that emanate from the gabbro plutons. This suggests that the mafic mylonites within the harzburgites represent deformed remnants of Transform Sequence mafic intrusions that were injected into actively-deforming shear zones.

In the field, the mylonites are marked by the development of planar and linear fabrics of markedly variable intensity, in extreme cases forming ultramylonites. Their senses of shear are often apparent from obliquities of the fabric or from rotation of passive markers (Figs 6, 7, and see below). Individual mylonitic shears are typically of the order of a few metres wide, but may form belts over a hundred metres across, consisting of several mylonite bands separating zones of lower strain. The mylonite shear zones do not appear to be laterally continuous: we have been unable to trace them for more than a kilometre along strike. The largest such mylonite zone (at map reference (5)070 (38)527, *c.* 3 km WSW of Dhierona; Fig. 5) is approximately 100 m wide. It has mafic mineralogy, is sharp-sided, and is mantled at both margins by zones of widespread, lower temperature, later serpentinite shearing that form a composite vertical E–W-trending deformation zone at least 500 m wide.

**Fig. 6.** Mylonite shear zone in Transform Sequence gabbro. The sharp contact with the less-deformed wall of the shear zone indicates efficient strain weakening. Clockwise obliquity of the mylonite foliation with respect to the walls indicates sinistral shear. Viewed vertically downwards, with axis of the camera in the plane of the E–W-trending vertical foliation and perpendicular to the sub-horizontal lineation. Western Limassol Forest ((5)0792 (38)5152).

**Fig. 7.** E–W-trending mylonitic shear zone in Transform Sequence gabbro. Note the anticlockwise rotation by drag of the coarser-grained mylonitic fabric in the gabbro (above) into the higher strain ultramylonite (below), indicating sinistral shear. Western Limassol Forest ((5)0792 (38)5152).

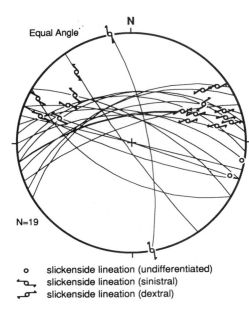

N=19

o        slickenside lineation (undifferentiated)
        slickenside lineation (sinistral)
        slickenside lineation (dextral)

**Fig. 8.** Equal angle lower hemisphere projection of mylonite shear zones from the locality (5)084 (38)517, western LFC. The great circle traces delineate the strikes and dips of the shear zones, and the white circles the slickenside lineations. The senses of shear are indicated where known.

The mylonites in the STTFZ have a strong preferred E–W orientation. Their average trend where they traverse the Transform Sequence gabbros is 085°, and very similar (at 091°) in harzburgite. In general they are steeply-dipping and have sub-horizontal lineations, with consistent sinistral senses of motion identified at outcrop. A more detailed examination of several of these mylonite zones at map references (5)085 (38)520 and (5)084 (38)513 reveals a mean foliation striking 080° and dipping 50° north, and mean lineation plunging 5° eastward (Fig. 8). Although the great majority of these mylonite shears show a sinistral shear sense, either from field or petrographic observation (see below, and Figs 6, 7, 9, 10), it is noteworthy that three samples show an unequivocal **dextral** sense in orientated thin section (samples 90CC15, 129B and 192B; Fig. 11). These dextral samples lie within and are exactly parallel to other structures in a zone of near E–W mylonitic shears at the margin of a large gabbro intrusion to the SSW of Dhierona (Fig. 5) that can be traced along strike for several hundred metres and which otherwise exhibit sinistral shear senses throughout (Fig. 8). It is thus extremely unlikely that they represent antithetic structures rotated into parallelism with the shear zone. Although under many circumstances the observation of a few conflicting shear sense indicators during the

**Fig. 9.** Brittle deformation of competent grains in plastically-deforming mylonitic matrix. The dextral sense of shear along antithetic fractures oblique to the foliation is opposite to the overall sinistral sense of shear in the rock (cf. Simpson & Schmid 1983, fig 9b). Sample 90CC16; plane polarized light; field of view 3.5 mm.

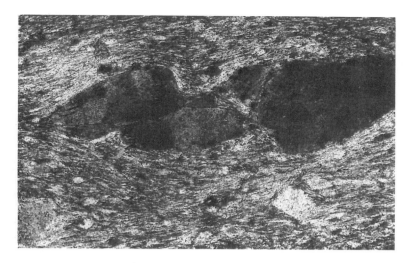

**Fig. 10.** Brittle deformation of porphyroclast (with undulose extinction) in plastically-deforming mylonitic matrix. Dextral antithetic and sinistral synthetic shear senses indicate unequivocal sinistral motion. Sample 203B; crossed polars; field of view 1.0 mm.

**Fig. 11.** Ribbon mylonite (above) and ultramylonite (below), cross-cut by post-kinematic chlorite vein. The ribbon mylonite fabric is being dragged clockwise into the ultramylonite and indicates dextral shear (White *et al.* 1986). Sample 90CC15; plane polarized light; field of view 3.5 mm.

kinematic analysis of a set of structures may not be deemed important, it is shown below that the overwhelming evidence is for dextral shear along the STTFZ. This clearly requires explanation and is therefore discussed at the end of this paper.

Deformation in mylonitic shear zones is accommodated by dynamic recrystallization and neomineralization processes (White *et al.* 1980).

Microfabric variations observed in petrographic thin section are interpreted as resulting from differences in mineralogy, total shear strain, strain rate and temperature. In general, the grain size of mylonites is reduced with increasing shear strain and strain rate and, to some extent, with decreasing temperature (Mercier *et al.* 1977; White *et al.* 1980). Complexities of fabric may be introduced in polymineralic mylonites (as with

the examples described herein) due to the differing rheological behaviours of the different constituent minerals. It is not the intention of this
paper to examine in detail fabric development
within the mylonites of the STTFZ, suffice to say
that the samples studied here obviously formed
under a range of temperature and strain conditions.

Discrete shear bands are common in many
Transform Sequence gabbros. Their hydrous
mineralogy, with green amphibole, suggests an
important role for water and temperature conditions estimated by Murton (1986b) to be in
the range 400–800°C. The presence of chlorite
within the matrix of some samples suggests that
deformation of these mylonites either took place
or continued at lower temperatures. Increasing
shear strain is indicated by an increase in the
proportion of fine-grained dynamically recrystallized matrix and/or the ribbon-like elongation
of plastically-deforming mineral phases (upper
part of Fig. 11). The end product of this deformation is an ultramylonite, in which the grain
size has been reduced to the submicroscopic (e.g.
the lower part of Fig. 11). Obliquity of fabric
and other internal structures observed in orientated thin sections of the mylonites, cut perpendicular to the foliation and parallel to the
stretching lineation, can indicate the slip sense of
the shear zone, complementing sense of shear
determinations made from outcrop observations.

## Serpentinite shear zones

Serpentinite shear zones are the principal transform-related structures in the Mantle Sequence
of the STTFZ, both in the western Limassol
Forest and in the Akapnou Forest. Most often
they form E–W-trending, vertical features (see
below), but may also bound brittlely-deformed
Axis Sequence blocks that have been incorporated into the transform zone. These shear zones
are, on average, some 20 m in width, but may
exceptionally be up to 500 m wide. They can be
traced along strike for 2 km directly, or intermittently for up to 8 km (Fig. 12). They comprise
tectonic mélanges, consisting of blocks, usually
phacoidal in shape, of exotic lithologies: principally harzburgite, dunite and pyroxenite, but
including wehrlites, gabbros and dolerites of
either the Transform or Axis Sequences, set in a
matrix of scaley schistose serpentinite (Fig. 13).
In the field the sheared serpentinite matrix has a
characteristic blue-silver sheen. The clasts range
in size from a few centimetres to approximately
50 m; the larger blocks are most commonly
pyroxenite or gabbro (often rodingitized), which
appear to be mechanically the most competent.
The serpentinite shears locally overprint, and
therefore post-date, the mylonite shear zones. At
map reference (5)082 (38)530 (2.5 km SW of
Dhierona) a serpentinite shear zone contains
clasts of a mafic mylonite. Serpentinite shears
both deform and are cut by Transform Sequence

**Fig. 12.** Outcrop of near-vertical, E–W-trending serpentinite shear zone. The schistose serpentinite fabric
within the shear zone is orientated slightly anticlockwise from the orientation of the shear zone as a whole
and suggests dextral strike-slip motion. Laxia tou Mavrou, 1.8 km south of Dhierona ((5)0950 (38)5180).

dykes (Fig. 14), confirming the synchroneity of transform tectonism and magmatism.

**Fig. 13.** Detail of a typical highly deformed serpentinite shear zone. Harzburgite and dunite clasts are incorporated into a scaley serpentinous matrix, whose proportion becomes greater with increasing shear strain. The fabric is characteristically irregular, and modified easily by later faulting, making analysis of the kinematics of the shear zones difficult.

The shear zones have a strong E–W preferred orientation, and are mostly near-vertical (Fig. 15). Sub-horizontal striae, often preserved on the surfaces of clasts, on internal fractures within clasts, and occasionally on the walls of the shear zone where well-defined (Fig. 16a), suggest a predominantly strike-slip mode of displacement. The schistose serpentinite foliation is usually very irregular, being deflected around blocks and modified with apparent ease by later cross-cutting fault lines, or by the plastic flow or protrusion of serpentinite (described below). Shear sense determinations, derived either from sigmoidal shears or 'S–C structures' (Berthé et al. 1979) within the matrix of the shear zone (Fig. 17), or from offset of brittlely disaggregated clasts (Gass et al. 1993), indicate dextral movement across the vast majority of the serpentinite shear zones. This dextral sense of movement is contrary to that originally deduced by Murton (1986b), and contrasts with the predominant sinistral shear sense of the mylonites. Possible reasons for the disparity in shear sense are discussed below.

Serpentinite shear zones not only affect the Mantle Sequence but occasionally separate Axis Sequence crustal lithologies. At a roadside locality, approximately 2 km south of Dhierona (map reference (5)090 (38)542), schistose serpentinite containing phacoidal blocks of harzburgite and dunite fills an E–W lineament separating Sheeted Dyke Complex from Axis Sequence high-level gabbro (Murton & MacLeod 1987). Its presence at this elevated stratigraphic level implies that some upward flow or protrusion of the serpentinite mélange has occurred. Murton (1986b) calculated that the density contrast

**Fig. 14.** Undeformed dolerite dyke intruding serpentinite shear zone, western LFC.

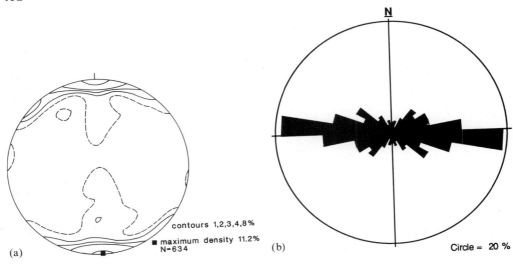

(a)

(b)                                                                   Circle = 20 %

contours 1,2,3,4,8%
■ maximum density 11.2%
N=634

**Fig. 15.** Orientations of serpentinite shear zones from the Limassol Forest Complex. (**a**) Lower hemisphere equal area projection of poles to planes of shear zones. Note that most shear zones are near vertical; (**b**) rose diagram of the same data emphasizing their strong E–W preferred orientation.

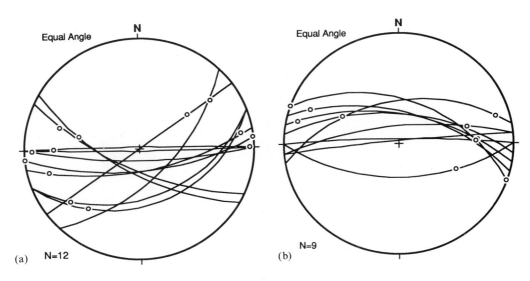

**Fig. 16.** (**a**) Equal-angle lower hemisphere projection of slickenside lineations on the walls of a serpentinite shear zone. The lineations are evidence for strike-slip motion; S–C fabrics within the adjacent schistose serpentinite indicate dextral shear. Akapnou Forest (1909 5205). (**b**) Equal-angle lower hemisphere projection of slickenside lineations on an E–W-trending fault plane in lavas/sheeted dykes, Akapnou village (1726 5539). The low-angle slickensides indicate strike-slip-dominated motion, and kinematic indicators nearby suggest dextral motion.

**Fig. 17.** Sigmoidal shear fabric indicating dextral shear in serpentinite shear zone near Vasa, Akapnou Forest.

between the serpentine and overlying crustal lithologies could have been sufficient to allow protrusion of serpentine to high crustal levels or even onto the sea floor. Seemingly analogous serpentinite protrusions have been reported from fracture zones in the Equatorial Atlantic (Bonatti 1976; Bonatti & Honnorez 1976). Such a mechanism is thought to be responsible for the local presence of serpentinite clasts within volcano-sedimentary breccias in the Extrusive Sequence in the vicinity of Akrounda; although since such clasts have not been reported from other localities within the STTFZ, or elsewhere in the Troodos ophiolite, protrusion of serpentinite onto the sea floor is thought to have been a rare phenomenon within the STTFZ.

Murton (1986b) and MacLeod (1988) demonstrated that serpentinization of ultramafic lithologies within the STTFZ commenced at a very early stage in its oceanic history. In the serpentinite shear zones, strain was clearly taken up by deformation of pre-existing serpentine. A decrease in the degree of serpentinization in unsheared wall-rocks away from the shear zones suggests that the latter may have acted as conduits along which sea water was introduced.

Experimental studies of the deformation of serpentinite (Bowen & Tuttle 1949; Raleigh & Paterson 1965) have shown that, at low temperatures and low–moderate pressures (0.1–0.2 GPa), dry serpentinized peridotite has an ultimate strength comparable to that of granite; however, at some temperature in the range 300–600°C (depending on confining pressure) it suddenly becomes very brittle and undergoes a very rapid reduction in cohesive strength, which marks the partial dehydration of serpentine to forsterite. The water so released enables local pore fluid pressures to build up, and allows a consequent reduction in overall confining pressure and frictional resistance to sliding (Murrell & Ismail 1976; Sibson 1977). The presence of pore fluid in a system below the dehydration temperature (as may be postulated in a tensional or transtensional oceanic regime) has the potential to decrease effective confining pressures still more, and further extend the range of pressure–temperature conditions under which serpentine behaves in a weak fashion (Hubbert & Rubey 1959; Murrell & Ismail 1976). It is clear that serpentinite in the shear zones of the STTFZ, particularly those within which protrusion has occurred, had a very low effective shear strength. In the most intensely deformed serpentinite shear zones, which have the highest proportion of scaley serpentinous matrix and most tectonically-rounded phacoidal clasts, boundaries between the shear zones and relatively undeformed wall-rocks are generally well-defined, implying that strain weakening was also an efficient tectonic process (MacLeod 1988).

### Brittle deformation styles in the Axis Sequence crust

Deformation of the styles described was confined principally to outcrops of the STTFZ Mantle Sequence and accompanying Transform Sequence intrusives. The expressions of these structures in the upper parts of the crustal sequence have frequently been modified by later tectonism, particularly in the eastern part of the LFC (MacLeod 1988, 1990). Mylonites have not been reported from the Axis Sequence crust within the STTFZ, although serpentinite shear zones often bound blocks of crustal sequence lithologies in the western LFC. Evidence for ductile deformation is extremely rare: it has been observed in the layered plutonic sequence, either in thin section or in outcrop, but appears similar to the style of deformation of the plutonic rocks of the main Troodos massif, which is ascribed to spreading-related processes (e.g. Malpas *et al.* 1989). One possible exception that might be transform-related is an E–W-trending, moderately-dipping contact between two apparently distinct units of plastically-deformed layered plutonics, 2 km south of Kellaki, across which dextral shear appears to have taken place (MacLeod 1988).

**Fig. 18.** Typical appearance of fault brecciated Sheeted Dyke Complex, Parsata. Unsorted, generally sub-angular fragments are set in an indurated matrix of comminuted diabase rock flour. Occasional shear strands may be visible, but more frequently the breccia is massive. Zones of such brecciation may be hundreds of metres in width and be traceable in an E–W direction for several kilometres.

Brittle deformation of the crustal sequence is, in contrast, exceptionally intense within most parts of the STTFZ. It is most markedly displayed in the Sheeted Dyke Complex outcrops of the AFB, described below. Most Sheeted Dyke Complex across virtually all of the AFB, and at least the northern parts of the LFC, has been fault brecciated to a greater or lesser degree. The extent of disruption is commonly such that fault breccias, with no dyke margins recognizable, predominate over distances of hundreds of metres or even a few kilometres. Sheeted dyke fault breccias are composed of unsorted angular to subrounded fragments, generally 0.01–0.5 m

in size, set in an indurated matrix of cataclastic rock flour (Fig. 18). The breccias are essentially monomictic, although occasional microgabbro clasts have been observed. Polishing marks or striations on some clast surfaces demonstrate their relationship to faulting. Simonian (1975) reported difficulty in distinguishing these fault breccias from sheeted dyke scree breccias in the field, although he was able to show that, in general, the scree breccias are more well-packed, more frequently polymictic (sometimes containing lava clasts), and more lenticular in their outcrop form than the fault breccias.

**Fig. 19.** Fault brecciation at the margin of a dyke within the Sheeted Complex, Parsata, eastern LFC. Such inter-dyke brecciation is common in the sheeted dykes, both within and adjacent to the transform fault zone. In many instances it appears to have been responsible for accommodating a significant proportion of the block rotations documented in the vicinity of the STTFZ.

Fault breccias grade in and out of occasional areas of more coherent Sheeted Dyke Complex. In these more coherent areas brecciation (often indurated) at dyke margins may be the only sign of deformation (Fig. 19). In the NE-striking sheeted dyke outcrops of the Troodos and Anti-Troodos plates, which border the STTFZ to the

**Fig. 20.** Minor E–W-trending fault plane near the Arakapas Dam, typical of many observed in the Extrusive Sequence and Sheeted Dyke Complex. Gently plunging slickenside lineations indicate strike-slip displacement. Sense of shear determinations on comparable structures suggest dextral motion.

north and south respectively, such inter-dyke breccias are common, and appear to have played an important role in accommodating vertical-axis block rotations (see below). Within the STTFZ itself the most intensely brecciated areas form E–W elongate linear zones that may be traced laterally up to 7 km. Such zones are up to several hundred metres wide, and anastomose along strike. They may also be accompanied by discrete fault planes or sets of fault planes, upon which sub-horizontal slickensides (Fig. 20 and Fig. 16b) occur, and which occasionally preserve evidence for dextral motion (cf. Lapierre *et al.* 1988; Grand *et al.* 1993). There is little doubt that the fault brecciation zones are the loci of significant strike-slip displacement.

The colour of the fault breccias varies from blue, through grey, to red/orange, depending upon the degree of oxidation. Many of the fault zones in the Arakapas Fault Belt are strongly Fe-oxide stained, although no major sulphide deposits have been discovered along transform-parallel structures (Adamides 1980). In thin sections, undeformed alteration minerals in the breccias demonstrate that hydrothermal activity post-dated deformation (Simonian 1975). More evidence for the early nature of the E–W wrench faulting is the observation that Transform Sequence lavas and intervolcanic sediments are frequently superposed directly on the fault-brecciated sheeted dyke basement (Gass *et al.*

1993). Simonian & Gass (1978) noted that the lava and sediment basins were often sited on the more brecciated portions of the Sheeted Dyke Complex in the AFB, whereas the palaeo-highs were generally more coherent.

Significant fault brecciation and strike-slip faulting appear to be most widespread in the AFB, i.e. in the northern part of the STTFZ. The geometry of deformation there is complex, with brecciated fault strands anastomosing along strike and isolating less-deformed elevated blocks and subsided basins. The style of this deformation appears to be characteristic of major strike-slip fault systems, within which less-deformed pips or 'duplexes' naturally develop between braided fault strands (Woodcock & Fischer 1986). In such systems transpressional or transtensional stresses are applied to the pre-existing oblique structures, leading to the relative uplift or subsidence of the duplexes respectively on a localized scale within the fault zone. Potentially, both transpressional and transtensional types of duplex can form within the same fault system at the same time, and their presence does not necessarily imply overall transpression or transtension on a regional scale.

In addition to the major fault brecciated zones associated with strike-slip faulting, a very large number of other faults, with a variety of orientations, occur within the STTFZ. Although many of these are associated with later post-volcanic deformation (MacLeod 1990), many others were active at a very early stage in the ocean-floor evolution of the complex in and adjacent to the transform zone. These faults appear to have normal displacements, throwing down on their south sides into the transform zone. Lavas are often brought down against Sheeted Dyke Complex, and where this occurs a substantial change in present-day relief is usually present. The timing of the normal displacement is not well constrained on the majority of the structures, and it is indeed possible that some of it may be associated with, for example, reactivation during the Tertiary–Quaternary uplift of Mount Olympus. Some evidence exists for reactivation in both reverse and strike-slip senses, probably in the late Cretaceous (Gass et al. 1993). At Perapedhi, however, E–W normal faults separating Sheeted Dyke Complex to the north from the Transform Extrusive Sequence to the south are associated with sheeted dyke scree breccias, against which lavas of the Transform Extrusive Sequence are banked. These have clearly built away from the fault scarps (Simonian 1975), and hence must be ocean-floor phenomena.

Analogous E–W-trending high-angle normal faults, but throwing down to the north, have been recognized along the southern margin of the STTFZ, within the eastern part of the Limassol Forest (Adamides 1980; MacLeod 1988, 1990). The two most important of these are the Mavridhia and Vasilikos Reservoir Faults, exposed in the vicinity of the Kalavasos Mines. These structures clearly controlled lava and sediment accumulation, with the Vasilikos Reservoir Fault forming the southern faulted margin to the 275 m + thick Dhrapia volcaniclastic sediment sequence (MacLeod 1990). The equivalent thickness of the deposit on the southern side of the fault is only 19 m; hence the Vasilikos Reservoir Fault has a cumulative normal component of displacement in excess of 250 m down on its northern side. The Vasilikos Reservoir and Mavridhia Faults are the most southerly originally transform-parallel structures identified in the eastern Limassol Forest, and limit the extent of the intervolcanic sediments to the south. For this reason MacLeod (1988, 1990) took them to mark the southern boundary to the STTFZ.

The observations presented above suggest that transform-parallel faults with normal or significant components of normal displacement stepped down towards the locus of principal strike-slip displacement, both to the north and south of the transform zone. It would indeed appear that the normal offset on these faults was largely responsible for the creation of the bathy-metric trough that was associated with the transform. The zone of most intense strike-slip faulting, or 'principal transform displacement zone', was probably little more than 1 km wide and was situated, at least at the eastern exposed end of the STTFZ, closer to the northern margin of the transform zone, largely coincident with the AFB. Overall, the transform trough at this longitude was estimated by MacLeod (1988, 1990) to have been probably 5 km in width. The structure of the STTFZ here, with a relatively narrow principal strike-slip displacement zone set somewhere within a broader overall trough, is directly comparable to most modern oceanic transform faults, be they low slip-rate (e.g. Vema: Macdonald et al. 1986) or high slip-rate (e.g. Clipperton: Gallo et al. 1986, Kastens et al. 1986; or Quebrada: Lonsdale 1978; Searle 1983) systems.

At the longitude of the western Limassol Forest the STTFZ appears to be wider than at its eastern exposed end. Important differences along strike between the eastern and western parts of the Limassol Forest Complex (MacLeod 1988, 1990; Murton 1990) complicate the relatively simple scenario outlined above. These differences, and their significance for the ocean-floor geometry of the STTFZ, are discussed at the end of this paper.

## Block rotations in and adjacent to the transform zone

It is evident from geological maps of the southern margin of the Troodos ophiolite (Gass et al. 1991a,b) that many of the fault-bounded blocks of the axis crustal sequence present within the STTFZ have differing orientations with respect to each other in the dips of their lava sequences, azimuths of their sheeted dykes, layered plutonics, etc. Bearing in mind the generally consistent and regular attitude of the crustal sequence on the northern flank of the Troodos massif, away from the effects of transform faulting, the highly irregular trends from the STTFZ suggest that the original attitudes of many of the axis-generated crustal blocks have been modified by rotational processes. Although it has been shown (MacLeod 1988, 1990) that the disposition of the crustal blocks, particularly in the eastern part of the LFC, is to some extent the result of post-volcanic tectonism, field relationships (see below) confirm that some disruption must be transform fault-related. The only means by which these purported rotations can be addressed in any quantitative way is by study of the palaeomagnetism of the crustal sequence rocks.

## Structural use of palaeomagnetism

In Cyprus, Vine & Moores (1969) and Moores & Vine (1971) found that primary remanent magnetization vectors isolated from samples at all stratigraphic levels within the Troodos massif consistently pointed westwards rather than towards the north. To explain this, they concluded that the entire ophiolite had been rotated as a coherent body by approximately 90° in an anticlockwise sense. The mechanisms and regional tectonic implications of the rotation of the 'Cyprus microplate' have been discussed by Clube & Robertson (1986), MacLeod (1990), and Murton (1990).

For the purposes of identifying rotations on a smaller scale, associated with the STTFZ, the significance of Vine & Moores' work is that a well-constrained 'Troodos Magnetization Vector' (TMV), with declination of 276° and inclination of 32°, is known. This can be treated as a reference vector, and deviations from it ascribed to structural rotations. In general, workers on Cyprus have assumed that rotation associated with the STTFZ has been about vertical axes, and thus simply assumed the difference in declination from 276° to be the tectonic rotation (e.g. Clube 1985; Clube & Robertson 1986; Bonhommet *et al.* 1988; MacLeod *et al.* 1990). However, a more sophisticated geometrical analysis has been devised by Allerton (1988) that allows calculation of inclined axes of rotation (Allerton & Vine, 1987). It is therefore useful in domains where oblique-slip faulting is suspected, and eliminates the declination errors inherent in making the simple strike-parallel bedding corrections made in most geometrical analyses of palaeomagnetic data (MacDonald 1980; Allerton & Vine 1987). It has been applied subsequently in Allerton (1989*a*) and Allerton & Vine (1990, 1991) for that portion of the Troodos Plate lying immediately north of the STTFZ (see below), and by Allerton & MacLeod (unpublished data, reported in part in MacLeod 1988 and Allerton 1988) for samples from the STTFZ and Anti-Troodos plate.

## Synmagmatic block rotations within the STTFZ: field evidence

Field evidence was presented by Murton (1986*b*) and MacLeod (1988) for the synmagmatic disruption and rotation of Axis Sequence crustal blocks within the STTFZ; this rotation they deduced was transform-related. MacLeod (1988, 1990), for example, described a progressive increase in the intensity of faulting and disruption of the Anti-Troodos Axis Sequence crust in a northerly direction (towards the AFB) within the eastern part of the LFC. At Palaeodhrapia the Lower Pillow Lava (LPL) sequence has been tilted steeply towards the south-southwest prior to the eruption of the Transform Sequence or Upper Pillow Lavas (UPL). Field mapping (MacLeod 1988; Gass *et al.* 1991*b*) clearly shows that the older lavas at this locality are contiguous with Anti-Troodos plate crust to the south rather than the Troodos plate to the north. It seems likely that most, if not all, of the other disrupted axis crustal blocks in the LFC were also generated at the Anti-Troodos ridge axis, and then subsequently incorporated into the transform zone.

Further evidence for synmagmatic block deformation and tilt rotation comes from the Kapilio area, at the northwestern margin of the LFC, where Murton (1986*b*) has documented a progressive unconformity within the transform lava sequence. The oldest lavas, to the northeast of Kapilio village, are overturned and dip steeply northeast; near the village itself they become vertical; and in the youngest parts of the sequence to the southwest of the village dips as low as 60° to the southwest are recorded (Fig. 21). Detailed study by Murton (1986*b*) of volcaniclastic Transform Sequence sediments intercalated with these lavas indicates a structural control along NE–SW faults during lava extrusion and sediment deposition, but that tilting of the sequence took place along an axis with NW–SE-trending horizontal component.

Another crustal block, deformed at a very early stage, is in the Venetou area *c.* 3 km north of Mathikoloni and 3–4 km east of Apsiou (eastings [050–070] northings [500–520] ). Disposition of outcrop suggests that a coherent crustal section, from the petrological Moho to the level of the Sheeted Dyke Complex, has been folded into a gently plunging open syncline about a WNW–ESE axis (Fig. 22). The syncline appears asymmetric, with the northern limb dipping at *c.* 60° to the south and the southern limb *c.* 20° to the north (Murton 1986*b*). Poles to planes of early sheeted dykes are distributed in a weak girdle pattern consistent with folding about an axis plunging 11° towards the ESE (Fig. 23). The entire crustal sequence has been invaded by a swarm of Transform Sequence picrite dykes, often multiple, with a tightly-clustered mean strike of 043° and dip of 86°SE ($\alpha_{95}$ cone of confidence of pole to plane = 2.9°; Fig. 23b). Although the pole to plane of the dykes is close to the axis of the fold, the consistency of orientation of these picrite dykes suggests that their emplacement post-dated folding of the Axis Sequence crust. Moreover, a second slightly

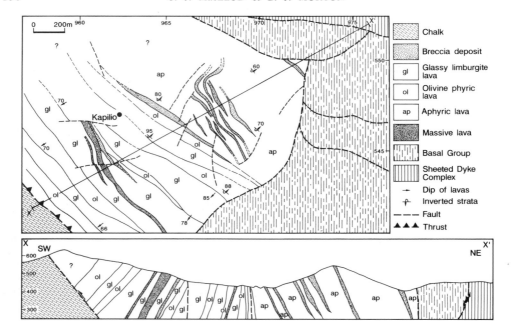

**Fig. 21.** Map and cross-section of the volcano-sedimentary sequence in the Kapilio area, western Limassol Forest, showing a progressive unconformity in the Transform Extrusive Sequence (Murton 1986*b*). The unconformity implies that synvolcanic disruption and tilting was affecting this part of the transform fault zone.

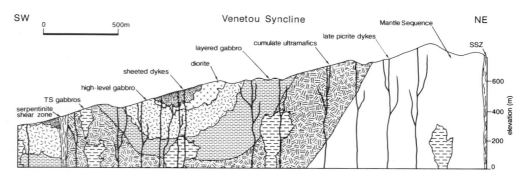

**Fig. 22.** Sketch cross-section of the Venetou area, *c.* 3 km north of Mathikoloni, western Limassol Forest, showing the folding of the Axis Sequence crust into a syncline prior to injection of Transform Sequence gabbros and picritic dykes (Murton 1986*b*).

younger cross-cutting dyke swarm recognized by Murton (1986*b*) **within** the Sheeted Dyke Complex of the Venetou area is also NE-trending, with mean strike of 046° and dip 87°SE, and $\alpha_{95}$ (pole to plane) = 6.4°, i.e. statistically identical to the later picrites (Fig. 23c). This further suggests that folding of the crustal sequence occurred between emplacement of the first and second generations of Sheeted Dyke Complex, in other words, extremely close to the (Anti-Troodos) ridge axis. Murton (1986*b*) speculated that this early folding was related to ocean-floor uplift of the central-western part of the Limassol Forest block (see below).

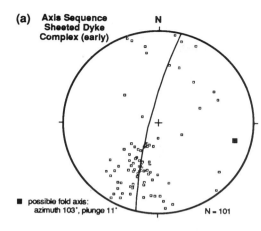

**(a) Axis Sequence Sheeted Dyke Complex (early)**

N

■ possible fold axis:
azimuth 103°, plunge 11°

N = 101

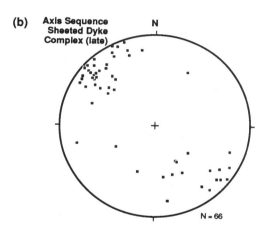

**(b) Axis Sequence Sheeted Dyke Complex (late)**

N

N = 66

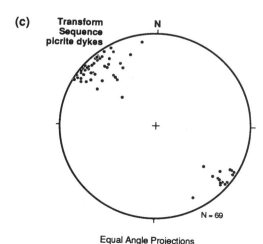

**(c) Transform Sequence picrite dykes**

N

N = 69

Equal Angle Projections
poles to planes

Cross-cutting sheeted dykes have been recognized elsewhere within the STTFZ. Although Simonian (1975) described dyke orientations in much of the AFB as random, detailed remapping in the AFB and the north of the LFC by Gass *et al.* (1993) has revealed domains of dykes with consistent orientation, often with intrusive relationships at their boundaries: in the Dhierona area, for example, dykes trend either E–W or N–S, the latter forming swarms of dykes tens of to a few hundreds of metres wide that cross-cut an earlier E–W sheeted complex (Fig. 24).

### Palaeomagnetic evidence for intra-transform block rotations

The first palaeomagnetic investigations specific to the STTFZ were made by Clube (1985) and Clube & Robertson (1986) as a minor part of a more regional study of Cyprus palaeomagnetism. They recorded 'anomalous' NW-declined stable remanent magnetization vectors, i.e. with declinations skewed clockwise from the westerly TMV reference direction, from three sites at Arakapas and Kapilio. These anomalous declinations, they suggested, recorded localized clockwise rotations of crustal blocks within the transform zone due to dextral strike-slip faulting. Measurement of westerly-directed magnetization vectors very similar to the TMV at sites from the Anti-Troodos plate (see below) suggested that these rotations were confined to the STTFZ.

The sites drilled by Clube and Robertson were taken from undeformed lava flows and volcaniclastic sediments that lie uncomformably on top of the brecciated sheeted dyke basement in the AFB, and thus deposited subsequent to the episode of deformation that gave rise to the brecciation (i.e. the main episode of strike-slip movement). The timing of these clockwise block rotations was therefore unconstrained and could have been due to post-volcanic processes (MacLeod 1988, 1990). More recent work by Morris

**Fig. 23.** Equal-angle lower hemisphere stereographic projections of poles to dyke planes from the Venetou syncline area, western Limassol Forest. Early sheeted dykes (**a**) show a spread of orientations compatible with the folding of the Axis Sequence inferred from outcrop relationships (Fig. 22); however, cross-cutting later generation sheeted dykes (**b**) and picrite dykes (**c**) have tightly clustered orientations identical to each other but distinct from the early dykes. This suggests that folding of the early sheeted dykes may well have occurred on the sea floor whilst the area was still in the transform domain.

**Fig. 24.** Cross-cutting sheeted dykes within the STTFZ near Dhierona. The photograph is taken looking northwards, and shows E–W-trending sheeted dykes at left (running from left to right) cut by a 100 m wide packet of N–S-trending dykes at right (running from top to bottom).

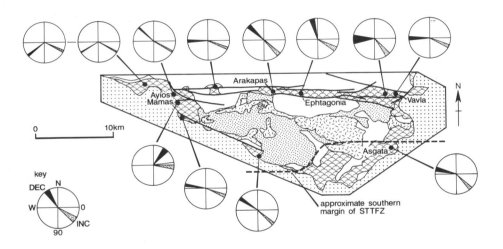

**Fig. 25.** Location of palaeomagnetic sites drilled in lavas and interlava sediments by Morris *et al.* (1990) in the STTFZ. The site at Asgata lies within the Anti-Troodos Plate, south of the southern margin of the transform zone as defined by MacLeod (1988, 1990). It shows a mean vector similar to the reference TMV (declination 276°, inclination 32°), indicating that no relative rotation has occurred between the Troodos and Anti-Troodos Plates. Northwesterly- or northerly-directed horizontal components of magnetic vectors in five sites in the STTFZ, indicative of clockwise block rotations, have been interpreted by Morris *et al.* (1990) as being due to dextral strike-slip along the STTFZ.

*et al.* (1990), also on lava flows and Transform Sequence volcaniclastic sediments, has confirmed Clube's (1985) original conclusions (Fig. 25); however, their discovery at one site in the AFB, near Ephtagonia, that cleaned magnetization directions obtained from pillow lavas are consistently skewed clockwise from cross-cutting dykes, suggests that at least some of the clock-

wise block rotation documented was indeed syn-volcanic, and therefore related to transform processes.

A reconnaissance study of the palaeomagnetism of the more coherent portions of the sheeted dyke basement in the STTFZ was made by Allerton (1988) and MacLeod (1988). They drilled two sites in the northeastern LFC, one

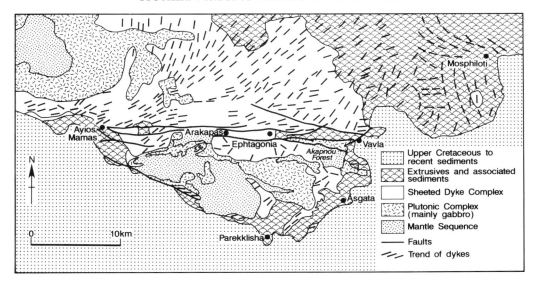

**Fig. 26.** Simplified geological map of the Limassol Forest Complex and the southern part of the main Troodos massif, showing the progressive change in the trend of dykes of the sheeted complex, from N–S (transform normal) to near transform parallel, over a distance of some 5–15 km as the transform is approached. Modified from Simonian & Gass (1978) and Morris *et al.* (1990).

north of Dhrapia ((5)2548 (38)5258) and the other between Kellaki and Akapnou ((5)1547 (38)5379) (Fig. 2). Using the geometrical analysis described in Allerton & Vine (1987) both sites suggest extreme clockwise rotations, of not less than 150°, about steeply plunging axes. The sites were drilled in metre-scale blocks of coherent dyke complex that were surrounded by extensive crush zones, all lying within the major strike-slip fault belt of the STTFZ. We suggest that such extreme rotations are a consequence of the small size of the blocks in relation to the overall size of the fault zone, in which they may be considered to be little more than clasts in a kilometre-scale fault breccia. This is discussed further at the end of this paper.

*Block rotations in the Troodos plate adjacent to the STTFZ*

One of the most striking and remarkable features of the internal structure of the Troodos plate is the progressive swing in the strike of the Sheeted Dyke Complex, over a radius of 5–10 km, from the average N–S orientation of the remainder of the massif, through NE–SW to E–W, as the STTFZ is approached (Fig. 26) (Wilson 1959; Moores & Vine 1971; Simonian 1975; Simonian & Gass 1978). Simonian & Gass (1978) noted that there was no noticeable change in the width or amount of internal deformation

of dykes from within the deviation zone. Three mechanisms for the origin of the change in dyke orientation have been proposed.

(1) One of two models proposed by Simonian & Gass (1978), suggesting that a requisite sigmoidal stress field could have been set up by the interaction of stresses created by spreading at two **sinistrally** offset ridge axes that were **not** connected by a transform fault; in this model the STTFZ would have been a dextral shear zone, but must have formed at a slightly later stage. In such a case the sigmoidal stress field, and hence the swing in dyke orientation, could not have been sustained once the transform had been initiated.

(2) Simonian & Gass's (1978) alternative model, that the sheeted dykes were originally N–S-trending throughout, and the swing in orientation was impressed upon those dykes adjacent to the STTFZ by clockwise block rotation due to fault drag along the (**dextrally**-slipping) transform (Fig. 27(b) ).

(3) The swing of sheeted dyke orientations is an original feature of the spreading fabric, due to dyke intrusion in a sigmoidal stress field at a **sinistrally**-slipping transform between dextrally-offset ridge crests (Varga & Moores 1985; Murton & Gass 1986; Murton 1986*a,b*; Moores *et al.* 1990; Dilek *et al.* 1990) (Fig. 27(a) ).

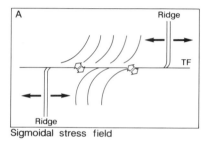

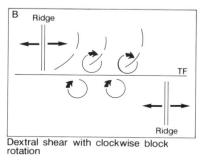

Sigmoidal stress field

Dextral shear with clockwise block rotation

**Fig. 27.** Sketches to explain two models for the origin of the dyke swing to the north of the STTFZ. In (**A**), dyke injection takes place in a sigmoidal stress field due to the interaction of transform and ridge stresses at the ridge–transform intersection. Ridge crests are dextrally offset and sinistral strike-slip occurs on the transform. In (**B**), however, dykes are injected perpendicular to the transform right up to the ridge–transform intersection; rotation of the dyke trend is instead effected by fault drag during dextral displacement along the transform, between sinistrally offset ridge crests.

All the models have geological precedent. Model (1) was proposed by Simonian & Gass (1978) following observation of sigmoidal structures in the Ethiopian Rift and Afar Depression by Gass & Gibson (1969). Curvature of the ridge tip into the active domain of transform faults (model (3)) is frequently observed at many modern oceanic fracture zones (e.g. Searle 1983). Fault block rotations at transform faults, as implied by model (2), appear to be much rarer, but have been reported from the Tjörnes fracture zone of northern Iceland (Young *et al.* 1985), from the Sovanco fracture zone on the Juan de Fuca rift (Cowan *et al.* 1987), and from the Bullard fracture zone of the Southern Atlantic (R. A. Livermore, pers. comm., 1990).

Implicit in the sigmoidal stress field hypothesis (model (3)) is that the NE–SW and E–W sheeted dykes are in their original orientations; in the fault drag model that these dykes were originally

near N–S and have been rotated subsequently. This being so, the models can be tested palaeomagnetically. Bonhommet *et al.* (1988) showed that the dyke magnetization vectors changed progressively from W-declined (i.e. close to the TMV) in N–S-trending dykes to N-declined in E–W-trending dykes (Fig. 28). They thus demonstrated beyond reasonable doubt that the fault drag hypothesis was correct. This was corroborated by an independent study at about the same time by Allerton (1988, 1989*a*) and Allerton & Vine (1990). These authors also recognized cross-cutting sheeted dyke relationships, with the older dykes rotated clockwise more than the younger, confirming that the rotations (and hence imposition of the dyke swing) were ocean-floor phenomena.

## Identification of a ridge-transform intersection in the Troodos plate

The processes that gave rise to the block rotations, and hence dyke swing, in the Troodos plate adjacent to the STTFZ have been investigated in detail by Allerton & Vine (1990, 1992) and MacLeod *et al.* (1990). MacLeod *et al.* (1990) noticed that the N–S to NE–SW to E–W dyke swing to the north of the westerly continuation of the Arakapas Fault Belt disappears a few kilometres to the west of Mandria (Fig. 29). Further west still, dykes trend uniformly N–S throughout and continue to do so across the entire western part of the ophiolite.

To the east of this boundary between domains of different dyke orientation, palaeomagnetic measurements show that the dyke swing is accompanied by a concomitant rotation of the magnetization vector, exactly as found by Bonhommet *et al.* (1988) and Allerton & Vine (1990); 060°–080°-trending sheeted dykes, for example, have near northerly-declined remanent magnetizations. A boss of massive microgabbro, at map reference ((4)813 (38)593), 3.5 km west of Mandria, cuts rotated lavas and NE-trending dykes but itself has a westerly-trending magnetic vector similar to the TMV; hence rotation of the dykes must have pre-dated its intrusion, and therefore that the rotation must have occurred at an early stage in the evolution of the oceanic crust (MacLeod *et al.* 1990).

To the west of the boundary, however, in the domain of uniform N–S dykes, all palaeomagnetic sites yield magnetization directions close to that of the TMV. Slightly steeper or shallower magnetic inclinations, together with the gentle easterly or westerly dips imparted to lava flows in the region, suggest that slight tilting about sub-horizontal axes has occurred, consistent

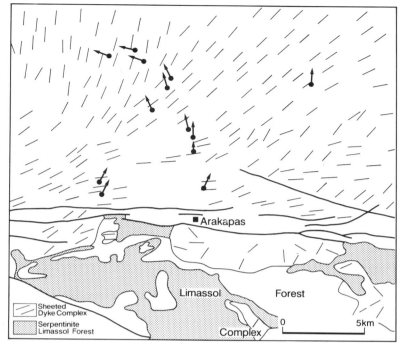

**Fig. 28.** Summary of the palaeomagnetic results of Bonhommet *et al.* (1988) in the zone of dyke deviation to the north of the Arakapas Fault Belt. These data show that N–S-striking sheeted dykes have magnetizations parallel to the westerly declined reference direction or 'Troodos Magnetization Vector' (Vine & Moores 1969; Moores & Vine 1971), but that as the strike of the sheeted dykes veers clockwise to NE–SW and E–W, their primary magnetizations are also slewed clockwise. This implies that the dyke swing is not an original feature of the spreading fabric, but that it has been impressed at a subsequent stage (as per Fig. 27 model B).

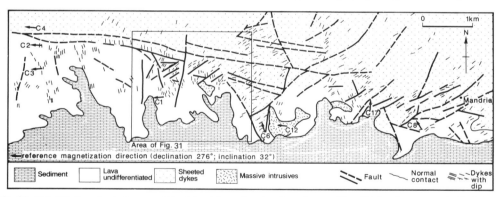

**Fig. 29.** Simplified geological map of the Mandria region (see location on Fig. 30). In the eastern half of the area sheeted dykes swing from N–S to NE–SW, as in the region to the north of the Arakapas Fault Belt (Fig. 26). In much the same way as demonstrated by Bonhommet *et al.* (1988; Fig. 28), MacLeod *et al.* (1990) showed that the magnetic vectors of these dykes (represented by arrows) were rotated clockwise from the Troodos reference direction; measurement of the Troodos reference vector, however, in a cross-cutting microgabbro boss (site C12 of MacLeod *et al.* 1990) confirms that these rotations were ocean-floor phenomena and almost certainly related to dextral movement on the STTFZ. In contrast, in the western half of the area of the figure, and everywhere further to the west, sheeted dykes do not change orientation as the transform is approached but remain N–S throughout. The magnetization vectors of the N–S dykes (sites C1–C4) are parallel to the reference direction and therefore have not been affected by any clockwise vertical axis rotation due to motion along the transform. The transition between the domains of NE–SW and N–S dykes lies in the boxed area, which is shown in more detail in Fig. 31 and discussed in the text.

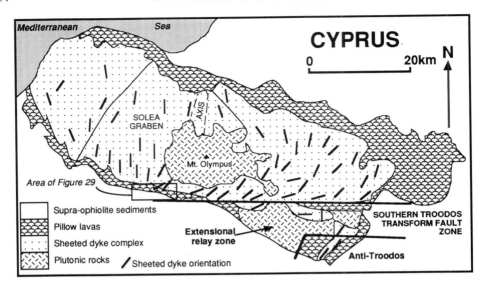

**Fig. 30.** Simplified geological map of the Troodos ophiolite, showing the principal features of the spreading geometry. The Solea graben (the area inside the fine lines) was identified by Varga & Moores (1985) and equated with an extinct ridge axis. MacLeod *et al.* (1990) observed that its intersection with the STTFZ approximately coincides with the disappearance of the clockwise swing of the Sheeted Dyke Complex and postulated that this area (boxed, and shown in more detail in Fig. 29) was therefore the site of a fossilized ridge–transform intersection. Also indicated is the approximate configuration of the STTFZ at the time of Transform Sequence magmatism, showing the widening of the transform-tectonized zone in the western LFC. The western LFC area is the site of ocean-floor disruption of the Axis Sequence crust, uplift of lithospheric mantle, and intrusion of geochemically distinct magmas into the active domain of the transform fault (shown diagrammatically in Fig. 33).

with minor normal faulting about N–S dyke-parallel structures observed in the field. The western domain does not, therefore, appear to have been affected by strike-slip faulting associated with the transform fault, but only to have suffered the effects of minor ridge-parallel normal faulting. No major displacive fault system exists between the two domains to account for the differing deformation styles, nor does the boundary appear to be the locus of a major intrusive contact between two different spreading systems, as has been proposed for superficially similar relationships in southeastern Troodos (Allerton 1989a; Allerton & Vine 1990, 1991, 1992). The relationship between the domains was therefore interpreted by MacLeod *et al.* (1990) to be a function of the original oceanic spreading fabric. They noted that the distribution of structural styles is exactly as predicted for a classic ridge–transform intersection (RTI), as originally envisaged by Wilson (1965). The eastern domain has been affected by dextral strike-slip faulting in the active portion of the transform fault, and the western domain affected by normal faulting only, in the inactive

'fracture zone' portion of the transform. MacLeod *et al.* (1990) therefore proposed that the region just west of Mandria represented an RTI, fossilized at the junction between the STTFZ and a ridge axis within the Troodos plate (Fig. 30).

The RTI lies close to the centre of the Solea graben, a 20–40 km wide N–S-trending (and hence ridge-parallel) fault-controlled ocean-floor structure within the Troodos massif that has previously been interpreted as a fossil axial valley (Varga & Moores 1985; Moores *et al.* 1990). It is defined by the tilt of rotated blocks such that sheeted dykes both to the east and west dip towards the graben axis, rotation having been effected about near-horizontal axes parallel to the axis of the graben (Allerton & Vine 1987; Hurst *et al.* 1992). Tilting of the dykes and lavas is thought to have taken place above a décollement horizon, the 'Kakopetria Detachment', located at the level of the base of the Sheeted Dyke Complex (Varga & Moores 1985, 1990; Varga 1991); these tectonic processes are believed to have resulted from continuing tectonic extension as magmatism at the spreading

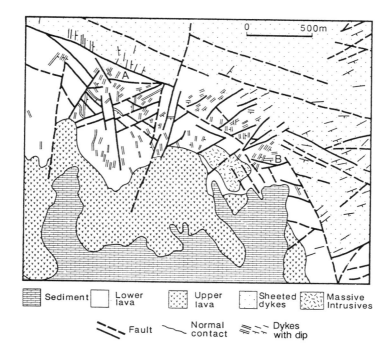

**Fig. 31.** Detailed geological map of the area (located on Fig. 29) of the boundary between the domains of rotated (NE–SW) and unrotated (N–S) dykes, suggested by MacLeod *et al.* (1990) to be the site of a ridge–transform intersection. The dyke swing dies away rapidly but not abruptly here over the space of 1–2 km in an E–W direction. Note the cross-cutting relationships between packets of dykes (e.g. at points A and B), always with an anticlockwise younging sense. See text for discussion.

axis waned (Allerton & Vine 1991; Varga 1991).

Detailed investigation of the boundary between the domains of rotated NE–SW and uniform N–S dykes has revealed much about the relationship between magmatism and tectonism at RTIs, and hence the origin of the swing of the sheeted dykes to the north of the STTFZ. The actual boundary between the two domains is situated some 4–5 km west of Mandria village. The changeover from unrotated (i.e. N–S) to fully rotated (ENE–WSW) dykes is rapid but not abrupt, occurring across a critical zone some 1–2 km wide, within which the LPL sequence is broken up by a network of small faults into blocks rarely coherent for more than 100–200 m across (Fig. 31). Many of the faults parallel to the NE and ENE-trending dykes are mineralized and have sinistral strike-slip senses of motion; conjugate NW-striking faults have a dextral sense (MacLeod *et al.* 1990).

Within the critical zone between the two dyke domains there is a spectrum of dyke orientations. A transition occurs from ENE–WSW-striking to N–S-striking dykes both from east to west and up-section within the LPL. Field observation shows that cross-cutting relationships occur: at point A (on Fig. 31), for example, packets of 010°-trending dykes cut 040°-trending dykes, and at point B 040°-striking dykes cut 060°–070° dykes. An anticlockwise younging sense is always observed. These observations, when taken with the palaeomagnetic evidence, suggest that bodily rotation of coherent packets of dykes clockwise from an original near N–S intrusion direction was occurring in this zone at the same time as dyke injection was taking place (MacLeod *et al.* 1990). Rotation was accommodated almost in situ by movement along closely spaced faults. The wedge-like form in map section of some of the packets of cross-cutting dykes (0–100 m in width, narrowing northwards; Fig. 31) may, by their very form, have helped to accommodate space problems created by the rotations.

The zone within which this rotation took place is only 1–2 km wide. To the east no further rotation is recorded in the dykes north of the transform: the dyke swing is fully established,

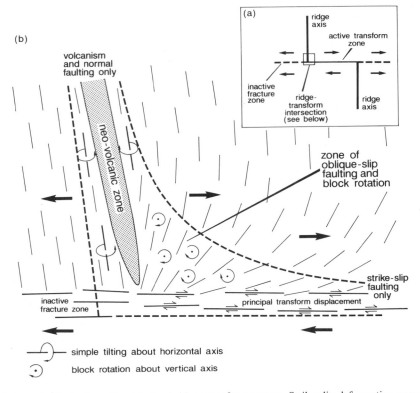

**Fig. 32. (a)** Schematic illustration of an idealized ridge–transform system. Strike-slip deformation occurs in the active transform zone between the two offet ridge crests; no strike slip occurs in the 'fracture zones' on either side as the crust is moving in the same direction. **(b)** Model for the Mandria ridge–transform intersection, based upon the field observations and palaeomagnetic studies of MacLeod *et al.* (1990) and theoretical modelling of Allerton (1989*b*). Block rotations occur predominantly at the ridge–transform itself rather than being accommodated progressively with increasing displacement along the transform.

and the radius of curvature of the dyke swing remains approximately constant along the entire 50 km exposed width of the massif (Fig. 30). This leads to the conclusion that the rotations documented by previous authors (Bonhommet *et al.* 1988; Allerton 1988, 1989*a*; Allerton & Vine 1990, 1991, 1992) occurred largely, if not totally, at the RTI itself, rather than having been accommodated with increasing displacement along the transform (MacLeod *et al.* 1990). This is consistent with and confirms relationships predicted in a recent generalized theoretical model of deformation processes at RTIs by Allerton (1989*b*). This model suggests that the strength of the lithosphere at a ridge–transform corner should increase rapidly as it moves away from the axis and cools, and so would soon become too rigid to accommodate major strains by fault block rotation. Distributed rotational deformation should therefore be largely confined to the inside corner of the RTI itself (Fig.

32), and subsequent strain be taken up by strike-slip faulting concentrated almost entirely within the transform valley or 'principal transform displacement zone'.

## Block rotations in the Anti-Troodos plate adjacent to the STTFZ

Earlier in this paper deformation of axis-generated crustal blocks in the STTFZ was discussed, and it was suggested that these blocks may have been originally generated at the Anti-Troodos ridge and subsequently incorporated into the transform zone. As identified by MacLeod (1988, 1990), a small fragment of Anti-Troodos plate crust (some 6–7 km wide in a N–S direction), that was not apparently incorporated into the transform, survives in the southeastern part of the LFC. A pronounced NE–SW structural grain is obvious in the strike of both the Sheeted Dyke Complex and major mineralized normal faults; hence we surmise that the Anti-Troodos ridge axis was also of this orientation.

The outcrop of ophiolitic rocks belonging to the Anti-Troodos plate is insufficient to determine whether or not this NE–SW ocean-floor fabric swings to a N–S orientation to the south of the present outcrop, i.e. to determine whether or not the NE–SW grain of the Anti-Troodos plate represents part of a dyke swing at the southern margin of the STTFZ complementary to that observed along the northern margin. Potentially, this question can once again be addressed by palaeomagnetic means, by looking within the Anti-Troodos plate for clockwise block rotations about steeply-plunging axes comparable to those found within the Troodos plate. Indeed Morris et al. (1990) have suggested that just such clockwise block rotations did occur, although their palaeomagnetic data show no evidence for vertical-axis rotations: their four sites at Asgata and Dhrapia (in UPL and Perapedhi Formation umbers), all show cleaned magnetization vectors close to the TMV. Sites reported by Clube & Robertson (1986) (from Clube 1985) in UPL at Parekklisha and the Kalavasos Mines are also statistically indistinguishable from the TMV. Further palaeomagnetic sampling from the Anti-Troodos plate has been undertaken by MacLeod & Allerton (in prep.).

Published data (including those of Morris et al. 1990) suggest that all of the sites drilled in UPL or Perapedhi Formation sediments show evidence for tilting about sub-horizontal NW- or SE-trending rotation axes. This tilting is thought to be due to post-volcanic extensional reactivation of the STTFZ described in MacLeod (1990). Sites from the Anti-Troodos Axis Sequence crust, however, i.e. from the SDC and Basal Group, appear to have suffered a more complex rotation history, with significant clockwise rotations having occurred about moderately to steeply plunging axes (MacLeod & Allerton in prep.; Allerton 1988; MacLeod 1988). Differing sample magnetization vectors between cross-cutting dykes in the UPL near Asgata allow an early clockwise rotation of some 50° about a steeply plunging axis to be identified prior to the later (post-volcanic) tilting about a gently plunging NW axis (MacLeod & Allerton in prep.). This leads us to the preliminary conclusion that the Anti-Troodos plate to the south of the southern margin of the STTFZ has indeed been modified by clockwise block rotation, and thus that the original orientation of the Anti-Troodos ridge was closer to N–S or even NW–SE. Rotation can presumably be ascribed to fault drag due to dextral slip along the STTFZ, in the same manner as that identified to the north of the STTFZ. The fact that such rotations are not observed in UPL from the Anti-Troodos plate (including all of those sites drilled by Clube & Robertson 1986 and Morris et al. 1990) is because the rotations largely pre-dated UPL extrusion (note the evidence from the Mandria ridge–transform intersection area, which shows that the swing of the dykes was impressed upon them at a very early stage, and that minor intrusives and overlying UPL all post-dated rotation: MacLeod et al. 1990).

## Ocean-floor evolution of the STTFZ

### Along-strike variations within the STTFZ

Allowing for the effects of post-volcanic tectonism, MacLeod (1988, 1990) estimated the original width of the STTFZ in the eastern part of the LFC, on structural grounds and with respect to the presence or absence of volcaniclastic sediments within the Extrusive Sequence, to have been approximately 5 km. This is significantly less than Murton's (1986a,b) estimate of not less than 10 km for the western LFC, based on the presence of serpentinite shear zones as far south as Akrounda, and occurrence of nearby volcaniclastic breccias.

In addition to this apparent along-strike difference in the width of the STTFZ, a significant disparity exists in the importance of Transform Sequence magmatism between the eastern and western parts of the LFC. Whereas Murton (1986b) estimated that Transform Sequence intrusions (plutonic and hypabyssal) accounted for dilation of up to 22% of the width of the western LFC, little evidence for such abundant magmatic activity has been observed in the eastern LFC (MacLeod 1988, 1990), even accounting for the difference in erosion levels between the two halves of the Complex. The Mantle Sequence in the Akapnou Forest is cut by rare bosses of poikilitic wehrlite, apparently similar to those of the Transform Sequence in the western LFC, except that they are only up to 50 m in diameter instead of 0.5–1 km. Transform Sequence doleritic dykes, common in the western LFC are observed cutting harzburgites and dunites in the Akapnou Forest, but are scattered, rarely multiple, and volumetrically insignificant.

A third along-strike difference between the western and eastern halves of the LFC is the presence of angular unconformities within the Extrusive Sequence of the former, and their absence in the latter (those sections bordering the AFB excepted: see above). The progressive

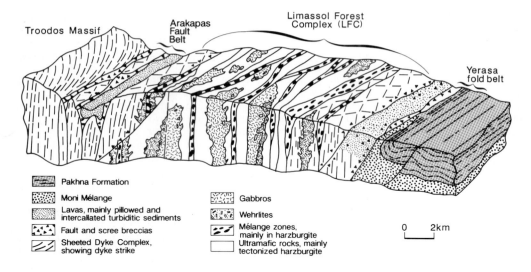

**Fig. 33.** Schematic cross-section of the western LFC, summarizing the principal tectonic and magmatic features identified there by Murton (1986*a,b*). Uplift of the lithospheric mantle was accompanied by disaggregation of the ridge axis-generated crustal sequence, and intrusion of ultramafic and then mafic plutons and dykes in a transtensional regime. The absence of evidence for comparable deformation and magmatism along strike in the eastern part of the LFC is taken to suggest that the western LFC was the site of an extensional relay zone within the STTFZ system.

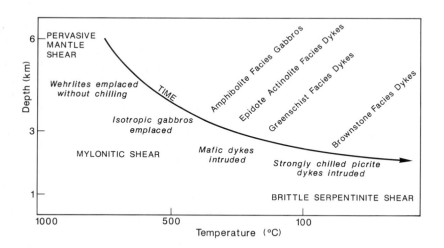

**Fig. 34.** Summary pressure (depth)–temperature–time path diagram for the western part of the LFC, from Murton (1986*b*). Lowering temperature and pressure conditions with time are deduced from the changing structural and intrusive styles, and from the change to progressively lower grades of metamorphism. Together these relationships suggest that the western part of the LFC was being uplifted and cooled progressively, but in an oceanic, syn-magmatic and intra-transform setting. Widespread serpentinization of the Mantle Sequence prior to intrusion of much of the Transform Sequence implies large-scale penetration of water beneath the Moho at an early stage.

unconformity at Kapilio (Fig. 21) is evidence for syn-volcanic tilting and extension within the STTFZ, supported by the observation of Transform Sequence plutonics cutting already-rotated axis-generated crustal sequence blocks in the western LFC. In the east, however, stratigraphic sections through the Extrusive Sequence in and to the north of the Kalavasos Mines are conformable throughout; although tilting of the successions has occurred it appears to have been a later, entirely a post-volcanic, phenomenon (MacLeod 1988, 1990).

These observations together suggest that the STTFZ in the vicinity of the western LFC was subjected to a period of transtension, following formation of the Axis Sequence, whilst in the active domain of the transform. Transtension was accommodated by disaggregation of the Axis Sequence crust and the simultaneous intrusion of a suite of geochemically distinct magmas (the Transform Sequence magmatic suite: see Murton 1986a,b, 1989, 1990; Figs 5 & 33). Uplift of the lithospheric mantle within this part of the STTFZ occurred at the same time, as demonstrated by the progressive change in deformation, intrusion and alteration styles of the Transform Sequence dykes (Fig. 34; Murton 1986a,b). It is likely that this uplift may also account for the present-day difference in erosion level between the western and eastern parts of the Limassol Forest Complex.

Murton & MacLeod (1987), MacLeod (1988, 1990) and Murton (1990) have interpreted the above to indicate that the western LFC became the site of a transtensional region, or 'extensional relay zone', across which the locus of principal transform displacement (approximately coincident with the AFB in the east) was relayed southward. Fragments of ophiolitic material incorporated into the Mamonia Complex of southwestern Cyprus have similar relationships to those described from the western LFC (e.g. boninitic dykes cutting harzburgites and clastic sediments occurring between lava flows) and Transform Sequence or Anti-Troodos Plate chemistry (Malpas & Xenophontos 1987; Malpas et al. this volume). This suggests either that there may have been more than one such relay zone, or that the western LFC relay zone may originally have had a greater extent than that preserved in the Limassol Forest and has subsequently been partially destroyed and incorporated into the Mamonia Complex.

Extensional relay zones analogous to that envisaged here have long been recognized in modern oceanic transform faults (e.g. the Tamayo (Macdonald et al. 1979), Orozco (Madsen et al. 1986) and Siqueiros (Fornari et al.

1989) transforms on the East Pacific Rise), particularly from medium to fast-slipping and/or short-offset systems, where strain rates are relatively high and the thermal and hence mechanical contrast between the two opposed slabs of lithosphere is small (Fox & Gallo 1984). The transtensional rifting and magmatism within these extensional relay zones tends to be short-lived, perhaps of the order of hundreds of thousands of years; continued extension within the transform zones appears to result in the organization of extension and magmatism into short inter-transform ridge segments, as has been documented within, for example, the Siqueiros (Fornari et al. 1989, 1991b) and Garrett (Hekinian et al. 1992) transform fault systems. We note with interest the recent discovery within both of these transform zones of very young, highly primitive picritic basalts (Siqueiros: Fornari et al. 1991a; Casey et al. 1991; Ridley et al. 1991; Garrett: Hekinian et al. 1992), which appear analogous in many respects to the primitive Transform Sequence extrusives of the STTFZ (Cameron 1985; Murton 1986b, 1989; MacLeod 1988; Rogers et al. 1989).

## Discussion: the sense of slip of the STTFZ

In previous sections reference has been made to various kinematic indicators that demonstrate the senses of slip on structures within the STTFZ and hence, by implication, the slip sense of the STTFZ itself. These sense-of-shear determinations are not consistent, i.e. both sinistral (e.g. Figs 6, 7, 9 & 10) and dextral (e.g. Figs 11, 12 & 17) indicators have been found. From this, it must be concluded that the evidence for one or the other sense of slip is flawed or has been misinterpreted, or else that both are valid. If the latter is true then the STTFZ must either have reversed its sense of slip at some time in its history or, alternatively, that both shear senses must somehow have been accommodated within a single regional shear regime.

The differing kinematic indicators have led previous authors to interpret the slip sense of the STTFZ in different ways. Simonian (1975) and Simonian & Gass (1978) interpreted the swing of strike of the Sheeted Dyke Complex to indicate dextral movement along the STTFZ. Murton (1986a,b) and Murton & Gass (1986), on the other hand, took shear sense indicators from mylonite zones and serpentinite shear zones, together with the predominantly NE–SW trend of Transform Sequence dykes (interpreted as tension gash infillings), as evidence that the STTFZ was a sinistrally-slipping system, between dextrally offset ridge crests. They,

Varga & Moores (1985), Moores et al. (1990) and Dilek et al. (1990) interpreted the swing of the strike of the SDC to the north of the AFB as a primary feature of the spreading fabric and therefore as additional evidence for sinistral motion. Palaeomagnetic data, however, show that the dyke swing is not an original feature of the spreading fabric, but has been imposed by clockwise block rotation due to transform drag (Bonhommet et al. 1988; Allerton 1989a; Allerton & Vine 1990; MacLeod et al. 1990); therefore that it instead provides evidence for dextral motion. The determination by palaeomagnetic means that clockwise block rotations were taking place between successive phases of magmatism at individual localities (Allerton 1989a; Allerton & Vine 1990; MacLeod et al. 1990; Morris et al. 1990) provides strong evidence that the dextral phase indeed relates to the ocean-floor history of the transform fault, rather than to emplacement-related tectonics, as proposed by MacLeod (1990). Further evidence for dextral slip is provided by direct structural observations by Allerton (1988), MacLeod (1988), Lapierre et al. (1988), Allerton & Vine (1990), Grand et al. (1993), Gass et al. (1993) and presented here (e.g. Figs 11, 12 & 17).

There appears little doubt that the evidence set out above in support of dextral slip along the STTFZ is genuine. Recent models for the spreading structure of the Troodos plate (e.g. Allerton & Vine 1991; MacLeod et al. 1992) claim to explain all of the complexity of its internal structure in terms of ephemeral spreading and ridge jumping adjacent to a dextrally-slipping transform fault system. Evidence for sinistral slip along the STTFZ, on the other hand, is more equivocal. The palaeomagnetic evidence discussed above has shown that the dyke swing north of the STTFZ cannot be taken as evidence for sinistral slip. Structural data from most of the serpentinite shear zones in the LFC are compatible with dextral motion (Fig. 17) (note that although Lapierre et al. (1988) and Grand et al. (1993) also report sinistral slickensides on some faults in the transform zone our own mapping and that of S. Allerton (pers. comm. 1992) suggests that the faults in question are rotated, originally ridge-parallel structures: see, for example, our description of the Mandria RTI region above). A few of the mylonites, too, appear to have been dextrally-slipping structures (Fig. 11). Murton's (1986a,b) interpretation of the NE–SW preferred orientation of Transform Sequence dykes as tension gashes in a sinistrally-slipping system assumes that this orientation is original and thus, unlike the NE–SW-trending Sheeted Dyke Complexes of both the Troodos

and Anti-Troodos plates to the north and the south, assumes that they alone have **not** been subjected to clockwise rotations about steeply plunging axes as a result of slip along the transform zone. We note that there is in fact a spread in Transform Sequence dyke orientation, leading Murton (1986a) to identify three 'generations' of dykes. Cross-cutting relationships between these dyke sets show a consistent anticlockwise younging sense: the earliest dykes are E–W trending and are cut by the predominant NE–SW set, and both are cut by late N–S-striking dykes. This relationship is similar to that described from the Mandria RTI (see above) and is compatible with clockwise rotations taking place during Transform Sequence intrusion. Palaeomagnetic investigations of the transform-intrusive dykes are in progress (Allerton & MacLeod, unpublished data), but at the time of writing are inconclusive.

Despite all other lines of 'evidence' for sinistral slip being dismissed, we are forced to accept that the majority of mylonites **do** show unequivocal sinistral slip senses. As discussed above, we cannot realistically explain away the sinistral mylonites as rotated antithetic structures in an overall right-lateral system. We are, therefore, left with the inescapable conclusion that both sinistral **and** dextral shear sense indicators from the STTFZ are reliable. Does this mean that the transform fault zone reversed its sense of slip, and therefore that wholesale reorganization of the Troodos–Anti-Troodos spreading geometry must have occurred?

Careful examination of the available evidence allows us to characterize the different episodes of slip more precisely. We note that all the evidence from the Troodos Axis Sequence to the north of the STTFZ indicates dextral shear; that evidence from the Anti-Troodos plate is less clear but probably also indicates dextral shear at an early stage in the evolution of its Axis Sequence. Evidence from the western half of the LFC, however, demonstrates both sinistral and dextral motion. We think it significant that **all** unequivocal indications of sinistral motion come from mafic mylonite shears from the extensional relay zone in the western LFC, within which the ocean-floor rifting and uplift of the pre-existing lithospheric mantle and Axis Sequence crust, accompanied by (Transform Sequence) magmatism, took place. We can therefore surmise that the local sinistral shears within the western STTFZ were formed or activated during Transform Sequence magmatism, at the time of formation of an extensional relay or relays across the transform.

The timing of the sinistral events is not completely constrained. However, structural evidence from shear zones within the western LFC clearly indicates that some at least of the dextral motion took place subsequent to the sinistral events; for example, the amphibolite facies mafic mylonite zone described earlier (map reference (5)070 (38)527) has sinistral shear sense indicators, but is flanked by a broad zone of demonstrably later, lower temperature serpentinite shearing with well-developed dextral slip indicators. We also recognize, however, that the magmatism and transtension in the western LFC must necessarily post-date formation of the Anti-Troodos axis crustal sequence and its consequent clockwise rotation (see above). This suggests that the sinistral slip phase was probably sandwiched between episodes of dextral strike-slip.

It is conceivable that the reversal of slip sense on the STTFZ may have come about because the Troodos and Anti-Troodos ridges temporarily jumped past each other, so as to be dextrally offset and thereby giving rise to an episode of sinistral slip along the STTFZ. Formation of the relay zone could possibly have been a response to a change in overall spreading direction at the same time as the ridge reorganization. We know that the spreading structure of the preserved portion of the Troodos plate is extremely complex, with indications that the spreading centres were ephemeral features: amagmatic extension and ridge jumping/propagation appear to have taken place (Varga & Moores 1985; Moores et al. 1990; Allerton & Vine 1991, 1992; Varga 1991), with possible slight changes of spreading direction between ridge jumps (Allerton 1988; Allerton & Vine 1990). Note, however, that because the western Limassol Forest portion of the transform zone must have remained in the active strike-slip domain at all times throughout the inferred ridge reorganizations, **both** the Troodos **and** Anti-Troodos ridge axes must have jumped past each other **twice** to effect the dextral-to-sinistral-to-dextral slip directions observed. It is not sufficient simply to invoke a single jump of the spreading axis from the Solea to the Larnaca grabens whilst keeping the Anti-Troodos axis fixed in between, as proposed by Grand et al. (1993). Although we cannot categorically discount such ridge jumping models we believe them to be contrived in the extreme, and we know of no other evidence elsewhere in Cyprus for such radical changes in the geometry of the Troodos spreading system.

We believe that the observations can be explained more simply, without such special pleading, and here propose an alternative model that does not require large-scale reorganizations of the spreading geometry. First of all we would like to emphasize the following points from the preceding account.

(1) **All** reliable sinistral shear indicators, without exception, come from the mafic mylonitic shear zones.

(2) Such mylonites are rare and are **only** found in close proximity to the Transform Sequence intrusions within the western LFC extensional relay zone.

(3) The mylonites have mafic mineralogies even when cutting mantle lithologies. Field relationships clearly show them to be the deformed remnants of Transform Sequence dykes fed from the plutons.

(4) Palaeomagnetic data indicate that the clockwise rotation of small (kilometre-sized or less) blocks about steeply plunging axes was widespread within the STTFZ. These rotations were apparently occurring at the same time as rifting and magmatism were taking place within the western LFC extensional relay zone.

To explain all of these observations we make an analogy with the kinematic complexities that have been observed in large-scale continental strike-slip fault zones (e.g. the Lake Mead fault system: Ron et al. 1986). Simple geometrical models show that contrary slip senses on shear zone-parallel structures can develop at the margins of rotating blocks within distributed shear zones, provided that the size of the blocks is small relative to the width of the deforming zone (Fig. 35). Space problems result in the imposition of localized extension and/or compression at block margins. For the STTFZ the size of the rotating blocks is sufficiently small relative to the overall width of the transform zone ($\geqslant 10$ km), for sinistral contra-shearing between clockwise-rotating blocks to be possible. Transform Sequence magmas injected into this deforming regime would be focused preferentially at block boundaries to accommodate space problems arising from the rotations. The sinistral mylonites we believe simply represent either sheared block boundaries or else remnants of dykes intruded along the contra-shear planes.

## Comparison with modern oceanic transform fault zones

Despite the aforementioned complexities in the tectonic evolution of the STTFZ, and the fact that the Troodos ophiolite formed in a supra-subduction zone, rather than mid-ocean ridge setting, we believe that the fundamental structural processes described herein are comparable to those of major transform plate boundaries at

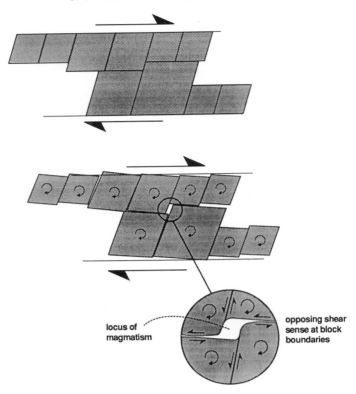

locus of magmatism

opposing shear sense at block boundaries

**Fig. 35.** Cartoon sketch indicating the means by which slip contrary to the overall sense of shear may develop at the boundaries of small rotating blocks within a much broader strike-slip shear regime. Blocks rotate clockwise about steeply plunging axes in response to an externally imposed dextral shear couple, but sinistral shear may develop at block boundaries within the deforming zone. Space problems at block boundaries may induce local compression or extension. Magma injected into the broad strike-slip shear zone is likely to be focused at extensional block boundaries, to form plutons that may be spatially associated with or cut by contra shears. This model, which has geological precedent (see text) is our preferred explanation for the presence of sinistral mylonites, formed within the regional, dextrally slipping STTFZ.

modern mid-ocean ridges. Observation of magnetic lineations, transform faults, propagating rifts and all scales of segmentation in modern marginal basins (e.g. Parson *et al.* 1990) suggest that, whatever the differences in magma composition, the **physical** processes of crustal formation and deformation at spreading ridges and transform faults are comparable whatever the geotectonic setting and plate boundary forces may be. This is borne out by comparison of features described herein from the STTFZ with those observed in modern oceanic transform faults. Lithological associations of tectonite peridotite, sheared serpentinite, and mylonite amphibolite, characteristic of the STTFZ, are common in most of the modern transform faults such as the Vema and Oceanographer transforms (Prinz *et al.* 1976; Honnorez *et al.* 1984; Karson *et al.* 1984; Cannat *et al.* 1991). Magma-

tism within the active transform domain, prominent within the western LFC area of the STTFZ, and once considered unlikely in modern oceanic transforms, is now being observed more and more widely, for example in the Eltanin (Lonsdale 1986), Panama (Lowrie *et al.* 1986), Siqueiros (Fornari *et al.* 1989) and Garrett transform fault zones (Hekinian *et al.* 1992). Much remains to be studied in the STTFZ: for example, palaeomagnetic studies on the NE–SW boninitic dykes within the western LFC intra-transform relay zone; further quantification of block rotations within the STTFZ, fluid pathway studies through and around transform displacement fault zones, detailed structural studies of the boundaries of the extensional relay zone etc.; however, the unique opportunity provided by the STTFZ to study transform processes will ensure it continues as a focus for future research.

We dedicate this paper to the memory of Ian Gass, our mentor and friend. Most of the ideas presented here have developed from ferocious debate with Ian over the years, either in the field or in Milton Keynes, and our wilder imaginings in earlier versions of this manuscript have been tempered by his wisdom and perspicacity. We would also like to thank Simon Allerton and Costas Xenophontos for much useful discussion, and John Taylor and Andy Lloyd for drawing many of the diagrams.

# References

ADAMIDES, N. G., 1980. The form and environment of formation of the Kalavasos ore deposits – Cyprus. In: PANAYIOTOU, A. (ed.) Proceedings of the International Ophiolite Symposium, Cyprus, 1979. Cyprus Geological Survey Dept, 117–127.

ALLERTON, S. 1988. Palaeomagnetic and structural studies of the Troodos ophiolite, Cyprus. PhD thesis, University of East Anglia.

—— 1989a. Fault block rotations in ophiolites: results of palaeomagnetic studies in the Troodos Complex, Cyprus. In: KISSEL, C. & LAJ, C. (eds) Palaeomagnetic Rotations and Continental Deformation. NATO ASI Series C, 254, Kluwer Academic Publishers, 393–410.

—— 1989b. Distortions, rotations and crustal thinning at ridge–transform intersections. Nature, 340, 626–628.

—— & VINE, F. J. 1987. Spreading structure of the Troodos ophiolite, Cyprus: some palaeomagnetic constraints. Geology, 15, 593–597.

—— & —— 1990. Palaeomagnetic and structural studies of the southeastern part of the Troodos complex. In: MALPAS, J., MOORES, E. M., PANAYIOTOU, A. & XENOPHONTOS, C. (eds) Ophiolites: Oceanic Crustal Analogues. Proceedings of the Symposium on Ophiolites and Oceanic Lithosphere, Troodos 87, Geological Survey Department, Nicosia, Cyprus, 99–111.

—— & —— 1991. Spreading evolution of the Troodos ophiolite, Cyprus. Geology, 19, 637–640.

—— & —— 1992. The structure of ridge–transform intersections: evidence from the Troodos ophiolite, Cyprus. In: PARSON, L. M., MURTON, B. J. & BROWNING, P. (eds) Ophiolites and their Modern Oceanic Analogues. Geological Society, London, Special Publication, 60, 251–261.

BAGNALL, P. S. 1960. The geology and mineral resources of the Pano Lefkara–Larnaca area. Cyprus Geological Survey Department Memoir, 5.

—— 1964. Wrench faulting in Cyprus. Journal of Geology, 72, 327–345.

BARTHOLOMEW, I. D. 1983. The primary structures and fabrics of the upper mantle and lower crust from ophiolite complexes. PhD thesis, Open University.

BEAR, L. M. 1958. Wrench fault zones in Cyprus. Cyprus Geological Survey Department Annual Report.

—— 1960. The geology and mineral resources of the Akaki–Lythrodonda area. Cyprus Geological Survey Department Memoir, 3.

—— & MOREL, S. W. 1960. The geology and mineral

resources of the Agros–Akrotiri area. Cyprus Geological Survey Department Memoir, 7.

BERTHÉ, D., CHOUKROUNE, P. & JEGOUZO, P. 1979. Orthogneiss, mylonite and non-coaxial deformation of granites: the example of the South Armorican shear zone. Journal of Structural Ecology, 1, 31–42.

BONATTI, E. 1976. Serpentinite protrusions in the oceanic crust. Earth and Planetary Science Letters, 32, 107–113.

—— & HONNOREZ, J. 1976. Sections of the Earth's Crust in the Equatorial Atlantic. Journal of Geophysical Research, 81, 4104–4116.

BONHOMMET, N., ROPERCH, P. & CALZA, F. 1988. Palaeomagnetic arguments for block rotations along the Arakapas fault (Cyprus). Geology, 16, 422–425.

BOWEN, N. L. & TUTTLE, O. F. 1949. The system MgO–SiO$_2$–H$_2$O. Geological Society of America Bulletin, 60, 439–460.

CAMERON, W. E. 1985. Petrology and origin of primitive lavas from the Troodos ophiolite, Cyprus. Contributions to Mineralogy and Petrology, 89, 239–255.

CANNAT, M., MAMALOUKAS-FRANGOULIS, V., AUZENDE, J.-M., BIDEAU, D., BONATTI, E., HONNOREZ, J., LAGABRIELLE, Y., MALAVIEILLE, J. & MEVEL, C. 1991. Geological cross-section of the Vema fracture zone transverse ridge, Atlantic Ocean. Journal of Geodynamics, 13, 97–118.

CARTER, N. L. & AVÉ LALLEMANT, H. G. 1970. High-temperature flow of dunite and peridotite. Geological Society of America Bulletin, 81, 2181–2202.

CASEY, J. F., FORNARI, D. J., PERFIT, M. R., RIDLEY, I. & XIA, C. 1991. ALVIN diving along strike-slip faults linking intra-transform spreading centers in the Siqueiros transform domain: documentation of plutonic exposures and evidence for 'leakage' along a PTDZ. EOS, 72, 525–526.

CEULENEER, G. 1986. Structure des ophiolites d'Oman: flux mantellaire sous un centre d'expansion oceanique et charriage à la dorsale. PhD Thesis, Université de Nantes.

——, NICOLAS, A & BOUDIER, F. 1988. Mantle flow patterns at an oceanic spreading centre: the Oman peridotites record. Tectonophysics, 151, 1–26.

CLUBE, T. M. M. 1985. The palaeorotation of the Troodos microplate. PhD thesis, University of Edinburgh.

—— & ROBERTSON, A. H. F. 1986. The palaeorotation of the Troodos microplate, Cyprus, in the Late Mesozoic–Early Cenozoic plate tectonic framework of the Eastern Mediterranean. Surveys in Geophysics, 8, 375–437.

COWAN, D. S., BOTROS, M. & JOHNSON, H. P. 1987. Bookshelf tectonics: rotated crustal blocks within the Sovanco Fracture Zone. Geophysical Research Letters, 13, 995–998.

DICK, H. J. B. & SINTON, J. M. 1979. Compositional layering in Alpine peridotites: evidence for pressure solution creep in the mantle. Journal of Geology, 87, 403–416.

DILEK, Y., THY, P., MOORES, E. M. & RAMSDEN, T. W. 1990. Tectonic evolution of the Troodos ophiolite within the Tethyan framework. *Tectonics*, **9**, 811–823.

FORNARI, D. J., GALLO, D. G., EDWARDS, M. H., MADSEN, J. A., PERFIT, M. R. & SHOR, A. 1989. Structure and topography of the Siqueiros transform fault system: evidence for the development of intra-transform spreading centers. *Marine Geophysical Researches*, **11**, 263–299.

——, PERFIT, M. R., CASEY, J. F., KASTENS, K., EDWARDS, M., KIRK, P., RIDLEY, I. & SIQUEIROS TRANSFORM TEAM 1991a. ALVIN diving and Seabeam surveying in the Siqueiros transform: the detailed volcanic and tectonic setting of intra-transform spreading centers. *EOS*, **72**, 525.

——, ——, KASTENS, K., EDWARDS, M. & CASEY, J. F. 1991b. Seabeam surveys in Siqueiros: the structural and kinematic history of a fast-slipping oceanic transform fault containing intra-transform spreading centers. *EOS*, **72**, 486–487.

FOX, P. J. & GALLO, D. G. 1984. A tectonic model for ridge transform–ridge plate boundaries: implications for the structure of oceanic lithosphere. *Tectonophysics*, **104**, 205–242.

GALLO, D. G., FOX, P. J. & MACDONALD, K. C. 1986. A Sea Beam investigation of the Clipperton Transform Fault: the morphotectonic expression of a fast-slipping plate boundary. *Journal of Geophysical Research*, **91**, 3455–3467.

GASS, I. G. & GIBSON, I. L. 1969. Structural evolution of the rift zones in the Middle East. *Nature*, **221**, 926–930.

——, MACLEOD, C. J., MURTON, B. J., PANAYIOTOU, A., SIMONIAN, K. O. & XENOPHONTOS, C. 1991a. *Geological map of the Southern Troodos Transform Fault Zone at 1:25,000: Sheet 1 (west)*. Geological Survey Department, Nicosia, Cyprus.

——, ——, ——, ——, & —— 1991b. *Geological map of the Southern Troodos Transform Fault Zone at 1:25,000: Sheet 2 (east)*. Geological Survey Department, Nicosia, Cyprus.

——, ——, ——, ——, & —— 1993. *Geology of the Southern Troodos Transform Fault Zone, Cyprus*. Cyprus Geological Survey Department Memoir, **9**, in press.

GEORGE, R. P. Jr. 1978. Structural petrology of the Olympus ultramafic complex in the Troodos ophiolite, Cyprus. *Geological Society of America Bulletin*, **89**, 845–865.

GEORGIOU, E. & XENOPHONTOS, C. 1990. Chromite occurrences and associated plutonic rocks in the Akapnou Forest. *In*: MALPAS, J., MOORES, E. M., PANAYIOTOU, A. & XENOPHONTOS, C. (eds) *Ophiolites: Oceanic Crustal Analogues*. Proceedings of the Symposium on Ophiolites and Oceanic Lithosphere, Troodos 87, Geological Survey Department, Nicosia, Cyprus, 585–592.

GRAND, T., LAPIERRE, H., MASCLE, G. H., OHNENSTETTER, M. & ANGELIER, J. 1993. Superimposed tectonics of the Cyprus ophiolitic massifs. *Tectonics*, **12**, 93–101.

HARTE, B. 1976. Rock nomenclature with particular relation to deformation and recrystallisation temperatures in olivine-bearing xenoliths. *Journal of Geology*, **85**, 279–288.

HEKINIAN, R., BIDEAU, D., CANNAT, M., FRANCHETEAU, J. & HÉBERT, R. 1992. Volcanic activity and crust-mantle exposure in the ultrafast Garrett transform fault near 13°28'S in the Pacific. *Earth and Planetary Science Letters*, **108**, 259–275.

HONNOREZ, J., MÉVEL, C. & MONTIGNY, R. 1984. Occurrence and significance of gneissic amphibolites in the Vema fracture zone, equatorial Mid-Atlantic Ridge. *In*: GASS, I. G., LIPPARD, S. J. & SHELTON, A. W. (eds) *Ophiolites and Oceanic Lithosphere*. Geological Society, London, Special Publication, **13**, 121–130.

HUBBERT, M. K. & RUBEY, W. W. 1959. Role of fluid pressure in mechanics of overthrust faulting: I. Mechanisms of fluid-filled porous solids and its application to overthrust faulting. *Geological Society of America Bulletin*, **70**, 115–166.

HURST, S. D., VEROSUB, K. L. & MOORES, E. M. 1992. Paleomagnetic constraints on the formation of the Solea graben, Troodos ophiolite, Cyprus. *Tectonophysics*, **208**, 431–445.

KARATO, S. I. 1984. Grain-size distribution and rheology of the upper mantle. *Tectonophysics*, **104**, 155–176.

KARSON, J. A., FOX, P. J., SLOAN, H., CRANE, K. T., KIDD, W. S. F., BONATTI, E., STROUP, J. B., FORNARI, D. J., ELTHON, D., HAMLYN, P., CASEY, J. F., GALLO, D. G., NEEDHAM, D. & SARTORI, R. 1984. The geology of the Oceanographer transform: the ridge–transform intersection. *Marine Geophysical Researches*, **6**, 109–141.

KASTENS, K. A., RYAN, W. B. F. & FOX, P. J. 1986. The structural and volcanic expression of a fast-slipping ridge–transform plate boundary: Sea MARC I and photographic surveys at the Clipperton Transform Fault. *Journal of Geophysical Research*, **91**, 3469–3488.

LAPIERRE, H., ANGELIER, J., COGNÉ, X., GRAND, T. & MASCLE, G. 1988. Tectonique superposée de la zone de faille d'Arakapas (Massif de Troodos, Chypre). *Geodinamica Acta (Paris)*, **2**, 197–206.

—— & ROCCI, G., 1967. Le massif pluto-volcanique basique de Kellaki, (Chypre) I-Étude pétrographique et structurale. *Sciences de la Terre*, **12**, 145–181.

LAPWORTH, C. 1885. The Highland controversy in British geology: its causes, course and consequence. *Nature*, **32**, 558–559.

LONSDALE, P. 1978. Near-bottom reconnaissance of a fast-slipping transform fault zone at the Pacific–Nazca plate boundary. *Journal of Geology*, **86**, 451–472.

—— 1986. Tectonic and magmatic ridges in the Eltanin fault system, South Pacific. *Marine Geophysical Researches*, **8**, 203–242.

LOWRIE, A., SMOOT, C. & BATIZA, R. 1986. Are fracture zones locked and strong or weak? New evidence for volcanic activity and weakness. *Geology*, **14**, 242–246.

MACDONALD, K. C., CASTILLO, D. A., MILLER, S. P., FOX, P. J., KASTENS, K. A. & BONATTI, E. 1986. Deep-tow studies of the Vema Fracture Zone, 1: tectonics of a major slow slipping transform fault and its intersection with the Mid-Atlantic Ridge.

*Journal of Geophysical Research*, **91**, 3334–3354.

——, KASTENS, K., MILLER, S. & SPIESS, F. N. 1979. Deep-tow studies of the Tamayo transform fault. *Mar. Geophys. Res.*, **4**, 37–70.

MACDONALD, W. D. 1980. Net tectonic rotation, apparent tectonic rotation, and the structural tilt correction in palaeomagnetic studies. *Journal of Geophysical Research* **B7**, 3659–3669.

MACLEOD, C. J. 1988. *The tectonic evolution of the Eastern Limassol Forest Complex, Cyprus*. PhD thesis, Open University, Milton Keynes.

—— 1990. Role of the Southern Troodos Troodos Transform Fault in the rotation of the Cyprus microplate: evidence from the Eastern Limassol Forest Complex. *In*: MALPAS, J., MOORES, E. M., PANAYIOTOU, A. & XENOPHONTOS, C. (eds) *Ophiolites: Oceanic Crustal Analogues*. Proceedings of the Symposium on Ophiolites and Oceanic Lithosphere, Troodos 87. Geological Survey Department, Nicosia, Cyprus, 75–85.

——, ALLERTON, S., GASS, I. G. & XENOPHONTOS, C. 1990. Structure of a fossil ridge–transform intersection in the Troodos ophiolite. *Nature*, **348**, 717–720.

——, ROBERTSON, A. H. F., ALLERTON, S., BROWNING, P., GASS, I. G., TAYLOR, R. N., VINE, F. J. & XENOPHONTOS, C. 1992. Comment on 'Tectonic evolution of the Troodos ophiolite within the Tethyan framework' by Dilek, Y., Thy, P., Moores, E. M. & Ramsden, T. W. *Tectonics*, **11**, 910–915.

MADSEN, J. A. FOX, P. J. & MACDONALD, K. C. 1986. Morphotectonic fabric of the Orozco transform fault: results from a Seabeam investigation. *Journal of Geophysical Research*, **91**, 3439–3454.

MALPAS, J., BRACE, T. & DUNSWORTH, S. M. 1989. Structural and petrologic relationships of the CY-4 drill hole of the Cyprus Crustal Study Project. *In*: GIBSON, I. L., MALPAS, J., ROBINSON, P. T. & XENOPHONTOS, C. (eds) *Cyprus Crustal Study Project: Initial Report, Hole CY-4*, 39–67.

——, CALON, T. & SQUIRES, G. 1993. The development of a Late Cretaceous microplate suture zone in SW Cyprus. (this volume).

—— & XENOPHONTOS, C. 1987. The Mamonia Complex and its reaction to the Troodos ophiolite. *In*: XENOPHONTOS, C. & MALPAS, J. (eds) *Troodos 87 Ophiolites and Oceanic Lithosphere, Field Excursion Guidebook*. Geological Survey Department, Nicosia, Cyprus, 234–259.

MERCIER, J. C., ANDERSON, D. A. & CARTER, N. L. 1977. Stress in the lithosphere: inferences from steady-state flow of rocks. *Pure and Applied Geophysics*, **115**, 199–226.

MENARD, H. W. & ATWATER, T. 1969. Origin of fracture zone topography. *Nature*, **222**, 1037–1040.

MOORES, E. M., VARGA, R. J., VEROSUB, K. L. & RAMSDEN, T. W. 1990. Regional structure of the Troodos dyke complex. *In*: MALPAS, J., MOORES, E. M., PANAYIOTOU, A. & XENOPHONTOS, C. (eds) *Ophiolites: Oceanic Crustal Analogues*. Proceedings of the Symposium on Ophiolites and Oceanic Lithosphere, Troodos 87. Geological Survey De-

partment, Nicosia, Cyprus, 27–35.

—— & VINE, F. J. 1971. The Troodos Massif, Cyprus and other ophiolites as oceanic crust: evaluation and implications. *Philosophical Transactions of the Royal Society of London*, **A268**, 443–466.

MORRIS, A., CREER, K. M. & ROBERTSON, A. H. F. 1990. Palaeomagnetic evidence for clockwise rotations related to dextral shear along the Southern Troodos Transform Fault (Cyprus). *Earth and Planetary Science Letters*, **99**, 250–262, 1990.

MURRELL, S. A. F. & ISMAIL, I. A. H. 1976. The effect of decomposition of hydrous minerals on the mechanical properties of rocks at high pressures and temperatures. *Tectonophysics*, **31**, 207–258.

MURTON, B. J. 1986a. Anomalous oceanic lithosphere formed in a leaky transform fault: evidence from the Western Limassol Forest Complex, Cyprus. *Journal of the Geological Society, London*, **143**, 845–854.

—— 1986b. *The tectonic evolution of the Western Limassol Forest Complex, Cyprus*. PhD thesis, Open University, Milton Keynes.

—— 1989. Tectonic controls on boninite genesis. *In*: SAUNDERS, A. D. & NORRY, M. J. (eds) *Magmatism in the Ocean Basins*. Geological Society, London, Special Publication, **42**, 347–377.

—— 1990. Was the Southern Troodos Transform Fault a victim of microplate rotation? *In*: MALPAS, J., MOORES, E. M., PANAYIOTOU, A. & XENOPHONTOS, C. (eds) *Ophiolites: Oceanic Crustal Analogues*. Proceedings of the Symposium on Ophiolites and Oceanic Lithosphere, Troodos 87. Geological Survey Department, Nicosia, Cyprus, 87–98.

—— & GASS, I. G. 1986. Western Limassol Forest Complex, Cyprus: part of an Upper Cretaceous leaky transform fault. *Geology*, **14**, 255–258.

—— & MACLEOD, C. J. 1987. The Limassol Forest and Arakapas fault Belt. *In*: XENOPHONTOS, C. & MALPAS, J. (eds) *Troodos 87 Ophiolites and Oceanic Lithosphere*. Field Excursion Guidebook. Geological Survey Department, Nicosia, Cyprus, 214–233.

NICOLAS, A. 1989. *Structures of ophiolites and dynamics of oceanic lithosphere*. Kluwer, Dordrecht.

——, BOUDIER, F. & CEULENEER, G. 1988b. Mantle flow patterns and magma chambers at ocean ridges: evidence from the Oman ophiolite. *Marine Geophysical Researches*, **9**, 293–310.

——, CEULENEER, G., BOUDIER, F. & MISSERI, M. 1988a. Structural mappng in the Oman ophiolites: mantle diapirism along an oceanic ridge. *Tectonophysics*, **151**, 27–56.

—— & POIRIER, A. 1976. *Crystalline plasticity and solid state flow in metamorphic rocks*. Wiley, New York.

—— & VIOLETTE, J. F. 1982. Mantle flow at oceanic spreading centres: models derived from ophiolites. *Tectonophysics*, **81**, 319–339.

NORRELL, G. T., TEIXELL, A. & HARPER, G. D. 1989. Microstructure of serpentinite mylonites from the Josephine ophiolite and serpentinisation in retrogressive shear zones, California. **101**, 673–682.

PANAYIOTOU, A. 1977. *Geology and geochemistry of the Limassol Forest plutonic complex and the associ-*

*ated Cu–Ni–Co–Fe sulphide and chromite deposits, Cyprus.* PhD thesis, University of New Brunswick.

PANTAZIS, Th. M. 1967. *The Geology and Mineral Resources of the Pharmakas–Kalavasos Area.* Cyprus Geological Survey Department Memoir, **8**.

PARSON, L. M., PEARCE, J. A., MURTON, B. J., HODKINSON, R. A. & RRS CHARLES DARWIN Scientific Party. 1990. Role of ridge jumps and ridge propagation in the tectonic evolution of the Lau back-arc basin, southwest Pacific. *Geology,* **18**, 470–473.

PRINZ, M., KEIL, K., GREEN, J. A., REID, A. M., BONATTI, E. & HONNOREZ, J. 1976. Ultramafic and mafic dredge samples from the Equatorial Mid-Atlantic Ridge and fracture zones. *Journal of Geophysical Research,* **81**, 4087.

PRINZHOFER, A. & NICOLAS, A. 1980. The Bogata peninsula, New Caledonia: a possible oceanic transform fault. *Journal of Geology,* **88**, 387–398.

RALEIGH, C. B. & PATERSON, M. S. 1965. Experimental Deformation of Serpentinite and Its Tectonic Implications. *Journal of Geophysical Research,* **70**, 3965–3985.

REUBER, I. 1985. Mylonitic ductile shear zones within tectonites and cumulates as evidence for an oceanic transform fault in the Antalya ophiolite, SW Turkey. *In:* DIXON, J. E. & ROBERTSON, A. H. F. (eds) *The Geological Evolution of the Eastern Mediterranean. Journal of Geophysical Research,* **17**, 319–334.

RIDLEY, W. I., PERFIT, M. R., KIRK, P., CASEY, J. & FORNARI, D. 1991. Picritic basalts and magnesian basaltic glasses from the Siqueiros transform fault. *EOS,* **72**, 526.

ROBERTSON, A. H. F. 1977. Tertiary uplift history of the Troodos massif, Cyprus. *Geological Society of America Bulletin,* **88**, 1763–1772.

ROGERS, N. W. MACLEOD, C. J. & MURTON, B. J. 1989. Petrogenesis of boninites from the Limassol Forest Complex, Cyprus. *In:* CRAWFORD, A. J. (ed.) *Boninites and related rocks.* Unwin Hyman, 288–313.

RON, H., AYDIN, A. & NUR, A. 1986. Strike Slip faulting and block rotation in the Lake Mead fault system. *Geology,* **14**, 1020–1023.

SEARLE, R. C. 1983. Multiple, closely spaced transform faults in fast-slipping fracture zones. *Geology,* **11**, 607–610.

SIBSON, R. H. 1977. Fault rocks and fault rock mechanisms. *Journal of the Geological Society, London,* **133**, 191–213.

SIMONIAN, K. O. 1975. *The geology of the Arakapas Fault Belt area, Troodos Massif, Cyprus.* PhD thesis, Open University, Milton Keynes.

—— & GASS, I. G. 1978. Arakapas fault belt, Cyprus: a fossil transform fault. *Geological Society of America Bulletin,* **89**, 1220–1230.

SIMPSON, C. & SCHMID, S. M. 1983. An evaluation of criteria to deduce the sense of movement in sheared rocks. *Geological Society of America Bulletin,* **94**, 1281–1288.

VARGA, R. J. 1991. Modes of extension at oceanic spreading centers: evidence from the Solea graben, Troodos ophiolite, Cyprus. *Journal of Structural Geology,* **13**, 517–537.

—— & MOORES, E. M. 1985. Spreading structure of the Troodos ophiolite, Cyprus. *Geology,* **13**, 846–850.

—— & —— 1990. Intermittent magmatic spreading and tectonic extension in the Troodos ophiolite: implications for exploration for black smoker-type deposits. *In:* MALPAS, J., MOORES, E. M., PANAYIOTOU, A. & XENOPHONTOS, C. (eds) *Ophiolites: Oceanic Crustal Analogues.* Proceedings of the Symposium on Ophiolites and Oceanic Lithosphere, Troodos 87. Geological Survey Department, Nicosia, Cyprus, 53–64.

VINE, F. J. & MOORES, E. M. 1969. Palaeomagnetic results from the Troodos igneous massif. *EOS,* **50**, 131.

WHITE, S. H. 1976. The effects of strain on the microstructures, fabrics and deformation mechanisms in quartzites. *Philosophical Transactions of the Royal Society of London,* **A283**, 69–86.

—— 1982. Fault rocks of the Moine Thrust Zone: a guide to their nomenclature. *Textures & Microstructures,* **4**, 211–221.

——, BRETAN, P. G. & RUTTER, E. H. 1986. Fault zone reactivation: kinematics and mechanisms. *Philosophical Transactions of the Royal Society of London,* **A317**, 81–97.

——, BURROWS, S. E., CARRERAS, J., SHAW, N. D. & HUMPHREYS, F. J. 1980. On mylonites in ductile shear zones. *Journal of Structural Geology,* **2**, 175–189.

WILSON, J. T. 1965. A new class of faults and their bearing on continental drift. *Nature,* **207**, 343–347.

WILSON, R. A. M. 1959. *The geology of the Xeros–Troodos area.* Cyprus Geological Survey Department Memoir **1**.

WOODCOCK, N. H. & FISCHER, M. 1986. Strike-slip duplexes. *Journal of Structural Geology,* **8**, 725–735.

YOUNG, K. D., JANCIN, M., VOIGHT, B. & ORKAN, N. 1985. Transform deformation of Tertiary rocks along the Tjörnes Fracture Zone, North Central Iceland. *Journal of Geophysical Research,* **90**, 9986–10,010.

# The development of a late Cretaceous microplate suture zone in SW Cyprus

J. MALPAS, T. CALON & G. SQUIRES

*Department of Earth Sciences, Memorial University, Newfoundland*

*Abstract:* Recent detailed mapping and volcanic geochemistry of rocks exposed in erosional windows through post-Cretaceous cover rocks in SW Cyprus have provided evidence for the development of a model for late Cretaceous microplate collision in the eastern Mediterranean. Two major juxtaposed terranes are recognized: the older Mamonia Complex consisting of Triassic ocean floor, accompanying seamounts and a series of continental rise prism sediments, and the younger Troodos Complex consisting of ophiolitic rocks formed in a supra-subduction zone environment, and modified in part by transform fault tectonics and magmatism. The two complexes were juxtaposed along an intricate suture zone, the evolution of which displays two main phases of contractional deformation of late Cretaceous age. These are a primary north- and northwest-directed thrusting, and a secondary backthrusting episode towards the west and southwest, that in places reorganized the initial structural stacking sequence. Extensional faulting of Troodos Complex rocks, that took place on the ocean floor prior to juxtaposition, clearly influenced the orientation of the later thin-skinned delamination. Although there is some evidence for strike-slip faulting, this process does not appear as extensive as proposed by previous workers.

The geology of the island of Cyprus, which lies in a region of complicated tectonics in the eastern Mediterranean (Fig. 1), is dominated by ophiolitic rocks. In the Troodos ranges, which form the core of the island and rise to an exposed height of 1951 m on Mount Olympus, an intact, complete ophiolite suite is preserved. Recent work, much of it part of the Cyprus Crustal Study Project (Malpas *et al.* 1990), has shown conclusively that this ophiolite was produced above a subducting oceanic slab in late Cretaceous times. This subduction further resulted in the juxtapositioning of two distinct geological terranes derived from either side of the convergent plate margin. Evidence of late Mesozoic plate collision is well preserved in SW

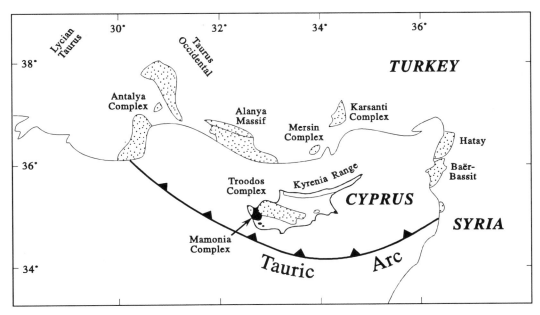

**Fig. 1.** Location of Cyprus in the eastern Mediterranean, showing relative positions of Troodos, Mamonia and other ophiolitic and related complexes.

*From* Prichard, H. M., Alabaster, T., Harris, N. B. W. & Neary, C. R. (eds), 1993,
*Magmatic Processes and Plate Tectonics,* Geological Society Special Publication No. 76, 177–195.

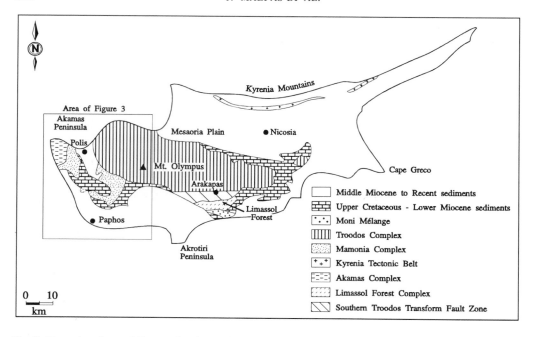

**Fig. 2.** General geology of Cyprus showing major terrane subdivisions.

Cyprus, which has proved an ideal area in which to study the geological evolution of the micro-plate boundaries.

The two juxtaposed terranes are the Mamonia Complex and the Troodos Complex (Fig. 2). The collision of these complexes was clearly along a structurally complicated zone, but there has been much debate on the nature of the collision and whether the structural style of the zone is dominated by thrust or strike-slip fault-ing. Interpretations of the available structural information have been used to support both and, indeed, more recent models favour a combi-nation of the two (Malpas *et al.* 1992). Whereas detailed work on the Troodos Complex has made it one of the best understood ophiolites in the world, the geological evolution of the Mamonia Complex has been somewhat neg-lected until recently, and is much less well under-stood. The provenance of the Mamonia Com-plex, in the context of eastern Mediterranean geology, will only be fully understood after res-olution of the nature of its collision with the Troodos Complex.

The suture zone along which the complexes are juxtaposed lies to the south of a line through the villages of Statos and Kannaviou and extends at least to the coast (Fig. 3). Its southern limit is likely concordant with the trend of the main Tauric Arc some 40 km offshore. Serpenti-nites outcrop throughout this zone as a series of apparently linear belts, e.g. that running through Akamas, Mavrokolymbos, Ayia Varvara and Phasoula. The significance of these belts in terms of the tectonic evolution of the area has not been fully explained. In this paper we review some aspects of each of the complexes as they are exposed in erosional windows situated in the south-central part of the suture zone, paying particular attention to the nature of volcanic rocks in each and the structural complexity of their juxtapositioning.

## Mamonia Complex rocks in SW Cyprus

Rocks of the Mamonia Complex occur in west and southwest Cyprus, where they are generally covered by a blanket of late Cretaceous to Quat-ernary sediments. Sporadic outcrops, the recog-nition of which is extremely important to the overall tectonic picture, are also present in the south and southeast of the island, and similar rock types are found associated with the Baer Bassit ophiolite in Syria (Fig. 1 & 2). The com-plex, a deformed late Triassic to mid-Cretaceous volcano-sedimentary terrane, outcrops in ero-sional windows through the cover, together with structural inliers of the Campanian to Maas-trichtian Troodos Complex.

The Mamonia Complex represents a highly

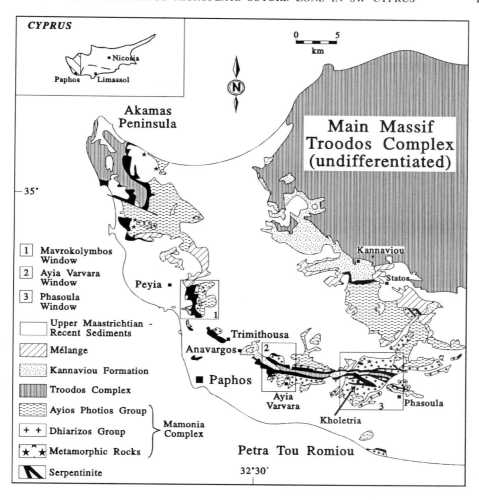

**Fig. 3.** Geology of SW Cyprus showing the location of the three erosional windows studied in this work.

tectonized and collapsed passive continental margin sequence, which formed within Neotethys, the Mesozoic Tethyan ocean now preserved in the eastern Mediterranean. Associated igneous rocks are remnants of the once widespread Upper Triassic alkalic volcanism which has most recently been interpreted as representing early ocean floor spreading and ocean island development in a series of small ocean basins along the northern margin of Gondwana, south of the Palaeotethys ocean (Malpas *et al.* 1992). Until the present work, however, no preserved Triassic oceanic basement to this alkalic volcanism had been reported, although amphibolites which occur as tectonic blocks within the Mamonia Complex may represent its metamor-

phosed equivalent (Malpas *et al.* 1992). The apparent absence of rocks representing Upper Jurassic to Lower Cretaceous ocean floor volcanism had been interpreted either as a result of the cessation of sea-floor spreading, or the subduction of any ocean crust produced during that time interval. In Cyprus, the ophiolitic rocks against which Mamonia lithologies are juxtaposed possess a supra-subduction zone (SSZ) geochemical signature (Robinson *et al.* 1983; Moores *et al.* 1984) supporting the latter argument. In this paper, however, we report the discovery of remnants of the Triassic oceanic basement for the first time.

After Upper Triassic rifting, the Jurassic to early Cretaceous in the eastern Mediterranean

saw the deposition of mainly deep-water pelagic
sedimentary rocks, indicating regional subsidence.


## Troodos Complex rocks in southern Cyprus

In general terms the Troodos Complex comprises a complete ophiolite suite disposed in a
domal structure forming the core of the island of
Cyprus but the southern portion of the massif,
both in the Limassol Forest Complex and where
the ophiolite is juxtaposed with the Mamonia
Complex, does not display a characteristic
ophiolite stratigraphy. Rather, a sequence of
intercalated lavas and breccias not found elsewhere in the complex, is interpreted to have
formed during the development of a transtensional transform fault and extensional relay zone
that offset transform movement along the fault
belt (Simonian & Gass 1978; Murton 1990; Mac-
Leod 1990; MacLeod & Murton this volume).
This Southern Troodos Transform Fault Zone
(STTFZ) (Fig. 2) is also underlain by a series of
ultramafic and gabbroic intrusions that were
emplaced at a shallow crustal level and were in
part exposed on the sea floor. In the eastern part
of the STTFZ, MacLeod (1990) has recognized
oceanic crust produced at the 'anti-Troodos
ridge' and has measured dextral movement
along the transform which he interprets as a late
reactivation of the zone in response to counter-
clockwise movement of the Troodos Complex in
late Cretaceous time. This tectonic picture is
similar to that proposed by Malpas *et al.* (1992),
who recognize the Limassol Forest Complex
itself as an integral part of the transform fault
zone.

Most workers agree that the transform fault
was magmatically active and, from the perspective of this paper, it is the geochemical nature of
the lavas erupted in the STTFZ that is of para-
mount importance in the tectonic interpretation
of the fossil suture zone which is exposed further
to the west. Cameron (1985) reported the
characteristic trace element contents that make
these lavas easily identifiable when compared
with other Troodos Complex lavas, i.e. their
extreme depletion in HFSE, high Mg and Si
contents which suggests a boninitic affinity. Until our work, these lavas were described only
from the mapped extent of the STTFZ (Fig. 2),
but we now know that they also occur considerably further west and are exposed in at least the
southern part of the Mamonia–Troodos suture
zone as seen in erosional windows through the
post-Cretaceous cover (Malpas & Xenophontos
1987; Malpas *et al.* 1992).


## Stratigraphy of rocks in the suture zone

This study concentrates on the geochemistry
and tectonic setting of volcanic, plutonic and
sedimentary rocks in three erosional windows
exposed through the Campanian to Recent sedimentary cover in southwest Cyprus. These are
the 'Phasoula window', the 'Ayia Varvara window' and the 'Mavrokolymbos window' (Fig. 3)
and they expose outcrops of Mamonia and
Troodos rocks in the southern portion of the
suture zone. The stratigraphy described here is
comparable to that of previous workers (Fig. 4).
For the most part we adhere to the nomenclature of Swarbrick & Robertson (1980). Those
rocks within the suture zone that comprise the
continental margin sediments of the Ayios
Photios Group and the Triassic volcanics of the
Dhiarizos Group form the major part of the
Mamonia Complex. Within the Mamonia Complex, the Ayios Photios Group can be further
subdivided into the Vlambouros, Marona and
Episkopi formations, generally a variety of
siliciclastics, calcareous and siliceous lutites,
arenites and rudites; the Dhiarizos Group is
divided into the Phasoula and Loutra tis Aphro-
ditis formations, mostly mafic rocks of late
Triassic age, and the Petra tou Romiou and
Mavrokolymbos formations, the former consisting of Mesozoic carbonates intimately associated with the volcanic rocks and the latter of
hemipelagic mudstones. Metamorphic rocks,
including psammitic and pelitic schists and
amphibolites, also form part of the Mamonia
Complex and are ubiquitously associated with
serpentinites in the region. They are assigned to
the separate Ayia Varvara Formation (Swarbrick & Robertson 1980; Malpas *et al.* 1992). We
note that the metamorphism that produced the
Ayia Varvara Formation was late Cretaceous in
age (Spray & Roddick 1981), and that rapid
disruption of the Mamonia Complex took place
in the Maastrichtian.

Within the suture zone, the Troodos Complex
is best exemplified by volcanic rocks and serpentinites with only sparse gabbros. The volcanic
rocks, and locally also the serpentinites, are
overlain in places by volcanogenic sandstones
and bentonitic clays of the Campanian to
Maastrichtian Kannaviou Formation. Locally,
notably in the Ayia Varvara window, the
Kannaviou sediments are interbedded with sedimentary melange consisting of a red mudstone
matrix with variably sized clasts (up to 2 m) of
volcanic rocks derived from both the Troodos
Complex and the Dhiarizos Group, as well as
cherts, sandstones and recrystallized limestones
of obvious Mamonia Complex provenance. This

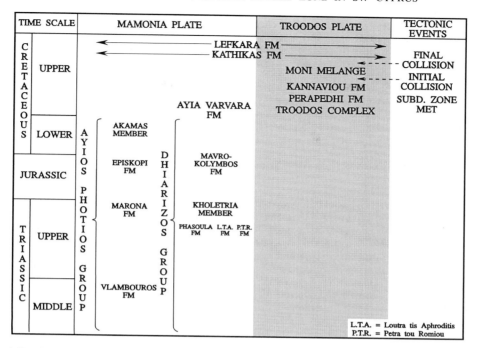

| TIME SCALE | | MAMONIA PLATE | | | TROODOS PLATE | TECTONIC EVENTS |
|---|---|---|---|---|---|---|

**Fig. 4.** Stratigraphy of the Mesozoic rocks of SW Cyprus.

depositional sequence can be correlated with the Moni Melange that lies in a trough along the southern margin of the STTFZ in the Limassol Forest (Robertson 1977). It is the first indication of the proximity of the advancing Mamonia microplate to the Troodos plate margin.

A younger olistostromal unit, the Maastrichtian Kathikas Melange, seals structural contacts within the Mamonia Complex, and the fundamental tectonic contacts between the Mamonia Complex and the Troodos Complex observed in the erosional windows. This unit consists of variably sized clasts of Mamonia rocks and rarer blocks of Troodos material that lie chaotically in a red argillaceous matrix. It appears undeformed and is considered to be largely post-orogenic. The melange passes upwards into deep water limestones of the Tertiary Lefkara Formation or is directly overlain by younger units of the cover sequence.

## Volcanic and related rocks of the suture zone

### Mamonia Complex

Earlier workers (e.g. Lapierre 1975; Swarbrick 1980) had designated all of the volcanic rocks of the Dhiarizos Group as alkali basalts and their fractionated products. As described below, one

of the major findings of our recent work is that more than 80% of the Mamonia volcanic rocks are, in fact, tholeiitic. We suppose that the discrepancy lies in the fact that previous workers relied on major element chemistry to indicate the geochemical affinity of these rocks and were unaware of the extent of the low temperature alteration and metasomatism they had undergone. In the field, the tholeiitic lavas comprise predominantly pillowed flows with individual pillows from 20–50 cm in diameter, orange-brown weathering, poorly amygdaloidal but copiously variolitic on their margins. Pillows are locally hollow or show some intra-pillow layering of alternating bands of chloritised basalt and zeolite. They are, no doubt, periodically evacuated lava tubes. Interpillow voids and radial shrinkage fractures are commonly filled with pink or grey calcilutite of the Triassic Kholetria Member. Rosettes of natrolite and some analcime are not uncommon. Less commonly red, green or brown chert, and black manganiferous chert are present as void infillings or discontinuous inter-pillow beds. Over significant areas, these tholeiites are covered by pelagic radiolarian cherts, shale and minor calcilutite, designated by Swarbrick & Robertson (1980) as the Mavrokolymbos Formation. The lavas are also associated with detached blocks of reefal limestone to interbedded pelagic limestone and chert of the Petra tou Romiou Formation, dated as Upper Triassic on the basis of pelagic bivalves, ammonites, corals and microfauna (Henson *et al.* 1949; Pantazis 1967; Ealy & Knox, 1975).

Approximately 15% of the Mamonia Complex volcanic rocks are alkali basalts and two equally abundant field types dominate. These are, essentially aphyric pillow lavas and heavily plagioclase-phyric pillow lavas with rare sheet flows and associated dikes. They are associated with the same range of sedimentary rocks as are the tholeiites. The aphyric lavas generally occur as burgundy to purple-weathering pillows averaging 50 cm in diameter. They are variably amygdaloidal, with amygdales filled with calcite and zeolite. Both pillowed and sheet flows have identical chemistries and their differing morphologies are probably a function of different volatile content, extrusion rate and depositional slope, and eruption depth. This lava type is locally observed to lie directly on the tholeiitic lava sequence and is clearly overlain by the plagioclase – phyric lavas. The latter occur as lightgrey weathering, spectacularly porphyritic pillows with calcite- and zeolite-filled amygdales. The pillows are relatively large, from 30 cm to more than 1 m, and the plagioclase phenocrysts range from 0.5–2 cm in length and can make up to 80% by volume of the flow.

Ankaramite, exhibiting cumulate titanaugite and olivine as well as subordinate plagioclase phenocrysts forms variably-sized blocks in deformed red shale matrix (Mavrokolymbos Formation). In the Petra tou Romiou area ankaramite flows are pillowed and associated with manganiferous cherts. As with the ankaramites, trachybasalts, trachytes and trachytic phonolites, ankaramites are poorly exposed and make up less than 5% of the Mamonia Complex volcanics. They occur as either flow-core blocks which are light-green in colour, sanidine–phyric and seriate textured or as flow-margin blocks which are pervasively carbonatized and locally flow-banded with abundant flow-flattened vesicles.

## Troodos Complex

Rocks which were derived from the Troodos ophiolite are intimately intercalated with Mamonia Complex lithologies along many portions of the suture zone. The minimum late Cretaceous age of these rocks is indicated by Maastrichtian Globotruncata (Mantis 1970; Ealy & Knox 1975) in Kannaviou Formation volcaniclastic sedimentary rocks which typically overlie Troodos volcanic rocks both here and within the main Troodos ophiolite to the north and west.

Two pillow lava units and their associated dikes can be recognized. The oldest is a pillowed flow sequence marked by small pillows (15–30 cm diameter) with fresh, black glassy rims. These lavas are usually amygdale-free and contain 5–15% fresh to pseudomorphed olivine phenocrysts. The glassy margins are only partly devitrified and contain skeletal olivine and augite micro-phenocrysts. In contrast to the limestone association of the Mamonia Complex volcanic rocks, these rocks have no associated carbonates. Where visible, the substrate upon which they were erupted is either gabbro or serpentinite. In their appearance and petrography, they are very similar to pillow lavas erupted within parts of the STTFZ. Their geochemistry, described below, confirms this and the rocks can be broadly defined as boninitic. They form the lower part of a volcanic pile ('lower boninites') and are overlain by a chemically similar, but physically quite distinct series of 'upper boninites'. Here, pillows are altered to a light greygreen colour with calcite and haematite interpillow fillings. They are frequently greater than 1 m in diameter, in places are flow-flattened and pillow breccias are well developed. Dikes which feed these upper boninites are seen to cut the lower series and the relationship between dike orientation and the dip of the lava sequence suggests some tilting of the lower lavas before extrusion of the upper lavas.

Both upper and lower boninite series lavas, and nearby serpentinites, are overlain by the onlapping Maastrichtian volcaniclastic sedimentary rocks of the Kannaviou Formation. These consist of grey-green bentonitic clays, radiolarian mudstones and volcanically derived siltstones and sandstones. The unit is particularly incompetent because of the clay content and has been tightly folded either by the thrust tectonics described below or later, quite recent gravity sliding.

Of considerable importance in unravelling the tectonic history of the Troodos Complex rocks in this region is the relationship between the serpentinites and boninites. There are several lines of evidence that suggest that the serpentinite was derived from anomalously shallow mantle, likely even exposed in part in fracture zone scarps. Immediately north of the village of Ayia Varvara, serpentinized harzburgites of the southern bounding serpentinite belt of the Troodos inliers are cut by numerous pegmatitic uralitized gabbro dikes, suggesting processes conducive to raising mantle to shallow depths at which gabbro intrusion would be possible. Secondly, fine-grained gabbro and chilled basaltic dikes intrude the serpentine immediately adjacent to

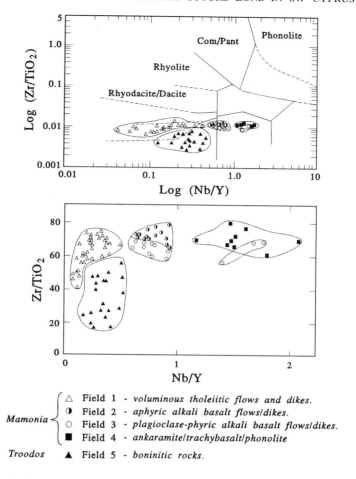

**Fig. 5.** Zr/TiO$_2$ vs. Nb/Y for rocks of the Dhiarizos Group and Troodos Complex. Explanation in text.

some outcrops of the boninitic rocks. This is particularly characteristic of early extensional fault contacts between the pillows and serpentinites and suggests that the faults may have developed along major dike trends. The chilled dikes are of similar chemistry to the boninites and thus indicate the presence of the host serpentinite in the highest parts of the crust at the time of diking. However, the most conclusive evidence of serpentinite on the sea floor is the occurrence of unconformable flow/serpentinite primary contacts in the Ayia Varvara area. Pillow lavas are found chilled against serpentinite and pillow breccias nearby are draped over a coarse gabbro-serpentinite body. Locally features reminiscent of the STTFZ are observed, including a polylithic (harzburgite, gabbro, basalt) talus breccia sitting immediately on harzburgite just north of Kholetria. Such evidence

strongly indicates that within the Troodos Complex as exposed in a number of the windows, serpentinite was exposed on the sea floor when the boninitic lavas were erupted. These relationships suggest a continuation of the STTFZ through this area (Malpas *et al.* 1992). Worth noting once again in this context, is the occurrence of Kannaviou volcaniclastic sediments on top of, or adjacent to, serpentinites in depressions controlled by early normal oblique faults.

### Geochemistry

Chemical classification of the volcanic rocks using major elements is considered ineffective due to the low temperature alteration which has severely modified the bulk major element analyses of many of the rocks. Using 'immobile'

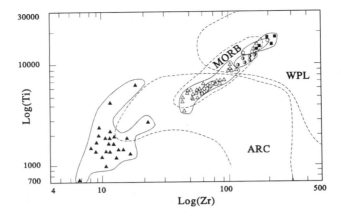

**Fig. 6.** Ti vs. Zr plot for Mamonia and Troodos volcanics of the suture zone. Fields as for Fig. 5.

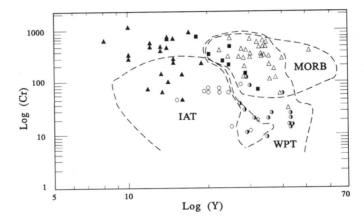

**Fig. 7.** Cr vs. Y for rocks of the Mamonia Complex and Troodos Complex in the suture zone. Fields as for Fig. 5.

trace elements, however, differentiation into distinct chemical fields is possible. In Figs 5a and 5b, $Zr/TiO_2$ acts as both an index of alkalinity and degree of differentiation, and Nb/Y acts as an alkalinity index. Field 1 represents the voluminous tholeiitic flows and dikes of Triassic age not previously recognized in Cyprus and Fields 2 and 3, the aphyric and plagioclase–phyric alkali basalt flows and dikes of the Mamonia Complex. The aphyric alkali basalts are slightly less depleted. Associated ankaramitic rocks are shown as Field 4. Thus the Mamonia Complex volcanic rocks seem to represent the development of ocean islands or seamounts upon a tholeiitic ocean crust basement. The remaining basalts on these plots are the sub-alkaline, boninitic basalts of the Troodos Complex (Field 5).

They are extremely depleted rocks and generally plot within the island arc field on appropriate diagrams (e.g Ti vs. Zr, Fig. 6). The Cr–Y diagram (Fig. 7) is particularly interesting in that separation of rock types within the individual complexes is possible. The Triassic Mamonia Complex tholeiites plot entirely within the MORB field, the alkali basalts within the WPB field and the Troodos Complex boninites entirely within the island arc field. Plots of V versus Ti (Shervais 1982; Fig. 8) likewise illustrate the dual nature of the suture zone volcanic rocks, with the Mamonia Complex lavas plotting dominantly in the ocean floor field, including more enriched ocean island basalts, and the Troodos Complex lavas clearly in the depleted arc field.

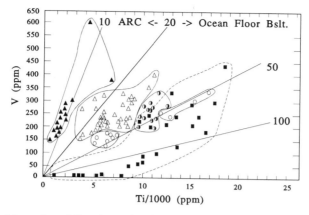

**Fig. 8.** V vs. Ti for Mamonia and Troodos rocks of the suture zone. Fields as for Fig. 5. 10, 20, 50 and 100 represent Ti/V trend lines.

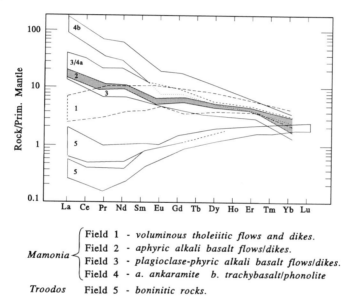

Mamonia
- Field 1 - *voluminous tholeiitic flows and dikes.*
- Field 2 - *aphyric alkali basalt flows/dikes.*
- Field 3 - *plagioclase-phyric alkali basalt flows/dikes.*
- Field 4 - *a. ankaramite   b. trachybasalt/phonolite*

Troodos    Field 5 - *boninitic rocks.*

**Fig. 9.** REE plot of volcanic rocks from the suture zone. Explanation in text.

Figure 9 is a primitive mantle-normalized plot of a range of REE from the volcanic rocks within the suture zone. Samples were taken from the Phasoula window and a variety of rock types from mafic to felsic are represented. Mamonia Complex lavas are represented by units 1 to 4. Unit 1 displays a typically flat to LREE-depleted trend and absolute concentrations consistent with MORB affinity. The alkaline, seamount volcanic rocks vary from aphyric alkali basalts (unit 2) to the most evolved rocks in the study area, phonolites and trachytes of unit 4. The Troodos Complex lavas are depleted in all REE with respect to MORB, with characteristc U-shaped patterns in the LREE found associated with boninitic rocks from present-day western Pacific forearc areas. In this supra-subduction zone environment, REE are initially depleted because of partial melting of a previously depleted mantle source, and the enrichment in the lightest REE is thought to result from a late mantle metasomatic event involving the passage of LREE-enriched fluids from the subducting slab.

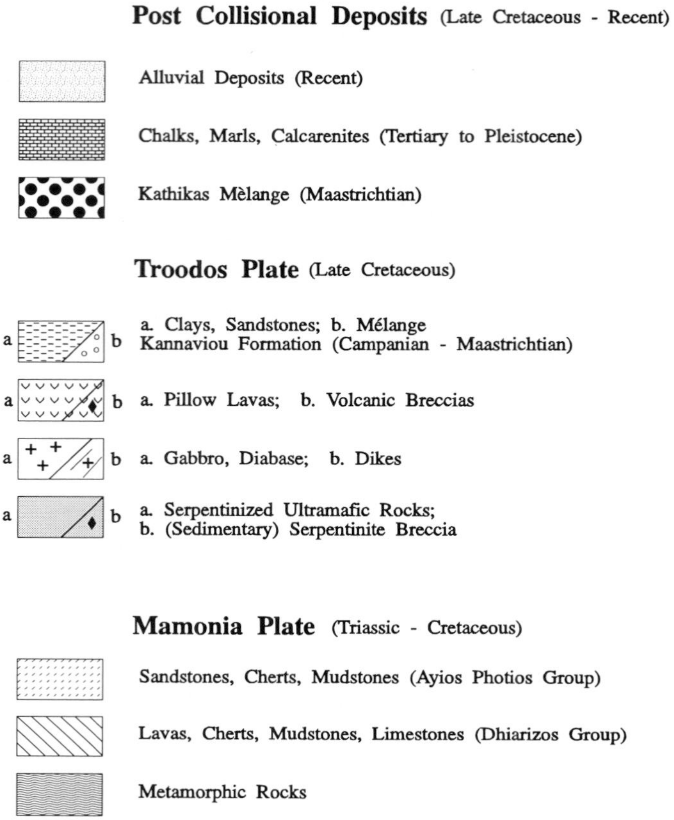

## Post Collisional Deposits (Late Cretaceous - Recent)

Alluvial Deposits (Recent)

Chalks, Marls, Calcarenites (Tertiary to Pleistocene)

Kathikas Mèlange (Maastrichtian)

## Troodos Plate (Late Cretaceous)

a ___ b   a. Clays, Sandstones; b. Mèlange
          Kannaviou Formation (Campanian - Maastrichtian)

a ___ b   a. Pillow Lavas;   b. Volcanic Breccias

a ___ b   a. Gabbro, Diabase;   b. Dikes

a ___ b   a. Serpentinized Ultramafic Rocks;
          b. (Sedimentary) Serpentinite Breccia

## Mamonia Plate (Triassic - Cretaceous)

Sandstones, Cherts, Mudstones (Ayios Photios Group)

Lavas, Cherts, Mudstones, Limestones (Dhiarizos Group)

Metamorphic Rocks

**Fig. 10.** Legend accompanying the geological maps and cross-sections of the Mavrokolymbos and Ayia Varvara windows, shown in Figs 11–14.

## Structural geometry and evolution of the suture zone

Considerable structural analysis has been carried out in the STTFZ in the Limassol Forest area (see MacLeod & Murton, this volume for review) but little to date on the suture zone further west (e.g. Robertson & Woodcock 1979; Swarbrick 1980, 1993). Here, we present the results of detailed structural analysis of areas within two of the erosional windows, at Mavrokolymbos in the north–south-trending part of the belt (Figs 11 and 13), and at Ayia Varvara in the east–west part of the belt (Figs 12 and 13). The legend for the geological maps and structural cross-sections that accompany the following descriptions is shown in Fig. 10.

The two windows expose parts of the southwest portion of the suture zone, marked by an arcuate serpentinite belt on the regional scale.

The tectonic significance of this arcuate belt is not fully understood at this stage and, indeed, it may simply be an artefact of exposure. Our preliminary investigation involved 1:5000 scale form surface mapping of lithostratigraphic units, extensive lava chemostratigraphy, and detailed mesoscopic to macroscopic geometric analysis of internal deformational structures, combined with kinematic analysis of unit contact relationships. Detailed documentation of the structural evidence for the model we have developed is presented elsewhere (Calon *et al.*, in prep.).

Two major groups of structures, each with a distinctive structural style and kinematic signature, are recognized within the tectonostratigraphic components of the southern part of the suture zone. In addition, metamorphic blocks of the Ayia Varvara Formation form an exotic component in the suture zone assemblage; their emplacement history remains enigmatic.

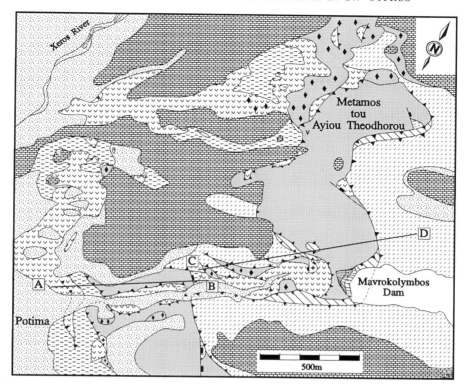

**Fig. 11.** Geological map of the Mavrokolymbos window. For legend see Fig. 10.

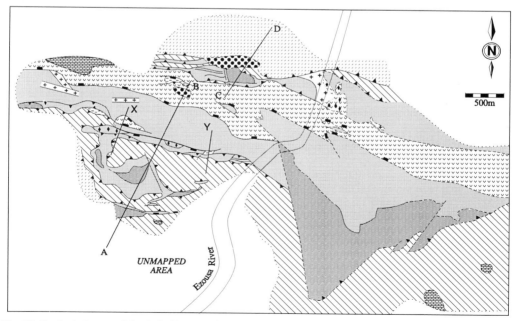

**Fig. 12.** Geological map of the Ayia Varvara window. For legend see Fig. 10.

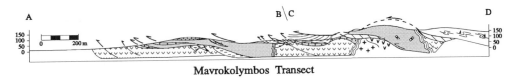

Mavrokolymbos Transect

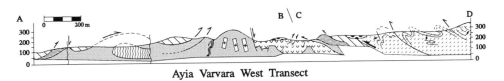

Ayia Varvara West Transect

**Fig. 13.** Structural cross-sections along section lines in Mavrokolymbos (ABCD) and Ayia Varvara (ABCD) windows. For legend see Fig. 10.

## Extensional structures affecting Troodos Complex rocks

The first group comprises extensional fault systems that are restricted to Troodos Complex inliers. They define narrow, linear horst and graben structures, with upthrown blocks occupied by serpentinite and gabbroic basement and downthrown blocks by volcanic rocks, sedimentary serpentinite breccias and Kannaviou Formation cover with locally interbedded Moni Melange. Where well preserved beneath the thrust systems of the Mamonia Complex, as in the northern part of the Ayia Varvara window (Figs. 12 & 13), planar rotational and listric normal faults with steep to gentle dips define geometrically complex linked systems with E–W–trending master faults and NE- and NW-trending transfer faults. Kinematic indicators on fault surfaces and in shear zones show consistently normal slip sense, corroborating the observed extensional stratigraphic separation. Nevertheless, slip directions vary from pure dip-slip to nearly strike-slip and normal dextral oblique-slip is predominant on the E–W–trending master faults. An example of the stratigraphic and structural features of a horst-graben bounding fault zone in the southern portion of the Ayia Varvara window is shown in Fig. 14. The extensional structures are interpreted as a continuation of similar fault systems recognized by Murton (1990) and MacLeod (1990) in the Southern Troodos Transform Fault Zone further east.

The field relationships concerning the relative timing of deformation and plutonism are ambi-

guous. However, a relatively high-temperature shear regime is postulated for the development of plastic serpentinite mylonite zones with C–S fabrics, that mark the margins of some ultramafic cumulates, suggesting that they developed during high-level intrusion of these plutons into already substantially cooled and perhaps serpentinized, mantle host rocks. The profusive development of wehrlitic, gabbroic and diabasic dikes in the mantle host rocks, particularly near and along faulted contact zones with pillow lavas, corroborates this interpretation. Sedimentary serpentinite breccias form characteristic talus deposits in the graben structures, particularly near the E–W–trending master faults. These breccias generally overlie the pillow lavas and are in turn overlain by Kannaviou sediments (Fig. 14), although in rare instances pillow lavas depositionally overlie the breccias, and breccias overlie Kannaviou sediments.

## Contractional structures of the suture zone:

We presently recognize two sets of contractional fault systems, which developed during the collisional stages of the evolution of the suture zone. Both display very similar stratigraphic stacking sequences which are well displayed in the western part of the Ayia Varvara window. They consist of a basal zone of sheared serpentinites entraining blocks of metamorphic rocks of the Ayia Varvara Formation, overlain by thrust sheets of the Dhiarizos Group, which in turn are overlain by imbricate thrust sheets of the Ayios Photios Group. Structural relationships deter-

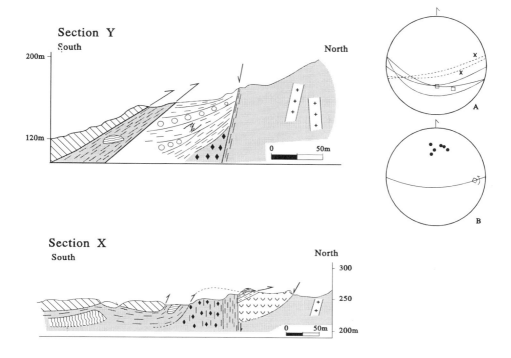

**Fig. 14.** Structural cross-sections along section lines X and Y in Ayia Varvara window, and orientation patterns (lower hemisphere, equal-area projections) of structural elements in section Y. (**A**) Normal fault surfaces (dashed great circles) with slickensides (crosses) in serpentinite along graben wall, and serpentinite foliations (full great circles) with slickensides (open squares) in the basal zone of the thrust system. (**B**) Poles to bedding, cleavage (great circle), and fold axis (open square) of north-verging minor folds related to inversion in graben fill.

mined on the basis of meticulous form surface mapping and careful cross-section construction (Figs 12, 13 & 14) show clearly that the basal portions of the Mamonia thrust systems truncate the lithological units and steep extensional structures of the underlying Troodos Complex. A similar stacking sequence and truncation relationship emerge from restoration of the structurally more complicated Mavrokolymbos section (Figs 11 & 13; see below).

The two thrust systems are distinguished on the basis of their inferred tectonic transport directions, the older to the north and northwest, and the younger to the southwest and west. Criteria used for the purpose of this distinction include a variety of small-scale kinematic indicators, such as slip line fibres, C–S fabrics and shearbands in foliated rocks, cleavage orientation in mesoscopic shear zones, and vergence of minor folds of bedding as well as cleavage, all of which are common features in the more penetratively deformed rocks in the lower portions of

the thrust systems. The predominantly ductile nature of these shear zone fabrics implies that they developed under load pressures exceeding several kilobars, indicating that the exposed portions of the thrust systems represent only the lower part of what was once an orogenic wedge of considerable thickness.

At present, the relative timing of the two thrust systems is not well constrained, although several lines of evidence suggest that structures recording north-directed emplacement are overprinted by the southwest-directed structures. North-directed, steeply inclined inversion structures observed in pillow lavas and Kannaviou Formation sandstones in the northern graben of the Troodos Complex in the Ayia Varvara window are truncated by serpentinite shear zones at the base of the south-directed system. Also, imbricates of the Ayios Photios Group in the south-directed systems of the Mavrokolymbos and Ayia Varvara windows contain mesoscopic and macroscopic fold interference patterns which indicate that rare north-facing and verging folds are overprinted by ubiquitous south-facing and verging folds related to the younger thrust system (Fig. 13).

The stacking of tectonostratigraphic units in the Mavrokolymbos window may provide further evidence for the sequence of development of the thrust structures. The thin duplex of Dhiarizos Group wedged between the two horses of Troodos Complex rocks in the north-eastern portion of the cross-section (Fig. 13), represents an out-of-sequence thrust relationship. One scenario explaining this is that the Mamonia Complex rocks were initially emplaced over a footwall of the Troodos Complex preserving some of the horst and graben structure. The stacking order established in this way was subsequently reorganized in a phase of west-directed thrusting, during which, part of a large horst consisting of massive ultramafic cumulates intruded by gabbroic dikes was emplaced over the sole of the Mamonia thrust system along a breaching thrust. Similar out-of-sequence thrust relationships, involving sheets of serpentinite breccia and pillow lava wedged between imbricates of the Ayios Photios Group along breaching thrusts, are observed in the central part of the Mavrokolymbos transect (Fig. 13).

In the Mavrokolymbos window, it is clear that west-directed thrusting occurred along a basal detachment situated within the Troodos Complex well below the floor thrust of the Mamonia Complex (Fig. 13). For example, in the south-western part of the cross-section, imbricated sheets of serpentinized harzburgites with rod-ingitized gabbro dikes and sheets of sedimentary serpentinite breccia (beneath the Mamonia sole thrust), are emplaced over a footwall of Troodos pillow lavas and Kannaviou clays, that is itself also imbricated along west-verging thrusts. In the southwestern part of the Ayia Varvara window, on the other hand, the original stacking sequence is well preserved in the older north-west-directed thrust system above the Troodos basement (Fig. 13). A blind, south-directed thrust may underlie this part of the section, to account for south-verging thrust structures observed in the southeastern part of the window (Fig. 12).

Inspection of the macroscopic geometrical relationships displayed in our maps and cross-sections shows that the early horst and graben structure of the Troodos Complex has exerted a profound control on the geometry and orientation patterns of the contractional structures that developed during the ensuing compressional phases. Overall, the thrust systems are character-ized by gentle to moderate dips along major detachment surfaces, although in a number of narrow belts the sheared serpentinites and Dhiarizos Group rocks at the base of the thrust systems display steep dips of both cleavage and bedding. These belts consistently correlate with the positions of steep graben-bounding faults in the Troodos Complex in the immediate footwall of the thrust systems (Figs 13 & 14). Inversion structures are typically observed in pillow lavas and Kannaviou lithologies situated near the steep extensional fault zones (Fig. 14, section Y). It is clear that the sole thrusts of the contractional systems have utilized not only shallowly dipping weak zones in the graben fill, particularly the Kannaviou cover and the talus deposits of serpentinite breccia, but also the steep serpentinite shear zones developed along the graben-bounding faults. This has created staircase fault trajectories, analogous to the ramp/flat trajectories of thrusts developed in bedded sedimentary sequences with large competence contrasts. In a number of instances, well illustrated in the Mav-rokolymbos window (Fig. 13), short-cut thrusts through the footwalls of the graben-bounding faults (e.g McClay & Buchanan 1992) have decapitated high-standing portions of the serp-entinite horst blocks, which were then emplaced along breaching thrusts into the base of the overlying orogenic wedge. The breaching thrusts show concave upwards trajectories, with rela-tively steep dips (partly along pre-existing exten-sional faults) in the Troodos Complex and gentle dips in the overlying Mamonia Complex, and some show hanging wall ramp anticlines. This geometry resembles the thrust trajectories of positive 'flower' structures (Harding 1985) associated with transpressive strike-slip regimes, but it is also a common product of dip-slip inversion of extensional faults (McClay & Buchanan 1992).

Kinematic indicators in the basal thrust zones invariably demonstrate reverse dipslip or reverse oblique-slip, with large pitch angles of slip lines on shear planes. These movement senses and directions differ markedly from those for the steep graben-bounding faults, which generally display normal oblique-slip with gently to moderately plunging slip lines (Fig. 14). Two contrasting kinematic patterns are recognized for the interactions of the thrust systems with the pre-existing, east–west-trending extensional structures of the Troodos Complex. The older northwest-directed thrusting phase effected dex-tral transpression in the Troodos basement. A good example in the Ayia Varvara window is the small duplex of serpentinites and Dhiarizos Group rocks, underlain by a thin veneer of

Kannaviou sandstones (too small to be shown on the map), which is situated 200 m east of section line Y (Fig. 12). This duplex developed against a short, northeast-striking segment of the main, south-dipping graben wall (shown in Fig. 14, section Y), which acted as a restraining bend on the sole of the northwest-directed thrust system. A portion of the Kannaviou fill of the graben was incorporated into the base of the thrust system. The younger, southwest- and west-directed thrusting phase, on the other hand, effected sinistral transpression in the Troodos basement. In the Mavrokolymbos window (Fig. 11), where the thrust direction is due west and the main graben walls strike northwest, this is shown by ubiquitous reverse sinistral oblique-slip indicators observed in sheared serpentinites along the steep contact (60–80° NE dip) with the Ayios Photios Group north of the dam (Fig. 13; cf. Swarbrick 1980). The serpentinite wall contains a small inlier of Troodos pillow lavas above a prominent normal dextral oblique-slip shear zone that is truncated by the floor thrust of the Ayios Photios Group. The wall is interpreted as an original graben-bounding fault that acted as a lateral to oblique ramp for the overriding Ayios Photios thrust sheets. The relay fault (30–50° ESE dip) of this graben at Ayiou Theodhorou acted as a frontal to oblique ramp to the overriding Mamonia thrust system. The serpentinite footwall contains a fault-bounded inlier of Kannaviou sandstones, representing the upper portion of the graben fill which now lies largely buried under the thrust system. Similar geometric and kinematic relationships may be postulated to explain the termination of the serpentinite horst block in the area around the dam.

## Metamorphic rocks

The thrust systems in the western part of the Ayia Varvara window contain a basal zone of highly sheared serpentinite entraining numerous blocks of metamorphic rocks of the Ayia Varvara Formation (Figs 12 & 13). The overall shape of the blocks is concordant with the shear fabric, but the metamorphic banding in the blocks is clearly oblique to this fabric. The serpentinite foliation locally occurs in steep belts where it wraps around the short edges of the larger blocks, but in general the fabric of the basal serpentinite zone has a shallow dipping attitude.

Locally, low strain domains occur in the serpentinites on the edges of the larger blocks. In one example, on the northeastern edge of the large block in the southwestern part of the map area, high-temperature peridotite mylonites are preserved, which show strong L–S fabrics more or less parallel to the foliation and mineral lineation in the adjacent metamorphic rocks. This association is strikingly similar to the contacts between basal peridotite mylonites and dynamothermal metamorphic aureoles observed in a number of obducted ophiolite complexes (Williams & Smyth 1973; Malpas 1979). Another informative example is the large strain shadow situated west of the block in the northern part of the area (Fig. 12). It contains two east–west-trending, sub-vertical shear zones truncated against the steep edge of the block in the east, and structurally overlain by a gently north-dipping thrust sheet of Dhiarizos lavas in the west. The northern shear zone is up to 5 m in width and contains small blocks of Dhiarizos Group lithologies in an intensely sheared serpentinite matrix with well-developed C–S fabrics and shearbands indicating dextral strike-slip with a gently east-plunging slip direction. The southern shear zone defines a contact between harzburgite to the north and massive wehrlite with pyroxenite and rodingitized gabbro dikes to the south, and shows composite shear fabrics indicating sinistral strike-slip. The presence of a virtually undeformed diabase dike along the margin of this shear zone suggests that the local strike-slip deformation along the intrusive contact may have occurred synmagmatically.

Internally, the metamorphic blocks display evidence of polyphase deformation under medium grade metamorphic conditions. Several generations of mesoscopic folds and associated planar and linear fabrics have been described in previous work (Spray & Roddick 1981; Malpas et al. 1992). Our observations corroborate the deformation history for the metamorphic rocks established by previous workers. It is important to note, however, that all synmetamorphic structures in the blocks, including the late stage kink fold systems, are clearly truncated at the contacts with the enveloping serpentinites. The effects of the entrainment of the blocks in the basal portions of the thrust systems are marked by pervasive shear fracturing and brecciation, associated with low-grade, chloritic alteration, and are particularly notable in the smaller blocks and exposed margins of the larger ones. Considering the present structural setting of the blocks, and the incompatibilities of their metamorphic history and that of their serpentinite host rocks, it is dubious that any valid structural correlations can be made between the two units. We are also doubtful that the structures in the blocks can be used to infer kinematic aspects of their displacement history prior to entrainment in the thrust systems.

## Discussion

The chemostratigraphy established for the volcanic rocks of the Mamonia Complex in southwest Cyprus has provided for the first time identification of a large tract of Triassic oceanic basement in the eastern Mediterranean. This oceanic crust, preserved as tholeiitic Dhiarizos Group lavas, together with associated seamount volcanics, subordinate pelagic sediments and fragments of atoll reef complexes, is now entrained in a late Cretaceous suture zone that marks the juxtaposition of the Mamonia Complex continental margin with the ophiolitic Troodos Complex. Malpas *et al.* (1992) have suggested that amphibolites and quartz-sericite schists of the Ayia Varvara Formation represent equivalents of these lithologies metamorphosed during subduction and later exhumed and incorporated in the thrust systems developed during the juxtapositioning of the two complexes. A good correlation has been established between the chemistry of lava types identified in the Dhiarizos Group and that of some mafic protoliths of the amphibolites. This correlation includes their MORB chemistry which is quite distinct from the supra-subduction zone geochemical signature of the Troodos Complex lavas. It is also corroborated by the correlation of the metasedimentary rocks in the metamorphic blocks and the sedimentary components of the Mamonia Complex noted by previous workers (Robertson Woodcock 1979).

These findings support the model proposed by Malpas *et al* (1992) that much of the Dhiarizos oceanic crust was consumed in a subduction zone dipping beneath the leading edge of the Troodos microplate. This process was the driving force for the generation of supra-subduction zone spreading within the Troodos microplate (Moores *et al.* 1984), as well as the dynamothermal metamorphism of Dhiarizos oceanic crust to give rise to the metamorphic rocks of the Ayia Varvara Formation (Malpas *et al.* 1992).

The new results of our mapping in three of the windows in the southern part of the suture zone establishes for the first time a detailed structural and stratigraphic framework for the Troodos Complex inliers of the suture zone. It is shown that the Troodos Complex preserves an east–west-trending horst and graben structure whose development started synchronous with extrusion of boninitic lavas onto, and intrusion of ultramafic and mafic plutonic rocks into, a substrate of uplifted and cooled mantle harzburgite. The

extensional deformation of the Troodos lithosphere continued amagmatically into the Campanian to early Maastrichtian, as witnessed by the deposition of the arc-related Kannaviou sediments together with locally derived talus deposits of serpentinite breccia in the grabens. The kinematic framework of this deformation remains uncertain at present, but it may have taken place in a dextral strike-slip regime similar to that of the STTFZ in the Limassol Forest (MacLeod 1990; MacLeod & Murton, this volume). We feel that it is now well established that the full range of stratigraphic, igneous and structural features which characterize the STTFZ are also present in the Troodos Complex of the southern part of the suture zone.

The first indication of the proximity of the Mamonia oceanic and continental margin rocks to the Troodos microplate edge in the southern windows of the suture zone is the synchronous deposition of Kannaviou sediments and melange with clasts of both Troodos and Mamonia Complex provenance in the graben structures of the Troodos Complex. This tectonostratigraphic setting is strikingly similar to that of the Campanian–early Maastrichtian Moni Melange which is found in a trough along the southern margin of the STTFZ in the Limassol Forest (Robertson 1977).

At present, no substantive model exists to explain the development of the Moni trough. The Moni Melange is inferred to have been emplaced by a short-lived gravity sliding event during the initial stage of collision of the Mamonia continental margin with the oceanic Troodos microplate (Robertson, 1977). Its material may have been derived by 'subduction erosion' of the Mamonia Complex (Murton 1990). The most likely plate margin setting for this trough is on the attenuated leading edge of the Troodos microplate, which is essentially a proto-forearc environment. The cause of the collapse of this forearc region remains uncertain, but it may at least in part be explained by anticlockwise rotation of the Troodos microplate, the main phase of which took place in Campanian to Maastrichtian time (Robertson 1990). The torsional pull of the microplate edge away from the subduction zone would stretch the eastern forearc region (present-day coordinates), creating a progressively eastwards widening basin that served as the depocentre for the Moni Melange. This model differs fundamentally from the configuration of the southern Troodos margin in the late Campanian proposed by MacLeod (1990), in that it places the Moni trough on top of the southern part of the STTFZ above a northerly inclined subduction zone, rather than at the edge of a major dextral strike-slip lineament between the Mamonia Complex and the Troodos Complex, for which we have found no evidence to date.

Robertson & Woodcock (1979) have described a pattern of contrasting facing and vergence directions of folds in the Ayios Photios Group in proximity to Troodos Complex inliers of the southern part of the suture zone that is similar to the basic pattern presented here. These authors suggest that north-facing and verging folds predominate across the width of the suture zone, and they have related these to an initial phase of emplacement of the Mamonia Complex in a northerly direction. The emplacement was considered to have occurred by gravity sliding of the Ayios Photios Group rocks over Dhiarizos basement at a time prior to docking with the Troodos Complex. The docking itself took place along steep serpentinite fault zones which truncated the already established thrust stack of the Mamonia Complex. Robertson & Woodcock (1979) viewed the development of the south- and west-facing folds as due to local effects associated with this docking process. Our new data corroborate the overprinting sequences and kinematic patterns of fold development in the Mamonia Complex described by Robertson & Woodcock (1979), but negate their arguments in three important aspects. Firstly, all contractional structures clearly affect rocks of the Troodos Complex. The macroscopic structural relationships observed by us in the Ayia Varvara and Mavrokolymbos windows, suggest that the Troodos Complex, rather than the Dhiarizos Group and its allochthonous Ayios Photios Group cover, defines the basement to the suture zone assemblage. Secondly, the development of the north-directed fold and thrust system was not limited to emplacement of the Ayios Photios Group over a Dhiarizos Group basement in a setting outboard of the Troodos microplate margin, but also involved emplacement of the assembled Mamonia units over the Troodos microplate edge. Thirdly, the south- and west-directed thrust system dominates the structural framework around the Troodos Complex inliers in the southern windows of the suture zone, and incorporates sizeable portions of the Troodos Complex.

Current models for the collisional stage in the tectonic evolution of the suture zone favour interleaving of segments of the Mamonia and Troodos complexes by dominant strike-slip movement along arcuate serpentinite belts, in an overall transpressive plate kinematic regime, with either dextral (MacLeod 1990; Murton 1990) or sinistral (Swarbrick 1980, 1993) shear

sense. In supporting arguments for these models, much emphasis has been placed on the anastomosing pattern, steep attitude and sheared nature of the serpentinite belts, as well as the presence of metamorphic blocks in these belts; the common occurrence of indicators for strike-slip or shallow plunging oblique-slip in the serpentinite shear zones; the map pattern suggesting that the serpentinite belts define microterrane boundaries in the northern and southern parts of the suture zone; the lack of documentation of low-angle structural contacts between the two complexes; and the lack of evidence for a two-stage deformation history involving horizontal emplacement followed by steep faulting, necessary to create the present distribution of the two complexes in the suture zone (cf. Swarbrick 1993).

Our new results, on the other hand, convincingly demonstrate the complexity of the structural evolution of the suture zone, with respect to its deformation history, megascopic geometry and kinematics. The polyphase deformation history, established by us, places renewed emphasis on the importance of contractional deformation, involving development of gently dipping thrust systems, in shaping the collisional framework of the suture zone, not only in its north–south-trending western portion, but also its west–east-trending southern portion. It negates many of the arguments presented by Swarbrick (1993) for a single-stage strike-slip dominated collisional history. Our detailed form surface mapping, although presently restricted to small but relevant portions of the suture zone, has failed to establish the presence of a through-going, linked network of steep serpentinite shear zones in the southern portion of the suture zone, where according to the current models strike-slip deformation should have been predominant (e.g. Swarbrick 1993). Much of the steep structure of the serpentinite belts can be convincingly shown on the basis of both structural geometrical, kinematic, and stratigraphic evidence to be inherited from the phase of extensional deformation to which the Troodos microplate margin was subjected prior to the ensuing collision. The common, local indicators for oblique movement with shallow plunging slip lines in the serpentinite shear zones represent a mixed group of structures, partly inherited from the extensional phase, and partly created by the superposed contractional deformations acting obliquely across the already established extensional structural framework of the Troodos microplate edge. Our form surface mapping has further failed to establish clear-cut truncations of the Mamonia thrust wedge by steep serpentinite belts; rather, the Dhiarizos Group basement of the Mamonia Complex is consistently seen to structurally overlie rocks of the Troodos Complex. Sharp truncations along a linked network of sub-vertical serpentinite shear zones are a prerequisite in any model that regards the boundaries of the Troodos Complex inliers as microterrane boundaries in a strike-slip dominated suture zone.

The emplacement of the early, north-directed thrust system of the Mamonia Complex over the southern margin of the Troodos Complex heralds, in our scenario, the docking of the two microplates. The deposition of the Moni Melange pre-dated, and is most likely the precursor to, the arrival of this thrust system on the Troodos crust. The mechanisms by which the early thrust wedge was transferred from the leading edge of the Mamonia microplate onto the Troodos microplate margin remain speculative. Robertson & Woodcock (1979) have presented valid arguments that the thrust system does not represent an accretionary wedge. Our findings lend further support to their arguments, in that both the observed stacking order of Mamonia Complex over Troodos Complex and the northerly polarity of the thrust system are opposite to those expected if the Mamonia Complex was telescoped in an accretionary wedge along a north-dipping subduction zone beneath the Troodos microplate. We favour, instead, a model wherein the surficial continental margin rocks of the Mamonia Complex were delaminated from their substrate upon arrival at the subduction zone, and emplaced onto the highly extended forearc region of the Troodos microplate. The emplacement may have occurred by massive gravity sliding, as originally proposed by Robertson & Woodcock (1979), presumably into the then established Moni trough. Much of the Dhiarizos oceanic crust was subducted, but some off-scraping took place of elevated volcanic edifices and their associated sediments which were incorporated into the base of the advancing thrust system.

The most enigmatic feature encountered by us to date, is the presence of metamorphic blocks of the Ayia Varvara Formation within the soles of the Mamonia thrust systems. This is contrary to their setting within steep serpentinite belts associated with major strike-slip faults, favoured by previous workers (e.g, Spray & Roddick 1981; Swarbrick 1993). We have argued earlier that these rocks were formed by subduction zone metamorphism of Dhiarizos oceanic crust beneath the Troodos microplate, and essentially constitute fragments of the dynamothermal metamorphic aureole of the Troodos ophiolite

(Malpas *et al.* 1992). The entrainment of these rocks within the soles of the Mamonia thrust systems requires that they were uplifted from their site of formation in the subduction zone, possibly transported across the overlying Troodos microplate edge, and exhumed prior to the arrival of the north-directed Mamonia thrust system in early (?) Maastrichtian time. We have found little field evidence, so far, for this complicated displacement path in the serpentinite host rocks of the metamorphic blocks. The steep shear zone with Dhiarizos Group blocks in the strain shadow of the northern metamorphic block in the Ayia Varvara window may be a feature related to the emplacement history of the blocks that survived the effects of the contractional deformations during the ensuing collision.

The cessation of deformation in the suture zone is marked by the deposition of the Maastrichtian Kathikas Melange, which seals the structural contacts created by the younger, south- and west-directed thrust event (e.g. Fig. 12; Swarbrick 1980). The development of the contractional framework of the suture zone in southwestern Cyprus thus took place largely in the Maastrichtian, over a period of approximately 3–7 Ma. During this period, notable changes occurred at least in the southern and southwestern portions of the suture zone with respect to the direction and polarity of thrusting, as well as the crustal level at which thrusting took place. The older northwest- to north-directed thrusting involved the development of a thrust wedge that incorporated mostly Mamonia Complex lithologies and moved surficially over the western extension of the STTFZ. The younger southwest- to west-directed thrust wedge, on the other hand, incorporated sizeable sections of the STTFZ assemblage at its base, creating locally notable reversals of the tectono-stratigraphic stacking order established during the older thrust event. The fundamental differences in the geometric and kinematic evolution of the thrust systems must be related in some way to changes in the boundary conditions of the deformation while the orogenic front migrated across the leading edge of the Troodos microplate. Considering that our detailed structural analysis of the suture zone is presently restricted to only its most southern and southwestern portions, we feel that it is unwarranted at this point in time to speculate in any great detail on the relationship between the deformation history of the suture zone and the plate kinematic evolution of the Mamonia and Troodos terranes as a whole.

This paper reports the findings of the Memorial

University group who were, in part, introduced to Cyprus geology by a good friend, the late Professor Ian Gass. The authors would like to thank D. Williams, D. Regular, J. Smith and the Cyprus Geological Survey Department, especially Dr C. Xenophontos, for their able assistance and continuing scientific discussions.

# References

CAMERON W. E. 1985. Petrology and origin of primitive lavas from the Troodos ophiolite, Cyprus. *Contributions to Mineralogy and Petrology*, **89**, 239–255.

EALY, P. J. & KNOX, G. J., 1975. The pre-Tertiary rocks of S.W. Cyprus. *Geologie en Mijnbouw*, **54**, 85–100.

HARDING, T. P. 1985. Seismic characteristics and identification of negative flower structures, positive flower structures, and positive structural inversion. *American Association of Petroleum Geologists Bulletin*, **69**, 582–600.

HENSON, F. R. S., BROWNE, R. V. & MCGINTY, J. 1949. A synopsis of the stratigraphy and geological history of Cyprus. *Quarterly Journal of the Geological Society of London*, **105**, 1–41.

LAPIERRE H., 1975. Les formations sedimentaires et eruptives des nappes de Mamonia (Chypre). *Comptes Rendus de l'Academie des Sciences, Paris*, **d276**, 32–35.

MACLEOD, C. J. 1990. Role of the Southern Troodos Transform fault in the rotation of the Cyprus microplate: evidence from the Eastern Limassol Forest Complex. *In*: MALPAS *et al.* (eds) *Ophiolites*. Proceedings of the international ophiolite symposium, Cyprus, 1987. Cyprus Geological Survey Department, Nicosia, 75–85.

MALPAS J. 1979. The dynamo-thermal aureole of the Bay of Islands ophiolite suite. *Canadian Journal of Earth Sciences*, **16**, 2086–2101.

——, MOORES, E. M., PANAYIOTOU A. & XENOPHONTOS, C. (eds) 1990. *Ophiolites*. Proceedings of the International ophiolite symposium, Cyprus, 1987. Cyprus Geological Survey Department, Nicosia.

—— & XENOPHONTOS, C. 1987. Mamonia Complex and its relation to the Troodos ophiolite. Excursion I. In: *Field Excursion Guidebook, International ophiolite symposium, Cyprus, 1987*. Cyprus Geological Survey Department, Nicosia, 234–259.

——, & WILLIAMS, D. 1992. The Ayia Varvara Formation of S.W. Cyprus, a product of complex collisional tectonics. *Tectonophysics*, **212**, 193–211.

MANTIS, M. 1970. *Upper Cretaceous–Tertiary foraminiferal zones in Cyprus*. Scientific Research Centre Cyprus, 227–241.

MCCLAY, K. R. & BUCHANAN, P. G. 1992. Thrust faults in inverted extensional basins. *In*: MCCLAY,
K. R. (ed.) *Thrust Tectonics*. Chapman & Hall, London, 93–104.

MOORES, E., ROBINSON, P. T., MALPAS, J. & XENOPHONTOS, C. 1984. A model for the origin of the Troodos massif, Cyprus and other mid-east ophiolites. *Geology*, **12**, 500–503.

MURTON, B. J. 1990. Was the Southern Troodos Transform Fault a victim of microplate rotation? *In*: MALPAS *et al.* (eds) *Ophiolites*. Proceedings of the International ophiolite symposium, Cyprus, 1987. Cyprus Geological Survey Department, Nicosia, 87–98.

PANTAZIS, T. M. 1967. *The geology and mineral resources of the Pharmakas–Kalavassos area*. Geological Survey of Cyprus Memoir **8**.

ROBERTSON, A. H. F. 1977. The Moni Mélange, Cyprus: an olistostrome formed at a destructive plate margin. *Journal of the Geological Society, London*, **133**, 447–466.

—— 1990. Tectonic evolution of Cyprus. *In*: MALPAS *et al.* (eds) *Ophiolites*. Proceedings of the International ophiolite symposium, Cyprus, 1987. Cyprus Geological Survey Department, Nicosia, 235–250.

—— & WOODCOCK, M. H. 1979. Mamonia Complex, S.W. Cyprus: evolution and emplacement of a Mesozoic continental margin. *Geological Society of America Bulletin*, **90**, 651–665.

ROBINSON, P. T., MELSON, W. G., O'HEARN, T. & SCHMINCKE, H-U. 1983. Volcanic glass composition of the Troodos ophiolite, Cyprus. *Geology*, **11**, 400–404.

SHERVAIS, J. W. 1982. Ti–V plots and the petrogenesis of modern and ophiolitic lavas. *Earth and Planetary Science Letters*, **59**, 101–118.

SIMONIAN, K. O. & GASS, I. G. 1978. Arakapas fault belt, Cyprus: a fossil transform fault. *Geological Society of America Bulletin*, **89**, 1220–1230.

SPRAY, J. G. & RODDICK, J. C. 1981. Evidence for Upper Cretaceous transform fault metamorphism in west Cyprus. *Earth and Planetary Science Letters*, **55**, 273–291.

SWARBRICK, R. E. 1980. The Mamonia Complex of S.W. Cyprus, a Mesozoic continental margin and its relationship to the Troodos Complex. *In*: PANAYIOTOU, A. (ed.) *Ophiolites*. Proceedings of the International ophiolite symposium, Cyprus, 1979. Cyprus Geological Survey Department, Nicosia, 86–92.

—— 1993. Sinistral strike-slip and transpressional tectonics in an ancient oceanic setting: the Mamonia Complex, southwest Cyprus. *Journal of the Geological Society, London*, **150**, 381–392.

—— & ROBERTSON, A. H. F. 1980. Revised stratigraphy of the Mesozoic rocks of S. Cyprus. *Geological Magazine*, **117**, 547–563.

WILLIAMS, H. & SMYTH, W. R. 1973. Metamorphic aureoles beneath ophiolite suites and alpine peridotites: tectonic implications with west Newfoundland examples. *American Journal of Science*, **273**, 594–621.

# Troodos revisited: the Mount Olympus gravity anomaly

A. W. SHELTON

*Department of Earth Sciences, Sultan Qaboos University, PO Box 32486 Al-Khod,*
*Sultanate of Oman.*

**Abstract**: Eighty new gravity stations have been established to define the intense gravity low reported by Gass & Masson-Smith in 1963. The anomaly is confirmed as circular; the implications of this, against a background 200 mGal positive with an E–W trend, are explored.

The residual anomaly has been isolated and an anomalous mass determined. From this, permissible volumes have been calculated assuming serpentinization of mantle material to be solely responsible for the anomaly. Within these constraints, modelling of the residual reveals a solution with a northerly dip consistent with the underlying subduction polarity. The modelling excludes causative bodies other than those near-surface, equidimensional in plan and having a high density contrast.

The anomalous mass allows an estimate of the uplift forces acting beneath the summit of Mt Olympus. These are shown to be three times the mass of the topography above the level of 1000 m. Implications for the rate of uplift are discussed.

Gravity surveys of Cyprus were carried out by the Iraq Petroleum Company (1946) and the Overseas Geological Survey (1958). Gass & Masson-Smith (1963) communicated the results and interpretation of those surveys with a perceptive geological understanding of the Troodos massif of Cyprus. Their data showed a surprisingly localized, negative gravity anomaly approximately coincident with the summit of Mt Olympus and the ultramafic outcrop.

This circular negative anomaly of $-120$ mGal was modelled as a cone-shaped mass deficiency extending to a depth of over 11 km. The low density material (density contrast $-0.8$ Mg $^{-3}$) was considered either as a granitic boss or, more probably, a serpentine body; the authors have identified problems with both of these interpretations.

At that time, serpentinite intrusions were popular geological interpretations of ultrabasic bodies, many of which have since been more satisfactorily modelled as thrust sheets following the plate tectonic revolution and the widespread acceptance of ophiolites as fragments of oceanic lithosphere. Gass & Masson-Smith, in the vanguard of the revolution, postulated diapiric emplacement of the serpentinite but recognized the difficulties in reconciling 'the cylindrical space-form of the boss with the pronounced north–south elongation of dykes in the Sheeted Intrusive Complex'. They did, however, emphasize the concentricity of the Olympus ultrabasic outcrop and the coincidence of the negative anomaly with the area of greatest uplift, stating that the potential uplift greatly exceeds the pres-

ent-day uplift and that the Olympus area is likely to have been experiencing continuous uplift since 'the emplacement of a mass deficiency', resulting in extensive erosion.

In 1985 I. G. Gass supported a grant application to fund a detailed survey, suggesting that the co-existence of such a pronounced mass deficiency and topographic expression deserved further investigation and might provide constraints on the history of uplift. The present work is intended to define more closely the shape and magnitude of the Olympus negative anomaly and to interpret it in the light of the present understanding of the Troodos ophiolite. The gravity data provide constraints on the forces involved and improved geomorphological mapping and dating of the surficial rocks (Houghton *et al.* 1990; Poole & Robertson 1991) constrain the rates of uplift.

## Gravity network

Working from a base in Paphos, approximately 80 new gravity stations were occupied in a 20 km wide N–S band between 480 and 500 000E (Universal Transverse Mercator). This strip extends from Episkopi Bay in the south over Mt Olympus to within 10 km of the northern coast (see Fig. 1). Station density was greatest over the reported position of the Olympus negative anomaly.

In 1973 a regional gravity survey was completed to a high degree of accuracy by the Royal Engineers. This island-wide survey was based on 14 secondary stations and over 370 measure-

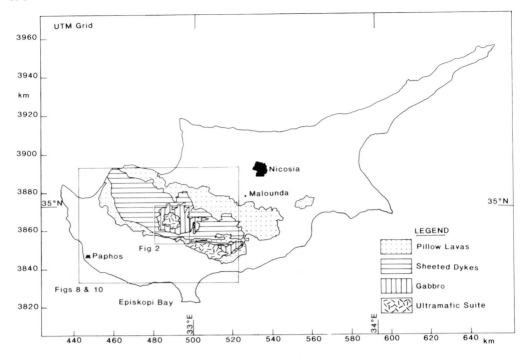

**Fig. 1.** Generalized geology of Cyprus showing the areas covered by Figs 2, 8 and 10. Mount Olympus, elevation $c$. 1950 m, corresponds to the circular outcrop of ultramafic and gabbroic rock. Areas without ornament are uppermost Cretaceous and Cenozoic sediments, principally carbonates. Ophiolite exposed on the Akamas peninsula at the extreme west of the island is not shown.

ments. In the area covered by the present survey a N–S traverse with stations at 5 km intervals (on average) was established. Through the generous cooperation of the Directorate of Military Survey, Feltham, details of these stations allowed reoccupation of one of their first-order bases and several of their secondary stations. In addition to the use of their tie into the world network, this provided a further 25 measurements in the region of interest, in particular measurements on the northern coast, to which access is now difficult.

The primary station in the 1973 survey at Nicosia is given as:

$$\text{CG}/73\text{A} - \text{IG} = 979834.34 \pm 0.3 \text{ mGal}$$

relative to Potsdam 981274 mGal. This is based largely on a reliable Beirut tie and has been checked against pre-existing Nicosia stations and found to be free of significant error. The secondary base at the centre of the present survey area is

$$\text{CG}/73\text{A} - 9\text{G} = 979546.049 \pm 0.007 \text{ mGal}$$

(error relative to the 1973 datum). This gives the present survey base value (tie $\pm 0.05$ mGal) as

$$\text{Paphos BG} = 979819.61 \pm 0.36 \text{ mGal}$$

The 1985 survey measurements were made with LaCoste & Romberg meter G-513 which settled after five days of the survey into an acceptable drift rate of 0.01 mGal per day. Higher drift affected a single return connection to one of the 1958 OGS stations at Malounda. A drift-corrected difference from Paphos of 25.84(8) mGal was obtained. The 1958 value at this station (599) is 979847.1 mGal based on a Cambridge value of 981268.1 mGal. The 1985 value for Malounda 599 is 979845.46, within 0.05 mGal when the 1.59 mGal reduction in base values for Mace Pendulum station 4 is taken into account. To convert to IGSN71 values a reduction of 14 mGal in the datum is required. For the present purposes Potsdam 981274 mGal is accepted so that the Gass & Masson-Smith (1963) data can be directly compared with recent measurements. This allows the use of both the 1958 and 1973 survey data to provide a regional gravity field against which the extent and magnitude of the Olympus gravity low can be assessed.

After correction for tidal drift, the 1985 gravity differences were least-squares adjusted on a

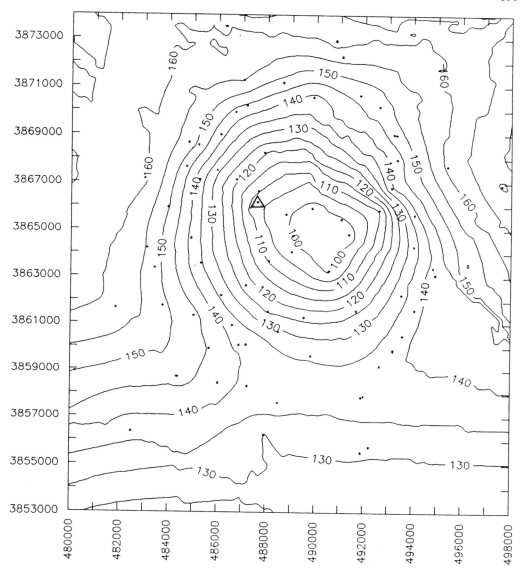

**Fig. 2.** The Mt Olympus gravity anomaly showing new station positions, summit marked with triangle. UTM grid in metres, SBA values are in mGal. Note the symmetry of the anomaly despite the strong E–W background field.

network from which it was apparent that the largest misclosure was 0.217 mGal. This was found to be due to an inexact reoccupation of a tertiary station, after which correction loop misclosures did not exceed 0.015 mGal per tie. Accuracy of gravity readings, including meter drift, appears better than ± 0.11 mGal.

**Altimetry**

Height differences were measured using two Thommens barometric altimeters and by making the maximum use of previously surveyed positions.

Many of the heights established by the Royal Engineers have been lost due to the recent re-

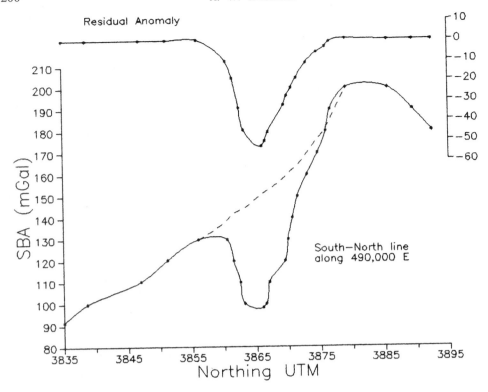

**Fig. 3.** 1985 data along a N–S transect through 490E. The residual of 53 mGal results from considering the regional as a third-order surface approximately represented by the dashed line. This simple background assumption results in an asymmetric residual anomaly and implies a northward dip for the causative body (residual anomaly scale at right in mGal).

newal of roads in the Troodos area. As a result, a greater dependency than was anticipated was placed on the barometric altimetry. After correction for air temperature, humidity and gravity values a barometric drift curve was drawn up for each day to satisfy multiple reoccupation of stations and measured drift at stations occupied for extended periods. Typically, barometric pressure rose by the equivalent of $-1.6\,m\,hr^{-1}$ until 12.30 pm after which a drop of $+1.8\,m$ $hr^{-1}$ occurred until 16.00 at which time pressure generally rose again. Readings were only rarely taken at intervals greater than 30 minutes and, therefore, drift corrections to measured height differences rarely exceeded 90 cm. The drift-corrected differences were then networked and compared with the surveyed height differences. The network loop misclosures did not exceed 7 m and the adjustment to any height difference was exceptionally 70 cm but generally between 10 and 30 cm.

Despite every possible care, barometric alti-

metry is prone to error in mountainous terrain. A careful analysis of the heighting showed unresolvable differences with the declared heights in the 1973 survey which reached 10 m in the worst case. There is some evidence for altimeter malfunction or abnormal pressure fluctuation during part of one day's survey and corrective steps have been taken; however the results are at variance with the surveying by as much as 1.7%. The barometric results are internally consistent and give a derived height only 70 cm different from that declared on the trig point at the summit of Mt Olympus. The uncertainties in the altitude may contribute as much as 3 mGal to any error in the Bouguer anomaly values.

## Simple Bouguer anomaly (SBA) results

The SBA (i.e. without terrain correction) values confirm the presence and shape of the Olympus negative anomaly (Fig. 2) as contoured by Gass & Masson-Smith (1963). The distribution of

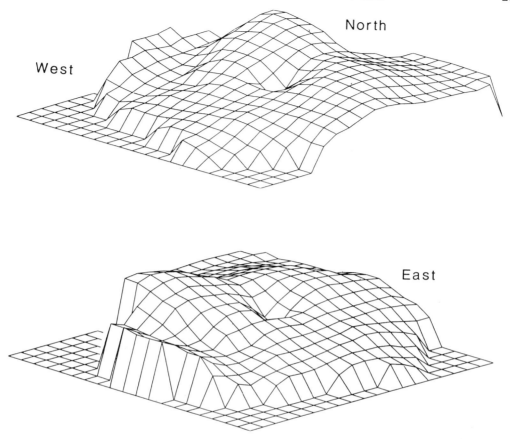

**Fig. 4.** Two views of the Bouguer gravity data of Gass & Masson-Smith (1963) reduced to zero at the coastline to aid orientation. Looking from the SE and SW, only western Cyprus is shown. The Mt Olympus low and the Pomos positive anomaly are both clear, the positive is less obviously separable from the overall positive for the Troodos Range.

gravity values in the most recent survey allows none other than a circular low impressed upon the otherwise E–W-trending contours associated with the ophiolite outcrop. The SBA values are not significantly different from the terrain-corrected complete Bouguer values of Gass & Masson-Smith (1963) but the size of the negative anomaly is called into question when compared with a regional field derived by plotting a N–S line through the centre of the low (Fig. 3). Such a line along UTM 490E has a residual of only −53 mGal.

A comparison with the Complete Bouguer Anomaly (CBA) values taken from the contours of the original paper (Fig. 5) shows an anomaly of approximately −67 mGal for the same line. The greater depth of the residual low is mostly due to the difference in Bouguer reduction values

(see later discussion). In order to achieve a residual anomaly approaching −120 mGal the low must be compared with N–S lines 20 km to the west of 490E. Thus the −120 mGal low was derived from a 3D treatment of the regional gravity field. There are problems with this approach in that to the northwest of the Olympus low there is a discrete positive anomaly called the Pomos positive anomaly in Gass & Masson-Smith (1963). This broad feature, only casually related to outcrop geology, controls the regional field to the west of Mt Olympus. Figure 4 illustrates the difficulties in selecting a representative regional field for western Cyprus.

As Gass & Masson-Smith acknowledge, the separation of residual and regional fields in Cyprus is largely subjective. The original amplitude of the Olympus low arises from their

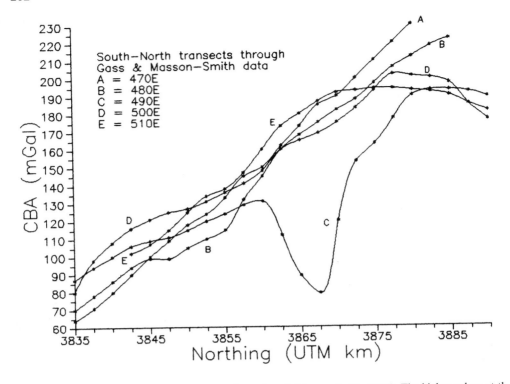

**Fig. 5.** Comparison of N–S data profiles taken from Gass & Masson-Smith (1963). The higher values at the northern end of the most westerly examples (A & B) are starting to show the influence of the positive Pomos anomaly.

assumption that the contours of the main (regional) anomaly would have a steady E–W trend and that any disturbance is due to a discrete source. Given the N–S overall dyke trend and the impressive definition of the Olympus negative, the E–W trend assumption is entirely reasonable but the anomaly amplitude needs reconsideration.

The terrain corrections for the 1985 data were not accessible at the time of writing. To estimate the effects of terrain, a large-scale map of the island was digitized and the 100 station elevations incorporated into the data set. These gave a measure of control in the area of the summit of Mt Olympus. Corrections were made out to Hammer zone M (22 km) using this approximation to the topography assuming a constant slope for zones C to F. These terrain correction estimates have a significant effect only in the area of the anomalous low. They add 1–3 mGals to the SBA values on the mountain flanks but may reduce the amplitude of the residual to −40 mGal.

The anomaly as seen in the complete Bouguer

anomaly map of Gass & Masson-Smith (1963) is almost perfectly circular. This has been confirmed with the additional data: it is not an artefact resulting from low data density in the less accessible area of the peak. To present a circular anomaly when obviously superimposed on an east–west linear background, the causative body ought to have a north–south elongation. This observation is reinforced by the examination of N–S profiles (Fig. 5) at regular intervals in Western Cyprus which shows the 490E transect to have lower overall values than its neighbouring profiles.

The N–S band of lower gravity values between Xeros on the north coast and Episkopi on the south raises the possibility that the Olympus low is part of a ridge or ridge-parallel structure. Indeed, structural studies (Varga & Moores 1985) have revealed north–south-trending grabens on the northern flank of the ophiolite thought to be the fossil axial valleys of slow-spreading ridges. Allerton & Vine (1987) see the listric normal faulting of the upper crustal section of the ophiolite as a later event, the grabens being structures formed on the side of a spreading ridge.

In this context, the separation of the residual low from a N–S regional field must be carefully considered. However, the anomaly is so intense and localized that the E–W-trending regional appears to have little effect upon it (cf. Residual separation, Fig. 10).

Before investigating the form of the causative body, the extent to which the Olympus negative anomaly could be an artefact of the gravity reduction process has to be considered. The correspondence of the negative anomaly and greatest elevation makes good sense from the point of view of isostasy. There is however the alternative possibility: that the correspondence means the anomaly arises from the derivation of the gravity values.

## Effects due to reduction assumptions

A radically simplified south–north geological section was constructed with the surface dips of the major interfaces assumed to continue to sea-level. Serpentinized harzburgite was assumed to occupy the highest ground, the ultramafic rocks were not differentiated.

The SBA values have been derived with a uniform reduction density of $2.67 \, \mathrm{Mg \, m^{-3}}$. The original authors used $2.4 \, \mathrm{Mg \, m^{-3}}$ for the Tertiary and Recent sedimentary rocks and $2.7 \, \mathrm{Mg \, m^{-3}}$ for the older ophiolitic suite. Using the approximation of the geology, a comparison of Bouguer values calculated at different densities has been made and the effects on the regional field are considered.

The effect of using 2.4 and $2.7 \, \mathrm{Mg \, m^{-3}}$ (scheme A) instead of 2.67 throughout (scheme C) is only significant over the elevated parts of the sedimentary succession where the more realistic density employed by Gass & Masson-Smith generates a profile up to 7 mGal more positive. This could affect the estimation of the regional anomaly level, increasing it by not greater than 10 mGal over the $2.67 \, \mathrm{Mg \, m^{-3}}$ version. In addition, the slightly higher densities over the elevated ultramafics would deepen the residual negative anomaly by approximately 2 mGal.

Scheme B investigates the effects of using densities appropriate for unserpentinized harzburgite in the traverse ($3.05 \, \mathrm{Mg \, m^{-3}}$). This results in a deepening of the low by approximately 25 mGal. Compare this with scheme D in which the harzburgite has been 100% serpentinized to give reduction densities of $2.60 \, \mathrm{Mg \, m^{-3}}$. This reduces the 2.67 derived anomaly by approximately 5 mGal (Fig. 6). In the field

serpentinization is approximately 70% near the present-day surface.

In summary, there is a large anomaly coincident with the elevated terrain. Assuming high (mantle) densities for the reduction makes that anomaly considerably deeper; however, assuming lower densities cannot flatten out the low without resorting to unrealistic values ($< 1.8 \, \mathrm{Mg \, m^{-3}}$).

The gravity low corresponding to the high ground has a value of approximately 60 mGal using a constant Bouguer reduction density of $2.67 \, \mathrm{Mg \, m^{-3}}$. If all the material down to sea-level is in reality harzburgite with only minor alteration (say not greater than 40% serpentinization), having a density of $3.05 \, \mathrm{Mg \, m^{-3}}$, then that low would be deepened to approximately 85 mGal. The use of a Nettleton approach to the estimation of the density of the summit of Mt Olympus is not a success. Such an approach is only properly applicable over topography of uniform composition. It does, nonetheless, confirm that the higher density alternatives are inappropriate. The remainder of the calculations are, therefore, carried out assuming an average density of $2.67 \, \mathrm{m^{-3}}$ for the mountain. This value would be appropriate for severely altered ultramafic rock and allows comparison with the data of Gass & Masson-Smith in the elevated area.

## 3D gravity modelling of the Olympus anomaly

Given that the Olympus negative anomaly is not merely an artefact of the reduction process it is instructive to consider the implications of the anomaly. The simple or complete Bouguer anomaly values represent the mass excess and a localized deficiency in that mass below sea-level. The magnitude and gradient, however, indicate a shallow source for the negative anomaly. Regionally, a substantial gravity high of up to 250 mGal has to be explained and within that a local deficiency of at least 55 mGal.

As a first approximation the low was modelled as a localized absence of the high-density material responsible for the regional high. A number of models were run with the CORDELL iterative 3D gravity modelling programme (Cordell & Henderson 1968). The residual low was investigated on a 2.5 km grid assuming a reference plane delimiting the top of the model. This programme attempts to account for the gravity field by iteratively adjusting the depths, or lengths in this case, of vertical prisms.

Using this grid, supposed sufficiently detailed for an anomaly some 35 km in diameter, solutions could not be obtained at density contrasts

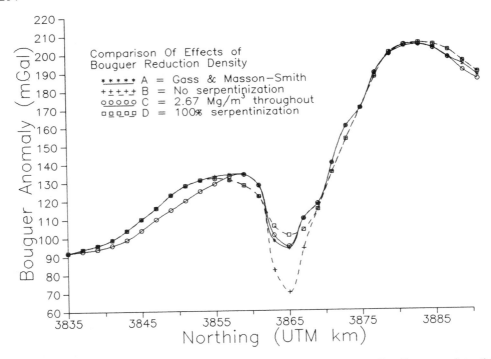

**Fig. 6.** Comparison of the effects of using different Bouguer reduction densities. The effects are substantial over such elevated ground, especially when a large range of densities is, theoretically, possible. C = 2.67 throughout. A = 2.40 for chalks, 2.70 for ophiolite. B = 2.40 chalks, 2.80 dykes, 2.90 gabbros and 3.05 harzburgite. D as C except ultramafics 100% serpentinized at 2.60 Mg m$^{-3}$.

smaller than $-0.8\,\mathrm{Mg\,m^{-3}}$. With a coarser grid of 5 km and subsequent greater fit errors, a density contrast of $-0.72\,\mathrm{Mg\,m^{-3}}$ gave a solution with a maximum model depth of $7.2\,\mathrm{km\,m^{-3}}$. Lower contrasts could not be modelled reliably.

The high density contrasts apparently necessary for solution are difficult to relate to the geology of the island. From data gathered from ophiolite samples in Oman (Shelton 1984), mantle rocks above sea-level appear to have densities of around $3.05\,\mathrm{Mg\,m^{-3}}$ indicating 40% serpentinization. The derived density of the alteration products in Oman was $2.68\,\mathrm{Mg\,m^{-3}}$. These results give a maximum contrast of $0.37\,\mathrm{Mg\,m^{-3}}$ which is much less than the stable limit. The two ophiolites may, however, not be even remotely comparable. Nowhere in Oman is there evidence of a serpentinite body on the scale necessary to cause the Mt Olympus negative anomaly.

At the other extreme the mineral density of harzburgite is 3.32 and serpentine in some iso-morphs has densities as low as $2.60\,\mathrm{Mg\,m^{-3}}$. This extreme density contrast of $0.72\,\mathrm{Mg\,m^{-3}}$ approaches the $0.8\,\mathrm{Mg\,m^{-3}}$ used by Gass & Masson-Smith (1963). Surface samples collected from Troodos were only 70% serpentinized on average. Because much of the gravity effect arises below sea-level and surficial weathering ought not to have much hold, lower density contrast and greater depth possibilities should be considered. Note that if the anomaly is larger than the 80 mGal modelled here, only the highest contrasts suffice to keep the problem within the bounds of reality.

## 2.5D modelling

Given the sensitivity of the 3D Cordell algorithm, a well-tried and trusted 2.5D method was used to experiment on the data set. The 1985 data set was sampled at 1 km intervals on a S–N line along UTM 490 000mE, the line is 60 km from 3835 000 to 3895 000mN. These data have been Bouguer reduced at $2.67\,\mathrm{Mg\,m^{-3}}$ and are not terrain corrected (as mentioned, the CBA values can be greater by as much as 20 mGal in extremely rugged stations, the overall effect being to reduce the depth of the anomalous low).

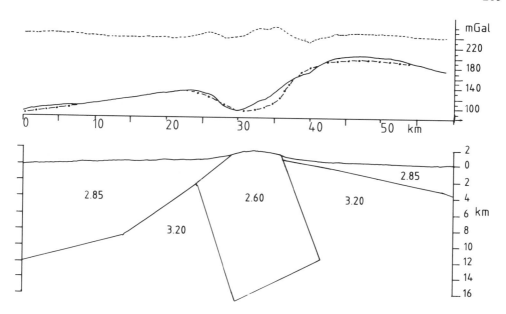

**Fig. 7.** 2.5D model and results for the S–N transect through 490E. The model shows oceanic crust at 2.85 Mg m$^{-3}$ over altered depleted mantle at 3.20 Mg m$^{-3}$. The central prism at 2.60 Mg m$^{-3}$ represents fully serpentinized mantle. Observed gravity is shown as solid line, calculated as a dotted and dashed line. The difference between these is a dotted line above. The largest errors with this deliberately simple solution occur on the northern flank of the mountain. These can be accounted for by introducing near-surface complications to the northern side of the low-density body. Vertical exaggeration 1:1.15.

The modelling is carried out to the land surface; topography is taken from 1:100 000 maps to within 20 m. The surface geological boundaries and dips are from the excellent mapping of the Cyprus Geological Survey (Wilson 1959).

To fit this work into the larger picture, the data were combined with a regional gravity line and bathymetry from Woodside (1977) along 33°E. This line extends 220 km south and 200 km north of the onshore data. A model was created that approximated this field in which it was found necessary to provide a shallowly (5°), northward-dipping Moho overlain by a crustal wedge (part of Turkey?). To the south the data are satisfied by a horizontal Moho at around 20 km depth. The regional field in the area of the Eratosthenes Seamount proved difficult to account for with the distribution of densities employed. It is possible that the 1–2 km of sediment overlying oceanic crust south of the island should not have been included. More importantly, the complex crustal structures associated with subduction in the vicinity of the Seamount were not attempted. This does not, however, affect modelling on the island.

Within this long-range framework the onshore regional high can be adequately modelled simply by assuming that the mantle rises rapidly under Western Cyprus as suggested in Gass & Masson-Smith (1963). In this model the Moho rises from a depth of 10 km at the southern coast to outcrop on Mt Olympus. On the northern flanks of the mountain a shallower dip of the crust/mantle interface satisfies the data. It drops from outcrop at 36 km to a depth of 4 km at 60 kmN (Fig. 7). The density contrast is 0.35 Mg m$^{-3}$ (e.g. 3.20 against 2.85 Mg m$^{-3}$). This contrast, or the depth to the interface, will be reduced if the Tertiary sediments are included in the regional model.

## Modelling the Mt Olympus gravity low

Having established a background model that is consistent with surface constraints and the established trends of the regional geology from seismic and seismological data (McKenzie 1972; Woodside 1977), the next step was to consider the form of bodies that could be responsible for the Mount Olympus Low. Polygons of hydrated mantle at density 2.65 Mg m$^{-3}$ were inserted into

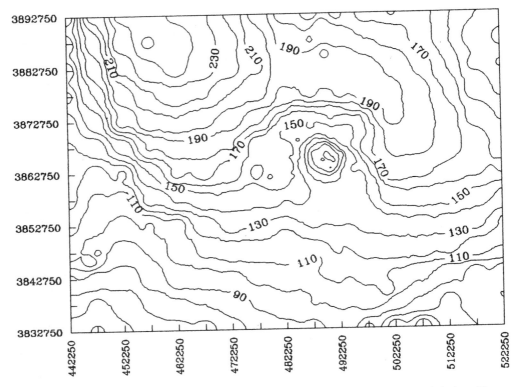

**Fig. 8.** Combined Gass & Masson-Smith regional data with the detailed 1985 results around the low. The Pomos high is centred at 3887 kmN, 457 kmE. The E–W trend in the southern portion of this 80 × 60 km area is clear.

the mantle wedge. These plugs of serpentinized mantle were initially given a half-width of 3.25 km in a good approximation to a 3D model.

Two classes of body were investigated: sheet-like structures striking N–S and cylindrical 'diapirs' as the two geologically reasonable contenders.

In order to match the amplitude of the anomaly with a sheet-like body, an extensive amount of low density material is required. Models with the mass deficiency as deep as 20 km with a N–S extent of 20 km were optimized but failed to provide a solution with density contrasts up to $-0.5\,\mathrm{Mg\,m^{-3}}$. Increasing the depth, as ever, provides diminishing returns. The alternative, much larger density contrasts, is considered less than likely in this geological context. The only option remaining is to increase the half-width.

Once this path is taken the modelling quickly evolves into a regular-shaped body, some 9 × 10 km in plan. To match the shape of the residual anomaly, the body requires a north-wards dip. In keeping the model as simple as

possible, the solution indicates that the southern flanks of the mountain are underlain by serpentinized material whereas the northern limits coincide with the outcrop.

The solution illustrated in Fig. 7 has a 'serpentinite body which contrasts with the background mantle material by $-0.6\,\mathrm{Mg\,m^{-3}}$. It extends to an average depth of 15 km and dips at approximately 65° to the north. The dip of this body is steeper by an order of magnitude than that attributed to the regional geology. This suggests that the effect responsible for the low is a deep-rooted phenomenon that post-dates and transcends the arrangement of oceanic lithosphere making up the island. It is also clear that the low is the result of an extreme density contrast situated at relatively shallow levels and formed subsequent to, or perhaps as a consequence of, subduction beneath Turkey.

## Regional–residual separations

The Gass & Masson-Smith data, digitized on a 5 km grid over Western Cyprus, are redisplayed in Fig. 8. It is clear that at least the southern half of these data conform to an E–W-trending regional. Plotting values in the 50 km swath surrounding the low allows a first-order field to be fitted to data west of the low (gradient + 3.9 mGal km$^{-1}$ northwards). The effect of subtracting this planar regional from the total is to create a serious mismatch north of 3868 000 (UTM) on the eastern side of the anomaly. The resultant residual is not fully isolated from the surrounding longer wavelength field.

Figure 9 shows two of the alternative regional field profiles derived from either side of the low. The western side can be successfully approximated by a constant gradient, the eastern side requires a cubic regional approximation, the two diverge some 40 km from the southern coast. The eastern alternative is preferred because the western side has a local positive; seen on the Gass & Masson-Smith data to partially close and labelled by those authors 'the Pomos positive anomaly'. It is not really part of the east–west regional of the Western Cyprus ophiolite.

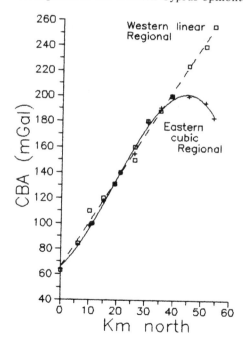

**Fig. 9.** Alternative approximations to the regional field based on Gass & Masson-Smith (1963) data to the west (linear version) and east (cubic version) of the Mt Olympus anomaly.

The Mt Olympus anomaly cannot be accurately isolated from the regional data-set which is very coarse, there are too few points defining

the gravity low. A merged data set of Gass & Masson-Smith (remapped to UTM values) and the 1985 data was created (Fig. 8) before subtraction of the regional field. The residual field resulting from subtraction of the cubic eastern alternative is shown in Fig. 10. The use of the CBA values as background and the SBA values for the local anomaly means that the residual amplitude should be regarded as a maximum.

With this separation the Mt Olympus anomaly is most successfully isolated; it is surrounded by zero values. The only quadrant from which interference might be suspected is the NW where the Pomos positive anomaly is now clearly defined. The even gradients between the positive and negative anomaly suggest that the interference between the two is minimal.

## Anomalous mass calculation

Having achieved a reasonable separation of the residual anomalous low, Gauss' Theory allows a straightforward calculation of the mass deficiency responsible for it. The combined data-set was gridded at 500 m intervals so that the anomaly is well defined. Areas outside the limits of the anomaly were blanked and an upper surface of zero mGal set. The 'volume' of the negative residual anomaly was computed by three methods and the results checked with a graphical approximation. The trapezoidal rule, Simpson's rule and Simpson's 3/8 rule gave an average 'volume' of $-1.53850 \pm 0.0003 \times 10^{10}$ m$^2$ mGal. This 'volume' is converted into a mass deficiency of $3.67 \times 10^{14}$ kg. The true volume of the deficient mass depends, of course, on the density contrast with the country rocks. However, the solutions can be constrained assuming that serpentinization is the prime cause of the anomaly – a not unreasonable assumption in mantle rocks above sea-level.

The volume of the causative body can be examined if it is considered as a cylinder. The modelling has indicated that such geometry is reasonable. Figure 11 shows extreme ranges of density contrast from 0.15–0.80 Mg m$^{-3}$ and the resulting volumes plotted as radius and length (depth) in km of a cylinder. The graphs converge at higher density contrasts and it is possible to constrain the options further by a consideration of the limits set on the radius of such a body. Identification of the inflection points and the resultant zero crossings in the second horizontal derivative is usually considered to define the margins of the causative body. Using N–S transects through the anomaly, the radius of the body is estimated at 3.25 km from the 1963 data and 2.5 km from the 1985 data although there is

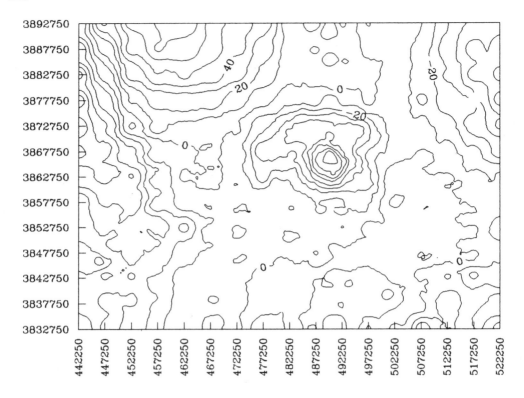

**Fig. 10.** Results of subtraction of the eastern based regional approximation. 10 mGal contour interval, Pomos positive anomaly +70 mGal, Olympus low −80 mGal. The amplitude of the low is greater than that derived in Fig. 2 because the regional field is here fitted as a surface to the area rather than a line through the depressed values along 490E.

considerable noise on the northern flank of the anomaly (Fig. 3). The anomaly is most strongly controlled by the near-surface geology; it is not coincidental that the outcrop of the harzburgite is approximately circular and has a mean radius of 3 km. The modelling indicated that a radius greater than 3 km was appropriate, it is thus apparent that the derivatives are obscured on the northern flanks of the anomaly and that after smoothing of the N–S profiles, radii up to 5 km are permissible.

The density contrast should not be greater than 0.65 Mg m$^{-3}$. This corresponds to 100% serpentinization of otherwise pristine harzburgite. Lower values for serpentinite density cannot play a significant role deeper than a few hundred metres and in this case a body with a depth of the order 20 km is required (radius 3 km). This quickly drops to 11.2 km depth for a 4 km radius body. It is also predicted that the obduction of the massif will have lead to wide spread alteration of the mantle, and although

this need not be at an advanced stage the likelihood of finding pristine mantle above sea-level is considered slim. Again, lower density contrasts and deeper-rooted bodies result. The 0.8 Mg m$^{-3}$ used in the 1963 interpretation provided a relatively tidy causative body which should probably have been much larger.

The present work indicates a body extending to depths of between 16 and 11 km depending on the density contrast with the country rock.

## Contribution of serpentinization to uplift

The Troodos Range encompasses a broad band of terrain over 1000 m, stretching 60 km with a WNW–ESE trend from the Paphos Forest to Mt Makheras. It seems clear that the ophiolite, as defined by the large positive anomaly, is uncompensated. The mega-scale fold is uplifted as a result of tectonic forces as the island is underthrust. The 10 km diameter 'plug' of Mt Olympus

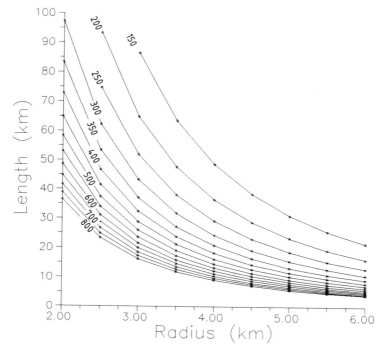

**Fig. 11.** Values of cylinder dimensions for a range of density contrasts exceeding those possible in this geological framework given the anomalous mass responsible for the Mt Olympus gravity low.

clearly plays no part in the uplift of the range as a whole. Indeed the anomalous mass fails by an order of magnitude to provide enough uplift for even a conical mountain of the height of Mt Olympus (1951 m) above sea-level. It is, however, sufficient to account for the uplift of Mt Olympus above the general level of the range.

The anomalous mass of $3.67 \times 10^{14}$ kg, if reduced by the portion above 1000 m (according to the modelling), is $2.21 \times 10^{14}$ kg. A calculation of the volume of the summit above 1000 m was attempted after fitting a surface to the digitized elevation data (as derived from 1:250 000 scale mapping). The approximate volume on a 1 km grid is $3.27 \times 10^{10}$ m³, if the average density is 2.70 Mg m⁻³ the required buoyancy is only $9 \times 10^{13}$ kg leaving 70% of the uplift to overcome frictional forces between the summit and its surroundings. There are numerous faults which would allow the summit area to be disengaged from the ophiolite around it. There is recorded seismic activity with foci (15–70 km) dipping beneath the south of the island confirming the activity of the subduction zone, it has been suggested that some of the seismic activity could result from uplift around Troodos (I. G. Gass, pers. comm. 1992). In view of the

modelled depth of the anomalous body it is not unreasonable to relate shallower events to uplift. The background level of 1000 m was selected as it is broadly consistent along the entire 'ridge' of the ophiolite. There are five major peaks above this level; Tripylos (Paphos Forest) at 1362 m, Mt Olympus at 1951 m, Adelphi at 1612 m, Papoutsa 1554 m and, further east, Makheras 1423 m. Of these, only Mt Olympus raises a significant area above 1500 m (3 km radius) and this is the only peak with an associated gravity anomaly. The correlation between the most elevated topography and the mass deficiency argues strongly for uplift aided by local isostatic forces.

If total disengagement of the supported mass is assumed (i.e. frictionless boundary faults) an interesting result emerges. The uplifted mass is approximated by a cone above 1500 m elevation and a cylinder below that level. The elevation of the datum level is then only dependent on the radius of the body. At 5 km, the preferred value from the modelling, the 'compensation depth' turns out to be sea-level. The mass deficiency is capable of supporting a cylinder of 5 km radius, 1500 m high and topped by a cone for the remaining 450 m. Clearly, such a case is unrealistic and sets a lower limit on the level. The degree

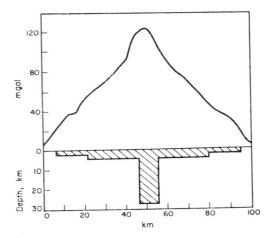

**Fig. 12.** The model of Harrison (1955) showing ultrabasic material arriving in a central feeder tube to spread laterally as it reaches the surface.

to which the load is transmitted to the surrounding rock is unknown but substantial, the level is probably below 1000 m but cannot be determined more precisely.

Houghton *et al.* (1990) confirmed the episodic nature of the uplift suggested by Robertson (1977) and presented new evidence of major erosion in the Late Pliocene. If that event were responsible for the planation of the summit area then very high rates of uplift are invoked (1 mm a$^{-1}$). Poole & Robertson (1991) infer rapid uplift in the early and mid-Pleistocene with rates reduced in the late Pleistocene. Terraces identified at levels up to 360 m have sediments derived principally from erosion of Mt Olympus.

The area of the summit is at least $3 \times 10^8$ m$^2$, for each millimetre eroded away some $8 \times 10^8$ kg of material are lost. However, uplift of 1 mm also raises a volume of the buoyant material above the datum level reducing the uplift by up to $4.7 \times 10^7$ kg (6% of the erosional loss). There appears to be a net gain with uplift and erosion, an increase in the 'power-to-weight ratio'. Such a process should lead to accelerating uplift, and the change of rate could be detectable in the geology and geomorphology. There are, however, imponderables such as the weather to consider, increased elevation does not of itself guarantee increased erosion.

It is assumed that the periodic uplift phases do not arise from changes in the serpentinization beneath Troodos. Either uplift occurs as isostatic stresses exceed friction along faults or the whole process is a response to changing tectonic conditions. A constant uplift force implies decreasing uplift rates. As the mass deficiency is entirely capable of raising the uppermost kilometre of Mt Olympus, and is assumed to be in the process of so doing, there must have been a time when less mountain was raised. At that time uplift rates should have been high and are decreasing as the summit mass is raised.

The result of the interplay of two opposing and rather speculative tendencies requires undue speculation to predict the outcome!

## Discussion

The model of Harrison (1955) showing ultrabasic material arriving in a central feeder tube to spread laterally as it reaches the surface (Fig. 12) looks unlikely now that we are used to such rocks arriving in tectonic slices. However, although the positive anomaly over Western Cyprus can be modelled with mass distributions in tune with current understanding of plate tectonics, the Mt Olympus negative anomaly cannot. Every effort to impose ridge or transform structures on this situation is resisted by the evident circularity and intensity of the anomaly. Cylinders must form an integral part of Western Cyprus, the residual anomaly is still circular and corresponds, as originally suggested, to exposed serpentinized, depleted mantle. Elongate ridge-parallel structures show vaguely across the summit with the swathe of lowered values but superimposed on that there is a local depletion in density. To account for such a unique? structure, Hurst *et al.* (1990) draw a comparison between Cyprus and a nodal basin formed at the intersection of a slow-spreading ridge and a transform fault. The comparison is compelling, the results in the ocean are extreme crustal thinning over a limited area. The possibility exists that this could lead to a localized increase in the degree of serpentinization and subsequent isostatic uplift.

The alteration has indeed to be severe, yet limited to a body less than 10 km across and up to twice that extent in depth. The intensity of the anomaly demands a sudden change in properties usually indicative of faulting. Serpentinization is known to penetrate to depth along transform faults yet the Arakapas fault zone, acknowledged to be transform related (Simonian & Gass 1978), does not display anomalies of the same order of magnitude as the Mt Olympus low (F. J. Vine, pers. comm.).

It may be that if the palaeoridge axis is now at 490E, there was a small offset or accommodation structure as documented by Karson (1991) in the axis that provided a channel for deep penetration of sea water. The evidence for ridge-related faulting is certainly abundant and long-standing, for example Searle & Panayiotou (1980) show a block-faulted, uplifted Mt Olympus. These authors date commencement of faulting as following close on the extrusion of the Basal Group lavas. Obduction and uplift are Tertiary events, serpentinization is assumed to have occurred at the same time. Why then only in one area of the range? The faulting is widespread and the putative mechanisms far-reaching, why is the alteration so localized? If fluids rising from a subducted slab are the mechanism, their passage through the fault-bounded block could have led to serpentinization which then acted to increase the permeability thus increasing the flow, intensifying the alteration and limiting the process to this single block.

More data have been collected, the regional tectonic picture has clarified, evidence of the timing and results of the uplift have been documented yet Mt Olympus remains unique. The Mt Olympus mass deficiency, a massive volume – apparently greater than $700 \text{ km}^3$ of intensely altered mantle – is as startling as it appeared in 1963.

The gravity survey was made possible by a research grant from the Open University, UK; The Directorate of Military Survey, Feltham, generously made available maps and data from their survey. The Geological Survey of Cyprus provided their usual warm welcome and valued assistance. I wish to thank Prof. F. J. Vine and an anonymous reviewer for their help in improving this paper.

# References

ALLERTON, W. S. Q. & VINE, F. J. 1987. Spreading structures of the Troodos ophiolite, Cyprus: some palaeomagnetic constraints. *Geology*, **15**, 593–597.

CORDELL, L. & HENDERSON, R. G. 1968. Iterative three-dimensional solution of gravity anomaly data using a digital computer. *Geophysics*, **33** (4), 596–601.

GASS, I. G. & MASSON-SMITH, D. 1963. The geology and gravity anomalies of the Troodos massif, Cyprus. *Philosophical Transactions of the Royal Society, London*, **1060** (255), 417–467.

HARRISON, J. C. 1955. An interpretation of the gravity anomalies in the eastern Mediterranean. *Philosophical Transactions of the Royal Society, London*, **A248**, 283–325.

HOUGHTON, S. D., JENKINS, D. G., XENOPHONTOS, C. & GASS, I. G. 1990. Microfossil evidence for a late Pliocene age for the Amathus and Khirokitia channel deposits, southern Cyprus and thereby the unroofing of the Troodos Massif. *In*: MALPAS, J., MOORES, E., PANAYIOTOU, A. & XENOPHONTOS, C. (eds) *Ophiolites and Oceanic Lithosphere. Proceedings of the International Symposium, Nicosia, Cyprus, October 1987*, 231–234.

HURST, S. D., KARSON, J. A. & MOORES, E. M. 1990. Nodal basins at slow-spreading ridge-transform intersections: a comparison to the central portion of the Troodos ophiolite. *In*: MALPAS, J., MOORES, E., PANAYIOTOU, A. & XENOPHONTOS, C. (eds) *Ophiolites and Oceanic Lithosphere. Proceedings of the International Symposium, Nicosia, Cyprus, October 1987*, 125–130.

KARSON, J. A. 1991. Accommodation zones and transfer faults: Integral components of Mid-Atlantic Ridge extensional systems. *In*: PETERS, Tj. *et al.* (eds) *Ophiolite Genesis and Evolution of the Oceanic Lithosphere*. Ministry of Petroleum and Minerals, Sultanate of Oman, 21–37.

MACE, C. 1939. Gravity measurements in Cyprus. *Monthly Notices of the Royal Astronomical Society, Geophysics. Supplement*, **4**, 473.

McKENZIE, D. P. 1972. Active tectonics of the Mediterranean region. *Geophysical Journal of the Royal Astronomical Society*, **30**, 109–185.

POOLE, A. J. & ROBERTSON, A. H. F. 1991. Quaternary uplift and sea-level change at an active plate boundary, Cyprus. *Journal of the Geological Society, London*, **148**, 909–921.

ROBERTSON, A. H. F. 1977. Tertiary uplift history of the Troodos Massif, Cyprus. *Geological Society of America Bulletin*, **88**, 1763–1772.

SEARLE, D. L. & PANAYIOTOU, A. 1980. Structural implications in the evolution of the Troodos Massif, Cyprus. *In*: PANAYIOTOU, A. (ed.) *Ophiolites: Proceedings of the International Ophiolite Symposium, Cyprus 1979*, 50–60.

SHELTON, A. W. 1984. *Geophysical studies on the Northern Oman Ophiolite*. PhD thesis, Open University, Milton Keynes.

SIMONIAN, K. O. & GASS, I. G. 1978. The Arakapas Fault belt, Cyprus: a fossil transform fault. *Geological Society of America Bulletin*, **89**, 1220–1230.

VARGA, R. J. & MOORES, E. M. 1985. Spreading structure of the Troodos ophiolite, Cyprus. *Geo-*logy, **13**, 846–850.

WILSON, R. A. M. 1959. The geology of the Xeros–Troodos area. *Memoir of the Cyprus Geological Survey Department*, **1**.

WOODSIDE, J. M. 1977. Tectonic elements and crust of the eastern Mediterranean Sea. *Marine Geophysical Research*, **3**, 317–354.

# Tectonic significance of the Hellenic–Dinaric ophiolites

ALAN G. SMITH

*Department of Earth Sciences, Downing Street, Cambridge CB2 3EQ, UK*

**Abstract**: Isotopic and biostratigraphic data show the Hellenic ophiolites (those SE of the Scutari-Pec transform zone in Albania) are of Middle to Late Jurassic age. They are of two contrasting types. The first type of ophiolite is complete, usually harzburgitic, forms allochthonous sheets, commonly develops metamorphic soles, generally includes significant chrome deposits and shows supra-subduction zone (SSZ) trace-element characteristics with an evolution from MORB to IAT and occasionally boninites. The second type is characterized by incomplete ophiolites which lack chrome and mantle tectonite rocks. In contrast to the first type, these are slightly younger, are exposed in situ, show contact metamorphism against the country rock, are similar to MORB and show little influence of a subduction zone.

The harzburgitic ophiolites form a western and an eastern outcrop belt. The relationship between the two is unclear, principally because of large, probably strike-slip, offsets in the Vardar zone, best documented in former Yugoslavia.

The western Hellenic ophiolites (Pindos, Vourinos, Othris, Evvia ( = Euboea) and Argolis) all formed above a SW-dipping subduction zone in early Middle Jurassic time. They are continuous with a similar belt in the Dinarides of Yugoslavia whose SW margin gradually becomes lherzolitic as it is traced northwards. It is totally lherzolitic at its termination in NW Yugoslavia. This gradual change in ultramafic character is speculatively linked to the changes in spreading rates in a wedge-shaped marginal basin.

Emplacement took place in later Middle to Late Jurassic time probably along a low-angle detachment zone that was close to the lithosphere/asthenosphere boundary shortly after spreading ceased. The SW half of the basin was pushed over the NE half, which was subducted to the SW but has left very little trace of its former existence. In the Hellenides the ophiolites were emplaced onto the Pelagonian continent and in the Dinarides onto the Drina-Ivanjica continent.

Precise analogues of the complete ophiolites appear to be absent in the present-day major ocean basins – because of their SSZ character – or any island arcs that border the present-day oceans – because their marginal stratigraphy shows no trace of arc sediments or volcanics.

The incomplete ophiolites, which appear to be restricted to the Axios zone in Greece, seem to be the expression of transient motion on short extensional segments of a plate margin whose geometry resembled the early stages of the opening of the Gulf of California.

This paper reviews the general nature and tectonic setting of the ophiolites in Greece, Albania and Yugoslavia (Fig. 1); gives a detailed account of some of the Greek ophiolites (Figs 2 & 3); and proposes a simple geometric model for their origin. It omits any detailed discussion of chemical composition except where this has tectonic implications. The literature is widely scattered and is written in several languages including Greek, Serbo-Croat and Albanian. Only the literature written in English or French is reviewed here, though some publications in other languages are given in the references. Much of the recent literature is readily found through papers published or referenced in *Ofioliti*. The Institute of Geology and Mineral Exploration in Greece has also begun to publish the results of a large EEC programme focused on the chromite deposits of Greece (Rassios *et al.* 1990).

## Role in tectonic theory

The Vourinos ophiolite, in particular, has played a significant role in tectonic theory. In the first major paper on one of the Hellenic ophiolites, Brunn (1956) interpreted the Vourinos Complex as a huge, essentially in situ, mafic–ultramafic complex formed by submarine eruptions that appeared to show a continuity from an ultramafic base to mafic rocks at the top. The in situ character was supported by the contact metamorphism at the ultramafic base of the complex, which seemed to point to an essentially autochthonous position of a vast differentiated extrusion.

Even before the advent of plate tectonics and ocean-floor spreading, Brunn (1959) had drawn an analogy between the rocks of the Vourinos Complex and the mid-Atlantic ridge. Aubouin (1965) later incorporated the submarine eruption

*From* Prichard, H. M., Alabaster, T., Harris, N. B. W. & Neary, C. R. (eds), 1993,
*Magmatic Processes and Plate Tectonics*, Geological Society Special Publication No. 76, 213–243.

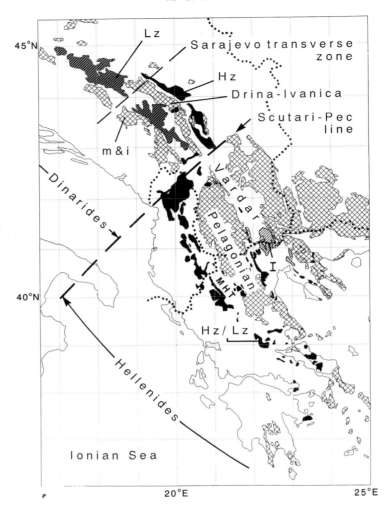

**Fig. 1.** Major features in the Dinarides and Hellenides. The Drina-Ivanica and Pelagonian zones are continental areas. The Mesohellenic (MHT) is a later Cenozoic basin that separates the western ophiolites from one
another. Major transverse structures are the Sarajevo transverse zone and the Scutari-Pec line. The latter is
probably a transform zone. The Dinarides lie NW of this line; the Hellenides to the SE. Solid fill are
ophiolites with predominantly harzburgitic ultramafics (Hz); dark diagonal stripes are predominantly lherzolitic (Lz); light diagonal stripes are incomplete ophiolites with well-developed dyke complexes but lacking
harzburgite, lherzolite or dunite (I); cross-hatched are granites, volcanics unrelated to ophiolites and metamorphic rocks (m & i). Heavy dots are political boundaries as in Fig. 2.

model into his elegant model of geosynclines,
which was based largely on his (Aubouin 1959)
and Brunn's (1956) work in the western Hellenides. The Vourinos and other mafic–ultramafic
complexes in the Alpine–Mediterranean region
were described as eugeosynclines, i.e. areas of
submarine igneous activity ultimately involved
in the formation of an orogenic belt.

Historically, Hess's interest in Alpine ophio-

lites (Hess 1955) eventually led to his ideas of
ocean-floor spreading (Hess 1965) and to the
investigation of the Vourinos Complex by
Moores (1969). That the Vourinos Complex
was a slice of ocean-floor emplaced onto the
continental rocks of the Pelagonian zone was
advanced as only one of four possible interpretations (Moores 1969). Only three years later the
Penrose Conference on ophiolites took place and

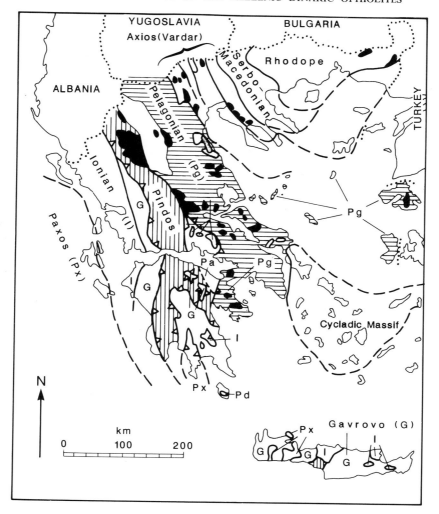

**Fig. 2.** Geotectonic zones of Greece and political boundaries of neighbouring countries (heavy dots). The ophiolites are in black. They are confined to two internal zones: the sub-Pelagonian (or Othris) zone west of the Pelagonian zone (Pg); and an eastern zone, the Axios (or Vardar) zone east of the Pelagonian zone. The western boundary of the Othris zone is conventionally taken as the boundary between the internal (eastern) zones which have undergone at least one phase of Mesozoic deformation and the external (western) zones which were not deformed until Cenozoic time. Pa: Parnassos; Pd: Pindos; G: Gavrovo-Tripolitza. Modified from 1:500 000 *Geological Map of Greece* (2nd edn) 1983, Institute of Geology and Mineral Exploration, Athens.

proposed a workable definition of an ophiolite complex (Anon. 1972).

A mafic sheeted-dyke complex is present in a fully developed ophiolite (Anon. 1972). The only known process that can cause such extension is ocean-floor spreading. For some geologists this requires them to be ocean floor, whereas for others the non-MORB chemistry of some ophiolites shows they cannot be ocean floor. This

semantic problem is avoided if it is recognised that the formation of complete ophiolites does require 100% extension. Such extension cuts through – and generates – the entire lithosphere and therefore takes place at an extensional plate margin. Thus all ophiolites are generated by spreading at plate margins with an extensional component. Such margins are today located mostly at mid-ocean ridges in the major ocean

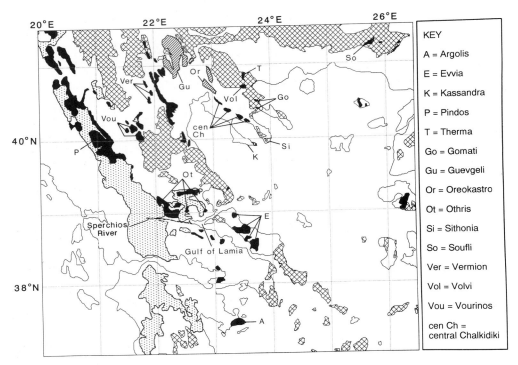

**Fig. 3.** Enlargement of Fig. 1, with named Hellenic ophiolites in Greece. Stipple shows extent of Pindos zone (mostly pelagic carbonates, cherts and flysch) and ophiolitic melange.

basins where adiabatic melting of peridotite forms the ocean floor, but a significant fraction are located in back arc basins where melting may well involve a subduction component (e.g. Woodhead *et al.* 1993).

The complete Hellenic ophiolites do not conform to simple plate tectonic expectations. The stratigraphy and structure of the continental margins that originally bordered the complete ophiolites suggest that these margins were passive, whereas ophiolite chemistry suggests the ophiolites formed above active subduction zones. This contradictory evidence is at the heart of the problem of interpreting precisely what they represent.

## Distribution

Tectonically the Greek ophiolites are part of the Hellenides, the orogenic belt that terminates in Albania along the Scutari (Skadar)-Pec line (Fig. 1). NW of the Hellenides lie the Dinarides, which start in Albania and continue throughout most of former Yugoslavia.

From the most northerly outcrop at about (45° N, 16°E) the ophiolites trend SE and then split into two outcrop belts. The major eastern belt shows a discontinuous roughly linear outcrop pattern in the Vardar zone, named after the Vardar River in former Yugoslavia, and the Axios zone, named after the Axios River, the continuation of the River Vardar in eastern Greece. The western branch forms the ophiolites nearest the Adriatic and Ionian coasts. The major offset along the Scutari (Skadar)-Pec line probably represents a former transform fault (Pamić 1983, fig 1).

Two other NE-trending offsets in the outcrop pattern of the Mesozoic carbonate platform near Sarajevo and Zagreb are also regarded as possible transform faults by Pamić. The Zagreb transverse structure terminates the ophiolite outcrop (not shown on Fig. 1); the Sarajevo transverse structure marks a change in trend of the ophiolite outcrop but the offset, if any, is small. The spacing between these possible transforms is about 325 km (Zagreb–Sarajevo) and 250 km (Sarajevo–Pec).

The outcrop of Hellenic ophiolites is offset across the Sperchios River and Gulf of Lamia. The offset is immediately S of the only plagioclase lherzolite in the Hellenic ophiolites and may represent a transform zone (see below). It is in the opposite sense to the offset on the Scutari-Pec line and about 410 km from it. Transverse structures exist in the Kastaniotikos region and Gulf of Corinth (Robertson *et al.* 1991, fig. 8, p. 309) but they do not markedly offset the ophiolite outcrop. It is unclear whether these were Jurassic transform faults.

The major transverse structures divide the ophiolites into three panels. The ultramafics in the area NW of the Sarajevo transverse structure are largely lherzolitic in composition with harzburgite just beginning to dominate the eastern ophiolites immediately adjacent to the structure (Pamić 1983). Between Sarajevo and the Scutari-Pec transform fault, harzburgite becomes dominant. SE of the Scutari-Pec faults, significant lherzolite is restricted to the NW corner of the panel. Apart from some lherzolite in the Dramala Complex of the Pindos ophiolite (Robertson *et al.* 1991, p. 303) and in western Othris (Fig. 3) the ultramafics of all the western Hellenic ophiolites are harzburgitic. The variations in the distribution of lherzolite and harzburgite are believed to provide important clues to the general nature of the ophiolite belt, discussed below.

The geology of Greece is complex and only a schematic outline is presented here. A much fuller account of the general setting, particularly of Triassic time and of the Jurassic stratigraphy and sedimentology is given in Robertson *et al.* (1991, pp. 293–302). The western limit of the Hellenic ophiolites conventionally marks the boundary between the so-called internal tectonic zones of the Hellenides – the Rhodope, Serbo-Macedonian, Axios ( = Vardar) Pelagonian and sub-Pelagonian (or Othris) zones – and the external zones – the Parnassos, Gavrovo, Pindos, Gavrovo, Ionian and Paxos zones (Fig. 2). The Mesozoic and Cenozoic rocks in the ophiolite-free external zones are unmetamorphosed and have undergone only one phase of compressional deformation, during the Cenozoic. By contrast, the internal zones in which the ophiolites occur, have been affected by at least two, and occasionally three, major phases of post-Palaeozoic compressional deformation: a Late Jurassic to Early Cretaceous phase (or phases) of emplacement onto adjacent continental margins; and Late Cretaceous to Tertiary thrusting.

## General nature

The western ophiolites themselves are all allochthonous, forming sub-horizontal sheets locally exceeding 11 km in thickness, as in Vourinos (Moores 1982). The sheets are commonly imbricated, with duplexes reflecting their emplacement history. The main outcrops in the western ophiolite belt in Greece are the Pindos (2500 km²), Vourinos (450 km²), Othris (800 km²) and Evvia ( = Euboea) (400 km²) ophiolites discussed below (Fig. 3). Smaller western ophiolites include Kastoria (Mountrakis 1982, 1984, 1986), Koziakas (Ferrière 1982; Capedri *et al.* 1985; Lekkas 1988), Vermion (Economou 1983), E Thessaly (Migiros & Economou 1988), Iti (Mitropoulos *et al.* 1987), and Argolis (Baumgartner 1985; Hatzipanagiotou 1990).

The main eastern ophiolites are the Guevgeli, central Chalkidiki (100 km²), Oreokastro, Kassandra and Sithonia ophiolites (Fig. 3). The small Ano Garefi ophiolite on the Yugoslav border has been described by Migiros & Galeos (1990). All these will be referred to as the Axios ( = Vardar) ophiolites, though they differ in age and character. All except central Chalkidiki and minor tectonized slices in the western Axios zone (Almopias zone) are unusual in having intrusive contacts with the country rock and are therefore interpreted as autochthonous (see below).

In addition, there are small meta-ophiolites within the Serbo-Macedonian massif (Dixon & Dimitriadis 1984) and scattered through the eastern Rhodope region (Magganas & Economou 1988) (Fig. 3). Many of the Greek islands, including Crete, have small ophiolite outcrops

The ultramafic components of all the western ophiolites and those of central Chalkidiki are dominated by harzburgite with associated tabular or podiform dunite (Economou *et al.* 1986; Rassios *et al.* 1990). Economic concentrations of chromite occur within the dunite, but its abundance as an economic mineral varies from extremely rare in Pindos (Rassios *et al.* 1990) to relatively common in Vourinos (Rassios *et al.* 1983, 1990) and central Chalkidiki (Christodoulou & Michaelides 1990). The disrupted eastern Rhodope ophiolites include dunites, harzburgites and chromite ores (Magganas & Economou 1988) and appear to resemble the central Chalkidiki and Vourinos ophiolites. Gabbros, dolerites and basalts are present in all the western ophiolites.

According to the definition given by the participants in the 1972 Penrose conference on ophiolites (Anon. 1972), the Axios ( = Vardar) ophiolites of Guevgeli, Kassandra and Sithonia are all incomplete, lacking ultramafic tectonite suites. Though all three show excellent pillow lavas, sheeted-dyke complexes are developed only at Guevgeli and Sithonia (Jung & Mussallam 1985; Bebien *et al.* 1987; Mussallam 1991); the exposure level at Kassandra stops within the

**Table 1**. *Ages assigned to Middle and Late Jurassic stages (Harland et al.* 1990)

| Stratigraphic unit | Age of base in Ma | | Difference in Ma | Estimated error in 1990 scale |
|---|---|---|---|---|
| | 1982 scale | 1990 scale | | |
| Base of Cretaceous | 144 | 146 | 2 | 9 |
| Late Jurassic | | | | |
| Tithonian | 150 | 152 | 2 | 11 |
| Kimmeridgian | 156 | 155 | −1 | 6 |
| Oxfordian | 163 | 157 | −6 | 7 |
| Middle Jurassic | | | | |
| Callovian | 169 | 161 | −8 | 7 |
| Bathonian | 175 | 166 | −9 | 7 |
| Bajocian | 181 | 173 | −8 | 11 |
| Aalenian | 188 | 178 | −10 | 11 |

pillow lavas; at Sithonia in hypabyssal rocks and at Guevgeli in gabbros.

The chemistry of the related Oreokastro ophiolite (Baroz & Remy 1985; Haenel-Remy & Bebien 1985), discussed below, is similar to Guevgeli, Kassandra and Sithonia. Oreokastro is regarded here as incomplete even though there is a small outcrop – <0.5 km² – of serpentinites and peridotites. The peridotites contain plagioclase, clinopyroxene and olivine. Mangle tectonite, harzburgite, dunite and chromite are absent.

The Serbo-Macedonian meta-ophiolites at Volvi include lavas, a sheeted-dyke complex and gabbros, but no significant ultramafic rocks. Meta-ophiolites containing ultramafics are present at Gomati and Therma (Dixon & Dimitriadis 1984, p. 604) and chrome ore is found at Gomati (Magganas & Economou 1988). Both these meta-ophiolites may have been formerly complete sequences.

# Ages

## Middle and Late Jurassic time-scale

The time span of interest is largely Middle Jurassic (Dogger) to Late Jurassic (Malm) time. Biostratigraphic dating can resolve Jurassic events with a precision equivalent to ±2 Ma or better; isotopic dating errors are of a similar magnitude (Table 1). However, unlike the Cenozoic and later Cretaceous time-scale, the links between isotopic and biostratigraphic scales for Jurassic stages are poorly determined. Though Harland et al. (1990, p. 139) consider their error estimates

for the numerical boundaries of stratigraphic boundaries are high (Table 1), the uncertainties in the numerical values of some Jurassic stages are probably at least 5 Ma and could be more.

## Crystallization ages

There are no precise dates from Hellenic ophiolites such as U–Pb dates from zircons in plagiogranites as in Oman (Tilton et al. 1981). Isotopic age determinations from the western ophiolites are limited to whole-rock K–Ar dates from the Othris ophiolite (Hynes et al. 1972; Ferrière 1982, p. 338) and show a very wide range. It is assumed that a reasonable approximation to the ophiolite crystallization age is given by the oldest dates which are listed in Table 2. More limited whole-rock K–Ar dates are available from the chromite-bearing Chalkidiki ophiolite in the eastern belt (Jung et al. 1980; Mussallam & Jung 1986). Both sets of dates suggest a Middle Jurassic crystallization age (Table 2).

Late Triassic within-plate-basalts (WPB) and WPB transitional to MORB basalts are known from melanges under the Pindos ophiolite (Jones & Robertson 1991, see below). Similar Triassic rocks are known from Othris (Hynes 1974), but none of the relatively intact ophiolites are known to be of Triassic age.

There are more modern K–Ar determinations of 149–163 Ma for minerals in the incomplete Guevgeli ophiolite (Table 2). These give late Middle to Late Jurassic dates, indistinguishable from the date of 155 Ma for the penecontemporaneous Fanos granite which intrudes the Guevgeli ophiolite (Table 2).

**Table 2.** *Isotopic dates from Hellenic ophiolites and associated rocks*

| Date and method | | Material dated | Reference |
|---|---|---|---|
| **Othris ophiolite** | | | |
| 187 ± 23 | K–Ar | Ophiolitic pillow lavas | Ferrière 1982, p. 338 |
| 178 ± 24 | | | |
| 185 ± 7 | | Rhyolite in ophiolite | Hynes *et al.* 1972 |
| 169 ± 4 | Ar–Ar | Amphibolite in sole | Spray *et al.* 1984 |
| **Pindos ophiolite** | | | |
| 176 ± 5 | K–Ar | Metamorphic sole | Thuizat *et al.* 1981 |
| 167 ± 4 | Ar–Ar | Amphibolite & other rocks in metamorphic sole | Spray *et al.* 1984 |
| **Vourinos ophiolite** | | | |
| 171 ± 4 | Ar–Ar | Amphibolite in sole | Spray *et al.* 1984 |
| **Chalkidiki ophiolite** | | | |
| 172 ± 5 | | Hornblende in hornblende gabbro dyke cutting dunite | Kreuzer, pers. comm. in Mussallam & Jung 1986 |
| 172 ± 4 | | Hornblende in gabbro dyke in ophiolite | Kreuzer, pers. comm. in Mussallam & Jung 1986 |
| **Guevgeli ophiolite** | | | |
| 149 ± 3 | K–Ar | Hornblende in gabbro | Spray *et al.* 1984 |
| 154 ± 3 | | Biotite in diorite | |
| 163 ± 3 | | Hornblende in diorite | |
| **Fanos granite** | | | |
| 155 ± 2 | Misc. | Mean age (range up to 158) | Borsi *et al.* 1966 |

## Metamorphic sole ages

When ophiolites are emplaced they commonly develop a metamorphic sole, as in Oman (e.g. Lippard *et al.* 1986). The soles reflect a time when the base of a hot oceanic sheet was first detached from its substratum and overrode the rocks that have been metamorphosed, commonly to greenschist or amphibolite grade.

Metamorphic sole rocks are known with certainty only from the western ophiolites of Pindos, Vourinos, Othris and Evvia (= Euboea) (Spray *et al.* 1984; Simantov *et al.* 1990) and Iti (S of W Othris) (unpublished data referred to in Robertson *et al.* 1991 p. 303), though sheared amphibolites at the base of the Chalkidiki ophiolites at Vavdos, 50 km SE of Thessalonika (Christodoulou & Michaelides 1990), may well be metamorphic sole rocks.

The amphibolites in the metamorphic soles of the Pindos, Vourinos and Othris ophiolites have been dated by $^{40}Ar/^{39}Ar$ methods (Spray & Roddick 1980), which when corrected (Spray *et al.* 1984), give consistent dates in the range 167–171 Ma or mid-Middle Jurassic. Thus the sole dates are all older than all the modern dates from the Guevgeli ophiolite and Fanos granite (Table 2 and Figs 1 & 3). Similar sole dates, reviewed by Spray *et al.* (1984), have been obtained from the soles of some Dinaric ophiolites.

However, Late Jurassic radiolarites in lower greenschist facies have been found under the Pindos ophiolite (Jones *et al.* 1992), implying that emplacement continued for several million years after amphibolite formation. Its precise duration is unknown because of uncertainties in the time-scale.

Major and trace element analyses show that the amphibolites include samples with MORB compositions (Spray & Roddick, 1980), together with other basaltic types (Robertson *et al.* 1991, p. 303). Thus the ages of the soles give the time since a low-angle fracture within the ocean floor was first exploited by emplacement, though the fracture itself may already have existed, e.g. as a ridge crest, transform fault or a subduction zone.

**Table 3.** *Biostratigraphic dates from sedimentary cover or post-emplacement sediments*

| Biostratigraphic age | Material dated | Reference |
|---|---|---|
| **Sediments contemporaneous with crystallization** | | |
| Pindos ophiolite: | | |
| Bathonian–E Kimmeridgian | Radiolarites *interthrust* with pillow lavas | Jones *et al.* 1992 |
| Evvia ophiolite: | | |
| Lt Bathonian–E Oxfordian | Radiolarites interbedded with pillow lavas | Simantov, in Baumgartner 1984, p. 74 |
| Oxfordian–mid-Kimmeridgian | | Ferrière *et al.* 1989 |
| Argolis ophiolite: | | |
| M Callovian–E Oxfordian | Radiolarites interbedded with pillow lavas | Baumgartner 1984, 1985 1987 |
| Sithonia ophiolite: | | |
| latest Kimmeridgian | Shallow-water sediments on top of 700 m pillow lava and 1200 m sheeted dykes | Jung & Mussallam 1985, p. 337 |
| **Sediments penecontemporaneous with ophiolite emplacement** | | |
| Pindos ophiolite: | | |
| E Bathonian–E Callovian | Ophiolite clasts in radiolarites | Jones *et al.* 1992 |
| Othris and Evvia ophiolites: | | |
| Kimmeridgian | Radiolarites just prior to ophiolite emplacement | Ferrière *et al.* 1989 |
| Argolis ophiolite: | | |
| Lt Oxfordian–Kimmeridgian | Radiolaria in melange | Baumgartner 1985 |
| Kimmeridgian | First appearance chrome spinel in sediments | Baumgartner 1985 |
| **Oldest post-emplacement sediments** | | |
| Vourinos Complex: | | |
| Kimmeridgian–Tithonian | Oldest sediment Krapa hills | Mavridis *et al.* 1979; Pichon 1979 |
| Vermion region (E of Vourinos): | | |
| Tithonian | Oldest sediment | |
| Oreokastro ophiolite: | | |
| Lt Jurassic | 'Molasse' cover to ophiolite | Jung & Mussallam 1985 pp. 337–338 |

The soles presumably represent the time when the extension that gave rise to the ophiolites changed into convergence. It would be expected that, as in other ophiolites where soles are developed, the sole dates would be younger than ophiolite crystallization ages but not by more than a few million years, otherwise the ophiolite would have cooled below the temperatures necessary for amphibolite-grade metamorphism. The whole-rock K–Ar dates are consistent with such an expectation but the sole dates probably set a better constraint on the youngest likely age of the ophiolite.

## Age of primary sedimentary cover

There are no ribbon radiolarian cherts in Vourinos (Rassios, pers. comm). Undated radiolarites associated with the igneous rocks of the Vourinos Complex (Pichon 1979, fig. 2a, p. 166) may be metalliferous sediments instead (Rassios, pers. comm.). These are unconformably overlain by a well-dated Late Jurassic carbonate sequence (see below). Rassios *et al.* (1983, p. 282) note a 40–90° rotation of the Vourinos diabase prior to deposition of these carbonates in the Krapa hills region. Metamorphic assemblages in the hypabyssal rocks of the Vourinos ophiolites immediately under the carbonates also suggest that up to 1 km of lavas may have been eroded prior to the deposition of the little-deformed sedimentary cover (Rassios *et al.* 1983, p. 304). Rotation, erosion and subsidence of the Vourinos ophiolite therefore took place prior to Late Jurassic time.

The only well-dated sediments that are clearly part of a lava sequence in the ophiolites are in Argolis, Evvia ( = Euboea) and Sithonia (Table 3), though radiolarites in the Pindos complex that are tectonically interleaved with ophiolitic lavas may originally have been interstratified with them (Jones *et al.* 1992). The Argolis and Evvia examples are both in the age range of Late Bathonian to Early Oxfordian and clearly older than Kimmeridgian sediments associated with the Sithonia lavas. The Argolis ultramafics were originally harzburgites, resembling those found in the Vourinos Complex (Hatzipanagiotou 1990), rather than the ophiolites of Guevgeli and Sithonia. Thus, the biostratigraphic dates show that the Sithonia ophiolite is younger than all the sole rocks and at least some of the other ophiolites.

## Age of emplacement

Of the western ophiolites, central Othris exposes the best-known Late Jurassic/Early Cretaceous thrust sheets associated with ophiolite emplacement in Greece (Hynes *et al.* 1972; Ferrière 1974, 1982; Smith *et al.* 1979). Ophiolite emplacement is assumed to be contemporaneous with the emplacement of thrusts onto a carbonate platform. Prior to the arrival of the thrusts the platform was eroded, probably subaerially, and overlain by well-bedded radiolarian chert and siltstones. Radiolaria in the cherts were originally assigned a late Tithonian or Early Cretaceous age (Riedel, *in* Smith *et al.* 1975), but are now regarded as Kimmeridgian to Tithonian (De Wever *in* Ferrière *et al.* 1988). These pass up into debris flows and olistostromes, which are then tectonized higher in the section. This sequence has been interpreted as representing the flexure of the platform as it approached the ophiolite; its rapid subsidence and then its overriding by the ophiolite which was emplaced from the W (see below). A similar age of emplacement and interpretation has been made for the Evvia ( = Euboea) ophiolite (Ferrière *et al.* 1988; Robertson 1991).

In Argolis, Baumgartner (1985) dated radiolaria in the Potami Formation, a melange probably contemporaneous with ophiolite emplacement, as of late Oxfordian to Kimmeridgian age.

Chrome spinel, assumed to represent exposure of the mantle sequence of the ophiolite, first appears in Kimmeridgian sediments, accompanied by thrusting (Baumgartner 1985).

The Othris, Evvia and Argolis radiolarian ages suggest emplacement of these ophiolites was underway in late Oxfordian to Kimmeridgian time.

Emplacement of the Pindos ophiolite seems to have begun somewhat earlier: Jones *et al.* (1992, p. 395) note that E Bathonian to E Callovian radiolarites are interbedded with ophiolite clasts that include chrome-rich harzburgite debris.

## Age of post-emplacement sediments

In the Vermion massif, just E of the eastern Vourinos Complex, the Pelagonian marbles are eroded and overlain unconformably by a variable but little-deformed Tithonian–Berriasian sequence (Pichon 1979; Fig. 4). This sequence can be traced from Vermion and westward to the Vourinos Complex where it lies directly on the ophiolites, ranging into the Late Cretaceous and reaching up to 300 m (Mavridis *et al.* 1979, Pichon 1979; Fig. 4). Thus between 171 Ma ago, when the Vourinos sole was formed, and Kimmeridgian time (*c.* 153? Ma ago), the ophiolites were emplaced onto the Pelagonian continent, perhaps 2–5 km removed by erosion (Rassios, pers. comm.), and the area had returned to its earlier history of relatively slow subsidence.

The incomplete Oreokastro ophiolite is overlain unconformably by a Late Jurassic molasse-like sequence (Jung & Mussallam 1985, pp. 337–338) derived from the metamorphosed Svoula Formation.

## Linking isotopic and biostratigraphic ages

The Greek ophiolites crystallized, were emplaced and then sealed by a sedimentary cover spanning no more than the Middle to Late Jurassic interval, or about 30 Ma. The time span for the formation of ophiolitic melange in the Dinarides is similar: ophiolitic melange includes fragments of rock as young as early Middle Jurassic overlain by rocks as old as Tithonian (Dimitrijević 1982, p. 17).

The soles dated at 167–171 Ma ago are most likely to be Bathonian in age, though time-scale uncertainties mean that they might be as old as Aalenian or as young as Bajocian. Similarly, the time gap between metamorphic sole formation in Vourinos at 171 Ma ago and the Kimmeridgian cover could range from 6–34 Ma. The possible range would be even greater if age-dating errors are taken into account.

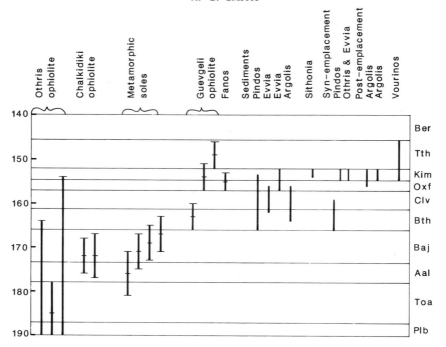

**Fig. 4.** Summary of isotopic and biostratigraphic dates from Hellenic ophiolites. Isotopic dates are shown as lines with error bars and a central bar. They suggest the western and Chalkidikian ophiolites are older than the Guevgeli complex. Biostratigraphic dates are shown as lines without error bars. They suggest that the western ophiolites are older than the Sithonia ophiolite. The metamorphic soles appear to be older than the sediments deposited on top of the ophiolites but this apparent anomaly may in part reflect errors in correlating isotopic and biostratigraphic ages.

Nevertheless, the biostratigraphic and isotopic data independently suggest that two of the eastern ophiolites – Guevgeli and Sithonia – are significantly younger than the central Chalkidiki ophiolites and probably all western ophiolites. This distinction between the ophiolites is identical to one made by Bebien *et al.* (1986) on structural, petrological and chemical evidence.

Clift & Robertson (1989) describe well-dated Late Cretaceous pelagic sediments deposited on basalts with MORB and island-arc tholeiite Y vs. Cr ratios (see below). The Cretaceous Arvi lavas of Crete may also be fragments of a Cretaceous ophiolite. Hornblende dates from gabbroic dykes in Rhodes and Carpathos are in the Late Cretaceous age range of 91–87 Ma (Koepke *et al.* 1985). None of these Cretaceous examples will be discussed further in this paper.

## Igneous stratigraphy, petrology and chemistry

### Stratigraphy

The thicknesses of individual igneous units in the complete ophiolite sequences are best known from Vourinos (Fig. 5). In Vourinos the thickness of the mafic rocks is about 75% of typical oceanic thicknesses (Moores 1982, fig. 4), but this figure may reflect the cumulative effects of thrusting and erosion, rather than being representative of the original thickness (Rassios, pers. comm.). The estimate of the thickness of the ultramafic–mafic cumulate section – about 5 km – (Jackson *et al.* 1975; Rassios *et al.* 1983) is considered much closer to the original thickness because ultramafic–cumulate units can be correlated across faults (Rassios, pers. comm.). In Pindos the equivalent section is less than 1 km thick (Rassios *et al.* 1990). The cumulate section in Pindos is also described by Capedri *et al.* 1982. Othris cumulates are petrologically similar to those of the Pindos. Multiple intrusive events in the Vourinos Complex are described by Harkins *et al.* (1980).

The remnant thickness of the Vourinos sheeted dykes varies from about 500 m to 1.5 km (Rassios *et al.* 1990). The thickness of the lavas and dolerites in some of the Chalkidiki ophiolites is disputed. Mussallam (1991, p. 687)

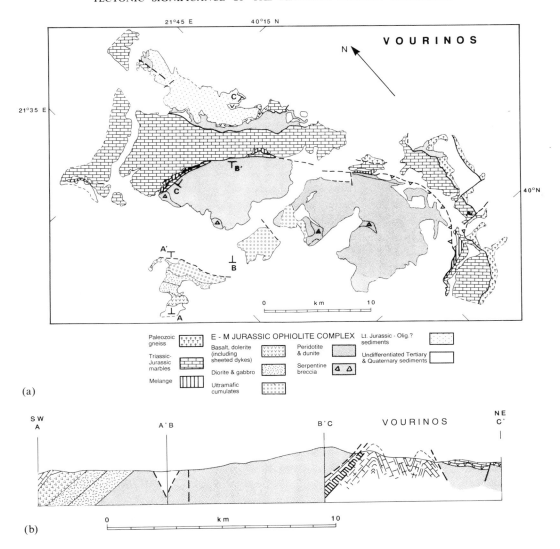

**Fig. 5. (a)** Map and **(b)** cross-section of the Vourinos Complex and surrounding rocks (modified from Moores 1969 and Zimmerman 1972).

suggests they are absent altogether, whereas Bebien *et al.* (1986, p. 1018) recognize their presence as notably thin units. Elsewhere, the total thickness of the mafic units is difficult to gauge because of faulting, e.g. in Othris (Smith *et al.* 1975).

*Petrology and chemistry*

Depleted harzburgite is dominant below the cumulate sections in all the complete ophiolites except western Othris, where plagioclase lherzo-lite dominates (Menzies & Allen 1974; Rassios & Konstantopoulou, in press).

The applicability of trace element discrimination to basalt petrogenesis has been extensively discussed elsewhere (Pearce & Cann 1973; Pearce & Norry 1979; Pearce *et al.* 1984).

Table 4 gives trace element results from the Hellenic ophiolites. It omits some preliminary work, data from melanges and references without location maps. As noted below, the presence of two or more basalt types commonly represents a sequence in which WPB or MORB are

**Table 4.** *Trace element discrimination results for basaltic rocks in Hellenic ophiolites*

| Ophiolite | Method | Tectonic setting | Reference |
|---|---|---|---|
| **Complete ophiolites** | | | |
| central | Ni vs. Ti/Cr | IAT/MORB | Bebien *et al.* 1987 |
| Chalkidiki | Ti vs. V | IAT? | |
| | Zr vs. Zr/Y | IAT | |
| Pindos | Ni vs. Ti/Cr | IAT | Beccaluva *et al.* 1979 |
| | Cr vs. Ti | MORB LKT | Capedri *et al.* 1980 |
| | Ni vs. Y | MORB LKT | Capedri *et al.* 1981 |
| | Y vs. Cr | MORB IAT | Jones *et al.* 1991 |
| | Zr vs. Zr/Y | MORB IAT | |
| Vourinos | Ni vs. Ti/Cr | IAT | Beccaluva *et al.* 1979 |
| | | LKT | Beccaluva *et al.* 1984 |
| | Y vs. Cr | MORB IAT | Jones *et al.* 1991 |
| **Incomplete ophiolites** | | | |
| Guevgeli | Ni vs. Ti/Cr | MORB | Bebien *et al.* 1987 |
| | Ti vs. V | MORB | |
| | Zr vs. Zr/Y | mostly MORB | Bebien *et al.* 1987 |
| | Zr vs. Zr/Y | mostly MORB | Haenel-Remy & Bebien 1985 |
| Kassandra | Y vs. Cr | MORB IAT | Mussalam 1991 |
| Metallikon | Ni vs. Ti/Cr | MORB | Bebien *et al.* 1987 |
| | Ti vs. V | MORB | |
| | Zr vs. Zr/Y | mostly MORB | |
| Oreokastro | Ni vs. Ti/Cr | MORB | Bebien *et al.* 1987 |
| | Ti vs. V | MORB | |
| | Zr vs. Zr/Y | mostly MORB | |
| Sithonia | Ti vs. Cr | MORB LKT | Jung & Mussallam 1985 |
| | Ti vs. Zr | WPB MORB VAB | |
| | Y vs. Zr | WPB? | |
| | Y vs. Cr | WPB MORB VAB | |
| | Ni vs. Ti/Cr | MORB | Bebien *et al.* 1987 |
| | Ti vs. V | MORB | |
| | Ti vs. Zr | MORB | Mussallam 1991 |
| | Y vs. Cr | MORB IAT | |

*Note*: Abbreviations are generally as given in the original publication. MORB: mid-ocean ridge basalt; LKT: low potassium tholeiite; IAT: island arc tholeiite; VAB: volcanic arc basalt; WPB: within-plate-basalt.

the initial magmas that change with time to another magma type rather than the coexistence of two magmas.

Other trace element and REE data include those of Simantov & Bertrand (1987) who suggest that basalts in an ophiolitic melange in Central Evvia ( = Euboea) are either island-arc or transitional to MORB; Hf/Th vs. Ta/Th and Hf vs. Zr data, and Nd/Sr isotopic ratios for Vourinos (Noiret *et al.* 1981); and REE data for Iti (Mitropoulis *et al.* 1987) suggesting a possible

MORB origin.

Central Chalkidiki, Pindos and Vourinos all show MORB to IAT (or LKT) trace element chemistry. All three are, therefore, SSZ ophiolites. By contrast, the incomplete eastern ophiolites – Guevgeli, Metallikon, Oreokastro and Sithonia – all appear to be MORB with minor subduction zone influences. Relevant trace element studies on Othris rocks are largely reconnaissance in nature.

Chromite deposits are scarce in MORB ophio-

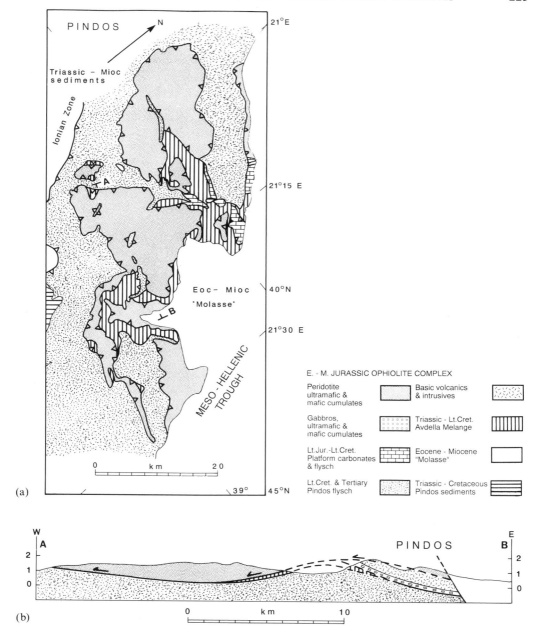

**Fig. 6. (a)** Map and **(b)** cross-section of the Pindos Complex and surrounding rocks (modified from Jones & Robertson 1991).

lites and relatively abundant in SSZ ophiolites (Roberts 1988) probably because during hydrous melting of peridotite the olivine and spinel both remain on the liquidus longer than they do during dry melting. Chromite deposits, redistributed in the western ophiolites by tectonic pro-

cesses (Rassios *et al.* 1990), are found in virtually all the complete ophiolites, i.e. all the western ophiolites (though rare in Pindos), the central Chalkidiki ophiolites and those in Rhodope. Their chromite content suggests they are all SSZ ophiolites. The chrome ores in western Othris are restricted to the top of a relatively small exposure of a harzburgitic nappe of presumed SSZ origin.

The incomplete eastern ophiolites would be expected to lack chrome, but the exposure level is not deep enough to test this expectation.

### Pindos

Parrot (1967, 1969) made the earliest detailed descriptions of the Pindos ophiolite. More recently Jones & Robertson (1991) have subdivided it into three tectonic units (Fig. 6): the Dramala Complex – the ultramafic and plutonic mafics; the Loumnitsa Unit – essentially the metamorphic sole sequence dated by Spray et al. (1984); and the Aspropotamos Complex – ophiolitic mafic units.

The Dramala complex, together with all other Pindos ultramafic units, consist of >5 km of harzburgite with abundant podiform dunite. Economic chromite deposits were probably originally present but have been reduced to sub-economic size by pervasive shearing during emplacement (Rassios et al. 1990).

The cumulates show a complex history and include plagioclase dunite–troctolite–anorthosite gabbro sequences (Jones et al. 1991) that lack significant orthopyroxene; other cumulates are interlayered with wehrlites.

Cr–Y and Zr/Y–Zr discrimination diagrams for the lower Aspropotamos Complex show a series ranging from MORB to boninites, which field relationships suggest is an evolution in time from N-MORB to MORB/IAT, then IAT and finally boninite series volcanics. A similar evolution from MORB to boninitic rocks is suggested by the chemistry and layering of the cumulates in the Dramala complex (Jones & Robertson 1991).

### Vourinos

Economic chromite, whose location is structurally controlled, is relatively abundant in Vourinos (Roberts et al. 1988; Rassios et al. 1990; Rassios 1991). Ore is confined to a tabular zone 0.5–2 km thick that is sub-parallel to the basal thrust. The zone is believed to represent the remnants of a deformed dunite/chromite-rich section in the upper mantle in which shearing was less pervasive than in Pindos.

Like the Pindos complex, Vourinos (Fig. 5) shows a range of magma types from MORB, island-arc tholeiites (IAT) to boninite series volcanics (Beccaluva et al. 1984). As in the Pindos ophiolite there is an older IAT series (the Krapa series) and a younger IAT series that is transitional to boninitic rocks (the Asprokambos series) with very low $TiO_2$ and high Mg. The Krapa crystallization sequence is initial olivine, then clinopyroxene, plagioclase, orthopyroxene and opaque minerals; the Asprokambos crystallization sequence is initial olivine, then simultaneous clinopyroxene and orthopyroxene, plagioclase and amphibole. The mineral sequence is quite different to MORB, which is simultaneous olivine and spinel, plagioclase, clinopyroxene, opaque minerals with low-Ca pyroxene. Both series are regarded as forming in an island setting with the boninitic series being formed in a fore-arc.

### Othris

The main ophiolite outcrops in Othris are in the west where they form a nappe complex. The most extensive nappe is in the Mega Isoma massif (Rassios & Konstantopoulou, in press), unique among the Hellenic ophiolites in that it consists principally of plagioclase lherzolite. Nevertheless, economic chrome deposits are found in western Othris, largely confined to the contact zone at the base of the lherzolite and the top of much smaller, structurally lower harzburgite nappe. The harzburgite is thrust, in turn, over ultramafic cumulates and tectonites; itself riding over a sheet of gabbroic cumulates and sheeted dykes that rests on lavas and cherts.

The plagioclase lherzolite shows typical MORB chemistry and little evidence for IAT and boninitic rocks (Rassios & Konstantopoulou, in press).

### Guevgeli

The Guevgeli igneous complex (Bebien 1982; Anon. 1983; Haenel-Remy & Bebien 1987) and its continuation into southern Yugoslavia (Ivanov et al. 1987) is unusual in that it consists of two incomplete ophiolite complexes (Bebien 1982), the eastern of which is intruded by the contemporaneous Fanos granite (Fig. 7). The western ophiolite is faulted against the granite, but cross-cutting relationships of acid and basic dykes in the eastern ophiolite show acid and basic magmas to have coexisted (for map see Bebien, 1982, fig. IV–1, p. 51). Even more unusual is that while trace element diagrams suggest the ophiolite closely resembles MORB (Table 4) – with a $K_2O$ content as low as 0.1% – the $K_2O$ content of the Fanos granite is about 5%. Bebien et al. (1986) have highlighted the cordierite/andalusite contact metamorphism between the gabbroic cumulates of the eastern Guevgeli ophiolite (and also the Oreokastro

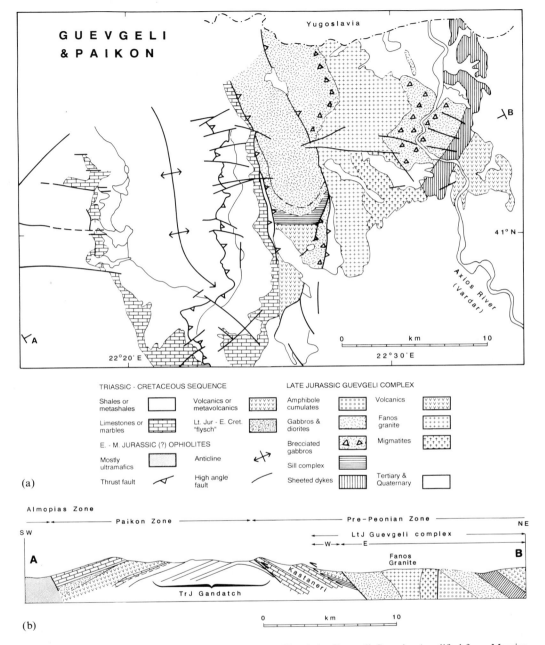

**Fig. 7.** (**a**) Map and (**b**) cross-section of the Paikon massif and the Guevgeli Complex (modified from Mercier 1968, Baroz *et al.* 1987 and Bebien 1982).

ophiolite) and the adjacent sediments of Early to Middle Jurassic age.

Pillow lavas and dikes are present in both ophiolites, but abundant only in the eastern ophiolite where a sheeted complex is developed. Gabbros are present in both ophiolites. The upper part of the plutonic rocks in the western Guevgeli complex shows diorites, ferrodiorites and trondhjemites similar to those found in oceanic fracture zones (Rassios *et al.* 1983).

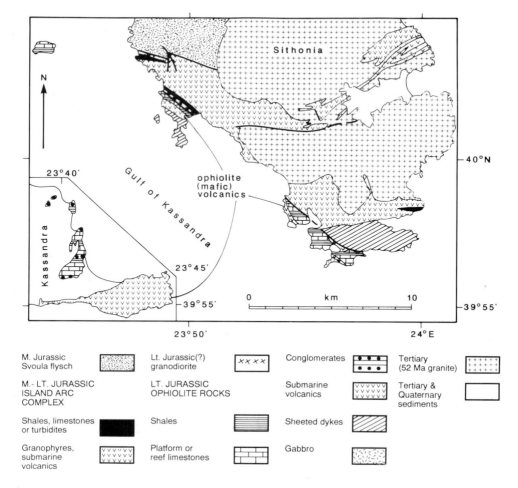

**Fig. 8**. Map of Sithonia and Kassandra ophiolite complex. (Modified from Mussallam 1991.)

Despite the similarity of some of the Guevgeli plutonics to oceanic fracture zone rocks, the prominent contact metamorphism at the contacts of the Guevgeli and Oreokastro ophiolites suggests to Bebien *et al.* (1986) that they are autochthonous with respect to the country rocks and have not been tectonically transported from root zones elsewhere.

## Sithonia and Kassandra

The incomplete Sithonia ophiolite developed on the site of a regionally metamorphosed M. to Late Jurassic arc (Mussallam 1991). The ophiolite is discontinuously exposed for 30 km along the W coast (Fig. 8). Sheeted dikes strike NE, are at least 3 km thick (Mussallam 1991, p. 691) and pass up into volcanics up to 750 m thick

with overlying sediments up to 1.5 m thick. Pillows are highly vesicular. Volcanics are mostly basic, but at the SE margin up to 300 m of rhyolite is present. The sediments include reef limestones with late Kimmeridgian faunas. The ophiolite is intruded by a Tertiary granite which has disrupted the original structure, but it is interpreted as a symmetrical rift at most 30 km across and 10 km long with a central graben, which is essentially in situ with respect to the country rock. Like Guevgeli and Oreokastro, the ophiolite is autochthonous and has not been transported to its present location as a thrust sheet.

The Kassandra ophiolite, 12 km W of Sithonia (Fig. 8), is the least complete of all the Hellenic ophiolites. It consists of 1.2 km of 'abyssal volcanics' with interbedded radiolarian chert, possibly connected to Sithonia by a transform fault. The shallow-water facies at Sithonia may reflect the initial phases of extension which had progressed further when the Kassandra lavas were erupted.

The underlying arc volcanics include early boninites with a gradual transition to IAT and finally minor MORB rocks chemically similar to the subsequent sheeted dykes of the ophiolite. On a Zr vs. Ti diagram sheeted dykes lie mostly within the MORB field. Rare earth element (REE) diagrams show the ophiolitic rocks as a whole – sheeted dykes and lavas – to be enriched in REE compared with MORB. The chemistry is similar to that of the Guevgeli ophiolite. They most closely resemble volcanics in the Bransfield Strait in the Antarctic peninsula region, formed during an early stage of extension, and are also comparable with the ensialic Sarmiento ophiolite in southern Chile.

The trace element and REE patterns of the Kassandra volcanics are very similar to MORB. The relatively enriched chemistry of the Sithonia ophiolite may reflect a lower degree of partial melting in the source and/or the presence of a small subduction component.

## Summary

There appears to be a clear distinction between the complete ophiolites and most of the incomplete ophiolites. The complete ophiolites are generally harzburgitic, allochthonous, commonly show the development of a metamorphic sole, generally include significant chromite often of economic importance and show SSZ trace element characteristics with an evolution from MORB to IAT and occasionally boninites. The incomplete ophiolites are younger, in situ, show contact metamorphism against the country rock, are similar to MORB and show little influence of a subduction zone. Because the incomplete ophiolites are essentially in situ, there is no problem in locating their margins. By contrast, the original positions of the margins of the allochthonous complete ophiolites are still controversial.

## Relations between the ophiolites

### Palaeomagnetic rotations

Both the external and the internal zones of much of NW and central Greece have been rotated by as much as 45° relative to stable Europe (Kissel & Laj 1988) in Late Oligocene (33 Ma) and later time, probably as a byproduct of the rapid extension of the Aegean Sea (Le Pichon & Angelier 1981). These Cenozoic rotations have blurred the original geometrical relationships that the ophiolite belts had to other areas that have not been rotated.

It is not yet clear how and where these rotations of Greece terminate to the NW, but a marked difference in the general trend of the Dinaric ophiolites (130°) and the Hellenic ophiolites (150°) takes place across the Scutari-Pec line (Fig. 1). This probable transform between the Hellenides and Dinarides is speculatively interpreted as having been reactivated in Cenozoic time as a plate margin across which some of the angular differences between Greece and areas to the north have been accommodated. The western edge of the ophiolite outcrop may originally have been linear, with a subsequent clockwise rotation of the Hellenic ophiolites by about 20° relative to the Dinaric ophiolites (see Fig. 14). If the pole was on or close to the line, the actual motions in the area would have been very small.

Other areas, such as Argolis have been rotated since Jurassic time through as much as 90° relative to some parts of the Pelagonian and Pindos zones (Pucher et al. 1974; Turnell 1988). Such rotations may in part account for the fact that as one moves S of the Gulf of Lamia, it becomes increasingly difficult to relate the highly disrupted, poorly exposed, scattered ophiolite outcrops of Beotia and Argolis to the more continuous exposures to the north of the Gulf (Fig. 3). Detailed discussion of the interrelationships among the western ophiolites is, therefore, confined to those north of the Gulf of Lamia.

### Pindos, Vourinos and Othris

It is likely that the western ophiolites – Pindos, Vourinos, Othris and other smaller bodies – were once connected. Over 30 years ago Aubouin et al. (1962) showed that the Pindos and Vourinos ophiolites were probably lateral continuations of one another, divided into two separate outcrop areas by the superposition of the relatively undeformed Cenozoic Mesohellenic trough onto a formerly continuous ophiolite thrust sheet, or sheets (Fig. 9). Certainly, as the Mesohellenic trough is traced N into Albania, the two western belts merge into one (Fig. 1).

This interpretation was elaborated by Smith (1979), who argued from the outcrop pattern that the Othris ophiolite was most probably part of the same tectonic unit as the Pindos and Vourinos ophiolites, the whole forming what had once been a large ophiolite nappe, or nappes. Detailed structural work (Rassios et al. 1990) shows that the initial emplacement strain – presumably within the ocean basin – is similarly

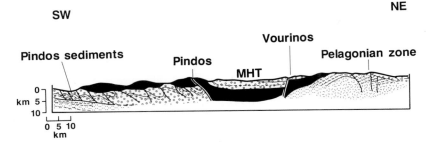

**Fig. 9**. Cross-section through the Pindos and Vourinos ophiolites (black) showing their probable lateral continuation under the undeformed Cenozoic Mesohellenic trough (MHT). Modified from Aubouin *et al.* (1962).

orientated for all three ophiolites, suggesting they were initially emplaced as a unit which has not undergone significant internal rotations. The similarity in orientation also implies that there has not been any significant relative rotation of the ophiolites relative to the Pelagonian zone since their emplacement onto the continental margin in Late Jurassic time.

### Other structures within the ophiolites

In Othris, Pindos and Vourinos the dominant fabrics trend NE, parallel to the emplacement direction – whether from the NE or the SW – or they trend NW, at right angles to it (Rassios *et al.* 1990; Rassios & Konstantopoulou, in press).

Most of the structures in the Vourinos ultramafics formed at about 1200°C at the ridge crest (Rassios, pers. comm.). There is a 'moderate' overprint by ductile fabrics formed at about 1000°C expressed in the deeper-level peridotites as distinct mylonite zones. These pass upward into abundant brittle shears. In Pindos cataclastic and mylonitic fabrics at the same structural level as the Vourinos mylonite are pervasive, rather than discrete. This difference in deformation leaves pyroxenite dykes intact in the Vourinos peridotites but reduces them to boudins in Pindos.

The pervasive ductile structures in the Pindos are attributed to overprinting of the initial 1200°C ridge crest structures by long-continued high strain in a lower temperature ductile state during ophiolite emplacement. Compared to Vourinos, the transition from ductile to brittle conditions took much longer in the Pindos. It is believed to be related to Pindos' trailing edge position, i.e. SW of Vourinos, which itself is assumed to have been closer to the leading edge of the ophiolite nappe (Rassios *et al.* 1990) and to have moved from SW to NE.

Structures internal to the ophiolites show consistent transport to the NE (Fig. 10). For example, Roberts *et al.* (1988, p. 253) showed that the entire spectrum of brittle to plastic structures throughout the Vourinos ophiolite 'show a more or less constant movement direction towards 050'. Similar NE-directed structures occur in the Pindos ophiolite (Robertson *et al.* 1991, p. 304).

In western Othris the nappe pile is cut by high-angle SW-dipping faults forming imbricate slices (duplexes). Faulting propagated from the NE to the SW. Each duplex is lined by low-grade amphibolite facies ophiolitic material, showing that these structures are contemporaneous with initial emplacement. Prior to their formation the nappes were emplaced in semi-ductile conditions with abundant folds showing top-to-the-NE displacement where the lherzolites override the harzburgites and local intrusion of gabbro, which is itself plastically deformed (Rassios & Konstantopoulou in press). The geometry of the imbrications within the lavas of central and eastern Othris (Rassios 1989; Rassios & Konstantopoulou in press) also suggests initial NE transport.

After allowing for Neogene rotations, brittle and ductile fabrics in the metamorphic sole under the ophiolite in Evvia also show NE-directed transport (Robertson 1991). The early ductile displacements in the sole rocks of the Zlatibor ophiolite in SW Yugoslavia were also to the NE (Dimitrijević & Dimitrijević 1979).

### Root zones of the western ophiolites

Where the root zones of the western ophiolites lay is an important question for any tectonic models of their origin and emplacement. In Greece there are essentially two schools of thought: one roots them SW of the Pelagonian

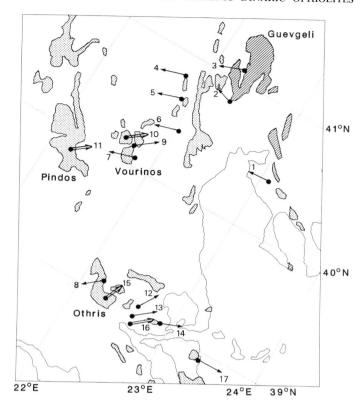

**Fig. 10.** Fold vergence and tectonic transport directions associated with ophiolite emplacement. Incomplete ophiolites are diagonally shaded; complete ophiolites or their erosional remnants are stippled. 1–8: mostly fold vergence (Vergely 1984 Fig. for phase JE1); 9: fold vergence (Naylor & Harle 1976, 1977; Vergely 1976, 1977); 10: NE-verging structures (Rassios et al. 1990, p. 10, Roberts et al. 1988, p. 253); 11: NE-verging structures (Rassios et al. 1990); 12–13: oldest tectonic structures in submarine fan (12) and pelagic basin (13) Smith et al. 1979; 14: general transport direction in E Othris (Rassios 1991); 15: imbrication and fold vergence in ophiolite (Rassios & Konstantopoulos, in press); 16: general transport direction (Rassios 1989); 17: structures in metamorphic sole (Robertson 1991, p. 38). Structures clearly of intra-oceanic origin have a double-lined arrow.

zone; the other NE of the Pelagonian zone, i.e. in the Axios = Vardar) zone.

The overall simplicity of the outcrop pattern of the western Dinaric–Hellenic ophiolites, particularly after removal of the post-Eocene rotation of the Hellenides (see Fig. 14), together with the gradual and systematic change in the nature of the ultramafic rocks (Fig. 1) all suggest an underlying tectonic simplicity. One view of the ophiolites in the Dinarides is that they are part of a marginal basin formed to the SW of the Dinaric analogue of the Pelagonian zone – the Drina-Ivanjica block – when it rifted away from Adria (Dimitrijević 1982). For example, the large Zlatibor ophiolite in the Dinarides is believed to have been emplaced initially from the SW (Dimitrijević 1982, p. 16). One would expect

a very similar model to apply to the western Hellenic ophiolites.

However, analogy with Alpine structure has led several geologists to root all the western ophiolites in the more internal parts of the Hellenides, i.e. in the Axios = Vardar) zone to the NE of the Pelagonian zone (e.g. Bernoulli & Laubscher 1972; Jacobshagen et al. 1976; Katsikastos 1977; Katsikatsos et al. 1982). Other geologists have proposed a similar origin for the Dinaric ophiolites.

Facies trends in sediments formed during emplacement of the Argolis ophiolite suggest SW-directed transport (Baumgartner 1985), a direction confirmed by the orientation of thrust duplexes, thrust geometry and facing directions in pelagic sediments interbedded with the ophio-

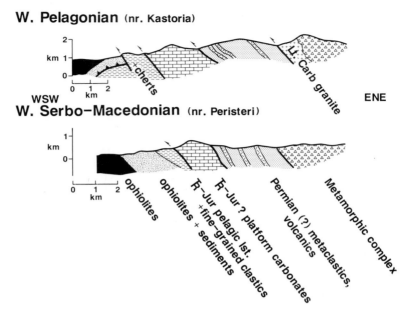

**Fig. 11.** Cross-sections of the western edge of the Pelagonian zone near Kastoria and the Serbo-Macedonian zone near Peristeri showing their remarkable similarities. Modified from Mountrakis (1986). Both appear to be continental margins of Triassic age.

litic lavas (Robertson *et al.* 1991, p. 304). However, after allowing for Neogene rotations emplacement is from the NW and cannot be used to support derivation from the Axios zone (Robertson *et al.* 1991).

*Fold vergences*

The movement sense of the structures associated with emplacement of the western ophiolites onto the SW margin of the Pelagonian zone should give unequivocal evidence for the location of the root zone, but the study of fold vergences has given rise to a divergence of opinion summarized in Fig. 10.

The reasons for disagreement include the interpretation of some structures as soft-sediment slumping rather than as folds formed under the ophiolite nappes. Slump folds will have an opposite vergence to those created shortly afterwards by the emplacement itself. This difference in view, together with the difficulty of determining whether folds that are within a few kilometres of an ophiolite nappe are related to nappe emplacement or are a different tectonic phase possibly with an opposite vergence, are the main sources of structural disagreement about the direction of emplacement onto the Pelagonian zone.

The time interval between the beginning of emplacement within the ocean basin and the arrival of the ophiolite on the Pelagonian zone was short (Fig. 4). The direction associated with the intra-oceanic emplacement is to the NE. While this is not necessarily the direction of subsequent emplacement onto the continental margin, it would be remarkable if the direction had changed to SW, for it would imply a marked discontinuity in what seems to have been a continuous process.

*Possible relations between the complete western and eastern ophiolites.*

Mountrakis (1986) showed that there are remarkable similarities between the margins of the western edge of the Pelagonian and Serbo-Macedonian zones (Fig. 11). Like Vergely (1984, Figs J.1(a) and J.2), Mountrakis interprets these as independent Triassic passive continental margins, that developed two SSZ marginal basins in Triassic and earlier Jurassic time on their western flanks, parts of which were emplaced simultaneously from the west as ophiolites onto the Pelagonian and Serbo-Macedonian zones. In Yugoslavia Karamata also envisages the simultaneous existence of two spreading oceans (Karamata 1988, fig. 3, p. 6).

An alternative explanation for these similarities is tectonic duplication by transcurrent faulting (Smith & Spray 1984). These authors speculated that the western and eastern Hellenic ophiolite belts were once continuous and had been duplicated by a transform fault at the eastern margin of the Pelagonian zone = western margin of the Axios or Vardar zone).

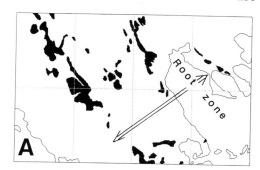

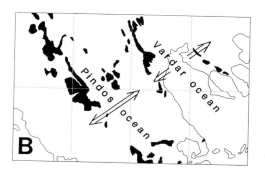

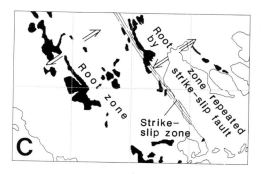

## Vardar zone

Dimitrijević (1982, p. 21) regards the Vardar zone as 'the most important movement zone in the Balkan Peninsula'. For example, between about 18°E and 21°E the Vardar zone is in contact with the Drina-Ivanjica block, the tectonic unit analogous to the Pelagonian zone in Greece (Fig. 1). The later Cretaceous cover of this block is mostly limestone and flysch, with a schistose source to the NE. At the present time the source area, which should be in the immediately adjacent Vardar rocks, is occupied instead by late Cretaceous rocks of largely reworked ophiolitic melange, a different kind of flysch and pelagic deposits. Dimitrijević (1982, p. 16) concludes 'that one part at least of this area has been lost after the Senonian'. In the writer's view the most likely explanation is that the missing source has been removed by strike-slip motions.

The general types of relationships that have been suggested between the complete western and eastern ophiolites are summarized in Fig. 12.

It seems entirely possible that the eastern ophiolites have been significantly offset with respect to the western ophiolites and that in the present state of knowledge only general correlations are possible between them. Spreading and emplacement models discussed here are, therefore, limited to the ophiolites west of the Axios ( = Vardar) zone. Even here there are significant differences of interpretation. For example, ophiolite fragments extend NE from the Vourinos more or less continuously to the Vermion range on the E side of the Pelagonian zone (Fig. 3), implying that the Pindos–Vourinos–Othris ophiolites once formed a nappe(s) that was at least 120 km in width. However, this apparent continuity of outcrop is regarded by some geologists as illusory. Vergely (1984, fig. J. 1–2(b), p. 155) believes the Vardar ophiolites were emplaced onto the eastern half of the Pelagonian zone in pre-Tithonian time, whereas the western half was covered by the western ophiolites shortly afterwards (Vergely 1984, fig. J.1–2(d) ).

**Fig. 12.** Schematic diagram of major types of ophiolite/ocean models for the Hellenides. (**A**) Remnants of an originally continuous ophiolite nappe rooted in the Axios ( = Vardar) zone that has since been eroded into two separate outcrop zones without any significant strike-slip motion between them (e.g. Bernoulli & Laubscher 1972; Vergely 1984; Ferrière 1985); (**B**) Two adjacent contemporaneous but quite independent ophiolite belts that were never connected together (e.g. Mountrakis 1986; Karamata 1988). (**C**) Formerly continuous single belt that has been tectonically duplicated by strike-slip faulting (Smith & Spray 1984). The sense of motion is not known but was speculated to be sinistral. Several other models exist in which the larger ophiolites are each regarded as small ocean remnants.

## Emplacement model for the western ophiolites

In the author's opinion, the balance of evidence from Greece cited above supports a root zone for the western ophiolites SW of the Pelagonian zone and suggests that western ophiolites once covered most of this zone.

### Sole rocks

The sole rocks provide important constraints on all emplacement models. The highest metamorphic grade is attained locally in W Othris in a garnet amphibolite at a temperature of 860°C (Spray & Roddick 1980). Garnets are also found in the carbonates under the ophiolites in eastern Othris (Vrinena) and locally in the carbonates and schist under the Vourinos Complex (Rassios, pers. comm.). However, the highest grade in the Othris sole is generally in the low-amphibolite facies, as is the N Pindos sole (Spray et al. 1984) and in the N Evvia ( = Euboea) and Vourinos soles it is generally in epidote–amphibolite facies.

Ti vs. Zr plots give MORB signatures for all 5 soles; Zr/Y vs. Zr gave WPB, except for Evvia which was IAT and Ti–Z–Y plots gave WPB for Pindos, Vourinos and Othris, with the Othris garnet–amphibolite as MORB and Evvia as LKT (Spray & Roddick 1980). They suggest that

the original rocks were mostly either MORB or WPB, with SSZ influences present in Evvia. In the Pindos zone the sole rocks are not cut by dykes, including the youngest (boninitic) dykes (Jones et al. 1991). Amphibolites of boninitic composition and IAT are found in the Pindos sole, though the most of the amphibolites are of MORB and within-plate-basalt (WPB) composition. The WPB rocks are presumed to have been derived from Triassic basalts.

Analogy with the Oman ophiolite, which has similar sole rocks at its base (e.g. Lippard et al. 1986), requires the ophiolite to have been detached at or near an active, or recently active, ridge crest at the lithosphere–asthenosphere boundary (Fig. 13). The temperature at the detachment zone was above 860°C – to make the Othris garnet – and below 1250°C, the melting temperature of peridotites at the corresponding depth (Boudier et al. 1988, p. 291). For Oman, Boudier et al. suggest a detachment temperature of about 1000°C, maintained initially at or close to this value by significant shear heating (Pavlis 1986).

### Position of the ridge

For the Dinaric–Hellenic ophiolites, emplacement from the SW onto the Pelagonian (or Drina-Ivanjica) zones implies that the ridge lay to the SW, that the western half of the ocean has

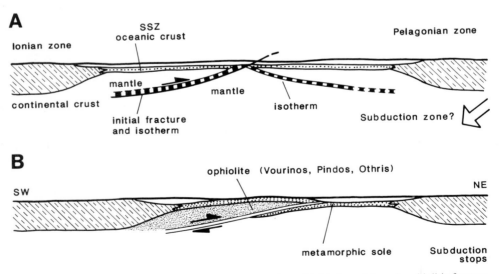

**Fig. 13.** (**A**) Schematic diagram of the marginal basin at the time of initiation of the sub-ophiolitic fracture along a geotherm intersecting at the ridge crest. (**B**) Emplacement is underway, with the hot ophiolite overriding the eastern half of the ocean floor and creating metamorphic sole rocks of oceanic composition. In Greece, the ocean basin was probably wider than depicted. During spreading it is speculated that a SW-dipping subduction zone existed NE of the Pelagonian zone.

been preserved and thrust onto the Pelagonian (and Drina–Ivanjica) zones, and that eastern half of the ocean disappeared as a Late Jurassic subduction zone dipping to the SW under the western half. The author has always been reluctant to accept the last conclusion because there is no obvious evidence for such a subduction zone anywhere SW of the Pelagonian zone. However, Jones & Robertson (1991) and Robertson (1991) plausibly interpret the structure of the rocks under the Pindos ophiolite and Evvia ( = Euboea) ophiolite, respectively, as the remnants of a Late Jurassic subduction complex. The absence of any volcanism can be attributed to the small amount of subduction involved (? <200 km).

A new convergent zone is created when the forces resisting convergence – the strength and bending resistance of the lithosphere, and the friction on the slip zone – are overcome by the driving forces – the hydrostatic head of the ridge crest and the gravitational pull of the subducted slab (McKenzie 1977). Convergence at ridge crests must be initiated by external forces, i.e. the ridge crest must be part of a plate network that is connected to nearby pre-existing convergent zones which can supply the necessary forces to overcome the initial resistance to convergent motion at the ridge crest. It is pointless to look for the source of the driving forces in the ophiolites themselves: in the case of the Dinaric–Hellenic ophiolites, connections must have existed to other subduction zones further E – since there are none to the W – but details are not discussed here.

## Spreading model for the western ophiolites

### Spreading rate

For ophiolites and ocean floor, the most important parameter is the spreading rate (Nicolas 1989, p. 85). Were they available, isotopic dates would probably be too imprecise to date spreading rates.

The continuity and thickness of the layered gabbros in Oman suggests fast spreading (Nicolas 1989). The Pindos, Othris and Vourinos complexes all contain layered gabbros but the gabbros as a whole appear to be about one half to one third the thickness of the equivalent Oman section (Jackson et al. 1975, fig. 6). The amount of postcumulus overgrowth in the Vourinos Complex is believed to indicate a slow-spreading ridge (Jackson et al. 1975).

In Oman the absence of transform faults for a ridge length of over 300 km (Nicolas 1989) is thought to indicate fast spreading. In the Dinarides possible spacing of large transforms seems to be at least 250 km and may be as much as 580 km if the Sarajevo and Zagreb transverse structures are not transform faults. If the Spherchios offset in Greece is a transform, the spacing of major transforms in the Hellenides exceeds 400 km. The overall spacing implies fast spreading rates, contrary to the evidence from the layered gabbros.

In Oman, the flat-lying shear planes in the uppermost mantle suggest fast, rather than slow, spreading (Nicolas 1989, p. 85). Mantle structural and fabric studies have been made for Vourinos (Ayrton 1968; Ross et al. 1980; Roberts et al. 1988; Rassios et al. 1990); for Pindos (Rassios 1990; Rassios et al. 1990) and Othris (Rassios et al. 1990; Rassios & Konstantopoulou, in press) but it is not clear what they reveal about the likely spreading rate.

### Ridge orientation

Areally extensive trends of sheeted-dyke complexes in ophiolites are important data for tectonic models. In the case of the western ophiolites good exposures of sheeted-dyke complexes are present in Vourinos trending NW and dipping moderately SW (Jackson et al. 1975). Elsewhere dyke complexes are fragmentary: in Pindos, MORB dykes trend at about 135°; exposures of multiple dykes trending at about 160° are known from western Othris (personal observations). High-temperature form lines in peridotites are thought to parallel the ridge axis (Nicolas 1989). In Vourinos, Pindos and Othris all form lines trend NW, parallel to the MORB sheeted-dyke complexes.

Unlike the Guevgeli, Sithonia and Kassandra ophiolites (see below) most of the extension in the western ophiolites was at right angles to the local trend of the Hellenides: the western ophiolites were not created in a basin resembling the Gulf of California that has been subsequently emplaced onto adjacent continents.

However, it is worth noting that, in Pindos, the later IAT and boninitic sheeted dykes show a range of orientations (Jones et al. 1991, fig. 7) but generally trend NE, as they do in Vourinos (Rassios, pers. comm.).

### Relation to Dinaric ophiolites

That the ophiolites represent the SW half of a marginal basin is independently supported by two different models for the lateral variations of ocean floor in a newly formed ocean basin.

In the first, summarised by Nicolas (1989, fig.

7.3), the initial ascent rate of the asthenosphere during continental rifting is small and little melt is extracted. The peridotites are spinel lherzolite. As the rift develops, the ascent rate increases and plagioclase lherzolites form. At still faster rates of asthenosphere ascent more melt is extracted and the peridotites are predominantly harzburgitic.

Nicolas (1989) highlights these differences as 'LOT' (lherzolitic ophiolite type) and 'HOT' (harzburgitic ophiolite type). He concludes (Nicolas 1989, pp. 194–195) that HOT typically forms where spreading is more than about 10 mm a$^{-1}$ and that LOT typifies areas of slow spreading and transform faulting. The lateral change in ultramafics is not related to subduction.

In the second model, water from a subduction zone plays an essential role (Pearce et al. 1984; Roberts 1988). Initially the ocean floor is MORB, but as water enters the magmatic system, the trace elements in the basalts take on a typical SSZ signature, chromite is precipitated and the mantle rocks are typically harzburgitic (see above).

In the first model the lateral change across the Dinaride ophiolites from lherzolites (LOT) in the SW to harzburgites (HOT) in the NE (Fig. 1) suggests that the spreading rate was slowest in the SW, probably because the SW side was the first-formed oldest ocean floor and was closer to a continental margin.

Lherzolite is rare but not absent in the western Hellenic ophiolites and is always on the western edge. As noted above, the Pindos ophiolite contains some lherzolite and western Othris contains a unique exposure – for the Hellenic ophiolites – of plagioclase lherzolite (Rassios & Konstantopoulou, in press) which Menzies (1976) interpreted as having formed in the initial stages of rifting. Its location, immediately N of the Sperchios offset, together with lherzolite in the Pindos ophiolite could also reflect the presence of a transform zone at the edge of the continent bordering the ophiolites, a view shared by Rassios (pers. comm.).

As noted by Robertson et al. (1991), the greater abundance of chrome in Vourinos compared with Pindos can be interpreted as representing a lateral transition from spreading in a normal oceanic setting to spreading above an active subduction zone. If, as seems likely, the transition is one in time as well as in space then the Pindos ophiolite is older than the Vourinos ophiolite.

Though differing fundamentally in explaining the origin of harzburgite and the abundance of chrome, both models lead to the conclusion that the preserved western ophiolites are the western half of a marginal basin.

These conclusions have not yet been verified by other methods of finding where the ridge lay, such as the preferential chilling direction in sheeted dykes; the slope direction of the floor in layered gabbros; and the dip of flow planes in sheared peridotites with respect to the Moho and the shear sense in them (Nicolas 1989).

## Margins of the ophiolites

In the thrusts of central Othris there is a Triassic to Late Jurassic facies progression from a Jurassic (?) ophiolite sequence (structurally highest sheet) down into a pelagic basin sequence then a submarine fan and finally a carbonate platform overlain by radiolarian chert (Smith et al. 1975). The sequence, together with the absence of any significant arc-related sediments and volcanics has been interpreted as recording the breakup of a continent in Triassic time and the formation of a passive eastern continental margin (Smith et al. 1975, 1979). Mid- to Late Triassic rifting is also documented in the Avdella melange of the Pindos Complex (Jones et al. 1991, p. 776). The associated rocks are within-plate-basalts (WPB) or transitional to MORB and interpreted as part of an eastern margin to the ophiolite (Robertson et al. 1991, fig. 7).

No sediments directly associated with any Hellenic ophiolite are older than mid-Jurassic. The hiatus in ages between the Triassic igneous rocks and the sediments overlying the ophiolites may represent a hiatus in the spreading history of the Pindos ocean. Triassic ocean floor could have formed the basement to the widespread allochthonous Triassic and younger pelagic sediments of the Pindos zone west of the ophiolites, whose substrate is unknown. These are mostly deep-water limestones and cherts with little trace of arc sediments or volcanism. The presumed ocean floor would have been subducted in Cenozoic time, with the sediments being scraped off to form a Cenozoic accretionary prism. The western margin of the Pindos zone is interpreted as a passive continental margin of Triassic age (Robertson et al. 1991, fig. 6).

Thus the stratigraphic evidence suggests the Pindos ocean formed between two Triassic passive margins that gradually separated. This view is entirely compatible with Nicolas' interpretation with the view that the lateral changes in the ultramafic rocks are unrelated to subduction, but is apparently incompatible with the interpretation of the trace elements from basalts and the relatively abundant chrome as indicators of a subduction zone. The changes in the basalts,

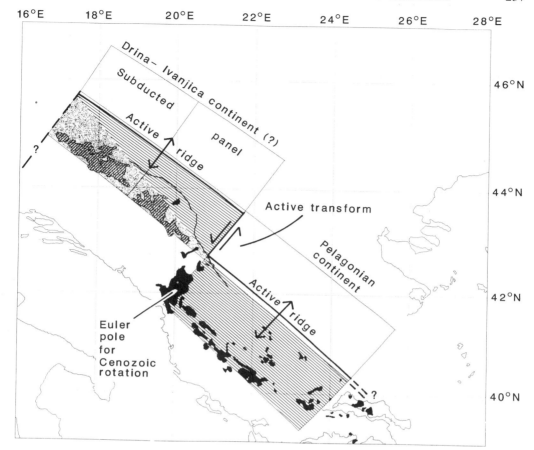

**Fig. 14.** A speculative model for the origin of the Dinaric–Hellenic ophiolites. The Hellenides have been rotated anticlockwise by 20° about 'the Euler pole for Cenozoic rotation'. The pole is on the Scutari-Pec line and the rotation brings the trends of the western Dinaric ophiolites into parallelism with the western Hellenic ophiolites. A schematic ridge-and-transform grid has been superposed on the map using a possible Jurassic spreading pole to the NW of the area. The grid depicts the area at the end of spreading just before emplacement began. The ridge is shown as orthogonal to the Scutari-Pec transform and a possible transform just S of Othris. Transverse trends near Sarajevo and Zagreb are also shown. The finely ruled area covers the harzburgitic massifs; the shaded area in the panels NW of the Scutari-Pec transform shows the largely lherzolitic massifs. Lherzolitic areas are speculatively attributed to slow spreading at the initiation of the marginal basin; harzburgitic areas to faster spreading. All the ocean floor to the NE of the ridge has been subducted by a SW-dipping subduction zone formed at the ridge crest. The SW panels have been emplaced NE onto the Drina-Ivanjica and Pelagonian continents.

from MORB to IAT and eventually boninites require some hydrous component in the mantle (Pearce *et al.* 1984). However, the absence of the thicknesses of IAT volcanics found in many arcs – several kilometres or more – from the western ophiolites as a whole suggests that they were never present, rather than having been present originally and subsequently eroded. Rather than envisaging a subduction zone as the source of the trace element chemistry, perhaps the mantle was amphibole-bearing and extension above it caused adiabatic melting and simulation of an SSZ environment. But were that the case, it is likely that the ophiolites would have started as IAT rather than evolving from MORB to IAT. Clearly, the conflicting views outlined above represent unsolved problems.

## Active margins

The coexistence of passive margins to a basin floored by SSZ magmas without any thick pile of arc volcanics can be reconciled by postulating a short-lived **west-dipping** subduction zone, a conclusion previously resisted by earlier workers (e.g. Smith *et al.* 1979; Jones *et al.* 1988, quoted in Jones & Robertson 1991).

Jones & Robertson (1991, fig. 13E) site such a subduction zone within the ophiolite basin itself, with sole formation overlapping spreading (Robertson *et al.* 1991, fig. 7). However, no dykes cut the Pindos sole (Jones & Robertson 1991) or any other metamorphic sole so far as the author is aware, suggesting that extension and convergence did not overlap in time. The author postulates a mid-Jurassic W-dipping subduction zone on the E side of the Pelagonian zone or beyond (Fig. 13) to create the SSZ ophiolites and a second W-dipping later Middle Jurassic fracture at the ridge crest to emplace them onto the Pelagonian zone.

The only andesites and other calc-alkaline lavas of probable Early–Middle Jurassic age are in the Axios ( = Vardar) zone: in the Paikon massif (Baroz *et al.* 1987) (Fig. 6) and next to the Oreokastro and Metallikon ophiolites (Bebien *et al.* 1987) and the Chortiatis magmatic suite of the circum-Rhodope belt (Mussallam & Jung 1986; Mussallam 1991). These lavas suggest the existence of an E–M Jurassic subduction zone in the Axios ( = Vardar) zone. Provided it dipped to the SW, it could have imprinted the SSZ signature on the western ophiolites.

Wherever it lay, the effect of the inferred subduction zone on magmatism within the basin seems to be limited to processes at the extensional margin only: there is no evidence for E–M Jurassic subduction-related volcanism anywhere else in the basin.

### A spreading model

The Dinaric ophiolite outcrops form essentially an inverted V, narrowing northwards (Fig. 1). The pattern suggests the Euler opening pole lay N of the northernmost outcrop, which would imply that spreading was least in the N and increased steadily S. According to Nicolas' (1989) model, this is independently implied by the existence of lherzolite only in the N and harzburgite only in the S. According to this model, the rate of asthenospheric ascent − and therefore spreading rate − in the N never reached the necessary velocity for harzburgite formation, whereas in the S the spreading velocity for harzburgite formation was reached early on. The migration of the lherzolite/harzburgite boundary northwards could reflect an increase in angular velocity about the Euler pole with time (Fig. 14). This simple model is consistent with all the

available data except for the contrary structural views discussed above. It provides a rationale for the lateral variations in the nature of the western Dinaric–Hellenic ophiolites. It is important to note that the model is largely independent of the problem of their root zone, though it has obvious implications for it. The model implies that the ophiolites are not randomly emplaced fragments of a former ocean but represent the bulk of its western half. The present western margin lies east of, but not far from, the original continental margin and the present eastern margin of the western ophiolites is not far from the position of the youngest ridge within the ocean basin.

Space does not permit discussion of the relationship of Jurassic spreading to possible Triassic spreading (e.g. Jones *et al.* 1991) and Triassic volcanism (e.g. Pamic 1984; Pe-Piper 1982), nor of how the required extensional and convergent Jurassic plate margins might have been linked together.

## Spreading models for the incomplete (younger) ophiolites

### Ridge orientation

The Sithonia rift, containing the Sithonia and Kassandra ophiolites, resembles the early stages of the opening of the Gulf of California, though no evidence for strike-slip faulting has been located (Mussallam 1991, p. 701). The sense of motion here is unknown, but the direction was presumably at right angles to the dyke trend of 27°. A local magnetic anomaly is present indicating that the ophiolite is an isolated body.

Dykes in the western Guevgeli complex are not well developed but originally trended at about 45°. A sheeted complex is well developed in the eastern ophiolite with two distinct orientations, one originally at 45° in a central block, the other at 160° in a block to the N and the S of the central block (Bebien *et al.* 1986, fig. 1). These orientations are interpreted as two conjugate extension directions brought about by wrench faulting with a dextral sense of motion on a transcurrent zone parallel to the central Chalkidiki ophiolite.

### Transient plate margins

The Guevgeli and Sithonia–Kassandra complexes are essentially transient pull-apart basins (Bebien *et al.* 1986) formed in the early stages of motion on a ridge-transform margin whose displacement did not exceed 30 km and whose duration was probably less than 1.5 Ma (Mus-

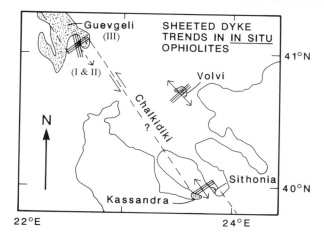

**Fig. 15.** Dyke trends for sheeted dykes in Guevgeli (I, II and III) from Bebien (1982); Volvi from Dixon & Dimitriadis (1984) and Sithonia from Mussallam (1991). The Kassandra ophiolite lacks sheeted dykes but is the lateral continuation of the Sithonia body. The spreading systems in Sithonia and Guevgeli have been joined by a long transform segment, as suggested by Bebien *et al.* (1986), but the sense of motion is speculatively shown here as dextral rather than sinistral. It is impossible to connect the Volvi complex into the Sithonia–Guevgeli system without postulating a subsequent displacement.

sallam 1991). In the author's view, the dyke orientations give inconclusive evidence for the sense of motion, but the geometry is suggestive of dextral motion (Fig. 15). The contemporaneous Fanos granite gives an age of 155 Ma.

It is tempting to see a similar pattern in the Volvi meta-ophiolite (Dixon & Dimitriadis 1984, fig. 1). Like the Sithonia dikes, the Volvi sheeted dykes have a NE strike (Dixon & Dimitriadis 1984 p. 610).

## Tectonic setting

Jones *et al.* (1991) liken the tectonic setting of the Pindos–Vourinos ophiolite to the initial setting of some present-day Pacific volcanic arcs such as the Marianas arc where boninitic crust is present. While similarities exist, the author suggests a more appropriate analogy, at least for the initial formation of the ocean floor, may be the present-day Mediterranean. In the western Mediterranean, a subduction zone appears to have 'rolled back', fragmenting the former southern continental margin of the Eurasian plate and causing rapid rotation and transport of areas such as Corsica, Sardinia, the Khabylies, Calabria and other areas with the generation of oceanic crust behind them (e.g. Livermore *et al.* 1986).

The Dinaric–Hellenic ophiolites can be regarded as forming in a similar fragmented continental setting as a side-effect of the suturing

Laurasia and Gondwana to form Pangea in Permo-Triassic time (Smith & Livermore 1991). In the case of the Dinaric–Hellenic ophiolites, convergence followed almost immediately on the cessation of spreading, causing a mid-ocean subduction zone to develop with the consequent emplacement of the ophiolites. In the western Mediterranean, emplacement of the young ocean floor will probably take place provided convergence starts when the former spreading ridges are still the weakest part of the lithosphere. If convergence is delayed long enough, the lithospheric fracture will probably take place at a continental margin, rather than within the ocean floor, and no ophiolites will be emplaced.

A preliminary version of this paper was presented as part of an EUG symposium organized by John Ramsay in 1989. Subsequently, it has benefited from the comments and criticisms of Andrew de Wet and John Waldren. Alastair Robertson and Anne Rassios extensively reviewed the manuscript and suggested numerous improvements. In addition, Anne Rassios generously provided invaluable reprints, preprints and otherwise difficult-to-obtain information. Earth Sciences Contribution number 3363.

## References

ANON. 1972. Penrose Field Conference on ophiolites. *Geotimes*, **17**, 24–25.
—— 1983. Preliminary report on the field excursion to Vourinos–Guevgeli ophiolites. *Ofioliti*, **8**, 303–306.

AUBOUIN, J. 1959. Contribution a l'étude de la Grèce septentrionale: les confins de l'Epire et de la Thessalie. *Annales Géologiques des Pays Helléniques*, **10**, 1–525.

—— 1965. *Geosynclines*. Elsevier, Amsterdam.

——, BRUNN, J.-H., CELET, P., DERCOURT, J., GODFRIAUX, I. & MERCIER, J. 1962. Esquisse de la géologie de la Grèce. *Bulletin de la Société Géologique de France*, **2**, 583–610.

AYRTON, S. 1968. Structures isoclinales dans les peridotites du Mont Vourinos (Macédoine grècque). Un exemple de deformation des roches ultrabasiques. *Schweizerische Mineralogische und Petrographische Mitteilungen*, **48**, 733–750.

BAROZ, F. & REMY, P. 1985. Calc-alkaline and tholeiitic magmas in a Mesozoic ophiolitic domain: the Oreokastro Range (eastern Hellenides). *Ofioliti*, **10**, 161–180.

——, BEBIEN, J. & IKENNE, M. 1987. An example of high-pressure low-temperature metamorphic rocks from an island arc: the Paikon Series (Innermost Hellenides, Greece). *Journal of Metamorphic Petrology*, **5**, 509–527.

BAUMGARTNER, P. O. 1984. A Middle Jurassic–Early Cretaceous low-latitude radiolarian zonation based on unitary associations and age of Tethyan radiolarites. *Eclogae Geologicae Helvetiae*, **77**, 729–837.

—— 1985. *Jurassic sedimentary evolution and nappe emplacement in the Argolis peninsula (Peloponnesus, Greece)*, Swiss Society for Nature Research, Basel, Switzerland.

—— 1987. Age and genesis of Tethyan Jurassic radiolarites. *Eclogae Geologicae Helvetiae*, **80**, 831–879.

BEBIEN, J. 1982 *L'association ignée de Guévgéli (Macédoine Grècque) expression d'un magmatisme ophiolitique dans une dechirure continentale*. PhD thesis, Université de Nancy I.

—— BAROZ, J., CAPEDRI, S. & VENTURELLI, G. 1987. Magmatismes basiques associés à l'ouverture d'un bassin marginal dans les Hellénides internes au Jurassique. *Ofioliti*, **12**, 53–70.

—— DUBOIS, R. & GAUTHIER, A. 1986. Example of ensialic ophiolites emplaced in a wrench zone: innermost Hellenic ophiolite belt (Greek Macedonia). *Geology*, **14**, 1016–1019.

BECCALUVA, L., OHNENSTETTER, D. & OHNENSTETTER, M. 1979. Geochemical discrimination between ocean floor and island arc tholeiites: application to some ophiolites. *Canadian Journal of Earth Sciences*, **16**, 1874–1882.

——, ——, & PAUPY, A. 1984. Two magmatic series with island arc affinities within the Vourinos ophiolite. *Contributions to Mineralogy and Petrology*, **85**, 253–271.

BERNOULLI, D. & LAUBSCHER, H. 1972. The palinspastic problem of the Hellenides. *Eclogae Geologicae Helvetiae*, **65**, 107–118.

BORSI, G., FERRARA, G., MERCIER, J. & TONGIORGI, E. 1966. Age stratigraphique et radiomètrique Jurassique supérieur d'un granite des zones internes des Hellénides. (Granite de Fanos, Macédoine, Grèce). *Revue de Géologie Dynamique et de Géographie Physique*, **8**, 279–287.

BOUDIER, F., CEULENEER, G. & NICOLAS, A. 1988. Shear zones, thrusts and related magmatism in the Oman ophiolite: initiation of thrusting on an oceanic ridge. *Tectonophysics*, **151**, 275–296.

BRUNN, J. H. 1956. Contribution à l'étude géologique du Pinde septentrional et de la Macédoine occidentale. *Annales Géologiques des Pays Helléniques*, **7**, 1–358.

—— 1959. La dorsale médio-atlantique et les épanchements ophiolitiques. *Comptes rendues sommaires Société géologique de France*, 234–237.

CAPEDRI, S., LEKKAS, E., PAPANIKAOU, D., SKARPELIS, N., VENTURELLI, G. & GALLO, F. 1985. The ophiolite of the Koziakas range, western Thessaly (Greece). *Neue Jahrbuch Mineralogie*, **152**(1), 45–64.

—— VENTURELLI, G., BEBIEN, J. & TOSCANI, L. 1981. Low and high Ti ophiolites in northern Pindos: petrological and geological constraints. *Bulletin Volcanologique*, **44**, 439–449.

——, BOCCHI, G., DOSTAL, J., GARUTI, G. & ROSSI, A. 1980. The geochemistry and petrogenesis of an ophiolite sequence from Pindos, Greece. *Contributions to Mineralogy and Petrology*, **74**, 189–200.

——, —— & TOSCANI, L. 1982. Petrology of an ophiolitic cumulate sequence from Pindos, Greece. *Journal of Geology*, **17**, 223–242.

CHRISTODOULOU, C. & MICHAELIDES, K. 1990. Petrology of the plutonic suites from the Chalkidiki ophiolites, northern Greece. Implications for parental magma characteristics and tectonic provenance. *Ofioliti*, **15**, 17–44.

CLIFT, P. D. & ROBERTSON, A. H. F. 1989. Evidence of a late Mesozoic ocean basin and subduction-accretion in the southern Greek Neo-Tethys. *Geology*, **17**, 559–563.

DIMITRIJEVIĆ, M. D. 1982. Dinarides: an outline of the tectonics. *Earth Evolution Sciences*, **1**, 4–23.

—— DIMITRIJEVIĆ, M. N. 1979. Struktura i kinematika metamorfnog oboda zlatisborg ultramafitsog masiva. *Vesnik Geol.*, **37**, 101–121.

DIXON, J. E. & DIMITRIADIS, S. 1984. Metamorphosed ophiolitic rocks from the Serbo-Macedonian Massif, near Lake Volvi, Northeast Greece. *In*: DIXON, J. E. & ROBERTSON, A. H. F. (eds) *The Geological Evolution of the Eastern Mediterranean*. Geological Society, London, Special Publication, **17**, 603–618.

ECONOMOU, M. 1983. A short note on the evolution of the Vermion ophiolite complex (Macedonia–Greece). *Ofioliti*, **8**, 333–338.

—— DIMOU, E., ECONOMOU, G., MIGIROS, G., VACONDIOS, I., GRIVAS, E., RASSIOS, A. & DABITZIAS, S. 1986. *Chromite deposits of Greece* (UNESCO's IGCP 197 Project Metallogeny of ophiolites). Series ed.: KARAMATA, S. Theophrastus Publications, S.A., Athens, Greece.

FERRIÈRE, J. 1974. Etude géologique d'un secteur des zones helléniques internes subpelagonienne et pelagonienne (massif de l'Othrys–Grèce continentale). Importance et signification de la période orogénique anté-Crétacé superieur. *Bulletin de la Société Géologique de France*, **XVI**, 543–562.

—— 1982. Paléogéographies et tectoniques super-posées dans les Hellénides internes: les massifs de l'Othrys et du Pelion (Grèce septentrional). *Société de la Géologique du Nord*, **8**, 1–970.

—— 1985. Nature et développement des ophiolites helleniques du secteur Othrys-Pelion. *Ofioliti*, **10**, 255–278.

——, BERTRAND, J., SIMANTOV, J. & DE WEVER, P. 1989. Comparaison entre des formation volcano-detritiques ('melanges') du Malm des Hellénides internes (Othrys, Eubée): implications géodynamiques. *Bulletin of the Geological Society of Greece*, **20**, 223–235.

HAENEL-REMY, S. & BEBIEN, J. 1985. The Oreokastro ophiolite (Greek Macedonia): an important component of the innermost Hellenic ophiolite belt. *Ofioliti*, **10**, 279–296.

—— & —— 1987. Basaltes et dolérites riches en magnesium dans l'association ignée de Guévgéli (Macédoine grècque): les temoins d'une évolution depuis des tholéiites abyssales jusqu'à des basaltes continentaux? *Ofioliti*, **12**, 91–106.

HARKINS, E., GREEN, H. W. & MOORES, E. M. 1980. Multiple intrusive events documented from the Vourinos ophiolite complex, northern Greece. *American Journal of Science*, **280A**, 284–295.

HARLAND, W. B., ARMSTRONG, R. L., COX, A. V., CRAIG, L. A., SMITH, A. G. & SMITH, D. G. 1990. *A geologic time scale 1989*. Cambridge University Press, Cambridge.

HATZIPANAGIOTOU, K. 1990. Petrography of the ophiolite complex in central Argolis (Peloponnesus, Greece). *Ofioliti*, **15**, 61–77.

HESS, H. H. 1955. Serpentines, orogeny and epeirogeny. *Geological Society of America Special Paper*, **62**, 391–408.

—— 1965. Mid-oceanic ridges and tectonics of the sea floor; submarine geology and geophysics. *In*: WHITTARD, W. F. & BRADSHAW, R. (eds) *Proceedings of the Seventeenth Symposium of the Colston Research Society*. Butterworths, London, 317–334.

HYNES, A. J. 1974. Igneous activity at the birth of an ocean basin in eastern Greece. *Canadian Journal of Earth Sciences*, **11**, 842–853.

——, NISBET, E. G., SMITH, A. G., WELLAND, M. J. P. & REX, D. C. 1972. Spreading and emplacement ages of some ophiolites in the Othris region (eastern central Greece). *Zeitschrift Deutsche Geologische Ges.*, **123**, 455–468.

IVANOV, T., MISAR, Z., BOWES, D. R., DUDEK, A., DUMURDZANOV, N., JAROS, J., JELINEK, E. & PACESOVA, M. 1987. The Demir Kapija-Gevgelija ophiolite massif, Macedonia, Yugoslavia. *Ofioliti*, **12**, 457–478.

JACKSON, E. D., GREEN, H. W. & MOORES, E. M. 1975. The Vourinos ophiolite, Greece: cyclic units of lineated cumulates overlying harzburgite tectonite. *Geological Society of America Bulletin*, **86**, 390–398.

JONES, G., DE WEVER, P. & ROBERTSON, A. H. F. 1992. Significance of radiolarian age data to the Mesozoic tectonic and sedimentary evolution of the northern Pindos Mountains, Greece. *Geological*

*Magazine*, **129**, 385–400.

—— & ROBERTSON, A. H. F. 1991. Tectono-stratigraphy and evolution of the Pindos ophiolite and associated units, northwest Greece. *Journal of the Geological Society, London*, **148**, 267–268.

——, & CANN, J. R. 1991. Genesis and emplacement of the supra-subduction zone Pindos ophiolite, northwestern Greece. *In*: PETERS, T., NICOLAS, A. & COLEMAN, R. G. (eds) *Ophiolite genesis and evolution of the oceanic lithosphere*. Kluwer Academic Publishers, London, 771–800.

JUNG, D. & MUSSALLAM, K. 1985. The Sithonia ophiolite: a fossil oceanic crust. *Ofioliti*, **10**, 329–342.

JUNG, G., MUSSALLAM, K., BURGATH, K., KOCKEL, F., MOHR, M. & RASCHKA, H. 1980. Ultramafic and related rocks of Chalkidiki. *In*: *Proceedings International Symposium on Metals in Mafic and Ultramafic Complexes* (Vol. 3). Institute of Geological and Mining Research, Athens, Greece, 24–42.

KARAMATA, S. 1988. 'The Diabase-chert formation' some genetic aspects. *Bull. Acad. Serb. Sci. & Arts, Class Sci. Nat. & Math.*, **XCV**, 1–11.

KATSIKATSOS, G. 1979. La structure tectonique d'Attique et de l'île d'Eubée. *In*: *6th Colloquium on the Geology of the Aegean region* (Vol. 1). Institute of Geological and Mining Research, Athens, Greece, 211–228.

——, MIGIROS, G. & VIDAKIS, M. 1982. La structure geologique de la region de la Thessalie orientale (Grèce). *Annales Société Géologique du Nord*, **CI**, 177–188.

KISSEL, C. & LAJ, C. 1988. The Tertiary geodynamical evolution of Greece: a paleomagnetic reconstruction. *Tectonophysics*, **146**, 183–201.

KOEPKE, J., KREUZER, H. & SEIDEL, E. 1985. Ophiolites in the southern Aegean arc (Crete, Karpathos, Rhodes) – linking the ophiolite belts of the Hellenides and the Taurides. *Ofioliti*, **10**, 343–354.

LE PICHON, X. & ANGELIER, J. 1981. The Aegean Sea. *Philosophical Transactions of the Royal Society of London*, **300A**, 357–372.

LEKKAS, E. 1988. Geological structure and geodynamic evolution of the Koziakis mountain range, western Thessaly. *University of Athens Geological Monographs*, **1**, 281.

LIPPARD, S. J., SHELTON, A. W. & GASS, I. G. 1986. *The Ophiolite of Northern Oman*. Geological Society, London, Memoir, **11**.

LIVERMORE, R. A., SMITH, A. G. & VINE, F. J. 1986. Late Palaeozoic to early Mesozoic evolution of Pangea. *Nature*, **B322B**, 162–165.

MAGGANAS, A. & ECONOMOU, M. 1988. On the chemical composition of chromite ores from the ophiolitic complex of Soufli, NE Greece. *Ofioliti*, **13**, 15–27.

MAVRIDIS, A., SKOURTSIS-CORONEOU, V. & TSAILA-MONOPOLIS, St. 1979. Contribution to the geology of the Subpelagonian zone (Vourinos area, West Macedonia). *In*: *VI Colloquium Geology of the Aegean region*. Institute of Geological and Mining Research, Athens, Greece, 175–195.

MCKENZIE, D. P. 1977. The initiation of trenches: a finite amplitude instability. *In*: TALWANI, M. & PITMAN, W. C. (eds) *Island arcs, deep sea trenches and back-arc basins* (Maurice Ewing Series, 1). American Geophysical Union, Washington, DC, 57–61.

MENZIES, M. A. 1976. Rifting of a Tethyan continent. Rare evidence of an accreting plate margin. *Earth and Planetary Science Letters*, **28**, 427–438.

—— & ALLEN, C. 1974. Plagioclase lherzolite-residual mantle: relationships within two eastern Mediterranean ophiolites. *Contributions to Mineralogy and Petrology*, **46**, 454–487.

MERCIER, J. 1968. Etude géologique des zones internes des Hellénides en Macédoine centrale (Grèce). *Annales Géologiques des Pays Helléniques*, **20**.

MIGIROS, G. & ECONOMOU, G. S. 1988. Chromites in the ultrabasic rocks East Thessaly complex (central Greece). *Ofioliti*, **13**, 127–136.

—— & GALEOS, G. 1990. Tectonic and stratigraphic significance of the Ano Garefi ophiolitic rocks (northern Greece). *In*: MALPAS, J., MOORES, E. M., PANAYIOTOU, A. & XENOPHONTOS, C. (eds) *Ophiolites: oceanic crustal analogues.* Geological Survey Department, Nicosia, Cyprus, 279–284.

MITROPOULOS, S. I., KALOGEROPOULOS, S. I. BALTAZIS, E. M. M. 1987. Geochemical characteristics of ophiolitic rocks from Iti, central Greece. *Ofioliti*, **12**, 37–42.

MOORES, E. M. 1969. Petrology and structure of the Vourinos ophiolitic complex of northern Greece. *Geological Society of America Special Paper*, **118**.

—— 1982. Origin and emplacement of ophiolites. *Reviews of Geophysics and Space Physics*, **20**, 735–760.

MOUNTRAKIS, D. 1982. Emplacement of the Kastoria ophiolite on the western edge of the Internal Hellenides. *Ofioliti*, **7**, 397–406.

—— 1984. Structural evolution of the Pelagonian Zone in NW Macedonia, Greece. *In*: DIXON, J. E. & ROBERTSON, A. H. F. (eds) *The Geological Evolution of the Eastern Mediterranean.* Geological Society, London, Special Publication, **17**, 581–590.

—— 1986. The Pelagonian zone in Greece: a polyphase deformed fragment of the Cimmerian continent and its role in the geological evolution of the eastern Mediterranean. *Journal of Geology*, **94**, 335–347.

MUSSALLAM, K. 1991. Geology, geochemistry and the evolution of an oceanic lithosphere rift at Sithonia, NE Greece. *In*: PETERS, T., NICOLAS, A. & COLEMAN, R. G. (eds) *Ophiolite genesis and evolution of the oceanic lithosphere.* Kluwer Academic Publishers, London, 685–704.

—— & JUNG, D. 1986. Petrology and geotectonic setting of salic rocks preceding ophiolites in the eastern Vardar zone, Greece. *Tschermaks Mineralogie und Petrographische Mitteilungen*, **35**, 217–242.

NAYLOR, M. A. & HARLE, T. J. 1976. Palaeogeographic significance of rocks and structures beneath the Vourinos ophiolite, northern Greece. *Journal of the Geological Society, London*, **132**, 667–675.

—— & —— 1977. Palaeogeographic significance of rocks and structures beneath the Vourinos ophio-

lite: a reply. *Journal of the Geological Society, London*, **133**, 506–507.

NICOLAS, A. 1989. *Structures of ophiolites and dynamics of oceanic lithosphere.* Kluwer Academic, London.

NOIRET, G., MONTIGNY, R. & ALLEGRE, C. J. 1981. Is the Vourinos complex an island arc ophiolite? *Earth and Planetary Science Letters*, **56**, 375–386.

PAMIĆ, J. 1983. Considerations on the boundary between lherzolite and harzburgite subprovinces in the Dinarides and northern Hellenides. *Ofioliti*, **8**, 153–164.

—— 1984. Triassic magmatism in the Dinarides. *Tectonophysics*, **109**, 372–380.

PARROT, J. F. 1967. Le cortège ophiolitique du Pinde septentrional (Grèce). *ORSTOM, Paris*, 1–14.

—— 1969. Etude d'une coupe de référence dans le cortège ophiolitique du Pinde septentrional (Grèce): la vallée de l'Aspropotamos. *Cahiers ORSTOM Séries Géologique*, **1**, 35–59.

PAVLIS, T. L. 1986. The role of strain heating in the evolution of megathrusts. *Journal of Geophysical Research*, **91**, 12 407–12 422.

PEARCE, J. A. & CANN, J. R. 1973. Tectonic setting of basic volcanic rocks using trace element analysis. *Earth and Planetary Science Letters*, **19**, 290–300.

——, LIPPARD, S. J. & ROBERTS, S. 1984. Characteristics and tectonic significance of supra-subduction zone ophiolites. *In*: KOKELAAR, B. P. & HOWELLS, M. F. (eds) *Marginal Basin Geology.* Geological Society, London, Special Publication, **16**, 77–94.

—— & NORRY, M. J. 1979. Petrogenetic implications of Ti, Zr, Y and Nb variations in volcanic rocks. *Contributions to Mineralogy and Petrology*, **69**, 33–47.

PE-PIPER, G. 1982. Geochemistry, tectonic setting and metamorphism of the mid-Triassic volcanic rocks of Greece. *Tectonophysics*, **85**, 253–272.

PICHON, J. F. 1979. Une transversale dans la zone pélagonienne, depuis les collines de Krapa (SW) jusqu'au massif du Vermion (NE): les premières séries transgressives sur les ophiolites. *In*: *VI Colloquium on the geology of the Aegean region.* Institute of Geological and Mining Research, Athens, Greece.

PUCHER, R., BANNERT, D. & FROMM, K. 1974. Paleomagnetism in Greece: indications for relative block movement. *Tectonophysics*, **22**, 31–39.

RASSIOS, A. 1989. *The geology and ore environment of the Limogardi copper deposit, Othris ophiolite.* Internal Report. Institute of Geology and Mining Exploration, Athens, Greece.

—— 1990. Geology and copper mineralization of the Vrinena area, east Othris ophiolite, Greece. *Ofioliti*, **15**, 287–304.

—— 1991. Internal structure and pseudo-stratigraphy of the Dramala peridotite massif, Pindos mountains, Greece. *Bulletin of the Geological Society of Greece*, **XXV**, 293–305.

——, BECCALUVA, L., BORTOLOTTI, V., MAVRIDES, A. & MOORES, E. M. 1983. The Vourinos ophiolitic complex: a field excursion guidebook. *Ofioliti*, **8**, 275–292.

—— & KONSTANTOPOULOU, G. In press. emplacement tectonism and the position of chrome ores in the Mega Isoma peridotites, SW Othris, Greece. *Bulletin of the Geological Society of Greece.*

——, ——, VACONDIOS, I. & GRIVAS, E. 1990. Part 1, synthesis. *In:* RASSIOS, A., KONSTANTOPOULOU, G. & VACONDIOS, I. (eds) *Tectonic controls on chrome ore localization in ophiolites, Greece.* Institute of Geology and Mineral Exploration, Athens, Greece, 1–35.

ROBERTS, S. 1988. Ophiolite chromite formation: a marginal basin phenomenon. *Economic Geology,* **83,** 1034–1036.

——, RASSIOS, A., WRIGHT, L., VACONDIOS, I., VRACHATIS, G., GRIVAS, E., NESBITT, R. W., NEARY, C. R., MOAT, T. & KONSTANTOPOULOU, G. 1988. Structural controls on the location and form of the Vourinos chromite deposits. *In:* BOISSONNAS, J. & OMENETTO, P. (eds) *Mineral deposits within the European Community.* Springer-Verlag, Berlin, 249–266.

ROBERTSON, A. H. F. 1991. Origin and emplacement of an inferred late Jurassic subduction-accretion complex, Euboea, eastern Greece. *Geological Magazine,* **128,** 27–41.

——, CLIFT, P. D., DEGNAN, P. J. & JONES, G. 1991. Palaeogeographic and palaeotectonic evolution of the Eastern Mediterranean Neotethys. *Palaeogeography, Palaeoclimatology, Palaeoecology,* **87,** 289–343.

ROSS, R. V., MERCIER, J. C., AVE LALLEMANT, H. G., CARTER, N. L. & ZIMMERMAN, J. 1980. The Vourinos ophiolite complex, Greece: the tectonite suite. *Tectonophysics,* **70,** 63–83.

SIMANTOV, J. & BERTRAND, J. 1987. Major and trace element geochemistry of the central Euobea basaltic rocks (Greece). Possible geotectonic implications. *Ofioliti,* **12,** 201–218.

——, ECONOMOU, C. & BERTRAND, J. 1990. Metamorphic rocks associated with the Central Euboea ophiolite (Southern Greece): some new occurrences. *In:* MALPAS, J., MOORES, E. M., PANAYIOTOU, A. & XENOPHONTOS, C. (eds) *Ophiolites: oceanic crustal analogues.* Geological Survey Department, Nicosia, Cyprus, 285–293.

SMITH, A. G. 1979. Othris, Pindos and Vourinos ophiolites and the Pelagonian zone. *In: 6th Colloquium on the geology of the Aegean region* (Vol. 3). Institute of Geological and Mining Research, Athens, Greece, 1369–1374.

——, HYNES, A. J., MENZIES, M., NISBET, E. G., PRICE, I., WELLAND, M. J. P. & FERRIÈRE, J. 1975. The stratigraphy of the Othris mountains, eastern central Greece: a deformed Mesozoic continental margin sequence. *Eclogae Geologicae Helvetiae,* **68,** 463–481.

—— & LIVERMORE, R. A. 1991. Pangea in Permian to Jurassic time. *Tectonophysics,* **187,** 135–179.

—— & SPRAY, J. G. 1984. A half-ridge transform model for the Hellenic–Dinaric ophiolites. *In:* DIXON, J. E. & ROBERTSON, A. H. F. (eds) *The Geological Evolution of the Eastern Mediterranean.* Geological Society, London, Special Publication, **17,** 629–644.

——, WOODCOCK, N. H. & NAYLOR, M. A. 1979. The structural evolution of a Mesozoic continental margin, Othris mountains, Greece. *Journal of the Geological Society, London,* **136,** 589–603.

SPRAY, J. G., BEBIEN, J., REX, D. C. & RODDICK, J. C. 1984. Age constraints on the igneous and metamorphic evolution of the Hellenic–Dinaric ophiolites. *In:* DIXON, J. E. & ROBERTSON, A. H. F. (eds) *The Geological Evolution of the Eastern Mediterranean.* Geological Society, London, Special Publication, **17,** 619–627.

—— & RODDICK, J. C. 1980. Petrology and $^{40}Ar/^{39}Ar$ geochronology of some Hellenic sub-ophiolitic metamorphic rocks. *Contributions to Mineralogy and Petrology,* **72,** 43–55.

THUIZAT, R., WHITECHURCH, H., MONTIGNY, R. & JUTEAU, T. 1981. K-Ar dating of some infra-ophiolitic metamorphic soles from the Eastern Mediterranean: new evidence for oceanic thrustings before obduction. *Earth and Planetary Sciences Letters,* **52,** 301–310.

TURNELL, H. B. 1988. Mesozoic evolution of Greek microplates from paleomagnetic measurements. *Tectonophysics,* **155,** 301–316.

VERGELY, P. 1976. Chevauchement vers l'Ouest et retrocharriage vers l'Est des ophiolites: deux phases tectoniques au cours du Jurassique supérieur-Eocrétacé dans les Hellénides internes. *Bulletin de la Société Géologique de France,* **18,** 231–244.

—— 1977. Discussion of the palaeogeographic significance of the rocks beneath the Vourinos ophiolite, northern Greece. *Journal of the Geological Society, London,* **133,** 506–507.

—— 1977. Ophiolites et phases tectoniques superposées dans les Hellénides. *In: 6th Colloquium on the geology of the Aegean region.* Institute of Geological and Mining Research, Athens, Greece.

—— 1984. *Tectonique des ophiolites dans les Hellénides internes (déformations, métamorphismes et phénomènes sédimentaires). Consequences sur l'évolution des regions tethysienne occidentales.* Docteur d'Etat Thesis, Université de Paris-Sud, Centre d'Orsay.

WOODHEAD, J., EGGINS, S. & GAMBLE, J. 1993. High field strength and transition element systematics in island arc and back-arc basin basalts: evidence for multi-phase melt extraction and a depleted mantle wedge. *Earth and Planetary Science Letters,* **114,** 491–504.

ZIMMERMAN, J. 1972. Emplacement of the Vourinos ophiolitic complex, Northern Greece. *Geological Society of America, Memoir,* **132,** 225–239.

# The interaction and geometries of diapiric uprise centres along mid-ocean ridges – evidence from mantle fabric studies of ophiolite complexes

## I. D. BARTHOLOMEW

*Oryx UK Energy Company, Charter Place, Vine Street, Uxbridge, Middlesex UB8 1EZ, UK*

**Abstract:** Detailed structural mapping and thin-section fabric studies of oceanic upper mantle sections exposed within 3 ophiolite complexes have shown that in all of the ophiolites studied two co-existing high-temperature mantle fabric orientations can be identified. The fabrics are related both in time and space in that one fabric is ductile shear-folded by a later one to varying degrees. Olivine and orthopyroxene crystal slip-system and fabric orientation studies show that all the fabrics identified are high-temperature 'primary' asthenospheric flow fabrics and that simple shearing is the main flow process. The fabrics observed are at varying angles to the orientation of the Moho plane, with the slip directions varying both along strike with the Moho as well as vertically down from the Moho plane.

The identified flow fabrics are considered to be indicative of mantle flow directions 'frozen' into the mantle as it cooled from being ductile asthenosphere to lithosphere. Each fabric is interpreted as originating from a different localized mantle diapiric uprise centre. The centres interact with each other both in space and time, the observable 'frozen' fabrics indicating the closeness and 'strength' of individual diapirs relative to the position of the data measurement point.

Mantle fabric studies have been conducted in many well-preserved ophiolite sequences from around the world (Antalya, Turkey – Juteau *et al.* 1977; Bay of Islands, Newfoundland – Malpas 1977; Casey & Karson 1981; Girardeau & Nicolas 1981; New Caledonia – Prinzhoffer *et al.* 1980; Cassard *et al.* 1981; Semail, Sultanate of Oman – Boudier & Coleman 1981; Bartholomew 1983; Smewing *et al.* 1984; Ceuleneer *et al.* 1988; Nicolas *et al.* 1988a, Ceuleneer 1991; Troodos, Cyprus – George 1978; Gass 1980; Bartholomew 1983; Vourinos, Greece – Jackson *et al.* 1975; Ross *et al.* 1980; Unst, Shetland – Prichard 1985, Bartholomew 1983).

These studies have shown that the dominant mantle flow fabric direction is normally sub-parallel to the palaeo-Moho and the flow lines normal to the sheeted dyke strike. Locally, however, they are highly variable in orientation. This has been attributed to the variation in spreading direction of the asthenosphere away from the diapiric uprise centre and the interaction of the regional spreading direction with more local features such as transform zones (Nicolas & Violette 1982; Bartholomew 1983; Lippard *et al.* 1986; Nicolas *et al.* 1988b; Nicolas 1989; Ceuleneer 1991).

The generally accepted model is that the asthenosphere rises vertically upwards towards local points that source mid-oceanic ridge magma chambers that are spaced along the ridge axis. The asthenospheric flow trajectory then makes a right-angled turn into an approximately horizontal flow plane away from the spreading centre. At some point along the flow trajectory, the asthenosphere will have cooled sufficiently in order that it will no longer flow (approx. 1000 °C). This transition zone is the asthenosphere–lithosphere boundary. The asthenospheric flow fabrics existing at this transition zone will be fossilized and will remain preserved within the lithosphere.

The purpose of this paper is to highlight that two co-existing mantle flow fabric directions have been identified from the ophiolites studied by the author (Semail, Sultanate of Oman; Troodos, Cyprus; and Unst, Shetland). These observations are incorporated into a more refined model of the behaviour of the asthenospheric flow beneath oceanic spreading centres.

## The areas of study

It is not the intention of this paper to describe in any detail each of the ophiolite complexes from which data were collected. A few introductory remarks, however, are given for each of the areas and a diagrammatic section of each ophiolite studied is shown in Fig. 1.

The mantle sequences of all 3 ophiolites contain a strong fabric which extends by variable amounts into the lower crustal sequences. The mantle is composed mainly of residual harzburgites which contain dunitic pods of very variable

*From* Prichard, H. M., Alabaster, T., Harris, N. B. W. & Neary, C. R. (eds), 1993, *Magmatic Processes and Plate Tectonics*, Geological Society Special Publication No. 76, 245–256.

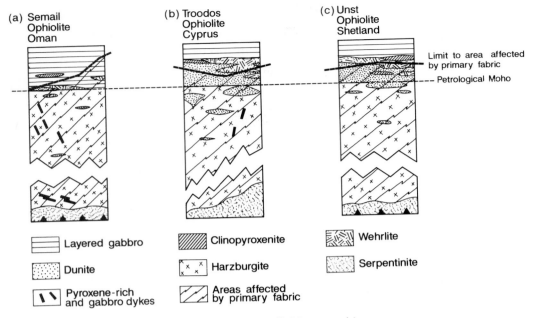

**Fig. 1.** Diagrammatic sections of the ophiolite areas studied (not to scale).

shapes and sizes. These pods are considered to have been cumulates crystallized from primary melts and are often connected by anastomosing 'feeder' sheets of dunite.

## The Semail Ophiolite, Sultanate of Oman

The Semail Ophiolite is one of the best exposed ophiolite sequences in the world. It is an obducted remnant of the Late Cretaceous Tethys Ocean. It covers a length of over 400 km and in places the mantle sequence has a vertical thickness of over 10 km. A location map is shown in Fig. 2. The ophiolite has been extensively described and the reader is directed to the comprehensive works of Lippard et al. (1986) and Boudier & Nicolas (1988) for further details.

Eleven different wadi transects were made totalling over 80 km in length along which fabric measurements were taken at over 750 locations. Fifty-seven samples were collected for fabric analysis with a universal stage microscope. Figure 2 identifies the main areas of study.

## The Troodos Ophiolite, Cyprus

The Troodos Ophiolite was one of the first ophiolite sequences described. As for the Semail Ophiolite, it is also a remnant of the Tethys Ocean. Gass (1980) summarizes the main features of the ophiolite. A 10 km length of mantle sequence is well exposed with a 2–3 km vertical thickness preserved of mainly unserpentinized harzburgites (Fig. 3). A particular feature of the Troodos mantle sequence is the presence of kilometre-wide sub-Moho dunitic magma chambers (Greenbaum 1972; Bartholomew 1983).

An area of 10 km² was mapped with fabric measurements made at over 700 locations and 31 samples collected for universal stage fabric analysis.

## The Unst Ophiolite, Shetland

The ophiolite of the Shetland Islands is the least known of the three ophiolites studied. It is thought to be Ordovician and is related to the Late Caledonian Orogenic event (Mykura 1976). Only the lower part of the ophiolite sequence is preserved (Fig. 4). A 5 km length of mantle sequence is well exposed and is up to 2 km thick. The ophiolite geology is best described by Prichard (1985) and Bartholomew (1983).

Areas of 14 km² and 9 km² were mapped on the islands of Unst and Fetlar, respectively, with fabric measurements made at over 600 locations. Fourteen samples were collected for universal stage fabric analysis.

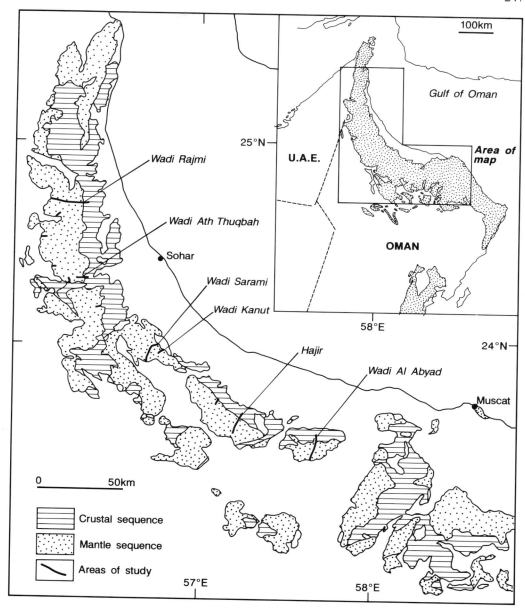

**Fig. 2.** Map of the Semail Ophiolite sequence, Sultanate of Oman showing the areas of study.

## The identification of mantle flow structures

The main mantle rock type in ophiolite complexes is harzburgite. The main mineral constituents are olivine (forsterite) (75–85%) and orthopyroxene (15–25%) with chrome spinel an ubiquitous accessory.

Olivine has specific temperature – and press-

ure-controlled crystallographic slip systems. Raleigh (1968) and Carter & Avé Lallement (1970) carried out the initial pioneering experiments on olivine crystallographic slip systems. Many workers have subsequently reviewed this subject (e.g. Nicolas & Poirier 1976; Lippard *et al.* 1986). For typical oceanic upper mantle/ lower crust confining pressures (5–10 kb) and

strain rates $(10^{-4} s^{-1})$, the olivine slip system
{0kl}[100] (i.e. slip in a [100] direction on {0kl}
planes) is activated at temperatures between
950–1300°C, and the (010)[100] slip system
above 1300°C (Carter & Avé Lallement 1970).
Below 950°C the olivine slip direction is [001].
Readers are referred to Nicolas & Poirier (1976)
for further details.

Orthopyroxene has a single non-temperature-
dependent crystal slip system of (100)[001]. This
is reviewed in Christensen & Lundquist (1982).

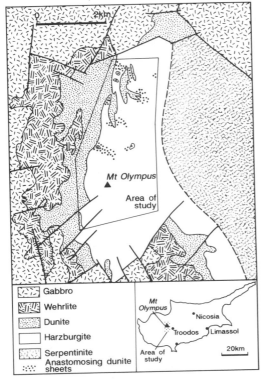

**Fig. 3.** Map of the Troodos Ophiolite sequence,
Cyprus, showing the area of study.

Olivine crystallographic studies have been carried out on most of the world's ophiolitic mantle
sequences. Observations of high-temperature
[100] (i.e. >950°C) olivine slip directions predominate from most workers. This implies that
the fabrics observed in most mantle sequences of
ophiolites are primary oceanic spreading structures rather than lower-temperature ophiolite
emplacement-related structures. The crystallographic textures observed confirm the primary
ocean spreading origin of these ductile flow
fabrics.

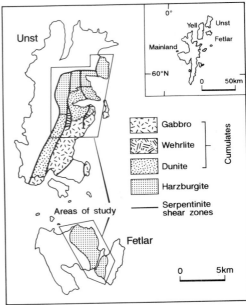

**Fig. 4.** Map of the Unst Ophiolite, Shetland, showing
the areas of study.

Emplacement-related fabrics tend to be concentrated at the edges of ophiolite bodies, both
along the metamorphic sole and also along
specific shear zones related to the large-scale
breakup of the ophiolite body during obduction
and emplacement. Serpentinization is commonly
associated with these late emplacement-related
structures which are easily distinguished from
the mantle fabrics considered in this paper.

The type of high-temperature flow taking
place within the asthenospheric mantle is a process of ductile simple shear (Nicolas & Poirier
1976). In order to study this mantle asthenospheric flow processes, the olivine crystallographic fabrics must be compared with the crystal shape fabrics. These are observable in thin
section by use of a 4-axis universal stage to
measure crystallographic orientations and crystal shape orientations. The angle between the
slip and mineral elongation direction gives the
sense of shear and shearing direction as illustrated in Fig. 5.

Olivine and orthopyroxene shape fabrics are
parallel to each other as are the crystallographic
slip directions. Chromite grains are typically
elongate and are orientated with their long axis
parallel to the olivine and orthopyroxene crystal
fabric shape long axis.

In the field, individual olivine crystals cannot
be made out in outcrop or hand specimen. In
some areas, distinct layering is visible as a result

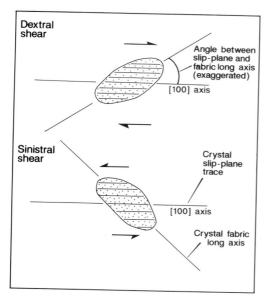

**Fig. 5.** Mantle shear sense determinations from crystallographic and shape fabric studies.

of differing concentrations of orthopyroxene. This layering is planar and is parallel to the shape fabric of the rock as measured in thin section. The elongate chromite grains are easy to identify and measure in the field and are ubiquitous. Both chromite planes (parallel to the overall harzburgite fabric) and lineations (measurement of the long axis of the chromite grain shapes) are usually measurable in most outcrop localities. The presence of chromite, therefore, allows a harzburgite shape fabric to be readily measured in the field.

An estimate of both the sense of shear and amount of shear is possible by comparing the crystallographic slip orientations with the shape fabric orientations. This is demonstrated in Fig. 6 for a rock undergoing a progressive dextral simple shear.

## Results of the mantle fabric studies

### The identification of two co-existing ductile fabrics

The main results of this study that impact existing models of asthenospheric flow fabrics are

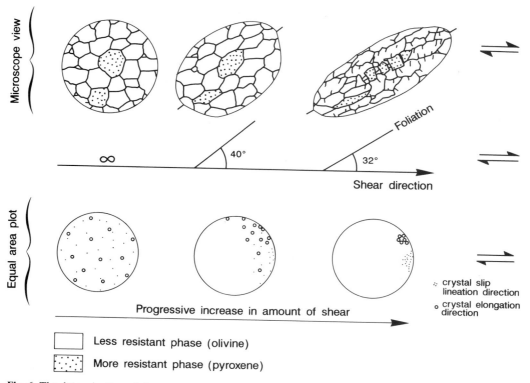

**Fig. 6.** The determination of shear strength from crystallographic and shape fabric orientation data (modified from Darot & Boudier 1975).

that two **co-existing** foliations have been ident-ified both in thin section and in field outcrop from many areas of the three ophiolite com-plexes studied. In all cases, both of the foliations have fabrics and crystallographic orientations that have been formed during high-temperature deformation. They must, therefore, be related to ocean-spreading-related ductile asthenospheric flow rather than to ophiolite obduction and emplacement processes.

In all areas studied, the emplacement-related fabrics are easy to identify in the field and are located in the metamorphic sole and along loca-lized shear zones running through the ophiolite. These shear zones separate ophiolite blocks that have been internally unaffected by obduction and emplacement.

If either of the two co-existing foliations were related to obduction and emplacement then they would be expected to rotate into the localized emplacement-related shear zones. This is not the case in any of the ophiolites studied, and it can, therefore, be concluded that both of the high-temperature fabrics are unrelated to obduction and emplacement and are indeed both related to ocean-spreading processes.

The preservation of a second high-tempera-ture foliation from a single specimen is highly dependent on the strength of flow (i.e. amount of shear) of the dominant flow fabric. Figure 7 illustrates this concept. Where the main fabric is the result of a strong flow, only a single lineation orientation and single foliation plane is measur-able (Fig. 7a). Where the main fabric has been formed by only a weak flow, remnant secondary flow lineations and foliations are preserved and plot as great circles (Fig. 7b-e). This is indicative of a temporal relationship between the ductile flow events forming the fabrics: the earlier fabric being folded by the later fabric.

## The importance of recrystallization in the preservation of ductile fabrics

Harzburgite textures grade from coarse equi-granular through porphyroclastic to mosaic porphyroclastic depending on the amount of recrystallization that has occurred. Textural classifications are after Harte (1977). A coarse equigranular texture is present in a rock which has recently recrystallized, the exact grain size depending on the amount of deviatoric stress. A high deviatoric stress will result in a finer grain

size. As the recrystallized rock is deformed, the texture progressively changes from equigranular, through porphyroclastic, to mosaic porphyro-clastic. A completely recrystallized rock will not preserve any of the fabrics formed prior to recrystallization and thus will only contain a single fabric. Partially recrystallized harzbur-gites, which form the majority of samples ana-lysed, will preserve earlier fabric orientations (if they existed), as well as the fabric formed after the recrystallization process.

The process of recrystallization appears to be cyclical and is directly related to the deformation process. As a recrystallized crystal is progressi-vely deformed it becomes more and more broken up and will eventually completely breakdown and recrystallize again and again whilst under-going ductile simple shear. Within a slowly cool-ing mantle rock, different crystals of the same mineral will be at different stages of recrystalliza-tion and breakdown: the most common rock texture that is observed, therefore, is a porphyro-clastic texture. An example of such texture is illustrated in Fig. 8.

When a mantle harzburgite undergoes ductile simple shearing with a constant shear direction then the rock texture will vary as illustrated in Fig. 8a. The olivine slip direction axes ([100] crystallographic orientation) will always plot as a cluster pattern as both the strained crystals and the newly recrystallised crystals will have ap-proximately the same slip direction orientations.

Figure 8b illustrates the expected textures and crytallographic orientations where the direction of shearing has a sudden change in orientation during the straining–recrystallization process. As the new shear direction ($S_2$) takes over from the earlier shearing direction ($S_1$), newly recrys-tallized olivines grow with their [100] axes almost parallel to the $S_2$ direction, whereas existing crystals are rapidly strained, break-down, and eventually recrystallize. The equal-area plots of olivine [100] axes change from a cluster in the $S_1$ slip direction to a girdle pattern, still with a cluster in the $S_1$ slip direction. As recrystalliza-tion proceeds, a cluster forms in the $S_2$ slip direction, the as yet un-recrystallized olivines forming a girdle pattern. The exact orientation of the girdle is dependent on the sense of the simple shearing. The girdle pattern in Fig. 8b illustrates a sinistral $S_2$ shearing.

Equal-area plots of olivine [100] axes from a number of harzburgite and dunite samples ana-

**Fig. 7.** Equal-area lower hemisphere plots from a sample of the areas studied illustrating the variations in interaction between two ductile flow directions.

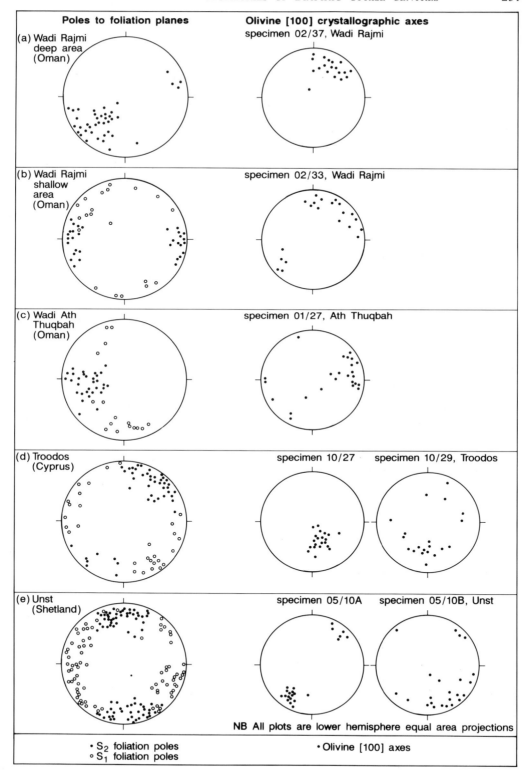

Poles to foliation planes

Olivine [100] crystallographic axes

(a) Wadi Rajmi deep area (Oman) — specimen 02/37, Wadi Rajmi

(b) Wadi Rajmi shallow area (Oman) — specimen 02/33, Wadi Rajmi

(c) Wadi Ath Thuqbah (Oman) — specimen 01/27, Ath Thuqbah

(d) Troodos (Cyprus) — specimen 10/27    specimen 10/29, Troodos

(e) Unst (Shetland) — specimen 05/10A    specimen 05/10B, Unst

NB All plots are lower hemisphere equal area projections

• S₂ foliation poles
○ S₁ foliation poles

• Olivine [100] axes

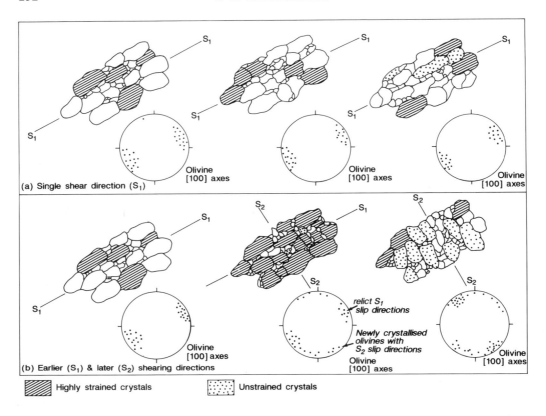

**Fig. 8.** Schematic illustration of the cyclical process of contemporaneous recrystallization and ductile simple shearing. (**a**) Single shear direction ($S_1$); (**b**) earlier ($S_1$) and later ($S_2$) shear directions.

lysed are shown in Fig. 7. All the samples have porphyroclastic textures. The plots illustrate the full spectrum of [100] orientations expected from the process of cyclical grain breakdown and recrystallization with two different shearing directions as described above.

Figure 7a is from an area where only one mantle foliation is measurable in the field. This implies that only one shear direction has ever existed, or that the $S_2$ shearing is so intense that it has destroyed any remnant $S_1$ shearing directions. As would be expected, the [100] axes from the specimen from this area have a cluster pattern.

Figures 7b–e are all from areas where both $S_2$ and $S_1$ foliations are measurable in the field. The poles to $S_2$ foliation planes plot as clusters and the poles to $S_1$ foliation planes plot as girdles lying on a great circle containing the poles to the $S_2$ foliation planes. The [100] axes equal-area plots from the specimens in Figs 7b and 7c have a cluster pattern with an associated girdle development similar to that illustrated in Fig. 8b.

Figures 7d and 7e are of particular note as in both figures two specimens are illustrated from the same area of study, one with a [100] axis cluster distribution and the other with a [100] axis girdle distribution. The specimens from Unst (Fig. 7e) were collected from outcrops only 5 m apart. Such a variation in the distribution of olivine [100] axes is evident from all of the 3 ophiolites studied. This highlights that the amount of $S_2$ shearing is highly variable both on a local and a more regional scale.

*Evidence for asthenospheric ductile shear folding*

The field measurement of $S_1$ and $S_2$ mantle foliations and detailed crystallographic studies of selected specimens have enabled maps to be constructed for all the areas of study of the sense of shear for the $S_2$ shearing direction within the mantle sequence. In all the areas of study, the shear sense is not consistent for any one area. On a regional scale the sense of shear is the same in

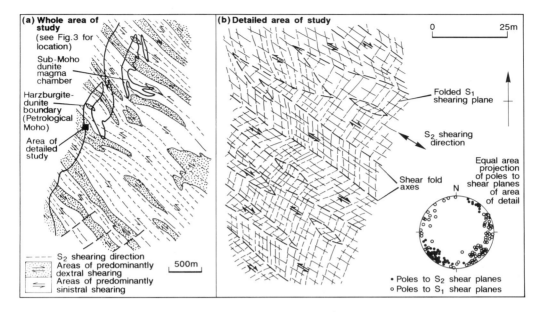

**Fig. 9.** Scales of ductile shear folding in the Troodos Ophiolite, Cyprus.

500–3000 m thick bands. Figure 9a illustrates the typical scale of shear banding of the mantle sequence of the Troodos Ophiolite. Similar scales of banding are also evident in a the areas of study in Oman and Unst.

On a local scale, the shear senses also vary markedly. Figure 9b shows a typical area from Troodos. The local variation in shear sense produces a folding effect which can best be described as 'ductile shear folding'. The fold 'axes' are between 10–20 m apart. A similar detailed area of study was mapped on the Unst Ophiolite where very similar scales of folding were also found to exist.

### The relationship between ductile mantle shearing and the formation of mantle and crustal melt sequences

In all of the areas studied the main mantle flow fabric extends into the lower crustal cumulate sequences (Fig. 1). The fabrics extend up to a few hundred metres into the cumulate sequences and gradually die out upwards. This observation implies that mantle flow was active during the early stages of crystallization of the ocean ridge crustal magma chambers, and then died out as the magma chamber expanded in size as a response to oceanic crustal spreading.

Dunitic bodies exist beneath the petrological Moho plane in all of the ophiolites studied.

These bodies are thought to represent initial melts which have crystallized before reaching the crustal-level magma chambers. They are often connected to each other by anastomosing sheets and veins of dunite which are most likely to have been magma feeder channels. The size, orientations and shapes of both the dunite bodies and sheets are highly variable and can be directly related to the amount of ductile flow that they have undergone.

The Troodos Ophiolite has particulary large sub-Moho dunitic magama chambers. Major swarms of anastomosing dunite sheets appear to have 'fed' these chambers with dunitic melt (Fig. 3). These sub-Moho magma chambers formed as the asthenosphere was shearing. The evidence for this is shown by the contacts between the harzburgites and massive dunites which are often highly irregular in nature and have clearly been deformed by the flow fabrics.

The Semail and Unst mantle sequences are devoid of very large-scale sub-Moho magma chambers. Many smaller pod features are, however, present, as are wider areas of anastomosing 'feeder' dykes and sheets. These have been variously deformed depending on the amount of shearing.

### The orientation of mantle flow directions

In the relatively small areas of the Unst and

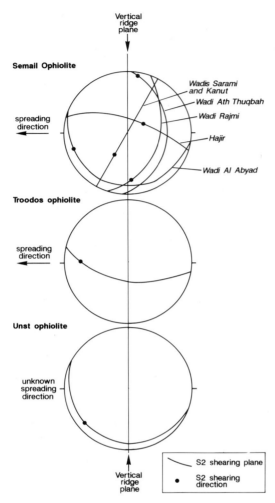

**Fig. 10.** The mean orientations of the $S_2$ shear planes and flow directions from the 3 ophiolites studied rotated back to their original palaeo-spreading orientation. The ridge plane is assumed to strike north–south and the ocean spreading direction is from east to west. All projections are equal-area lower hemisphere plots.

Troodos Ophiolites the main lineation trace and foliation plane orientation is remarkably constant. Traverses made in the larger Semail Ophiolite show major regional variation of shear orientations both laterally along the length of the Moho and also vertically downwards from the Moho plane. Figure 10 summarizes the regional $S_2$ shear orientations for each of the areas studied. The shear orientations have been rotated from their measured present-day orientation to their palaeo-spreading orientation.

This palaeo-spreading orientation has been calculated from a number of factors: the orientation of the sedimentary layers at the top of the ophiolite sequence; the trend of the sheeted dyke complexes; the orientation of the crustal cumulate layering; and the orientation of the petrological Moho plane. The techniques of using these various criteria are discussed in greater detail by Bartholomew (1983) and Smewing et al. (1984). It is not possible to show a palaeo-spreading orientation for the Unst Ophiolite due to lack of preservation of the relevent deterministic data.

As can be seen from Fig. 10, the regional $S_2$ shear orientations vary markedly between ophiolite blocks within the Semail Ophiolite and between the 3 ophiolites studied. This variation and the existence of an $S_1$ shear direction is discussed in the section below.

## Discussion of the findings of this study: a refined model for asthenospheric flow at oceanic spreading centres

Detailed crystallographic studies of over 100 specimens have shown that the shear orientations measured in all 3 of the ophiolites studied have been formed during high-temperature asthenospheric flow. As has been described above, this is thought to have been a cyclical process involving repeated phases of recrystallization. The measured fabrics and crystallographic orientations are those that existed as the asthenosphere cooled through the asthenosphere – lithosphere boundary. The existing flow orientations are 'frozen' as a 'snap-shot' of the asthenospheric flow directions.

The generally accepted model of the behaviour of the asthenosphere at a mid-oceanic ridge is that the asthenospheric residual material flows approximately horizontally away from each mantle diapiric uprise centre (Nicolas & Violette 1982; Lippard et al. 1986; Nicolas 1988b; Nicolas 1989; Cueleneer 1991). The variation of the $S_2$ asthenospheric shear directions measured in this study, relative to the palaeo-spreading direction and the Moho plane observed in the Semail Ophiolite, agrees well with general model. The varying orientations can be attributed to the relative positions of the diapiric uprise centres along the spreading centre. In the Semail Ophiolite the variation in shear directions indicate the existence of localized mantle diapiric uprise centres with an along-ridge spacing of between 20 and 30 km. The areas of preserved mantle sequence within the Troodos and Unst Ophiolite complexes are not large enough to postulate on the location and spacing of mantle diapiric centres.

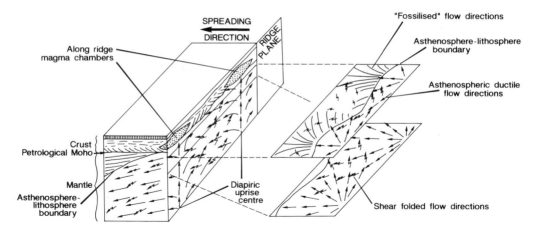

**Fig. 11.** Diapiric flow systems from two diapiric uprise centres illustrating the concept of the interaction between different flow systems.

The existence of an earlier shearing plane is clear evidence that there has been more than one shearing direction in any one locality. This can best be explained by the hypothesis that the ductile flow paths from more than one diapric uprise centre interact with one another, the stronger and/or later shear flow folding the earlier and/or weaker shear flow. The main controlling factors would be the vicinity of a diapiric uprise centre, the diapiric flow strength of the uprise centre, and also whether the uprise centre is active or extinct. Figure 11 illustrates the model of the interaction of two diapiric uprise centres along a mid-ocean ridge along with the corresponding 'fossilized' flow directions.

The changes in the sense and the amount of shear of the dominant foliation direction are most likely to have occured as a result of a pulsing in the asthenospheric flow behaviour: the relative velocities of the ductile shearing producing varying amounts and sense of shear.

## Conclusions

The recognition and detailed measurement of two temporally related high-temperature ductile shearing events from 3 ophiolite complexes has enabled a more refined model for the behaviour of the asthenosphere along mid-oceanic ridges to be constructed. The key points of the model are as follows:

- sub-horizontal ductile shear flow lines from different mantle diapiric uprise centres interfere with each other;
- the 'stronger' diapir shear flow deforms the 'weaker' diapir shear flow;

- flow pulsing occurs during the shearing process causing 'ductile shear folding' both on the large and small scale;
- sub-Moho dunitic pods are the crystallization products of early melts: these pods form at the same time as the 'ductile shear folding' is taking place and are themselves sheared;
- asthenospheric ductile flow fabrics extend into the lower part of the oceanic crust indicating that the asthenospheric shearing has an integral part to play in the actual spreading process at a mid-oceanic spreading centre.

The main part of this work was completed whilst in receipt of a NERC studentship. My thanks go to colleagues from the Open University Earth Sciences Department and specifically to John Taylor for all the draughting work.

## References

BARTHOMEW, I. D. 1983. *The primary structures and fabrics of the Upper Mantle and Lower Crust from ophiolite complexes.* PhD thesis, Open University.

BOUDIER, F. & COLEMAN, R. G. 1981. Cross section through the peridotite in the Semail ophiolite, southern Oman mountains. *Journal of Geophysical. Research,* **86,** 2573–2592.

—— & NICOLAS, A. 1988. (eds) The ophiolites of Oman. *Tectonophysics* (Special Issue) **151.**

CARTER, N. L. & AVÉ LALLEMENT, H. G. 1970. High temperature flow of dunite and peridotite. *Geological Society of America Bulletin,* **81,** 2181–2202.

CASEY, J. F. & KARSON, J. A. 1981. Magma chamber profiles from the Bay of Islands ophiolite complex. *Nature,* **292,** 295–301.

CASSARD, D., NICOLAS, A., RABINOVITCH, M., MOUTTE, J., LEBLANC, M. & PRINZHOFFER, A

1981. Structural classification of chromite pods in Southern New Caledonia. *Economic Geology*, **76**, 805–831.

CEULENEER, G. 1991. Evidences for a Paleo-Spreading Center in the Oman Ophiolite: Mantle Structures in the Maqsad Area. *In:* PETERS, Tj., NICOLAS, A. & COLEMAN, R. G. (eds) 'Ophiolite Genesis and Evolution of the Oceanic Lithosphere' *Proceedings of Ophiolite Conference Oman, 1990*, 147–174.

——, NICOLAS, A. & BOUDIER, F. 1988. Mantle flow patterns at an oceanic spreading centre: The Oman peridotites record. *Tectonophysics*, **151**, 1–26.

CHRISTENSEN, N. I. & LUNDQUIST, S. M. 1982. Pyroxene orientation within the upper mantle. *Geological Society of America Bulletin*, **93**, 279–288.

DAROT, M. & BOUDIER F. 1975. Mineral lineations in deformed peridotites: kinematic meaning. *Petrologie*, **1**, 225–236.

GASS, I. G. 1980. The Troodos massif: its role in the unravelling of the ophiolite problem and its significance in the understanding of constructive plate margin processes. *In:* PANAYIOTOU (ed.) 'Ophiolites'. *Proceedings of the International Ophiolite Symposium Cyprus, 1979*. Cyprus Geological survey Department, Nicosia, Cyprus, 23–35.

GEORGE, R. P. Jr. 1978. Structural petrology of the Olympus Ultramafic Complex in the Troodos Ophiolite, Cyprus. (A), *Geological Society of America Bulletin*, 845–865.

GIRARDEAU, J. & NICOLAS, A. 1981. The structures of two ophiolite massifs, Bay-of-Islands, Newfoundland: a model for oceanic crust and upper mantle. *Tectonophysics*, **77**, 1–34.

GREENBAUM, D. 1972. Magmatic processes at ocean ridges, evidence from the Troodos Massif, Cyprus. *Nature* (Physical Sciences), **288**, 18–21.

HARTE, B. 1977. Rock nomenclature with particular relation to deformation and recrystallisation textures in olivine-bearing xenoliths. *Journal of Geology*, **85**, 279–288.

JACKSON, E. D., GREEN, H. W. II & MOORES, E. M. 1975. The Vourinos ophiolite, Greece: cyclic units of lineated cumulates overlying harzburgite tectonite. *Geological Society of America Bulletin*, **86**, 390–398.

JUTEAU, T., NICOLAS, A., DUBESSY, J., FRUCHARD, J. C. & BOUCHEZ, J. L. 1977. Structural relationships in the Antalya ophiolite complex, Turkey:

possible model for an oceanic ridge. *Geological Society of America Bulletin*, **88**, 1740–1748.

LIPPARD, S. J., SHELTON, A. W. & GASS, I. G. 1986. *The Ophiolite of Northern Oman*. Geological Society, London, Memoir **11**.

MALPAS, J. 1977. Petrology and tectonic significance of Newfoundland ophiolites with examples from the Bay of Islands. *North American Ophiolites Bulletin*, **95**, 13–23.

MYKURA, W. 1976. *British regional geology: Orkney and Shetland*. (BGS), HMSO, Edinburgh.

NICOLAS, A. 1989. *Structures of ophiolites and dynamics of oceanic lithosphere*. Kluwer Academic Publishers.

——, CEULENEER, G., BOUDIER, F. & MISSERI, M. 1988*a*. Structural mapping in the Oman ophiolites: mantle diapirism along an oceanic ridge. *Tectonophysics*, **151**, 27–56.

——, POIRIER, J. P. 1976. *Crystalline plasticity and solid state flow in metamorphic rocks*. John Wiley & Sons.

——, REUBER, I. & BENN, K. 1988*b*. A new magma chamber model based on structural studies in the Oman ophiolite. *Tectonophysics*, **151**, 87–105.

——, VIOLETTE, J. F. 1982. Mantle flow beneath oceanic ridges: Models derived from ophiolites. *Tectonophysics*, **81**, 319–339.

PRICHARD, H. M. 1985. The Shetland ophiolite. *In:* GEE, D. G. & STURT, B. A. (eds) *The Caledonide orogen – Scandinavia, and related areas*. Wiley, New York, 1173–1184.

PRINZHOFFER, A., NICOLAS, A., CASSARD, D., MOUTTE, J., LEBLANC, M., POIRIER, J. P. & RABINOVITCH, M. 1980. Structures in the New Caledonia peridotites – gabbros: implications for oceanic mantle and crust. *Tectonophysics*, **69**, 85–112.

RALEIGH, C. B. 1968. Mechanisms of plastic deformation of olivine. *Journal of Geophysical Research*, **73**, 5391–5406.

ROSS, J. V., MERCIER, J-C. C., AVÉ LALLEMANT, H. G., CARTER, N. L. & ZIMMERMAN, J. 1980. The Vourinos ophiolite complex, Greece: the tectonic suite. *Tectonophysics*, **70**, 63–83.

SMEWING, J. D., CHRISTENSEN, N. I., BARTHOLOMEW, I. D. & BROWNING, P. 1984. The structure of the oceanic upper mantle and lower crust as deduced from the northern section of the Oman ophiolite. *In:* GASS, I. G., LIPPARD, S. G. & SHELTON, A. W. (eds) *Ophiolites and Oceanic Lithosphere*. Geological Society, London, Special Publication **14**, 41–54.

# Petrogenesis of ophiolitic chromitite

STEPHEN ROBERTS[1] & CHRISTOPHER NEARY[2]

[1] *Department of Geology, The University, Highfield, Southampton SO9 5NH, UK*
[2] *Natural Environment Research Council, Polaris House, North Star Avenue,
Swindon SN2 1EU, UK*

**Abstract**: Chromite deposits comprise an integral part of the mantle sequences observed within many ophiolite complexes; in particular, those where a harzburgite is the dominant mantle sequence lithology. The chromite segregations are invariably contained within a dunite envelope and show a wide variety of ore textures, some of which are directly analogous to those observed within major layered intrusions. The majority of chromite segregations contain chromite and olivine of variable modal proportions although in certain instances a wide variety of interstitial silicates may be preserved including plagioclase, orthopyroxene, clinopyroxene and amphibole. Evidence of deformation linked to increasingly lower temperatures is invariably present which can be linked either to high temperature 'flow fabrics' away from the spreading axis, the obduction of the ophiolite or post-obduction regional deformation events.

Analysis of chromite grains from a variety of ophiolitic chromite segregations shows them to be chrome-spinels with variable $Cr^*$ values ($Cr/(Cr + Al)$), typically between 0.4 and 0.85, with $Mg^*$ values ($Mg/(Mg + Fe^{2+})$) between (0.5 and 0.8) and invariably restricted $Fe^{3+}$ contents. By way of a simple contrast to major layered intrusions the ophiolitic chromite segregations tend to range to lower $Cr^*$ values and show higher and more restricted $Mg^*$ ratios. The variation of the $Cr^*$ ratio from chromite segregations within an individual ophiolite can be related to the position of the segregation within the mantle sequence. The more aluminous deposits being located towards the petrological moho, whereas the more chrome-rich horizons tend to occur deeper within the sequence, in particular toward the harzburgite lherzolite transition.

A model is described which considers the chromite deposits to represent the early fractionates of ascending magmas within highly depleted mantle, likely to have developed above subduction zones, or at fast spreading centres. Transport of the mantle away from the spreading zone results in deformation of the chromite deposits within a falling P–T regime involving both ridge-axis and post-obduction deformation.

In describing the association between large peridotite bodies and economically significant chromite mineralization, Thayer (1946) drew attention to the distinct chemistry of the Alpine chromite segregations compared to those of Stillwater and the Bushveld. This geochemical distinction became reinforced as the contrasting form and setting of the deposits became realized (Wells *et al.* 1946; Thayer 1963, 1964) and as Alpine-type peridotites, for the larger part, evolved into ophiolite complexes. Not surprisingly, the ideas on the petrogenesis of ophiolitic chromite have reflected this evolution.

Early workers, based their ideas on the formation of Alpine chromitite on the work of Bowen & Tuttle (1949). They envisaged that the chromite segregations resulted from the solid emplacement of chromite within a peridotite crystal mush following differentiation from a magma within the lower part of the crust and mantle (Thayer 1964, 1969, 1970). The development of the ophiolite theory as recognized today, and the broad acceptance of ophiolites as land-bound

fragments of oceanic lithosphere correspondingly began to influence ideas on the formation of the contained chromite segregations. In particular, the basal ultramafic tectonite unit, which contains the majority of the chromite segregations was increasingly recognized as the residuum following the extraction of a basaltic melt (Moores & Vine 1971; Greenbaum 1972; Menzies & Allen 1974). Despite the residual nature of the mantle sequence many features of the contained chromite deposits were indicative of cumulate processes. This led to several hypotheses which attempted to accommodate these observations. Dickey (1975) considered the chromite deposits as autoliths of cumulate chromite which initially formed within crustal magma chambers and which then sank into the mantle residuum after formation. Alternatively, Greenbaum (1977) considered the deposits to represent the early fractionates of the magma chamber which were then infolded into the tectonized harzburgite. The recognition that olivine and chrome-spinel represent the most likely early

*From* Prichard, H. M., Alabaster, T., Harris, N. B. W. & Neary, C. R. (eds), 1993,
*Magmatic Processes and Plate Tectonics*, Geological Society Special Publication No. 76, 257–272.

257

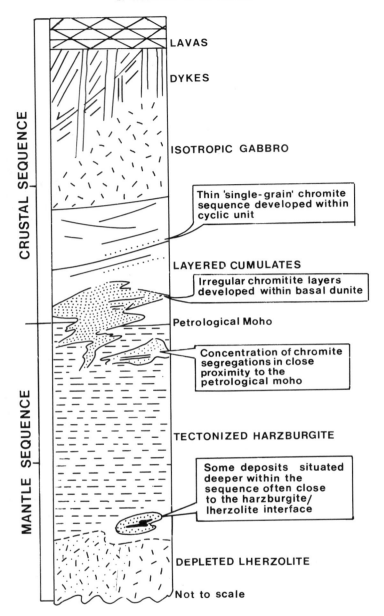

**Fig. 1.** Idealized ophiolite stratigraphy emphasizing the position of chromite segregations through the sequence (not to scale).

fractionates of rising picritic melts (Menzies & Allen 1974) provided a new insight into the problem and prompted the development of several models which envisaged the chromite deposits as the first segregations of rising picritic melts which ascended through the uppermost

mantle at the sites of palaeospreading centres (Neary & Brown 1979; Brown 1980; Lago *et al.* 1982).

Despite the development of a broad consensus on the basic origin of the deposits, much unresolved detail remains. In particular, the relative importance and influence of the partial melting regime, the precipitation mechanisms involved in the production of 'chromite-only' layers, composition of the magma, role of fluids, and the importance of deformation in the genesis of the deposits are poorly understood. This paper aims to review the key characteristics of ophiolitic chromitite deposits and using these observations develop a model to account for their multi-stage evolution.

## Petrological characteristics

### Setting

Chromite deposits comprise an integral part of the mantle sequence observed within many ophiolite complexes. In particular those where harzburgite is the dominant mantle sequence lithology as opposed to more 'fertile' lherzolite-dominated sequences; a feature particularly well observed within the Tethyan ophiolites of the Mediterranean region (Den Tex 1969; Jackson & Thayer 1972; Nicolas & Jackson 1972). The major chromite segregations are invariably situated within the ultramafic rocks of the ophiolite succession, tending to be more abundant within the tectonized mantle sequence, but also present within the lowermost cumulates (Fig. 1). Within the mineralized ophiolite sequences there is often a tendency for the number of deposits to increase in proximity to the petrological moho (Rossman et al. 1959; Smith 1958; Peters & Kramers 1974; Brown 1980). The chromite segregations are invariably situated within a dunite envelope irrespective of the size of the deposit, although it is widely reported that the size of the dunite envelope bears no direct relationship to the amount of chromite present (Peters & Kramers 1974; Cassard et al. 1981). Despite the common occurrence within the tectonized harzburgite and the presence of the dunite envelope, the actual form of the deposits varies widely from simple tabular lenses to highly irregular masses (Fig. 1).

### Ore types

The chromite segregations display a wide variety of ore types and textures. Dunite bodies, which contain the chromite segregations, show all gradations between dunite containing only accessory chromite through to almost 100 modal % chromite. A classification devised by Greenbaum (1977) to describe these modal variations within the ore is shown in Table 1. This variation in modal chromite is often accompanied by a variety of textures with many papers devoted to

a description of the wide variety of textures observed (Greenbaum 1977; Brown 1980; Ahmed 1982). Illustrations of some of the more commonly observed textures are shown in Fig. 2.

**Table 1.** *Classification used to describe compositional variations in chromitiferous rocks after Greenbaum (1977).*

| | |
|---|---|
| Dunite (with accessory chromite) | :less than 5% chromite |
| Chromitiferous dunite | :5–50% chromite |
| Olivine-chromitite | :51–90% chromite |
| (Massive) chromitite | :more than 90% chromite |

Many of the textural relationships observed within the chromite segregations are directly analogous to those observed within chromite segregations of the major layered intrusions. These include chromite net, occluded silicate and chain textures (Thayer 1969) and cross-laminations and inverted flame structures (Brown 1980; Auge & Roberts 1982). Others are unique to ophiolitic chromitite e.g. nodular and orbicular ore (Thayer 1969; Greenbaum 1977). However, as a cautionary note to the endeavour of a simple comparison of similar looking textures, Christiansen & Roberts (1986) described the development of 'relict igneous crescumulate textures' during deformation under subsolidus conditions of olivine-spinel lithologies within both the Semail and Vourinos ophiolites.

The exact type or spatial distribution of ore textures encountered either within particular ophiolites (even within a given chromite-deposit) or between different ophiolites is difficult to predict. For example, the chromite ores of the Vourinos Complex, Greece, are dominated by schlieren ore with occasional deposits showing well-developed nodular ore which tends to be virtually absent at other localities from the area (Burgath & Weiser 1980). By contrast, many of the chromite deposits described from the northern Semail ophiolite, Oman, are dominated by massive ore with only local to rare development of schlieren and nodular ore respectively (Brown 1980; Auge & Roberts 1982).

### Interstitial silicates

The majority of described ophiolitic chromite deposits are dominated by olivine and chromite of variable modal proportions. However, in certain instances a wide variety of interstitial silicates may be preserved, particularly within

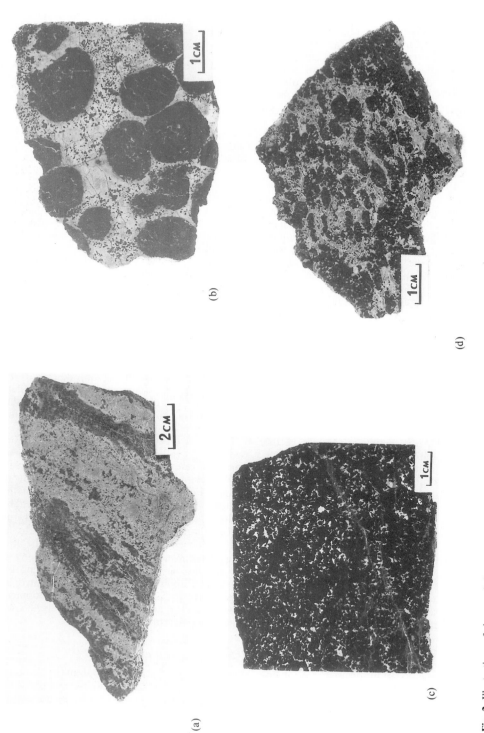

**Fig. 2.** Illustrations of characteristic textures from ophiolitic chromitite segregations: (**a**) schlieren ore; (**b**) nodular ore; (**c**) massive ore; (**d**) deformed nodular ore. All samples from the Vourinos massif, Greece.

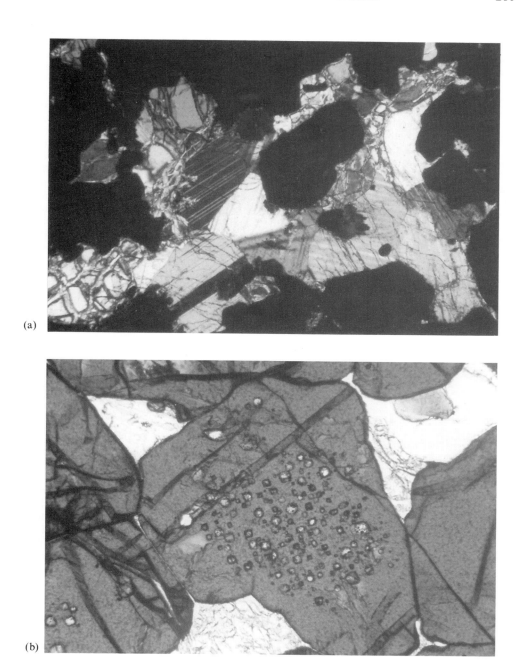

(a)

(b)

**Fig. 3. (a)** Interstitial silicates (olivine plus plagioclase) to subhedral chromite grains from the Mahara 1 chromite deposit, Semail ophiolite, Oman. Field of view 8 mm. **(b)** Silicate inclusions within a spinel grain from a chromite segregation within the Semail ophiolite. Field of view 3.5 mm.

sequences where more massive types of ore are present, for example in the Semail. Here, plagioclase, ortho- and clinopyroxene and in some instances pargasitic amphibole, in addition to olivine, are preserved as interstitial phases (Auge & Roberts 1982; Auge 1987; Leblanc & Ceuleneer 1992). Often the ortho- and clinopyroxene occur as large plates up to 8 mm long poikilitically enclosing the chromite grains and occasionally other interstitial olivine grains (Fig. 3a).

Another feature of the Semail chromitites are the presence of silicate inclusions within many of the chromite grains. These often occur as negative crystal forms up to 0.4 mm in diameter, preserved within euhedral chromite grains (Fig. 3b). The mineralogy is diverse and similar to the interstitial silicates with a notable increase in the amount of pargasitic amphibole present as inclusion compared to its abundance as an interstitial phase. The population of silicate inclusions within a single grain is often polyphase and Roberts (1986) suggested that the abundance of inclusions increases towards the top of a deposit. Inclusions within chromite grains showing a similar mineralogy and form have been described from both the Bushveld (McDonald 1965) and Stillwater (Jackson 1961) chromite segregations.

## Deformation

Intuitively, chromite segregations formed within the mantle sequence at some constructive plate margin are likely to encounter tectonism, linked either to the high temperature deformation 'flow-fabrics' away from the spreading axis, the obduction of the ophiolite or post-obduction regional deformation events. Given that all three of the above may act to a variable degree it is perhaps not surprising that a vide variety of shapes and forms to the various chromite deposits have been described. Indeed, one of the most distinctive characteristics of ophiolitic chromite segregations compared to their major layered intrusion counterparts is their irregular nature, with the similarity in form of many deposits to seed pods promoting the term podiform (Wells et al. 1946). Thayer (1969) referred to 'pull-apart' textures within grains and the moderate to strong deformation resulting in the elongation of nodules within nodular ore whilst Christiansen (1985) described the presence of dislocations due to high temperature deformation, and evidence of deformation to increasingly lower temperatures with the subsequent development of cataclastic textures and cracks.

A consideration of the micro- and macro-scale structures associated with ophiolitic chromite segregations has resulted in a number of classifications being erected, based on the shape, size, internal structures and relation to host rock structures in an attempt to provide some systematic description of their form (Cassard et al. 1981; Christiansen 1986). The model of Christiansen (1986) suggests that the form of a chromite deposit can be influenced by early high temperature (ridge-axis) fabrics through to later syn- and post-emplacement thrusting and faulting.

The role of emplacement fabrics influencing the form of the chromite deposits was further described by Roberts et al. (1988) for the Vourinos Complex. They indicated that emplacement fabrics are prevalent throughout the mantle sequence, with their influence on the present form and distribution of the chromite deposits differing between the various localities depending on its location with regard to a major emplacement structure (Fig. 4).

Despite the obvious importance of deformation in the **ultimate** shape and form of ophiolitic chromitite deposits, there is a broad agreement that the initial formation and location of the deposits is more likely the direct result of magmatic processes. However, understanding the structural relationships in detail is a necessary prerequisite to the determination of ore reserves and the prediction of any 'downdip' extension of known mineralization.

## Geochemistry

### Chromite geochemistry

Chrome-spinels from chromite segregations show straightforward compositions, simplified as $(Mg, Fe^{2+}) (Cr, Al, Fe^{3+})_2O_4$ (Irvine 1965). The major divalent ions are $Mg^{2+}$ and $Fe^{2+}$ and the major trivalent species $Cr^{3+}$, $Al^{3+}$ and $Fe^{3+}$. Analysis of chromite grains from a variety of ophiolitic chromite segregations shows them to be chrome-spinels with variable $Cr^*$ values ($Cr/(Cr+Al)$), typically between 0.4 and 0.85, with $Mg^*$ values ($Mg/(Mg+Fe^{2+})$) between 0.5 and 0.8) (Fig. 5) and invariably restricted $Fe^{3+}$ contents. They show minor contents of $TiO_2$ (0.8–0.3 wt%), $NiO$ (0.1–0.4 wt%) with $MnO$ values around 0.1 wt %. By way of a simple contrast to major layered intrusions the ophiolitic chromite segregations tend to range to lower $Cr^*$ values and show higher and more restricted $Mg^*$ ratios (Fig. 5).

Various authors have related the variation of the $Cr^*$ ratio from chromite segregations within an individual ophiolite to the position of the

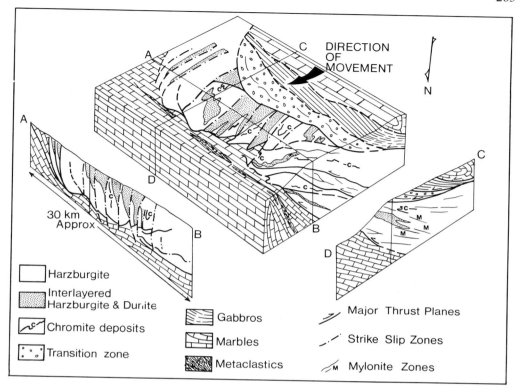

**Fig. 4.** Schematic block diagram of the Vourinos Complex showing the geometry of the emplacement structures (from Roberts *et al.* 1988)

segregation within the mantle sequence. Neary & Brown (1979) for the Semail and Leblanc & Violette (1983) in the Zambales both drew attention to the more aluminous deposits being located towards the petrological moho, whereas the more chrome-rich horizons tend to occur deeper within the sequence, in particular toward the harzburgite lherzolite transition observed within the lowermost portions of many ophiolite complexes.

*Interstitial silicates*

The majority of ophiolitic chromitite are dominated by olivine and chromite of variable modal proportions. The olivine compositions are typically highly fosteritic with fosterite (Fo) values of $Fo_{96}$ reported in some instances. The very high fosterite contents and the variation in olivine composition ($Fo_{94-96}$) are best explained by postcumulus/subsolidus processes. The commonly observed positive correlation between the modal percent chromite and the fosterite content of olivine reflects an Fe–Mg exchange reaction between chromite and olivine. With falling temperature the chromite grains exchange $Mg^{2+}$ for $Fe^{2+}$, as outlined by Irvine (1965) and demonstrated experimentally by Roeder *et al.* (1979). Such an exchange reaction in chromitite, where the high modal proportion of chromite buffers the Mg loss of chromite grains to the interstitial olivine produces the anomalously high Mg values in the subordinate olivine grains.

In addition to the olivine within the Semail ophiolite clinopyroxene, orthopyroxene, plagioclase and pargasitic amphibole are reported. Comparing data from the interstitial silicates of the Semail chromitite to that encountered within the cumulate sequence (Fig. 6) indicates that the silicates contained within the chromite ore from within the mantle sequence show the least evolved mineral compositions.

*Isotope systematics*

Few isotope data are available for ophiolitic chromite; however, Dunlop & Fouillac (1986) completed a O,H,Sr & Nd study of the chromite

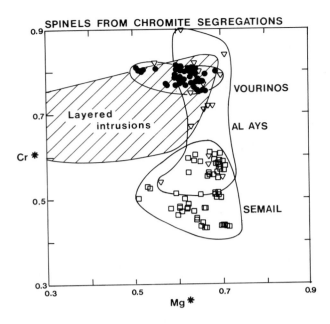

**Fig. 5.** Cr* vs. Mg* for chromite grains from chromite segregations within dunite pods from the Semail, Vourinos and Al 'Ays ophiolite complexes. Data sources – Semail: Roberts 1986; Vourinos: Roberts 1992; field for layered intrusions after Duke 1983.

deposits of the northern Semail ophiolite. The oxygen data reported from mineral separates from the chromite ore gave $\delta O_{18}$ values of between 4.7 and 5.7 per mil. with radiogenic isotope ratios for chromitite $\varepsilon Nd = +8.5$ and diopside $\varepsilon Nd = +9.2$, Sr87/Sr86 of 0.70385 compatible with data reported for the overlying crustal sequence. In particular they report data from fluid inclusions within the spinel with $\delta D = -56$ to $-79$ per mil. typical of magmatic water, which is consistent with the harzburgite data which suggests that the fluid phase observed within the chromite grains was unlikely to be derived from marine or meteoric waters.

## Discussion

For any model to fully account for the formation of ophiolitic chromitite it must explain the characteristics outlined above, in particular the presence of relict cumulus textures yet the ubiquitous deformational overprint. Below is a discussion of a multi-stage evolution of ophiolitic chromite deposits.

### Role of the partial melting regime

Not all ophiolitic mantle sequences contain major chromite segregations. Empirically it is evident that major ore deposits are restricted to the harzburgite dominant sequences (Den Tex 1969; Jackson & Thayer 1972; Roberts 1988). If we accept the view that the harzburgites represent the residua following extraction of a basaltic component then it appears the presence of more depleted residua in some way reflects the importance of a process which ultimately influences the likelihood of significant chromite mineralization. The magma fractionating the chromite segregations is unlikely to have derived directly from the associated harzburgite host. However, the apparent linkage between the chemistry of the residua and the presence or absence of chromite deposits and their respective chemistry, suggests that they are sufficiently related in time and space to be considered as consanguineous. Nevertheless, if the partial melting episode plays a crucial role in the formation of chromite mineralization it would appear that this is not a simplistic relationship. By comparing a series of increasingly depleted peridotites within a Ni/Al vs. Cr/Al diagram (Fig. 7), it is clear that the Lizard and Appenine ophiolites constitute reasonably 'fertile' mantle compared to the highly depleted peridotites of the Vourinos ophiolite. However, in plotting the

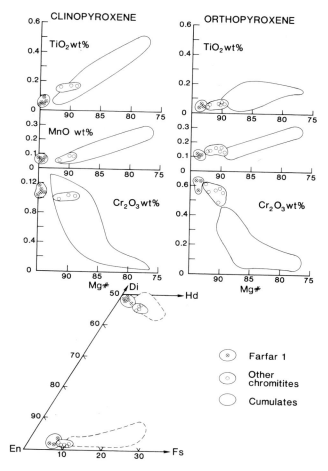

**Fig. 6.** Interstitial silicate data from chromite deposits within the mantle sequence of the Semail ophiolite with fields of data reported for the lowermost cumulates for comparison. Farfar 1 is a chromite deposit within a dunite body situated close to the petrological moho. Data source: Roberts (1986). Cumulate sequence data from Browning (1982).

Ni and then Cr value for these peridotites against the Ni/Al ratio as an indicator of the degree of depletion, although the Ni content of the peridotite increases with increasing depletion (Fig. 8a), the Cr content of an array of peridotites from fertile lherzolites through to depleted harzburgites (Fig. 8b) shows an almost constant Cr value (see also Liang & Elthon 1990). This observation is consistent with the experimental work which showed that during the partial melting of a spinel-lherzolite, the presence of spinel in the residuum ensures that chromium is partitioned into the spinel phase within the residuum even after extensive degrees of partial melting (Dickey & Yoder 1972; Jaques & Green 1980). The result is chromium-rich spinel grains in

the residuum compared to the source. Thus increased degrees of partial melting cannot become a significant factor until the spinel phase itself begins to melt, at which point the melt would rapidly become saturated with chromite.

By contrast, if we examine the Cr content of a series of basalts, generated in a variety of tectonic regimes (Fig. 9), it is apparent that for basalts of similar Mg values, to negate the effects of fractional crystallization, the Cr content increases as we move from MORB to Arc-Tholeiites through to Low-Ti Basalts and Boninites. Accepting the view that these basalts are derived from increasingly depleted sources (Sun et al. 1989) it appears that whereas the residuum suggest a constant Cr input to the

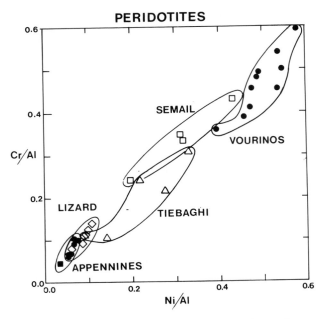

**Fig. 7.** Cr/Al vs. Ni/Al diagram for peridotites from a series of ophiolitic mantle sequences. The trend from low Ni/Al, Cr/Al ratios (Lizard, Appenines) to high Ni/Al, Cr/Al ratios (Semail, Vourinos) is one of increasing depletion. Data sources: this study and Beccaluva *et al.* 1984.

melt, the basalts associated with the more depleted sources show higher Cr contents. This conundrum is best resolved if we consider the 'capacity of the melt' to transport the Cr from the source region to the surface as an important factor. Irvine (1976) demonstrated experimentally that increasing silica content of basalts results in a higher Cr content of the associated spinel. Dick and Bullen (1984) supported this view with a natural data set following analysis of basalt assemblages from a variety of tectonic assemblages. The partial melting of increasingly depleted lithosphere results in the production of $SiO_2$-enriched melts (Green 1973; Nicholls 1974), and suggests that ophiolites which show the more depleted mantle sequences, tending to be in equilibrium with $SiO_2$-rich melts, would exhibit Cr-rich segregations. This is certainly the case for the Vourinos, where a highly depleted mantle sequence hosts Cr-rich deposits (Roberts 1992) and follows a relationship between the geochemistry of the mantle sequence and the enclosed chromite mineralization outlined by Johan & Auge (1986). Interestingly, a similar theory has recently been advanced to explain the relatively high PGE content of low-Ti basalts compared to their mid-ocean ridge counterparts (Hamlyn *et al.* 1985).

What does this increased depletion represent

and how is it achieved? Lowering the peridotite solidus by hydration of the source region is recognized as a significant factor in the formation of many of the ophiolites which show depleted mantle sequences (Pearce *et al.* 1984). Moreover, the hydrated nature of the mantle sequences will ensure the expansion of the olivine-spinel phase volume with olivine and spinel remaining liquidus phases for longer and enhancing the potential for chromite mineralization (Roberts 1988). Field evidence in support of this process can be found at the Semail, Troodos and Vourinos ophiolites where the mantle sequences comprise up to 20% dunite. The processes outlined above may also in part explain the presence of only minor chromite segregations within more fertile terranes. It suggests that when the amount of melting and more importantly the degree of depletion are low, as in lherzolite-dominated sequences, the melt precipitates the contained Cr as Cr-spinel prior to any significant removal of the melt from the source region. However, the melting of previously depleted mantle produces '$SiO_2$-enriched' melts which allows them to depart the source region and amalgamate into significant pockets of melt or infiltrate melt-filled structures.

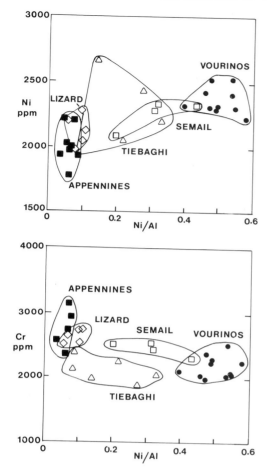

**Fig. 8.** (**a**) Ni (ppm) vs. Ni/Al for peridotites as in Fig. 7. Note the expected increase in Ni with increasing depletion of the peridotites. (**b**) Cr (ppm) vs. Ni/Al. Note the almost constant Cr values despite the increasing depletion of the peridotites. (See text for discussion.)

## Melt extraction and mantle magma chambers

Given the highly compatible nature of Cr into chrome-spinel, the formation of significant chromite segregations must involve the successful extraction and focusing of melt. Recent data suggest that the shape of the partial melting regime may be considered as a 'tent-like' structure with an apex, which consists of the zone of extensive melt extraction being coincident with the ridge axis (McKenzie 1985). A model of 'point sourced' diapirs rising to specific sites along a spreading axis as proposed by Dick (1989) provides an elegant mechanism for the focusing of melt and is in keeping with the observation of the clustering of chromite segregations at points close to the petrological moho and often below significant ultramafic cumulates, which are often of dunite. The presence of significant chromite mineralization deeper within the mantle sequence close to the lherzolite harzburgite transition may represent the early fractionates of melts at a point where they significantly depart from the molten matrix of the peridotite at *c.* 20–30 km below the ridge axis coincident with the onset of the zone of extensive melt extraction. Deposits located higher in the sequence may represent the focusing of melts towards small axial magma chambers. Indirect evidence in support of this view may be the observed fractionation of chromite deposit geochemistry between these two end-member situations, with those situated deep within the sequence tending to be Cr-rich whereas those situated close to the petrological moho tend to be Al-rich.

It is perhaps notable that the ophiolites which show more fertile mantle sequences and commonly lack significant chromite mineralization, also tend to show many features now commonly observed at slow spreading centres. For example, lherzolites with small amounts of dunite are reported, the lack of a well-developed ultramafic cumulate sequence in many instances, the predominance of gabbroic cumulates, and the presence of multiple dyke sequences with associated 'ridge-axis' tectonics are all in keeping with observations from slow spreading centres (Karson 1990). Given that the successful extraction and focusing of melt is probably essential for the formation of significant chromite mineralization, it would seem reasonable that a faster spreading rate may facilitate this process by developing a greater magma budget than is the case for slow-spreading environments.

The nature of the site of chromitite precipitation is difficult to establish. Lago *et al.* (1982) and more recently Leblanc & Ceuleneer (1992) have produced elegant models to account for chromite precipitation in dyke-like structures. The 'open-systems' they maintain and complex magma dynamics which are envisaged produce both the chromite segregations and may account for some of the unusual textures which are observed. They argue that the dyke-like nature of the original site is rarely preserved due to rotation and deformation of these earlier structures during further ascent and rotation to off-axis. However, the tabular nature of some of the Northern Semail chromite deposits, which preserve 'relict igneous textures' indicating way-up and which are discordant to the prevailing

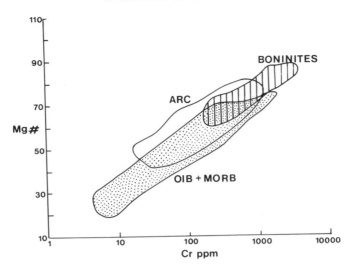

Fig. 9. Mg # vs. Cr (ppm) for basalts representative of a range of geotectonic setting of MORBs through to Boninites. Data from Catell & Taylor (1990).

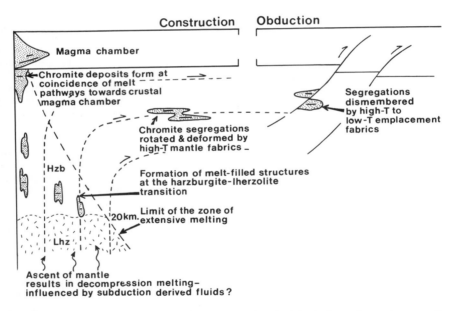

Fig. 10. Schematic illustration of constraints and processes involved in the formation and preservation of ophiolitic chromite deposits. Initial formation within melt-filled dyke structures within the uppermost mantle followed by deformation within a declining P–T regime from the ridge axis through obduction.

foliation, suggests that the dyke-scenario is certainly not all embracing.

Although melt-filled dyke structures within the mantle may be the sites for chromite segregation, the mechanisms involved in the formation of chromite-only layers remains a problem which has vexed workers on both major layered intrusions and ophiolites for a considerable period of time. Virtually every available physical parameter which can be varied realistically at the site of mineralization has been cited as the cause of the chromitite segregation. These include changes in fO$_2$ (Cameron 1977; Ulmer 1969), total pressure (Cameron 1977, 1980), temperature (Murck & Campbell 1986), P$_{H_2O}$ (Johan *et al.* 1983) and magma mixing (Irvine 1977; Irvine & Sharpe 1986). Based on experimental data, Irvine (1977) suggested that the mixing of two chemically distinct magma pulses can result in a hybrid-melt which resides in the chromite-only phase volume resulting in chromite precipitation. Murck & Campbell (1986) have described experiments which suggest that the solubility of the Cr$^{3+}$ ion within the melt is strongly temperature dependent and that any significant lowering of the temperature would result in the saturation of the melt with respect to chromitite. Given the very high distribution coefficient for chromium between chromite grains and melt (100–1000, Hill & Roeder 1974) an open-system must be maintained in order to produce a significant chromite-only segregation, without any drastic fractionation in the Cr values of the spinel grains within the deposit. Thus magma mixing appears an attractive scenario. However, whether it is the actual geochemical consequences of the mixing process or the resultant changes in T, fO$_2$ which cause chromite-only precipitation remains an open question.

## Role of deformation

High temperature structures within ophiolite peridotites (foliation and lineation) are usually ascribed to plastic flow associated with diapiric and/or horizontal flow of the lithosphere/asthenosphere away from the ridge axis (Nicolas & Poirier 1976). Evidence of high temperature plastic deformation can commonly be observed at sites of chromite mineralization. If these deposits developed originally within sub-vertical dyke-like structures within the mantle they have been progressively deformed, rotated and thinned, due to strong horizontal plastic flow, as the mantle moved away from the palaeo-spreading zone (Nicolas & Jackson 1982).

However, in addition to the ubiquitous presence of plastic structures of presumed mantle origin it is clear that in many instances ductile and brittle/ductile fabrics, of emplacement and post-emplacement origin, largely influence the present nature and form of the chromite deposits. Mylonitic fabrics superimposed on earlier high temperature fabrics within the basal portions of tectonized peridotites are well documented (Boudier *et al.* 1982) and have been related to the intra-oceanic displacement and thrusting of the ophiolite (Reuber 1986). In evaluating the tectonism of an individual deposit it is important to discern the relative importance of plastic over brittle/ductile fabrics as this can vary between sites within the same ophiolite, and exert strong influence on the observed and predicted shape of the chromite segregation (Roberts *et al.* 1988).

Irrespective of the actual origin of the tectonism there can be little doubt that the present nature and form of the chromites are strongly structurally controlled. Structural classifications based on high temperature fabrics alone, appear not to appreciate fully all the structural elements concerned. More expansive models, similar to those proposed by Christiansen (1986) are required.

## Summary

Ophiolitic chromite deposits represent the early fractionates of rising magmas within the mantle sequence at sites of palaeospreading (Fig. 10). The deposits tend to be restricted to more depleted mantle sequences (harzburgite dominant over lherzolite) and within these sequences the major segregations tend to be located either close to the petrological moho or near the harzburgite lherzolite transition zone often located deeper within the sequence. The deposits show a variety of forms and can preserve complex chromite-textures.

The association of chromite segregations with depleted sequences suggests a connection between the partial melting regime and enhanced chromite segregations. Sites where strongly depleted peridotites may be produced, including hydrated mantle above subduction zones, mantle formed below fast-spreading centres may be considered likely sites for present-day chromite mineralization.

Mass balance calculations indicate that the segregations require an open-system and models of dyke-like systems within the upper mantle appear to preserve the necessary magma budget and complex magma dynamics to produce both the chromite segregation and the complex chromite textures which are reported.

Transport of the mantle away from the palaeospreading zone results in deformation of the chromite deposits within a falling temperature regime, during ridge-axis through to post-obduction deformation.

Despite the emergence of some consensus views for the origins of ophiolitic chromitite some fundamental problems remain for both the igneous petrologist and the explorationist. For example, what is the mechanism controlling chromite-only precipitation; what experiments can we devise in order to further understand the nature of this process? What are the apparent reasons for the generation of mineralized and barren dunite bodies? A reasoning of this process is clearly not simply an academic exercise as it would significantly impact on exploration strategies. Perhaps we are really only at the beginning of an understanding of the petrogenesis of ophiolitic chromite deposits.

This paper is based largely on studies completed at the Open University under the aegis of Ian Gass. Ian's guidance and support was gratefully appreciated and will be greatly missed. Thierry Auge, Hazel Prichard & Robert Nesbitt are thanked for thorough and constructive reviews of the manuscript. Anthea Dunkley is thanked for cartography.

# References

AHMED, Z. 1982. Porphyritic-nodular, nodular and orbicular chrome ores from the Sakhakot-Qila Complex, Pakistan, and their chemical variations. *Mineralogical Magazine*, **45**, 167–178.

AUGE, T. 1987. Chromite deposits in the Southern Oman Ophiolite – Mineralogical constraints. *Mineralium Deposita*, **22**, 1–11.

—— & ROBERTS, S. 1982. Petrology and geochemistry of some chromitiferous bodies within the Oman ophiolite. *Ofioliti*, **2/3**, 133–154.

BECCALUVA, L., MACCIOTTA, G., PICCARDO, G. B & ZEDA, O. 1984. Petrology of Iherzolitic rocks from the northern Appenine ophiolites. *Lithos*, **17**, 299–316.

BOUDIER, F., NICOLAS, A. & BOUCHEZ, L. 1982. Kinematics of oceanic thrusting and subduction from basal sections of ophiolites. *Nature*, **296**, 825–828.

BOWEN, N. L. & TUTTLE, O. F. 1949. The system $MgO–SiO_2–H_2O$. *Geological Society of America Bulletin*, **60**, 439–460.

BROWN, M. A. 1980. Textural and geochemical evidence for the origin of some chromite deposits in the Oman Ophiolite. *In*: PANAYIOUTOU, A. (ed.) *Ophiolites: Proceedings of the International Ophiolite Symposium, Cyprus 1979*. Geological Survey of Cyprus, Nicosia, 714–721.

BROWNING, P. 1982. *The petrology, geochemistry and structure of the plutonic rocks of the Oman Ophiolite*. PhD thesis, Open University, Milton Keynes.

BURGATH, K. & WEISER, T. 1980. Primary features and genesis of Greek podiform chromite deposits. *In*: PANAYIOUTOU, A. (ed.) *Ophiolites: Proceedings of the International Ophiolite Symposium, Cyprus 1979*. Geological Survey of Cyprus, Nicosia, 675–690.

CAMERON, E. N. 1977. Chromite in the central sector of the Eastern Bushveld Complex, South Africa. *American Mineralogist*, **62**, 1082–1096.

—— 1980. Evolution of the lower critical zone, Central Sector, Eastern Bushveld Complex and its chromite deposits. *Economic Geology*, **75**, 845–871.

CASSARD, D., NICOLAS, A., RABINOVITCH, M., LEBLANC, M. & PRINZHOFER, A. 1981. Structural classification of chromite pods in Southern New Caledonia. *Economic Geology*, **76** (4), 805–831.

CATELL, A. C. & TAYLOR, R. N. 1990. Archaean basic magmas. *In*: R. P. HALL & D. J. HUGHES (eds) Early Precambrian basic magmatism. Blackie, Glasgow, 11–39.

CHRISTIANSEN, F. G. 1985. Deformation fabric and microtextures in ophiolite chromitites and host ultramafics, Sultanate of Oman. *Geologische Rundschau*, **74**, 61–76.

—— 1986. Structural classification of ophiolitic chromite deposits. *In*: GALLAGHER, M. J., IXER, R. A., NEARY, C. R. & PRICHARD, H. M. (eds) *Metallogeny of basic and ultrabasic rocks*. Institute of Mining and Metallurgy, 279–289.

—— & ROBERTS, S. 1986. Formation of olivine pseudo-crescumulates by syntectonic axial planar growth during mantle deformation. *Geological Magazine*, **123**, 73–79.

DEN TEX, E. 1969. Origin of ultramafic rocks, their tectonic setting and history: A contribution to the discussion of the paper 'The origin of basic and ultrabasic rocks' by P. J. Wyllie. *Tectonophysics*, **7**, 457–488.

DICK, H. J. B. 1989. Abyssal peridotites, very slow spreading ridges and ocean ridge magmatism. *In*: SAUNDERS, A. D. & NORRY, M. J. (eds) *Magmatism in the Ocean Basins*. Geological Society, London, Special Publication **42**, 71–105.

—— & BULLEN, T. 1984. Chromian spinel as a petrogenetic indicator in abyssal and alpine-type peridotites and spatially associated lavas. *Contributions to Mineralogy and Petrology*, **86**, 54–76.

DICKEY, J. S. 1975. A hypothesis of origin for podiform chromite deposits. *Geochimica et Cosmochimica Acta*, **39**, 1061–1074.

—— & YODER, H. S. 1972. Partitioning of chromium and aluminium between clinopyroxene and spinel. *Carnegie Institute Washington Yearbook*, **71**, 384–392.

DUKE, J. M. 1983. Ore deposit models 7. Magmatic segregation models of chromite. *Geoscience Canada*, **10**, 15–24.

DUNLOP, H. M. & FOUILLAC A. M. 1986. Isotope geochemistry of Oman basic–ultrabasic rocks and chromite deposits. *In*: GALLAGHER, M. J., IXER, R. A., NEARY, C. R. & PRICHARD, H. M. (eds) *Metallogeny of basic and ultrabasic rocks*. Institute of Mining and Metallurgy, 291–304.

GREEN, D. H. 1973. Experimental melting studies on model upper mantle compositions at high pressure under water saturated and water undersaturated conditions. *Earth and Planetary Science Letters*, **19**, 37–53.

GREENBAUM, D. 1972. Magmatic processes at ocean ridges, •evidence from the Troodos Massif, Cyprus. *Nature*, **288**, 18–21.

—— 1977. The chromitiferous rocks of the Troodos Ophiolite Complex, Cyprus. *Economic Geology*, **72**, 1175–1194.

HAMLYN, P. R., KEAYS, R. R., CAMERON, W. E. CRAWFORD, A. J. & WALDRON, H. M. 1985. Precious metals in magnesian low-Ti lavas: Implications for metallogenesis and sulfur saturation in primary magmas. *Geochimica et Cosmochimica Acta*,

**49**, 1797–1811.

HILL, R. & ROEDER, P. 1974. The crystallization of spinel from basaltic liquid as a function of oxygen fugacity. *Journal of Geology*, **82**, 709–729.

IRVINE, T. N. 1965. Chromian spinel as a petrogenetic indicator. Part 1. Theory. *Canadian Journal of Earth Science*, **2**, 648–672.

—— 1976. Chromite crystallisation in the join $Mg_2SiO_4$–$CaMgSi_2O_6$–$CaAl_2Si_2O_8$–$MgCr_2O_4$–$SiO_2$. *Carnegie Institute Washington Yearbook*, **76**, 465–472.

—— 1977. Origin of chromitite layers in the Muskox intrusion and other stratiform intrusions: A new interpretation. *Geology*, **5**, 273–277.

—— & SHARPE, M. R. 1986. Magma mixing and the origin of stratiform oxide ore zones in the Bushveld and Stillwater complexes. *In*: GALLAGHER, M. J., IXER, R. A., NEARY, C. R. & PRICHARD, H. M. (eds) *Metallogeny of basic and ultrabasic rocks*. Institute of Mining and Metallurgy, 183–198.

JACKSON, E. D. 1961. Primary textures and mineral associations in the ultramafic zone of the Stillwater Complex, Montana. *United States Geological Survey, Professional Paper*, **358**.

—— & THAYER, T. P. 1972. Some criteria for distinguishing between stratiform, concentric and alpine peridotite-gabbro complexes. *International Geological Congress, 24th, Montreal, 1972*, **2**, 297–302.

JAQUES, A. L. & GREEN D. H. 1980. Anhydrous melting of peridotite at 0–15 kb pressure and the genesis of tholeiitic basalts. *Contributions to Mineralogy and Petrology*, **73**, 287–310.

JOHAN, Z. & AUGE, T. 1986. Ophiolitic mantle sequence and their evolution: mineral chemistry constraints. *In*: GALLAGHER, M. J., IXER, R. A., NEARY, C. R. & PRICHARD, H. M. (eds) *Metallogeny of basic and ultrabasic rocks*. Institute of Mining and Metallurgy, 305–318.

——, DUNLOP, H., LE BEL, L., ROBERT, J. L & VOLFINGER, M. 1983. Origin of chromite deposits in ophiolite complexes: Evidence for a volatile and sodium-rich reducing fluid-phase. *Fortschritte der Mineralogie*, **61**, 105–107.

KARSON, J. A. 1990. Seafloor spreading on the Mid-Atlantic Ridge: Implications for the structure of ophiolites and oceanic lithosphere produced in slow-spreading environments. *In*: MALPAS, J., MOORES, E. M., PANAYIOTOU, A. & XENOPHONTOS, C. (eds) *Ophiolites: Oceanic Crustal Analogues*. Cyprus Geological Survey, 547–553.

LAGO, B. L. RABINOWICZ, M. & NICOLAS, A. 1982. Podiform chromite ore bodies: a genetic model. *Journal of Petrology*, **23**, 103–126.

LEBLANC, M. & CEULENEER, G. 1992. Chromite crystallisation in multicellular magma flow: Evidence from a chromitite dyke in the Oman ophiolite. *Lithos*, **27**, 231–257.

—— & VIOLETTE, J. F. 1983. Distribution of aluminium-rich and chromium-rich chromite pods in ophiolite peridotites. *Economic Geology*, **78**, 293–301.

LIANG, Y. & ELTHON, D. 1990. Evidence from chromium abundances in mantle rocks for extraction

of picritic and komatiite melts. *Nature*, **343**, 551–555.

McDONALD, J. A. 1965. Liquid immiscibility as one factor in chromite seam formation in the Bushveld Igneous Complex. *Economic Geology*, **60**, 1674–1685.

McKENZIE, D. 1985. The extraction of magma from the crust and mantle. *Earth and Planetary Science Letters*, **74**, 81–91.

MENZIES, M. A. & ALLEN, C. 1974. Plagioclase lherzolite residual mantle relationships within two eastern Mediterranean ophiolites. *Contributions to Mineralogy and Petrology*, **45**, 197–217.

MOORES, E. M. & VINE, F. J. 1971. The Troodos massif Cyprus and other ophiolites as oceanic crust: Evaluations and Implications. *Philosophical Transactions of the Royal Society, London*, **A268**, 443–466.

MURCK, B. W. & CAMPBELL, I. H. 1986. The effects of temperature, oxygen fugacity and melt composition on the behaviour of chromium in basic and ultrabasic melts. *Geochimica et Cosmochimica Acta* **50**, 1871–1887.

NEARY, C. R. & BROWN, M. A. 1979. Chromites from the Al Ays Complex, Saudi Arabia and the Semail Complex, Oman. *In*: AL SHANTI, A. M. S. (ed.) '*Evolution and mineralisation of the Arabian Shield*', *Institute of Arabian Geologists Bulletin*, **2**, 193–205.

NICHOLLS, I. A. 1974. Liquids in equilibrium with peridotite mineral assemblages at high water pressures. *Contributions to Mineralogy and Petrology*, **45**, 289–316.

NICOLAS, A. & JACKSON, E. D. 1972. Repartition en deux provinces des peridotites des chaines alpines longeant la Mediterranee; implications geotectoniques. *Bulletin Suisse Mineralogische und Petrographische*, **52**, 479–495.

—— & ——. 1982. High temperature dikes in peridotites: Origin by hydraulic fracturing. *Journal of Petrology*, **23**, 568–582.

—— & POIRIER, J. P. 1976. *Crystalline plasticity and solid state flow in metamorphic rock*. Wiley, New York.

PEARCE, J. A., LIPPARD, S. J & ROBERTS, S. 1984. Characteristics and tectonic significance of suprasubduction zone ophiolites. *In*: KOKELAAR, B. P. & HOWELLS, M. F. (eds) *Marginal Basin Geology*. Geological Society, London, Special Publication, **16**, 77–94.

PETERS, T. & KRAMERS, J. D. 1974. Chromite deposits in the ophiolite complex of Northern Oman. *Mineralium Deposita*, **9**, 253–259.

REUBER, I. 1986. Geometry of accretion and oceanic thrusting of the Spontang ophiolite, Ladakh-Himalayas. *Nature*, **321**, 592–596.

ROBERTS, S. 1986. *The role of igneous processes in the formation of ophiolitic chromitite*. PhD thesis, Open University, Milton Keynes.

——, 1988. Ophiolitic chromitite formation: A marginal basin phenomenon? *Economic Geology*, **83**, 1034–1036.

——, 1992. Influence of the partial melting regime on the formation of ophiolitic chromitite. *In*:

PARSON, L. M., MURTON, B. J. & BROWNING, P. (eds). *Ophiolites and their modern ocean analogues.* Geological Society, London, Special Publication, **60**, 203–218.

——, RASSIOS, A., WRIGHT, L., VACONDIOS, I., VRACHATIS, G., GRIVAS, E., NESBITT, R. W., NEARY, C. R., MOAT, T. & KONSTATOPOLOU, L. 1988. Structural controls on the location and form of the Vourinos chromite deposits. *In*: BOISSONNAS, J., & OMENETTO, P. (eds) *Mineral Deposits of The European Community. Springer*, 249–266.

ROEDER, P. L., CAMPBELL, I. H. & JAMIESON, H. E. 1979. A re-evaluation of the olivine-spinel geothermometer. *Contributions to Mineralogy and Petrology*, **68**, 325–335.

ROSSMAN, D. L., FERNANDEZ, N. S., FONTANOS, C. A. & ZEPEDA, Z. C. 1959. Chromite deposits on Insula Chromite reservation number 1., Zambales, Philippines. *Philippines Bureau of Mines Special Programme Publication*, **19**, 1–12.

SUN, S. S., NESBITT, R. W. & McCULLOCH, M. T. 1989. Geochemistry and petrogenesis of Archaean and early proterozoic siliceous high magnesian basalts. *In*: CRAWFORD, A. J. (ed.) *Boninites.* Unwin–Hyman, London, 149–173.

SMITH, C. H. 1958. Bay of Islands Igneous Complex, Western Newfoundland. *Memoir of the Geological Survey of Canada*, **290**.

THAYER, T. P. 1946. Preliminary chemical correlation of chromite with the containing rocks. *Economic Geology*, **41**, 202–217.

——, 1963. Flow layering in Alpine Peridotite–Gabbro complexes. *Mineralogical Association of America Special Paper*, **1**, 55–61.

——, 1964. Principal features and origin of podiform chromite deposits and some observations on the Guleman–Soridag district, Turkey. *Economic Geology*, **59**, 1497–1542.

——, 1969. Gravity differentiation and magmatic-re-emplacement of podiform chromite deposits. *Economic Geology Monograph*, **4**, 132–146.

——, 1970. Chromite segregations as petrogenetic indicators. *Geological Society of South Africa Special Publication*, **1**, 380–390.

ULMER, G. C. 1969. Experimental investigations of chromite-spinels. *Economic Geology Monograph*, **4**, 114–131.

WELLS, F. G., CARTER, F. W. & RYNEARSON, G. A. 1946. Chromite deposits of Del Norte County, California. *Bulletin of California Division of Mines*, **134**, 1–76.

# An overview of the PGE concentrations in the Shetland ophiolite complex

H. M. PRICHARD & R. A. LORD

*Department of Earth Sciences, The Open University, Walton Hall, Milton Keynes MK7 6AA UK*

**Abstract**: Extremely anomalous platinum-group element (PGE) concentrations are known at one site, Cliff, in the Shetland ophiolite complex. Systematic PGE analysis of all the mafic and ultramafic igneous and alteration lithologies in the ophiolite has revealed many lower grade anomalous PGE occurrences throughout the cumulate ultramafic sequence and their distribution is described here. More sites with PGE enrichments as anomalous as those at Cliff have not been found.

At Cliff the anomalous values of over 60 ppm Pt + Pd are restricted to a chromite-rich sulphide-bearing dunite forming a small part of a 200 m dunite lens in mantle harzburgite close to the basal thrust of the ophiolite. Lower values of up to 6.4 ppm Pt + Pd occur in chromite-poor, sulphide-rich dunites also within this dunite lens. The only other chromite-rich dunite lens in the Cliff area also has detected Pt and Pd but with low Pt + Pd values of 200 ppb. In contrast, harzburgites, metasediments underlying the basal thrust, serpentinites from the basal thrust and internal faults are all barren of Pt and Pd (detection limit = 20 ppb). In the Cliff area, therefore, detected PGE values are restricted to magmatic chromite-rich dunite lenses. PGE analyses of drill core from beneath the disused chromite quarries at Cliff are low (227 ppb Pt + Pd) indicating that the extremely anomalous PGE values are very restricted. This supports the idea that PGE, concentrated magmatically within the dunite lens at Cliff, may have been remobilized locally to produce extremely anomalous PGE values in an alteration zone only a few metres in diameter.

Elsewhere in the ophiolite, anomalous Pt + Pd values of up to 4 ppm occur in chromite-rich, sulphide-bearing dunite within the dunite unit, which stratigraphically overlies the harzburgite. Pt + Pd concentrations of up to 1 ppm are present in the pyroxenites and wehrlites of the upper part of the ultramafic sequences. High-level wehrlites and pyroxenites within the gabbro unit, representing late ultramafic differentiates, contain lower levels of PGE of up to 310 ppb Pt + Pd. The gabbros all have less than 20 ppb Pt and Pd. This distribution indicates that the PGE concentrations occur in specific primary magmatic lithologies and pathfinder analysis shows that they are associated with Ni, Cu, Au and Cr. PGE have not been found above detection limits in fault zones away from primary PGE mineralization sites and it is concluded that PGE are not significantly hydrothermally reconcentrated. At Cliff, remobilization may have occurred over short distances of only a few metres at most.

The basic and ultrabasic igneous complex, forming the lower part of a Caledonian ophiolite complex (Gass *et al.* 1982; Prichard 1985; Flinn 1985), occurs (exposed area of approximately 70 km²) on Unst and Fetlar, the most northeastern islands in Shetland and the British Isles. Residual mantle harzburgite and gabbro are the two main lithologies on Fetlar, which lies to the south of Unst. In Unst, harzburgite, containing dunite lenses, some of which are enriched in chromite (Prichard & Neary 1981, 1982), is overlain by a cumulate ultramafic sequence of dunite, with discontinuous layers of chromite, grading stratigraphically upwards into wehrlite and clinopyroxenite. Above these ultramafic lithologies lies gabbro containing ultramafic wehrlites and pyroxenites at upper stratigraphic levels in the gabbro and which is intruded at the top by

dykes, probably representing the lower part of a sheeted dyke complex. Some of these dykes have arc tholeiitic geochemistry suggesting that this ophiolite complex has a supra-subduction zone origin (Prichard & Lord 1988).

Ophiolite complexes were initially thought to contain platinum-group elements (PGE) at grades of less than 1 ppm. Os, Ir and Ru concentrations associated with podiform chromitite were described (Agiorgitis & Wolf 1978; Page *et al.* 1982*a,b*, 1984; Page & Talkington 1984). Recently Pt and Pd concentrations have been documented from a number of ophiolite complexes (Bacuta *et al.* 1988; Corrivaux & La Flamme 1990; Edwards 1990; Prichard & Lord 1990; Lachize *et al.* 1991, Ohnenstetter *et al.* 1991, Prichard & Neary 1991; Prichard *et al.* 1992 and Pedersen *et al.* 1993) often at con-

*From* Prichard, H. M., Alabaster, T., Harris, N. B. W. & Neary, C. R. (eds), 1993, *Magmatic Processes and Plate Tectonics*, Geological Society Special Publication No. 76, 273–294.

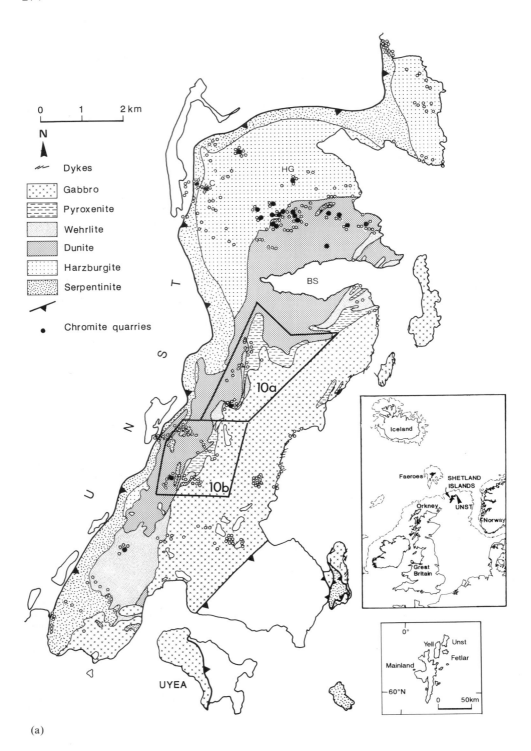

(a)

centrations of 1–2 ppm. PGE were recorded in Shetland in the early part of the century (Hitchen 1929) with 1 dwt Pt metals per ton (1.3 ppm) in chromite concentrate taken from the chromite crushing mill and the presence of Pd, Ir and osmiridium were noted. Hitchen concluded that platinum was present in the chrome concentrates but in variable amounts. Subsequently Os, Ir and Ru platinum-group minerals (PGM) were described enclosed in chromite from dunite lenses in harzburgite and from discontinuous layers in the dunite cumulate sequence (Prichard et al. 1981). More recently an abundant variety of PGM, including all 6 PGE, was discovered during an EC funded survey (Prichard et al. 1987; Prichard & Tarkian 1988). A limited number of analyses confirmed that two localities, Cliff and Harold's Grave contain anomalously enriched PGE values (Prichard et al. 1984; Neary et al. 1984 and Prichard et al. 1986) associated with chromite-rich dunite lenses within harzburgite. At Harold's Grave, PGE are enriched in Os, Ir and Ru at 3–4 ppm levels whereas at Cliff Pt, Pd and Rh are enriched with respect to Os, Ir and Ru with Pt + Pd values of over 60 ppm and 1 ppm Rh common (Prichard

et al. 1986). These values have been endorsed by a number of analytical companies and by Gunn et al. (1985) and Gunn (1989).

Previous studies for PGE and PGM in the Shetland ophiolite complex were confined essentially to chromite-rich lithologies, although there was evidence that anomalous PGE concentrations were more widespread. For example, PGM had been observed in sulphide-rich dunites at Cliff (Prichard & Lord 1988). A geochemical survey was undertaken in order to examine the distribution and concentrations of the PGE and potential pathfinder elements throughout the ophiolite sequence and so produce a model for the behaviour of PGE in this ophiolite complex (Prichard & Lord 1990; Lord & Prichard 1989b, 1991). The mineralogy and textures of PGM in samples with PGE anomalies, discovered as a result of this survey, are described in Prichard & Lord (1989), (1990) and in Prichard et al. (in press). The PGE distribution and their association with pathfinder elements in the least altered and best preserved part of the ophiolite complex, in the north around Balta Sound (Fig. 1), is recorded in Lord (1991) and Prichard & Lord (1990). This paper presents an overview of

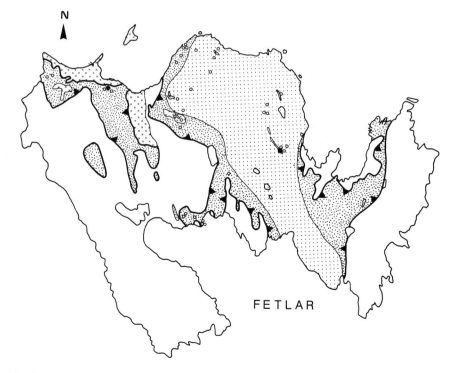

(b)

**Fig. 1.** Distribution of sample sites on (**a**) Unst and (**b**) Fetlar. Positions of maps (Fig. 10 a and b) are shown by black outlines. C marks the position of the Cliff locality, HG of Harold's Grave and BS of Balta Sound.

**Table 1.** *Analyses of all PGE 6 and Au (in ppb) and As, Cu and Ni (in ppm) for igneous and alteration lithologies from Cliff, mid-Unst and Fetlar. Many of these analyses have been used for the chondrite-normalized plots in Fig. 11.*

| Number | Os | Ir | Ru | Rh | Pt | Pd | Au | As | Cu | Ni | Rock | Locality |
|---|---|---|---|---|---|---|---|---|---|---|---|---|
| CL2-12 | 24 | 2 | 8 | 1 | 12 | 8 | 15 | 17 | 3 | 3110 | dunite | Cliff drill core adjacent to CL2-13 (north) |
| CL2-13 | 50 | 40 | 165 | 12 | 4 | 3 | 5 | 5 | 32 | 1976 | chromitite | Cliff drill core |
| CL2-14 | 26 | 4 | 20 | 2 | 8 | 4 | 15 | 24 | 2 | 2905 | dunite | Cliff drill core adjacent to CL2-13 (south) |
| MR292 | 50 | 97 | 190 | 55 | 500 | 520 | 0 | 0 | 183 | 1580 | Cr-rich S-bearing dunite | Cliff spoil tip |
| MR293 | 34 | 83 | 170 | 69 | 370 | 180 | 31 | 123 | 32 | 2578 | Cr-rich S-bearing dunite | Cliff spoil tip |
| MR4 | 470 | 1400 | 1800 | 950 | 10000 | 8600 | 91 | 121 | 7 | 2816 | Cr-rich S-bearing dunite | Cliff N wall of quarry 2, Locality B, Fig. 8 |
| CL1-10 | 38 | 34 | 64 | 15 | 155 | 72 | 10 | 5 | 7 | 2407 | dunite + thin chromitite layer | Cliff drill core |
| MR2 | 6 | 4 | 8 | 1.5 | 6 | 6 | 5 | 4 | 12 | 2676 | dunite | Cliff N wall of quarry 2 |
| CL1-14 | 10 | 4 | 14 | 1 | 6 | 6 | 5 | 4 | 7 | 2417 | dunite | Cliff drill core |
| MR11 | 290 | 300 | 500 | 230 | 2400 | 4000 | 111 | 51 | 752 | 5667 | Cr-poor S-bearing dunite | Cliff Locality C, Fig. 8 |
| MR12 | 225 | 245 | 380 | 180 | 1850 | 1850 | 54 | 12 | 163 | 3500 | Cr-poor S-bearing dunite | Cliff Locality C, Fig. 8 |
| MR1 | 30 | 4.5 | 8.5 | 1.5 | 10 | 13 | 12 | 29 | 9 | 2363 | harzburgite | Cliff S wall of quarry 2 |
| CL1-04 | 8 | 4 | 14 | 2 | 10 | 6 | 15 | 9 | 2 | 2233 | transitional harzburgite | Cliff drill core |
| CL1-06 | 6 | 4 | 10 | 2 | 12 | 4 | 5 | 8 | 5 | 2263 | transitional harzburgite | Cliff drill core |
| CL2-10 | 14 | 6 | 18 | 2 | 16 | 12 | 3 | 14 | 4 | 2385 | transitional harzburgite | Cliff drill core |
| CL2-11 | 16 | 2 | 18 | 2 | 10 | 6 | 15 | 27 | 2 | 2576 | transitional harzburgite | Cliff drill core |
| CL1-17 | 4 | 4 | 14 | 1 | 10 | 2 | 15 | 18 | 7 | 2210 | Sheared talc carbonate | Cliff drill core |
| MR3 | 4 | 4 | 8.5 | 1.5 | 5.5 | 3.5 | 15 | 10 | 14 | 2233 | serpentinite | Cliff fault adjacent to MR4 |
| MR128 | 22 | 30 | 57 | 16 | 130 | 68 | 75 | 231 | 0 | 2157 | chromite-rich dunite | Cliff west Locality A, Fig. 8 |
| MR284 | 54 | 50 | 150 | 25 | 89 | 190 | 0 | 39 | 24 | 1676 | Cr-rich S-bearing dunite | Quarries SW of Sobul, mid-Unst, |
| MR283 | 150 | 150 | 300 | 45 | 200 | 340 | 18 | 30 | 59 | 2526 | Cr-rich S-bearing dunite | Quarries SW of Sobul, mid-Unst, |
| MR57 | 200 | 200 | 420 | 37 | 170 | 270 | 16 | 29 | 21 | 1908 | Cr-rich S-bearing dunite | Quarries SW of Sobul, mid-Unst, |
| MR187 | 6 | 6.5 | 12 | 6.5 | 80 | 170 | 34 | 0 | 460 | 3087 | dunite | Caldback, mid-Unst |
| MR45 | 0 | 1.5 | 3.5 | 3 | 86 | 39 | 0 | 0 | 0 | 670 | wehrlite/pyroxenite | South Unst |
| MR103 | 4 | 1 | 1.5 | 3 | 51 | 75 | 31 | 0 | 87 | 1261 | wehrlite/pyroxenite | Watlee, mid-Unst |
| MR63 | 4 | 2.5 | 4 | 3 | 44 | 62 | 0 | 4 | 34 | 1000 | wehrlite/pyroxenite | Hellier's water, mid-Unst |
| MR65 | 6 | 5.5 | 13 | 9.5 | 100 | 220 | 33 | 28 | 608 | 742 | wehrlite/pyroxenite | Hellier's water, mid-Unst |
| MR56 | 20 | 25 | 2.5 | 1.5 | 1 | 0 | 0 | 28 | 18 | 1534 | sheared dunite | SW Sobul, mid-Unst |
| HW1 | 0 | 3 | 7 | 2 | 5 | 6 | 0 | 18 | 6 | 1480 | sheared pyroxenite | Hellier's water, mid-Unst |
| 713 | 80 | 140 | 710 | 49 | 71 | 39 | na | na | na | na | chromitite in pyroxenite | Ordale |
| NA25 | 4 | 30 | 18 | 27 | 510 | 590 | 0 | 34 | 204 | 645 | wehrlite/pyroxenite | South of Unst airport |
| SA2 | 8 | 68 | 56 | 40 | 480 | 440 | 0 | 6 | 206 | 384 | wehrlite/pyroxenite | South of Unst airport |
| SA3 | 0 | 4 | 5 | 2 | 5 | 5 | 0 | 13 | 467 | 638 | wehrlite/pyroxenite | Sandwick |
| MR16 | 5 | 2 | 19 | 4 | 48 | 18 | 0 | 276 | 21 | 746 | high level pyroxenite | Coast mid-Unst |
| MR17 | 0 | 6.5 | 11 | 7.5 | 120 | 110 | 0 | 47 | 11 | 729 | high level pyroxenite | Coast mid-Unst |
| MR169 | 0 | 1 | 4.5 | 7 | 120 | 190 | 18 | 38 | 73 | 806 | high level pyroxenite | Coast mid-Unst |
| MR86 | 00 | 0.5 | 2 | 0 | 3 | 5.5 | 15 | 22 | 114 | 16 | gabbro | Coast mid-Unst |
| MR233 | 0 | 0 | 0.5 | 0 | 1 | 2 | 63 | 11 | 250 | 133 | gabbro | Stackerberg, Fetlar |

Na: not available

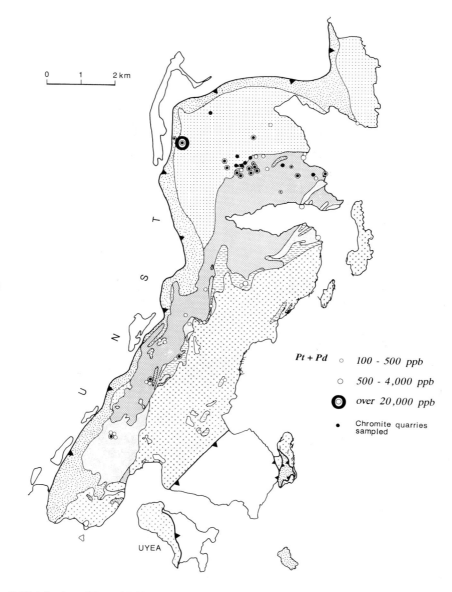

0  1  2 km

*Pt + Pd*  ○  *100 - 500 ppb*

○  *500 - 4,000 ppb*

◎  *over 20,000 ppb*

•  Chromite quarries
sampled

UYEA

**Fig. 2.** Distribution of Pt and Pd in the ophiolite complex on the island of Unst. Note the close relationship between chromite and Pt + Pd concentrations with black circles representing chromite quarries often surrounded by open circles representing Pt + Pd concentrations.

all the results of the PGE and pathfinder geochemical study for the whole ophiolite, including both the islands of Unst and Fetlar. Two areas are described in detail to illustrate the different types of PGE mineralization within the ophiolite sequence: (i) Cliff in mantle harzburgite and (ii) mid-Unst, where dunite, wehrlite and pyroxenite crustal cumulates are preserved.

## Techniques

Samples of 1 kg in size were crushed and the powders were analysed for Pt, Pd and Au. Pt and Pd were collected using a Ni sulphide fire assay and Au was extracted using Pb collection. The button concentrates were analysed for Pt, Pd and Au using ICP-ES. The detection limit for

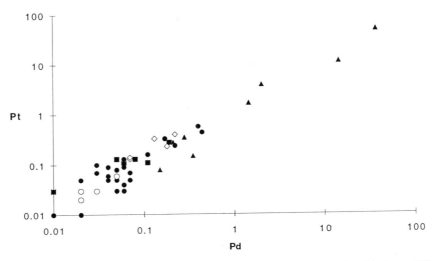

**Fig. 3.** Graph showing the correlation between Pt and Pd (in ppm) for all samples with detected Pt and Pd from the 477 samples analysed. Varying Pt and Pd values for different lithologies are also shown. ■: dunites; ◇: chromitites; ●: wehrlites and pyroxenites; ○: high-level wehrlites; ▲: samples from Cliff.

all 3 elements, for these analyses, was quoted as approximately 20 ppb. Selected samples shown to have Pt or Pd anomalies or representing typical lithologies were analysed for all 6 PGE using Ni sulphide fire assay and ICP-MS (Table 1). The detection limit for these analyses was approximately 2 ppb for each PGE. In all cases SARM 7 was run as a standard and gave results similar to the quoted values. All PGE-bearing samples studied, were found to contain PGM in numbers proportionate to the analysed PGE values. Ni, Cu and As were analysed by ED XRF using powder pellets.

## Distribution of Pt and Pd

Initially 477 samples were collected from all the different types of primary igneous and alteration lithologies in the ophiolite complex to provide a comprehensive geological and geographical cover (Fig. 1). Pt and Pd were found to be concentrated in certain lithologies. The highest proportion of samples with detected Pt and/or Pd occurs in chromite-rich lithologies (43 samples analysed) with just over half having detected Pt and/or Pd. Approximately one quarter of all the dunites from lenses in harzburgite (79 samples analysed), dunites from the unit overlying the harzburgite (92 samples analysed), wehrlites (30 samples analysed), pyroxenites (27 samples analysed) and high-level ultramafics within gabbro (23 samples analysed) also had

detected Pt and/or Pd. In stark contrast the harzburgites (60 samples analysed), serpentinites and talcs (74 samples analysed) gabbros (34 samples analysed), dykes (3 samples analysed) and metasediments (12 samples analysed) are characterized by the complete absence of detectable Pt and Pd. All samples (31) collected from Fetlar have Pt and Pd values below the detection limit of 20 ppb. These data are summarized (Fig. 2) on a map of the ophiolite complex on Unst showing the association of PGE in pyroxene-rich ultramafics and with chromite both in dunite lenses in harzburgite and the overlying cumulate dunite. Maps and diagrams revealing the close relationship between PGE occurrences and specific igneous lithologies for the area north of Balta Sound are given in Lord (1991) and Lord & Prichard (submitted).

Pt and Pd are usually either recorded together in samples or are both absent and Pt < Pd is normal for magmatic concentrations but Pt > Pd is present in more altered samples, e.g. Cliff; Pt/Pd ratios usually varying between 0.5 and 1.5 (Fig. 3). The concentrations of Pt and Pd, however, vary systematically with lithology. Extremely anomalous values of over 60 ppm total Pt + Pd (Prichard et al. 1986) occur in chromite-rich sulphide-bearing dunites in the dunite lens surrounded by harzburgite at Cliff, although the highest value recorded in this study is only 18.6 ppm (Table 1). Typically 0.5–2 ppm Pt + Pd values occur in sulphide-bearing dunites associated with chromitites situated both in dunite

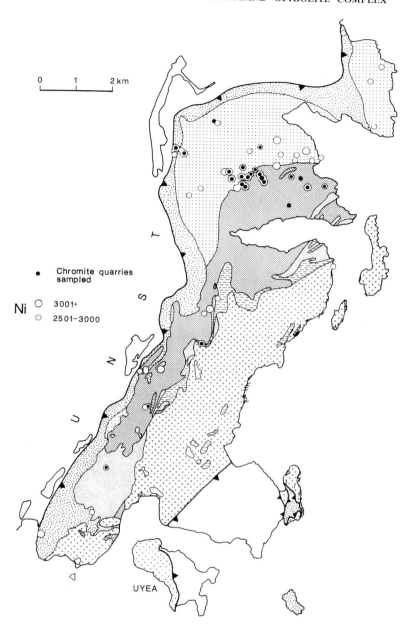

**Fig. 4.** Distribution of Ni in the ophiolite complex on the island of Unst. Note the close relationship between chromite and Ni concentrations with black circles representing chromite quarries often surrounded by open circles representing Ni concentrations. Values in ppm.

lenses within the harzburgite and more abundantly in the overlying dunites; this is especially well demonstrated in the area north of Balta Sound where the highest Pt + Pd value is 4 ppm (Lord 1991). 100–200 ppb Pt + Pd values are common in the upper part of the ultramafic sequence in sulphide-bearing wehrlites and pyroxenites and the highest Pt + Pd value recorded in the pyroxenites in the Shetland ophiolite complex is as high as 1 ppm. Two areas of high-level ultramafic lithologies within the gabbros contain low levels of Pt + Pd ranging from detected to 310 ppb; the highest value occurring in a sulphide-bearing sample taken from the junction of a pyroxene-rich and an olivine-rich layer.

## The distribution of base metals, gold and arsenic

Ni, present in olivine, is concentrated in the ultramafic parts of the ophiolite rather than the gabbro (Fig. 4). Comparison of whole-rock Ni concentrations with the presence of Ni sulphides, arsenides, antimonides or alloys, in thin section shows that Ni values of over 2500 ppm generally correspond to the presence of Ni in an additional phase to olivine. The highest Ni levels (over 3000 ppm) have extra Ni-bearing phases clearly visible in hand specimen and occur in dunites in close proximity to chromite concentrations, both in lenses within harzburgite, as at Cliff, and in the lower part of the ultramafic cumulate sequence. Cu is concentrated (over 200 ppm) in the same types of igneous lithologies as those with Ni values of over 2500 ppm, in the vicinity of chromite quarries (Fig. 5). In addition, enriched Cu values are recorded in high-level PGE-poor gabbros along the coast of eastern Unst. These may represent the first stages of hydrothermal sulphide concentration which might, at a higher level, form volcanogenic massive sulphides, characteristic of other ophiolite complexes. The distribution (Lord & Prichard 1989a) of the more anomalous Au values (over 50 ppb) is also similar to that of Ni and Cu within the ultramafic part of the complex, with highest values near the chromite quarries. Low levels of Au (less than 50 ppb) are present in a few gabbros and in altered lithologies along fault zones.

The preceding paragraph indicates that the highest base metal and Au concentrations occur in similar ultramafic igneous lithologies in the vicinity of the chromite quarries. This is also the location of the most anomalous PGE values. Anomalous Ni, Cu, Au and Cr values within the ultramafic sequence of this ophiolite are, therefore, very good indicators that anomalous PGE concentrations are likely to occur in the vicinity, although in detail, for reasons discussed later, these pathfinders are poor markers of the richest PGE values. Chromite concentrations without associated Ni or Cu sulphides are not Au, Pt or Pd enriched and nor are Ni or Cu sulphides which are not associated with chromite.

The distribution of arsenic is quite different from that of PGE, Ni, Cu, Au and Cr. Arsenic is concentrated along the basal thrust zone (Fig. 6) in serpentinites and other altered lithologies such as talc and is concentrated in faults internal to the complex. Large arsenic concentrations (up to 0.2 per cent along the basal thrust in south Unst) in altered and sheared lithologies are not associated with PGE-rich magmatic lithologies. Arsenic does not, therefore, correlate with Pt and Pd concentrations and is not a pathfinder within the Shetland ophiolite complex. The only exception to this is the occurrence of anomalous As values with the extremely anomalous Pt- and Pd-enriched samples at Cliff.

The correlation of (Pt + Pd) with Ni, Cu and As can be illustrated graphically. The (Pt + Pd)-bearing samples which are most Ni enriched are chromitites and dunites whereas wehrlites and pyroxenites, which are higher in the stratigraphic sequence, are less Ni enriched (Fig. 7a). Gabbros are least Ni enriched. Cu shows a positive correlation with (Pt + Pd) (Fig. 7b) but high Cu values in the high-level gabbros are (Pt + Pd) barren. (Pt + Pd) shows a poor correlation with As (Fig. 7c).

In order to demonstrate the close association of PGE with certain igneous lithologies two areas have been chosen for detailed description.

### 1. The Cliff area

Dunite forms a number of sub-parallel lenses trending in a NE–SW direction situated in harzburgite in the Cliff area. Only two of these lenses have chromite concentrations; the largest concentration is at the Cliff quarries, themselves, where five en echelon pits mark the position of five discontinuous chromite-rich lenses (for ease of description numbered 1–5 from SW to NE on Fig. 8), the other occurrence is a small chromite concentration in a dunite lens to the west of Cliff (locality A, Fig. 8). The igneous lithologies are cut by numerous faults, represented by zones of serpentinite, and the main Cliff quarries are situated 300 m from the serpentinized basal thrust contact of the ophiolite. All the various lithologies in the Cliff area were collected (sample sites are shown on Fig. 8) and analysed for Pt, Pd, Au, base metals and As.

Pt and Pd were detected at only two localities in this area, both in the vicinity of chromite concentrations associated with dunite lenses. At the Cliff quarries two very anomalous values of PGE occur. Firstly chromite-rich (up to 30% chrome-spinel) sulphide-bearing dunites located in situ in the northern wall of quarry 2 (locality B, Fig. 8) have extremely anomalous total PGE values of 18.6 ppm Pt + Pd (Table 1), similar material from spoil tips has recorded values over 60 ppm Pt + Pd' (Prichard et al. 1986). Secondly

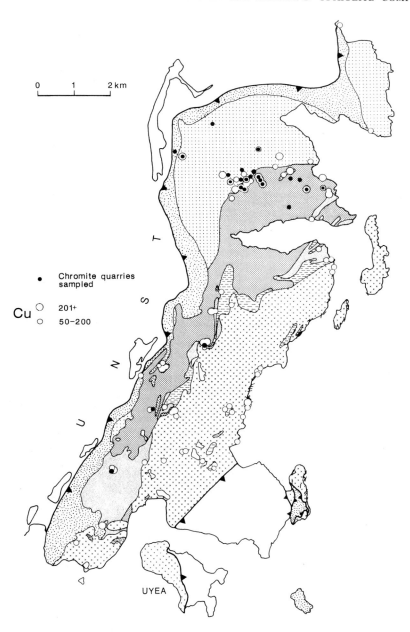

**Fig. 5.** Distribution of Cu in the ophiolite complex on the island of Unst. Note the close relationship between chromite and Cu concentrations with black circles representing chromite quarries often surrounded by open circles representing Cu concentrations. Values in ppm.

chromite-poor sulphide-bearing dunites containing some unaltered olivine, from a spoil tip, (locality C, Fig. 8) contain concentrations of up to 6.4 ppm Pt + Pd (Table 1). Chromitites have low Pt and Pd values (7 ppb) but show slight enrichment in Os, Ir and Ru (Os + Ir + Ru = 255 ppb) (CL2–13, Table 1). Dunite barren of sulphides within the dunite lens at Cliff and a serpentinite in a fault less than 2 m from the extremely PGE-enriched site in quarry 2 are barren of PGE as are the sulphide-poor dunites from other nearby chromite-poor dunite lenses.

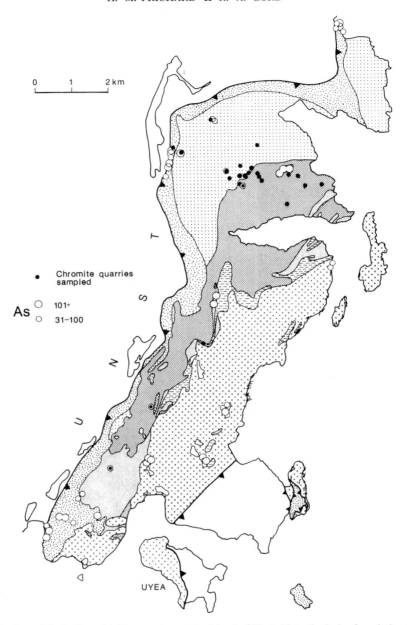

**Fig. 6.** Distribution of As in the ophiolite complex on the island of Unst. Note the lack of a relationship between chromite and As concentrations with black circles representing chromite quarries and open circles representing As concentrations situated along the basal thrust and on internal fault zones. Values in ppm.

Away from the main Cliff chromite quarries, the only Pt and Pd value above the detection limit is in a chromite-rich sample from the small chromite quarry in the altered basal thrust zone to the west of Cliff (locality A, Fig. 8). All the harzburgites, serpentinites, talcs and metasedi-ments (green schists, black schists and meta-limestones) have Pt and Pd values below the detection limit. Pt and Pd were not detected in whole-rock analysis of samples from the basal contact but, although very rare, trace Pt and Rh have been recorded in sulpharsenide minerals

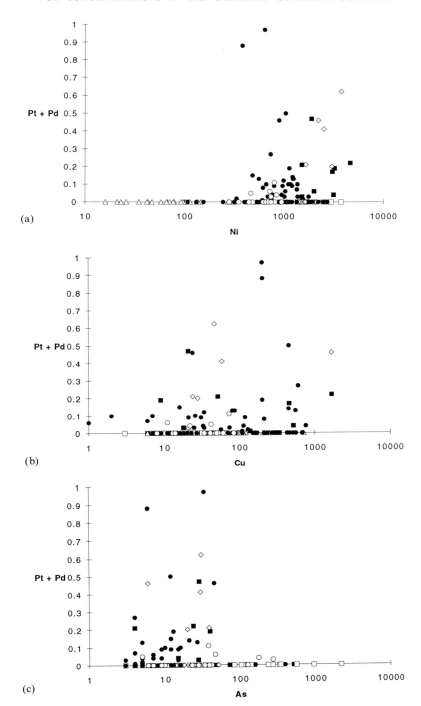

**Fig. 7.** Graphs of (Pt+Pd) vs. (**a**) Ni, (**b**) Cu and (**c**) As, for samples other than in the Cliff area. ■: dunites; □: serpentinites; ◆; harzburgites; ◇: chromitites; ●: wehrlites and pyroxenites; ○: high-level wehrlites and pyroxenites; △: gabbros. Values in ppm.

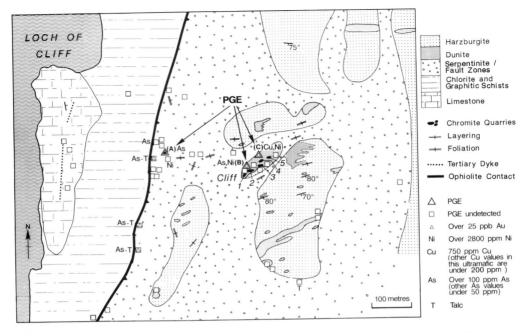

**Fig. 8.** Map of the Cliff area showing the geology and sample sites. Locality (A) is a small chromite quarry west of the main Cliff quarries. Locality (B) is the site in the wall of quarry 2 with the extremely anomalous Pt + Pd values of 18.6 ppm. Locality (C) is a spoil tip just north of quarry 4 from which were collected samples of sulphide-rich, chromite-poor dunite with anomalous PGE values of up to 6.4 ppm total PGE.

from the basal thrust at Cliff (Prichard *et al.* in press). In summary, therefore, the occurrences of significant Pt and Pd concentrations in the Cliff area are not markedly affected by brittle deformation associated with the emplacement faults but are closely associated with primary igneous chromite-rich sulphide-bearing dunite lenses. Sulphides are only found in significant quantities (1–3%) within the dunite lenses (the harzburgites are sulphide barren) and, although now present as a low-temperature alteration assemblage, probably represent original in situ magmatic sulphides. The concentration of sulphides only in the dunite lenses is demonstrated by the pathfinder element Ni and Cu data.

At Cliff, Ni, Cu and Au are good pathfinders for the PGE as elsewhere in the ultramafic sequence. Samples with Ni values of over 3000 ppm are found only within the immediate vicinity of the Cliff quarries and at the small chromite quarry to the west of Cliff. At Cliff, anomalous Ni values occur in the highly anomalous PGE-bearing chromite-rich sulphide-bearing dunites (locality B, Fig. 8) and in PGE-bearing chromite-poor sulphide-bearing dunites (locality C, Fig. 8). The correlation between Pt + Pd and Ni, in the Cliff area, is illustrated in Fig. 9a. Back-

ground Ni values of 2000–2500 occur in the dunites and harzburgites due to the presence of Ni in olivine. Enriched-Ni values do not occur in the local internal faults zones or the basal thrust. In the most serpentinized, silicified and talc-impregnated parts of the basal thrust in this area, Ni depletion has occurred with values of less than 2000 ppm.

In the Cliff area, Cu values of over 30 ppm are only found in samples from the Cliff quarries. The highest Cu value of 750 ppm occurs in the chromite-poor sulphide-rich dunite with anomalous Pt and Pd values (locality C, Fig. 8). The correlation between Cu and Pt + Pd is shown in Fig. 9b. The most anomalous Au values in this area, and from the whole ophiolite, occur at the Cliff quarries in PGE-rich samples. The highest Au value (7.6 ppm) is in a chromite-rich dunite with 10.4 ppm Pt and 64.9 ppm Pd (Lord 1991). Generally at the Cliff quarries, PGE-bearing samples have Au values equal or more than 75 ppb, including the PGE-bearing sample in the small chromite quarry, west of Cliff. In contrast PGE-barren dunites and harzburgites have undetected Au (less than 20 ppb). Values of Au of 75 ppb or more are very good indicators of the presence of PGE in the samples from dunite lenses in the Cliff area (Fig. 9c). In addition, Au is slightly enriched in samples from the basal contact at Cliff with values of 25–50 ppb in the most talc-enriched samples. Au values of more than 25 ppb were not found elsewhere along the basal thrust of the ophiolite on Unst or Fetlar despite extensive sampling (64 samples) (Fig. 9d). Thus, the Au in the talc-rich serpentinites from the basal thrust at Cliff may represent a secondary hydrothermal concentration from the magmatic source in the chromite-bearing dunite lens at Cliff.

At the Cliff quarries, and at the small quarry west of Cliff, high As values (over 100 ppm) often occur in the PGE-bearing samples. Arsenic is also equally enriched along the basal thrust of the ophiolite both at Cliff and elsewhere in samples which are completely barren of PGE. Arsenic is, therefore, a poor pathfinder (Fig. 9e), but within the Cliff quarries high As is associated with the highest PGE values (Lord 1991; Lord & Prichard 1991).

Massive chromitite at the Cliff quarries is only present on the surface in the spoil tips and in order to determine the exact relationship between PGE-rich lithologies, chromitites and dunites forming the lenses in harzburgite, 3 holes were drilled at 45° from north of the quarries, in a southerly direction, below quarries 1 (hole CL 0, 25 m), 2 (hole CL 1, 50 m) and 3 & 4 (hole CL 2, 50 m) (Fig. 8). CL 0 traversed a serpentinized fault. CL1 encountered dunite and intersected two thin (1 cm and 2.5 cm) layers of chromitite within dunite immediately below quarry 1, before traversing out of the dunite into harzburgite. CL2 traversed harzburgite with zones of dunite beneath quarries 3 and 4 and intersected a 1 cm chromitite layer below quarry 4 and a 10 cm width of chromitite under quarry 3. The dunites from both CL1 and CL2 contained sparse sulphides in the vicinity of the chromitite layers. Cores were analysed for PGE and the highest Pt and Pd values are 155 and 72 ppb respectively, associated with a chromitite layer in CL1. Anomalous Ni values of approximately 3000 ppm occur only in dunites on either side of the 10 cm layer of chromitite in CL2 but these are not associated with particularly anomalous values of PGE, Cu or As (Table 1). Cu values are generally low, less than 30 ppm, except for serpentinized samples veined by native Cu. Arsenic values in the cores are also low, nearly all less than 30 ppm, with the highest value of 91 ppm in a harzburgite with much serpentine veining. Analyses of As, noble and base metals in the drill core are low especially compared with the PGE-rich samples from quarry 2.

## 2. Mid-Unst

In order to understand the distribution of the PGE in mid-Unst the area was remapped using aerial photographs (Figs 10a and b, locations shown on Fig. 1). This revealed abundant faulting of syn- or post-emplacement origin which divides the ophiolite into tectonic blocks. Within a block, igneous layering, defined by varying proportions of clinopyroxene, olivine and to a lesser extent chrome-spinel, shows a consistent orientation which is different to the orientation of the layering in adjacent blocks. Usually this is approximately parallel to the strike of the igneous lithologies as illustrated by chromite layers approximately parallel to the dunite/harzburgite junction north of Balta Sound (Gass et al. 1982; Prichard & Neary 1982; Lord 1991). In mid-Unst a pseudostratigraphy strikes north–south with dunites to the west and gabbros to the east. Adjacent different lithologies are often in different blocks separated by faults. The rotation of the blocks has been so extreme that the layering is, in places, east–west, striking at right angles to the pseudostratigraphy. The new mapping made it possible to locate the stratigraphic position of a particular lithology. This enabled recognition of continuous igneous stratigraphic sequences of dunite through wehrlite and pyroxenites to gabbro, within a fault block, so that PGE-bearing samples could be located exactly within the stratigraphy.

Anomalous Pt and Pd values occur in a number of lithologies but systematically those which are both Cr-rich and sulphide-bearing. PGE-rich sulphide-bearing chromite-rich dunites from the disused chromite quarries in cumulate dunite in mid-Unst may have Pt + Pd values of c. 500 ppb. Sulphide-bearing dunites not associated with surface exposure of chromite-rich lithologies have lower Pt + Pd values. Sulphide-bearing wehrlites and pyroxenites commonly have anomalous Pt + Pd levels of between 100–200 ppb. Rarely discontinuous chromitite layers occur near the base of the lowest wehrlites and they are usually associated with disseminated sulphides. Pt and Pd values tend to be higher in these wehrlites as illustrated by a value of Pt 240 and Pd 400 ppb in a sulphide-bearing wehrlite adjacent to a previously unknown small chromite layer. This is located at the transition from dunite to wehrlite in a block where the complete stratigraphic sequence from dunite to gabbro is preserved (Fig. 10b, section X–Y). In mid-Unst, as elsewhere in the ophiolite complex, the PGE are concentrated with specific igneous lithologies rather than in fault zones.

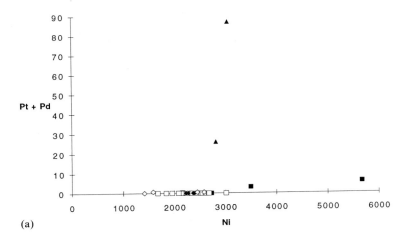

(a)

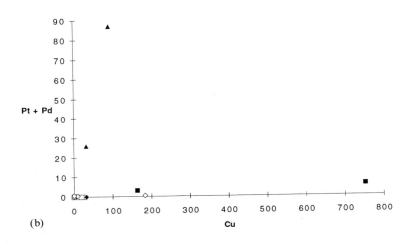

(b)

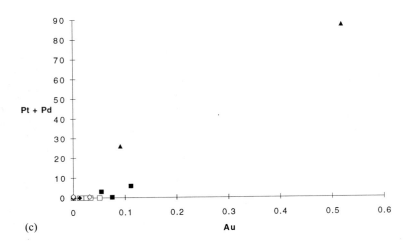

(c)

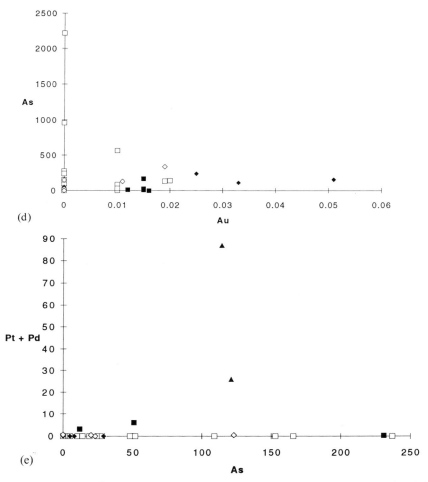

**Fig. 9.** Graphs of pathfinder elements in the Cliff area. (**a**) Ni vs. (Pt + Pd); (**b**) Cu vs. (Pt + Pd); (**c**) Au vs. (Pt + Pd); (**e**) As vs. (Pt + Pd). ■: dunites; □: serpentinites; ◆: harzburgites; ◇: chromitites; ▲: sulphide-bearing chromite-rich dunites. (**d**) Comparison of Au vs. As for – ■: talc-poor serpentinites form Cliff; □: talc-poor serpentinites from elsewhere; ◆: talc-rich serpentinites from Cliff; and ◇: talc-rich serpentinites from elsewhere. Values in ppm.

## 6 PGE patterns

The relative proportions of PGE can be shown on a chondrite-normalized diagram with values for the PGE plotted in melting point order from high to low, that is Os, Ir, Ru, Rh, Pt and Pd (Naldrett *et al.* 1979). Chondrite-normalized Os, Ir, and Ru enrichment over Rh, Pt and Pd gives a negative slope pattern whereas Rh, Pt and Pd enrichment gives a positive slope pattern. In Shetland, both types of pattern were known to exist; negative slope patterns were first described at Harold's Grave and positive slope patterns were described from Cliff (Prichard *et al.* 1986). Further analysis, described here, has shown that

the relative abundances of PGE vary according to lithology (Table 1). Negative slope patterns only occur in very chromite-rich samples (Fig. 11a), but these are present at all levels in the ultramafic part of the complex, from low-level dunite lenses in harzburgite such as at Cliff to high-level chromitite within the wehrlite/pyroxenite sequence (Fig. 1a).

Positive slope patterns are widespread throughout the PGE-bearing part of the ophiolite sequence occurring in chromite-rich sulphide-bearing dunites in dunite lenses such as at Cliff (Figs 11b and c), in the overlying dunite unit (Fig. 11c), in sulphide-bearing wehrlites and

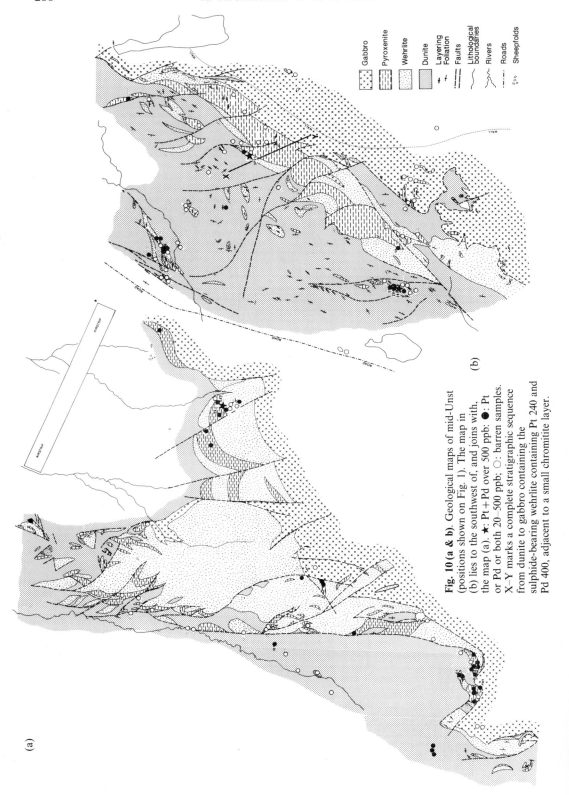

**Fig. 10 (a & b).** Geological maps of mid-Unst (positions shown on Fig. 1). The map in (b) lies to the southwest of, and joins with, the map (a). ★: Pt + Pd over 500 ppb: ●: Pt or Pd or both 20–500 ppb; ○: barren samples. X–Y marks a complete stratigraphic sequence from dunite to gabbro containing the sulphide-bearing wehrlite containing Pt 240 and Pd 400, adjacent to a small chromitite layer.

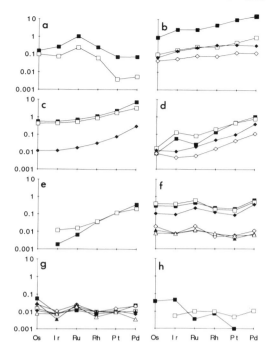

**Fig. 11.** Chondrite-normalized graphs showing the typical patterns for the different lithologies in the Shetland ophiolite complex. Samples, numbers given in brackets, are described in Table 1. **(a)** Chromitites, high-level sample from wehrlite ■ (713) and a low-level sample from Cliff □ (CL2–13); **(b)** chromite-rich (up to 30% chrome-spinel) sulphide-bearing dunites from Cliff, ■ MR4, □ MR292, ◆ MR293, and from Cliff west ◇ MR128; **(c)** sulphide-bearing chromite-poor dunites, ■ MR11 and □ MR12 from Cliff and ◆ MR187 from cumulate dunite; **(d)** sulphide-bearing pyroxenites and wehrlites, ■ NA25, □ SA2, ◆ MR65, ◇ MR63; **(e)** high-level wehrlites and pyroxenites, ■MR169 and □ MR17; **(f)** sulphide-bearing chromite-rich (up to 30% chrome-spinel) dunites associated with chromite quarries in mid-Unst, ■ MR283 and □ MR57 and ◆ MR284 and barren dunites from Cliff, ◇ CL1–14 and ▲ MR2 and a serpentinite from Cliff △ MR3; **(g)** barren harzburgites, ■ MR1, □ CL1–04, ◆ CL1–06, ◇ CL2–10, ▲ CL2–11 and △ CL1–17; **(h)** sheared rocks from mid-Unst, a dunite ■ MR56 and a pyroxenite □ HW1. Points not plotted have values below the detection limit.

pyroxenites within the ultramafic part of the sequence (Fig. 11d) and in the high-level ultramafic lens within the gabbro (Fig. 11e). At Cliff, the chromite-rich sulphide-bearing dunites have the most enriched positive chondrite-normalized pattern (Fig. 11b) and a positive slope pattern also characterizes the sulphide-bearing dunites,

although this pattern has a slightly concave-upwards shape (Fig. 11c). Sulphide-bearing chromite-rich dunites from mid-Unst have patterns with peaks at Ru and Pd (Fig. 11f) probably representing a combination of negative slope patterns (Fig. 11a) and positive slope patterns (Fig. 11b). The mantle harzburgites (Fig. 11g), sulphide-barren dunites (Fig. 11f) and sheared lithologies (Fig. 11h) have rather flat patterns in contrast to the samples containing more anomalous PGE concentrations.

## PGE in ophiolite and layered complexes

The sequence of lithologies which comprise an ophiolite complex are thought to have been formed at an oceanic spreading centre (Gass 1980). Dunite lenses in mantle harzburgite represent crystal precipitates remaining after the resulting basaltic melt has risen to feed the overlying magma chamber, preserved as dunite, wehrlite and pyroxenite ultramafic magmatic cumulates overlain by gabbro. Chromite-rich lithologies are thought to represent early, high-temperature, crystal cumulates (Neary & Brown 1979; Lago et al. 1982; Roberts 1988) associated with early dunite cumulates and this has been suggested for the Shetland chromitites (Prichard & Neary 1982). Os, Ir and Ru are the higher melting point PGE and often occur as PGM within chromitite as laurite and alloys (Constantinides et al. 1980; Prichard et al. 1981; Talkington et al. 1984; Stockman & Hlava 1984; Augé 1985, 1986, 1988; Prichard & Neary 1991). These PGE are very compatible, crystallizing very early from the melt, commonly prior to chromite (Barnes et al. 1985). In contrast, Pt and Pd are often associated with sulphides in the ultramafic cumulates of ophiolite complexes (Oshin & Crocket 1986; Orberger et al. 1988) and in gabbros (Prichard & Lord 1990; Lachize et al. 1991). Exceptions occur where Pt, Fe alloys are not in association with sulphides (Ohnenstetter et al. 1991). In Shetland, as in other ophiolite complexes, Os, Ir and Ru are concentrated in chromite-rich lithologies (30% or more chrome-spinel). Pt and Pd are concentrated in ultramafic lithologies, often close to chromite-rich lithologies. They are chalcophile and usually have associated anomalous base metal concentrations, represented mineralogically by Ni and Cu sulphides. Os, Ir and Ru crystallize earlier than the Rh, Pt and Pd as shown by the platinum-group mineralogy where Os, Ir and Ru minerals occur within the chromite whereas Rh, Pt and Pd occur with sulphides in the interstitial matrix to the chromite (Prichard & Tarkian 1988; Prichard et al. in press).

Similar situations to those described for ophiolite complexes are commonly described from layered complexes. Ru, sometimes Os- and Ir-bearing, forms laurites enclosed within chromite in the Bushveld (von Gruenewaldt *et al.* 1986) and geochemical evidence suggests that Os, Ir and Ru are concentrated in the lower earlier ultramafic parts of layered complexes (Keays & Campbell 1981; Davies & Tradoux 1985). Pt and Pd are known to be associated with sulphides in a number of types of complex (Naldrett & Duke 1980; Naldrett 1981; Campbell & Barnes 1984), for example in layered complexes (Wagner 1929; Kinloch 1982; McLaren & De Villiers 1982; Gain 1985; Barnes *et al.* 1988) and in nickel sulphide deposits (Chyi & Crocket 1976; Ross & Keays 1979). The magmatic associations of the PGE with chromite and sulphides as observed in the Shetland ophiolite complex are similar to those described from other types of complex. From this it can be inferred that the magmatic processes which concentrate the PGE in ophiolite complexes are similar to those operating in other types of mafic and ultramafic complexes including layered complexes. If this is the case it follows that positive and negative chondrite-normalized patterns will be present in both ophiolite and layered complexes. In ophiolite complexes, however, regular, continuous and extensive PGE-enriched layers are absent due to the discontinuous nature of the igneous layering in ophiolite complexes.

In the Shetland ophiolite complex there is a close spatial association of Pt and Pd with chromite both in dunite lenses in harzburgite and in the overlying dunites, wehrlites and pyroxenites. These chromite concentrations are most abundant in the thickest and best preserved part of the ophiolite complex north of Balta Sound. Significant Pt and Pd concentrations are present in mid- and southern Unst, in similar lithologies to those in the north, but occurrences are less common corresponding to less chromite in this southern area. The total lack of any detected Pt or Pd concentrations on Fetlar may be accounted for by the absence of suitable host lithologies including the virtual lack of chromitite.

## Noble and base metal associations

The maps showing the distribution of PGE, Ni, Cu and Au, especially in relation to the chromite quarries indicate a close relationship between these elements. This is thought to have been produced by magmatic processes whereby all these elements crystallized from the melt approximately together. However, the lack of exact correlation between these elements and the PGE (Figs 7a and b) is likely to be the result of two processes:

1. PGE may have crystallized from the melt at a slightly different, perhaps earlier, time than that of Ni and Cu, resulting in an igneous separation of these elements within the stratigraphic sequence. This is now a well-recognized phenomenon in PGE-bearing layered sequences, resulting in 'out of sequence profiles' (Prendergast 1991; Hoatson & Keays 1989) where Pt and Pd crystallize from the magma just prior to Ni and Cu sulphides and therefore are located lower in the stratigraphic sequence.

2. The effects of alteration may cause the noble and base metals to be remobilized at slightly different rates to each other and so, even if they were magmatically concentrated all together in one site, alteration is likely to have caused separation of these elements. There is, indeed, clear evidence of the mobility of base metals during alteration. Cu is obviously mobile as it can be observed commonly as native copper in secondary serpentinized veinlets cross-cutting the ultramafic sequence. Ni is also mobile as shown by Ni depletion along the intensely altered basal thrust at Cliff (Table 1). Evidence of Au mobility is demonstrated by low-grade Au values in the basal thrust zone in the Cliff area suggesting that the Au is being mobilized from its primary source and reconcentrated within the shear zone. Such associations of Au concentrations in serpentinites with arsenides, including cobalt, are commonly described as listwaenites (Buisson & Leblanc 1986).

Experimental evidence suggests that Pt and Pd are less mobile than base metals and Au (Crerar & Barnes 1976). This is confirmed in Shetland where, in contrast to Ni, Cu and Au, PGE appear to be less mobile because: (i) there is a consistent primary igneous stratigraphic association of the PGE with chromite layers and adjacent sulphides; (ii) unlike Au, significant reconcentrations of PGE have not been located in the altered shear zones of the ophiolite suggesting that mobilization and reconcentration is not occurring to any great extent for the PGE. Pd is thought to be more mobile than Pt during weathering processes (Fuchs & Rose 1974). This is also the case in Shetland where Pt/Pd ratios in soil samples were found to be higher than those in the underlying rock (Prichard *et al.* 1993). The variability of Pt/Pd ratios in the rocks (Fig. 2) could be primary but is more likely to be due to greater Pd mobility during alteration.

In detail, these two processes, that is primary igneous concentration and secondary alteration, result in spatial separation of the highest noble and base metal values and in a local, extremely complicated, pathfinder and PGE distribution pattern.

## PGE concentrations at Cliff

The processes producing the extremely enriched PGE values at Cliff are still debatable. The chromite-rich dunite lens hosting the PGE represents a small trapped magma body which did not reach the overlying magma chamber; such chromite-rich dunite lenses are common in the mantle harzburgite sequences of ophiolite complexes. The initial low ppm concentrations of the PGE are thought to be the result of magmatic processes because the PGE are concentrated within the magmatic dunite lens and have a textural magmatic relationship: Pt and Pd are enriched in sulphide-bearing dunites adjacent to chromitite layers, both in the drill core and in spoil tip samples. This is similar to the lithological position of the Pt and Pd concentrations in the overlying ultramafic cumulates. PGE are not concentrated in the surrounding harzburgite or serpentinized fault zones associated with the nearby basal thrust.

The distribution of As along the basal thrust and in internal fault zones (Fig. 5) indicates that it was introduced late, during or post emplacement of the ophiolite. The Cliff quarries are situated near the basal thrust contact of the ophiolite and the highly anomalous PGE-bearing samples have been impregnated by As. This is known to immobilize Pt and Pd (Mountain & Wood 1988) and the extremely high PGE grades at Cliff may be the result of local reconcentration of the PGE within the dunite lens (Lord 1991; Lord & Prichard 1991; Lord *et al.* 1992) with immobilization of the PGE on contact with As introduced by late hydrothermal syn- or post-emplacement fluids.

So at Cliff the lithological position of the low ppm PGE concentrations is in sulphide-bearing dunites adjacent to chromite-rich layers. Analysis of the drill core, however, shows that the extremely anomalous PGE grades (60 ppm Pt + Pd) are not continuous along the length of the chromitite layers (Table 1, CL2-12 and 14) and are not present at depth in any of the quarries (1–4) sampled by the drilling. In fact, these extremely anomalous PGE-bearing, As-rich, chromite-rich sulphide-bearing dunite samples are probably restricted to surface outcrop in

quarry 2 and its associated spoil tips. The lack of high As, Pt or Pd values in igneous associations of sulphides adjacent to chromite layers, in the drill core samples, supports the idea that the extremely high Pt and Pd concentrations at Cliff are not magmatic in origin but are the result of local remobilization of Pt and Pd from their lower concentration magmatic source.

## Conclusions

PGE occur in the Shetland ophiolite in (1) chromite-rich dunites and in the associated chromite-poor sulphide-bearing dunites in dunite lenses in harzburgite; (2) sulphide-bearing dunites associated with chromitite layers in the cumulate dunite overlying the harzburgite; (3) sulphide-bearing pyroxenites and wehrlites, not necessarily with chromite, in the upper part of the ultramafic sequence; (4) high-level ultramafic lenses within gabbro. Anomalous Pt and Pd values occur together and can be related to specific igneous lithologies indicating concentration by magmatic processes. The association of Ni, Cu and Au with the PGE in the less altered ultramafic part of the sequence suggests that the noble metals behaved in a chalcophile manner during concentration and segregation from the magma. The occurrence of PGE only with the chromite-rich dunite lenses in the Cliff area indicates an original magmatic concentration but evidence from drill core samples from beneath the Cliff quarries supports the idea that the extremely anomalous PGE values are the result of local reconcentration.

In addition to the negative slope chondrite-normalized patterns, characteristic of ophiolite complexes, positive slope chondrite normalized patterns are common within the ultramafic part of the Shetland ophiolite complex. Both patterns are now known to be present in other ophiolite complexes, as in layered complexes, suggesting that there are similarities in the processes of concentration of the PGE in all these complexes.

We have great admiration for the perceptive vision and constant encouragement freely given to us by Professor Ian Gass. We are also very grateful to MIRO (Mineral Industry Research Organisation) and the sponsors including RTZ who made this extensive study financially possible and to the Royal Society for funding a fellowship for Dr H. M. Prichard and the Open University for funding Dr R. A. Lord for a PhD studentship. We much appreciate the helpful and detailed comments from Dr C. J. Morrissey and two reviewers, Dr Steve Roberts and Dr Thierry Augé. We would like to thank 4 analytical companies for PGE and Au analysis and in all cases were impressed by the analysts' concern over the accuracy of their results. So our thanks go to Ron Hanson and Geoff Ibbs of Caleb Brett laboratories Ltd, St Helens, Merseyside; John Smith of Anamet, Avonmouth, and T. K. Chan of Analytical Services and then of Genalysis, Western Australia. At the Open University we would like to thank John Watson for much help with the XRF analyses and sample collection and John Taylor for drawing the maps.

# References

AGIORGITIS, G. & WOLF, R. 1978. Aspects of osmium, iridium and ruthenium contents in some Greek chromites. *Chemical Geology*, **23**, 267–272.

AUGÉ, T. 1985. Platinum-group mineral inclusions in ophiolitic chromitite from the Vourinos complex, Greece. *Canadian Mineralogist*, **23**, 163–171.

—— 1986. Platinum-group mineral inclusions in ophiolitic chromitites from the Oman ophiolite. *Bulletin de minéralogie*, **109**, 301–304.

—— 1988. Platinum-group minerals in the Tiebaghi and Vourinos ophiolitic complexes: genetic implications. *Canadian Mineralogist*, **26**, 177–192.

BACUTA, G. C. Jr., LIPIN, B. R., GIBBS, A. K. & KAY, R. W. 1988. Platinum-group element abundance in chromite deposits of the Acoje ophiolite block, Zambales ophiolite complex, Philippines. *In*: PRICHARD, H. M., POTTS, P. J., BOWLES, J. F. W. & CRIBB, S. J. (eds) *Geo-platinum 87*. Elsevier, London, 381–382.

BARNES, S-J., BOYD, R., KORNELIUSSEN, A., NILSSON, L-P., OFTEN, M., PEDERSEN, R. B. & ROBINS, B. 1988. The use of mantle normalisation and metal ratios in discrimination between the effects of partial melting, crystal fractionation, and sulphide segregation on platinum-group elements, gold, nickel, and copper: examples from Norway. *In*: PRICHARD, H. M., POTTS, P. J., BOWLES, J. F. W., & CRIBB, S. J. (eds) *Geo-Platinum 87*. Elsevier Applied Science, London, 113–143.

——, NALDRETT, A. J. & GORTON, M. P. 1985. The origin of the fractionation of Pt group elements in terrestrial magmas. *Chemical Geology* **53** (3–4), 303–323.

BUISSON, G. & LEBLANC, M. 1986. Gold-bearing list-waenites (carbonatised ultramafic rocks) from ophiolite complexes. *In*: GALLAGHER, M. J., IXER, R. A., NEARY, C. R. & PRICHARD, H. M. (eds) *Metallogenesis of basic and ultrabasic rocks*. Institute of Mining and Metallurgy Symposium volume, Edinburgh, 121–131.

CAMPBELL, I. H. & BARNES, S. J. 1984. A model for the geochemistry of the platinum-group elements in magmatic sulphide deposits. *Canadian Mineralogist*, **22**, 151–160.

CHYI, L. L. & CROCKET, J. H. 1976. Platinum-partition of platinum, palladium, iridium and gold among coexisting minerals from the deep ore zone Strathcona mine, Sudbury, Ontario. *Economic Geology*, **71**, 1196–1205.

CONSTANTINIDES, C. C., KINGSTON, G. A. & FISHER, P. C. 1980. The occurrence of platinum-group minerals in the chromitites of the Kokkinorotsos chrome mine, Cyprus. *In*: PANAYIOTOU, A. (ed.) *Ophiolites: proceedings of the international ophiolite symposium*. Cyprus Geological Survey Department, Nicosia, 93–101.

CORRIVAUX, L. & LAFLAMME, J. H. G. 1990. Minéralogie des éléments du groupe du platine dans les chromitites de l'ophiolite de Thetford mines Québec. *Canadian Mineralogist*, **28**, 579–595.

CRERAR, D. A. & BARNES, H. L. 1976. Solubilities of chalcopyrite and chalcocite assemblages in hydrothermal solution at 200° to 350°C. Ore solution chemistry volume. *Economic Geology*, **71**, 772–794.

DAVIES, G. & TRADOUX, M. 1985. The platinum group element and gold contents of the marginal rocks and sills of the Bushveld complex. *Economic Geology*, **80**, 838–848.

EDWARDS, S. J. 1990. Harzburgites and refractory melts in the Lewis Hills massif, Bay of Islands ophiolite complex: the base metals and precious metals story. *Canadian Mineralogist*, **28**, 537–552.

FLINN, D. 1985. The Caledonites of Shetland. *In*: GEE, D. G. & STURT, B. A. (eds) *The Caledonide Orogen – Scandinavia and related areas*. Wiley, New York, **2**, 1159–1172.

FUCHS, W. A. & ROSE, A. W. 1974. The geochemical behaviour of platinum and palladium in the weathering cycle in the Stillwater complex, Montana. *Economic Geology*, **69**, 332–346.

GAIN, S. B. 1985. The geologic setting of the platiniferous UG-2 chromitite layer on the farm Maandagshoek, eastern Bushveld complex. *Economic Geology*, **80**, 925–943.

GASS, I. G. 1980. The Troodos massif; its role in the unravelling of the ophiolite problem and its significance in the understanding of constructive plate margin processes. *In*: PANAYIOTOU, A. (ed.) *Ophiolites: proceedings of the international ophiolite symposium*. Cyprus Geological Survey Department, Nicosia, 23–35.

——, NEARY, C. R., PRICHARD, H. M. & BARTHOLOMEW, I. D. 1982. *The chromite of the Shetland ophiolite: a reappraisal in the light of new theory and techniques*. Report for the EEC CREST raw materials programme.

VON GRUENEWALDT, G., HATTON, C. J., MERKLE, R. K. W. & GAIN, S. B. 1986. Platinum-group element–chromite associations in the Bushveld complex. *Economic Geology*, **81**, 1067–1079.

GUNN, A. G. 1989. Drainage and over burden geochemistry in exploration for platinum-group element mineralisation in the Unst ophiolite, Shetland, UK. *Journal of Geochemical Exploration*, **31**, 209–236.

——, LEAKE, R. C., STYLES, M. T. & BATESON, J. H. 1985. *Platinum-group element mineralisation in the Unst ophiolite, Shetland*. Mineral Reconnaissance Programme Report, British Geological Survey, 85/73.

HITCHEN, C. S. 1929. Unst and its chromite deposits. *Mining Magazine*, **40**, 18–24.

HOATSON, D. M. & KEAYS, R. R. 1989. Formation of platiniferous sulfide horizons by crystal fractionation and magma mixing in the Munni Munni layered intrusion, west Pilbara block, western Australia. *Economic Geology*, **84**, 1775–1804.

KEAYS, R. R. & CAMPBELL, I. H. 1981. Precious metals in the Jimberlana intrusion, western Australia. Implications for the genesis of platiniferous ores in layered intrusions. *Economic Geology*, **76**, 1118–1141.

KINLOCH, E. D. 1982. Regional trends in the platinum-group mineralogy of the critical zone of the Bushveld complex, South Africa. *Economic Geology*, **77**, 1328–1347.

LACHIZE, M., LORAND, J. P. & JUTEAU, T. 1991. Cu–Ni–PGE magmatic sulfide ores and their host layered gabbros in the Haymiliyah fossil magma chamber (Haylayn block, Semail ophiolite nappe, Oman). *In*: PETERS, T. J., NICOLAS, A. & COLEMAN, R. G. (eds) *Ophiolite Genesis and Evolution of the oceanic lithosphere.* Proceedings of the ophiolite conference held in Muscat, Oman. Kluwer Academic Publishers, 209–229.

LAGO, B. L., RABINOWICZ, M. & NICOLAS, A. 1982. Podiform chromite ore bodies: a genetic model. *Journal of Petrology*, **23**, 103–126.

LORD, R. A. 1991. *Platinum-group element mineralisation in the Shetland ophiolite complex*. PhD thesis, Open University, Milton Keynes.

—— & PRICHARD, H. M. 1989*a*. An igneous source for gold in the Shetland ophiolite. Extended abstract for IMM commodity meeting on gold. *Institute of Mining and Metallurgy*, **98**, B44–46.

—— & —— 1989*b*. Magmatic fractionation of PGE in the Shetland ophiolite complex. Abstract for the 5th International Platinum Symposium in Helsinki, August 1989. *Bulletin of the Geological Society of Finland*, **61**, 38.

—— & —— 1991. Magmatic distribution and fractionation of platinum-group elements in the Shetland ophiolite complex. *In*: BARNES, S.-J. (ed.) *IAGOD Commission on ore deposits in mafic and ultramafic rocks, 6th International Platinum Symposium programme and abstracts.* Astral Press, Wembly, W.A, 32–33.

——, —— & NEARY, C. R. 1992. The distribution of platinum-group elements in the Shetland ophiolite complex: evidence for localised hydrothermal remobilisation and upgrading of an original magmatic concentration at the Cliff chromite quarry. *In*: FOSTER, R. P. (ed.) *Mineral deposit modelling in relation to crustal reservoirs of ore-forming elements.* Abstract volume Institute of Mining and Metallurgy, London.

MCLAREN, C. H. & DE VILLIERS, J. P. R. 1982. The platinum-group chemistry and mineralogy of the UG-2 chromitite layer of the Bushveld complex. *Economic Geology*, **77**, 1348–1366.

MOUNTAIN, B. W. & WOOD, S. A. 1988. Solubility and transport of the platinum-group elements in hydrothermal solutions: thermodynamic and physical chemical constraints. *In*: PRICHARD, H. M., POTTS, P. J., BOWLES, J. F. W. & CRIBB, S. J. (eds) *Geo-Platinum 87*. Elsevier Applied Science, London, 57–82.

NALDRETT, A. J. 1981. Nickel sulfide deposits: classification, composition and genesis. *Economic Geo-logy*, **75**, 628–655.

—— & DUKE, J. M. 1980. Pt metals in magmatic sulfide ores; the occurrence of these metals is discussed in relation to the formation and importance of these ores. *Science*, **208**, 1417–1424.

——, HOFFMAN, E. L., GREEN, A. H., CHOU, C. L., NALDRETT, S. R. & ALCOCK, R. A. 1979. The composition of Ni sulfide ores with particular reference to their content of PGE and Au. *Canadian Mineralogist*, **17**, 403–415.

NEARY, C. R. & BROWN, M. A. 1979. Chromites from the Al Ays complex, Saudi Arabia and the Semail complex, Oman: Jeddah, Saudi Arabia, King Abdulaziz University. *Institute Applied Geology*, **3**, 193–205.

——, PRICHARD, H. M. & POTTS, P. J. 1984. Chromite, platinoids, gold and moly in the Shetlands. *Mining Magazine*, 559–560.

OHNENSTETTER, M., KARAJ, N., NEZIRAJ, A., JOHAN, Z. & CINA, A. 1991. Le potentiel platinifere des ophiolites: minéralisations en éléments du groupe du platine (PGE) dans les massifs de Tropoja et Bulquiza, Albanie. *Comptes Rendus de l'Academie des Sciences*, Paris, **313**, Série II, 201–208.

ORBERGER, B., FREDRICH, G. & WOERMANN, E. 1988. Platinum-group element mineralisation in the ultramafic sequence of the Acoje ophiolite block, Zambales, Philippines. *In*: PRICHARD, H. M., POTTS, P. J., BOWLES, J. F. W. & CRIBB, S. J. (eds) *Geo-Platinum 87*. Elsevier Applied Science, London, 361–380.

OSHIN, I. O. & CROCKET, J. H. 1986. Noble metals in the Thetford Mines ophiolites, Quebec, Canada. II. Distribution of gold, silver, iridium, platinum and palladium in the Lac de l'Est volcano-sedimentary section. *Economic Geology*, **81**, 931–945.

PAGE, N. J, CASSARD, D. & HAFFTY, J. 1982*a*. Palladium, platinum, rhodium, ruthenium, and iridium in chromitites from the Massif du Sud and Tiebaghi Massif, New Caledonia. *Economic Geology*, **77**, 1571–1577.

——, ENGIN, T., SINGER, D. A. & HAFFTY, J. 1984. Distribution of platinum-group elements in the Bati Kef chromite deposit, Guleman-Elazig area, eastern Turkey. *Economic Geology*, **79**, 177–184.

——, PALLISTER, J. S., BROWN, M. A., SMEWING, J. D. & HAFFTY, J. 1982*b*. Palladium, platinum, rhodium, ruthenium, and iridium in chromite-rich rocks from the Samail ophiolite, Oman. *Canadian Mineralogist*, **20**, 537–548.

—— & TALKINGTON, R. W. 1984. Palladium, platinum, rhodium, ruthenium, and iridium in peridotites and chromites from ophiolite complexes in Newfoundland. *Canadian Mineralogist*, **22**, 137–149.

PEDERSEN, R. B., JOHANNESEN, G. M. & BOYD, R. 1993. Stratiform PGE mineralisations in the ultramafic cumulates of the Leka ophiolite complex, central Norway. *Economic Geology*, **88**, 782–803.

PRENDERGAST, M. D. 1991. The Wedza-Mimosa platinum deposit, Great Dyke Zimbabwe: layering and stratiform PGE mineralisation in a narrow mafic magma chamber. *Geological Magazine*, **128**, 235–249.

PRICHARD, H. M. 1985. The Shetland Ophiolite. *In*: GEE, D. G. & STURT, B. A. (eds) *The Caledonide Orogen – Scandinavia and related areas*. Wiley, New York, **2**, 1173–1184.

—— IXER, R. A., LORD, R. A., MAYNARD, J. & WILLIAMS, N. In press. Platinum-group mineral assemblages in silicate lithologies and chromite-rich rocks within the Shetland ophiolite sequence. *Canadian Mineralogist*.

—— & LORD, R. A. 1988. The Shetland ophiolite: Evidence for a supra-subduction zone origin and implications for PGE mineralisation. *In*: BOISSONNAS J. & OMENETTO, P. (eds) *Mineral Deposits in the European Community*, Springer Verlag, 289–302.

—— & —— 1989. Magmatic and secondary PGM in the Shetland ophiolite complex. Abstract for the 5th International Platinum Symposium in Helsinki, August 1989. *Bulletin Geological Society Finland*, **61**, 39.

—— & —— 1990*a*. Platinum and palladium in the Troodos ophiolite complex, Cyprus. *Canadian Mineralogist*, **28**, 607–617.

—— & —— 1990*b*. *Platinum mineralisation in the Shetland ophiolite complex*. Final report for the Minerals Industry Research Organisation Contract RC 48.

——, ——, MAYNARD, J. & IXER, R. A. 1993. Secondary remobilization of PGE in the Shetland ophiolite complex. *Terra nova*, **5**, 43.

—— & NEARY, C. R. 1981. Chromite in the Shetland Islands ophiolite complex. *In: An international symposium on metallogeny of mafic and ultramafic complexes*. UNESCO Project 169, Athens, **3**, 343–360.

—— & —— 1982. Some observations on the Chromite in the Shetland Ophiolite complex. *Ofioliti*, **2/3**, 455–466.

—— & —— 1991. PGM in the chromitites of the Al 'Ays complex, Saudi Arabia. *In*: BARNES, S.-J. (ed.) *IAGOD Commission – ore deposits in mafic and ultramafic rocks, 6th International Platinum Symposium programme*. Astral Press, Wembly, W.A., 45.

——, —— & LORD, R. A. 1992. New evidence of platinum-group element concentrations in the Al 'Ays ophiolite complex, Saudi Arabia: Significance for prediction in other ophiolite complexes. *In*: FOSTER, R. P. (ed.) *Mineral deposit modelling in relation to crustal reservoirs of ore-forming elements*. Abstract volume Institute of Mining and Metallurgy, London.

——, —— & POTTS, P. J. 1984. Platinum and gold in the Shetland ophiolite. *Mining Journal*, **303** (7772), 77.

——, —— & —— 1986. Platinum-group minerals in the Shetland ophiolite complex. *In*: GALLAGHER, M. J., IXER, R. A., NEARY, C. R. & PRICHARD, H. M. (eds) *Metallogenesis of basic and ultrabasic rocks*. Institute of Mining and Metallurgy Symposium volume, Edinburgh, 395–414.

——, POTTS, P. J. & NEARY, C. R. 1981. Platinum group minerals in the Shetland ophiolite complex. *Institute of Mining and Metallurgy Transactions*, **90**, B186–B188.

——, ——, ——, LORD, R. A. & WARD, G. R. 1987. *Development of techniques for the determination of the PGE in ultramafic rock complexes of potential economic significance: mineralogical studies*. Report for the EEC. Published by the EEC 1989.

—— & TARKIAN, M. 1988. Pt and Pd minerals from two PGE-rich localities in the Shetland ophiolite complexes. *Canadian Mineralogist*, **26**, 979–990.

ROBERTS, S. 1988. Ophiolitic chromitite formation: a marginal basin phenomenon. *Economic Geology*, **83**, 1034–1036.

ROSS, J. R. & KEAYS, R. R. 1979. Precious metals in volcanic type nickel sulphide deposits in Western Australia, I. Relationship with the composition of the ores and their host rocks. *Canadian Mineralogist*, **17**, 417–435.

STOCKMAN, H. W. & HLAVA, P. F. 1984. Platinum-Group Minerals in alpine chromitites from southwestern Oregon. *Economic Geology*, **79**, 491–508.

TALKINGTON, R. W., WATKINSON, D. H., WHITTAKER, P. J. & JONES, P. C. 1984. PGM and other solid inclusions in chromite of ophiolitic complexes: occurrence and petrological significance. *Tscher-maks Mineralogische und Petrographische Mitteilungen* **32**, 285–301.

WAGNER, P. 1929. *Platinum deposits and mines of South Africa*. Oliver and Boyd, London.

# Geochemical and thermal fluxes, high-temperature venting and diffuse flow from mid-ocean ridge hydrothermal systems: the TAG hydrothermal field, Mid-Atlantic Ridge 26°N

## H. ELDERFIELD, R. A. MILLS & M. D. RUDNICKI

*Department of Earth Sciences, The University of Cambridge, Downing Street, Cambridge CB2 3EQ, UK*

**Abstract:** Submarine hydrothermal activity provides a source of many elements to sea water at rates of a similar order to those of input by rivers. Estimates of hydrothermal fluxes from geophysical models which attribute only about 20% of the advection to the axial region are up to an order of magnitude lower than those based upon geochemical budgets (from $^3$He, Mg and $^{87}$Sr/$^{86}$Sr). Evidence for ridge-flank and on-axis low-temperature hydrothermalism is reviewed. Diffuse flow appears to account for about $\frac{3}{4}$ to $\frac{6}{7}$ of the total heat flux of 500–900 MW for the TAG vent field, but is poorly characterized chemically. Processes in hydrothermal plumes moderate the primary hydrothermal fluxes of trace elements to the oceans. Recent studies of the plume above the TAG hydrothermal field are discussed. Oxyanions and particle-reactive trace metals are co-precipitated with iron oxyhydroxides that form during mixing in the buoyant plume. Particle-reactive metals are further scavenged during lateral transport of the plume whereas chalcophile elements are removed from the plume. The overall effect of plume reactions is that hydrothermal activity acts as an oceanic sink for several trace elements.

The transport of sea water through oceanic crust was recognized as an important process from studies of ophiolites before hydrothermal vents were discovered (Gass 1968; Gass & Smewing 1973; Spooner 1976). The mapping of metal-rich deep-sea sediments associated with mid-ocean ridges (Bostrom & Peterson 1966, 1969) provided important circumstantial evidence of the input of hydrothermal solutions to the sea floor. However, it was the direct observation of submarine hydrothermal activity (Corliss *et al.* 1979; Edmond *et al.* 1979) which first led to an appreciation that the input of hydrothermal fluids to sea water at ocean ridges is of quantitative importance in oceanic chemical budgets. Now, it is recognized, as a consequence of the enrichment or depletion of elements in hydrothermal fluids, that submarine hydrothermal activity provides a pathway for the transfer of many of the major and minor dissolved chemical constituents of sea water to or from the oceans at rates that possibly rival input rates by the world's rivers (Fig. 1). The global hydrothermal water flux transfers the whole of the oceanic volume through the mid-ocean ridge system every *c.* 10 Ma, making the processes within the oceanic crust that change the chemistry of sea water into that of hydrothermal fluids as important to ocean chemistry as the processes of chemical weathering on the continents that define the chemistry of rivers.

The principal purpose of this paper is to review recent work on hydrothermal activity at the Mid-Atlantic Ridge at 26°N. Two main points are emphasized which are important in determining the role of hydrothermal activity in global geochemical budgets. Firstly, there are considerable uncertainties in estimates of hydrothermal heat fluxes. Here, we emphasize the importance of low-temperature flow and summarize the evidence for on-axis diffuse flow. Secondly, we show that hydrothermal activity acts as a sink for many of the trace elements in sea water because of reactions within hydrothermal plumes. Submarine hydrothermal plumes are the sites of the initial mixing of hydrothermal fluids with sea water. This boundary zone is one of extremely high reactivity where primary input fluxes to the oceans are strongly moderated. A number of studies of the chemistry of hydrothermal plumes have been made since the important work on far-field dispersion of plume tracers such as He and Mn (e.g. Lupton *et al.* 1980; Craig & Lupton 1981), focusing on the formation of plumes and their mixing behaviour during the first stages of dispersion. These geochemical studies have been mainly, but not exclusively, in two areas: the Juan de Fuca Ridge–Endeavour Ridge area in the Pacific Ocean (e.g. Baker *et al.* 1985; Feely *et al.* 1987; Dymond & Roth 1988) and the TAG area at 26°N in the Atlantic Ocean, which provides the principal source of information used here.

After summarizing how primary hydrother-

*From* Prichard, H. M., Alabaster, T., Harris, N. B. W. & Neary, C. R. (eds), 1993, *Magmatic Processes and Plate Tectonics,* Geological Society Special Publication No. 76, 295–307.

mal fluxes of elements are obtained from fluid chemical data, evidence for on-axis diffuse flow is reviewed and chemical data presented. Next, chemical distributions and processes in hydrothermal plumes are outlined, distinguishing behaviour in the buoyant plume and the neutrally-buoyant plume. Finally, the impact of plumes in modifiying the primary hydrothermal fluxes of elements to the oceans is discussed.

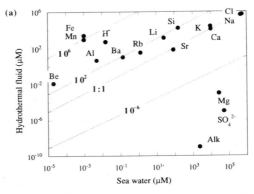

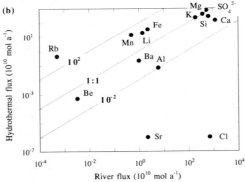

**Fig. 1.** (a) Concentrations of major and some minor elements in hydrothermal fluids compared with sea water; data from von Damm *et al.* (1985); (b) comparison of river fluxes and hydrothermal fluxes, assuming a hydrothermal water flux of $10^{14}$ kg a$^{-1}$ (see text).

## Hydrothermal circulation

### Advection at ocean ridges and global geochemical budgets

Hydrothermal circulation through young oceanic crust is a fundamental consequence of sea-floor spreading. Heat flow measurements over ridge crests indicate a discrepancy between observed and theoretical values that is attributed

to convective cooling of the crust by circulating sea water (Lister 1972). The balance between off-axis and axial heat advection by the circulation of water is a matter of some dispute between geochemical and geophysical investigators. Principally, this argument results from the need for convective cooling to be extended a considerable distance from the ridge axis for the observed and the calculated heat flow to coincide, whereas geochemical mass balance arguments (using Mg or $^{87}$Sr/$^{86}$Sr ratios) and the observation of $^{3}$He plumes within the oceans require the axial high temperature flux to dominate (Jenkins *et al.* 1978; Palmer & Edmond 1989). Recent estimates of hydrothermal fluxes based upon geochemical work on ophiolites (Bickle & Teagle 1992) are in agreement with the calculations based on $^{3}$He, Mg and $^{87}$Sr/$^{86}$Sr in the modern oceans.

The coincidence of the original estimate of total hydrothermal flux of Wolery & Sleep (1976) with the $^{3}$He method of Jenkins *et al.* (1978) and the geochemical budget calculations (about $10^{14}$ kg a$^{-1}$) has now been revised. Recent estimates of the high-temperature flux using thermal models are as much as an order of magnitude lower than previously calculated (Morton & Sleep 1985). This discrepancy presents problems when attempting global budget calculations. For example, measurements of strontium isotopes in off-axis circulation systems at Galapagos (Hess *et al.* 1992) indicate that high-temperature axial systems must be the major source of mantle strontium to the oceans and that low-temperature activity does not modify the Sr isotopic composition of sea water. A further complication is the recent suggestion (Sleep 1991) that much of the recharge is at the axis in order to account for the absence of a major anhydrite reservoir in the oceanic crust.

Thus, the attribution of the majority of the heat advection to low-temperature circulation as required by the geophysical constraints produces a major problem in balancing global geochemical budgets with attendant ramifications for evaluating geochemical fluxes from mid-ocean ridge hydrothermal circulation. The total heat available in oceanic crust limits > 350°C fluids to $c. \frac{1}{2}$ or, more realistically, $c. \frac{1}{5}$ of the flux necessary to account for $^{87}$Sr alteration.

### Low-temperature hydrothermal circulation

Sediment pore water studies provide evidence for substantial off-axis low-temperature circulation as predicted by heat flow discrepancies. Heat flow studies on the Galapagos mound flanks have identified individual low-temperature circulation cells away from the main high-temperature field (Becker & von Herzen 1983). Advective fluid flow through sediments in the off-axis Mariana mounds field has also been identified (Leinen *et al.* 1987; Wheat & McDuff 1987). Pore water Mg, Ca and F provide useful tracers of upwelling low-temperature hydrothermal fluids and element fluxes for the Galapagos mounds area suggest that this process is a potentially important sink for Mg (Maris & Bender 1982; Maris *et al.* 1984). Other useful tracers of low-temperature activity have been identified, including Li and B, which are removed from sea water during low temperature alteration of oceanic crust (Seyfried *et al.* 1984), $\delta^{11}B$ (Spivack & Edmond 1987) and $\delta^{18}O$ (Bowers & Taylor 1985).

However, ridge flanks are not the only foci for low-temperature hydrothermal activity. A second type is that of *on-axis* low-temperature hydrothermal activity. Experiments to quantify the balance between diffuse (low temperature) and discrete (high temperature) sources on the Juan de Fuca Ridge (e.g. Rona & Trivett 1992; Schultz *et al.* 1992) have suggested that discrete flow only accounts for $\frac{1}{5}$ to $\frac{1}{10}$ of the axial heat flow. Thus, determination of the relative importance of these two flow paths is vital.

Although high-temperature venting is, in general, well characterized, the documentation of the chemistry of the diffuse flow on axis is extremely poor. It relies principally on (a) pore–water studies for off-axis regions, as described above; and (b) inferences based on the composition of hot spring deposits: for example, in the Galapagos mounds area, nontronite is apparently forming from hydrothermal solutions at 4–10°C (Corliss *et al.* 1979); Haymon & Kastner (1981) suggest a number of processes that might cause low-temperature formation of hydrothermal mineral deposits; Alt *et al.* (1987) describe Fe- and Mn-oxides from seamounts on the East Pacific Rise that are actively forming at 10–15°C from mixing of low-temperature iron-rich solutions with sea water and suggest a bacterially-mediated origin.

Although it seems certain from the lines of evidence outlined above that the chemistry of low-temperature diffuse flows must differ from that of the high temperature vents, there are very few direct observations reported and this represents a significant gap in knowledge and understanding. As discussed later, it has major implications for the investigation of chemical budgets even if the diffuse flow system is driven by sub surface mixing of high-temperature fluid and sea water, since the impact on sea-water chemistry of the fraction of pristine fluid reacted in this way is severely modified.

## Mid-Atlantic Ridge hydrothermal activity and evidence for low-temperature fluid flow

### Hydrothermal activity at the Mid-Atlantic Ridge, 26°N

Until 1985, all the hydrothermal vents that had been found were from fast-to-medium spreading ridges in the Pacific. Work using manganese as a tracer of venting (Klinkhammer *et al.* 1985, 1986) provided evidence that led to the discovery of black smokers at the TAG site on slowly-spreading crust at the Mid-Atlantic Ridge at 26°N (Rona *et al.* 1986). In the same year, hydrothermal vents were discovered during a site survey for deep-sea drilling at the Snakepit site nearby at 23°N (Scientific Party, ODP Leg 106, 1986). There is now a considerable body of observational data available on hydrothermal activity at TAG (e.g., Campbell *et al.* 1988; Klinkhammer *et al.* 1985, 1986; Rona *et al.* 1986, 1990; Metz *et al.* 1988; Trocine & Trefry, 1988; Speer & Rona 1989; Trefry & Metz 1989; Elderfield 1990; German *et al.* 1990, 1991*a,b*, 1993; Thompson *et al.* 1990; Lunel *et al.* 1990; Mills *et al.* 1993; Elderfield & Rudnicki 1992; Elderfield *et al.* 1993; Mitra *et al.* 1993; Rudnicki & Elderfield 1992*a,b*,1993).

### Evidence for low-temperature venting at TAG

Through application of a mathematical plume model (see the later discussion on formation of plumes), Rudnicki & Elderfield (1992*a*) have calculated a total thermal flux of 500–900 MW for the TAG vent field, a figure which compares with 120 MW for the main black smoker venting complex at the summit of the TAG mound (Rona *et al.* 1990). This result indicates that possibly $\frac{3}{4}$ to $\frac{6}{7}$ of the total TAG heat flux derives from low-temperature systems which are entrained into the plume. CTD profiles obtained through this area in 1990 identified bottom water with a temperature anomaly that is thought to arise from low-temperature venting (see Fig. 2). This source of water may exhibit chemical anomalies in conjunction with this thermal anomaly which has not been considered in any budget calculations to date. Similarly, at the Snakepit site, submersible work identified large volumes of *c.* 4°C near-bottom sea water surrounding the vent site; it is unclear whether all such anomalous bottom-water is incorporated into the buoyant plume.

Data on the chemical composition of low-temperature fluids at TAG, as elsewhere, is

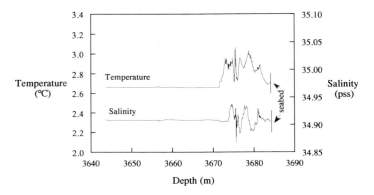

**Fig. 2.** CTD profile through bottom anomaly at TAG; data from Alvin dive series, 1990 (unpublished data).

sparse. Lunel *et al.* (1990) found that bottom-waters near the TAG vent site were enriched in Al. Rudnicki & Elderfield (1992*b*) found that these enrichments were associated with enrichments in $^{222}Rn$. Rudnicki & Elderfield (1992*b*) have compared the $^{222}Rn$ measured directly in end-member vent fluid sampled from submersible with a theoretical $^{222}Rn$ end-member value obtained by extrapolating measurements in the neutrally buoyant plume back to the high-temperature end-member using $^3He$ as a conservative tracer. This showed that the high-temperature systems can only account for <2.5% of the radon in the plume. This is shown by the term $\gamma$ in Fig. 3 which is the ratio of the extrapolated end-member $^{222}Rn$ concentration based on the plume data to the measured concentration in hydrothermal fluids; the gradient of the helium vs. Rn plot in Fig. 3 is 1/68 of that expected from the fluid data. The excess $^{222}Rn$ must, therefore, be derived from low-temperature systems. Also, comparison of $^{222}Rn$, He isotopes and Mn at the level of neutral buoyancy have revealed water of possible low temperature origin intermixed with the plume which may have been derived from the walls of the median valley (see Fig. 3). This water falls on a Mn-Si mixing line with a negative gradient, implying that the low-temperature end-member is enriched in Si but depleted in Mn. It appears that $^{222}Rn$ and $^3He$ can be used as tracers of low- and high-temperature venting: $^3He$ has an entirely high-temperature source whereas $^{222}Rn$ is dominated by low-temperature input (Rosenberg *et al.* 1988).

Related evidence comes from a comparison of compositions of different types of hydrothermal fluid. Edmond *et al.* (1990) summarize the compositions of black-smoker ($363 \pm 3°C$) and lower-temperature ($265–300°C$) 'clear fluids'/white smokers from TAG, showing that the

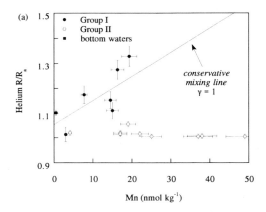

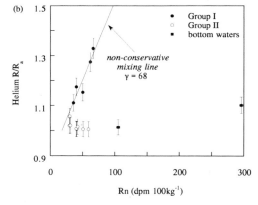

**Fig. 3.** $^3He/^4He$, $^{222}Rn$ and Mn in sea waters from the region of the TAG plume (Rudnicki & Elderfield 1992*b*). The Group I samples are from the neutrally buoyant plume, whereas the Group II samples are also from the height of neutral buoyancy but from the region between the plume and the east wall of the median valley. The bottom waters are also enriched in Al (Lunel *et al.* 1990)

latter contain less Fe and have higher pH suggestive of conductive cooling of the end-member fluids, and sulphide precipitation, rather than sub-surface dilution of the end-member fluids. A detailed study of TAG mound material (Mills 1992) suggests that hydrothermal fluids **evolve** within the TAG mound. REE and Nd isotopic distributions in TAG ochres and oxides indicate that these phases are not derived from oxidation of pristine sulphides by sea water. Instead, they appear to be undergoing oxidation in, or precipitation from, a silica- and REE-enriched environment.

The white-smoker fluids have lower concentrations of REEs than black-smoker fluids but much enhanced positive Eu anomalies (Mitra *et al.* 1993). Figure 4 shows that they have almost identical $^{87}Sr/^{86}Sr$ ratios to the black smokers. This means that Sr isotopic measurements may be used to test whether the diffuse flow at TAG has the same origin as the white-smoker fluids. This would be important in the light of the observation of Hess *et al.* (1992) that the Sr in ridge-flank systems is of sea water origin.

What is, as yet, uncertain is whether the lower-temperature fluids are originally high-temperature fluids cooled by conduction in the upper part of the crust or whether they represent fluid from flow paths which never reached high temperatures. This is important in terms of how focused the circulation systems are and how significant geochemically are the waning stages of evolving flow systems.

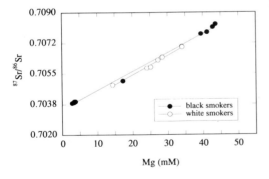

**Fig. 4.** $^{87}Sr/^{86}Sr$ for TAG hydrothermal fluids vs. Mg as an index of proportion of hydrothermal end-member (unpublished data).

Surface Fe and Mn staining has been widely observed by submersible within the median valley at TAG which is indicative of upwelling of low-temperature solutions rich in Fe and Mn, although it seems more likely that this represents deposition from the hydrothermal plume. Three types of metalliferous sedimentation have been identified at TAG: (a) Mn-rich deposits, interpreted as late-stage low-temperature precipitates, which occur on the eastern wall of the axial valley, above the height of the neutrally buoyant plume (Scott *et al.* 1974; Thompson *et al.* 1985). There is evidence that lower-temperature fluids are channelled up the eastern wall by the intense faulting and fissuring at TAG (Karson & Rona 1990); (b) particle fall-out from the neutrally buoyant plume, which provides a substantial sink for some elements. This represents that part of the hydrothermal flux that is involved in the plume system and associated precipitation/scavenging reactions therein; (c) material derived from mass wasting of sulphidic material deposited in the near-field environment. The second two sources have distinct chemical signatures (Mills *et al.* 1993; German *et al.* 1993).

## Chemical distributions and processes in hydrothermal plumes

### Formation of plumes

Primary hydrothermal fluxes of many elements are modified by reactions in hydrothermal plumes and ultimate storage of elements in metalliferous hydrothermal sediments. Recent advances in understanding of the behaviour of elements in hydrothermal sediments at TAG have been made by the recognition that they have a dual origin, from plume input and by alteration of hydrothermal sulphides (German *et al.* 1993; Mills *et al.* 1993), but this is beyond the scope of the present review. However, it must be recognized that the ultimate fate of the products of plume reactions depends on their behaviour within hydrothermal sediments and a detailed evaluation of this is of pressing importance.

Hydrothermal plumes form above sites of venting because of the negative buoyancy of the hot hydrothermal fluids which rise, entraining ambient sea water with a consequent continuous increase in plume volume, until neutral buoyancy is achieved after which the plume disperses laterally. It is convenient to distinguish the **vent**, from which the buoyant plume emanates, from the **buoyant** portion of the plume and the **neutrally-buoyant** plume. Information on all three are important for an evaluation of the role of plumes in moderating hydrothermal fluxes of elements to the oceans. Studies of the chemistry of the buoyant plume (these are difficult to make and are rare) need information on the time-scale of plume formation but this may be readily obtained from a plume model calibrated against physical properties. Similarly, studies of the neutrally-buoyant plume (easier to make) need information on the time-scale of plume dispersion; this must be obtained experimentally from naturally occurring radioactive isotopes.

Models describing the physical and chemical properties of the hydrothermal plume at TAG have been presented by Speer & Rona (1989), Lunel *et al.* (1990) and Rudnicki & Elderfield (1992*a*), all based upon the principles for turbulent entrainment in plumes described by Morton *et al.* (1956) and Turner (1973). The relevance of these studies to the present work is that it is possible (a) to calculate heat fluxes from plume data (data are given earlier in this paper for TAG); and (b) to predict the entrainment ratio (the ratio of entrained sea water to hydrothermal fluid) as a function of plume height and also the final entrainment ratio at the height of neutral buoyancy. During plume rise, ambient sea water is entrained from a range of depths such that the chemical and physical composition of the water arriving at the height of the neutrally-buoyant plume is a function of both the vent fluid endmember concentration, and its flux, and of the background profile of a property integrated over the whole of the depth range of the buoyant plume. Thus, the property anomalies seen at neutrally-buoyant plume height are the result of these various factors. For example, the temperature anomaly at TAG is negative (i.e. the water is colder than other water at plume height) because the background depth gradients of both temperature and salinity are negative and the density deficiency caused by the entrainment of relatively fresh water is balanced by its lower temperature. However, heat fluxes can be obtained from plume heights together with knowledge of the background temperature and salinity gradients and exit temperatures of vent fluids. Also, by comparing volume fluxes at the vent with those at the height of neutral buoyancy, it is also possible to obtain the final entrainment ratio. This ratio is about $10^4$ at TAG, although the situation is more complex in detail because the TAG plume is multi-layered, each layer having a characteristic entrainment ratio (Rudnicki & Elderfield 1992*a*).

## The neutrally-buoyant plume

Far-field studies of the TAG hydrothermal plume were used in the identification of the TAG hydrothermal field (Klinkhammer *et al* 1985, 1986). Mn is a useful tracer of plume dispersion because its concentration in sea water is low

($c.$ 0.1 nmol kg$^{-1}$) compared with vent fluid concentrations ($c.$ 600 μmol kg$^{-1}$ at TAG), an enrichment factor of 6 million, and can therefore be detected after significant dilution as the plume is dispersed laterally. The maximum measured concentration in the neutrally-buoyant plume is just below 60 nmol kg$^{-1}$, an entrainment ratio of $10^4$, as predicted by the plume model. Apparently Mn behaves conservatively (or near-conservatively) in the plume because of the slow oxidation kinetics of Mn$^{2+}$.

In contrast to Mn, there is no detectable dissolved Fe in the TAG plume but particulate Fe concentrations approach 250 μmol kg$^{-1}$ as compared with hydrothermal fluid values of $c.$ 6 mmol kg$^{-1}$ (Trefry *et al.* 1985; German *et al.* 1990). This is because about half of the iron in the fluids is removed from solution in the form of sulplides during the first stage of mixing with sea water in the buoyant plume, and is largely removed from the plume. The remaining Fe is removed from solution in the form of Fe oxyhydroxide particles (see below) which are transported upwards with the plume and appear to behave conservatively. Thus, the Fe/Mn ratio of hydrothermal fluids is $c.$ 10 whereas that of neutrally-buoyant plume particles is $c.$ 5.

Fe may be used as an index of the hydrothermal component in particles from the neutrally-buoyant plume and there is now a good body of data showing the relationship between the contents of many minor and trace elements and that of iron in particles collected from the neutrally-buoyant plume. The patterns show 3 types of form (Fig. 5) and this has led to a characterization of element behaviour into the following categories (Trocine & Trefry 1988; Trefry & Metz 1989; German *et al.* 1990, 1991*a,b*; Feely *et al.* 1987, 1991):

*(i) The oxyanions (V, Cr, As, P, Mo, U)* show a linear relationship with Fe (Fig. 5a). As the concentrations of these elements in 'background' particles (clays, biogenic material etc.) are very low, this type of relationship represents simple mixing between hydrothermal Fe oxyhydroxides and background particles. The slope of such lines approximates to the oxyanion/Fe ratios of the hydrothermal particles. These elements are considered to be added to the hydrothermal Fe oxyhydroxides during the process of their formation with no further reaction, and the oxyanion/Fe ratios must represent the ratios of the particles delivered to the height of neutral buoyancy.

*(ii) Particle-reactive metals (Th, REEs, Y, Be)* show element–Fe plots with positive curvature

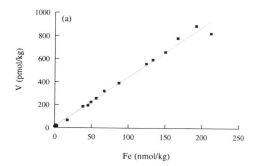

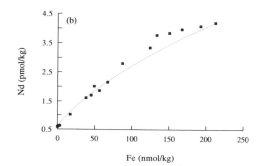

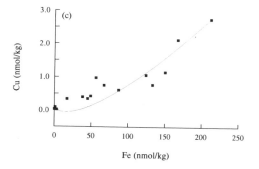

**Fig. 5.** Element–Fe plots for particulate matter from the TAG neutrally-buoyant plume waters showing 3 types of reactivity (see text); from Rudnicki & Elderfield (1993) modified from German *et al.* (1991*b*)

(Fig. 5b). Therefore, in addition to uptake of elements by newly formed hydothermal oxyhydroxides, there is continuous additional uptake within the neutrally-buoyant plume. This is a classic pattern of non-conservative behaviour. The highest element/Fe ratios (or, better, the ratio for an extrapolated Fe content equivalent to an entrainment ratio of $10^4$) similarly must represent the ratios delivered to the base of the neutrally-buoyant plume.

*(iii) The chalcophile elements (Cu, Zn, Pb, Co, Sn, Cd, Ag)* show element–Fe plots with negative curvature (Fig. 5c). Thus, in contrast to category (ii), there is removal of the elements from the neutrally-buoyant plume. It has been assumed that these elements are largely associated with sulphides transported with the plume and that this removal pattern reflects either their dissolution or their fallout by gravitational settling.

### The buoyant plume

There are, as yet, few descriptions of the behaviour of elements in buoyant hydrothermal plumes. Mottl & McConachy (1990) have described the chemistry of plume particles from the East Pacific Rise near 21°N, including the crucial observation that about half of the iron in the hydrothermal fluids is removed in the buoyant plume as sulphides, as inferred (above) for the TAG plume. Campbell (1991) has identified the Fe oxyhydroxide that subsequently forms at TAG as nano-phase haematite.

Recently, measurements have been made of the dissolved concentrations of certain trace elements in the buoyant plume at TAG. Figure 6 shows plots of dissolved Mn, REEs, and Al (Elderfield *et al.* 1993; Mitra *et al.* (1993) vs. dissolved Si or Mg as an index of entrainment ratio (vent fluid Si is *c.* 20 mmol kg$^{-1}$; Mg = 0). The distribution of Mn is shown for comparative purposes (Figs 6a,c) and shows conservative mixing between hydrothermal fluids and sea water. Apparently, the REEs behave similarly to Mn (Fig. 6b; Nd is shown but all REEs behave similarly) but this is misleading as the minimum dilution shown is that of 10% of the hydrothermal end-member. When the data for the dilution range 1.5–0.1% hydrothermal end-member (entrainment ratios of 67–1000) are examined (Fig. 6d) it is clear that the REEs behave highly non-conservatively. Concentrations are below levels in normal sea water: the chemical reactivity in the buoyant plume is such that REEs are removed from both hydrothermal fluid and sea-water end-members. A similar behaviour is seen for Al. Although the mixing lines at low entrainment ratios (<5) are linear (Fig. 6e) they do not extrapolate to sea-water values and inspection of the data for high entrainment ratios (Fig. 6f) shows the same effect as for REEs: Al concentrations have been reduced to sub-sea-water levels.

These data provide the first direct evidence of element removal within the buoyant plume. However, caution must be exercised when making quantitative interpretations from these results. The reason for this is that the time for

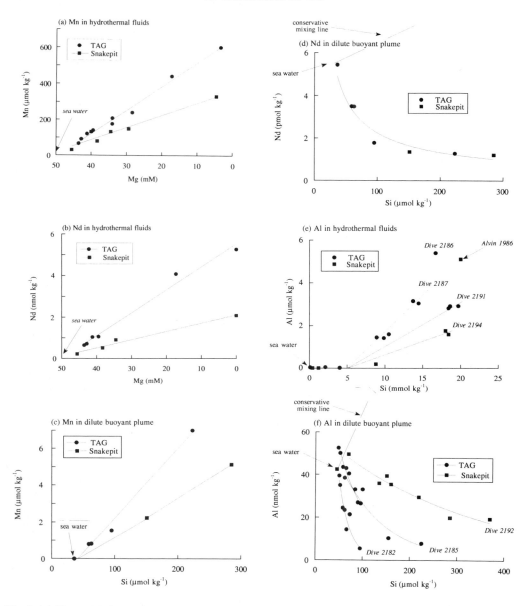

**Fig. 6. (a)** Mn vs. Mg in hydrothermal fluids; **(b)** Nd vs. Mg in hydrothermal fluids; **(c)** Mn vs. Si in dilute portion of buoyant plume; **(d)** Nd vs. Si in dilute portion of buoyant plume; **(e)** Al vs. Si in hydrothermal fluids; **(f)** Al vs. Si in dilute portion of buoyant plume.

plume rise to neutral buoyancy is only *c.* 40 minutes (Rudnicki & Elderfield 1992*a*) which means that reaction rates in the buoyant plume are extremely rapid and therefore are likely to continue after sampling of plume waters. In situ separation of particles from the buoyant plume is now required to estimate element removal rates directly.

## Chemical processes in plumes

It is apparent that, apart from the chalcophiles which are removed from solution as metal sulphides, elements behave conservatively over the very early stages (first few seconds) of dilution but show significant removal once Fe oxyhydroxide precipitation takes place. From a survey

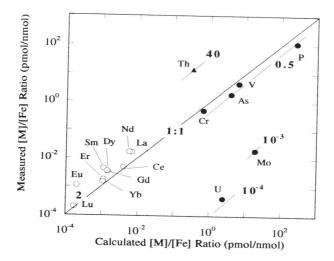

**Fig. 7.** Comparison between measured element/Fe ratios in hydrothermal plume particles and calculated ratios for quantitative co-precipitation of elements with Fe in the buoyant plume (from Rudnicki & Elderfield 1993).

of chemical and physical properties in the buoyant plume at TAG, Rudnicki & Elderfield (1993) have shown that $Fe^{2+}$ oxidation occurs early in the development of the plume and the half-life oxidation time is c. 2 minutes. As discussed above, data from neutrally-buoyant plume particles may be used to obtain element/Fe ratios that correspond to the average composition of the particles formed in the buoyant plume and, therefore, reflect the total element uptake within the buoyant plume.

Two possible mechanisms may be envisaged: (i) instantaneous co-precipitation of elements with the newly formed Fe oxyhydroxides, and (ii) 'scavenging', i.e. kinetically-controlled adsorption of elements onto this Fe phase during the period of plume rise, c. 40 minutes. From the study of Fe(II) oxidation kinetics it was possible to obtain an average entrainment ratio of 570 for mixture of sea water and hydrothermal fluid from which the oxide precipitation occurs (Rudnicki & Elderfield 1993). This is a useful number as it allows calculation of the element/Fe ratios for hydrothermal fluids–seawater mixtures of this ratio (all of the Fe being derived from the fluid and the elements derived from both fluid and entrained sea water) which, therefore, represents the theoretical maximum ratio for quantitative co-precipitation of elements with Fe. Comparison of this theoretical ratio with measured ratios obtained from neutrally-buoyant plume particle data allows the process or processes responsible for removal of the various groups of elements to be identified

(Fig. 7). It can be seen that the behaviour of the oxyanions can be accounted for by co-precipitation alone, whereas the element/Fe ratios of the reactive metals Th and the REEs reflect removal by both co-precitation and scavenging. Of the oxyanions, Mo and especially U are inefficiently co-precipitated with Fe. This is consistent with their sea-water speciation: both form large stable oxyanions in solution.

As may be inferred from element/Fe plots for neutrally-buoyant plume particles (Fig. 5), those elements which undergo scavenging in the buoyant plume also undergo scavenging within the neutrally-buoyant plume, whereas those that only undergo co-precipitation do not. A further complication is that there is evidence that chalcophile elements removed from solution in hydrothermal fluids as metal sulphides may be released to sea water by oxidative dissolution (Metz & Trefry 1993). Thus, hydrothermal activity may add the chalcophile elements to sea water and remove oxyanions and particle-reactive trace elements from sea water.

## Impact on hydrothermal activity on ocean chemistry

The time-scale of dilution of the neutrally-buoyant plume at TAG has been estimated from $^3He$–$^{222}Rn$ dating of plume waters and $^{234}Th$–$^{228}Th$–$^{230}Th$ dating of plume particles (Rudnicki & Elderfield 1992b, 1993) and the dilution half-time is about 25 days. On this basis it is possible to determine the rates of element removal within

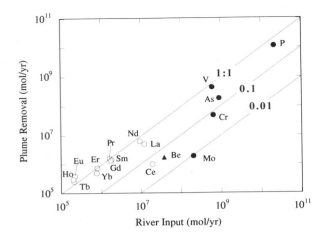

**Fig. 8.** Comparison of plume removal rates and river input rates (from Rudnicki & Elderfield 1993)

the plume. Similarly, element removal within the buoyant plume may be readily obtained by comparing element/Fe ratios with hydrothermal Fe fluxes. This information may be used to determine the moderation of hydrothermal fluxes by reactions in hydrothermal plumes.

As can be seen from Fig. 8, the primary hydrothermal fluxes of the reactive metals studied have been eliminated by plume removal. Furthermore, scavenging by plume particles has removed significant quantities of these elements from ambient sea water such that, overall, hydrothermal activity acts as an oceanic sink for such elements and not a source. For the oxyanions, for which hydrothermal activity is not a significant source, co-precipitation with hydrothermal Fe oxyhydroxides acts an oceanic sink of some significance too.

A quantitative evaluation of this process is difficult because of the problems discussed earlier of calculating a global hydrothermal flux estimate, knowledge of the relative importance of diffuse flow versus high-temperature venting, the representivity of the TAG hydrothermal field and the periodicity in hydrothermal activity. The estimates given here should be regarded within this framework. Much more work is needed on chemical processes and budgets of individual vent areas and ridge segments containing hydrothermal vents, including an evaluation of lower-temperature diffuse flow systems as well as the more spectacular manifestations of high-temperature venting. In addition, the ultimate fate of plume particles needs to resolved. For example, if additional amounts of Fe are removed sub-surface prior to diffuse flow then the influence on particulate Fe oxide formation

on sea-water chemistry may be highly complex.

Nevertheless, it is now certain that reactions in hydrothermal plumes act as important chemical sinks for many of the trace constituents in sea water. It has been long accepted that the chemistry of the oceans is controlled to a significant extent by the degree to which the elements are removed from sea water rather than added to it. The discovery and documentation of submarine hydrothermal activity has revealed both a source and a sink for the elements.

The research at Cambridge summarized in this paper has been generously supported by grants and studentships from NERC. A draft of this manuscript was prepared when one of the authors (H. E.) was Lady Davis Professor at the Hebrew University, Jerusalem, and it is a pleasure to acknowledge the hospitality of colleagues at the Institute of Earth Sciences of the University and the Lady Davis Trust. Cambridge Earth Sciences Series, contribution 3191.

# References

ALT, J. C., LONSDALE, P., HAYMON R. & MUEHLEN-BACHS, K. 1987. Hydrothermal sulfide and oxide deposits on seamounts near 21°N, East Pacific Rise. *Geological Society of America Bulletin*, **98**, 157–168.

BAKER, E. T., LAVELLE, J. W. & MASSOTH, G. J. 1985. Hydrothermal particle plumes over the southern Juan de Fuca Ridge. *Nature*, **316**, 342–344.

BECKER, K. & VON HERZEN R. P. 1983. Heat transfer through the sediments of the Mounds Hydrothermal area, Galapagos Spreading Center at 86°W. *Journal of Geophysical Research*, **88**, 995–1008.

BICKLE, M. J. & TEAGLE, D. A. H. 1992. Strontium alteration in the Troodos ophiolite: implications for fluid-fluxes and geochemical transport in mid-ocean ridge hydrothermal systems. *Earth and Planetary Science Letters*, **113**, 219–237.

BOSTROM K. & PETERSON, M. N. A. 1966. Precipitates from hydrothermal exhalations on the East Pacific Rise. *Economic Geology*, **61**, 1258–1265.

—— & —— 1969. Origin of aluminum-poor ferro-manganoan sediments in areas of high heat flow on the East Pacific Rise. *Marine Geology*, 7, 427–447.

BOWERS, T. S. & TAYLOR, H. P. 1985. An integrated chemical and stable-isotope model of the origin of midocean ridge hot spring systems. *Journal of Geophysical Research*, **90**, 12583–12606

CAMPBELL A. C. 1991. Mineralogy and chemistry of marine particles by synchroton X-ray spectroscopy, mossbauer spectroscopy and plasma-mass spectrometry, *Monograph of the American Geophysical Union*, **63**, 375–390.

——, PALMER, M. R., KLINKHAMMER, G. P., BOWERS, T. S., EDMOND, J. M., LAWRENCE, J. R., CASEY, J. F., THOMPSON, G., RONA, P. & KARSON, J. A. 1988. Chemistry of hot springs on the Mid-Atlantic Ridge. *Nature*, **335**, 514–519.

CORLISS, J. B., DYMOND, J, GORDON, L. I., EDMOND, J. M., VON HERZEN, R. P., BALLARD, R. D., GREEN, K., WILLIAMS, D., BAINBRIDGE, A., CRANE, K. & VAN ANDEL Tj. H., 1979. Submarine thermal springs on the Galapagos rift. *Science*, **203**, 1073–1083.

CRAIG, H. & LUPTON, J. E. 1981. Helium-3 and mantle volatiles in the ocean and oceanic crust. *In*: EMILIANI, C. (ed.) *The Sea*, **17**, John Wiley, Chichester, 391–428.

DYMOND, J. & ROTH, S. 1988. Plume dispersed hydrothermal particles: a time-series record of settling flux from the Endeavour Ridge using moored sensors. *Geochimica et Cosmochimica Acta*, **52**, 2525–2536.

EDMOND, J. M., CAMPBELL, A. C., PALMER, M. R. & GERMAN, C. R. 1990. Geochemistry of hydrothermal fluids from the Mid-Atlantic Ridge: TAG and MARK 1990. *Transactions of the American Geophysical Union*, **71**, 1650–1651.

——, MEASURES, C. I., MCDUFF, R. E., CHAN, L. H., COLLIER, R., GRANT, B., GORDON, L. I. & CORLISS, J. B. 1979. Ridge crest hydrothermal activity and the balance of the major and minor elements in the ocean: the Galapagos data. *Earth and Planetary Science Letters*, **46**, 1–18.

ELDERFIELD, H. 1990. Hydrothermal springs, plumes and mineral deposits at the Mid Atlantic Ridge. *NERC News*, **15**, 27–29.

——, GREAVES, M. J., RUDNICKI, M. D. & HYDES D. J. 1993. Aluminium reactivity in hydrothermal plumes at the Mid Atlantic Ridge. *Journal of Geophysical Research*, **98**, 9667–9670.

—— & RUDNICKI, M. 1992. Iron fountains on the seabed. *New Scientist*, **134**, 31–35.

FEELY, R. A., LEWISON, M., MASSOTH, G. J., ROBERT-BALDO, G., LAVELLE, J. W., BYRNE, R. H., VON DAMM, K. L. & CURL, H. C. 1987. Composition and Dissolution of Black Smoker Particulates From Active Vents on the Juan de Fuca Ridge. *Journal of Geophysical Research*, **92**, 11,347–11,363.

——, TREFRY J. H., MASSOTH, G. J. & METZ, S. 1991. A comparison of the scavenging of phosphorus and arsenic from seawater by hydrothermal iron oxyhydroxides in the Atlantic and Pacific Oceans. *Deep-Sea Research*, **38**, 617–623.

GASS, I. G. 1968. Is the Troodos Massif of Cyprus a fragment of Mesozoic ocean floor? *Nature*, **220**, 39–42.

—— & SMEWING, J. D. 1973. Intrusion, extrusion and metamorphism at constructive margins: evidence from the Troodos Massif, Cyprus. *Nature*, **242**, 26–29.

GERMAN, C. R., CAMPBELL, A. C. & EDMOND, J. M. 1991*b*. Hydrothermal scavenging at the Mid-Atlantic Ridge: Modification of trace element dissolved fluxes. *Earth and Planetary Science Letters*, **107**, 101–114.

——, FLEER, A. P., BACON, M. P. & EDMOND, J. M. 1991*a*. Hydrothermal scavenging at the Mid Atlantic Ridge: radionuclide distributions. *Earth and Planetary Science Letters*, **105**, 170–181.

——, KLINKHAMMER, G. P., EDMOND, J. M., MITRA A. & ELDERFIELD H. 1990. Hydrothermal scavenging of rare earth elements in the ocean. *Nature*, **345**, 516–518.

——, MILLS, R. A. BLUSZTAJN, J. FLEER, A. P., BACON, M. P., HIGGS, N. C., ELDERFIELD, H. & THOMSON, J. 1993. A geochemical study of metalliferous sediment from the TAG hydrothermal field, 26°08′N, MAR, *Journal of Geophysical Research*, **98**, 9683–9692.

HAYMON, R. M. & KASTNER, M. 1981. Hot spring deposits on the East Pacific Rise at 21°N: preliminary description of mineralogy and genesis. *Earth and Planetary Science Letters*, **53**, 363–381.

HESS, J., BENDER, M. & SCHILLING, J. G. 1992. Assessing seawater/basalt exchange of strontium isotopes in hydrothermal processes on the flanks of mid-ocean ridges. *Earth and Planetary Science Letters*, **103**, 133–142.

JENKINS, W. J., EDMOND, J. M. & CORLISS J. B. 1978. Excess ³He and ⁴He in the Galapagos submarine hydrothermal waters. *Nature*, **272**, 156–158.

KARSON, J. A. & RONA, P. A. 1990. Block tilting, transfer faults, and structural control of magmatic and hydrothermal processes in the TAG area, Mid-Atlantic Ridge 26°N. *Geological Society of America Bulletin*, **102**, 1635–1645.

KLINKHAMMER, G. ELDERFIELD, G. H., GREAVES, M., RONA, P. & NELSON, T. 1986. Manganese geochemistry near high-temperature vents in the Mid-Atlantic Ridge rift valley. *Earth and Planetary Science letters*, **80**, 230–240.

——, RONA, P., GREAVES, M. & ELDERFIELD, H. 1985. Hydrothermal Mn plumes in the Mid-Atlantic Ridge rift valley. *Nature*, **314**, 727–731.

LEINEN, M., MCDUFF, R., DELANEY, J., BECKER, K. & SCHULTHEISS, P. 1987. Off-axis hydrothermal activity in the Mariana Mounds field. *Transactions of the American Geophysical Union*, **68**, 1531.

LISTER, C. R. B. 1972. On the thermal balance of a mid-ocean ridge. *Geophysical Journal of the Royal Astronomical Society*, **26**, 515–535.

LUNEL T., RUDNICKI, M., ELDERFIELD, H. & HYDES, D. 1990. Aluminium as a depth-sensitive tracer of entrainment in submarine hydrothermal plumes. *Nature*, **344**, 137–139.

LUPTON J. E., KLINKHAMMER, G. P., NORMARK, W. R., HAYMON, R., MACDONALD, K. C., WEISS, R. F. & CRAIG, H. 1980. Helium-3 and manganese at the 21°N East Pacific Rise hydrothermal site. *Earth and Planetary Science Letters*, **50**, 115–127.

MARIS, C. R. P. & BENDER, M. L. 1982. Upwelling of hydrothermal solutions through ridge flank sediments shown by pore water profiles. *Science*, **216**, 623–626.

——, ——, FROELICH, P. N., BARNES, R. & LUEDTKE, N. A. 1984. Chemical evidence for advection of hydrothermal solutions in the sediments of the Galapagos Mounds Hydrothermal Field. *Geochimica et Cosmochimica Acta*, **48**, 2331–2346.

METZ, S. & TREFRY, J. H. 1993. Field and laboratory studies of metal uptake and release by hydrothermal precipitates. *Journal of Geophysical Research*, **98**, 9661–9666.

——, —— & NELSEN, T. A. 1988. History and geochemistry of a metalliferous sediment core from the Mid-Atlantic Ridge at 26°N. *Geochimica et Cosmochimica Acta*, **52**, 2369–2378.

MILLS, R. A. 1992. *A geochemical and isotopic study of hydrothermal sediments from the Mid Atlantic Ridge, 26°N.* PhD thesis, University of Cambridge.

—— ELDERFIELD, H. & THOMSON, J. 1993. A dual origin for the hydrothermal component within metalliferous sediment core from TAG, *Journal of Geophysical Research*, **98**, 9671–9681.

MITRA, A., ELDERFIELD, H. & GREAVES, M. J. 1993. Rare earth elements in submarine hydrothermal fluids and plumes from the Mid-Atlantic Ridge. *Marine Chemistry*, submitted.

MORTON, B. R., TAYLOR, G. & TURNER, J. S. 1956. Turbulent gravitational convection from maintained and instantaneous sources. *Philosophical Transactions of the Royal Society of London*, **A234**, 1–23.

MORTON, J. L. & SLEEP, N. H. 1985. A mid-ocean ridge thermal model: constraints on the volume of axial hydrothermal heat flux. *Journal of Geophysical Research*, **90**, 11,345–11,353.

MOTTL, M. J. & McCONACHY, T. F. 1990. Chemical processes in buoyant hydrothermal plumes on the East Pacific Rise near 21°N. *Geochimica et Cosmochimica Acta*, **54**, 1911–1927.

PALMER, M. & EDMOND, J. M. 1989. The strontium isotope budget of the modern ocean. *Earth and Planetary Science Letters*, **92**, 11–26.

RONA, P. A., HANNINGTON, M. D. & THOMSON, G. 1990. Evolution of hydrothermal mounds, TAG hydrothermal field, Mid-Atlantic Ridge 26°N, 45°W, *EOS Transactions of the American Geophysical Union*, **71**, 1650.

—— KLINKHAMMER, G., NELSON, T. A., TREFRY, J. H. & ELDERFIELD H. 1986. Black smokers, massive sulphides and vent biota at the Mid-Atlantic Ridge. *Nature*, **321**, 33–37.

—— & TRIVETT, D. A. 1992. Discrete and diffuse heat transfer at ASHES vent field, Axial Volcano, Juan de Fuca Ridge. *Earth and Planetary Science Letters*, **109**, 57–71.

ROSENBERG, N. D., LUPTON, J. E., KADKO, D., COLLIER, R., LILLEY, M. & PAK, H. 1988. Estimation of heat and chemical fluxes from a seafloor hydrothermal vent field using radon measurements. *Nature*, **334**, 604–607.

RUDNICKI, M. D. & ELDERFIELD, H. 1992a. Theory applied to the Mid-Atlantic Ridge hydrothermal plumes: the finite difference approach. *Journal of Volcanology and Geothermal Research*, **50**, 163–174.

—— & ELDERFIELD, H. 1993. A chemical model of the buoyant and neutrally buoyant plume above the TAG vent field, 26°N, Mid-Atlantic Ridge. *Geochimica et Cosmochimica Acta*, **57**, 2939–2957.

SCHULTZ, A., DELANEY, J. R. & McDUFF, R. E. 1992. On the partitioning of heat flux between diffuse and point source seafloor venting. *Journal of Geophysical Research*, **97**, 12,299–12,314.

SCIENTIFIC PARTY, LEG 106. 1986. Drilling the Snakepit hydrothermal sulfide deposits on the Mid-Atlantic Ridge. *Geology*, **14**, 1004–1007.

SCOTT, R. B., RONA, P. A., McGREGOR, B. A. & SCOTT, M. R. 1974. The TAG hydrothermal field. *Nature*, **251**, 301–302.

SEYFRIED, W. E., JANECKY, D. R. & MOTTL, M. J. 1984. Alteration of the oceanic crust: implications for geochemical cycles of lithium and boron. *Geochimica et Cosmochimica Acta*, **48**, 557–569.

SLEEP, N. H. 1991. Hydrothermal circulation, anhydrite precipitation, and thermal structure at ridge axes. *Journal of Geophysical Research*, **96**, 2375–2387.

SPEER, K. G. & RONA, P. A. 1989. A Model of an Atlantic and Pacific Hydrothermal Plume. *Journal of Geophysical Research*, **94**, 6213–6220.

SPIVACK, A. J. & EDMOND, J. M. 1987. Boron isotope exchange between seawater and the oceanic crust. *Geochimica et Cosmochimica Acta*, **51**, 1033–1043.

SPOONER, E. T. C. 1976. The strontium isotopic composition of seawater–oceanic crust interaction. *Earth and Planetary Science Letters*, **31**, 167–174.

THOMPSON, G., MOTTL, M. J. & RONA P. A. 1985. Morphology, mineralogy and chemistry of hydrothermal deposits from the TAG area, 26°N MAR. *Chemical Geology*, **49**, 243–257.

——, RONA P., BEAVERSON, C., MILLER, T., NELSEN, T., CAMPBELL, A., EDMOND, J., GERMAN, C., ELDERFIELD, H., GREAVES, M., RUDNICKI, M., HANNINGTON M., HUMPHRIS S., MOLYNEAUX, S., TIVEY, M., WIRSEN, C. & TAYLOR, P. 1990. Mid-Atlantic Ridge hydrothermal processes. *Transactions of the American Geophysical Union*, **71**, 726.

TREFRY, J. H. & METZ, S. 1989. Role of hydrothermal precipitates in the geochemical cycling of vanadium. *Nature*, **342**, 531–532.

——, TROCINE, R. P., KLINKHAMMER, G. P. & RONA, P. A. 1985. Iron and copper enrichment of suspended particulates in dispersed hydrothermal plumes along the Mid-Atlantic Ridge. *Geophysical. Research. Letters*, **12**, 506–509.

TROCINE, R. P., & TREFRY, J. H. 1988. Distribution and chemistry of suspended particles from an active hydrothermal vent site on the Mid-Atlantic Ridge at 26°N. *Earth and Planetary Science Letters*, **88**, 1–15.

TURNER, J. S. 1973. *Buoyancy effects in fluids*. Cambridge University Press, Cambridge.

VON DAMM, K. L., EDMOND, J. M., GRANT, B., MEASURES, C. I., WALDON, B. & Weiss, R. F. 1985. Chemistry of hydrothermal solutions at 21°N, East Pacific Rise. *Geochimica et Cosmochimica Acta*, **49**, 2197–2220.

WHEAT, C. G. & McDUFF, R. E. 1987. Advection of pore waters in the Mariana Mounds hydrothermal region as determined from nutrient profiles. *Transactions of the American Geophysical Union.* **68**, 1531.

WOLERY, T. J. & SLEEP, N. H. 1976. Hydrothermal circulation and geochemical flux at mid-ocean ridges. *Journal of Geology*, **84**, 249–275.

# MORB peridotite–sea water interaction: experimental constraints on the behaviour of trace elements, $^{87}Sr/^{86}Sr$ and $^{143}Nd/^{144}Nd$ ratios

MARTIN A. MENZIES,[1] ANDREW LONG,[1] GERRY INGRAM,[1]
MATTHEW TATNELL[1] & DAVID JANECKY[2]

[1]*Department of Geology, Royal Holloway University of London, Egham, Surrey TW20 0EX, UK*

[2]*Los Alamos National Laboratory, Los Alamos, New Mexico 87545, USA*

**Abstract**: The geochemical changes associated with the experimental serpentinization of peridotite are due to reaction with sea water and to the growth of new mineral phases. Since the rare earth elements (REE) and Sr are primarily ensconced in clinopyroxene, it is the unreactive nature of this phase in the presence of sea water that determines the REE content, the $^{87}Sr/^{86}Sr$ and $^{143}Nd/^{144}Nd$ ratio of the experimentally produced serpentinites. Serpentinites (after lherzolite and dunite) have chondrite-normalized REE abundance patterns similar to the initial peridotite indicating that the light REE (LREE) are not selectively mobilized by peridotite–sea water interaction at 300°C. However, the serpentinites produced as a result of harzburgite–sea water experiments show an increase in LREE content. Despite the sporadic behaviour of the LREE, the $^{143}Nd/^{144}Nd$ ratios in experimentally produced serpentinites (after lherzolite and harzburgite) are identical to primary clinopyroxene in the unaltered peridotite. In contrast, a marked change in the strontium isotopic composition of the peridotites occurs during experimental serpentinization due to the growth of hydrous and Ca-rich phases which facilitates the uptake of sea water Sr. Whereas harzburgite and dunite alter to produce serpentinites with high Sr contents and $^{87}Sr/^{86}Sr > 0.709$, lherzolites tend to alter to serpentinites with $^{87}Sr/^{86}Sr < 0.709$. This behaviour invalidates the use of Rb–Sr data in understanding the origin of oceanic and ophiolitic peridotites, but the relative immobility of the light REE (in clinopyroxene-bearing peridotites) and the low REE content of sea water encourages the careful use of the REE and neodymium isotopes as a petrogenetic indicator for elucidating the origin of serpentinized abyssal peridotites.

Serpentinized oceanic peridotites were first reported from Atlantic ocean islands by Darwin (1845) and later studied by Tilley (1947), Hess (1954) and Melson *et al* (1972). Hess (1954) believed these rocks to be of mantle origin related to basalt genesis. More recently, serpentinites have been recovered in dredge hauls from the large fracture zones of the Atlantic, Indian and Antarctic oceans extending from mid-ocean ridges (e.g. Dick *et al.* 1984). Whereas the provenance of exposed oceanic peridotites is believed to be the upper mantle, serpentinized peridotites found within fragments of ancient oceanic lithosphere (ophiolites) may represent a metamorphic (i.e. mantle) or igneous protolith (Hess 1955; Gass 1968; Gass & Smewing 1973; Gass *et al.* 1984). The ubiquitous serpentinization of peridotites on the sea floor is due to interaction with sea water at temperatures that can reach 500°C.

The main oceanic rock types to undergo serpentinization are dunites, harzburgites and lherzolites. These are altered to lizardite-bearing assemblages which also contain chrysotile and antigorite with the less common occurrence of brucite (e.g. Prichard 1979). The geochemistry of oceanic peridotites is affected by serpentinization and although the major element chemistry is not drastically affected by sea water interaction, trace elements and isotopes of petrogenetic significance are affected to an unknown degree. The rare earth elements (REE), $^{87}Sr/^{86}Sr$ and $^{143}Nd/^{144}Nd$ isotopic ratios are the most important as they are pivotal in understanding the genesis of the oceanic lithosphere.

## Previous work

Experiments were undertaken (Janecky 1982; Janecky & Seyfried 1986) in an attempt to evaluate the chemical changes that would occur within sea water when equigranular peridotites (mixtures of mantle minerals) (Fig. 1) were reacted with Pacific sea water (IAPSO standard sea water; 19.3755 per mil Cl). The primary minerals used to reconstitute the peridotites were

*From* Prichard, H. M., Alabaster, T., Harris, N. B. W. & Neary, C. R. (eds), 1993, *Magmatic Processes and Plate Tectonics*, Geological Society Special Publication No. 76, 309–322.

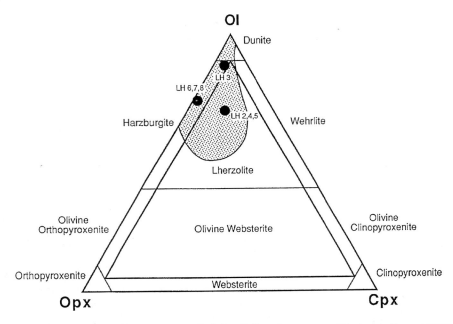

**Fig. 1.** Modal proportions in volume percent of olivine (O1), orthopyroxene (Opx) and clinopyroxene (Cpx) in peridotites used in serpentinization experiments (Janecky & Seyfried 1986). These compositions compare favourably with natural peridotites shown by the shaded field which encompasses oceanic and ophiolitic peridotites (Menzies 1990). The samples studied here are plotted as filled circles.

separated from a large basalt-borne xenolith (Fig. 2). Three lherzolite–sea water experiments were run at 200 and 300°C and water/rock (W/R) ratios of 10 and 30 and three harzburgite–reacted sea water experiments were run using various solutions similar in chemistry to reacted sea water all at 300°C and a W/R ratio of 10 and 20. A dunite–sea water experiment was run at 300°C and a W/R ratio of 10. Janecky & Seyfried (1986) studied the reacted solutions and noted that sea water chemistry changed significantly during the experiments. The concentrations of Mg, Ca and sulphate decreased as did the acidity. According to Janecky & Seyfried (1986) the peridotites were significantly altered, a factor that is consistent with the radical change to the sea water chemistry. All the orthopyroxene, substantial amounts of olivine, and relatively minor amounts of diopside dissolved during these experiments. From these data, Janecky & Seyfried (1986) concluded that the reaction rates of olivine to enstatite to diopside during 300°C lherzolite–sea water experiments were approximately 1.0:1.0:0.1. Serpentine (lizardite) was the dominant alteration product and anhydrite ($CaSO_4$) was identified in experiments in which sulphate was present. Other Ca-rich phases (e.g. truscottite and possibly carbonate)

were identified in the runs involving harzburgite and Mg and $SO_4$-free solution (i.e. reacted sea water). The serpentinized peridotites show an overall increase in silica and a decrease in aluminium, magnesium and the alkaline earths relative to their initial composition.

## Analytical techniques

Whole-rock serpentinites from these peridotite–sea water experiments and mineral separates used to reconstitute the starting peridotite compositions (i.e. lherzolite, harzburgite and dunite) were analysed at the University of London Radiogenic Isotope Laboratory (Royal Holloway) for elemental concentrations and isotopic compositions. Samples for REE abundances, $^{87}Sr/^{86}Sr$ and $^{143}Nd/^{144}Nd$ ratios were prepared using standard ion exchange techniques and the REE fractions were analysed using the technique of Thirlwall (1982) modified for a multicollector mass spectrometer. For isotopic analysis, Sr was loaded onto single Ta filaments and Nd onto single Re filaments and analysed in a VG354 multicollector mass spectrometer (Thirlwall 1991a,b). Values for standards during the period of analysis were SRM987 $^{87}Sr/^{86}Sr = 0.710241$ (22)(2SD) and La Jolla $^{143}Nd/^{144}Nd = 0.511857$

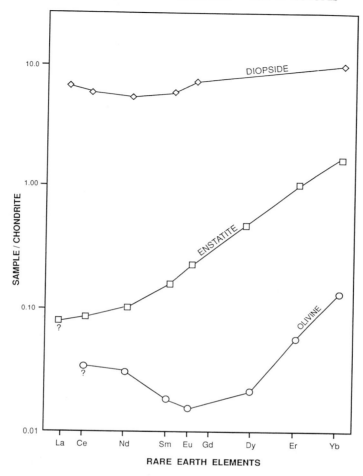

**Fig. 2.** Chondrite-normalized rare earth element abundance patterns for the primary minerals used to reconstitute the peridotites for the peridotite–sea water experiments. Normalization data for this and other diagrams taken from Evensen *et al.* (1979).

(7)(2 SD). Typical blanks for the REE are given in Table 1, together with an estimate of the magnitude of blank correction and the REE concentrations in Table 1 have been blank corrected. Blank correction has little effect on the majority of the data except in the case of La, Ce and to a lesser degree Nd. Similarly the Sr blank of 2.5 ng, with an $^{87}Sr/^{86}Sr$ isotopic composition of 0.70947 (9), has little effect on the $^{87}Sr/^{86}Sr$ ratio of the serpentinites (Table 2).

## Analytical results

### Primary minerals

The clinopyroxene (Cr-diopside) was found to be characterized by a slightly U-shaped profile with $(Ce)_N = 5.71$ and $(Yb)_N = 10.24$. The orthopyroxene (enstatite) has a light REE depleted profile with $(Ce)_N = 0.08$ and $(Yb)_N = 1.75$. Olivine has a U-shaped chondrite normalized REE pattern with $(Ce)_N = 0.03$ and $(Yb)_N = 0.15$. Diopside is the major repository for all the REE containing 30 times and 65 times the Ce content, and 6 times and 70 times the Yb content, of the orthopyroxene and olivine respectively. Diopside contains 78 ppm Sr and has an $^{87}Sr/^{86}Sr = 0.70280$ and $^{143}Nd/^{144}Nd = 0.51308$ (Table 2).

### Peridotites

Reconstituted lherzolites used in this study contain olivine: orthopyroxene: clinopyroxene: spinel = 70.5 : 18 : 10 : 1.5 (LH2; LH4; LH5). The

**Table 1.** *Rare earth abundance data for primary mantle minerals, recalculated whole rocks and experimentally altered peridotites.*

| Sample | La | Ce | Nd | Sm | Eu | Dy | Er | Yb |
|---|---|---|---|---|---|---|---|---|
| **Unaltered peridotite minerals** | | | | | | | | |
| Olivine | — | 0.019 | 0.013 | 0.003 | 0.001 | 0.006 | 0.010 | 0.024 |
| Opx. | 0.023 | 0.051 | 0.048 | 0.027 | 0.014 | 0.156 | 0.184 | 0.290 |
| Cpx | 1.688 | 3.640 | 2.636 | 0.946 | 0.448 | — | — | 1.690 |
| **Lherzolite–sea water interaction** | | | | | | | | |
| LHZ (WR) | 0.198 | 0.409 | 0.289 | 0.104 | 0.049 | — | — | 0.243 |
| LH2(300/10) | 0.186 | 0.397 | 0.290 | 0.105 | 0.040 | — | — | 0.168 |
| LH4(200/10) | 0.186 | 0.397 | 0.293 | 0.106 | 0.042 | — | — | 0.159 |
| LH5(300/30) | — | 0.487 | 0 300 | 0.135 | 0.058 | — | — | — |
| **Dunite–sea water interaction** | | | | | | | | |
| DUN(WR) | 0.078 | 0.138 | 0.097 | 0.033 | 0.015 | — | — | 0.094 |
| LH3(300/10) | 0.060 | 0.129 | 0.107 | 0.038 | 0.015 | — | — | 0.081 |
| **Harzburgite–sea water interaction** | | | | | | | | |
| HZB(WR) | — | 0.034 | 0.024 | 0.009 | 0.004 | — | — | 0.091 |
| LH6(300/10) | — | 0.045 | 0.037 | 0.012 | 0.005 | — | — | 0.057 |
| LH7(300/10) | — | — | 0.025 | 0.010 | — | — | 0.048 | 0.079 |
| LH8(300/20) | — | 0.065 | 0.032 | 0.011 | 0.005 | — | 0.046 | 0.075 |
| Blank pg (Range) | 1750 | 100–1400 | 50–400 | 20 | 5 | 5 | 5 | 5 |
| Chondrite | 0.2446 | 0.6379 | 0.4738 | 0.1540 | 0.0580 | 0.2541 | 0.166 | 0.165 |

**Table 2.** *Strontium and neodymium isotope ratios and Sr abundance data for primary minerals and altered peridotites.*

| Sample | Sr | $^{87}Sr/^{86}Sr$ | $^{143}Nd/^{144}Nd$ |
|---|---|---|---|
| VISS 01 (cpx) | 77.9 | 0.70280 (3) | 0.513088 (6) |
| LH2 (300/10) | 61.2 | 0.70855 (2) | — |
| LH4 (200/10) | 30.5 | 0.70872 (2) | 0.513104 (12) |
| LH6 (300/10) | 54.7 | 0.71018 (5) | 0.513136 (13) |
| ,, | — | 0.71020 (3) | — |
| LH7 (300/10) | 21.5 | 0.71017 (2) | — |
| LH8 | 63.7 | 0.70992 (4) | — |

*Note*: Numbers in brackets after $^{87}Sr/^{86}Sr$ and $^{143}Nd/^{144}Nd$ ratios are the two sigma errors.

chondrite-normalised REE abundance pattern is essentially LREE depleted with a slight enrichment in La because their REE geochemistry is dominated by diopside (Fig. 3, Table 1). Reconstituted harzburgites contain olivine: orthopyroxene = 75:25 (LH6; LH7; LH8) and the reconstituted dunite contains olivine: orthopyroxene: clinopyroxene: spinel = 88.6:7.2:3.0:1.2 (LH3). The harzburgites have a LREE depleted chondrite-normalized REE abundance profile at a low level of enrichment, a factor that reflects the lack of diopside and the abundance of olivine (Fig. 4, Table 1). The dunite has a light REE depleted chondrite-normalized REE abundance pattern with a slight enrichment in La (Fig. 4,

Table 1) due to the presence of 3% clinopyroxene.

### Serpentinites

The experimentally produced serpentinites (after lherzolite) have a chondrite-normalised REE abundance profile similar to the lherzolite (Fig. 3, Table 1). In the case of LH5 the serpentinite has elevated Ce,Nd,Sm and Eu contents. In LH4 and LH2 the Yb content in the serpentinite is less than in the lherzolite. Overall the LREE do not appear to be preferentially mobilized during lherzolite–sea water alteration at 300°C. The experimentally produced serpentinite (after

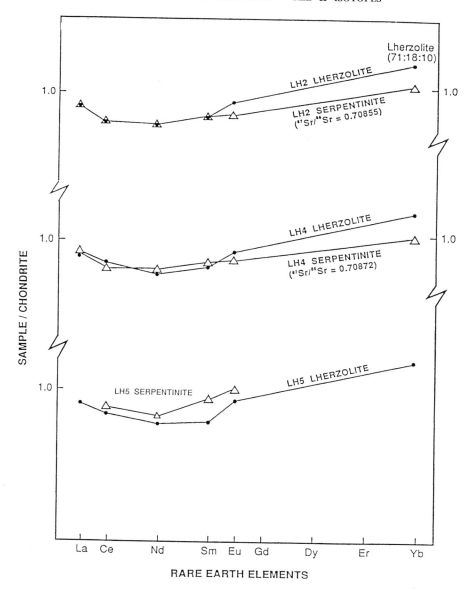

**Fig. 3.** Chondrite-normalized rare earth element abundance patterns for experimentally produced serpentinites after lherzolite (71:18:10 = olivine: orthopyroxene:clinopyroxene). Note that the light rare earth elements (LREE) are not systematically enriched over their abundance in the lherzolite despite a marked change in $^{87}Sr/^{86}Sr$ ratio from N-MORB to almost that of Pacific sea water (Elderfield *et al.* 1982). The different level of enrichment in LH5 serpentinite (bottom) may be due to inaccuracies in sample weight.

dunite) has a chondrite-normalized REE abundance pattern identical to the dunite (Fig. 4a, Table 1) again indicating that the REE were not mobilized by sea water alteration at 300°C.

The experimentally produced serpentinites (after harzburgite) have chondrite-normalized REE abundance patterns that mimic that of the harzburgite (Fig. 4b, Table 1). However, in some cases the light and middle REE (Ce, Nd, Sm, Eu) have concentrations at a higher level of enrichment. Er concentrations are close to the harzburgite whereas Yb data are lower than the

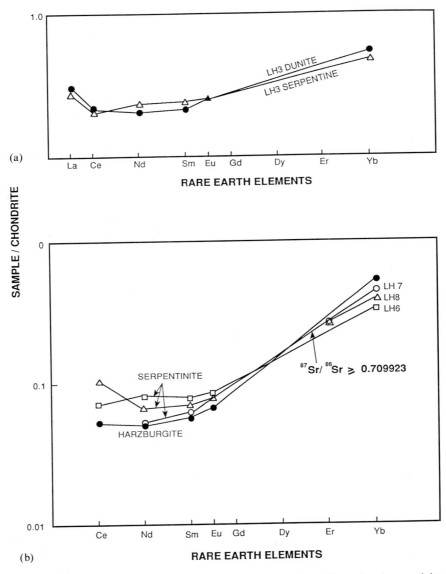

**Fig. 4. (a)** Chondrite-normalized REE abundance patterns for experimentally produced serpentinite after dunite (89:7:3:2 = olivine:orthopyroxene:clinopyroxene:spinel). Note that the REE are identical in the fresh initial peridotite and the serpentinite. **(b)** Chondrite-normalized REE abundance patterns for experimentally produced serpentinites after harzburgite (75:25 = olivine:orthopyroxene). Note that the LREE are elevated in the serpentinite relative to the unaltered harzburgite (clinopyroxene free). The difference between (a) and (b) may be that the effects of alteration are only apparent in peridotites with very low abundances of REE (i.e. harzburgites and clinopyroxene-free dunites).

unaltered harzburgite. Although the LREE in the serpentinites (after harzburgites) are at very low levels, where errors on data and blanks are significantly higher than in the serpentinites produced from lherzolites, these data provide some indication that Ce, Nd and Sm abundances in the serpentinites (after harzburgite) were increased by interaction with sea water.

The serpentinites contain 21–64 ppm Sr relative to an initial maximum concentration of 8 ppm in the lherzolites and ≪1 ppm in the harzburgites. No correlation exists between $^{87}Sr/$

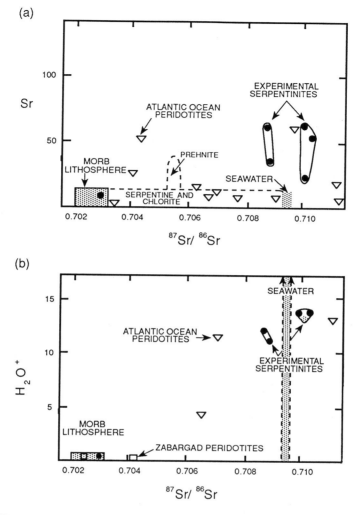

**Fig. 5. (a)** $^{87}Sr/^{86}Sr$ versus $H_2O^+$ in naturally and experimentally serpentinized peridotites. Note that the Sr abundances in some serpentinites are higher than in sea water or the initial unaltered peridotite. This is due to the growth of Ca-rich phases which accommodate high levels of sea water Sr. The occurrence of both naturally and experimentally produced serpentinites with $^{87}Sr/^{86}Sr$ > sea water remains problematical. Serpentine, chlorite and prehnite data from Atlantic Ocean peridotites are taken from Kimball & Gerlach (1986). The Pacific sea water data are from Piepgras & Wasserburg (1980) and Elderfield *et al.* (1982). **(b)** $^{87}Sr/^{86}Sr$ versus Sr in naturally and experimentally serpentinized peridotites. Note that natural and experimental serpentinites have comparable water contents and $^{87}Sr/^{86}Sr$ ratios. The Atlantic peridotite data are taken from Bonatti *et al.* (1970) and the Zabargad peridotite data from Brueckner *et al.* (1988). The Pacific sea water data are from Piepgras & Wasserburg (1980) and Elderfield *et al.* (1982).

$^{86}Sr$ ratio and Sr abundance (Fig. 5a) but it is apparent that the serpentinites with the highest $^{87}Sr/^{86}Sr$ ratios are the most hydrated (Fig. 5b). In the serpentinites (after lherzolite) $^{87}Sr/^{86}Sr$ = 0.7085–0.7087 and in the serpentinites (after harzburgite) $^{87}Sr/^{86}Sr$ = 0.7099–0.7102 the latter

being beyond that of Pacific sea water (Table 2). Two of the experimentally produced serpentinites (LH4 and LH6) have $^{143}Nd/^{144}Nd$ = 0.51310–0.51314, within error of the value for the clinopyroxene that comprises part of the fresh peridotite (Table 2).

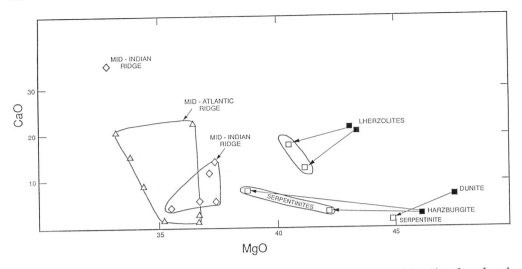

**Fig. 6.** MgO–CaO variation in unaltered peridotites, experimentally produced serpentinites (data from Janecky 1982; Janecky & Seyfried 1986) and oceanic peridotites from the Atlantic and Indian oceans (data from Bonatti 1968; Miyashiro *et al.* 1969; Vinogradov *et al.* 1969).

## Discussion

Peridotite–sea water interaction has important implications for the chemistry of sea water and the modification of the oceanic lithosphere. Seyfried & Dibble (1980) noted that most of the alteration minerals produced by peridotite–sea water experiments have been reported in natural oceanic serpentinites, with the exception of anhydrite. Seyfried & Dibble (1980) and Janecky & Seyfried (1986) studied the change in sea water chemistry and observed a marked decrease in Mg, Ca and sulphate, in the reacted sea water, due to the uptake of these elements during serpentinization of the peridotite and concomitant growth of anhydrite ($CaSO_4$). The changes in Mg and Ca observed in the experimentally produced serpentinites project toward the field of natural serpentinites from the Atlantic and Indian oceans (Fig. 6). The concentrations of Na, K, Cl, Ni and B, in the reacted sea water, remained constant during the peridotite–sea water experiments (Seyfried & Dibble 1980), the implication being that they were not significantly changed by dissolution of the primary minerals in the peridotite. Interestingly at the end of the experiments, when the system is cooled, the concentrations of Fe, Mn and B decreased in the sea water (increased in the serpentinite) and strontium increased in the sea water (decreased in the serpentinite) (Fig. 5a). This points to the importance of both higher temperatures (greenschist facies) during the production of serpentinites and low temperature sea floor weathering (zeolite facies) conditions.

### Growth of Ca-rich phases

The concentration of Sr in all the experimentally produced serpentinites was elevated above that of the initial peridotite (< 8 ppm) and Pacific sea water (7 ppm) (Fig. 5a). Compared to the unaltered peridotite and unreacted Pacific sea water, the serpentinites, after lherzolite, have 4–8 times as much Sr and the serpentinites, after harzburgite, have up to 3–9 times as much Sr. If we assume that the unaltered olivine and orthopyroxene contain negligible Sr then much of the Sr in the serpentinites (LH6,7 & 8) must be accounted for by (a) the growth of new phases, or (b) the survival of primary clinopyroxene, a major repository for Sr. It is known that Sr tends to be encorporated in Ca-rich phases and consequently Sr should be a sensitive indicator of the growth of Ca-rich phases. Analysis of experimentally altered basalt (Menzies & Seyfried 1979) demonstrated significantly lower Sr in the unaltered basaltic glass relative to the altered whole rock (anhydrite + smectite + basaltic glass). This was interpreted to mean that a considerable amount of Sr was contained within the anhydrite. Anhydrite formed in the lherzolite experiments and truscottite/carbonate in the harzburgite experiments (Janecky & Seyfried 1986). The variable amount of Sr observed in the serpentinites (Fig. 5a,b) is probably a response to several factors including the retrograde solubility of anhydrite during the 3-hour quench at the end of experiments where the temperature is reduced from 300–25°C. The serpentinites which formed as a result of experimental alteration of harzburgite (< 1 ppm Sr) have gained more Sr from sea water than the serpentinites after lherzolite (8 ppm Sr). This is believed to be due to the growth of carbonate in the harzburgites and the more effective uptake of Sr by this phase. The Sr content of the experimentally produced serpentinites is similar to that reported for abyssal serpentinites and their constituent minerals (Bonatti *et al.* 1970; Kimball & Gerlach 1986).

The majority of natural serpentinites from the Atlantic Ocean (Bonatti *et al.* 1970) have Sr contents and $^{87}Sr/^{86}Sr$ ratios between MORB peridotite and Atlantic sea water (Fig. 5a,b) but several samples have elevated Sr contents at variable $^{87}Sr/^{86}Sr$ ratios, one sample being close in composition to the experimentally produced serpentinite LH8. As in the case of the experimentally produced serpentinites this may be due to the growth of Ca-rich phases. Although the precise Sr content of the Ca-rich phases produced in these experiments is not known it should be noted that natural aragonites from oceanic serpentinites (Bonatti *et al.* 1980) contain around 1% Sr with $^{87}Sr/^{86}Sr = 0.7097$, similar to present-day sea water.

The $^{87}Sr/^{86}Sr$ ratios in the experimentally produced serpentinites are higher than the initial composition of the peridotite (Fig. 5a,b). Higher $^{87}Sr/^{86}Sr$ ratios than Pacific sea water are evident in all the carbonate/truscottite-bearing serpentinites after harzburgite. In contrast, the $^{87}Sr/^{86}Sr$ ratios in the anhydrite-bearing serpentinites after lherzolite lie between the initial peridotite and Pacific sea water. It is also evident from the relationships between Sr and $^{87}Sr/^{86}Sr$ ratio that simple mixing of peridotite and sea water does not explain the data. Whilst the elevated Sr contents have been explained by the growth of Ca-rich phases the occurrence of serpentinites with $^{87}Sr/^{86}Sr$ > Pacific sea water needs to be further investigated. It is unlikely to be caused by the mass spectrometric procedural blank, as this is small in relation to the Sr separated from the serpentinites (Table 1).

## Dissolution rate with respect to elemental and isotopic data

Orthopyroxene initially dissolved faster than olivine but as reactions proceeded olivine reacted at an approximately equal rate to orthopyroxene.

In the harzburgite, lherzolite and dunite experiments olivine reacted slightly faster than orthopyroxene. Orthopyroxene was totally dissolved when only part of the olivine had reacted. The total loss of orthopyroxene and the relatively unreacted status of clinopyroxene has important implications for elemental and isotopic data. The serpentinites (after lherzolite), containing 10% diopside, are less hydrated (Fig. 5b) and have lower $^{87}Sr/^{86}Sr$ ratios than the serpentinites (after harzburgite) that contained no diopside. In contrast the $^{143}Nd/^{144}Nd$ ratio remains unchanged in the serpentinites (after lherzolite and harzburgite) despite alteration to serpentine. The behaviour of $^{87}Sr/^{86}Sr$, $^{143}Nd/^{144}Nd$, Sr and the total REE concentration reflects (a) the survival of diopside during serpentinization and hence the retention of 'primary' neodymium isotopic compositions and REE concentrations, (b) the loss of anhydrite at the termination of the experiments, and (c) the more effective uptake of sea water Sr by carbonate. Overall, the experimentally produced serpentinites display similar changes in $^{87}Sr/^{86}Sr$ and water (Fig. 5b) to natural serpentinites from the Atlantic Ocean (Bonatti *et al.* 1970; Kimball & Gerlach 1986).

## REE mobility or immobility during serpentinization

For some time the possibility of selective mobilization of the REE has been alluded to by various authors but no unequivocal evidence exists in the literature. Studies of the rare earth geochemistry of variably serpentinized peridotites from the Lizard (Frey 1969), Pindos (Montigny *et al.* 1973), Vourinos (Montigny 1975), Anatalya (Montigny 1975) and Troodos ophiolites (Kay & Senechal 1976) revealed that peridotites are enriched in the LREE (Ce–Nd), depleted in the middle REE (Sm–Gd) and enriched in the heavy REE (Dy–Lu). This compared favourably with that observed in oceanic peridotites (Shih 1972) and led to the suggestion that the LREE were perhaps mobilized by water/rock interaction. Sun & Nesbitt (1978) reported possible mobility of $Eu^{2+}$ during serpentinization and Shih (1972) noted that 38% of the Nd in a serpentinized oceanic peridotite could be removed by 1 N nitric acid. In addition, Ottonello *et al.* (1979) concluded that the LREE were mobilized during serpentinization. However, a case for the relative immobility of the LREE during serpentinization has been made by several authors who have argued that there is no correlation between REE abundances and serpentinization (Frey *et al.* 1983; Loubet *et al.* 1975). Frey (1983) reviewed the available literature regarding REE mobility and concluded that early work on the Lizard peridotite (Frey 1969) indicative of LREE mobility was probably in error. High-precision data (Frey *et al* 1991; Gruau *et al.* 1991) on variably serpentinized mantle peridotites indicate that the LREE are not preferentially mobilized at the temperatures associated with serpentinization. Serpentinized lherzolites and harzburgites from the Horoman peridotite, Japan, (Frey *et al.* 1991) have light REE depleted profiles with no evidence for enrichments in La, Ce or Nd. Similarly, serpentinized lherzolites and harzburgites from China Mountain, California, (Gruau *et al.* 1991) have LREE depleted profiles at concentrations as low as <0.01 × chondrite for the LREE. No anomalously enriched LREE concentrations are reported.

The data reported herein provide a more precise picture of REE mobility in that the conditions of serpentinization (temperature, pressure, water/rock ratio) and the composition of the water and the starting materials are tightly constrained. While one can state, in general terms, that no unequivocal evidence exists for a systematic change in the abundance of the light REE during experimental serpentinization of lherzolite and dunite (both clinopyroxene-bearing rocks), some indication exists for anomalous behaviour of some of the light REE during experimental serpentinization of clinopyroxene-free rocks (i.e. harzburgite). In the case of the serpentinites produced from harzburgite, uptake of the LREE (La? > Ce > Nd) from sea water may be enhanced by the growth of carbonate rather than anhydrite. The mobility of the LREE during serpentinization of harzburgite is consistent with earlier observations made by Shih (1972) and Ottonello *et al.* (1979). However, the similarity in $^{143}Nd/^{144}Nd$ isotopic ratio between the experimentally produced serpentinites and the fresh, unaltered clinopyroxene (Table 2) indicates that the bulk of the Nd in the experimentally produced serpentinites is 'primary'.

### Implications for the geochemistry of oceanic and ophiolitic peridotites

In naturally serpentinized peridotites the relative reaction rates tend to be olv = opx ≫ cpx but in experimentally serpentinized peridotites olv = opx ≫ cpx. Janecky & Seyfried (1986) concluded that this may be due to a surface area effect and reaction rates. However, it does not significantly affect discussions of the application of the isotopic and elemental data to natural systems since the most significant mineral repository for the LREE and Sr is diopside and

it tends to be the least reactive phase according to both natural and experimental data.

Early studies of $^{87}Sr/^{86}Sr$ ratios and Sr variation in oceanic and ophiolitic peridotites recorded a vast range in $^{87}Sr/^{86}Sr = 0.7028–0.7290$ that did not match that reported from mid-ocean ridge magmas or, in some cases, sea water (e.g. Melson *et al.* 1972; Bonatti *et al.* 1970) (Fig. 6b). Melson *et al.* (1972) believed that the range in strontium isotopic composition of St Paul's Rocks was due to involvement of Atlantic sea water in serpentinization ($^{87}Sr/^{86}Sr = 0.7092$) (Elderfield *et al.* 1982). In contrast, Bonatti *et al* (1970) considered that sea water contamination may have produced the high $^{87}Sr/^{86}Sr$ ratios in oceanic peridotites, but disregarded it for several reasons.

(1) Fifty per cent of the dredged peridotites from the Atlantic Ocean had $^{87}Sr/^{86}Sr$ ratios greater than sea water, thus invalidating sea water contamination (Bonatti *et al.* 1970). However, it is evident from the sea water–basalt experiments that some of the experimentally produced serpentinites also have isotopic ratios higher than average Pacific sea water. From the variation in $^{87}Sr/^{86}Sr$ and Sr (Fig. 5a) it is apparent that a simple mixing process does not apply to these experiments. Given the concentrations of Sr in these serpentinites and the blank data (Table 1), the high $^{87}Sr/^{86}Sr$ ratios cannot be accounted for by laboratory contamination. The presence of $^{87}Sr/^{86}Sr$ ratios higher than sea water in natural serpentinites does not invalidate sea water as a potential (or, in the case of the experiments, a known) contaminant but it may point to an undefined process occurring both in nature and in the laboratory.

(2) Serpentinized peridotites from the Atlantic Ocean, with very low Sr contents, did not have $^{87}Sr/^{86}Sr$ ratios closest to that of sea water (Bonatti *et al.* 1970). Low Sr peridotites would not necessarily have an isotopic ratio closest to sea water. If we consider the experimental data it is apparent that of the two serpentinites with the highest $^{87}Sr/^{86}Sr$ ratios (Fig. 5a), one has the lowest Sr content (i.e. LH7). The Sr content of any serpentinite is rather complex being governed by the initial Sr content of the unaltered rock, the amount of Sr leached during interaction with sea water, the growth of Ca–Sr minerals during alteration and the possible loss of these Ca–Sr minerals due to their retrograde solubility (as in the case of anhydrite).

(3) Serpentinized peridotites from the St Peter–

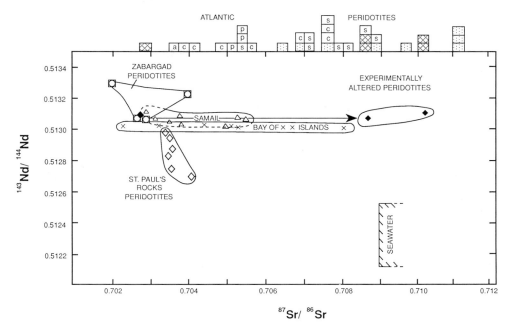

**Fig. 7.** $^{87}Sr/^{86}Sr$ versus $^{143}Nd/^{144}Nd$ for peridotites and basalts. Note the dispersion of altered basalts and experimentally produced serpentinites toward higher $^{87}Sr/^{86}Sr$ ratios with little or no change in the $^{143}Nd/^{144}Nd$ ratio. Two of the natural peridotites from Zabargad Island, with the lowest $^{143}Nd/^{144}Nd$ ratios, (Brueckner *et al.* 1988) are joined by a tie line to demonstrate the effect of leaching on the $^{87}Sr/^{86}Sr$ ratio. The high $^{87}Sr/^{86}Sr$ ratio in one of the Zabargad peridotites may be the result of sea water exchange. The histogram on the $^{87}Sr/^{86}Sr$ axis includes whole-rock data from St Paul's Rocks (Bonatti *et al.* 1970; Melson *et al.* 1972) and mineral data from the Islas Orcadas peridotites (a: amphibole; c: chlorite; s: serpentine; p: prehnite) (Kimball & Gerlach 1986). Recent analyses of peridotites from St Paul's Rocks (Roden *et al.* 1984) plot in a field similar to that of ocean island basalts and differ from earlier analyses. Roden *et al.* (1984) commented that these earlier analyses ($^{87}Sr/^{86}Sr$ = 0.7028–0.7083) (Melson *et al.* 1972) should be disregarded. The ophiolitic basalt data (Samail and Bay of Islands) are taken from Jacobsen & Wasserburg (1979) and McCulloch *et al.* (1980), the Atlantic peridotite data from Melson *et al.* (1972) and Bonatti *et al.* (1970) and the Pacific/Atlantic sea water data from Piepgras & Wasserburg (1980), Elderfield *et al.* (1982) and Palmer & Elderfield (1986).

Paul Islets show no indication of sea water contamination (i.e. high $^{87}Sr/^{86}Sr$ ratio) despite being highly serpentinized (Bonatti *et al.* 1970). While the degree of serpentinization (i.e. $H_2O^+$) appears to relate systematically to the $^{87}Sr/^{86}Sr$ ratio (Fig. 5b), the $^{87}Sr/^{86}Sr$ is also be governed by the amount of diopside in the original peridotite, the extent to which it has survived serpentinization and the degree to which new minerals have grown with concomitant uptake of sea water Sr. One could conceive of a situation where a clinopyroxene-rich peridotite maintains a relatively low $^{87}Sr/^{86}Sr$ when hydrated due to the unreactive nature of the main repository for Sr and $^{87}Sr/^{86}Sr$ (i.e. clinopyroxene).

To overcome the complex problems associated with whole-rock systems, recent isotopic work

has concentrated on careful separation of primary minerals from peridotites (Brueckner 1974; Menzies & Murthy 1978; Polve & Allegre 1980; Richard & Allegre 1980; Zindler *et al.* 1983; Reisberg & Zindler 1986; Brueckner *et al.* 1988; Reisberg *et al.* 1989; Bodinier *et al.* 1991; Downes *et al.* 1991; Gruau *et al.* 1991) or careful selection of rock types (Roden *et al.* 1984). In particular, clinopyroxene has been chosen because of the high concentration of Sr and REE and its generally unreactive character (Janecky & Seyfried 1986). Brueckner *et al.* (1988) compared $^{87}Sr/^{86}Sr$ ratios in clinopyroxenes with whole rocks before and after leaching and concluded that leaching significantly reduced the $^{87}Sr/^{86}Sr$ ratio in the peridotite. However, Bodinier *et al.* (1991) demonstrated that at very high degrees of serpentinization (>50%) even the $^{87}Sr/^{86}Sr$ ratio of the clinopyroxene can be adversely affected. This increase in $^{87}$Sr/$^{86}$Sr may also be associated with an increase in Rb/Sr ratio.

On a $^{87}$Sr/$^{86}$Sr versus $^{143}$Nd/$^{144}$Nd diagram the fresh, unaltered clinopyroxene used in these experiments and the experimentally produced serpentinites lie on a sub-horizontal array (Fig. 7) due to marked changes to the $^{87}$Sr/$^{86}$Sr ratio and no change to the $^{143}$Nd/$^{144}$Nd ratio during conversion of the fresh peridotite to a serpentine + anhydrite + carbonate assemblage. Little or no change to the $^{143}$Nd/$^{144}$Nd ratio and a marked change to the $^{87}$Sr/$^{86}$Sr ratio with serpentinization/alteration has been demonstrated elsewhere on ophiolitic and oceanic rocks (Fig. 7). While the bulk of the peridotites from St. Paul's Rocks and Zabargad Island define a linear anti-correlation between $^{87}$Sr/$^{86}$Sr and $^{143}$Nd/$^{144}$Nd ratio, the elevated $^{87}$Sr/$^{86}$Sr ratio in one of the Zabargad Island peridotites may reflect secondary processes. For these rocks, Brueckner *et al.* (1988) demonstrated that leaching experiments can lower the $^{87}$Sr/$^{86}$Sr ratio but that leached whole rocks, unleached whole rocks and clinopyroxenes had identical $^{143}$Nd/$^{144}$Nd ratios. Gruau *et al.* (1991) measured $^{143}$Nd/$^{144}$Nd ratios in serpentinized lherzolites and harzburgites from the Trinity Ophiolite California and found that the mantle rocks (i.e peridotites) and the crustal rocks (i.e. granites) defined a linear array in an Sm–Nd isochron diagram. This may indicate that the $^{143}$Nd/$^{144}$Nd ratio was not severely modified by post-consolidation processes and that it had retained primary magmatic information. This is further verified by the ages obtained by Gruau *et al.* (1991) which are identical to zircon ages from elsewhere in the Trinity massif. Had the $^{143}$Nd/$^{144}$Nd ratios of the peridotites been affected by serpentinization one would not have expected such systematics to survive in rocks with such low REE contents.

## Conclusions

High temperature serpentinization of MORB peridotite (i.e.lherzolite, dunite & harzburgite) by Pacific sea water provides the following information regarding the geochemistry of serpentinites.

(1) The 'unreactive' nature of clinopyroxene during high temperature serpentinization of peridotite is crucial in determining the $^{87}$Sr/$^{86}$Sr ratio and REE content of serpentinites as it is the main repository for Sr ($^{87}$Sr/$^{86}$Sr ratio) and the REE ($^{143}$Nd/$^{144}$Nd ratio).

(2) The LREE are not preferentially mobilized during serpentinization of clinopyroxene-

bearing peridotites (e.g.lherzolites or dunites) at 300°C.

(3) The LREE are preferentially encorporated into secondary minerals (i.e. lizardite, carbonate, truscottite) during alteration of clinopyroxene-free peridotites (i.e. harzburgites).

(4) The $^{143}$Nd/$^{144}$Nd ratio is unaffected by alteration of peridotite to serpentinite at the conditions prevailing during these experiments.

(5) The growth of Ca-rich phases during serpentinization has important implications for the $^{87}$Sr/$^{86}$Sr ratio due to the uptake of sea water Sr by phases like anhydrite, truscottite and carbonate.

(6) The $^{87}$Sr/$^{86}$Sr ratio of peridotite is dramatically changed during experimental serpentinization and is most marked in clinopyroxene-free serpentinites.

(7) The $^{143}$Nd/$^{144}$Nd ratio and, to some degree, REE abundance data, should be carefully used to elucidate the origin of abyssal peridotites particularly those containing relict primary clinopyroxene. The Rb–Sr systematics of such rocks should be treated with extreme caution.

(8) While it is generally accepted that extremely high water/rock ratios ($> 10^4$) are required to promote the exchange of REE between basaltic rocks and sea water, the low water/rock ratios ($\ll 10^2$) used in the experimental serpentinization of harzburgite were associated with slight changes to the LREE content, marked changes to the $^{87}$Sr/$^{86}$Sr ratio and no change to the $^{143}$Nd/$^{144}$Nd ratio.

This work was supported by the National Science Foundation and Royal Holloway, University of London. H. Elderfield, F. Frey and M. Thirlwall are thanked for their comments on an earlier version of this manuscript. Sandra and Lynn are thanked for their skill with computer graphics.

## References

BODINIER, J.-L., MENZIES, M. A. & THIRLWALL, M. F. 1991. Continental to Oceanic Mantle Transition – REE and Sr–Nd isotopic geochemistry of the Lanzo Lherzolite Massif. *Journal of Petrology*, Special Lherzolites Issue, 191–210.

BONATTI, E. 1968. Ultramafic rocks from the mid-Atlantic ridge. *Nature*, **219**, 363–367.

——, HONNEREZ J. & FERRARA, G. 1970. Equatorial Mid-Atlantic Ridge: petrologic and Sr isotopic evidence for an alpine-type rock assemblage. *Earth and Planetary Science Letters*, **9**, 247–256.

——, LAWRENCE, J. R., HAMLYN, P. R. & BREGER, D. 1980. Aragonite from deep sea ultramafic rocks. *Geochimica et Cosmochimica Acta*, **44**, 1207–1214.

BRUECKNER, H. K. 1974. Mantle Rb/Sr and $^{87}$Sr/$^{86}$Sr

ratios from clinopyroxenes from Norwegian garnet peridotites and pyroxenites. *Earth and Planetary Science Letters*, **24**, 26–32.

——, ZINDLER, A., SEYLER, M. & BONATTI, E. 1988. Zabargad and the isotopic evolution of the sub-Red Sea mantle and crust. *Tectonophysics*, **150**, 163–176.

DARWIN, C. 1845. *Journal of Researches during the Voyage of H.M.S. 'Beagle'*. T. Nelson and Sons, Ltd. London.

DICK, H. J. B., FISHER, R. L. & BRYAN, W. B. 1984. Mineralogic variability of the uppermost mantle along mid-ocean ridges. *Earth and Planetary Science Letters*, **69**, 88–106.

DOWNES, H., BODINIER, J.-L., THIRLWALL, M. F., LORAND, J.-P. & FABRIES, J. 1991. REE and Sr–Nd isotopic geochemistry of eastern Pyrenean peridotite massifs: sub-continental lithospheric mantle modified by continental magmatism. *Journal of Petrology*, Special Lherzolites Issue, 97–116.

ELDERFIELD, H., GIESKES, J. M., BAKER, P. A., OLDFIELD, R. K., HAWKESWORTH, C. J. & MILLER, R. 1982. $^{87}Sr/^{86}Sr$ and $^{18}O/^{16}O$ ratios, interstitial water chemistry and diagenesis in deep-sea carbonate sediments of the Ontong Java Plateau. *Geochimica et Cosmochimica Acta*, **46**, 2259–2268.

EVENSEN, N., HAMILTON, P. J. & O'NIONS, R. K. 1978. Rare earth abundances in chondritic meteorites. *Geochimica et Cosmochimica Acta*, **42**, 1199–1212.

FREY, F. A. 1969. Rare earth abundances in a high-temperature peridotite intrusion. *Geochimica et Cosmochimica Acta*, **33**, 1429–1447.

——, 1983 Rare earth element abundances in upper mantle rocks. *In*: HENDERSON, P. (ed.) *Rare Earth Element Geochemistry*. Elsevier, Amsterdam, 153–203.

——, SUEN, C. Y. J. & STOCKMAN, H. W. 1983. The Ronda high-temperature peridotite: geochemistry and petrogenesis. *Geochimica et Cosmochimica Acta*, **49**, 2469–2491.

——, SHIMIZU, N., LEINBACH, A., OBATA, M. & TAKAZAWA, E. 1991. Compositional variations within the lower layered zone of the Horoman Peridotite, Hokkaido, Japan: constraints on models for melt-solid segregation. *Journal of Petrology*, Special Lherzolites Issue, 211–228.

GASS, I. G. 1968. Is the Troodos Massif of Cyprus a fragment of Mesozoic Ocean Floor? *Nature*, **220**, 39–42.

—— & SMEWING, J. D. 1973. Intrusion, extrusion and metamorphism at a constructive margin: evidence from the Troodos massif Cyprus. *Nature*, **242**, 26–29.

——, LIPPARD, S. J. & SHELTON, A. W. 1984. *Ophiolites and Oceanic Lithosphere*. Geological Society London, Special Publication, **13**.

GRUAU, G., LECUYER, C., BERNARD-GRIFFITHS, J. & MORIN, N. 1991. Origin and petrogenesis of the Trinity Ophiolite complex (California): new constraints from REE and Nd isotopic data. *Journal of Petrology*, Special Lherzolites Issue, 229–242.

HESS, H. H. 1954. Geological hypotheses and the earth's crust under the oceans. *Proceedings of the Royal Society of London*, **222A**, 341–348.

—— 1955. Serpentinites, orogeny and epeirogeny. *Geological Society of America Special Paper*, **62**, 391–408.

JACOBSEN, S. B. & WASSERBURG, G. J. 1979. Nd and Sr isotopic study of the Bay of Islands Ophiolite Complex and the evolution of the source of midocean ridge basalts. *Journal of Geophysical Research*, **84**, 7429–7445.

JANECKY, D. R. 1982. *Serpentinization of peridotite within the oceanic crust – experimental and theoretical investigations of sea water–peridotite interaction at 200°C and 300°C 500° bars*. PhD thesis, University of Minnesota

—— & SEYFRIED, W. E. 1986. Hydrothermal serpentinization of peridotite within the oceanic crust: Experimental investigations of mineralogy and major element chemistry. *Geochimica et Cosmochimica Acta*, **50**, 1357–1378.

KAY, R. & SENECHAL, R. 1976. Rare earth geochemistry of the Troodos ophiolite. *Journal of Geophysical Research*, **81**, 964–970.

KIMBALL, K. L. & GERLACH, D. C. 1986. Sr isotopic constraints on hydrothermal alteration of ultramafic rocks in two oceanic fracture zones from the South Atlantic Ocean. *Earth and Planetary Science Letters*, **78**, 177–188.

LOUBET, M., SHIMIZU, N. & ALLEGRE, C. 1975. Rare earth elements in alpine peridotites. *Contributions to Mineralogy and Petrology*, **53**, 1–12.

MCCULLOCH, M. T., GREGORY, R. T., WASSERBURG, G. J. & TAYLOR, H. P. 1980. A neodymium, strontium and oxygen isotopic study of the Cretaceous Samail ophiolite and implications for the petrogenesis and sea water–hydrothermal alteration of oceanic crust. *Earth and Planetary Science Letters*, **46**, 201–211.

MELSON, W. G., HART, S. R., & THOMPSON, G. 1972. St. Paul's rocks, equatorial Atlantic: petrogenesis, radiometric ages and implications on sea floor spreading. *Geological Society of America*, **132**, 241–272.

MENZIES, M. A. 1990. Oceanic Peridotites. *In*: FLOYD, P. (ed.) *Oceanic basalts*. Blackie, Glasgow, 363–385.

—— & MURTHY, V. R. 1978. Strontium isotope geochemistry of alpine tectonite lherzolites: data compatible with a mantle origin. *Earth and Planetary Science Letters*, **38**, 346–354.

—— & SEYFRIED, W. E. Jr. 1979. Basalt–sea water interaction: trace element and strontium isotopic variation in experimentally altered basalt. *Earth and Planetary Science Letters*, **44**, 463–472.

MIYASHIRO, A., SHIDO, F. & EWING, M. 1969. Composition and origin of serpentinites from the mid-Atlantic ridge near 24° and 30° north latitude. *Contributions to Mineralogy and Petrology*, **23**, 117–134.

MONTIGNY. R. 1975. *Geochimie comparee des corteges de roches oceaniques et ophiolitiques – problemes de leur genese*. PhD thesis, University of Paris.

——, BOUGAULT, H., BOTTINGA, Y. & ALLÈGRE, C. J. 1973. Trace element geochemistry and genesis of the Pindos ophiolite suite. *Geochimica et Cosmo-*

*chimica Acta*, **37**, 2135–2148.

OTTONELLO, G., PICCARDO, G. B. & ERNST, W. G. 1979. Petrogenesis of some Ligurian peridotites, II Rare earth element chemistry. *Geochimica et Cosmochimica Acta*, **43**, 1273–1284.

PALMER, M. R. & ELDERFIELD, H. 1986. Rare earth elements and neodymium isotopes in ferromanganese oxide coatings of Cenozoic foraminifera from the Atlantic Ocean. *Geochimica et Cosmochimica Acta*, **50**, 409–417.

PIEPGRAS, D. J. & WASSERBURG, G. J. 1980. Neodymium isotopic variation in sea water. *Earth and Planetary Science Letters*, **50**, 128–138.

POLVE, M. & ALLEGRE, C. J. 1980. Orogenic lherzolite complexes studied by $^{87}Rb/^{87}Sr$: a clue to understand the mantle convection process. *Earth and Planetary Science Letters*, **51**, 71–93.

PRICHARD, H. M. 1979. A petrographic study of the process of serpentinisation in Ophiolites and the Ocean Crust. *Contributions to Mineralogy and Petrology*, **68**, 231–241.

REISBERG, L. & ZINDLER, A. 1986/87. Extreme isotopic variations in the upper mantle: evidence from Ronda. *Earth and Planetary Science Letters*, **81**, 29–45

——, —— & JAGOUTZ, E. 1989. Further Sr and Nd isotopic results from peridotites of the Ronda Ultramafic Complex. *Earth and Planetary Science Letters*, **96**, 161–180.

RICHARD, P. & ALLEGRE, C. J. 1980. Neodymium and strontium isotope study of ophiolite and orogenic lherzolite petrogenesis. *Earth and Planetary Science Letters*, **47**, 65–74.

RODEN, M. K., HART, S. R., FREY, F. A. & MELSON, W. G. 1984. Sr, Nd and Pb isotopic and REE geochemistry of St. Paul's Rocks: the metamorphic and metasomatic development of an alkali basalt mantle source. *Contributions to Mineralogy and Petrology*, **85**, 376–390.

SEYFRIED, W. E. & DIBBLE, W. E. Jr 1980. Sea water–peridotite interaction at 300°C and 500 bars: implications for the origin of oceanic serpentinites. *Geochimica et Cosmochimica Acta*, **44**, 309–321.

SHIH, C. Y. 1972. *The rare earth geochemistry of oceanic igneous rocks.* PhD thesis. Columbia University, New York.

SUN, S. S. & NESBITT, R. W. 1978. Petrogenesis of Archean ultrabasic and basic volcanics: evidence from rare earth elements. *Contributions to Mineralogy and Petrology*, **65**, 301–325.

THIRLWALL, M. F. 1982. A triple filament method for rapid and precise analysis of rare earth elements by isotope dilution. *Chemical Geology*, **35**, 155–66.

—— 1991a. Long-term reproducibility of multicollector Sr and Nd isotope ratio analysis. *Chemical Geology*, **94**, 85–104.

—— 1991b. High-precision multicollector isotopic analysis of low levels of Nd as oxide. *Chemical Geology*, **94**, 13–22.

TILLEY, C. E. 1947. The dunite-mylonites of St. Paul's rocks (Atlantic). *American Journal of Science*, **246**, 483–491.

VINOGRADOV, A. P., UDINSTEV, G. B., DMITRIEV, V. F., KANAEV, V. F., NEPROCHNOV, Y. P., PETROVA, G. N. & RIKNOUV, L. 1969. The structure of the mid-oceanic rift zone of the Indian Ocean and its place in the world rift system. *Tectonophysics*, **8**, 377–389.

ZINDLER, A., STAUDIGEL, H., HART S. R., ENDRES, R. & GOLDSTEIN, S. 1983. Nd and Sr isotopic study of a mafic layer from Ronda ultramafic complex. *Nature*, **304**, 226–230.

**Tectonics and convergent margins**

# Orogenic uplift and collapse, crustal thickness, fabrics and metamorphic phase changes: the role of eclogites

J. F. DEWEY,[1] P. D. RYAN[2] & T. B. ANDERSEN[3]

[1]*Department of Earth Sciences, Parks Road, Oxford OX1 3PR, UK*
[2]*Department of Geology, University College, Galway*
[3]*Department of Geology, University of Oslo*

**Abstract**: Coesite-bearing eclogites in several deep crustal metamorphic assemblages now exposed in extensionally-collapsed orogens indicate the tectonic denudation of more than 90 km of crustal rocks and pre-collapsed crustal thicknesses of at least 120 km. For mountain ranges and orogenic plateaux up to 5 km in elevation and average crustal densities of about 2.8, crustal thickness cannot exceed about 80 km unless pre-shortening crustal/lithosphere thickness ratios were less than 0.135 or some way can be found to preferentially thicken the lithospheric mantle. This problem can be avoided and very thick orogenic crusts built up if granulite facies rocks transform to denser eclogite facies during shortening, where the petrographic Moho is continuously depressed below a density/seismic velocity Moho buffered at about 70 km and mountains at about 3 km. Advective thinning of the lithosphere combined with the resultant heating and eclogite to sillimanite–granulite/amphibolite transformation causes surface uplift of about 2 km, a rapid change in isostatic compensation level, and a switch from a shortening to an extensional/collapse regime. We have developed a simple numerical model based upon field observations in southwestern Norway in which coherent regional-scale transformation of lower crustal rocks to eclogite facies during lithospheric shortening is followed by heating, transformation of eclogite to amphibolite and granulite, extension, and crustal thinning by coaxial then non-coaxial mechanisms. The model also explains strong lower crustal layering (eclogite and other lenses in horizontally-extended amphibolites), regionally horizontal gneissic fabrics, rapid return from orogenic to 'normal' crustal thickness with minor erosion, the lateral and vertical juxtaposition of low-grade and high-grade rocks and rapid marine transgression shortly after orogeny.

Young orogens have maximum regional average elevations of about 5 km; their crustal thicknesses, determined directly from seismic reflection/refraction studies or indirectly from gravity anomalies, do not exceed about 70 km (Meissner 1986). The pre-plate tectonic view was that the surface elevation ($e$) of a mountain belt in perfect isostatic balance is related to its compensating root ($r$) and crustal thickness ($C_z$) by the relative densities of crust ($\rho_c$) and mantle ($\rho_m$), the floating iceberg principle in which the mantle was considered to behave as a fluid (Stokes 1849; Airy 1855; Heiskanen & Vening Meinesz 1958). The plate tectonic view is that the crust forms part of the lithospheric boundary conduction layer (thickness $l_z$) with a mantle density of $\rho_m$. The whole $l_z$ column of crust and mantle is compensated to the asthenospheric mantle of density $\rho_a$. The crust 'floats', whereas the mantle portion 'sinks', the lithosphere; therefore, the level at which the surface sits relative to the oceanic ridges depends upon $l_z$ and $C_z/l_z$. Also, the cooler upper portion of the boundary layer acts as a strong flexural beam to support loads, which allows a departure from pure zero-strength Airy isostasy and the support of loads and elevations higher than those for a pure Airy model and the development and maintenance of substantial positive gravity anomalies. The elevation of a mountain range is, therefore, a function of the vertical density distribution within and the flexural strength of the lithosphere, although, for most mountain belts, there is insufficient knowledge of these parameters yet to draw conclusions that clearly relate crustal thickness to elevation. In this paper, we wish to draw attention to some general principles of vertical density distribution in relation to elevation and crustal/lithospheric thickness that may be important in understanding orogenic evolution, although we emphasize that crust/lithospheric thickness beneath mountain ranges is poorly constrained.

Assuming homogenous bulk strain and pre-shortening crustal ($C_z$) and lithospheric ($l_z$) values of 32 km and 120 km respectively, crustal thickening, caused by vertical stretching, is buffered at about 70 km beneath a surface elevation of about 3 km by vertical compression caused by isostatic compensation in a thickened crust that

*From* Prichard, H. M., Alabaster, T., Harris, N. B. W. & Neary, C. R. (eds), 1993,
*Magmatic Processes and Plate Tectonics*, Geological Society Special Publication No. 76, 325–343.

balances horizontal compression caused by plate convergence (Dewey 1988; England & Houseman 1988, 1989). Elevations above 3 km may be achieved by crustal underplating or by mechanisms that thin the lithosphere without thinning the crust such as hot-spot jetting, delamination, or rapid advective thinning. The general picture that has emerged for the wide Tibetan Himalayan zone of crustal thickening is one of Palaeogene vertical plane strain crustal thickening to about 65 km, caused by the India/Eurasia convergence, succeeded by a phase of horizontal plane strain followed, in turn, by a phase of post-Miocene uplift to the present 5 km average elevation accompanied and followed by lithospheric extension and magmatism (Dewey *et al.* 1988), a phase of so-called orogenic extensional collapse (Dewey 1988). Many Phanerozoic orogens appear to follow this general pattern of shortening followed by extensional collapse (Dewey 1988), which is related probably to lithospheric shortening followed by the rapid advective removal of the lithospheric mantle root. (Houseman *et al.* 1981; England & Houseman 1988, 1989). During shortening by roughly vertical plane strain and vertical bulk stretching, buoyant crustal and negatively buoyant lithospheric mantle roots develop, rocks are progressively buried and geothermal gradient and heat flow are reduced. During shortening, the principal axis of compression is horizontal and the axis of least compression vertical. Crustal thickness is buffered at about 70 km, and the intermediate axis of compression becomes vertical, a wrench regime is developed and shortening must spread laterally if convergence continues, one possible explanation of the lateral progradation of thrust sheet complexes. Advective removal of the mantle root leads to uplift to about 5 km, a rapid increase in geothermal gradient and vertical shortening/extensional collapse in a stress regime of vertical compression.

There is sufficient seismic data to indicate that the Moho, as defined by that data, does not exceed depths of about 70 km beneath Cenozoic mountain ranges (Meissner 1986). If 70 km is the limit to which normal density (2.8) continental crust may be thickened by bulk vertical stretching, there are substantial implications for the structural and metamorphic history of orogenic belts. First, gross orogenic shortening values achieved by bulk vertical plane strain expressed by orogenic structure and fabrics cannot exceed about 50% if we start with a 'normal' thickness continental crust of about 35 km. Many orogenic belts have shortening values, at least locally, greatly in excess of 50%. Of course, shortening may be increased in several

ways such as by substantial erosion during shortening, and/or by starting with a thin crust, which would be expected at a colliding rifted margin. Both of these have operated in the Himalayas; some 20 km has been lost over large areas by erosion and some of the highest thrust sheets probably had a thin starting crust, although these factors alone are insufficient to account for Himalayan shortening. Horizontal plane strain by lateral escape tectonics will also allow increased shortening values without increasing $C_z$ although it is likely to generate steep structures and cannot generate thrust regime structures and fabrics.

A $C_z$ limit of 70 km places even greater constraints on crustal metamorphism. Rocks now at the surface in older orogens have up to 35 km of continental crust below them so that, if orogenic thickness was 70 km, erosional denudation can have removed a maximum of only 35 km and extensional collapse reduces this figure still further. Tectonic denudation mechanisms such as motion towards the surface in the footwalls of major normal faults above zones of 'replacive' lower crustal flow may allow deeper crustal levels to be exposed but we are still limited by a $C_z$ maximum of 70 km. Therefore, we would expect the regional exposure of metamorphic rocks of greenschist/amphibolite granulite facies recording pressures of around 10–12 kb with localized zones of blueschist/eclogite facies indicating maximum pressures of about 20 kb. The rocks of the Tauern window in Austria experienced peak pressures of 20 kb and yet appear to be part of a regionally-coherent metamorphic terrain now at the surface of a 50 km crust suggesting a peak $C_z$ of 100 km. In the western Alps, Chopin (1984, 1987) and Chopin *et al.* (1991) have described coesite/pyrope-bearing rocks and, in the Dabie Shan, Enami & Zhang (1990), Hirajima *et al.* (1990), Okay & Şengör (1992), Wang & Liou (1991), Wang *et al.* (1989, 1992) and Xu *et al.* (1992) have recorded and described diamond- and coesite-bearing eclogites indicating pressures of 39–40 kb. In southwestern Norway, coesite-bearing eclogites form part of the regionally-coherent Western Gneiss Region (Smith 1984; Austrheim 1987, 1991; Smith & Lappin, 1989; Andersen & Jamtveit 1990; Andersen *et al.* 1991), and experienced minimum peak pressures of 28 kb (Fig. 1) and have 35 km of subjacent crust indicating a peak $C_z$ of at least 120 km.

We are, therefore, forced into the apparent paradox that observation and theory indicate that $C_z$ cannot exceed about 70 km and yet metamorphic rocks indicate $C_z$ values of at least 120 km. The problem is how to get rocks down

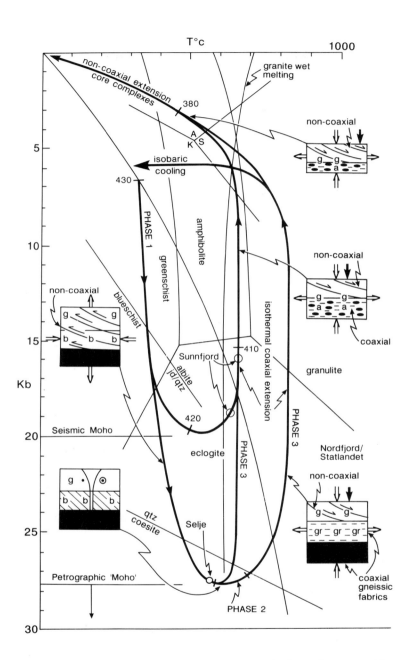

**Fig. 1.** Suggested PTt (pressure, temperature, time) paths (heavy lines) for footwall metamorphic core complex rocks beneath the Kvamshesten Detachment in southwestern Norway. a: amphibolite; b: blueschists; g: greenschist; gr: granulite; black: eclogite; A: andalusite; K: kyanite; S: sillimanite; solid short arrow: motion of surface. Data to construct the PTt paths from Brueckner (1972), Krogh (1977, 1980), Bohlen & Boettcher (1982), Smith (1984), Griffin & Brueckner (1985), Griffin et al. (1985), Lux (1985), Steel et al. (1985), Kullerud et al. (1986), Jamtveit (1987), Smith & Lappin (1989), Andersen & Jamtveit (1990), Carswell (1990), Cuthbert & Carswell (1990), Andersen et al. (1991), Cuthbert (1991), Chauvet et al. (1992).

to depths of over 100 km (burial) during shortening/thickening and then back up again (denudation) to and almost to the surface during extensional collapse and crustal thinning (Fig. 1); erosional denudation by itself is far too slow a mechanism, as will be shown in a later section for western Norway. If crust of 'normal' (*c.* 2.8) density is stretched vertically to values greatly in excess of 70 km, we would get absurdly high mountains, which would be buffered and reduced by extensional collapse. $C_z$ values of greater than 70 km could be achieved in one of two ways. First, the uplift and surface elevation of a mountain belt is partly dependent upon $C_z/l_z$, uplift increasing as the ratio increases; for $C_z/l_z$ <0.1375, shortening actually produces subsidence (Dewey 1982). A smaller $C_z/l_z$ allows a crust thicker than 70 km without the buffering effect of orogenic collapse, although this does not explain the geophysically-determined limit of $C_z$ *c.* 70 km. Secondly, if the density of crustal rocks can increase during shortening, the uplift and elevation caused by vertical stretching of the crust is reduced. If petrographically crustal rocks increase their density to mantle values during shortening, there is no obvious limit to crustal thickness and, therefore, to shortening values. Passing rocks into the eclogite facies during shortening and back out again during extensional collapse is a simple way of changing density and transforming petrographically continental crust from geophysically continental crust into 'geophysical' mantle and back again. Such metamorphic phase transitions and density changes do indeed occur as will be shown in the next section and may be related to the development of very thick orogenic crusts and the rapid denudation of high-grade metamorphic rocks during extensional collapse.

Richardson & England (1979) were the first to suggest that eclogitization of lower continental crusts may play an important role in decreasing crustal buoyancy and, therefore, in reducing surface elevation by 'weighting' the crust of orogens. This concept was taken to an 'extreme' position by Butler (1986) who argued that crustal balancing, by comparing cover shortening with cross-sectional areas in the French Alps, demands a substantial volume of 'missing' crust thrust or subducted beneath the Po Plain; that the Po Plain is not elevated, yet is supposed to have had a large amount of Alpine crust thrust beneath it, is accounted for by the view that this 'missing' crust is eclogitized. Le Pichon *et al.* (1988) and Laubscher (1990) suggested that crustal volume cannot have been preserved in the Alps and that substantial loss of crust into the mantle, or perhaps conversion of crust into

'mantle' by eclogitization must have occurred. However, the concept of permanent crustal loss into the mantle does not help us to understand the passage of crustal rocks into coesite–eclogite facies rocks to depths in excess of 100 km and their subsequent rapid denudation to upper crustal and surface positions.

England & Holland (1979) developed a model for the subduction of crustal rocks to eclogite facies and the subsequent ejective upward flow of blocks in a 'subduction' shear zone. Austrheim (1991) argued for the detachment of crustal blocks into the mantle to explain high-pressure metamorphic rocks of the southern Norwegian Caledonides. These block detachment models are implausible in at least three respects. First, if eclogitization resulted from the inclusion of crustal blocks to mantle depths it is not obvious what caused them to sink into the mantle except possibly major thrust imbrication of the Moho. Also, the subsequent denudation of such a thrust imbricated complex would surely include both eclogites and mantle ultramafics, which could scarcely explain the separation and rise of eclogite blocks from the mantle. Secondly, although in principle, eclogite blocks might rise in the mantle to the base of the crust, it is difficult to see how they could rise into lighter encasing crustal granulites and amphibolites. Thirdly, they fail to account for the regional coherence of many eclogite terrains in which eclogite-facies metamorphism, although not necessarily wholly penetrative, affected sufficient of the lower crust to make it clear that tectonic juxtaposition of eclogite blocks and amphibolite facies regional 'host' rocks has not occurred.

Exhumation during convergence has been suggested for a subduction–accretion setting in two ways. Cowan & Silling (1978) and Cloos (1982) have argued for a circulation model involving the down flow of hanging wall material as blocks of high-pressure metamorphism rocks in a low-viscosity matrix and the upward flow of the resulting mélanges against the subduction–accretion backstop. Platt (1986) showed that underplating and extension in a critically tapered subduction–accretion wedge will exhume high-pressure rocks. Both mechanisms, however, are likely to generate 'block in matrix' associations rather than exposed coherent high-pressure terrains. Furthermore, the subduction–accretion environment cannot generate pressures higher than about 10 kb.

Two further models for coesite–eclogite facies metamorphism and the subsequent denudation of regionally structurally-coherent terrains have been suggested, both of which involve rapid uplift caused by the catastrophic advective thin-

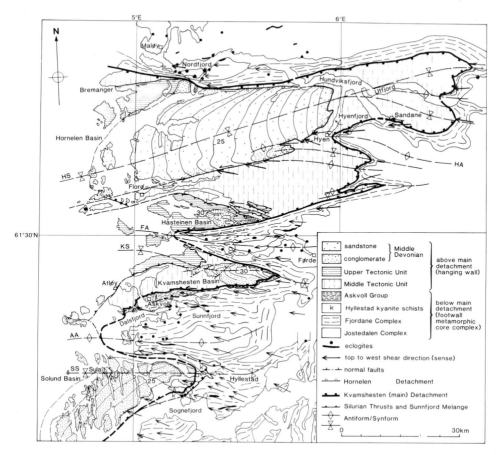

**Fig. 2.** Tectonic map of southwestern Norway between Nordfjord and Sognefjord. AA: Askvoll Antiform; FA: Førde Antiform; HA: Hyen Antiform, HS: Hornelen Synform; KS: Kvamshesten Synform; SS: Sula Synform.

ning of a thickened lithospheric root beneath the orogen. Okay & Sengör (1992) argued a model for the Dabie Shan whereby erosional denudation occurs during uplift caused by progressive thrust-stacking above an advectively thinned lithosphere. Andersen *et al.* (1991) developed a model for the western Norwegian Caledonides in which coherent crustal rocks are pulled down in a continental subduction zone by a cold heavy lithospheric root, followed by the extensional eduction of the deep crust during orogenic collapse.

The model that we propose in this paper draws upon many of the principles and ideas expressed in the works cited above and on the geology of the southwestern Norwegian Caledonides. It accounts for the development of very thick (*c.* 150 km) orogenic crusts without

absurdly high mountain belts, the rapid exhumation of regionally coherent high-pressure metamorphic terrains by tectonic denudation, limited erosional denudation and relatively small volumes of 'molasse' clastics, the widespread preservation of supracrustal rocks adjacent to high pressure rocks, the superposition of non-coaxial upon coaxial fabrics in metamorphic core complexes, pervasive lower crustal layering in collapsed orogens, and catastrophic local marine transgression during or just after extensional collapse.

## Southwestern Norway

The Caledonides of southwestern Norway illustrate extremely well the five-phase orogenic evolution model of Dewey (1988) involving lithospheric shortening, decrease in heat flow and low temperature–high pressure metamorphism (Phase 1), a commonly very short period of slow uplift during horizontal plane strain and strike-slip faulting (Phase 2), catastrophic advective removal of the negatively buoyant lithospheric orogenic root causing uplift and rapid crustal heating (Phase 3), a period of rapid lithospheric extension, subsidence, and the development of metamorphic core complexes, extensional detachments and sedimentary basins (Phase 4, extensional collapse), followed by exponentially slowing subsidence during lithospheric cooling (Phase 5). In this paper, Phase 3 and Phase 4 are combined into a single phase 3. Also, Phase 2, although well-developed in Tibet (Dewey *et al.* 1988) and other orogens is apparently absent in southwest Norway where the shortening phase is closely followed by extensional collapse. We believe that we see, in southwestern Norway, an orogenic structural/metamorphic sequence that provides most of the facets in piecing together an orogenic shortening/collapse model, particularly the critical clue in understanding the development of very thick orogenic crusts, namely a regional Silurian eclogite-facies metamorphism and its structural relationships.

The geology of the region between Sognfjord and Nordfjord, in southwestern Norway (Fig. 2) is dominated by spectacular and superbly-exposed extensional detachment tectonics (Hossack 1984; Norton 1986, 1987; Seranne & Seguret 1987; Andersen & Jamtveit 1990; Andersen *et al.* 1991). The principal extensional detachment zone, the Kvamshesten Detachment, is disposed in a series of roughly east–west-striking major antiforms and synforms plunging gently westward; shear sense indicators in the associated thick mylonite zones (Askvoll Group; Swensson & Andersen 1991) show consistent down-to-west motion of the hanging wall along a gently-dipping trajectory very roughly parallel with the axes of the antiforms and synforms. There is a profound structural and metamorphic contrast across the Kvamshesten Detachment between footwall metamorphic core complex rocks that show enormous coaxial and non-coaxial strains in coesite–eclogite to greenschist facies metamorphic grades (Fjordane & Jostedalen Complexes) and low-grade hanging wall rocks that have been affected by the extensional strains only along earlier contractional faults; all eclogite bodies are in the footwall complexes. The hanging wall and footwall assemblages preserve quite different components and facets of the Caledonian history of southwestern Norway and each is critical in developing an understanding of the kinematics and timing of structural and metamorphic events.

The hanging wall contains three fundamental components (Figs 2 & 3) from base to top: Middle Tectonic Unit (Middle Allochthon); Upper Tectonic Unit (Upper Allochthon); and Devonian basins. The Middle Tectonic Unit (Andersen *et al.* 1990) consists of a mainly igneous basement, the Dalsfjord Suite, of anorthosites, mangerites, syenites, charnockites, granites and gabbros, commonly gneissic or foliated (Brynhi 1989), which has been correlated (Milnes & Koestler 1985) with the rocks of the Jotun Nappe in south-central Norway. The Dalsfjord Suite is overlain unconformably by upper greenschist facies metasediments of the late Precambrian Hoyvik Group, which is overlain, in turn unconformably, by the low-grade lower and middle Silurian shallow-marine Herland Group. The Upper Tectonic Unit comprises the Ordovician Solund–Stavfjord Ophiolite Complex (Furnes *et al.* 1990), dated at $443 \pm 3$ Ma (Dunning & Pedersen 1988) overlain by greywackes with mafic sills, the whole comprising a thrust sheet emplacement eastwards onto the Herland Group across a basal shear carpet of the Sunnfjord Mélange during middle Silurian (Wenlock) times (Andersen *et al.* 1990). Middle Devonian non-marine red beds rest unconformably on both Middle and Upper Tectonic Units and are disposed in four main basins (Fig. 2), which appear to exhibit three types of basin morphology and evolution. The Solund and Hasteinen basins are sheets of mainly conglomerates resting unconformably or along a faulted unconformity (Solund Fault) on older rocks of the hanging wall. The Kvamshesten Basin is a series of at least three normal fault-bounded tilt sub-basins, the bounding northeast striking faults merging downwards into the main Kvamshesten Detachment (Per-Terge Osmundsen, pers. comm. 1992). The Hornelen Basin rests mainly upon an upper extensional detachment, the Hornelen Detachment, with a top to the west sense of motion, and occupies the core of the Hornelen Synform. From the basal unconformity, Hornelen strata dip monotonically eastward from about 25–40° and are truncated downward by the Hornelen Detachment; to the north and south, Hornelen strata curve and steepen into dextral and sinistral portions, respectively, of the detachment. The Devonian basins contain detritus derived wholly from older rocks of the hanging wall; not a single boulder or pebble can be matched with the high-grade rocks of the footwall metamorphic core complexes (Cuthbert 1991), in spite of the fact that Devonian sediments and footwall are in contact across the Kvamshesten Detachment in the Hasteinen and Kvamshesten Basin. This indicates that hanging wall and footwall juxta-

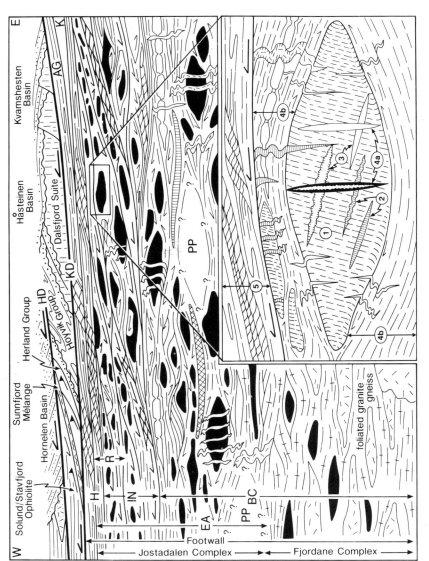

**Fig. 3.** Schematic illustration (fully described and discussed in text) based upon Andersen (1992), not to scale, illustrating the structural style and sequence of a notional EW section through Sunnfjord. AG: Askvoll 'Group'; BC: bulk coaxial deformation; EA: zone of preserved eclogite bodies in matrix of eclogite retrograded to amphibolite during bulk coaxial extension; H: zone of homogeneous, penetrative top down to the west non-coaxial deformation; HD: Hornelen Detachment; IN: zone of inhomogeneous top down to the west non-coaxial superposed upon coaxial deformation; K: Hyllestad kyanite schists; KD: Kvamshesten Detachment; PP: remnant Proterozoic footwall protolith bodies of uncertain distribution, size and shape; R: zone of heavily and pervasively retrograded eclogites; black: eclogites; vertical lines: ultramafic lenses probably part of Proterozoic protolith; oblique cross-hatch: gabbro probably Siluro-Devonian; random lines: granite, granodiorite, quartz–diorite. Inset: schematic illustration of details of kinematic sequence characteristic of preserved eclogite bodies, their coaxial amphibolite 'envelopes' and superposed top down to the west non-coaxial deformation. 1: constrictional L to L > S eclogite fabric; 2: eclogite facies extensional veins; 3: early amphibolite facies extensional veins; 4a: amphibolite facies extensional veins in eclogite bodies; 4b: amphibolite facies bulk coaxial extensional deformation in regional 'matrix'; 5: superposed top down to the west non-coaxial deformation.

position occurred across the Kvamshesten Detachment after or very late during the Middle Devonian accumulation of the basin fills and that the footwall was exhumed after Middle Devonian times.

Thus, the hanging wall records a Caledonian history of middle Silurian shortening probably driven by Greenland/Baltica plate convergence followed by a middle Devonian extensional detachment event that, as we will show below, was the end stage of a profound late Silurian/Devonian extensional collapse event recorded mainly in the footwall metamorphic core complexes. The main Kvamshesten Detachment must have originated as a regionally gently-dipping normal fault/shear zone in almost its present orientation (rejuvenated as a flat-lying brittle extensional detachment in Permian and Mesozoic times; Torsvik *et al.* 1992, although it is probable that portions of the detachment originally dipped more steeply westwards. The detachment probably nucleated on a major Scandian thrust that emplaced the Middle and Upper Tectonic Units eastwards across rocks that were subsequently extensionally displaced by rocks of the footwall metamorphic core complexes. The Askvoll Group, forming most of the mylonitic basal shear zone beneath the Kvamshesten Detachment consists principally of greenschist facies, mafic igneous and sedimentary protoliths (Skjerlie 1969; Swensson & Andersen 1991) distinct from core complex rocks below and may partly represent either an ophiolitic suture or, more likely, portions of a high-level ophiolitic nappe 'tucked in' by out-of-sequence Scandian thrusting.

Apart from the Hornelen Detachment and normal faults of the Kvamshesten Basin and Staveneset, the structure of the low-grade hanging wall rocks show little evidence of Siluro-Devonian extension. Brynhi's (1989) detailed mapping of lithological contacts in the Middle and Upper Tectonic Units in rocks throughout the hanging wall terrain south of the Hornelen Basin shows that they are unaffected by normal faults. Seranne *et al.* (1989) record extensional strains in the Devonian sediments of the Solund Basin. However, the basal contact of the Solund Basin is everywhere an unconformity or faulted unconformity and we support Nilsen's (1968) view that the NW–SE orientation of clast long axes is principally a sedimentary fabric. East–west extension occurred in the Solund Basin but it was mainly a late Palaeozoic to Mesozoic event associated with North Sea extension (Torsvik *et al.* 1992). We can find no evidence of the pervasive top-to-the-west shear sense recorded south of the Hornelen Basin between

the Hornelen Detachment and Kvamshesten Detachment by Seranne *et al.* (1989), who did not recognize that these rocks (Dalsfjord Suite and Hyvik Group) lie above the principal detachment. The penetrative structure of these rocks is Scandian (Wenlockian) or older in which the Dalsfjord Suite and Hyvik Group are tightly folded together and commonly strongly foliated (Brynhi 1989). Thus the hanging wall is largely a low-grade semi-coherent slab with modest and localized brittle extension. The origin of the east–west antiforms and synforms is unclear. They may have been formed by a late or post–Middle Devonian north–south Svalbardian (Solundian) shortening or, we believe more likely, reflect an original megagrooved shape of the Kvamshesten Detachment formed and enhanced during east–west extension.

The highest unit of the footwall is the Askvoll Group, an almost wholly reconstituted amphibolite to greenschist facies mylonite sequence with a consistent top to the west shear sense (Fig. 3). The footwall metamorphic core complexes, the Fjordane and Jostedalen Complexes of Brynhi (1966), consist of orthogneiss, paragneiss, anorthosites, gabbros, rapakivi granites, peridotites, and amphibolites with eclogites occurring in most lithologies with, in appropriate rock types, various combinations of omphacite, jadeite, pyrope, kyanite, clinozoizite, phengite, glaucophane and coesite. Coesite-bearing eclogites occur in the northwest of the region, north of Nordfjord whereas glaucophane-bearing eclogites occur in the Sunnfjord region. The Fjordane Complex is extremely heterogeneous and consists mainly of strongly-foliated amphibolites, migmatic and augen gneisses and anorthosites with lenses and pods of abundant eclogite and less common gabbro and ultramafics. The Jostedalen Complex consists of quartz-feldspathic and granite gneisses and migmatites with eclogite and ultramafic lenses and pods and is dominated by large amounts of massive and foliated granite, granodiorite and quartz-diorite. Within both Fjordane and Jostedalen complexes, Proterozoic ages of up to 1760 Ma ago are recorded (Kullerud *et al.* 1986). These ages occur in blocks/lenses, whose size, distribution and shape are as yet unknown, within a footwall metamorphic core complex whose bulk structure and metamorphism was developed predominantly in a milieu of Siluro-Devonian extensional collapse dominated by a foliation sub-parallel with the Kvamshesten Detachment and arranged in the same gently westward-plunging antiforms and synforms, with a sub-horizontal regional stretching lineation, and characterized by a lenticular style at all scales from a few

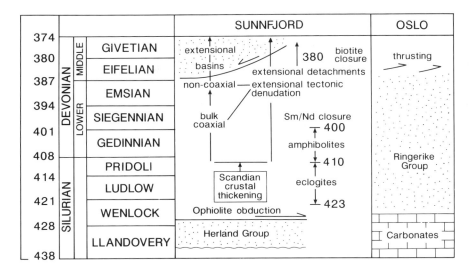

**Fig. 4.** Timing of Siluro-Devonian structural events in the Sunnfjord and Oslo regions. Data from Brueckner (1972), Bjorlykke (1983), Griffin & Brueckner (1985), Griffin *et al.* (1985), Lux (1985), Steel *et al.* (1985), Kullerud *et al.* (1986), Dunning & Pedersen (1988), Andersen & Jamtveit (1990), Andersen *et al.* (1990), Cuthbert & Carswell (1990), Andersen *et al.* (1991), Cuthbert (1991).

metres to kilometres.

In Figure 3, an attempt is made to show, schematically and not to scale, structures and relationships in the footwall Jostedalen and Fjordane complexes. The key to the orogenic evolution of the crust of southwestern Norway lies in the distribution, shape and structural/ metamorphic sequences in the numerous eclogite bodies that are enveloped in a regional principally amphibolite facies matrix. The eclogite bodies vary from a few centimetres up to about 5 km, the largest being typically within and near the base of the Jostedalen Complex. They are characteristically elongate roughly east–west with their shortest dimension normal to the regional amphibolite facies foliation. Most of the eclogite bodies are mafic, dominated by omphacite and garnet and, from the outcrop to mapping scale, have the amphibolite facies folia-tion 'wrapping' around them during the develop-ment of which they were clearly more rigid, higher viscosity, bodies. However, within the regional amphibolite 'matrix', a ghost-like rem-nant mafic eclogite mineralogy is heavily over-printed and patchy 'shadows' of the distinctive omphacite/garnet coloration within the more pervase dark-green colour of the overprinted amphibolite mineralogy can be seen in outcrop. It is quite clear that the preserved eclogites, which now constitute perhaps 10% of the foot-wall, are not merely isolated exotic bodies tecto-nically emplaced into the amphibolite but rep-resent remnants of a once pervasive or widespread eclogite facies terrain that was largely reconstituted by deformation and meta-morphism in a later amphibolite facies event.

The eclogite bodies and their immediate amphibolite envelopes preserve and illustrate, in great detail and clarity, a structural/metamor-phic sequence and history that records and de-fines a pressure/temperature/time loop (Fig. 1) of 10 Ma of Scandian crustal shortening during late Wenlockian to Pridoli times (Fig. 4) fol-lowed by about 20 Ma of Lower Devonian roughly east–west coaxial stretching, terminated during Middle Devonian times by the superposi-tion of extensional detachments with associated high-level non-coaxial top down to the west shear that juxtaposed low-grade hanging wall rocks against high-grade footwall metamorphic core complex rocks. Several eclogite bodies in Dalsfjord, most notably at Vardalsneset, to be described in detail elsewhere (Andersen, in press), illustrate the structural/metamorphic se-quence (Fig. 3, inset). A pervasive NNE-striking lineation defined by omphacite, amphibole, kya-nite, clinozoizite, and elongate garnet aggregates in a weak foliation defined mainly by phengite, constitutes an L > S fabric in the eclogite bodies, indicating an early prolate/constrictional defor-mation in the eclogite facies (Fig. 1). This fabric (1 in Fig. 3, inset) is transected by veins (2), roughly normal to the eclogite facies lineation, which evolved in eclogite to amphibolite facies. The earliest, quartz-dominated veins, up to 20 cm wide, contain garnet, omphacite, kyanite, clinozoizite, phengite, rutile and, in places, tourmaline with kyanite aggregates up to 15 cm and omphacites up to 5 cm normal to the vein walls and in continuity with the early eclogite facies lineation. Parallel with these early eclogite facies veins are later amphibole-quartz veins (3) some of which are axial to, and continue the opening of, earlier eclogite veins. Some of these earlier veins show small-scale buckling of vein walls indicating a small amount of penetrative shortening normal to the early eclogite facies lineation. These fabrics and veins are cut by N-striking amphibole/quartz veins (4a) that cut the early eclogite lineation at a low angle and the early veins at a high angle. Some of these N–S veins have symplectite hornblende/plagioclase (after clinopyroxene) margins. The eclogite bodies are surrounded by an amphibolite facies matrix with a strong and pervasive foliation (4b) that 'wraps' symmetrically around the eclogite bodies. Quartz and granite leucosome veins cut the eclogite bodies parallel with the phase 4 amphibolite veins and show variable degrees of shortening normal to foliation outside the eclogite bodies. Both granite and quartz veins, between which there is a complete compositional variation involving quartz, feldspar, amphibole, epidote, phengite and biotite, show synchronous and superposed garnet amphibolite facies metamorphism with syntaxial mineral growth from the margins of hydrofracture veins. The general picture during amphibolite facies metamorphism retrogressing the eclogites, is of a regionally bulk coaxial deformation with vertical shortening and roughly east–west extension (Andersen & Jamtveit 1990). The evidence for bulk regionally coaxial vertical shortening across the amphibolite facies foliation is symmetrical boudin development, roughly symmetrical fish-like lenses and pods of eclogites with respect to the regional foliation, roughly symmetrical boudinage of foliation at all scales with respect to the regional attitude of foliation, and especially changing sense of shear around lenses at all scales. The vertical shortening of granite sheets and quartz veins across foliation gives shortening values of up to 70% and foliation 'wrapping' around eclogite bodies gives vertical shortening values of 80% and horizontal east-west extension of about 500%. Lenses at all scales show variable senses of marginal shear that give an impression of bulk coaxial strain. However, local superposition of dextral on sinistral and sinistral on dextral is common because of changing strain/

displacement distribution and bulk coaxial lens size. This illustrates the necessity of exercising great care in 'establishing' polyphase deformation sequences and the importance of using a kinematic approach in analysing and understanding regional strain evolution rather than the somewhat arid polyphase approach typical of British structural geology during the 1950s and 1960s.

Superimposed upon the bulk coaxial fabric is a top down to the west non-coaxial deformation (5), which increases in penetration intensity upwards towards the Kvamshesten Detachment (Andersen and Jamtveit 1990). Within the Askvoll 'Group' and a zone of penetration below, non-coaxial fabrics are pervasive. In the Askvoll 'Group', the fabrics are in amphibolites to greenschists; in the penetrative non-coaxial zone beneath, they are in greenschist superimposed on amphibolite. Below this, top down to the west shear zones are inhomogeneously distributed, cutting earlier amphibolite coaxial fabrics, and diminish and die out downwards in the Jostedalen Complex (Andersen & Jamtveit 1990). Top down to the west non-coaxial shear zones and fabrics consistently cut the earlier amphibolite facies coaxial fabrics and structures.

In the Fjordane and lower parts of the Jostedalen Complex (Andersen & Jamtveit 1990), the proportion of granite, granodiorite and quartz diorite increases dramatically downwards from a small percentage of quartz and granite veins to a pervasive granite gneiss with a sub-horizontal foliation (Fig. 3). The general picture is one of increasing ductility and lower viscosities downwards during extension, heating and partial melting. In places, the lit-par-lit injection of granite veins and sheets indicates local east–west extensions of up to 500% and the development of granite-dyke complexes analogous to the mafic sheeted complexes of ophiolites. The veins show mineral growth normal to their walls, are commonly folded, and suggest a possible origin for gneissic foliation by multiple granite sheet injection rather than, or in addition to, the commonly supposed metamorphic differentiation across layering (Andersen 1992).

A major feature of the footwall complexes is the regional dominance of fabrics and structures formed during extensional collapse. Evidence for Silurian Scandian orogenic shortening (Fig. 4) is contained only in the hanging wall and in the eclogite bodies. The core complexes, representing part of the middle and lower orogenic crust, are dominated by a pervasive sub-horizontal layering consisting of a bulk coaxial gneissic foliation formed during vertical shortening and horizontal extension and containing elongate pods and lenses of eclogite up to 5 m long, together with elongate granitoid bodies, ultramafic lenses up to 3 km long and gabbro lenses up to 7 km long, of probable post-eclogite age synchronous with heating and horizontal extension (Fig. 3).

In Fig. 1, a series of smoothed PTt metamorphic loops are shown that characterize the footwall core complexes of southwestern Norway from the lower pressure (12–19 kb)/temperature (550–650°C) Sunnfjord region with glaucophane-bearing eclogites (Krogh 1980) to the higher pressure (28 kb)/temperature (> 750°C) coesite-bearing eclogites north of Nordfjord. All show an early eclogite facies metamorphism during crustal shortening from about 420–410 Ma ago with a superposed coaxial extensional amphibolite facies event, which is consistent with early heating and partial melting (granites in the footwall complex) followed by rapid roughly isothermal decompression for about 20 Ma during the Lower Devonian. North of Selje, the early heating was sufficient to carry the later isothermal decompression loop into the sillimanite–granulite field. Large amounts of water must have been involved in the metamorphic transformations, particularly that from eclogite to amphibolite; the origin of the water must await oxygen isotope studies.

It is clear that denudation of the footwall occurred mainly during Lower Devonian coaxial vertical thinning of the crust. Moreover, denudation of the footwall occurred mainly prior to the deposition of the Middle Devonian basin redbeds and final exhumation of the footwall and its juxtaposition against the hanging wall occurred after red-bed accumulation (Cuthbert 1991) during the latest stages of extensional detachment development. Neither erosion nor extensional detachment faulting have played a major role in denuding the footwall and bringing up middle and lower crustal rocks. Erosional denudation and denudation by hanging wall draw-down across an extensional fault give denudation rates that are uniform with depth, whereas denudation by vertical shortening gives rates that are depth dependent, increasing linearly downwards. At present, there is insufficient PTt data to discriminate among denudation mechanisms on this criterion. The structural sequence and PTt history of the footwall gives a clear and unequivocal picture of denudation by bulk coaxial horizontal extension, which can be roughly quantified. In the Sunnfjord region, a vertical shortening of about 80% and east–west horizontal extension of about 500% can be deduced consistently in three ways. First, flattening of foliation around eclogite bodies gives values of

between 75% and 85%. Secondly, PTt loops in the Sunnfjord region involve rocks at about 60 km at 410 Ma ago and at about 10 kb at 380 Ma ago giving a denudation rate during isothermal coaxial stretching of about $1.5 \, \text{mm a}^{-1}$, a strain rate of about $10^{-15} \, \text{s}^{-1}$ and a vertical shortening of 83%. Thirdly, if we take a present value for $C_z$ of about 30 km and a peak shortening $C_z$ of 150 km, we get a vertical shortening of 80%. Clearly, however, bulk coaxial extension cannot explain the final juxtaposition of the footwall core complex, consisting of lower crustal rocks, and the supracrustal hanging wall rocks. A large part of the upper and middle crust is 'missing' and its absence can be explained only by a major excision across the extensional Kvamshesten Detachment. If the Kvamshesten Detachment originated in its present gently westward-dipping attitude, extensional displacement along it must be at least 100 km to juxtapose lower crustal and supracrustal rocks.

These large extensions are, at least partly, synchronous with eastward thrusting over the Baltic Shield along the eastern margin of the Scandinavian Caledonides (Fig. 4). The Ringerike Group of Wenlock to Lower Devonian age is a clastic foreland basin sequence reflecting the growth of the Norwegian Caledonides (Bjorlykke 1983). The Silurian part of the Ringerike Group was deposited synchronously with Scandian shortening but the Lower Devonian was synchronous with interior bulk coaxial extension. Moreover, Middle Devonian thrusting in the Oslo region developed simultaneously with southwest Norwegian extensional detachments and basins. This suggests that, although the earliest shortening and foreland basin development along the eastern margins of the Scandian Caledonides was driven probably by Silurian Baltica/Greenland plate convergence, Lower Devonian foreland basin development and Middle Devonian thrusting may have been driven by extensional collapse (Andersen et al. 1991).

## The model

The geological data from southwestern Norway outlined in the previous section may be used to constrain a simple numerical model, shown qualitatively in Fig. 5 and quantitatively in Figs 6 and 7. The modelling work is part of an ongoing research programme by Dewey and Ryan involving the effects of varying $C_z$, $l_z$ and $C_z/l_z$ on orogenic evolution. In southwestern Norway, some 10–20 Ma of Scandian crustal shortening and lower crustal eclogite facies metamorphism was followed by about 20 Ma of vertical shor-

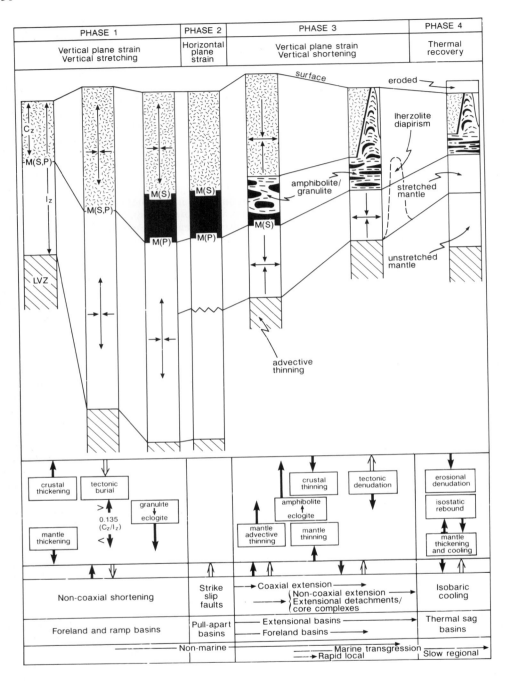

**Fig. 5.** Qualitative illustration of model for the shortening and extensional collapse and surface elevation of orogenic belts. $C_z$: crustal thickness; LVZ: low velocity zone; $l_z$: thickness of lithosphere (boundary conduction layer); M: Moho (P: petrographic; S: seismic); black: eclogite; horizontal broken lines: horizontal extension; random ornament: continental crust; solid arrows: motion of the surface; open arrows: motion of rocks with respect to the surface (burial or denudation).

tening and crustal extension in amphibolite/granulite facies both in an approximate east–west direction and both roughly bulk plane strain. Clearly, the bulk eclogitization of the lower crust during Scandian shortening was accompanied by a substantial increase in density, whereas the subsequent amphibolization caused a corresponding decrease in density. During crustal/ lithospheric shortening, crustal ($C_z$) thickening and mantle ($l_z$) thickening work in opposition, the former causing uplift, the latter subsidence. Generally, uplift occurs because $C_z$ ratios are commonly greater than 0.1375 (Dewey 1982); for an initial $C_z$ of 35 and $l_z$ of 120, shortening is buffered at 50% with a crustal thickness of about 70 km and a surface elevation of 3 km. If a substantial amount of the lower crust transforms to eclogite, let us say to the average density of the lithospheric mantle, the transformation will 'assist' the mantle in enhancing its subsidence role and, furthermore, will allow shortening values in excess of 50% and the development of orogenic crusts much greater than 70 km (Fig. 5). This will lead to a situation in which the seismically-defined Moho will lie within petrographic crust, a lower zone of which will be geophysically-indistinguishable from the lithospheric mantle, which illustrates our concept of a seismic Moho and a petrographic 'Moho' (Fig. 5), sandwiching a mantle density lower crust during shortening. The mineralogy of the southwestern Norwegian eclogites does not lead to a simple calculation of bulk densities during peak Scandian shortening because the exact peak proportions of omphacite (3.29–3.97), garnet (3.51–3.75), clinozoizite (3.12–3.38), kyanite (3.53–3.65), phengite (2.6–2.9), jadeite (3.24–3.43) and coesite (2.92), are hard to define. From field observations, we have made an estimate of peak bulk density towards the low end of the eclogite range of about 3.1 to 3.3 corresponding with compressional wave velocities ($Vp$) of about 7.8 to 8.1, approximately corresponding with lithospheric upper mantle densities and velocities (Meissner 1986), to avoid the positive gravity anomaly that would be caused by higher densities. Advective removal of the negatively buoyant lithospheric mantle root leads to lithospheric thinning, uplift, an increase in geothermal gradient and heat flow, and heating of the crust, which leads, in turn, to lithospheric stretching, conversion of eclogite to amphibolite (Fig. 5). Stretching causes subsidence, where $C_z/l_z >$ 0.1375), which is partially offset by the density reduction intrinsic to the eclogite/amphibolite transformation (Fig. 5). Finally, progressive thermal recovery leads to lithospheric thickening and slowing subsidence. The crust is denuded

principally by vertical shortening with extensional detachment and erosion contributing smaller amounts of denudation (Fig. 5).

We have modelled the crustal structure, thickness, compressional wave velocity/seismic structure and surface elevation during plane strain shortening, catastrophic lithospheric advective thinning and extensional collapse through a 60 Ma orogenic cycle for a rifted margin, an island arc, and active continental margin (Fig. 6). We have used a 100 km thick lithospheric element of 1 km² surface area in the orogen divided into 100 cells with an initial thickness of 1 km assuming pure Airy isostasy. We have not included a component of flexural isostasy for reasons of simplicity; such a component would allow support of higher elevations with a corresponding positive gravity anomaly. The initial variation of density with depth was computed from the P-wave velocity ($V_p$) profiles for various crustal types (Meissner 1986; Mooney & Meissner 1991) using the Nafe-Drake velocity/ density curves (Ludwig et al. 1970). The element was subjected to an initial phase of vertical plane strain until shortening exceeded 72%, sufficient to produce an orogenic $C_z$ of 120 km from an initial $C_z$ of 35 km; this corresponds with Phase 1 of Dewey (1988). Subsequent advective thinning of the lithosphere was modelled by exponentially thinning the lithospheric mantle by a predetermined amount over 10 Ma (Phase 2). Finally, the lithosphere was subjected to extensional vertical plane strain during the collapse phase until shortening equalled zero (Phases 3 and 4). Tectonic denudation during collapse was simulated by stretching the crust a faster rate than the mantle during this phase. Strain rates used were from 1.5 to $2.0 \times 10^{-15}\,s^{-1}$

Crustal rocks were allowed to eclogitize progressively during Phases 1 and 2 and the rate and minimum pressure of this reaction were preselected. The consequent density change within each cell was computed from the proportion of crust eclogitized and a compositional parameter that allowed bulk crustal composition to be varied from silicic to mafic, the densities of which were taken from Austrheim & Mørk (1988). Amphibolitization was allowed to proceed during collapse (Phases 3 and 4), maximum pressure and reaction rate could be varied in each experiment, and the density changes computed. Both granulite–eclogite and eclogite–amphibolite were assumed first-order ($-\delta c/\delta T$ $kC^1$) kinetics, where $c$ is concentration of reactants, $T$ is time and $k$ a rate constant. Values were chosen for the rate constants that allowed the reactions to proceed to completion in between 10 and 30 Ma as indicated by data from

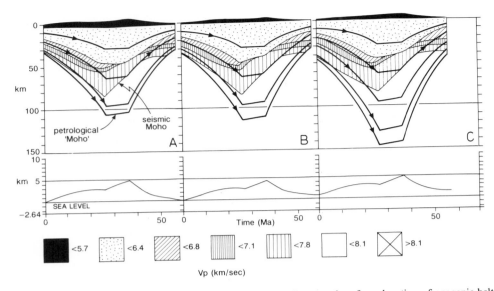

**Fig. 6.** Quantitative model for the shortening and extensional collapse and surface elevation of orogenic belts. The upper plot shows the evolution of P-wave velocity structure through time of an element in the centre of an orogen. The lower curve shows the elevation of this element above mid-oceanic ridge altitude (− 2.64) during the same time interval. A, B and C are for rifted continental margin, island arc and an active continental margin, respectively. Initial P-wave structures were taken from Mooney & Meissner (1991). Heavy lines in the upper plots represent particle paths for material at 10 km intervals and the Moho of the starting model. Note that, during eclogitization, the petrological Moho is beneath the seismic Moho. The following parameters were used: time interval for each step is 10 000 years; first-order kinetics; eclogitization took place at a 'half life' of 6.4 Ma, converted up to 100% of rock and initiated at pressures >13.2 kb; amphibolitization had a 'half life' of 3 Ma, converted up to 95% of rock at pressures <12 kb; strain rate during the shortening vertical plane strain phase was $1.5 \times 10^{-15}\,\mathrm{s}^{-1}$, during lithospheric advective thinning was 0, during extensional vertical plane strain was $2.0 \times 10^{-15}\,\mathrm{s}^{-1}$ for the crust and $1.5 \times 10^{-15}\,\mathrm{s}^{-1}$ for the mantle; the erosion constant was $1.5 \times 10\mathrm{E}-4/1000$ years; asthenospheric density was 3.32 tonnes m$^{-3}$; 50% of the lithospheric mantle was delaminated; the crustal composition was 60% granite and 40% basalt.

southwestern Norway (Fig. 1). The variation in $V_p$ of the element was calculated from the resultant density and thickness of each cell using the Nafe-Drake curves and the topographic elevation of the element was computed using an Airy 'iceberg' model where:

$$H_z \cdot \int_0^{H_z} \rho_c(z)\delta_z = (l_z - H_z).\rho_l(\rho_a - \rho_l)$$

and

$$\rho_l = \int_{H_z}^{C_z} \rho_c(z)\delta_z + \int_{C_z}^{l_z} \rho_m(z)\delta_z$$

where $H_z$ is elevation above oceanic ridge (−2.64 km), $\rho_c(z)$ and $\rho m(z)$ are density functions for crust and mantle respectively and $\rho_a$ is density of the asthenosphere low velocity zone. The crust and mantle density functions are calculated from the density and thickness of each cell in the lithospheric element. The amount of

material removed by erosion in each time step was calculated from

$$H_z = H_{z0} \cdot \exp\left\{-1(1 - (\rho_c/\rho_m)).K.T\right\}$$

where $H_{z0}$ is regional elevation at the beginning of time interval ($T = 0$), $\rho_c$ and $\rho_m$ are crust and mantle density functions and $K$ is an erosion constant $(1.0 \pm 1.0 \times 10^{-4}/10^3\,\mathrm{a})$ (W.C. Pitman, pers. comm., 1988). Thermal and elastic effects were ignored as they are small compared with those of the metamorphic phase changes. Mass was conserved in each element, except where removed by erosion.

The models of Fig. 6 show that, during the periods of maximum shortening and advective lithospheric thinning, the P-wave velocities of crustal rocks below 70 km exceed 7.8 km s$^{-1}$ but are less than 8.1 km s$^{-1}$, overlain by a thin layer of rocks with P-wave velocity in the range 7.1–7.8 km s$^{-1}$, these layers corresponding with eclo-

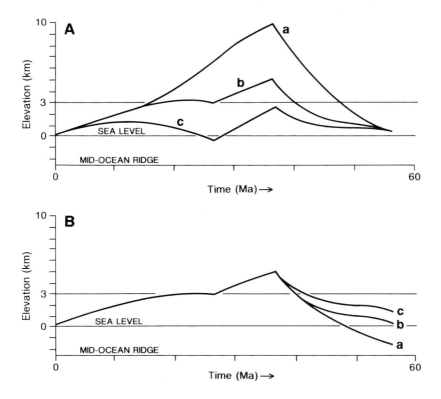

**Fig. 7.** Curves showing the elevation through time, with respect to that of the mid-oceanic ridge, of an element in the centre of an orogen formed from a rifted continental margin. The parameters used are the same as in Fig. 6 unless otherwise stated. (**A**) shows the effect, on topography, of variable eclogitization during the vertical plane strain phase. In curve (a) there is no eclogitization, in curve (b) the conditions are the same as those for Fig. 6 and in curve (c) the 'half life' for eclogitization = 3.0 Ma and the minimum pressure is 10 kb. (**B**) shows the effects of amphibolitization and tectonic denudation upon uplift history. In curve (a) there is no amphibolitization and tectonic denudation is modelled as for Fig. 6; curve (b) is identical to that in Fig. 6 and has both amphibolitization and tectonic denudation; in curve (c) there is no tectonic denudation and the conditions for amphibolitization are the same as those for curve (b).

gitized and partially eclogitized crust, respectively. Such a velocity structure is recorded in Cenozoic mountain belts (Meissner 1986). Thus, a substantial amount of the lower crust exhibits seismic velocities considered typical of mantle; Austrheim & Mork (1988) have noted that this must have been the case for Caledonian eclogites in the Bergen region of Norway and implies that estimates of crustal volumes based on the P-wave structure of orogens, late in the shortening or early in the collapse phase, may be considerably too low. The normal thickness crust generated by collapse has less high velocity material near its base as a consequence of amphibolitization, a structure observed in the now-collapsed Hercynian and Caledonian orogens of Europe (Mooney & Meissner 1991).

These processes are reflected in topographic elevation profiles. During shortening, elevation tends not to exceed 3 km as it is buffered by vertical stress and eclogitization. Advective removal of about half of the lithospheric mantle is required to produce an elevation of 5 km. Amphibolitization during the collapse phase can 'float' and maintain relatively elevated topography, delay subsidence below sea-level, and produce internal extensional molasse basins. The relative importance of these effects are illustrated in Fig. 7. Uplift during shortening was dependent upon rates of eclogitization (Fig. 7A). In Fig. 7A curve (a), shortening progressed without eclogitization and produced mountains in excess of 10 km, further exaggerated by a low erosion rate. Curve (c) illustrates the effect of a high rate of eclogitization of a mafic crust at low threshold pressure producing uplift followed by subsidence during shortening as $C_z/I_z$ falls below 0.1375, a condition that may have been important during Archaean times when heat flow was higher. The rate of subsidence during the extensional collapse phase was controlled primarily by the amount and rate of amphibolitization and tectonic denudation (Fig. 7B). A low rate of amphibolitization and substantial tectonic denudation caused subsidence below sea-level in less than 200 Ma (Fig. 7B curve (a)), whereas rapid amphibolitization and no tectonic denudation buffered the effects of stretching and subsidence to sea-level, which did not occur until after 50 Ma (Fig. 7B, curve(c)). The reference curves (b) in Figs 7A and B were derived from Fig. 6A. Finally, all models show that rocks subjected to peak metamorphic pressures in the range 20–30 kb remain at depths of between 20 and 30 km after collapse, that coaxial crustal stretching and erosion alone are insufficient for the exposure of coherent eclogite terrains, and that some form of hanging wall–footwall detachment relationship is necessary to exhume high grade terrains.

## Conclusions

The Caledonian structural and metamorphic history of southwestern Norway, together with our simple numerical modellings, leads to the conclusion that orogens may develop very thick continental crusts, perhaps up to 150 km, during shortening, because lower crustal rocks are transformed, pervasively and regionally into mafic and silicic eclogites of bulk lithospheric mantle density. This allows orogenic shortening, driven by plate convergence, to achieve average values greatly in excess of the commonly expected 50%, perhaps as high as 80%. Furthermore, this allows the development of a thick continental crust supporting mountains of reasonable average height (*c.* 3 km) rather than the impossibly (*c.* 10 km high mountains given by a 150 km thick crust of normal crustal density. Following catastrophic advective lithospheric thinning and consequent uplift, the resulting massive increase in geothermal gradient is accompanied by tectonic denudation by vertical bulk coaxial shortening and horizontal extension at strain rates of about $10^{-15}\,\mathrm{s}^{-1}$. This phase has been called extensional collapse (Dewey 1988) but, during the earliest phases of vertical thinning, elevation increases rapidly to a peak value of about 5 km (Figs 6, 7). During vertical thinning, eclogite facies rocks are largely transformed to amphibolites and granulites thus lowering lower crustal density and

enhancing uplift. Lower crustal rocks (amphibolite with residual eclogite lenses) reach upper crustal levels by coaxial vertical thinning but neither this form of tectonic denudation nor erosion can exhume these rocks. Exhumation can occur only in the footwalls of superimposed extensional detachments, which leads to the juxtaposition of high-grade footwall rocks against low-grade hanging wall rocks and the superimposition of greenschist/low amphibolite facies extensional non-coaxial structures and fabrics on the earlier coaxial structures and fabrics.

Thus, older mountain belts such as the Caledonides and Hercynides are characterized over large areas by high-grade metamorphic terrains adjacent to lower grade upper crustal rocks with extensional sedimentary basins, a situation achieved by extensional 'collapse' tectonics with very little erosional denudation. This may be the principal explanation for the widespread preservation of supracrustal rocks, including internal 'molasse' basins, in mountain belts and insufficient external molasse for erosional denudation to be the principal mechanism for returning the crust from orogenic to 'normal' thickness.

The structure of the high-grade parts of extensionally collapsed orogens is dominated by sub-horizontal bulk coaxial gneissic foliation developed by vertical thinning of up to 80% and horizontal extensions of up to 500%, much of which occurs during rapid uplift. These strains, in southwestern Norway, induced a strong and pervasive irregular layering at all scales from centimetres to kilometres, made up of the gneissic foliation itself with strong lithological contrasts across layers and lenses of eclogite, gabbro, peridotite, amphibolite and granite gneiss. Such regionally sub-horizontal gneissic fabrics are common in deeply-denuded orogens and may account, at least partly, for the widespread layered lower crusts in areas of active extension and extended areas of offshore Britain recognized by COCORP and BIRPS seismic reflective profiling (Blundell 1990) and in orogens generally (Dewey 1988; Sandiford 1989).

The massive conversion of rocks into eclogite in orogenic lower crusts has substantial implications for balancing calculations in convergent plate boundary zones. Butler (1986), Le Pichon *et al.* (1988) and Laubscher (1990) have pointed out the apparent shortfall of crust in the Alps when shortening from supracrustals is compared with the cross-section of crustal area and have argued 'loss' of crust into the mantle. We do not subscribe to the view that crustal material is permanently lost into the mantle because the Norwegian evidence indicates that eclogitized crust is largely transformed back into crustal densities by amphibolitization and 'returned' to the crust. However, calculations of the volume of crust in active collision zones like the Himalayan/Tibetan/Asian convergent system (Tapponnier *et al.* 1986; Dewey *et al.* 1989) may be seriously underestimated if large parts of the lower crust are eclogitized and, correspondingly, lateral escape tectonics may be overestimated.

Lastly, extensional collapse, contrasted with erosion, is a very rapid way of reducing the elevation of orogens and allowing rapid marine transgression and the development of post-orogenic unconformities while extension continues. This leads to a very close geometric relationship between extensional detachments and marine transgressive unconformities. Death Valley in the extant extensional Basin and Range Province lies below sea-level and is, therefore, potentially liable to instantaneous marine flooding. We should, perhaps, revise our views of the gradual erosional wearing-down of mountain ranges with progressive marine transgression long after orogenesis. The surfaces of many, perhaps most, mountain belts return to near or below sea-level by extensional rather than erosional denudation.

This work was financially assisted by grants to Andersen for fieldwork (NAVF 440-90-92/007) and a sabbatical leave in Oxford (NAVF 440-92/002), by British Petroleum funding to Dewey, and by EOLAS funding to Ryan (SC/91/003).

# References

AIRY, G. B. 1855. On the computation of the effect of the attraction of the mountain masses as disturbing the apparent astronomical latitude of stations in geodetic surveys. *Philosophical Transactions of the Royal Society*, **A145**, 101–104.

ANDERSEN, T. B. 1993. Structural relationships between eclogite tectonites and mylonites in extensional detachments; an example from Sunnfjord, western Norway. *Journal of Structural Geology*, in press.

—— & JAMTVEIT, B. 1990. Uplift of deep crust during orogenic extensional collapse: a model based upon field studies in the Sogn-Sunnfjord region of western Norway. *Tectonics*, **9**, 1097–1111.

——, ——, DEWEY, J. F. & SWENSSON, E. 1991. Subduction and eduction of continental crust: major mechanisms during continent–continent collision and orogenic extensional collapse, a model based on the south Norwegian Caledonides. *Terra Nova*, **3**, 303–310.

——, SKJERLIE, K. P. & FURNES, H. 1990. The Sunnfjord Mélange, evidence of Silurian ophiolite accretion in the West Norwegian Caledonides. *Journal of the Geological Society, London*, **146**, 59–68.

AUSTRHEIM, H. 1987. Eclogitization of lower crustal granulites by fluid migration through shear zones. *Earth and Planetary Science Letters*, **81**, 221–232.

—— 1991. Eclogite formation and dynamics of crustal roots under continental collision zones. *Terra Nova*, **3**, 492–499.

—— & MORK, M. B. E. 1988. The lower continental crust of the Caledonian mountain chain: evidence from former deep crustal sections in western Norway. *Norges Geologiske Undersøkelse Special Publication*, **3**, 102–113.

BJØRLYKKE, K. 1983. Subsidence and tectonics in late Precambrian and Palaeozoic sedimentary basins of Southern Norway. *Norges Geologiske Undersøkelse Bulletin*, **380**, 159–172.

BLUNDELL, D. J. 1990. Seismic images of continental lithosphere: *Journal of the Geological Society, London*, **147**, 895–913.

BOHLEN, S. R. & BOETTCHER, A. L. 1982. The quartz ↔ coesite transformation: a precise determination and the effects of other components: *Journal of Geophysical Research*, **87**, 7073–7078.

BRUECKNER, H. B. 1972. Interpretation of Rb–Sr ages from the Precambrian and Palaeozoic rocks of southern Norway. *American Journal of Science*, **272**, 334–358.

BRYNHI, I. 1966. Reconnaissance studies of gneisses, ultrabasites, eclogites and anorthosites in Outer Nordfjord, western Norway. *Norges Geolegiske Undersøkelse*, **241**.

—— 1989. Status of the supracrustal rocks in the Western Gneiss Region, S. Norway. *In*: GAYER, R. (ed.) *The Caledonian Geology of Scandinavia*. Graham & Trotman, London, 221–228.

BUTLER, R. W. H. 1986. Thrust tectonics, deep structure and crustal subduction in the Alps and Himalayas. *Journal of the Geological Society, London*, **143**, 857–873.

CARSWELL, D. A. 1990. Eclogites and eclogite facies: definition and classification. *In*: CARSWELL, D. A. (ed.) *Eclogite Facies Rocks*. Blackie, Glasgow, 1–13.

CHAUVET, A., KIENAST, J. R., PINARDEN, J. L. & BRUNEL, M. 1992. Petrological constraints and PT path of Devonian collapse tectonics within the Scandian mountain belt (Western Gneiss Region, Norway). *Journal of the Geological Society, London*, **149**, 383–400.

CHOPIN, C. 1984. Coesite and pure pyrope in high-grade blueschists of the Western Alps: a first record and some consequences. *Contributions to Mineralogy and Petrology*, **86**, 107–118.

—— 1987. Very-high-pressure metamorphism in the western Alps: implications for subduction of continental crust. *Philosophical Transactions of the Royal Society of London*, **A321**, 183–197.

——, HENRY, C. & MICHARD, A. 1991. Geology and petrology of the coesite-bearing terrain, Dora Maira Massif, Western Alps. *European Journal of Mineralogy*, **3**, 263–291.

CLOOS, M. 1982. Flow mélanges: Numerical modelling and geologic constraints on their origin in the Franciscan subduction complex, California. *Geological Society of America Bulletin*, **93**, 330–345.

COWAN, D. S. & SILLING, R. M. 1978. A dynamic scaled model of accretion at trenches and its implications for the tectonic evolution of subduction complexes. *Journal of Geophysical Research*, **83**, 5389–5396.

CUTHBERT, S. J. 1991. Evolution of the Hornelen Basin, west Norway: new constraints from petrological studies of metamorphic clasts. *In*: MORTON, A. C., TODD, S. P. & HAUGHTON, P. D. W. (eds) *Development in Sedimentary Provenance Studies*. Geological Society, London, Special Publication, **57**, 343–360.

—— & CARSWELL, D. A. 1990. Formation and exhumation of medium-temperature eclogites in the Scandinavian Caledonides. *In*: CARSWELL, D. A. (ed.) *Eclogite Facies Rocks*. Blackie, Glasgow, 180–203.

DEWEY, J. F. 1982. Plate tectonics and the evolution of the British Isles. *Journal of the Geological Society, London*, **132**, 371–412.

—— 1988. Extensional collapse of orogens. *Tectonics*, **7**, 1123–1139.

——, CANDE, S. & PITMAN, W. C. 1989. Tectonic evolution of the India/Eurasia collision zone. *Eclogae Geologicae Helvetiae*, **82**, 717–734.

——, SHACKLETON, R. M., CHANG CHENGFA & SUN YIYIN. 1988. The tectonic evolution of the Tibetan Plateau. *Philosophical Transactions of the Royal Society of London*, **327**, 379–413.

DUNNING, G. R. & PEDERSEN, R. B. 1988. U/Pb ages of ophiolites and arc-related plutons of the Norwegian Caledonides: implications for the development of Iapetus. *Contributions to Mineralogy and Petrology*, **98**, 13–23.

ENAMI, M. & ZHANG, Q. 1990. Quartz pseudomorphs after coesite in eclogites from Shandong province, eastern China. *American Mineralogist*, **75**, 381–386.

ENGLAND, P. C. & HOLLAND, T. J. B. 1979. Archimedes and the Tauern eclogites: the role of buoyancy in the preservation of exotic eclogite blocks. *Earth and Planetary Science Letters*, **44**, 287–294.

—— & HOUSEMAN, G. A. 1988. The mechanics of the Tibetan Plateau. *Philosophical Transactions of the Royal Society of London*, **A326**, 301–320.

—— & —— 1989. Extensional collapse during continental convergence with application to the Tibetan Plateau. *Journal of Geophysical Research*, **94**, 17,561–17,579.

FURNES, H., SKJERLIE, K. P., PEDERSEN, R. B., ANDERSEN, T. B., SILLMAN, C. J., SUTHREN, R. J., TYSSELAND, M. & GARMANN, L. B. 1990. The Solund-Stavfjord Ophiolite Complex and associated rocks, west Norwegian Caledonides: geology, geochemistry and tectonic environment: *Geologist Magazine*, **127**, 209–224.

GRIFFIN, W. L., AUSTRHEIM, H., BRASTAD, K., BRYNHI, I., KRILL, A. G., KROGH, E. J., MORK, J., QVALE, M. B. E. & TORUDBAKKEN, B. 1985. High pressure metamorphism in the Scandinavian Caledonides. *In*: GEE, D. G. & STURT B. A. (eds) *The Caledonide Orogen – Scandinavia and related areas*. Wiley, New York, 783–801.

—— & BRUECKNER, H. K. 1985. REE, Rb-Sr and Sm-Nd studies of Norwegian-eclogites. *Chemical Geology*, **52**, 249–271.

HEISKANEN, W. A. & VENING MEINESZ, F. A. 1958. *The Earth and its Gravity Field*. McGraw Hill, New York.

HIRAJIMA, T., ISHIWATARI, A., CHANG, B., ZHANG, R., BANNO, S. & NOZAKA, T. 1990. Coesite from Mengzhong eclogite at Dhonghai county, northeastern Jiangsu province, China. *Mineralogical Magazine*, **54**, 579–583.

HOSSACK, J. R. 1984. The geometry of listric faults in the Devonian basins of Sunnfjord, W. Norway. *Journal of the Geological Society, London*, **141**, 629–637.

HOUSEMAN, G. A., MCKENZIE, D. P. & MOLNAR, P. 1981. Convective instability of a thickened boundary layer and its relevance for the thermal evolution of continental convergence belts. *Journal of Geophysical Research*, **86**, 6115–6132.

JAMTVEIT, B. 1987. Metamorphic evolution of the Eiksundal eclogite complex, western Norway, and some tectonic implications. *Contributions to Mineralogy and Petrology*, **95**, 82–99.

KROGH, E. J. 1977. Evidence for a Precambrian continental collision in western Norway. *Nature*, **267**, 17–19.

—— 1980. Geochemistry and petrology of glaucophane-bearing eclogites and associated rocks from Sunnfjord, western Norway. *Lithos*, **13**, 355–380.

KULLERUD, L., TORUDBAKKEN, B. O. & ILEBEKK, S. 1986. A compilation of radiometric age determinations from the Western Gneiss Region, South Norway. *Norges Geologiske Undersøkelse Bulletin*, **406**, 17–42.

LAUBSCHER, H. 1990. The problem of the Moho in the Alps. *Tectonophysics*, **182**, 9–20.

LE PICHON, X., BERGERAT, F. & ROULET, M. J. 1988. Plate kinematics and tectonics leading to the Alpine belt formation; a new analysis. *Geological Society of America Special Paper*, **218**, 111–131.

LUDWIG, W. J., NAFE, J. E. & DRAKE, C. L. 1970. Seismic Refraction. *In*: A. E. MAXWELL (ed.) *The Sea*. Wiley Interscience, New York, 53–84.

LUX, D. R. 1985. K/Ar ages from the Basal Gneiss Region, south Norway. *Norsk Geologisk Tidsskrift*, **65**, 277–286.

MEISSNER, R. 1986. *The Continental Crust, a Geophysical Approach*. Academic Press, London.

MILNES, A. G. & KOESTLER A. G. 1985. Geological structure of Jotunheim, South Norway (Sognefjell–Valdres cross-section). *In*: GEE, D. G. & STURT B. A. (eds) *The Caledonide Orogen – Scandinavia and related regions*. John Wiley, 457–474.

MOONEY, W. D. & MEISSNER, R. 1991. Continental crustal evolution observations. *EOS*, **72**, 537–541.

NILSEN, T. H. 1968. The relationship of sedimentation to tectonics in the Solund area of Southwestern Norway. *Norges Geologiske Undersøkelse*, **259**.

NORTON, M. G. 1986. Late Caledonian extension in western Norway, a response to extreme crustal thickening. *Tectonics*, **5**, 195–204.

—— 1987. The Nordfjord–Sogn Detachment, W. Norway. *Norsk Geologisk Tidsskrift*, **67**, 13–106.

OKAY, A. I. & SENGÖR, A. M. C. 1992. Evidence for intracontinental thrust-related exhumation of the ultra-high pressure rocks in China. *Geology*, **20**, 411–414.

PLATT, J. P. 1986. Dynamics of orogenic wedges and the uplift of high-pressure metamorphic rocks. *Geological Society of America Bulletin*, **97**, 1037–1053.

RICHARDSON, S. W. & ENGLAND, P. C. 1979. Metamorphic consequences of crustal eclogite production in overthrust orogenic zones. *Earth and Planetary Science Letters*, **42**, 183–190.

SANDIFORD, M. 1989. Horizontal structures in granulite terranes: a record of mountain building or mountain collapse. *Geology*, **17**, 449–452.

SERANNE, M., CHAUVRET, A., SEGURET, M. & BRUNEL, M. 1989. Tectonics of the Devonian collapse basins of western Norway: *Bulletin de la Société Géologique de France*, **8**, 489–499.

—— & SEGURET, M. 1987. The Devonian basins of western Norway: tectonics and kinematics of an extending crust. *In*: COWARD, M. P., DEWEY, J. F. & HANCOCK, P. L. (eds) *Continental Extensional Tectonics*. Geological Society, London, Special Publication, **28**, 537–548.

SKJERLIE, F. J. 1969. The pre-Devonian rocks in the Askvoll–Gaular area and adjacent districts, Western Norway. *Norges Geologiske Undersøkelse Bulletin*, **258**, 325–359.

SMITH, D. C. 1984. Coesite in clinopyroxene in the Caledonides and its implications for geodynamics. *Nature*, **310**, 641–644.

—— & LAPPIN, M. A. 1989. Coesite in the Straumen kyanite-eclogite pod, Norway. *Terra Nova*, **1**, 47–56.

STEEL, R., SIEDLECKA, A. & ROBERTS, D. 1985. The Old Red Sandstone basins of Norway and their deformation: a review. *In*: GEE, D. G. & STURT, B. A. (eds) *The Caledonide Orogen – Scandinavia and related regions* John Wiley, 293–315.

STOKES, G. G. 1849. On the variation of gravity and the surface of the earth.

SWENSSON, E. & ANDERSEN, T. B. 1991. Contact relationships between the Askvoll Group and the basement gneiss of the Western Gneiss region (WGR), Sunnfjord, Western Norway. *Norsk Geologisk Tidsskrift*, **71**, 15–27.

TAPPONNIER, P., PELTZER, G. & ARMIJO, R. 1986. On the mechanics of the collision between India and Asia. *In*: COWARD, M. P. & RIES, A. C. (eds) *Collision Tectonics*. Geological Society, London, Special Publication, **19**, 115–157.

TORSVIK, T. H., STURT, B. A., SWENNSEN, E., ANDERSEN, T. B. & DEWEY, J. F. 1992. Palaeomagnetic dating of fault rocks: evidence for Permian and Mesozoic movements and brittle deformation along the extensional Dalsfjord Fault, western Norway. *Geophysical Journal International*, **109**, 565–580.

WANG, X. & LIOU, J. G. 1991. Regional ultrahigh-pressure coesite-bearing eclogite terrane in central China: evidence from country rocks, gneiss, marble and metapelite. *Geology*, **19**, 933–936.

——, —— & MAO, H. K. 1989. Coesite-bearing eclogite from the Dabie Mountains in central China. *Geology*, **17**, 1085–1088.

——, —— & MARAYUMA, S. 1992. Coesite-bearing eclogites from the Dabie Mountains, central China: petrogenesis, P-T paths, and implications for regional tectonics. *Journal of Geology*, **100**, 231–250.

XU, S., OKAY, A. I., SHOUJAN, J., SENGOR, A. M. C., SU, W., LIU, Y. & JIANG, L. 1992. Diamond from the Dabie Shan Metamorphic rocks and its implications for tectonic setting. *Science*, **256**, 80–82.

# Tectonics of the Mozambique Belt in East Africa

## ROBERT M. SHACKLETON

*The Croft Barn, Church Street, East Hendred, Oxon OX12 8LA. UK*

**Abstract**: The Late Proterozoic Mozambique Belt in East Africa is reviewed, using new geochemical and other data. This review leads to the following tectonic interpretation.

A first collision, between 750 and 800 Ma ago, after the obduction of the Baragoi and associated ophiolites of north-central Kenya, produced intense regional recumbent fabrics and structures, a trans-Mozambique Belt stretching lineation, crustal thickening and metamorphism reaching granulite-facies in the lower crust.

Uplift and erosion were followed by closure of a second oceanic area, obduction of the West Pokot ophiolite and collision along the West Pokot suture, possibly about 580 Ma ago. This second collision produced strong within-plate deformation (Baragoian–Barsaloian) especially in N–S dextral shear zones over 100 km east of the West Pokot suture. The shear zones are associated with late Barsaloian within-plate granites.

It is inferred that eastward subduction led to the successive accretion of plates to an eastern foreland, perhaps represented by Malagasy, culminating in the collision of east and west Gondwana.

Most of Ian Gass's fundamental contributions to the Earth Sciences, notably the recognition and interpretation of ophiolites, the geochemistry of granitoids associated with plate collision, and the accretion of island arcs to form new continental crust were based on work in Sudan, Cyprus, Arabia and Oman. It seems appropriate, therefore, for this work in his honour, to discuss a region farther south – the Mozambique Belt – which is thought to be a more deeply eroded continuation of the array of late Proterozoic terranes which Ian studied in Sudan and Arabia. Although a major orogenic belt, it is still far from being understood.

In Kenya and Tanzania, the deeply eroded (down to 25 km) late Proterozoic Mozambique Belt exposes migmatitic gneisses, amphibolite-facies metasediments and, more locally, granulite facies rocks. A number of well-authenticated ophiolites are known (Vearncombe 1983*b*; Berhe 1990), though fewer than in the higher-level late Proterozoic terranes of NE Africa and Arabia.

The Mozambique Belt trends N–S through Tanzania and Kenya (Fig. 1), with a well-defined western front, a zone of mylonites and thrusts separating it from the Archaean rocks of the Tanzanian Craton (Shackleton 1986). The eastern front, less clearly defined, probably runs through northeastern Kenya or Malagasy and Somalia. Stratigraphically, the belt exposes metasediments which include conspicuous shelf-facies quartzites, marbles and graphitic schists and gneisses. Most clearly towards the west, and probably elsewhere, these metasediments form a cover, underlain unconformably by basement.

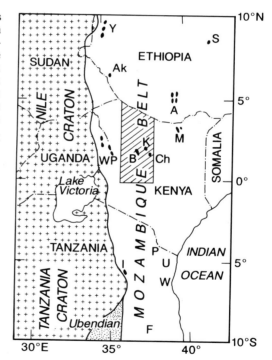

**Fig. 1.** Map of East Africa to show localities. Shaded area: north-central Kenya project area; crosses: cratonic areas west of Mozambique Belt; stipple: Ubendian. Black: Mozambiquian ophiolites – Y: Yubdo; S: Soka; Ak: Akobo; A: Adola; WP: West Pokot; B: Baragoi; K: Khor; Ch: Chaparkom; M: Moyale; I: Itiso. Granulites – P: Pare Mountains; U Usambara Mountains; W: Wami River; F: Furua.

*From* Prichard, H. M., Alabaster, T., Harris, N. B. W. & Neary, C. R. (eds), 1993,
*Magmatic Processes and Plate Tectonics*, Geological Society Special Publication No. 76, 345–362.

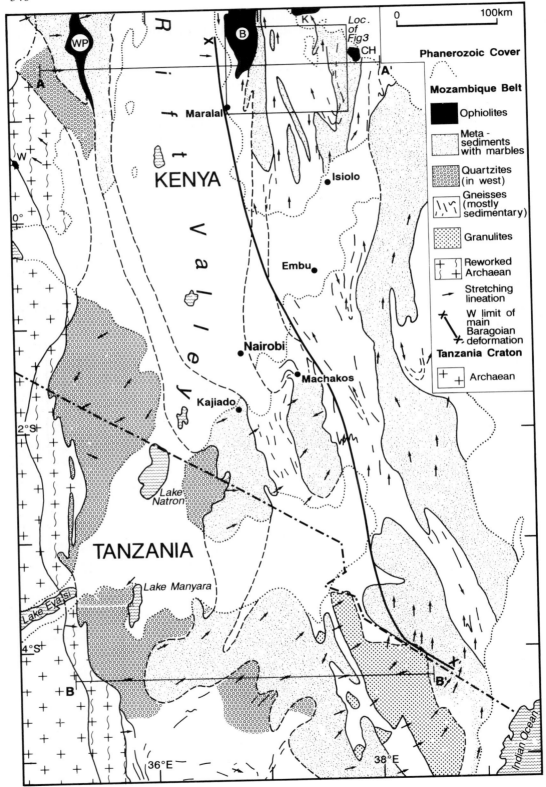

Phanerozoic Cover

**Mozambique Belt**

Ophiolites

Meta -
sediments
with marbles

Quartzites
(in west)

Gneisses
(mostly
sedimentary)

Granulites

Reworked
Archaean

Stretching
lineation

W limit of
main
Baragoian
deformation

**Tanzania Craton**

Archaean

This basement is Archaean in the west, where it can be traced at least 100 km into the belt (Sanders 1965; Hepworth 1972; Fig. 2), but further south in Tanzania Lower Proterozoic (Ubendian: c. 1700–1900 Ma) is recognized (Gabert & Wendt 1974; Priem et al. 1979), in north-central Kenya perhaps a Middle Proterozoic (c. 1200 Ma old) basement (Key et al. 1989) and in Malagasy widespread Archaean (Cahen & Snelling 1984). The relations between these various pre-Mozambiquian basements is unknown: the deformation in the belt is intense and complex.

Nearly all of Kenya and Tanzania is covered by 1:125 000 geological maps, mostly published between 1950 and 1970, but most of the Tanzanian maps only have brief descriptions printed on the sheets. Important later work includes a photogeological and field-based study of the western front of the Mozambique Belt in Tanzania (Hepworth 1972), detailed work in the West Pokot area in NW Kenya (Vearncombe 1983a,b; Ries et al. 1992), and a major co-operative UK/Kenya project in north-central Kenya (Fig. 1; Mines & Geological Department, Kenya, Reports 103–110). Despite all this and other work, tectonic interpretation of the belt remains uncertain, especially the relative ages of the known ophiolites, the positions of the sutures to which they relate, and the direction of subduction. The aim here is to clarify these problems, using the published data as well as some that are new. Geochronological, geochemical and structural data are discussed, as a basis for a tectonic interpretation.

## Geochronology

Age determinations up to about 1980 were assessed by Cahen & Snelling (1984). Subsequent work includes dates from Tanzanian granulites (Coolen et al. 1982; Maboko et al. 1985; Muhongo 1989), dates of granitoids related to a series of deformations in north-central Kenya (Key et al. 1989), dates from rocks in the West Pokot area, NW Kenya (Ries et al. 1992) and from W Ethiopia (Ayalew et al. 1990). The results are summarized in Table 1.

The data from an area c. 100 km SW of Yubdo, W Ethiopia (Fig. 1), are especially important because they allow comparison of U–Pb and Rb–Sr dates from the same rocks. These show that while those for the late- or post-tectonic granitoids agree, the Rb–Sr ages for the pre-tectonic granitoids are lower, in one by nearly 200 Ma, than the U–Pb ages. The same appears to be the case with the Furua and Wami River granulites from Tanzania. There, Rb–Sr ages of amphibolite-facies gneisses from 10–20 km outside the granulite-facies areas were interpreted by the authors as dating $M_2$. This implies, contrary to the evidence, that the granulites alone were affected by $M_1$ (granulite-facies) and so lie unconformably below the gneisses. Here, these $M_1$ and $M_2$ metamorphisms are correlated, the difference in ages being attributed to the different methods (see Table 1). These comparisons must throw doubt on all of the Rb–Sr dates of the rocks that were metamorphosed at depth and strongly deformed.

The geochronological data show that the East African Mozambique Belt evolved as a tectono-metamorphic complex between about 850 and 500 Ma ago, essentially during the same time as the Arabian–Nubian Shield (Cahen & Snelling 1984). The metasediments in the belt were probably deposited between 1200 and 900 Ma ago, this being the estimated age range of the sediments (Bukoban & Kisii) which rest on the Archaean of the Tanzanian Craton (Cahen & Snelling 1984), and with which the orthoquartzites (Fig. 2) and, less definitely, the other metasediments of the belt, are correlated (Macfarlane 1969).

The significance of many of the age determinations is unclear. Those of the Tanzanian granulites given in Table 1 were interpreted as ages of granulite metamorphism. The $652 \pm 10$ Ma age for the Furua granulite-facies $M_1$ metamorphism (Fig. 1; Coolen et al. 1982) is a lower intercept zircon age: the upper intercept age of between 2 and 3 Ga was tentatively interpreted as the age of volcanic crystallization of cores in the younger metamorphic zircons (Priem et al. 1979). The age of the Wami River (Fig. 1) granulite-facies metamorphism, $714 \pm 49$ Ma, is the lower intercept value from a regression analysis through all 17 zircons from five suites, excluding three fractions with conspicuous older components (Maboko et al. 1985). Of the two alternative interpretations of Rb–Sr dates from the Pare granulites, the lower ($812 \pm 37$ Ma) was

**Fig. 2.** Map of the Mozambique Belt in part of East Africa to show some of the significant tectonic features. X–X′: western limit of main N–S Baragoian–Barsaloian lineations associated with upright folds. Lineations west of X–X′ are associated with recumbent, and in West Pokot, westward-overturned folds and thrusts. Ophiolites – WP: West Pokot; B: Baragoi; CH: Chaparkom; K: Khor. W: Webuye. A–A′ & B–B′: lines of sections on Fig. 4. Box outlines location of Fig. 3.

**Table 1** *Selected and interpreted late Proterozoic radiometric dates (in Ma) from the East African Mozambique Belt*

| Ma | NW Kenya | W Ethiopia | N Central Kenya | S Kenya & Tanzania |
|---|---|---|---|---|
| | | | Final uplift & cooling 470–500[4] | |
| | | | P (post-tect) $474 \pm 20$[1] | |
| 500 | D$_4$ E–W open folds | $541 \pm 10$ ⎫[6] | | |
| | D$_3$ N–S folds | G$_4$ (post-tect.) $552 \pm 41$ ⎬[6] | E–W open folds *c.* 530[4] | |
| | | $571 \pm 5$ ⎭[6] | E–W mD dykes $593 \pm 8$[4] | |
| | | Q Monzonite $540 \pm 10$ | G$_4$ (G, Gd)      $566 \pm 22$[4] | |
| | | M$_2$           $(582 \pm 30)$[6] | G$_3$                 $573 \pm 5$[4] | |
| | P (post-tect) 597[1] | | D$_4$ N–S dextral shear zones, folds | |
| | M$_2$; D$_2$ tight N–S folds | | | |
| | $584 \pm 25$[5] | | | P(N–S)          $597 \pm 10$[1] |
| 600 | G$_2$ (Marich) $(593 \pm 58)$ | | D$_3$ (NNW–SSE folds) *c.* 620[4] | |
| | D$_1$ (imbrication of ophiolites | D (Birbir NNE–SSW Shear zone)      $632 \pm 8$[6] | | M$_1$ Gr (Furua)        $(652 \pm 10)$ ⎱[2] |
| | Marich mV   $663 \pm 49$[5] | | | M$_1$(M$_2$ auct.) $589 \pm 20$ ⎰[2] |
| 700 | Ophiolites | | | M$_1$ G (Wami R) $714 \pm 49$ ⎱[3] |
| | | | | M$_1$(M$_2$ auct.)      $478 \pm 5$ ⎰[3] |
| | | M$_1$ (regional)   $759 \pm 18$[6] | | G(Mbooni)      $774 \pm 14$[1] |
| | | G (syntect.)   $783 \pm 15$[6] | | |
| 800 | | G$_1$(pre-tect) Gd $814 \pm 2$ ⎱[6] | | M$_1$Gr (Pare)   $812 \pm 37$[1]? |
| | | subduction Gd $759 \pm 18$ ⎰[6] | | |
| | | QD $828 \pm 5$ ⎱[6] | | |
| | | QD $632 \pm 8$ ⎰[6] | G$_2$ (syntect) subduction $826 \pm 33$[4] | |
| | | | D$_2$ thrusts, folds, trans-Moz. B. lineation | |
| | | mV & mSed ophiolites | D$_1$ sub-horiz. foliation ophiolites | |

Sources: [1] Cahen & Snelling (1984); [2] Coolen *et al.* (1982); [3] Maboko *et al.* (1985); [4] Key *et al.* (1989); [5] Ries *et al.* (1992); [6] Ayalew *et al.* (1990).

Figures underlined U–Pb, in brackets () if lower intercept; not underlined Rb–Sr, pairs of samples linked by large brackets G: Granite; Gd: granodiorite; QD: quartz diorite; P: pegmatite; Gr: granulite facies; M: metamorphic phase; D: deformation phase; mD: metadolerite; mSed: metasediments; mV: metavolcanics. |→alternative correlations of NW Kenya. G$_2$ & Marich volcanics after Ayalew *et al.* (1990).

preferred to the higher ($908 \pm 38$ Ma), but both are little more than speculative (Cahen & Snelling 1984). Because the Pare-Usambara granulites (Fig. 1) differ from the others in the virtual absence of any of the later Mozambiquian defor-mations and because the fabrics and structures in the Usambara granulites are correlated with the D$_2$ Sabachian phase of north-central Kenya which is dated at 820 Ma ago (Key *et al.* 1989), the older, though imprecise, date for the Pare granulites might be preferred to the Wami River and Furua dates – assuming that all these granulites are contemporaneous. However, the granulites may have remained at high T and P for a long time; if so, the dates probably indicate the end of that period rather than a major tectonic phase.

The Rb–Sr whole-rock isochron ages from West Pokot (Fig. 2; Ries *et al.* 1992) are also difficult to interpret. That for the Marich metasediments, (five garnet biotite schists), $584 \pm 25$ Ma, must be a metamorphic age since those rocks are demonstrably older than the Marich granite. The age for the Marich granite ($593 \pm 50$ Ma), is not significantly older than the schist age; on field evidence it is thought to have been intruded just before, or during, the main ($D_2$) deformation and amphibolite-facies metamorphism (Vearncombe 1983a). The high initial ratio ($Sr_i = 0.7072 \pm 0.005$), and low $\varepsilon_{Nd}(T)$ show that it was derived from continental crust and the Nd model ages, 1650 Ma and 1950 Ma (Harris *et al.* 1984), imply a pre-Pan-African source. On an Sr evolution diagram the granite has a maximum age of c. 1090 Ma. On available evidence, the age was taken to be the intrusion age.

The age of $663 \pm 49$ Ma for the Marich Volcanic Series may also represent either an eruptive or a metamorphic age; a maximum eruptive age of c. 1000 Ma is calculated from an Sr evolution diagram (Ries *et al.* 1992). Close study (Price 1984) showed coherent inter-element chemistry, suggesting little deviation from the original composition; the initial ratio (0.7035) is within the range for island-arc volcanics at time of formation, and there is nothing to suggest that those volcanics were metamorphosed before the Marich metasediments. They are younger than, but successor to, the West Pokot ophiolites. For these reasons the age was taken as the eruptive age. Finally, an age of $982 \pm 40$ Ma as obtained (Ries *et al.* 1992) from an amphibolite and two associated impure dark calcareous bands. These amphibolites have MORB-like chemistry like that of the pillow lavas of the ophiolites. Being based on only three samples, and three which do not form a convincing suite, this age is best ignored. The West Pokot ages are discussed further in relation to structural correlation. The Rb–Sr ages of the granites from north-central and south Kenya have all been interpreted as approximating to intrusion ages. From north-central Kenya (Key *et al.* 1989), the $G_2$ granite age of $826 \pm 39$ Ma, $R_i = 0.7040 \pm 0.0005$, is based on ten samples. The age is an errorchron (MSWD 6.9) but was considered (Key *et al.* 1989) to be close to the time of

intrusion. It should be noted, however, that it has been subjected to a much higher grade of metamorphism than affected the West Pokot area and comparisons of U–Pb$_3$ and Rb–Sr ages discussed above reinforce doubts. Two $G_3$ granites yield a composite isochron of $573 \pm 5$ Ma, $R_i = 0.7045 \pm 0.0001$, and the $G_4$ granite yielded $566 \pm 30$ Ma, $R_i = 0.7042 \pm 0.0004$. These ages are all convincingly tied to a structural and metamorphic sequence. The Mbooni granitoid gneiss from the Machakos area of S Kenya (Fig. 2) yielded a Rb–Sr isochron age of 774 $\pm 14$ Ma (Shibata & Suwa 1979, revised Cahen & Snelling 1984). The low initial ratio of $R_i = 0.7037 \pm 0.0008$ is consistent with an intrusion age.

## Geochemistry of granitoids

There is little published geochemical information on the rocks of the Mozambique Belt in East Africa, so samples of granites dated from north-central Kenya by Rundle (Key *et al.* 1989), kindly supplied by Dr Rundle, were analysed at the Open University by John Watson, and processed and viewed by Peter Webb. These and analyses of other dated rocks from the region are given in Table 2, and also two other analyses from the Machakos area of S Kenya whose ages are thought to be close to that of the Mbooni granite.

All of the analyses were used to estimate the tectonic setting of the rocks analysed, both from major elements using the method of Maniar & Piccoli (1989) and, when trace element data were available, by the method of Pearce *et al.* (1984).

Of the granitoid gneisses from the Machakos area, S Kenya, the one which is dated, Mbooni, is identified using the Maniar & Piccoli method clearly as a continent/continent collision granite (CCG). The Muumandu intrusion also falls in the CCG field, but also just on the edge of the post-orogenic (POG) field. The third group of analyses, those from localities (unspecified) in S Machakos other than Mbooni and Muumandu, yields an ambiguous result, either continental arc granite (CAG) or possibly CCG. The Mbooni granite gneiss forms a dome, with concentric folds indicative of intrusion pressures. Muumandu is a concordant sheet; the others may include Uvete, another dome (Miyake & Suwa 1981). All were interpreted as metamorphosed and foliated magmatic granites. It thus seems likely that the date from Mbooni ($774 \pm 14$ Ma) indicates (with reservations about Rb–Sr dates) the time of a continent/continent collision.

**Table 2.** *Major and trace element analyses of dated granitoids from the East African Mozambique Belt*

| wt% | S Machakos | | | CRK1 Il Poloi G$_2$ (n = 8) | CRK2 Morupusi G$_3$ (n = 10) | CRIK3 Lauraki G$_3$ (n = 9) | CRK8 Lolmungi G$_4$ (n = 8) | Marich G (n = 6) |
|---|---|---|---|---|---|---|---|---|
| | Mbooni G gn (n = 4) | Muumandu G gn (n = 3) | S Machakos (others) (n = 8) | | | | | |
| SiO$_2$ | 76.90 | 71.80 | 71.86 | 77.09 | 66.60 | 64.21 | 65.53 | 74.48 |
| TiO$_2$ | 0.22 | 0.08 | 0.26 | 0.09 | 0.89 | 1.00 | 0.94 | 0.09 |
| Al$_2$O$_3$ | 13.40 | 14.72 | 14.55 | 12.59 | 14.35 | 14.66 | 14.32 | 15.04 |
| Fe$_2$O$_3$ | 0.91 | 1.48 | 0.60 | 1.03 | 5.58 | 6.64 | 6.33 | 0.59 |
| FeO | 0.92 | 1.29 | 0.92 | — | — | — | — | — |
| MnO | 0.04 | 0.09 | 0.04 | 0.04 | 0.09 | 0.11 | 0.10 | 0.03 |
| MgO | 0.26 | 0.48 | 0.44 | 0.08 | 0.78 | 1.07 | 0.91 | 0.14 |
| CaO | 0.97 | 1.76 | 1.30 | 0.54 | 2.09 | 2.66 | 2.49 | 1.24 |
| Na$_2$O | 2.50 | 3.46 | 4.99 | 4.36 | 3.43 | 3.89 | 3.28 | 4.84 |
| K$_2$O | 3.75 | 3.28 | 4.23 | 3.78 | 5.22 | 4.67 | 5.06 | 4.18 |
| P$_2$O$_5$ | 0.06 | 0.12 | 0.13 | 0.18 | 0.30 | 0.39 | 0.39 | ND |
| H$_2$O$^+$ | 0.03 | 0.44 | 0.42 | — | — | — | — | — |
| H$_2$O$^-$ | 0.17 | 0.20 | 0.12 | — | — | — | — | — |
| L.O.I. | | | | 0.19 | 0.40 | 0.49 | 0.52 | 0.16 |
| **ppm** | | | | | | | | |
| Rb | — | — | — | 61 | 139 | 95 | 108 | 114 |
| Sr | — | — | — | 42 | 202 | 363 | 317 | 508 |
| Ba | — | — | — | 984 | 1609 | 1685 | 2233 | 1016 |
| Nb | — | — | — | 5 | 46 | 44 | 36 | 6 |
| Zr | — | — | — | 74 | 607 | 385 | 520 | 95 |
| Y | — | — | — | 45 | 46 | 47 | 51 | 6 |
| Cr | — | — | — | — | — | — | — | 4 |
| Pb | — | — | — | — | — | — | — | 54 |
| Th | — | — | — | — | — | — | — | 11 |

G: granite; gn: gneiss

The oldest (826 ± 33 Ma old) suite from north-central Kenya, representing the Il Poloi G$_2$ granite, is indicated as an island arc (IAG) or continental arc (CAG) granite by the Maniar & Piccoli method and as a volcanic arc granite by the method of Pearce *et al.* (1984). This suite forms a fractionated sequence of peraluminous biotite granites with some highly siliceous magmas (possibly pegmatitic) with SiO$_2$ > 77%. (N. Harris, pers. comm.). Fractionation appears to have been controlled by alkali feldspar. The least fractionated magmas (samples CRK-1 G, I & J) are either subduction-related or post-collisional in tectonic setting. However, a subduction origin is favoured since the initial Sr-isotope ratios are low enough to exclude any mature crustal material from the source. Post-collisional magmas often have some crustal component because of unusual crustal thickness.

The three younger (*c.* 570–580 Ma old) granites – the metaluminous Morupusi G$_3$ granite, the metaluminous monzonite (G$_3$) of Lauraki, and Lolmungi (G$_4$) metaluminous granite – are all, by both the Maniar & Piccoli and Pearce *et al.* methods, within-plate in character, with low Sr$_i$ ratios. It has been commented (N. Harris, pers. comm) that their emplacement may well be rift-related, and they have a deep source (lower crust or mantle); similar intrusions occur in Arabia associated with a late Pan-African strike-slip fault system post-dating subduction. They could be regarded as post-collisional, but associated with extension, not crustal thickening. However, this would imply that these plutons post-date the associated local high-grade metamorphism, contrary to the interpretation of Key *et al.* (1989).

The G$_3$ Morupusi and Lauraki granites are slightly irregular N–S-trending bodies in the Isiolo area (Hackman *et al.* 1989). Both have a weak foliation defined by biotite flakes, parallel to the N–S Barsaloian (Table 3) fold axial planes. The Morupusi intrusion appears to be synclinally folded (Hackman *et al.* 1989, map and section BB'). These granites are cut by the approximately E–W Sinyai and related metadolerites (593 ± 38 Ma in age: Key *et al.* 1989) and displaced by NE–SW sinistral faults. The structural correlation of the G4 granites depends partly on evidence from a zone of multiple intrusions near the Seya River (Charsley 1987) which are classified as G$_4$. One small dyke

**Table 3.** *Tectonothermal history, north-central Kenya*

| Events | Structures | Thermal & magmatic effects | Tectonic level & process |
|---|---|---|---|
| Kipsingian | E–W asymmetric warps. | | High tectonic levels. Post-orogenic uplift. |
| Loldaikan | Asymmetric upright folds, axes plunging NE (& SW). Axial planar cleavage (NE–SW). Fractures in arc NE–SE. SSE sinistral shears. | Variable local reheating; minor dykes & veins. | High tectonic levels; stress field as Barsaloian. |
| Barsaloian | $D_4$. N-trending shear zones with isoclines plunging gently N (rarely S). Dextral shears. | Linear granite sheets, mantled gneiss domes. Variable met. grade. | High tectonic levels. ENE–WSW compression. En echelon dextral shear zones on Baragoian fold limbs. |
| Baragoian | $D_3$. Regional upright folds trending & gently plunging NNW. Local fracture cleavages; NW-trending mineral lineations; parallel brittle shears. | Variable up to Upper amphibolite facies. Local remelting. | |
| Sabachian | $D_2$. Overturned to recumbent folds (nappes) with related imbricate thrust system originating at gneiss/basal migmatite interface. ESE fold axes with low variable plunges. | Upper amphibolite facies | Low tectonic level. E–W tension across orogen with gravity-controlled deformation. |
| Samburuan | $D_1$. Horizontal coarse gneissosity. Minor folds of discordant veins. | Upper amphibolite facies. Granite sheets. | Low tectonic level – local pressure at least partly controlling horizontal fabrics. |
| 'Mukogodo' | Disharmonic structures in basal migmatites. | High grade, possibly polyphase. | (Pre-Mozambique Belt) |

Based on Key *et al.* (1989) table 5.

crosses the N–S Barsaloian (Table 3) structures at 60° but is itself marginally foliated with biotites aligned N–S.

Considering that the final uplift and cooling of the belt is dated by K–Ar at about 500–470 Ma ago (Key *et al.* 1989) and that post-$G_4$ basic dykes and associated faults indicate continuing E–W $P_{max}$ after the $G_4$ granites, it seems clear that on the field evidence, the $G_3$ and $G_4$ granites should be regarded as post-collisional rather than within-plate in the sense that the interplate compression was still being applied, in this case to rocks which were still hot, as it had been across the Tibet Plateau and north to the Tien Shan for more than 30 Ma after collision started. The main Barsaloian deformation, however, clearly preceded the $G_4$ granites but perhaps not $G_3$ if the Morupusi granite really was folded rather than injected into a pre-existing fold. As to the source of these granites, it was argued (Key *et al.* 1989) that they could have been derived by anatexis of pre-existing gneissic basement; this is not supported by the new geochemical evidence (see above).

The chemistry of the Marich granite (West Pokot; Fig. 2; Table 2) has been studied by Price (1984). It is a true granite (Streckeisen 1967); the small variation of major elements between samples implies little or no fractionation. The high initial $^{87}Sr/^{86}Sr$ ratio of $0.7072 \pm 0.0005$ (Ries *et al.* 1992) points to a crustal rather than a mantle origin. From the trace element chemistry and field evidence, Price concluded that the Marich granite shows an overlap with the characteristics of arc and collision settings. From the major elements, the Maniar & Piccoli method gives an ambiguous result, more probably continental arc (CAG) or island arc (IAG) but possibly continental collision (CCG). The method of Pearce *et al.* (1984), based on trace elements, also gives an ambiguous result but tends to indicate volcanic arc granite (VAG). Taking the evidence as a whole, a continental arc setting seems most probable, but continental collision granite (CCG) is possible.

## Geochemistry of the ophiolites and associated rocks

The geochemistry of the West Pokot ophiolites (Vearncombe 1983a,b) was studied in detail by Price (1984). The components, dismembered and tectonically interleaved with other rocks, include serpentinized dunite with podiform chromite chemically similar to Alpine ophiolite chromites; layered and isotropic metagabbros; dykes cutting gabbro and forming 20% of the outcrop; pillow lavas and spessartite quartzites which are interpreted as manganiferous metacherts (Vearncombe 1983b). The chemistry of the dykes, based on immobile trace elements, indicates MORB or IAT (island arc tholeiites); the pillow lavas (Downstream Series) are alkali within-plate and transitional alkaline MORB (Price 1984). The Marich Volcanic Series, supposedly stratigraphically above the ophiolite, is chemically similar to island arc volcanics; trace element evidence points to a transitional tholeiitic-calcalkaline magmatic affinity, suggesting an arc source which is transitional between immature and mature (Price 1984).

The Baragoi ophiolite (Baker 1963; Key 1987; Berhe 1990) in north-central Kenya (Fig. 2) is also tectonically imbricated and dismembered. It too includes mantle dunite and wehrlite, gabbro, sheeted dykes (20%) and volcanics classified as MORB, IAT and boninite compared to an average Mariana arc lava (Berhe 1990). The assemblage has not been dated but must be older than 830 Ma since the thrusting and imbrication which disrupted it is Sabachian or older. Comparison of the geochemical assessments of the West Pokot and Baragoi ophiolites shows no significant difference between them.

## Structure

The aspects of the structures which are discussed here are those which help in correlating structural sequences established in different areas; those which are needed to draw sections and to interpret generalized sequences across the Mozambique Belt; those, especially shear-sense indicators, which give evidence of transport direction and, hopefully, relative plate motions; and those which help to extrapolate the course of sutures away from any locality where these can be demonstrated to exist.

### Correlation of structures

Deformation sequences have been determined in most detail in north-central Kenya (Key 1987; Charsley 1987; Hackman 1988; Hackman et al. 1989), in NW Kenya (Sanders 1965; Vearncombe 1983b) and in north Tanzania (Hepworth & Kennerley 1970; Hepworth 1972). Direct correlation from north-central Kenya to NW Kenya (West Pokot), crucial since these areas include two clearly established ophiolite complexes, is hindered by the 100 km wide cover of Rift volcanics which separates them; east–west correlation is not so hindered in S Kenya and Tanzania. Tables 3, 4 and 5 show the sequences proposed in north-central and NW Kenya and northeast Tanzania.

### North-central Kenya

The earliest, 'Mukogodo', structures are irrelevant here for correlation because they are generally obliterated by the subsequent Mozambiquian deformations and because no other basement of their age (if it is indeed c. 1200 Ma) is known in the region considered.

The **Samburuan and Sabachian** may be regarded as phases of a single continuous process. The generally recognizable Samburuan structure is a coarse gneissic fabric, developed in amphibolite- or granulite-facies conditions. There are also small isoclinal folds parallel to the foliation. The main recognizable early structures, and tectonically the most significant, are the Sabachian. These include a complex of flat thrusts and recumbent folds, and a stretching lineation transverse to the overall N–S run of the Mozambique Belt. In the Maralal (Fig. 2) area, the recumbent folds have moderate westerly plunges and axial traces mostly trending ESE–WNW. A typical Sabachian SL fabric has axes 8:6:1 (Key 1987). The sub-horizontal attitude of these structures was compared to the root structures of major thrust belts, such as the Moine Thrust as revealed seismically. These early structures were said to indicate southeastward movement of the upper plate (Key et al. 1989). These recumbent structures, with roughly E–W fold axes and stretching lineations, were interpreted, following Hepworth (1972), as being formed during a period of extension across the width of the orogen. The folds were explained by assuming that the E–W extension, and vertically-acting gravity, would leave the intermediate (Y) axis N–S and that this pattern would explain the folds. This interpretation seems totally at odds with the facts. There is abundant evidence, from the western margin right across the belt, that the flat thrusts produce duplication, not omission. The ophiolites were obducted up from the ocean floor. The associated magmatism implies subduction or collision, not rifting (see under the earlier section 'Geochemistry'). The metamorphic evidence (PT) (Sanders 1954; Coolen 1980; Miyake 1984 indicates metamorphism at depths of *c.* 20 km for rocks now at surface over much of the Mozambique Belt of Kenya and Tanzania, although these rocks are still underlain by about 35 km of crust, implying major crustal thickening.

The fold axes, roughly parallel to the relative convergent plate motion, as suggested here, might be interpreted as sheath folds like the Turoka fold near Kajiado (Fig. 2; Shackleton 1993) or as developed on lateral ramps, or as flattened corrugations (cf. corrugated iron) produced by shear over irregular surfaces.

A major erosional break is inferred before the end-Precambrian onset of 'vertical tectonic regimes' recorded by the structures of the **Baragoian and Barsaloian** domains (Key 1987). Characteristic Baragoian structures are steep shears and folds with steep axial planes and usually low NW plunge, trending between NNW–SSE and NW–SE. Fabrics vary from S to SL to L. In the Maralal area, the type area for the Baragoian, typical SL fabrics have $X:Y:Z = 20:7:1$ (Key 1987). The Barsaloian structures are major N–S-trending shear or straightening zones (Hepworth 1967), arranged en echelon, up to 20 km wide and several hundred kilometres in length. Individual shears are defined by mylonites and augen gneisses with pseudotachylite. Folds are upright, tight to isoclinal. Minor fold axes plunge gently, usually northwards. Mineral lineations (sillimanite etc.) also generally plunge gently northwards (Fig. 2). The main shear zones are dextral. Typical axial ratios of fabrics are $10:10:1$ (Key 1987).

The metamorphism attributed to the Baragoian and Barsaloian varies but is often of amphibolite-facies. Sillimanite is common. There was said to be local anatexis, confined to major fold closures (Key 1987). Key *et al.* (1989) interpret the Baragoian structures as earlier (*c.* 620 Ma old), based on a Rb–Sr isochron age (Rundle 1983), than the Barsaloian (*c.* 570 Ma old) but the latter is only a minimum age for this deformation, based on ages from the $G_3$ and $G_4$ granites. The two deformations are distinguished essentially by trend. The Barsaloian shear zones are thought to represent pure shear, with the main mass-movement direction vertical; the gently plunging N–S lineations are thought not to represent the movement direction (a) but to be b-lineations parallel to the Barsaloian fold axes, the a-axis being vertical (Key 1987; Hackman *et al.* 1989).

These interpretations present difficulties. Firstly, the very straightness of the Barsaloian shear zones suggests mainly horizontal movement, since the straightest line on a shear surface is usually parallel to the movement. Secondly, the magnitude of the implied vertical movement is difficult to accept: shortening across the belt to a quarter, by pure shear (Hackman *et al.* 1989), implies extending it up to four times its previous thickness, so presumably more in the shear zones. Thirdly, the ubiquitous mineral lineation has to be interpreted not as parallel to the supposedly upward stretching direction, but normal to it. It would have to be mimetic, following crenulations, which is unusual. Fourthly, the maps show the Baragoian folds curving continuously into the Barsaloian (Fig. 3).

The interpretation preferred here is that the Baragoian and Barsaloian structures together reflect typical shear zone patterns (Ramsay & Graham 1970). This would imply that the major movement on the N–S shear zones was dextral, the maximum pressure being between NE–SW and ENE–WSW (Fig. 3). A decisive test to discriminate between these alternatives would be to find the orientation of stretched objects, as distinct from mineral lineations. They should be vertical according to one view, horizontal according to the other. In the Embu Series (around Embu, Fig. 2), which is thought to be unconformable on older sediments of the Mozambique Belt, boulders in a conglomerate were seen to be stretched with a plunge of 15° towards 165°. One such boulder measured $2.0 \times 0.6 \times 0.3$ m. Other nearby localities in the Embu Series showed stretching with low plunges to the SSE and SE. There is a steeply dipping schistosity striking SSW, presumably Baragoian/Barsaloian, but no sign of earlier (Samburuan/Sabachian) structures or fabrics. This evidence supports the view of Key *et al.* (1989) that there was a period of uplift and unconformity between the Samburuan/Sabachian and the Baragoian/Barsaloian deformations, which were also quite different in character, but it seems to contradict fairly conclusively their interpretation of the nature of the Baragoian/Barsaloian deformation: the N–S Baragoian/Barsaloian mineral lineation seems to be a stretching lineation. It even seems possible that the supposedly Barsaloian sillimanite, oriented N–S, is re-oriented and originally much older (cf. rotated Samburuan–Sabachian stretching lineation demonstrated in S Kenya and NE Tanzania (Fig. 2)).

## NW Kenya (West Pokot)

Large-scale open E–W folds were recognized in the Sekerr area, which includes West Pokot (McCall 1964) and elsewhere in Kenya (Sagger-

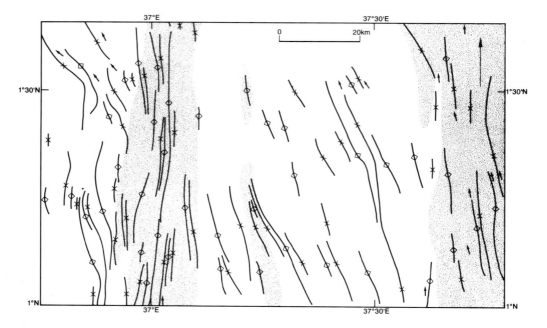

**Fig. 3.** Map of axial traces of folds in part of north-central Kenya showing 'Baragoian' NNW–SSE folds curving into N–S 'Barsaloian' shear zones (shaded), taken from maps of Laisamis (Charsley 1987) and Maralal (Key 1987) areas. The pattern is interpreted here as a single dextral shear system (Ramsay & Graham 1970). Arrows: stretching lineation.

son *et al.* 1960), as well as open folds trending about N–S. Both seem to die out to the west in the Webuye (Broderick Falls) area (Sanders 1965). Correlation of the $D_1$ and $D_2$ westward thrusts and overfolds of West Pokot with the westward thrusting and tight folding and the two NW-trending lineations, mapped by Sanders at the west front of the Mozambique Belt at Webuye, is approximate.

### S Kenya and NE Tanzania

The structural interpretation of this area is discussed (Shackleton 1993) with particular reference to deep crustal structures in the granulites of the Usambara Mountains, NE Tanzania (Bagnall 1964); structures in the Kajiado area, S Kenya, (Fig. 2) which were studied in detail by Weiss (1959); and a regional tectonic analysis based on photointerpretation, field control and analysis of published maps by Hepworth (Hepworth & Kennerley 1970; Hepworth 1972), extending from the Tanzania Craton across much of the Tanzanian Mozambique Belt.

Weiss (1959) studied the structures in the Kajiado area, S Kenya (Fig. 2), especially the

Turoka fold. This is an irregularly crescentic structure, outlined by an almost continuous band of marble, in turn surrounded by a discontinuous quartzite. Another fold a few kilometres to the SE shows a similar arrangement but the outer quartzite is more continuous. Weiss concluded that lineations and minor fold axes are parallel, plunging regularly 20° ENE. The lineation, conspicuous on most foliation surfaces, is a fine regular ribbing but varies from a fine striation to a coarse mullioning. It is commonly defined by an elongation of mineral grains, especially hornblende, and by streaky tracts of feldspar and mica. It is clearly not only a mineral lineation but also a stretching lineation. Weiss postulated first the tearing of the beds into long ENE-trending strips; then one such was rolled into a cylinder which was finally tilted ESE (to account for the plunge). This model is rejected and the Turoka fold reinterpreted as a sheath fold, the lineation being in the movement direction (Shackleton 1993).

East of Kajiado, teams from Nagoya University, Japan, studied the Machakos area (Fig. 2), and particularly the Mbooni and Uvete domes of granite gneiss and their surroundings. These

**Table 4.** *Tectonothermal history, West Pokot, NW Kenya*

| | | |
|---|---|---|
| $D_4$ | Large-scale folding on E–W axes | |
| $D_3$ | Open folds plunging gently N or N by E. Asymmetry variable, more to E. No associated fabric (but lineation mapped by McCall may be $l_3$). | |
| $D_2$ | Tight to isoclinal folds; axial planes dip E; plunge to N & NE; LS fabrics; mineral elongation lineation $l_2$ plunges E. Thrusts to W. Dykes, veins & major intrusion of granite, partly along ductile shear zones, may be early- or syn-$D_2$. | amphibolite facies (staurolite–kyanite sub-facies). |
| $D_1$ | Heterogeneous (locally undetected) planar fabric. Thrusts & folds. Dismemberment and imbrication of ophiolite. | amphibolite facies? |

Based on Vearncombe (1983*b*).

domes are surrounded by concentric folds and, from a study of strain ellipsoids based mainly on deformation of pegmatite and quartz veins, the Japanese researchers concluded that the strains and the concentric folds round the Uvete dome were accounted for by the uprise of the granitic core (Miyata & Saka 1981). The metasediments were interpreted as an essentially continuous stratigraphic sequence, some 8 km thick, and since some right-way-up sedimentary structures were found at one horizon (Saka & Miyata 1981), the whole sequence was inferred to have been right way up, dipping gently, before the granites were intruded. This simplicity of structure is in quite remarkable contrast to the evident complexity of the structures just to the west around Kajiado. It is recorded that tight minor folds are common, with axial surfaces parallel or sub-parallel to the gneissic foliation. Less ductile layers have been torn into lenses or boudins. It seems likely, therefore, that before the intrusion of the domes, dated for Mbooni at $774 \pm 14$ Ma (Cahen & Snelling 1984; Shibata & Suwa 1979), there were earlier phases of intense deformation on gently inclined surfaces, pre-dating the pegmatite and quartz vein strain markers. The stratigraphic sequence may be far from simple. The Kajiado and Usambara areas are unusual in that the later N–S folds and shear zones and the still later open E–W cross folds hardly affect them at all so they provide little evidence of structural sequence, but it is clear that the lineation which is conspicuous in both areas is the same. The lineation in the Usambara granulites is similar, both in character and orientation, to that at Kajiado. In intervening areas, where the basement is not covered by younger volcanics, the orientation is also similar: correlation from Kajiado to Usambara is clear, and the very large extensional strain (X:Y:Z = 30:2:1) measured in the Usambara mountains (Shackleton 1993)

leaves no doubt that the lineation marks the direction of transport or shear. Fold axes trend close to this stretching lineation.

Correlation of the stretching lineation further westwards across Tanzania to the western front of the Mozambique Belt is more uncertain. This is partly because, while some lineations are plotted on the 1:250 000 map sheets, their nature is not indicated: the maps were published with only very brief summaries at the sides of the sheets, unlike Kenya where they were published with Reports. The available data for each sheet, plotted stereographically (Hepworth 1972), often show several maxima, which cannot all be stretching lineations; successive differently orientated incremental strains would normally combine to give a single strain ellipsoid representing the cumulative strain. The correlation of particular maxima from different areas must, at present, depend on continuity of trend, in places helped by map evidence of structural sequence and on my own field data. The Usambara lineation curves continuously from N–S north of the Usambara Mountains, through NE–SW across the mountains and ENE–WSW at their SW side, to E–W. Some 100 km west (1:250 000 sheets 87 & 127), the stereograms show interruptions of the regular trend (Hepworth 1972). Still further west (sheets 126, 125), the previous pattern appears to be resumed though the trend is now ESE–WNW. Approaching the western front of the Mozambique Belt, the trend is similar though irregular but the SE plunge is steeper as it usually is along the front (e.g. Sanders 1965). One must conclude that on the basis of continuity of trend alone, one cannot definitely correlate the trans-Mozambiquian lineations right across the belt. Those in the east (Samburuan/ Sabachian domain of north-central Kenya and Pare-Usambara granulites in NE Tanzania) and westwards to the Kajiado area (Fig. 2) are *c*.

810–830 Ma old; those further west could be different.

The structural sequence in a large part of the Mozambique Belt in northeast Tanzania was studied by Hepworth (Hepworth & Kennerley 1970; Hepworth 1972). He distinguished domains characterized by the dominance of structures with a particular trend: those he recognized in the Mozambique Belt are shown in Table 5.

**Table 5.** *Structures of domains in the Mozambique Belt of NE Tanzania*

| Domain | Structures |
|---|---|
| Bongan | NE–SW or NNE–SSW fold axes. Local axial plane cleavage dips steeply E. Statistical maximum of lineation & fold axes 16°/048° |
| Kondoan | Intense folding on SE-plunging axes; flat or E-dipping axial planar foliation with planar preferred orientation of platy minerals. Strong lineation parallel to intersection at 5° of two S-surfaces; QF prisms or pencils: point maximum 16°/132°; to east, flattens and trends due E. |
| Parangan | Indistinct wavy or irregular foliation, little mesoscopic fabric or mineral orientation. Lineation weak – short ripples, rude fold axes, scaly elongation. Lineation maximum 14°/160°. Early Parangan isoclinal folding in quartzite and amphibolite. Late Parangan refolding to small folds with crenulations. Fold axes maximum 16°/180°. |

(A series of large eyed folds was also mapped, suggesting superimposed folding possibly of WSW–ESE or NW–SE folds by one of NE fold sets.)
From Hepworth 1972.

In the region studied by Hepworth, the late, Bongan, deformation was only recognized in small areas near the western Mozambique front and in one isolated area on sheet 127 (Hepworth 1972). The Parangan was recognized 100 km eastward from the front and the Kondoan about the same distance. No dates are available for these deformations. The Bongan is similar to, and probably to be correlated with, the Baragoian. Correlation of the trans-Mozambiquian Kondoan with the Samburuan/Sabachian, via the Usambara Mountains, is plausible but equally plausible is correlation with the trans-Mozambiquian $D_2$ structures of West Pokot further north along the western side of the belt which, if the geochronological evidence is accepted, are younger. This is discussed later.

## Shear sense indicators

Shear sense indicators, essential for determining transport direction, and thus plate motions, have unfortunately seldom been recorded in the East African Mozambique Belt. At the western front, movement was clearly westwards. At Webuye (Broderick Falls), lineations plunge mostly NW. The transport direction in the post-Archaean cover was towards the NW (Sanders 1965). This reflects the influence of the Aswa sinistral shear zone which trends NW across the Uganda basement.

East from the front at Webuye, and structurally upwards, foliation flattens and the transport direction was towards the west rather than NW. In West Pokot, where sedimentary structures give good facing directions, the facing directions of the $D_2$ folds are contradictory indicating pre-$D_2$ reversals, but the $D_1$ folds are indecipherable. However, the transport direction is still clearly WSW (Vearncombe 1983b), towards the Archaean foreland.

In north-central Kenya, on the other hand, the thrust direction during the Samburuan/Sabachian tectonism is thought to have been southeastwards (Key 1987; Charsley 1987): downdip lineation on thrust planes is said to indicate southeastward movement of upper plates (Key *et al.* 1989), but with no detailed evidence, it is difficult to assess this important conclusion. On the contrary, sections (Key 1987, AA′ & BB‴; Charsley 1987, AA′, BB′ & CC′; Hackman 1988 AA′; Hackman *et al.* 1989 AA′; sections on 1:250 000 maps) all show folded recumbent folds, presumably Sabachian, facing westwards, indicating westward transport. The facing is shown by the direction towards which cores of units shown as stratigraphically older close, or younger units open, in these folds. The reference to downdip lineations on thrust planes is hard to understand since the thrusts are folded and have no consistent dip. One section, AA′ in Key *et al.* (1987) does show some reverse faults dipping west but these are clearly post-Sabachian.

Important evidence of shear sense comes from north of the area covered by the present paper. In the Adola area of southern Ethiopia (Fig. 1), the tectonic contact between the ophiolite complex and 'basement' gneisses is associated with E–W or NW–SE stretching lineations. The sense of shear deduced from pressure shadows, rotated porphyroblasts and quartz c-axis fabrics indicates eastward tectonic transport (Bogliotti 1989). Berhe (1990) also states (without presenting evidence) that the major obduction and nappe transport was to the east in the Yubdo,

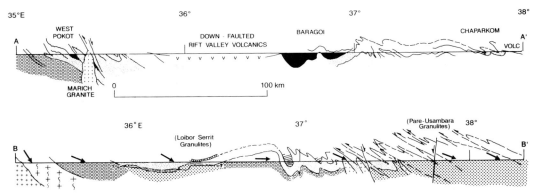

**Fig. 4.** Diagrammatic sections across the East African Mozambique Belt: A–A′ at 1°30′N; B–B′ at 4°15′S (Fig. 2). Ornament as on Fig. 2.

Adola and Moyale ophiolites in southern Ethiopia and at Baragoi in north-central Kenya. Thus, there is clearly a fundamental difference between the interpretation adopted here and that of many others. More shear sense data, with geochronological control, are needed.

*Cross sections*

Some indication of possible tectonic interpretation may be obtained from sections across the belt. Two very simplified and generalized sections are shown in Fig. 4, one across north-central Kenya on 1°30′N, the other across NE Tanzania on 4°15′S. The former shows recognized ophiolites (West Pokot, Baragoi, Chaparkom) but the relations between West Pokot and the others is obscured by the 100 km wide Rift volcanics cover. The southern section is more continuous but less detailed and no ophiolites are seen. However, the folded, overall flattish recumbent structures in the northern section and the general low eastward lineation plunge in the southern one together give no indication of a reversal of transport direction, away in either direction from a root zone under the Rift (cf. Key *et al.* 1989). They suggest rather that the West Pokot ophiolite is at a lower structural level than the Baragoi and Chaparkom ophiolites, that the transport was westwards throughout, and that the West Pokot and Baragoi ophiolites are distinct units.

*Structural controls on extrapolation of ophiolite sutures*

There is no decisive evidence for the existence of any sutures in the East African Mozambique Belt, but at least the West Pokot ophiolite looks like a good candidate; it dips eastwards below surface and does not reappear; the West Pokot zone of imbrication and thrusts is comparable with other sutures; and zones with ophiolites continue northwards or NNW through western Ethiopia. If it is a suture between plates, it must also continue southwards unless it only represents the closure of an ocean basin (backarc?) of limited extent. Archaean basement is recognized west of it, but none further east until Malagasy. Reworked Archaean basement is also recognized at least 100 km eastwards from the western Mozambiquian front in Tanzania (Hepworth 1972). A map of the belt in Kenya and Tanzania (Shackleton 1986) indicates probable continuity of formations across the area in a general SSE direction. These relationships place some control on the possible course of a suture southwards from West Pokot. West of the West Pokot ophiolite line, orthoquartzites, thought to be unconformable on Archaean, extend southwards to at least 4°30′S, while east of the ophiolite there is a zone with marble horizons (Shackleton 1986, Fig. 4; Fig. 2) which also extends (if extrapolated under Rift volcanic cover) far to the south. A suture between these two could run towards a suspected ophiolite (Shackleton 1986, p. 338) near Itiso (36°E, 5°30′S). However, there is at present no strong shearing or other structural evidence to support this 900 km extrapolation.

**Discussion**

There have been various different and contradictory interpretations of the East African Mozambique Belt. The trans-Mozambiquian lineation and the associated thrusting and folding (Hepworth's Kondoan) were attributed by Hepworth (1972) to E–W extension, a view accepted by Key *et al.* (1989) for the Samburuan/Sabachian deformations with similar trans-Mozambiquian lineation in north-central Kenya. These authors inferred a period of crustal extension between *c.* 840 and 766 Ma ago, when new oceanic crust, represented by the Baragoi, Korr and Chaparkom ophiolites, was formed, followed, before *c.* 620 Ma ago, by collision. The collision was thought to have produced a granulite root zone centred beneath the East African Rift Valley, forming an axis of bilateral symmetry with nappes in western Kenya facing northwest (Sanders 1965) while those to the east were stated to face southeast as the result of backfolding (Key 1987; Key *et al.* 1989). Structural objections to this interpretation have already been explained. It is also implausible because it implies that ophiolites were thrust away from the suture on both sides – almost 100 km westwards and about 200 km eastwards. Moreover, collision is supposed to have occurred between about 766 and 620 Ma ago, but no deformation phase in this interval was recognized (Key *et al.* 1989).

Berhe (1990) thought that sutures through West Pokot and Baragoi (Fig. 2) and Moyale (Fig. 1), further NE, could be identified and correlated with sutures postulated in the Arabian–Nubian Shield. A suture through the Baragoi ophiolite zone is difficult to accept because this extensive ophiolite mass is synformal (Baker 1963; Key *et al.* 1989; Fig. 4 section AA') and is correlated (Hackman 1988) with the Chaparkom ophiolite. The suture would, therefore, be either east of Chaparkom or west of the Baragoi ophiolite, depending on the direction of transport. The Moyale ophiolite, and those of Adola further N in Ethiopia, also appears to be synformal.

The demonstration in north-central Kenya (Key *et al.* 1989) of two separate Mozambiquian tectonisms some 200 Ma apart, the confirmation as ophiolites of the West Pokot and Baragoi complexes (Vearncombe 1983*b*; Price 1984; Berhe 1990), the geochemical identification of the tectonic setting of granitoids (this paper), and the dating of rocks from West Pokot (Ries *et al.* 1992) together perhaps make it possible to come closer to a convincing interpretation of the belt in East Africa.

There appears to be a conflict between the geochronological data and the proposed correlation of structures across the Mozambique Belt. If the ages of the Marich volcanics ($663 \pm 99$ Ma) and Marich granite ($593 \pm 50$ Ma) are accepted as approximating to magmatic ages (Ries *et al.*

1992), the West Pokot ophiolite must have been obducted after the first date, and probably after the second if the geochemical indication of tectonic setting of the Marich granite (continental arc) is accepted; if so, collision is probably indicated by the major metamorphism dated at *c.* 580 Ma. But in north-central Kenya, the evidence seems clear that the Baragoi, Korr and Chaparkom ophiolite complexes had already been obducted, deformed and dismembered no later than 820–830 Ma ago, the date of the Samburuan/Sabachian tectonism. The age data, if valid, thus imply two entirely separate periods of ophiolite obduction and collision in western and north-central Kenya. At first sight, the structural evidence seems to indicate (Key *et al.* 1989) the correlation of the intense flat Samburuan/Sabachian structures in north-central Kenya with the similarly orientated Kondoan structures in the west of the belt in Tanzania (Hepworth 1972) and, by further extrapolation, with the early ($D_1$–$D_2$) deformations at West Pokot. The trans-Mozambiquian lineations in all these areas seem to fall into a single pattern (Shackleton 1993; Fig. 2). If so, the obduction, imbrication and dismemberment of the West Pokot and Baragoi ophiolites would have been contemporaneous and earlier than *c.* 820 Ma ago. Either the dates or the structural correlation must have been misinterpreted. The two crucial West Pokot dates, of the volcanics and the Marich granite, were interpreted as magmatic rather than metamorphic ages, because both deformation and metamorphism (staurolite-kyanite sub-facies) are much less than in north-central Kenya for which the dates were also interpreted as primary magmatic. In the Marich volcanics, both blocks and phenocrysts in agglomerates are still clearly outlined (as well as vesicles and pillows in pillow lavas). If the ages, or even their relative values, are accepted one must look again at the structural correlation. There are gaps in the continuity of the lineation pattern in Tanzania (see Hepworth 1972, fig. 2, stereograms of sheets 87 & 127); stretching lineations transverse to orogenic belts are characteristic of most of them, often associated with intense deformation on recumbent structures, so if there are two superimposed orogenic deformations in the Mozambique Belt it is to be expected that both produced transverse stretching lineations on flat structures and these could be miscorrelated to infer a single event. There are also gently inclined Baragoian folds (Key *et al.* 1989). Axes of inclined $D_2$ folds at West Pokot trend N–S, like Baragoian folds in N Central Kenya whereas axes of Sabachian folds there trend *c.* E–W. On balance, correlation using the relative ages indicated by the

**Table 6.** *Proposed correlation and interpretation of tectonic sequences in the Mozambique Belt of Kenya (see Table 1 for alternative correlation of Ayalew et al. 1990)*

| Approx. age (Rb/Sr) Ma | | NW Kenya | N. Central & S. Kenya | Tectonism (Key et al. 1989) |
|---|---|---|---|---|
| 500 | | Final uplift | Final uplift | |
| | 530 | E–W folds ($D_4$) | E–W warps | Kipsingian |
| | | Open N–S folds ($D_3$) | NE–SW cylindrical folds & sinistral shears. E–W dykes | Loldaikan |
| | 570 | | $G_3$ & $G_4$ (WPG & PCG). | |
| | | Collision: W-vergent N–S folds, thrusts ($D_2$) | Major N–S dextral shears & folds | Barsaloian & |
| 600 | | Marich G (CAG or CCG) | NW–SE to NNW–SSE upright | Baragoian |
| | 620 | Obduction of ophiolites from E ($D_1$) | folds & shears | |
| | 670 | Subduction (extended period) | Embu Series | |
| | | Marich Volcanics | Unconformity, uplift | |
| 700 | | W. Pokot ophiolite | & erosion | |
| | 770 | | Mbooni G | |
| 800 | | | Collision. Flat thrusts & folds. | |
| | | | Trans-Mozambique Belt lineation | Sabachian |
| | 830 | | $G_2$ granites. Gneissic foliation | Samburuan |
| | | | Obduction of ophiolites from E | |
| | | | Subduction (eastwards) | |
| | | | Baragoi ophiolite | |
| | | Deposition of shelf sediments | Deposition of shelf-sediments | |

CAG: continental arc granites; CCG: continent–continent collision granites; WPG: within-plate granites; PCG: post-collision granites.

dates (Tables 1 & 6) is preferred to the east-to-west correlation of the trans-Mozambiquian linear structures of West Pokot and the regions to the east.

The metamorphic evidence should also help to discriminate between the hypothesis of a single collision under the Rift, between c. 766 and 620 Ma ago (Key et al. 1989) or two collisions, one east of Chaparkom at about 800 Ma ago and a second in the West Pokot zone at about 600 Ma ago, as advocated here. Two periods of metamorphism, both producing migmatites and upper-amphibolite facies (sillimanite gneiss etc) were recognized in north-central Kenya. They were dated at c. 830–820 Ma and c. 620–570 Ma (Key et al. 1989). The first phase, affecting the whole north-central Kenya area studied, was supposed to have been before the postulated time of collision; the second, considerably after the collision, was attributed to shear heating. No metamorphic phase was recognized at the supposed time of collision. However, the times of the two major metamorphisms do coincide with the two separate collisions postulated here. The distance between the West Pokot collisional suture and the metamorphism associated with the

N–S shear zones in north-central Kenya is about 200 km.

Assessing the structural, geochronological and metamorphic evidence together, it is concluded that despite the apparent continuity of the early recumbent structures and associated trans-Mozambique Belt stretching lineation, the most convincing interpretation is that there were two separate collisional orogenies, one at about 800 Ma ago on a suture east of the Baragoi and Chaparkom ophiolites and the other, at about 600 Ma ago, in the West Pokot zone.

A different chronology to that shown for NW Kenya (Table 6) is proposed in a tentative correlation based on both U/Pb zircon ages and Rb/Sr isochron ages of five granitoids from the Birbir domain in western Ethiopia (Ayalew et al. 1990). The area sampled there is about 750 km N of West Pokot (NW Kenya) and covers part of a N–S trending ophiolite-bearing zone of low-grade (greenschist facies) metasediments and metavolcanics which is in tectonic contact on both sides with upper amphibolite-facies gneisses regarded as the continuation of the Mozambique Belt gneisses in Kenya. While zircon and Rb/Sr ages of the two late- to post-kinematic plutons agree, the Rb/Sr isochron age of a syntectonic leucogranite is 54 Ma younger than the zircon age and those of two pre-tectonic granitoids are 196 and 195 Ma younger. These results strongly suggest that the comparable Rb/Sr ages from the Mozambique Belt in Kenya are also too low.

However, the tentatively proposed correlation (Ayalew *et al.* 1990) seems unconvincing. It implicitly assumes that throughout a region extending from Kenya to Saudi Arabia there was just a single arc accretion at a continental margin, with widespread regional metamorphism at 760 Ma ago, and later a continent/continent collision, regional metamorphism and granite plutonism at 580–550 Ma ago. The NW Kenya sequence is fitted into this interpretation, as an arc-accretion suture zone, by putting the age of the Marich granite (Rb/Sr *c.* 593 Ma) at between 780 and 800 Ma and the Marich Volcanic Series (Rb/Sr *c.* 663 Ma) at between 800 and 830 Ma. Such a reinterpretation of the West Pokot ages would by supported by a correlation of the Birbir and West Pokot ophiolite-bearing zones, but this is improbable; they are 750 km apart, with few intervening basement exposures, and the Birbir domain ends in the south against the major 25 km wide Surma (Akobo) sinistral shear zone, which may have displaced it from alignment with the Baragoi ophiolites rather than those of West Pokot. Moreover, West Pokot is the westernmost ophiolite zone in Kenya, but the Birbir zone is not the westernmost in W Ethiopia (Berhe 1990). To fit the N Central Kenya chronology (Key *et al.* 1989) into the scheme as well, those Rb/Sr ages would have to be accepted almost unchanged, unlike all the others and despite the higher grade of metamorphism there; the regional metamorphism and associated crustal thickening at *c.* 820 Ma ago would be attributed to arc accretion, while the more localized deformation concentrated in N–S shear zones and the associated metamorphism and the magmatism which has been identified as post-collisional or within-plate would represent continent–continent collision at *c.* 580–550 Ma ago. The Birbir domain represents the arc accretion zone; the location of the continent–continent collision suture is not suggested. The proposed correlations and general interpretation seem unconvincing.

I conclude that while all of the Kenya Rb/Sr ages are probably too low, the relative age relationships and interpretations suggested in Table 6 best fit the present evidence. Tighter geochronological control by zircon ages is urgently needed.

Another problem is the position of the suture to which the Baragoi, Korr and Chaparkom ophiolites (Key 1987; Charsley 1987) belong. Firstly, this depends on interpretation of the direction from which they were obducted and transported – from the northwest (Key 1987; Key *et al.* 1989; Berhe 1990) or from the east (Shackleton 1986 and this paper). If the combination of the Korr, Chaparkom and Baragoi ophiolites (Charsley 1989) is accepted, the suture must be west of Baragoi (Key *et al.* 1987) or east of Chaparkom and so at least 100 km east of Baragoi. The suture suggested (Berhe 1990) through the Moyale ophiolite would be some 150 km still further east. It seems that whether the Baragoi and associated ophiolites were obducted from the east or west, the horizontal transport distance from the suture must have been very large. The general overall eastward plunge of the trans-Mozambiquian stretching lineations (Figs 2 & 4) and the structures shown on the published sections (Baker 1963; Charsley 1987; Key 1987) seem to indicate a suture to the east and westward transport for the Baragoi and associated ophiolites.

The direction of subduction, in the East African Mozambique Belt and in the regions north to the Arabian–Nubian Shield, is controversial. Because the stretching lineation of the recumbent structures consistently plunges eastwards, most clearly across Tanzania (Fig. 4, section BB'), the transport direction in this part of the East African Mozambique Belt crust is considered here to have been westwards. Although it is possible that the sense of relative plate movement in the mantle might not be the same as in the crust, it is perhaps more likely that the crustal transport direction is a direct reflection of the subduction direction and that subduction was, therefore, eastwards. If so, and if the later (West Pokot) collision zone was west of the earlier one, it would appear that the plates or microplates accreted successively to an eastern foreland, probably Malagasy, with its widespread Archaean, representing East Gondwana. There is, as yet, insufficient evidence either to confirm or disprove the eastward direction of subduction in the Mozambique Belt from the distribution or polarity of supra-subduction zone magmas, as Ian Gass attempted (Nasseef & Gass 1980) in the Arabian Shield.

## Conclusions

The main conclusions (summarized in Table 6) are as follows:

1. The Il Poloi G$_2$ granite and the Marich granite are probably subduction-related volcanic

arc granites, the Mbooni granite (Machakos area) syn-collisional; the $G_3$ and $G_4$ granites of north-central Kenya are identified geochemically as probably within-plate, rift-related, although the field evidence favours post-collisional.

2. The N–S- or NNW–SSE-trending Baragoian/Barsaloian lineations, like the Samburuan/Sabachian and Kondoan trans-Mozambiquian lineations, indicate the direction of relative movement; the great Barsaloian shear zones are essentially dextral strike-slip shears, not zones of flattening and upward movement.

3. Many of the folds are sub-parallel to the direction of movement. They may be sheath folds, or developed at lateral ramps, or corrugations due to passage over irregularities.

4. The Baragoi and related ophiolites in north-central Kenya were obducted and involved in collisional tectonics at c. 800 Ma ago (Samburuan/Sabachian orogeny). The West Pokot ophiolite complex in NW Kenya was obducted and involved in collision at c. 600 Ma ago, (if the geochronological interpretation is correct).

The effects of this second collision include the Baragoian/Barsaloian deformation, with major N–S dextral shear zones, in N Central Kenya.

5. The West Pokot ophiolite was obducted from the E-dipping Pokot suture; the location of the suture from which the Baragoi and associated ophiolites were obducted is unknown, but they too are thought to have been thrust from the east.

6. The subductions which led to the collision along a suture thought to be east of the Chaparkom ophiolite, and to a later collision in the West Pokot zone, are thought to have been eastwards. Plates and microplates were successively accreted to an eastern foreland (East Gondwana) probably represented by Malagasy.

I wish to thank Mike Coward, Nigel Harris and Alfred Kröner for helpful critical comments, and my wife Peigi for transforming my illegible handwriting into typescript. This paper is a contribution to IGCP 348, 'The Mozambique and related belts'.

# References

AYALEW, T., BELL, K., MOORE, J. M. & PARRISH, R. R. 1990. Pb and Rb-Sr geochronology of the Western Ethiopian Shield. *Geological Society of America Bulletin*, **102**, 1309–1316.

BAGNALL, S. 1964. Geological relationships in NE Tanganyika and their bearing on the granulite problem. *Annual Report of the Research Institute of African Geology, University of Leeds*, **8**, 31–32.

BAKER, B. H. 1963. *Geology of the Baragoi Area*. Report of the Geological Survey of Kenya, **53**.

BERHE, S. M. 1990. Ophiolites in Northeast and East Africa: implications for Proterozoic crustal growth. *Journal of the Geological Society, London*, **147**, 41–57.

BOGLIOTTI, C. 1989. A re-interpretation of the large-scale structure of Precambrian rocks in the Adola Goldfield (Ethiopia) based on two generations of interference pattern. *Precambrian Research*, **44**, 289–304.

CAHEN, L. & SNELLING, N. J. 1984. *The Geochronology and Evolution of Africa*. Clarendon Press, Oxford.

CHARSLEY, T. J. 1987. *Geology of the Laisamis Area*. Report of the Mines and Geology Department, Kenya, **106**.

COOLEN, J. J. M. M. M. 1980. *Chemical Petrology of the Furua Granulite Complex, Southern Tanzania*. G.U.A. (University of Amsterdam), *Papers of Geology*, **1/13**, 1–258.

——, PRIEM, H. N. A., VERDURMEN, E. A. Th. & VERSCHURE, R. H. 1982. Possible zircon U-Pb evidence for Pan-African granulite facies metamorphism in the Mozambique Belt of Southern Tanzania. *Precambrian Research*, **17**, 31–40.

GABERT, G. & WENDT, I. 1974. Datierung von granitischen Gesteinen im Dodoman- und Usagaran-System in der Ndembera-Serie (Tanzania) *Geologisches Jahrbuch*, **11**, 3–55.

HACKMAN, B. D. 1988. *Geology of the Baringo–Laikipia area*. Report of the Mines and Geology Department, Kenya, **104**.

——, KAGASI, J., KEY, R. M. & WILKINSON, A. F. 1989. *Geology of the Isiolo Area*. Report of the Mines and Geology Department, Kenya, **103**.

HARRIS, N. B. W., HAWKESWORTH, C. J. & RIES, A. C. 1984. Crustal evolution in north-east and east Africa from model Nd ages. *Nature*, **309**, 773–776.

HEPWORTH, J. V. 1967. The photogeological recognition of ancient orogenic belts in Africa. *Quarterly Journal of the Geological Society of London*, **123**, 253–292.

—— 1972. The Mozambique orogenic belt and its foreland in northeast Tanzania: a photogeologically based study. *Journal of the Geological Society, London*, **128**, 461–500.

—— & KENNERLEY, J. B. 1970. Photogeology and structure of the Mozambique orogenic front near Kolo, north-east Tanzania. *Journal of the Geological Society, London*, **125**, 417–479.

KEY, R. M. 1987. *Geology of the Maralal Area*. Report of the Mines and Geology Department, Kenya, **105**.

——, CHARSLEY, T. J., HACKMAN, B. D., WILKINSON, A. F. & RUNDLE, C. C. 1989. Superimposed Upper Proterozoic Collision-controlled Orogenies in the Mozambique Orogenic Belt of Kenya. *Precambrian Research*, **44**, 197–225.

MABOKO, M. A. H., BODRYK, N. A. J. M., PRIEM, H.

N. A. & VERDURMEN, E.A.Th. 1985. Zircon U-Pb and biotite Rb-Sr dating of the Wami River granulites, eastern granulites, Tanzania: evidence for approximately 715 Ma old granulite facies metamorphism and final Pan-African cooling approximately 475 Ma ago. *Precambrian Research*, **30**, 361–378.

McCALL, G. J. H. 1964. *Geology of the Sekerr Area.* Report of the Geological Survey of Kenya, **65**.

MACFARLANE, A. 1969. Preliminary report on the Geology of the Central Serengeti, NW Tanzania. *Annual Report of the Research Institute of African Geology, University of Leeds*, **13**, 14–16.

MANIAR, P. D. & PICCOLI, P. M. 1989. Tectonic discrimination of granitoids. *Geological Society of America Bulletin*, **101**, 635–643.

MIYAKE, A. 1984. Phase equilibria in the hornblende-bearing basic gneisses of the Uvete area, central Kenya. *Journal of Metamorphic Geology* **2**, 105–177.

—— & SUWA, K. 1981. Geological structure of the Uvete dome, Kenya. *6th Preliminary Report of African Studies, Nagoya University (Earth Sci. 4)*, 33–41.

MIYATA, T. & SAKA, Y. 1981. Strain distribution around the Uvete dome, Machakos, Kenya. *6th Preliminary Report of African Studies, Nagoya University (Earth Sci. 4)*, 67–71.

MUHONGO, S. 1989. Tectonic setting of the Proterozoic metamorphic terrains in eastern Tanzania and their bearing on the evolution of the Mozambique Belt. *IGCP no. 255 Newsletter/Bulletin*, **2**, 43–50.

NASSEEF, A. O. & GASS, I. G. 1980. Arabian Shield granite traverse. In 'Evolution and mineralization of the Arabian-Nubian Shield'. *Institute of Applied Geology (Jeddah), Bulletin.* **3**(4), 77–82.

PEARCE, J. A., HARRIS, N. B. W. & TINDLE, A. G. 1984. Trace Element Dissemination Diagrams for the Tectonic Interpretation of Granitic Rocks. *Journal of Petrology*, **25**, 956–983.

PRICE, R. C. 1984. *Late Pre-Cambrian mafic-ultramafic complexes in Northeast Africa.* PhD thesis, Open University, Milton Keynes.

PRIEM. H. N. A., BOELRIJK, N. A. I. M., HIBEDA, E. H., VERDURMEN, E. A. Th., VERSCHURE, R. H., OEN, I. S. & WESTRA, L. 1979. Isotopic age determinations on granitic and gneissic rocks from the Ubendian–Usagaran System in Southern Tanzania. *Precambrian Research*, **9**, 227.

RAMSAY, J. G. & GRAHAM, R. H. 1970. Strain variation in shear belts. *Canadian Journal of Earth Science*, **7**, 786–813.

RIES, A. C., VEARNCOMBE, J. R., PRICE, R. C. & SHACKLETON, R. M. 1992. Geochronology and geochemistry of the rocks associated with a Late Proterozoic ophiolite in West Pokot, NW Kenya. *Journal of African Earth Sciences*, **14**(1), 25–36.

RUNDLE, C. C. 1983. *Rb-Sr dating of granitic intrusions into the Mozambiquian Belt of Central Kenya.* Report of the Isotope Geology Unit, Institute of Geological Sciences, 83/11 (unpublished).

SAGGERSON, E. P., JOUBERT, P. McCALL, G. J. H. & WILLIAMS, L. A. J. 1960. Cross-folding and refolding in the Basement System of Kenya Colony. *Report of the 21st International Geological Congress, Norden*, Pt XVIII, 335–346.

SAKA, Y. & MIYATA, T. 1981. Primary sedimentary structures found in the gneisses of the Mozambique metamorphic belt near Machakos, Kenya. *6th Preliminary Report of Africa Studies, Nagoya University (Earth Sci. 4)*, 33–41

SANDERS, L. D. 1954. The status of sillimanite as an index of metamorphic grade in the Kenya Basement system. *Geological Magazine*, **91** 144–152

—— 1965. Geology of the contact between the Nyanza Shield and the Mozambique Belt in western Kenya. *Bulletin of the Geological Survey of Kenya*, **7**.

SHACKLETON, R. M. 1986. Precambrian Collision Tectonics in Africa. *In*: COWARD, M. P. & RIES, A. C. (eds), *Collision Tectonics*, Blackwell, Oxford, 329–349.

—— 1993. Tectonics of the lower crust: a view from the Usambara Mountains, NE Tanzania. *Journal of Structural Geology*, **15**, 663–671.

SHIBATA, K. & SUWA, K. 1979. A geochronological study on gneiss from the Mbooni Hills, Machakos area, Kenya. *4th Preliminary Report of African Studies, Nagoya University (Earth Sci. 3)* 143–167.

STRECKEISEN, A. L. 1967. Classification and Nomenclature of Igneous Rocks. *Neues Jahrbuch fur Mineralogie Abhandlungen* **107**, 144–214.

VEARNCOMBE, J. R. 1983a. A proposed continental margin in the Precambrian of western Kenya. *Geologisches Rundschau*, **72**, 663–670.

—— 1983b. A dismembered ophiolite from the Mozambique Belt, West Pokot, Kenya. *Journal of African Earth Sciences*, **1**, 133–143.

WEISS, L. E. 1959. Structural analysis of the basement system at Turoka, Kenya. *Overseas Geological Mineral Resources*, **7**, 3–35 & 123–153.

# The growth of continental crust during the Late Proterozoic: geochemical evidence from the Arabian Shield

N. B. W. HARRIS, C. J. HAWKESWORTH & A. G. TINDLE

*Department of Earth Sciences, Open University, Milton Keynes MK7 6AA, UK*

**Abstract**: Proterozoic magmatic provinces that result from active subduction provide a critical link between contrasting styles of crustal growth during the Archæan and Phanerozoic. The Arabian Shield is an excellent example of Late Proterozoic (860–560 Ma ago) felsic magmatism that is largely calc-alkaline in composition and displays the selective enrichment of LIL elements indicative of subduction. Juvenile Nd and Sr isotope ratios confirm that the Arabian Shield represents a collage of island arcs that were responsible for a significant proportion of global crustal growth (as measured by volume of magma extracted from the mantle per unit time) during the Pan-African tectonothermal event.

The high Rb/Sr ratios and low Sr concentrations of the majority of granitoids from the Arabian Shield suggest that they may be modelled as the products of intra-crustal feldspar fractionation from a basaltic source. However, about 25% of Arabian granitoids, mostly formed between 860 and 820 Ma ago, are characterized by high Sr and depleted Y abundances, indicative of melts which have not undergone fractional crystallization of feldspar, derived from a garnet-rich source. In the absence of tectonic thickening this suggests that these magmas were generated by melting the subducted slab, a process observed in contemporary arcs where unusually young, hot crust has been subducted.

The average composition of the Arabian crust at its present level of exposure is highly silica rich ($SiO_2 = 66\%$), and mass balance constraints on the composition of the continental crust of the Arabian Shield together with seismic evidence for a lower crust of gabbroic composition, require that either delamination of a mafic lower crust has occurred or the average composition of the mantle-to-crust flux was intermediate rather than basic in composition. The latter explanation is preferred since crustal delamination implies unrealistically high crustal growth rates during the Pan-African event. A flux of intermediate composition is indicative of slab melting during subduction.

Thus trace element and mass balance considerations support the hypothesis that a significant proportion of Arabian granitoids formed during the early stages of the Pan-African event were derived from partial melting of the subducted slab, indicating that subduction of young, hot oceanic lithosphere was widespread at that time.

One implication of the plate-tectonic paradigm is that the growth of continental crust is most likely to occur at destructive plate margins. Geochemical evidence from the Andes, a well-documented contemporary destructive margin, suggests that such growth is a consequence of a basaltic flux generated within the mantle wedge above the subduction zone (Ellam & Hawkesworth 1988). However, there is a growing body of evidence to suggest that Archæan continental crust may have resulted from processes quite distinct from those that are associated with contemporary plate tectonics. In this case, the principle of uniformitarianism clearly breaks down, and studies of Proterozoic destructive margins become crucial to our understanding of the transition from Archæan processes to those that are operating today.

The Afro-Arabian Shield provides an excellent example of Proterozoic destructive plate margins. The plutonic rocks of the western Arabian Shield have been the subject of numerous geochemical projects (Marzouki *et al.* 1982; Jackson & Odell 1984; Jackson *et al.* 1984; Stoeser 1986) including many initiated by Professor Ian Gass, at the Open University (Nasseef & Gass 1977; Duyverman 1981; Harris *et al.* 1986). This paper has drawn on a database of 150 published and unpublished major and trace element analyses of western Arabian plutons to provide a geochemical overview of processes responsible for Late Proterozoic magmatism.

## Magmatic evolution in the Afro-Arabian Shield

The crystalline basement of the Afro-Arabian Shield is of broadly Pan-African age (860–567 Ma old) and it is now separated into Arabian and African segments by the late Tertiary opening of the Red Sea. In Arabia, the exposed geology of the shield is dominated by intrusive

*From* Prichard, H. M., Alabaster, T., Harris, N. B. W. & Neary, C. R. (eds), 1993,
*Magmatic Processes and Plate Tectonics,* Geological Society Special Publication No. 76, 363–371.

363

**Table 1.** *Proportion of plutonic rocks exposed in the Arabian Shield*

|  | %<br>(by area<br>exposed) | Average<br>SiO$_2$<br>(wt%) |  |
|---|---|---|---|
| Gabbro | 6 | 53 ⎫ |  |
| Diorite | 13 | 58 ⎬ | Calc-alkaline 860–620 Ma |
| Tonalite | 16 | 63 ⎭ |  |
| Granodiorite | 19 | 68 ⎫ | Calc-alkaline 770–560 Ma |
| Monzogranite | 37 | 73 ⎭ |  |
| Alkali granite | 8 | 75⎬ | Peralkaline 670–560 Ma |
| Weighted average crustal<br>composition | — | 66.7 |  |
| Mean value of calc-alkaline<br>analyses | — | 65.8 |  |

Data from Stoeser (1986) and Jackson & Odell (1984)

rocks (*c.* 60%) with relatively minor volcanics and volcanoclastic sediments (Fig. 1). Although geochemical and petrological surveys in NE Africa are less detailed than in Arabia, the broad divisions of Late Proterozoic lithologies are present in similar proportions (Vail 1988; Harris *et al.* 1990; Kroner *et al.* 1991).

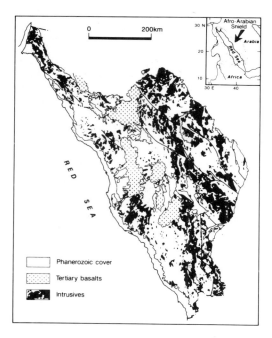

**Fig. 1.** Geological sketch-map of the Arabian Shield showing distribution of felsic intrusives (after Stoeser 1986). Heavy lines show major strike-slip faults.

Mafic–ultramafic complexes occurring within both sectors of the shield have been identified as ophiolitic sequences (Bakor *et al.* 1976; Al Shanti & Mitchell 1976; Gass 1977). Geochemical studies of the great majority of magmatic rocks that characterize the shield suggest an arc (supra-subduction zone) tectonic environment and consequently the sub-parallel ophiolite zones have been interpreted as marking inter-arc sutures. Structural and geochemical studies suggest that a series of arcs accreted to the African craton by the end of the Pan-African event to form the Afro-Arabian Shield (Greenwood *et al.* 1976; Gass 1977).

Of the many radiometric studies published from the Arabian Shield, few reliable ages have been recorded outside the range 860–560 Ma (Stoeser 1986; Stoeser & Stacey 1988 and references therein). A general trend towards more evolved magmas with time has been recognized: syn-orogenic basic to intermediate intrusives (gabbros, diorites and tonalites) were emplaced at 860–620 Ma ago (Table 1) which comprise 30–40% of all exposed plutons, and syn- to post-orogenic acid intrusives (granodiorites to monzogranites) were emplaced between 770–560 Ma ago and make up 50–60% of exposed plutons. Trace-element trends indicate fractionation of Rb with increased silica contents together with low abundances of HFS elements such as Nb and Y (Fig 2). Such trends are characteristic of subduction-related petrogenesis (Pearce *et al.* 1984). Where crustal melting of continental crust occurs, pelites provide low-temperature sources for granitic melts. Such melts are characterized by strong enrichment in Rb (Fig. 2) due to the incongruent melting of mica. It is interesting that none of the analysed samples from the Arabian Shield has sufficiently high Rb contents to be readily derived from pelitic sources. The absence of high-Rb melts suggests that continental sediments were largely absent in the melt zone during the Pan-African tectonothermal event, which in turn argues against the incorporation of significant pre-existing continental fragments in the island-arc collage.

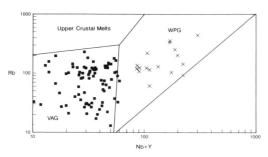

**Fig. 2.** Discriminant diagram (Rb vs. Nb + Y) for felsic intrusives ($SiO_2 > 55\%$) from the Arabian Shield (after Pearce et al. 1984). VAG: volcanic-arc granites; WPG: within-plate granites. Data from Marzouki et al. 1982; Jackson & Odell 1984; Jackson et al. 1984; Duyverman 1981; Nasseef & Gass 1977; Harris et al. 1986. ■: calc-alkaline suite; ×: peralkaline granites.

Towards the end of the Pan-African event, magma compositions indicate a marked change in geochemical characteristics. From 670–560 Ma ago post-orogenic hypersolvus alkali granites, invariably low in calcium and usually of peralkaline composition, were emplaced as discrete plutons throughout the shield. The plutons are rarely associated with intermediate compositions, although a syenitic facies may be present in some peralkaline plutons. Their geochemistry demonstrates the strong enrichment in HFS elements that is characteristic of within-plate magmatism (Fig. 2). Although the peralkaline granites comprise less than 10% of exposed plutons, they mark a significant change in tectonic style from magmatism in subduction-related to within-plate settings. The latter are more commonly associated with rift environments in continental regions. The timing of this geochemical transition is diachronous across the shield but it is significant that in many instances the emplacement of peralkaline granites in Arabia can be related to development of a major strike-slip fault system (the Nadj fault zone) associated with final cratonization of the Afro-Arabian Shield (Davies 1982; Agar 1986).

Since the end of the Pan-African orogenic event the Afro-Arabian Shield has been remarkably stable, post-orogenic magmatism being restricted to minor alkalic intrusions in NE Africa (Harris & Gass 1981). Present exposure levels throughout much of the shield are at depths of c. 5 km (Gass et al. 1990).

## Crustal growth or crustal reworking?

Trace element abundances from both the granitoids and the ophiolitic suites within the Afro-Arabian shield are indicative of subduction-related magmatism, but considerable debate has evolved over the proportion of pre-Pan-African crust that was incorporated within the Pan-African terranes of Arabia and NE Africa. Examples of pre-Pan-African ages in the shield have been reviewed by Harris et al. (1984) and Kroner et al. (1988). Crystallization ages indicate the presence of pre-900 Ma old crust in southeastern Arabia and west of the Nile. In southeastern Arabia, three upper intercept zircon ages from magmatic rocks lie in the range 1800–1600 Ma old indicating the presence of some pre-Pan-African basement. This region has sometimes been described as a discrete terrane (Stacey & Hedge 1984) although there is little evidence for tectonic boundaries that would demark it from the rest of the Arabian Shield. Isotopic evidence clearly indicates that although the southeastern Arabian Shield includes an anomalous fragment of pre-Pan-African basement, the great majority (>85%) of the shield of western Arabia provides no evidence, at the present level of exposure, for detectable contributions from pre-Pan African material.

In NE Africa, early Proterozoic zircon ages characterize sedimentary rocks from the Eastern Desert of Egypt and to the southeast of Lake Nasser. Undoubtedly a pre-Pan-African source region lying to the west of the present-day course of the Nile is required for some sediments. An Archæan craton of unknown size certainly exists in the Uweinat inlier on the Egyptian–Libyan border where Rb-Sr isochrons of 2600 Ma old have been obtained (Klerkx & Deutsch 1977). Much further south, ion microprobe ages of 1000–2700 Ma from zircons in the Sabaloka basement north of Khartoum (Kroner et al. 1987) confirm the presence of mid-Proterozoic or Archæan source regions in western Sudan.

It could be argued that Rb–Sr and zircon geochronology identify emplacement ages, and Sr, Pb or Nd isotope systematics are required to detect the presence of pre-emplacement basement. In general, the variations of well-constrained initial $^{87}Sr/^{86}Sr$ ratios lie in the range 0.707 to 0.702 throughout the Arabian Shield. Initial ratios in excess of 0.705 are restricted to lithologies younger than 650 Ma in the southern shield (Jackson *et al.* 1984). Spatial trends within this range are masked by analytical uncertainties although Stoeser & Camp (1985) record a slightly higher range (0.707–0.7035) in the eastern shield compared with values of 0.7035–0.702 to the west. Available Sr data do not support the presence of significant continental fragments within the island-arc collage, but younger (post-650 Ma) magmatism may result in part from reworking earlier magmatic rocks.

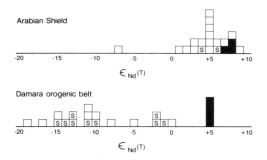

**Fig. 3.** $\varepsilon_{Nd}(T)$ ratios for basic ($SiO_2 < 53\%$; filled squares), and felsic ($SiO_2 > 55\%$; open squares) samples from the Arabian Shield and the Damara orogenic belt. S: metasediment, remaining samples are igneous. Data from Duyverman *et al.* 1982; Stacey & Hedge 1984; McDermott & Hawkesworth 1990.

Pb–Pb isotopic data from the Afro-Arabian Shield indicate a relatively unradiogenic province, that must have grown rapidly during the period of Late Proterozoic igneous activity. An exception lies in the southeastern shield where elevated $^{208}Pb/^{204}Pb$ and $^{207}Pb/^{204}Pb$ ratios are preserved (Stacey & Stoeser 1983). Perhaps the best evidence for rapid crustal growth comes from a comparison of the initial $^{143}Nd/^{144}Nd$ isotopic ratios of magmatic and metasedimentary rocks from the Afro-Arabian Shield and from the Damara belt of SW Africa. Both regions are sites of voluminous magmatic activity during the Pan-African orogenic event, but whereas magmatism in Arabia is largely calc-alkaline in character, in the Damaran orogen, suites of strongly peraluminous granites with elevated initial Sr isotope ratios ($^{87}Sr/^{86}Sr > 0.71$) suggest a crustal source for much of the igneous rocks (McDermott & Hawkesworth 1990). A compilation of their initial Nd isotopic ratios (in epsilon notation) is provided in Fig. 3. From this it is clear that for the Namibian samples, the

basic rocks have positive $\varepsilon_{Nd}(T)$ indicative of their mantle source, but both granitic and sedimentary rocks have negative $\varepsilon_{Nd}(T)$ values indicating an ancient source relative to their emplacement or deposition age. Such an array is indicative of crustal reworking of old material during magma genesis. In contrast, in the Arabian Shield, basic, granitic and sedimentary rocks have positive $\varepsilon_{Nd}(T)$ values, suggesting that all are derived from the mantle with only a minimal pre-emplacement crustal history. The single exception comes from the anomalous southeastern shield. In summary, available isotopic evidence identifies the Arabian Shield and its continuation into NE Africa, at least as far west as the Nile, as a classic example of rapid crustal growth during 300 Ma of magmatic activity.

## Crustal growth rates

The geochemical evidence suggests that the Afro-Arabian Shield is continental crust that grew rapidly by Late Proterozoic subduction processes. The geophysical evidence (reviewed in Gass 1977) suggests that the crust beneath Arabia is typical continental crust in terms of its thickness (35–40 km), density (2.7–2.9 g cm$^{-3}$) and average heat flow (50–100 mW m$^{-2}$). The rate of continental crust generation in the shield in comparison with contemporary rates at active subduction zones clearly has implications for continental growth rates throughout Earth history (Reymer & Schubert 1984, 1986; Duyverman *et al.* 1982; Dixon & Golombek 1988; Harris *et al.* 1990; Pallister *et al.* 1990). However, such calculations are poorly constrained because of large uncertainties in three parameters: the total volume of the Pan-African crust generated; the length of arcs active over the 300 Ma period; and the time period through which individual arcs were active.

The area of Pan-African crust in the Afro-Arabian Shield assumed in the various published models varies widely from $6.8 \times 10^6$ km$^2$ (Reymer & Schubert 1984) to $1.2 \times 10^6$ km$^2$ (Harris *et al.* 1990). The present-day crustal thickness is exposed at an average erosional depth of about 5 km, suggesting an original thickness of at least 40 km. If calculations are restricted to known exposures of Pan-African age (excluding the small enclave of earlier basement identified by isotopic studies) a minimal estimate for the volume of juvenile crust of $48 \times 10^6$ km$^3$ is obtained. The volume of new continental crust generated would be increased either by delamination at the base of the crust, or by intraplate magmatism.

The length of arcs active in the region is equally uncertain. Over 1200 km of arc can be inferred by adding the lengths of ophiolite sutures in Arabia alone (Stoeser & Camp 1985) and a value of 36 km has been obtained from identifications of linear granitic zones of calc-alkaline character throughout the Afro-Arabian shield (Gass 1982). If it is assumed that crustal growth rates (as measured as volume of magma extracted from the mantle per unit time per unit arc length) have remained unchanged from the Late Proterozoic to present day, 4000 km of arc are required, which is broadly consistent with arc lengths estimated from field studies (Harris et al. 1990).

The time period through which each arc was active is arguably the most poorly constrained parameter of all. Although most estimates assume that all arcs were active throughout the 300 ma of magmatic activity, Pallister et al. (1990) point out that an average arc lifespan of 70 Ma is a more realistic estimate. Clearly a reduced arc lifespan results in a requirement either for more arcs, or for substantially higher accretion rates (per unit arc length).

Despite all these uncertainties, recent reviews of crustal growth rates in the region concur that crustal growth could have occurred through active subduction at broadly similar rates per unit arc length to those at contemporary destructive margins. Harris et al. (1990) estimate that about 20–50% of crustal growth world-wide (as measured as total volume of magma extracted from the mantle per unit time irrespective of arc length) must be represented by the Afro-Arabian Shield during the Late Proterozoic. Pallister et al. (1990) place this estimate as high as 78%, but given that the component island arcs probably represent accretionary terranes scavenged from the margins of a wide ocean basin, even the higher figure is possible. However, such figures do not support a process of crustal delamination that would require even greater volumes of crust to be generated than is represented by present thicknesses.

## Chemical flux during crustal growth

Since the chemistry and bulk volumes of different magma types are well known in the Arabian Shield, it provides an excellent case-study for examining the processes involved in the rapid growth of continental crust during the Late Proterozoic. In a recent geochemical study of Phanerozoic subduction-zone magmas it was found that although basaltic rocks have Rb/Sr ratios indicative of MORB compositions, andesites and dacites reflect increased Rb and de-pleted Sr, indicating that the evolution of these rocks is controlled, in part, by feldspar fractionation (Ellam & Hawkesworth 1988). Since plagioclase is not stable at subcrustal pressures this indicates that magmas of intermediate composition are generated by intra-crustal fractional crystallization of mantle-derived basic magmas rather than by melting of the subducted slab. The chemical flux between mantle and crust is therefore basaltic ($SiO_2 < 53\%$) rather than andesitic in composition.

There are two ways of resolving the apparent conundrum that the average composition of continental crust is more siliceous than the composition of mantle-to-crust flux at contemporary plate margins:

(1) mafic, cumulate material from the lower crust is resorbed into the mantle through delamination;
(2) Phanerozoic processes do not reflect the mechanisms by which much of the continental crust has formed.

Some evidence for the latter hypothesis is provided by the compositions of Archæan basaltic rocks that have similar Rb and Sr abundances to the associated intermediate rocks. This implies that during the Archæan, formation of magmas of intermediate composition took place at greater depths than those at which plagioclase fractionation occurs.

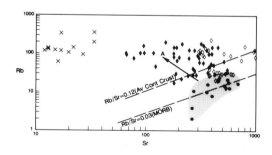

**Fig. 4.** Rb vs. Sr plot for intrusives from the Arabian Shield. ●: basic samples ($SiO_2 < 53\%$); ◆: ADR suite ($SiO_2 > 53\%$); ◇: TTD suite ($SiO_2 > 53\%$); ×: peralkaline granites. Shaded area indicates parental magma compositions from the mantle wedge. Vector A indicates trend resulting from fractional crystallization of feldspar for Andean samples (from Ellam & Hawkesworth 1988). For sources of data see Fig. 2.

For intrusives from the Arabian Shield the Th/U ratio of the chemical flux from mantle to crust, identified from Pb isotope systematics, is low and therefore similar to that found above modern subduction zones (Ellam et al. 1990).

The Rb versus Sr plot for calc-alkaline intrusives from Arabia (Fig. 4) indicates that intermediate and acid compositions are generally displaced to higher Rb and lower Sr than the basic rocks that comprise the island arcs. As with the Andean data, many evolved intrusives from Arabia can be derived from feldspar fractionation of more basic samples (or equally remelting gabbroic crust with a feldspar-rich restite). These low Sr compositions are also characterized by high Y abundances (Fig. 5), indicative of a garnet-free source, and are defined as ADRs (andesites, dacites and rhyolites) by Drummond & Defant (1990). Such melts can be modelled from intracrustal feldspar fractionation of basaltic magmas, thus indicating a basic mantle-to-crust flux.

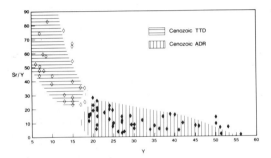

**Fig. 5.** Y vs. Sr/Y plot for calc-alkaline, felsic intrusives from the Arabian Shield. ◆: ADR suite (SiO$_2$ > 53%); ◇:TTD suite (SiO$_2$ > 53%). For sources of data see Fig. 2. Cenozoic fields taken from Drummond & Defant (1990).

In contrast, a significant group of high-Sr, calc-alkaline samples lie off the feldspar fractionation vector in Fig. 4, and so cannot be derived from a basaltic parent by feldspar fractionation. These also have low Y abundances and therefore high Sr/Y ratios (Fig. 5), indicative of a garnet-rich source. The Arabian island arcs provide little isotopic evidence for pre-existing crust and no evidence for crustal thickening, so that garnet-rich protoliths are probably indicative of melting of a subducted slab through the incongruent reaction

$$\text{Hornblende} + \text{Plagioclase} =$$
$$\text{Garnet} + \text{Pyroxene} + \text{Quartz} + \text{Melt}$$

which occurs in rocks of gabbroic composition at temperatures of about 960°C and pressures > 15 kbars (Rushmer 1991).

Defant & Drummond (1990) have argued that slab-derived melts do occur in Phanerozoic island arcs, albeit rarely, where young (< 25 Ma) and hot lithosphere is subducted. Such

melts are evolved (SiO$_2$ = 56–73%), aluminous (Al$_2$O$_3$ > 15%) and depleted in HREE (Yb < 1.9, Y < 18 ppm) due to the presence of residual garnet. They are categorized as high-Al TTDs (tonalites, trondhjemites and dacites).

In considering Precambrian magmatism, Drummond & Defant (1990) identified a group of *c.* 800 Ma intrusives from the Arabian Shield with high Al–TTD characteristics. The present study confirms that about 25% of analysed samples from Arabia fall within their definition of TTD magmas (Fig. 6). The TTD samples lie on a curve of strongly increasing Sr/Y with decreasing Y, controlled by the degree of melting from the eclogitic or garnet-amphibolite source in the slab. The consequence of slab melting is a mantle-to-crust flux which is intermediate in composition.

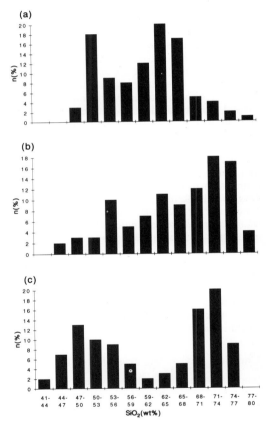

**Fig. 6.** Silica histograms for igneous rocks: (**a**) Andean extrusives (< 30 Ma) from the Central and South Volcanic Zones (*n* = 685); (**b**) Pan-African intrusives (860–560 Ma) from the Arabian Shield (*n* = 101); (**c**) Archæan greenstone and granite gneiss terrains from Zimbabwe (*n* = 230).

For the alkaline granites, which post-date subduction, the high Rb/Sr ratios cannot result from fractionation of calc-alkaline magmas and no plausible crustal source has sufficiently low Sr to act as a contaminant in their petrogenesis (Fig. 4). The Rb–Sr data reinforce the conclusion that the origin of peralkalic magmatism requires a distinct source-region that may be related to the influence of fault-controlled, mantle-derived volatiles (Harris & Marriner 1980; Harris et al. 1986).

The inference that the overall mantle-to-crust flux was not entirely basaltic in composition during the formation of the Afro-Arabian island arcs has implications for the bulk chemistry of the crust. The weighted average $SiO_2$ content of the proportion of the Arabian Shield that is made up of calc-alkaline intrusives (Table 1) is 67% (at present levels of exposure). A figure of 66% $SiO_2$ is obtained from averaging the available major element analyses of calc-alkaline rocks from the shield. This mean value for Arabian intrusives is more silica-rich than most magmatic rocks from the Central and Southern Volcanic Zones of the Andes (Rogers 1985; Ellam & Hawkesworth 1988; Hildreth & Moorbath 1988). This is best illustrated by comparing silica histograms from the two orogenic belts (Fig. 6). For the Andean data, a bimodal distribution results from the abundance of andesitic magma ($SiO_2 = 50$–53%), derived from fractional crystallization of mantle-derived basalts, and from the abundance of ignimbrites ($SiO_2 = 60$–68%) which result from crustal melting. In contrast, the Arabian data indicate a high proportion of magmas with $SiO_2 > 68\%$. The silica abundances therefore confirm that 800–600 Ma ago, magmatic processes at destructive margins resulted in more silica-rich magmas, at least at present levels of exposure in the Arabian Shield, than the composition of magmas erupted at contemporary arcs.

Seismic profiles through the Arabian crust indicate that P-wave velocities of 6.2–6.4 km s$^{-1}$, indicative of granitic rocks, characterize the upper 20 km of crust (Healey et al. 1980). If we assume that the upper 20 km of crust has an average silica content of 66%, that the original crust was 40 km thick, and that the average silica composition of the total crust was 53% (the composition of a basaltic mantle-to-crust flux), then the unexposed deep crust must have an average silica composition of 40%. This implausibly low value equivalent to an ultramafic rock would be increased if the average composition of the upper crust is considerably less siliceous than that revealed at present erosional levels. However, seismic evidence does not support regional compositional variations with depth in the upper crust.

Alternatively, lower crustal delamination can be invoked to increase the average silica content of the preserved crust but in the light of the high rates of crustal growth discussed above, and the buoyancy problems of delaminating feldspar-rich cumulates, this alternative seems unlikely.

The constraints on the composition of the lower crust can be relaxed if some component of the sub-crustal flux was more silica-rich than 53% $SiO_2$. The average silica composition of TTD magmas from Arabia is 67% $SiO_2$. If 25% of the subcrustal flux was characterized by melts of this composition, and the remainder by a mantle-derived basaltic composition, then the net flux contributing to crustal growth would have a silica content of 56%. Such a silica-rich flux allows the granitic upper crust to be complemented by a lower crust of gabbroic composition ($SiO_2 = 46\%$). Although more basic than global estimates for the average composition of the lower crust the unusually high P-wave velocities ($V_p$ c. 7.8 km s$^{-1}$) of the lowermost 10 km of the Arabian crust (Healey et al. 1980) provide independent evidence for an unusually mafic lower crust within the lithosphere of the Arabian Shield.

Mass-balance constraints therefore support the conclusion based on trace-element considerations, that slab melting played an important role in the formation of the Arabian granitoids.

## Discussion

Geochemical data from plutonic rocks in the Arabian Shield indicate that both mantle-derived and slab-derived calc-alkaline magmas were formed. The slab-derived melts (high-Al TTD) appear to be most prevalent in the early period of calc-alkaline magmatism (860–620 Ma) and are largely tonalitic or tronhjemitic in composition. This trend extends to NE Africa where early-Pan-African tronhjemites (850–870 Ma) have been recognized in eastern Sudan (Kroner et al. 1991) that share TTD characteristics.

The Arabian data suggest that rapid growth of continental crust occurred along multiple subduction zones during the Late Proterozoic by processes similar to those operating today. During the early phase of island-arc accretion a significant proportion of magmas had a slab rather than a mantle source due to the subduction of young ($< 25$ Ma) hot oceanic lithosphere. The mantle-to-crust flux may have been more silica-rich than at the present-day destructive margin of the Central Andes for example, since the Andean margin results from the subduction of relatively old (>40 Ma) lithosphere.

Archæan magmas are characterized by trace element abundances indicative of remelting basaltic source rocks, possibly in subducted slabs similar to, but hotter than, those in the Phanerozoic (Ellam & Hawkesworth 1988; Drummond & Defant 1990). Silica abundances from Archæan provinces are bimodal, reflecting komatiitic and basic magmas from the greenstone belts, and highly silica-rich granitoids from the gneissic belts (Fig. 6c). A general comparison of silica abundances from Arabia with those from a modern destructive margin and from the Archæan (Fig. 6) suggests that the Arabian data combine characteristics from both tectonic styles; the peak of intermediate compositions is similar to that observed in the Andes, whereas the high-silica peak is similar to the Archæan distribution. We propose that the latter characteristic is indicative of slab-melting at destructive margins during the Late Proterozoic.

Recent island-arcs that result from slab melting are rare today since only a small proportion of oceanic lithosphere, away from the immediate vicinity of the constructive margins, is sufficiently young and hot for slab melting to occur. It is tempting to conjecture that the distinctive geochemistry of Late Proterozoic magmatism from the Arabian Shield reflects a secular change in planetary processes. The slightly higher geothermal gradients prevalent 800 Ma ago (about 10% higher than contemporary values) may have contributed to more rapid plate movement, and therefore a higher proportion of slab-derived magmatism at destructive margins than occurs today.

The Arabian Shield provides a classic example of subduction-related magmatism at a critical period in Earth history. In being one of the first earth scientists to recognize the tectonic significance of the Arabian Shield, Ian Gass has made a crucial contribution to our understanding of how the continental crust has evolved.

We thank Dr Norman Jackson for his help in preparing this manuscript. This paper is a contribution to IGCP348 'The Mazambique and related belts – crustal evolution and mineralization'.

# References

AGAR, R. A. 1986. Structural geology of felsic plutonic rocks in the Arabian Shield: styles, modes and levels of emplacement. *Journal of African Earth Sciences*, **4**, 105–121.

AL-SHANTI, A. M. S. & MITCHELL, A. H. G. 1976. Late Precambrian subduction and collision in the Al Amar-Idsas region, Arabian shield, Kingdom of Saudi Arabia. *Tectonophysics*, **31**, 41–47.

BAKOR, A. R., GASS, I. G. & NEARY, C. R. 1976. Jabel Al-Wasq, northwest Saudi Arabia: an Eo-cambrian back-arc ophiolite. *Earth and Planetary Science Letters*, **30**, 1–9.

DAVIES, F. B. 1982. Pan-African granite intrusion in response to tectonic volume changes in a ductile shear zone from northern Saudi Arabia. *Journal of Geology*, **90**, 467–483.

DEFANT, M. J. & DRUMMOND, M. S. 1990. Derivation of some modern arc magmas by melting of young subducted lithosphere. *Nature*, **347**, 662–665.

DIXON, T. H. & GOLOMBEK, M. P. 1988. Late Precambrian crustal accretion rates in northeastern Africa and Arabia. *Geology*, **16**, 991–994.

DRUMMOND, M. S. & DEFANT, M. J. 1990. A model for trondhjemite–tonalite–dacite genesis and crustal growth via slab melting: Archean to modern comparisons. *Journal of Geophysical Research*, **95**, 21503–21521.

DUYVERMAN, H. J. 1981. *Late Precambrian volcanic rocks of the Arabian Shield, Saudi Arabia.* PhD thesis, Open University, UK.

——, HARRIS, N. B. W. & HAWKESWORTH, C. J. 1982. Crustal accretion in the Pan African: Nd and Sr isotope evidence from the Arabian Shield. *Earth and Planetary Science Letters*, **59**, 315–326.

ELLAM, R. M. & HAWKESWORTH, C. J. 1988. Is average continental crust generated at subduction zones? *Geology*, **16**, 314–7.

——, —— & MCDERMOTT, F. 1990. Pb isotope data from late Proterozoic subduction-related rocks: Implications for crust-mantle evolution. *Chemical Geology*, **83**, 165–81.

GASS, I. G. 1977. The evolution of the Pan African crystalline basement in NE Africa and Arabia. *Journal of the Geological Society, London*, **134**, 129–38.

—— 1982. Upper Proterozoic (Pan African) calc-alkaline magmatism in north-eastern Africa and Arabia. *In*: THORPE, R. S. (ed.) *Andesites.* John Wiley & Sons, London, 571–609.

——, RIES, A. C., SHACKLETON, R. M. & SMEWING, J. D. 1990. Tectonics, geochronology and geochemistry of the Precambrian rocks of Oman. *In*: ROBERTSON, A. H. F. & RIES, A. C. (eds) *Geology and Tectonics of the Oman Region.* Geological Society, London, Special Publication, **49**, 585–99.

GREENWOOD, W. R., ANDERSON, R. E., FLECK, R. J. & SCHMIDT, D. L. 1976. Late Proterozoic cratonisation in southwestern Arabia. *Philosophical Transactions of the Royal Society, London*, **A280**, 517–27.

HARRIS, N. B. W. & GASS, I. G. 1981. Significance of contrasting magmatism in North East Africa and Saudi Arabia. *Nature*, **289**, 395–6.

——, —— & HAWKESWORTH, C. J. 1990. A geochemical approach to allochthonous terranes: a Pan-African case-study. *Philosophical Transactions of the Royal Society, London*, **A331**, 533–48.

——, HAWKESWORTH, C. J. & RIES, A. C. 1984. Crustal evolution in north-east Africa from model Nd ages. *Nature*, **309**, 773–6.

—— & MARRINER, G. F. 1980. Geochemistry and petrogenesis of a peralkaline granite complex from the Midian Mountains, Saudi Arabia. *Lithos*, **13**, 325–37.

——, MARZOUKI, F. M. H. & ALI, S. 1986. The Jabel Sayid Complex: geochemical constraints on the origin of peralkaline and related granites. *Contributions to Mineralogy and Petrology*, **143**, 287–95.

HEALEY, J. H., MONEY, W. D., BLANK, H. R. & GETTINGS, E. 1980. Deep structure of the Arabian Shield from the 1978 USGS/DGMR seismic refraction profile. *Faculty of Earth Sciences, KAU Jeddah, Research Series*, **13**, 136–7.

HILDRETH, W. & MOORBATH, S. 1988. Crustal contributions to arc magmatism in the Andes of Central Chile. *Contributions to Mineralogy and Petrology*, **98**, 455–89.

JACKSON, N. J. & ODELL, J. 1984. Geochemistry of felsic plutonic rocks. *Directorate General of Mineral Resources, Jeddah, Open File Report*, DGMR-OF-29.

——, WALSH, J. N. & PEGRAM, E. 1984. Geology, geochemistry and petrogenesis of late Precambrian granitoids in the Central Hijaz Region of the Arabian Shield. *Contributions to Mineralogy and Petrology*, **87**, 205–19.

KLERKX, J. & DEUTSCH, S. 1977. Resultats preliminaires obtenues par la methode Rb/Sr sur l'age des formations precambriennes de la region d'Uweinat (Libye). *Musée royal de l'Afrique centrale, Département de Géologie et Minéralogie, Rapport annuel 1976*, 83–94.

KRONER, A., LINNEBACHER, P., STERN, R. J., REISCHMANN, T., MANTON, W. & HUSSEIN, I. M. 1991. Evolution of Pan-African island arc assemblages in the southern Red Sea Hills, Sudan, and in southwestern Arabia as exemplified by geochemistry and geochronology. *Precambrian Research*, **53**, 99–118.

——, REISCHMANN, T., WUST, H. J. & RASHWAN, A. A. 1988. Is there any pre-Pan-African (>950 Ma) basement in the Eastern Dessert of Egypt? *In*: EL GABY, S. & GREILING, R. (eds) *The Pan African Belt of NE Africa and adjacent areas*. Friedr. Vieweg und Sohn, Braunschweig, Germany, 95–120.

——, STERN, R. J., DAWOUD, A. S., COMPSTON, W. & REISCHMANN, T. 1987. The Pan-African continental margin in northeastern Africa: evidence from a geochronological study of granulites at Sabaloka, Sudan. *Earth and Planetary Science Letters*, **85**, 91–104.

MARZOUKI, F. M. H., JACKSON, N. J. & RAMSAY, C. R. 1982. Composition and origin of two Proterozoic diorite-tonalite complexes in the Arabian Shield. *Precambrian Research*, **19**, 31–50.

McDERMOTT, F. & HAWKESWORTH, C. J. 1990. Intracrustal recycling and upper-crustal evolution: a case study from the Pan-African Damara belt. *Chemical Geology*, **85**, 263–80.

NASSEEF, A. O. & GASS, I. G. 1977. Granitic and metamorphic rocks of the Taif area, western Saudi Arabia. *Geological Society of America Bulletin*, **88**, 1721–30.

PALLISTER, J. S., COLE, J. C., STOESER, D. B. & QUICK, J. E. 1990. Use and abuse of crustal accretion calculations. *Geology*, **18**, 35–9.

PEARCE, J. A., HARRIS, N. B. W. & TINDLE, A. G. 1984. Trace element discrimination diagrams for the tectonic interpretation of granitic rocks. *Journal of Petrology*, **25**, 956–83.

REYMER, A. & SCHUBERT, G. 1984. Phanerozoic addition rates to the continental crust and crustal growth. *Tectonics*, **3**, 63–77.

—— & SCHUBERT, G. 1986. Rapid growth of some major segments of continental crust. *Geology*, **14**, 299–302.

ROGERS, G. 1985. *A geochemical traverse across the north Chilean Andes*. PhD thesis, Open University, UK.

RUSHMER, T. 1991. Partial melting of two amphibolites: contrasting experimental results under fluid-absent conditions. *Contributions to Mineralogy and Petrology*, **107**, 41–59.

STACEY, J. S. & HEDGE, C. E. 1984. Geochronologic and isotope evidence for Early Proterozoic crust in the eastern Arabian Shield. *Geology*, **12**, 310–13.

—— & STOESER, D. B. 1983. Distribution of oceanic and continental leads in the Arabian–Nubian Shield. *Contributions to Mineralogy and Petrology*, **84**, 91–105.

STOESER, D. B. 1986. Distribution and tectonic setting of plutonic rocks of the Arabian Shield. *Journal of African Earth Sciences*, **4**, 21–46.

—— & CAMP, V. E. 1985. Pan-African microplate accretion of the Arabian Shield. *Geological Society of America Bulletin*, **96**, 817–26.

—— & STACEY, J. S. 1988. Evolution, U-Pb geochronology and isotope geology of the Pan-African Nabitah Orogenic belt of the Saudi Arabian Shield. *In*: EL GABY, S. & GREILING, R. (eds) *The Pan African Belt of NE Africa and adjacent areas*. Friedr. Vieweg und Sohn, Braunschweig, Germany, 227–88.

VAIL, J. R. 1988. Tectonics and evolution of the Proterozoic basement on Northeastern Africa. *In*: EL GABY, S. & GREILING, R. (eds) *The Pan African Belt of NE Africa and adjacent areas*. Friedr. Vieweg und Sohn, Braunschweig, Germany, 195–226.

# Trace element models for mantle melting: application to volcanic arc petrogenesis

JULIAN A. PEARCE & IAN J. PARKINSON

*Department of Geological Sciences, University of Durham, Durham DH1 3LE, UK*

**Abstract:** Understanding mantle melting above subduction zones requires an evaluation of the behaviour of elements for which the mantle contribution greatly exceeds any subduction contribution. In this paper we present a compilation of partition coefficients for a suite of these elements (Nb, Zr, Y, Yb, Ca, Al, Ga, V, Sc, Fe, Mn, Co, Cr, Mg, Ni) for temperatures of 1200–1300°C, oxygen fugacities of QFM $\pm$ 1 and sub-alkaline compositions. These coefficients yield good-fit mantle depletion trends for abyssal, orogenic and trench-wall peridotites. Modelling of pooled melts from mantle melting columns, presented as FMM (fertile MORB mantle) normalized patterns, give signatures of the composition and degree of melting of the mantle wedge that are generally independent of the subduction component. In particular, patterns formed from melting of fertile mantle exhibit normalized element abundances in the order VHI > HI > MI (VHI = very highly incompatible, HI = highly incompatible and MI = moderately incompatible) at low degrees of melting, becoming VHI = HI = MI at high degrees of melting. With derivation from progressively depleted sources, the patterns for moderate degrees of melting change to VHI < HI = MI at moderate degrees of depletion and VHI < HI < MI at high degrees of depletion.

The details, but not the principles, can be varied by changing the shape of the melting column, the porosity of the mantle during melting, the potential temperature of the mantle, and the temperature and depth of initiation of melting. Bivariate plots of elements of contrasting compatibilities (Cr–Yb, Sc–Yb, Nb–Yb) can be contoured according to the degree of depletion or enrichment of the mantle and the degree of melting, with selected plots also emphasizing the role of garnet (Ti–Yb) and oxygen fugacity (V–Yb). Evaluation of data from present-day volcanic arcs suggests that: (1) intra-oceanic arcs with associated active backarc basins are derived principally from fertile MORB mantle that has lost up to about 3% melt in a previous melting event; (2) this depletion takes place in spinel lherzolite facies, supporting models that relate it to backarc basin melting events; (3) oceanic arcs with no associated backarc basins are derived principally from fertile MORB mantle, though enriched sources can be important locally; (4) intra-continental arcs are commonly derived from enriched mantle, probably because of the involvement of sub-continental lithosphere; (5) degrees of melting are probably high (in the order of 25–30%) in intra-oceanic arcs on thin crust, decreasing to 15% or less in areas of thicker lithosphere; (6) some 10% melting can be explained by volatile addition to the mantle, the remainder by decompression.

Melt compositions in intraplate and mid-ocean ridge settings have been explained with general success by models of decompression melting and the pooling of melt increments from the melting column (e.g. Klein & Langmuir 1987; McKenzie & Bickle 1988; Niu & Batiza 1991). Application of the same principles to melting above subduction zones is less easy, because mantle flow and melt separation are more varied and complex (e.g. Spiegelman & McKenzie 1987), because mantle temperatures are known with less certainty and because the solidi for hydrated mantle are less well-defined than for dry mantle. Our aim in this paper is to present geochemical criteria which might contribute to the understanding of mantle melting above subduction zones, with particular reference to intra-oceanic volcanic arcs.

## Supra-subduction zone melting models

Most recent models for arc magmatism ascribe magma generation to decompression melting in the mantle wedge augmented by fluid advection from the subduction zone. Theoretical studies of the water transport mechanism suggest that fluids driven off the subducted slab into the wedge first hydrate the mechanical boundary layer between the top of the subduction zone and the convecting mantle (Tatsumi *et al.* 1983; Davies & Bickle 1991; Davies & Stevenson 1992). They argue that this fluid is released once this hydrated mantle is dragged below the depth of amphibole stability (*c.* 100 km), after which it migrates laterally into the base of the melting column as shown in Fig 1. The degree of melting is then a reflection of the combination of the

*From* Prichard, H. M., Alabaster, T., Harris, N. B. W. & Neary, C. R. (eds), 1993,
*Magmatic Processes and Plate Tectonics*, Geological Society Special Publication No. 76, 373–403.

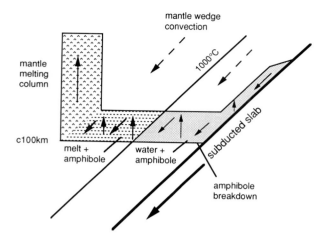

**Fig. 1.** Mechanism for melting above subduction zones, as proposed by Tatsumi *et al.* (1983), Davies & Bickle (1991) and Davies & Stevenson (1992). The arrows indicate transport of mantle (dashed line), aqueous fluid (thin line), melt (intermediate line) and subducted slab (thick line).

depression of the mantle solidus, the extent of adiabatic upwelling above the solidus, and the composition of the mantle before melting.

Figure 2 shows the types of melting behaviour that can be predicted for the melting column. Figure 2a (from Eggins (1992) based on the work of Klein & Langmuir (1987), McKenzie & Bickle (1988) and others) illustrates a schematic melting column for ridge magmatism. In the simplest scenario, shown here, the degree of melting increases uniformly as a function of the distance travelled by the column above the point of intersection between the adiabat and the MORB mantle solidus. Instantaneous melts from the base of the column are generated from fertile MORB mantle, whereas those from the top of the column are generated from mantle that has already undergone 15–20% melting. These instantaneous melts accumulate and mix to produce pooled melts.

In the mantle wedge, input of fluids into fertile MORB mantle of average potential temperature at depths shallower than about 100 km should depress the mantle solidus sufficiently to initiate melting even without decompression. The extent of this fluid-induced melting has been quantified as 2–8% by Davies & Bickle (1991) using the experimental results of Green (1973, 1976). Green's experimental work also suggests that this melt will be generated at temperatures close to the hydrated solidus and below the adiabat. Thus, if Fig. 1 is broadly correct, the first stage should be fluid-induced melting at the depth of

fluid addition, about 100 km if the fluids are generated by amphibole breakdown. If melting takes place at the base of an upwelling melting column, a second stage of melting should then result from decompression at shallower depths. If melt is extracted during the first stage of melting, the consequent depletion of the mantle requires that the second stage should start at a depth slightly shallower than that for decompression melting at the mid-ocean ridges. For a given fluid input, the maximum amount of melt generation in the mantle wedge should then be achieved if decompression can proceed as far as the Moho. The simple shape of the melt generation curve is then that shown in Fig. 2b.

If melting proceeds only to the base of a thick lithospheric cap, then the amount of decompression melting is correspondingly reduced, giving a pattern similar to that in Fig. 2c with the degree of melting depending on the thickness of that cap (Plank & Langmuir 1988; White & McKenzie 1989; Watson & McKenzie 1991). According to this principle, we expect more melting beneath arcs built on thin lithosphere, i.e. more melting in intra-oceanic arcs. If the mantle wedge has been depleted, by prior melting in a backarc basin or by recycling within the wedge itself (e.g. Ewart & Hawkesworth 1987), the solidi are displaced to higher temperatures and the percentage of melt generated is also reduced (Fig. 2d). These figures are also affected by mantle potential temperatures which determine the position of intersection of the dry mantle solidus

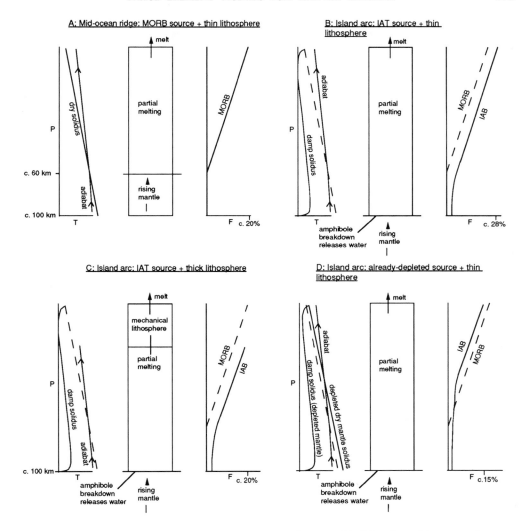

**Fig. 2.** Melt generation for (**a**) a mid-ocean ridge, (**b**) an arc volcano on thin lithosphere, (**c**) an arc volcano on thicker lithosphere and (**d**) an arc volcano on thin lithosphere with depleted mantle. The figures show the approximate percentage of melt likely to be generated during ascent of a mantle column in each case.

(e.g. McKenzie & Bickle 1988). The high temperatures associated with mantle plumes are unlikely to be found in mantle wedges. More critical may be a reduction in the mantle temperature within the wedge by heat exchange with the cooler subducting slab.

The question we address here is how to test and refine these simple models and apply them to some 'real' arc-basin systems. It is well-known that most of the incompatible elements used to investigate magma genesis in mid-ocean ridge and intraplate settings are also introduced into the mantle wedge from the subducted oceanic lithosphere. In order to understand the melting

behaviour of the mantle wedge, we need to concentrate specifically on those elements for which subduction flux is negligible relative to the mantle wedge contribution.

## Choice of mantle-derived elements to monitor the supra-subduction zone melting process

To a first-order approximation, the concentration of a given element in a lava erupted in a supra-subduction zone setting can be viewed in terms of partial melting and fractional crystalli-

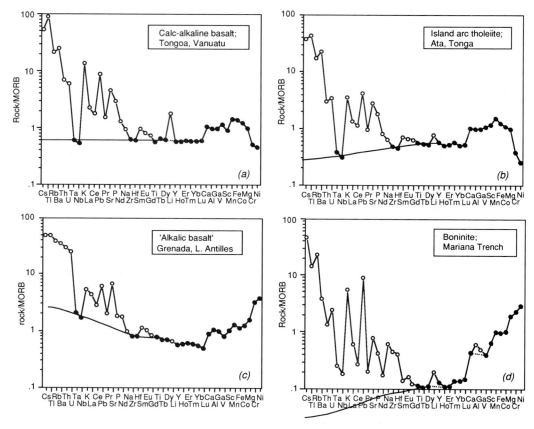

**Fig. 3.** MORB-normalized patterns for some representative arc volcanoes with values thought to be derived almost entirely from the mantle wedge shown as solid circles, and those thought to involve a significant subduction contribution shown as open circles. For the latter, the line at a lower composition gives the probable interpolated or extrapolated composition for the mantle wedge, the area above this line thus representing the slab contribution for the element in question (Pearce 1983). Normalizing values used (see text for sources) are: Cs (0.007); Tl (0.0014); Rb (0.56); Ba (6.3); Th (0.12); U (0.047); Ta (0.13); Nb (2.33); $K_2O$ (0.13); La (2.5); Ce (7.5); Pb (0.3); Pr (1.32); Sr (90); $P_2O_5$ (0.072); Nd (7.3); $Na_2O$ (2.75); Zr (74); Hf (2.05); Sm (2.63); Eu (1.02); Gd (3.68); $TiO_2$ (1.27); Tb (0.67); Dy (4.55); Li (4.3); Y (28); Ho (1.01); Er (2.97); Tm (0.456); Yb (3.05); Lu (0.455); $Al_2O_3$ (16); Ga (16); V (300); CaO (12); Sc (40); Mn (0.13); $Fe_2O_3$ (9); Co (40); MgO (7.5); Cr (275); Ni (100).

zation processes operating on a mantle source region containing a mantle-derived and slab-derived component, both of which may vary considerably in composition. The composition of the slab-derived component will depend on the thermal structure of the slab–wedge interface and the composition of the subducted crust and its sedimentary cover. The mantle-derived component will vary according to the fertility of the mantle, which in turn depends on the effects of any previous melting events, the presence or absence of a plume component and the extent of incorporation of inherited components from enriched lithosphere. Pearce (1983) proposed a

simple method using MORB-normalized plots to estimate the relative contributions of the mantle and slab for a range of incompatible elements. This calculation is based on the assumption that some elements, including Nb, Zr, Ti, Y, and Yb, are dominantly mantle-derived and can be used to estimate, by interpolation and extrapolation, the concentrations of other elements before subduction. A second assumption, justified in the conclusions to this paper, is that melt–residue interactions in the melting column (Navon & Stolper 1987; Keleman et al. 1990) have only a small effect on pattern shape. Variations due to partial melting and fractional crystallization are taken into account because the patterns depict enrichment of slab-derived elements relative to mantle-derived elements of similar bulk distribution coefficient.

MORB-normalized geochemical patterns for some representative supra-subduction zone basalts are shown in Fig. 3 but we have extended the element set to include Na and the more compatible elements, namely Sc, V, Ga, Al, Ca, Fe, Mn, Co, Cr, Mg and Ni. We have placed the elements in order of relative incompatibility with a fertile spinel-lherzolite mantle. Up to Lu, N-MORB values and the order of incompatibility are taken from Sun & McDonough (1989), except that the order of Gd and Ti is reversed. For elements between Na and Ni, N-MORB values are taken from the authors' MORB database. To ensure compatibility of the two sets of normalizing values, we have matched our $TiO_2$ value with the Sun & McDonough $TiO_2$ concentration of 1.27%. The order of incompatibility for the more compatible elements is explained in this paper. The geochemical data used in Fig. 3 come from the references cited, augmented by our own ICP-MS trace element analyses. These, and other unpublished data used in this paper, are available on request.

The first pattern, from Tongoa in the Marianas arc (Dupuy et al. 1982), illustrates the case where all the incompatible elements ascribed to a dominantly mantle-derived origin (Nb, Ta, Zr, Hf, Ti, Y and the HREEs) have compositions that form a trend parallel to the N-MORB normalizing value, although at lower absolute levels. Such a pattern does not require residual minor phases or residual amphibole in the wedge, as the latter should significantly fractionate the high field strength elements (e.g. Ti from Zr). For the same reason it does not require complex melt-residue interactions in the melting column. Our first-order interpretation is, therefore, that this feature can be explained by a simple increase in degree of melting relative to MORB. The second pattern, from Ata in the Tofua arc (Vallier et al. 1985), shows a progressive depletion in the mantle-derived elements. The extent of depletion is in order of incompatibility, the most incompatible elements (Nb and Ta) being most depleted. The smoothness of this pattern again does not require residual mantle phases. Moreover, variations in the degree of partial melting are not by themselves sufficient to reduce the ratios of the more incompatible elements to less incompatible elements. Our first-order explanation for this pattern is, therefore, that source depletion is the most important variable.

The remaining patterns represent the melting products of more complex mantle sources. The third pattern, from an alkali olivine basalt from Grenada in the Lesser Antilles (Brown et al. 1977), represents the enrichment, rather than depletion, of Nb, Ta, Zr, and Hf. Petrologists attribute this enrichment to the mantle rather than the slab, either to small degrees of melting with residual garnet (Shimizu & Arculus 1975) or to an enriched mantle source (De Long et al. 1975). The fourth pattern, an Eocene boninite from the Mariana trench (Pearce et al. 1992), also exhibits enrichment in these four elements. In this case, however, the origin is more controversial. Many papers also ascribe these enrichments to enriched mantle in the wedge (an 'ocean island basalt (OIB)' component) (e.g. Stern et al. 1991). However, unlike Grenada, the degree of enrichment does not follow the usual order of incompatibility during mantle melting, Zr and Hf being more enriched than the more incompatible elements Nb and Ta. Pearce et al. (1992) summarize isotopic and elemental evidence that the enrichment in Zr and Nb is the result of slab melting in amphibolite facies. They argue that the greater Zr enrichment could result from the fact that Zr is less compatible than Nb in residual amphibole. If correct, Zr and Nb may not always be reliable indicators of mantle behaviour. However, they are useful for most arc basalts as an indicator of melting and mantle composition and we therefore use them with caution in the work that follows.

Of the more compatible elements on the right of the pattern, levels are close to those of MORB in most cases, with no indication of any slab contribution. For the major elements, and compatible trace elements, this may be a consequence of mass balance, the high concentrations in the mantle masking any slab contribution. The greatest question concerns the behaviour of Al (and Ga). Pearce et al. (1992) suggest that some boninites, such as that in Figure 3d, may carry a significant slab component for Al and Ga, because they are derived from mantle depleted in these elements and because the slab component is an aluminous melt. Al is also susceptible to other processes such as sediment assimilation by arc magma (e.g. Davidson 1987). Al and Ga are included in this work, but used only in cases where no slab or crustal component is evident.

## Partition and bulk distribution coefficients for the mantle-derived elements

A substantial data set now exists on mineral–liquid partition coefficients for the elements

**Table 1.** The working set of partition coefficients and bulk distribution coefficients used in this paper. Major element coefficients are for wt% oxides. Data sources used are 1: Bartels *et al.* (1991); 2: Beattie (1993); 3: Beattie *et al.* (1991); 4: Colson *et al.* (1988); 5: Colson & Gust (1989); 6: Dostal *et al.* (1983); 7: Duke (1976); 8: Dunn (1987); 9: Dunn & McCallum (1982); 10: Dupuy *et al.* (1980); 11: Fujimaki *et al.* (1984); 12: Green *et al.* (1989); 13: Hervig *et al.* (1986); 14: Irving (1978); 15: Irving & Frey (1984); 16: Johnson & Kinzler (1989); 17: Kato *et al.* (1987); 18: Kinzler & Grove (1992); 19: Leeman & Scheidegger (1977); 20: Lindstrom & Weill (1978); 21: Liu *et al.* (1992); 22: McCallum & Charette (1987); 23: McKay & Mitchell (1988); 24: McKay (1986); 25: Nielsen *et al.* (1992); 26: Ohtani *et al.* (1989); 27: Onuma *et al.* (1968); 28: Ray *et al.* (1983); 29: Roeder & Emslie (1970); 30: Shervais (1982); 31: Stosch (1981); 32: Stosch & Seck (1980); 33: Takahashi (1978); 34: Tormey *et al.* (1987); 35: Watson *et al.* (1987). Coefficients based on a single value, or a series of inconsistent values, are given in italics.

**Partition coefficients**

| | ol/l 1300°C | ol/l 1200°C | opx/l 1300°C | opx/l 1200°C | cpx/l 1300°C | cpx/l 1200°C | gt/l 1300° | gt/l 1200°C | hbl/l 1300°C | hbl/l 1200°C | Al-sp/l 1300°C | Al-sp/l 1200°C | data sources |
|---|---|---|---|---|---|---|---|---|---|---|---|---|---|
| Ni | 9.0 | 15 | 2.5 | 4.5 | 1.5 | 2.5 | 1.3 | 2.5 | 1.5 | 2.0 | 7.5 | 12 | 3, 4, 10, 14, 15, 19, 31, 32 |
| Cr | 1.0 | 1.5 | 3.0 | 7.0 | 5.0 | 10 | 5.0 | 10 | 4.0 | 8.0 | 100 | 200 | 7, 10, 13, 14, 19, 31 |
| Mg | 3.9 | 4.2 | 2.8 | 3.2 | 1.9 | 2.1 | 2.2 | 2.4 | 1.5 | 1.6 | 3.0 | 3.5 | 8, 10, 18, 19, 21, 24, 34 |
| Co | 2.5 | 4.0 | 1.4 | 2.0 | 0.65 | 1.0 | 0.6 | 1.0 | *1.4* | *1.4* | 3.0 | 4.5 | 4, 7, 10, 15, 20, 27, 31 |
| Fe | 0.95 | 1.2 | 0.9 | 1.1 | 0.65 | 0.8 | 1.4 | 1.6 | 1.6 | 1.8 | 1.5 | 1.7 | 3, 5, 10, 18, 21, 29, 34 |
| Mn | 0.8 | 1.1 | 0.8 | 1.2 | 0.9 | 1.2 | 2.0 | 3.0 | 0.8 | 1.0 | 0.8 | 1.0 | 3, 4, 8, 10, 14, 18, 20, 21, 34 |
| Sc | 0.16 | 0.25 | 0.5 | 1.0 | 0.85 | 2.0 | 6.0 | 15.0 | 1.0 | 2.0 | 0.1 | 0.3 | 3, 4, 5, 13, 14, 15, 19, 25, 28, 31, 32 |
| V | 0.03 | 0.03 | 0.2 | 0.4 | 0.4 | 0.8 | 0.8 | *1.3* | 1.0 | 2.0 | 5.0 | 12.0 | 7, 10, 13, 14, 20, 30 |
| Ga | *0.04* | *0.1* | *0.3* | *0.4* | *0.35* | *0.6* | *0.6* | *1.2* | *1.0* | *1.2* | *4.0* | *4.0* | 22 |
| Al | *0.03* | *0.1* | 0.03 | 0.5 | 0.3 | 0.5 | *1.5* | *1.5* | *1.0* | *1.0* | *4.0* | *4.0* | 3, 4, 5, 10, 18, 21, 34 |
| Ca | 0.025 | 0.03 | 0.18 | 0.2 | 1.2 | 1.3 | 0.45 | 0.6 | 1.0 | 1.0 | 0.02 | 0.03 | 3, 4, 5, 8, 10, 19, 21 |
| Yb | 0.015 | 0.025 | 0.11 | 0.2 | 0.5 | 0.75 | 4.0 | 7.0 | 0.6 | 1.0 | 0.001 | 0.01 | 3, 4, 5, 8, 11, 15, 16, 21, 24, 25, 35 |
| Y | 0.005 | 0.015 | 0.08 | 0.15 | 0.5 | 0.7 | 1.0 | 1.0 | 0.6 | 1.0 | 0.001 | 0.01 | 3, 4, 5, 8, 11, 12, 15, 16, 21, 24, 25 |
| Ti | 0.01 | 0.04 | 0.11 | 0.25 | 0.35 | 0.4 | 0.3 | 0.4 | *1.2* | 2.0 | 0.1 | 0.15 | 1, 2, 7, 10, 12, 15, 16, 17, 18, 21, 28, 34 |
| Zr | 0.005 | 0.008 | 0.04 | 0.06 | 0.15 | 0.18 | 0.2 | 0.3 | *0.25* | 0.4 | *0.01* | *0.02* | 8, 11, 12, 15, 17, 22, 26, 35 |
| Nb | 0.001 | 0.001 | 0.01 | 0.01 | 0.06 | 0.08 | 0.1 | 0.01 | 0.3 | 0.6 | *0.01* | *0.02* | 8, 12, 14, 15, 16, 22 |
| Al (15kb): | | | 0.4 | 0.6 | 0.8 | 1.6 | :V(QFM−1) | | | | | | |
| Al (1atm): | | | 0.08 | 0.1 | 0.2 | 0.4 | :V(QFM+1) | | | | | | |

Cr-sp/l

| | | |
|---|---|---|
| Cr | 300 | 600 |
| Al, Ga | 1 | 1 |

**Bulk distribution coefficients**

| | sp. lhz. | | gt. lhz. | | hbl. lhz. | | hz. | |
|---|---|---|---|---|---|---|---|---|
| | 1300°C | 1200°C | 1300°C | 1200°C | 1300°C | 1200°C | 1300°C | 1200°C |
| Ni | 6.19 | 10.39 | 6.19 | 10.42 | 6.25 | 10.45 | 7.95 | 13.29 |
| Cr | 4.01 | 8.00 | 2.18 | 4.27 | 1.99 | 3.93 | 4.31 | 8.37 |
| Mg | 3.30 | 3.61 | 3.32 | 3.63 | 3.28 | 3.58 | 3.72 | 4.03 |
| Co | 1.96 | 3.06 | 1.91 | 3.01 | 1.99 | 3.09 | 2.33 | 3.69 |
| Fe | 0.90 | 1.12 | 0.97 | 1.20 | 1.00 | 1.23 | 0.95 | 1.19 |
| Mn | 0.80 | 1.13 | 0.95 | 1.35 | 0.80 | 1.12 | 0.80 | 1.12 |
| Sc | 0.34 | 0.67 | 0.95 | 2.24 | 0.37 | 0.70 | 0.21 | 0.37 |
| V | 0.22 | 0.47 | 0.18 | 0.31 | 0.19 | 0.37 | 0.11 | 0.21 |
| Ga | 0.23 | 0.32 | 0.18 | 0.33 | 0.22 | 0.32 | 0.09 | 0.16 |
| Al | 0.20 | 0.28 | 0.26 | 0.32 | 0.20 | 0.26 | 0.06 | 0.09 |
| Ca | 0.21 | 0.23 | 0.19 | 0.23 | 0.22 | 0.23 | 0.05 | 0.06 |
| Yb | 0.10 | 0.16 | 0.53 | 0.92 | 0.12 | 0.21 | 0.03 | 0.05 |
| Y | 0.09 | 0.14 | 0.17 | 0.32 | 0.11 | 0.18 | 0.02 | 0.04 |
| Ti | 0.08 | 0.14 | 0.09 | 0.15 | 0.18 | 0.32 | 0.03 | 0.07 |
| Zr | 0.03 | 0.04 | 0.05 | 0.07 | 0.05 | 0.07 | 0.01 | 0.02 |
| Nb | 0.01 | 0.01 | 0.02 | 0.01 | 0.04 | 0.07 | 0.003 | 0.003 |

**Mantle compositions**

Spinel lherzolite
0.575 ol + 0.27 opx + 0.125 cpx + 0.02 Al–sp
Garnet lherzolite
0.6 ol + 0.21 opx + 0.075 cpx + 0.115 gt
Hornblende herzolite
0.6 ol + 0.25 opx + 0.04 cpx + 0.11 hbl
Harzburgite
0.83 ol + 0.16 opx + 0.01 Cr–sp

under consideration. These data include information on dependencies on temperature, pressure, oxygen fugacities and mineral and melt compositions. In order to model supra-subduction zone processes, we have selected values that may best represent wedge melting, namely temperatures of 1200–1300°C, pressures of 1–30 kb, oxygen fugacities of QFM ± 1, and liquid and crystal compositions consistent with sub-alkalic primary melts and the minerals with which they should be in equilibrium. Despite this filter, there is considerable variability in measured values. We have plotted the values on Onuma-plots (Onuma *et al.* 1968) to ensure internal consistency and, in certain cases, to enable unknown values to be obtained by interpolation. The coefficients used, and the data sources, are listed in Table 1. Note that we determine major element coefficients as wt % oxides for ease of application.

Several points need to be made on the construction and use of this table. Where possible, values have been taken using experimental data for which there is good evidence for equilibration and for which melting conditions are known. We place most reliance on experiments on natural compositions. Experiments on simple systems rarely give realistic results but have been used to place limits on the values used. In the absence of experiments, other methods of estimating mineral–melt equilibria have been adopted. Finally, in the absence of even these data, as with many garnet–liquid equilibria, we obtain values by combining clinopyroxene–liquid and clinopyroxene–garnet partition coefficients. Values for 1200°C and 1300°C are obtained by extrapolation and interpolation on diagrams of lnK vs. 1/T. For pressure-dependent coefficients, especially Al and Ca (Colson & Gust 1989), we use values for 10 kb. In principle, coefficients can be varied with changing P, T and composition in the melting column, but we have not done this in order to keep the models as simple as possible. Errors have not been quoted because the data sets are rarely sufficient to define errors properly. Where sufficient data do exist, the standard error on lnK is about 0.2 log units.

Most of our values fall sufficiently close to those of most published compilations that they do not merit comment or represent estimates that require ratification by experimental work. However, there are some significant deviations in the most critical coefficients, notably the clinopyroxene/liquid coefficients for Ti, Y, Yb, Sc and V. For Ti, our value of 0.35 at 1300°C falls in the range of synthesis values of 0.3 (Pearce & Norry 1979), 0.35 (Johnson &

Dick 1992), 0.4 (Elthon 1992; Keleman *et al.* 1992), 0.44 (Johnson *et al.* 1990). The experimental data set from which our synthesis value is derived ranges from 0.2 in the pure diopside–plagioclase system (e.g. Ray *et al.* 1983; Irving, 1978) to about 0.6 in experiments on alkali- and alumina-rich melt compositions (e.g. Bartels *et al.* 1991) suggesting strong compositional, as well as temperature, dependence for which our chosen value is an approximate average. The implication is that compositional dependence may prove significant for more precise modelling. For Yb (and Y), synthesis values for 1300°C (or MORB mantle melting temperatures) range from 0.2–0.3 (Ottonello *et al.* 1984), 0.45 (Elthon 1992). 0.5 (Johnson *et al.* 1990), 0.49 (Johnson & Dick 1992) and 0.52 (Keleman *et al.* 1992). Our value of 0.5 best fits the low rate of depletion of Yb relative to Ti in residual peridotites (see Fig. 5). The clinopyroxene/liquid coefficient for Sc is given as 1.3 at 1300°C in the Ottonello *et al.* (1984) compilation. However, this leads to more depleted Sc values in residual peridotites than are observed. Irving's (1978) synthesis of Lindstrom's (1976) unpublished data gives a value of 1.6 in the pure plagioclase–diopside system but with lower values at a given temperature for natural compositions. Ray *et al.* (1983), however, obtain values of about 0.85 in their experiments in the pure plagioclase–diopside system and we elect to use their value. Bearing in mind that natural clinopyroxenes are less calcic than pure diopside, the true coefficient may even be less than this.

Clinopyroxene/liquid coefficients for V show a very strong dependence on oxygen fugacity, varying from 5 at a fugacity of $10^{-12}$ when $V^{3+}$ dominates, through 1 at a fugacity of $10^{-10}$, to 0.05 at a fugacity of $10^{-6}$ at mantle melting temperatures when $V^{4+}$ and $V^{5+}$ dominate (Irving 1978; Shervais 1982). A mean value (at QFM) is about 0.4. However, MORB magma genesis is thought to take place closer to QFM − 1, giving a coefficient of about 0.8, whereas magma genesis in oceanic arcs may take place at a fugacity of QFM + 1 or more (Carmichael & Ghiorso 1990) giving a coefficient of about 0.2 or less. These values must be regarded as approximate as their composition and temperature dependences are poorly known, but they do indicate that there may be a clear difference in behaviour of V between ridges and subduction zones. Partition coefficients for V between melt and other phases are also likely to exhibit oxygen fugacity dependence, although the extent of this dependence has not been evaluated. In the absence of the necessary data, we assume that the partition coefficients between clinopyroxene and other

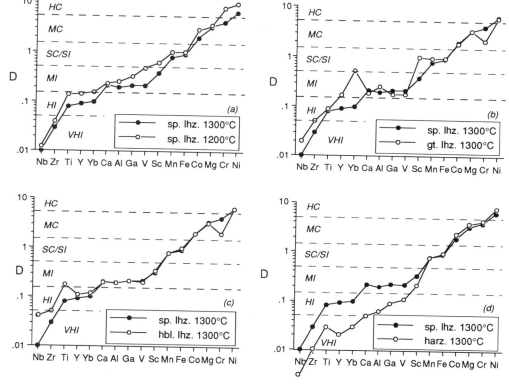

**Fig. 4.** Bulk distribution coefficients (D) for mantle wedge melting based on the values compiled in Table 1. Elements are subdivided into highly compatible (HC), moderately compatible (MC), slightly compatible or incompatible (SC/SI), moderately incompatible (MI), highly incompatible (HI), very highly incompatible (VHI) on the basis of their D values. sp.: spinel; Gt.: garnet; lhz.: lherzolite; harz.: harzburgite. Elements are placed in order of incompatibility with fertile spinel lherzolite at 1300°C, 10 kb and an oxygen fugacity at the QFM buffer.

phases are dependent in a similar way on oxygen fugacity.

Garnet/liquid and amphibole/liquid coefficients are approximate in many cases. Many required extrapolation of mineral/clinopyroxene coefficients to melting temperatures and multiplication of these values by clinopyroxene/melt coefficients; some amphibole/melt coefficients are based on phenocryst/matrix coefficients, again with extrapolation to high temperatures. However, the principal point is valid, that Ti is partitioned into amphibole, and Y, Yb and Sc into garnet, in preference to elements of otherwise comparable compatibilities.

Chromium is a special case in mantle melting as its solubility in the melt can be exceeded during mantle melting, the saturation concentration depending particularly on oxygen fugacity and temperature. We use Roeder & Rey-

nolds' (1991) experiments to define saturation concentrations for 1300°C and 1200°C at an oxygen fugacity corresponding to the QFM buffer and 10 kb. These indicate saturation concentrations of about 800 ppm at 1300°C and 400 ppm at 1200°C. If the theoretical concentration exceeds this value, the saturation concentration is taken. Thus, given a mantle concentration range for Cr of 2350 ppm, the effective bulk distribution coefficients must be less than about 3 at 1300°C and about 6 at 1200°C.

The elements are then ordered according to incompatibility with respect to a spinel lherzolite at 1200° and 1300°C (Fig. 4a). Using this plot, we classify the mantle-derived elements into six classes:

(1) HC or highly compatible elements (Ni) with values greater than 5;

(2) MC or moderately compatible (elements Cr, Mg, Co) with values between 1.5 and 5;

(3) SC/SI or slightly compatible/slightly incompatible elements (Fe, Mn) with values between 1.5 and 0.5;

(4) MI or moderately incompatible elements (Sc, V, Ca, Ga, Al) with values between 0.5 and 0.15;

(5) HI or highly incompatible elements (Yb, Y, Ti) with values between 0.15 and 0.05; and

(6) VHI or very highly incompatible elements (Zr, Nb) with values less than 0.05.

Comparable plots for garnet lherzolite (Fig. 4b), hornblende lherzolite (Fig. 4c) and harzburgite (Fig. 4d), indicate how the order of compatibility depends on the composition and degree of depletion of the mantle source. In particular, the trivalent ions, Sc, Yb and Y are strongly partitioned into a garnet lherzolite residue, with the result that Y and Yb now behave as MI elements and Sc as a SI element. Ti can behave as a MI element during melting of amphibole peridotite. In harzburgite, when the clinopyroxene content of the residue is very low, many of the MI elements become HI, and HI elements become VHI, and the order of compatibility can change: for example, Ca is less incompatible than Al with respect to fertile lherzolite, but more incompatible with respect to the more residual harzburgite. The presence of phlogopite in mantle residues will also have a marked effect, especially on Nb and V, but we do not consider this relatively rare case here.

## Patterns of mantle-derived elements in supra-subduction zone mantle source

The subduction component can be added to a mantle wedge which has a fertile MORB mantle composition, which is enriched through mixing with a plume, or other type of enrichment component, or which is residual from an earlier melting episode or episodes. The main upper mantle reservoir is generally taken to be the source of N-type MORB, described in isotope space as 'depleted MORB mantle' or DMM (Zindler & Hart 1986) to distinguish it from the sources of T- or E-type MORB. This term is slightly ambiguous in an elemental context, because there are two different types of depletion: the depletion that the mantle has experienced during melting processes in the backarc basin and mantle wedge, and the global processes that have generated the MORB mantle reservoir from Bulk Earth. We, therefore, define the following terms:

(1) fertile MORB mantle (FMM) – the global convecting upper mantle reservoir from which N-type MORB is derived;

(2) residual MORB mantle (RMM) – the residues from partial melting of this reservoir;

(3) enriched upper mantle (EUM) – any enriched portion of the upper mantle, which can be subdivided into enriched fertile mantle (EFM) and enriched residual mantle (ERM) depending on whether or not the mantle has been depleted by melting before enrichment.

(4) primitive upper mantle (PUM) composition – the mantle composition immediately after internal segregation of the Earth.

Note that EUM has a variable composition and incorporates mantle that produces both enriched MORB and hot-spot volcanoes. PUM is taken as an approximation to a deep-seated plume on the basis that its source is more primordial than that of MORB. This is not meant to imply, however, that any plume has this actual composition.

Table 2 gives the estimated compositions of the elements of interest in these mantle types and references to the sources of data. The PUM composition is taken from Sun & McDonough (1989) and McDonough & Frey (1989). The FMM composition is taken largely from published data on samples from orogenic lherzolite massifs (Ronda, Pyrenees, Zabargad) and nodules (Hungary, France, Mexico) that have no reported metasomatic enrichment. A further constraint is that this composition should form the end-member to depletion trends for mantle peridotites (see, for example, McDonough & Frey 1989). We also use the depletion trends to define residual mantle compositions and, more important, melting behaviour. These plots are presented in the form of concentration against modal abundance of clinopyroxene in Fig. 5.

Perhaps because of mantle tectonism and refertilization (e.g. Elthon 1992), there is no consensus on the precise mineralogical composition of FMM. We have taken a value of 14 modal % clinopyroxene, which lies within the range of published estimates of 12.5–17.5%. The plots give coherent trends from this FMM composition toward RMM compositions. Accepting evidence from equilibrium experiments for disappearance of free (non-exsolved) clinopyroxene at about 25% ($\pm 5\%$) melting, we have used these plots to determine RMM compositions for the residues to 5%, 10%, 15%, 20% and 25% melting assuming a constant rate of depletion of clinopyroxene during melting. Note that the depletion trends are not theoretically linear on this

**Table 2.** Data used to define a range of supra-subduction zone mantle compositions. Primitive Upper Mantle (PUM) is from Sun & McDonough (1989) and McDonough & Frey (1989). Fertile and residual MORB Mantle (FMM and RMM) compositions are from: Jagoutz *et al.* (1979) and Jochum *et al.* (1989) (France and Mexico); Frey *et al.* (1985) (Ronda); Bonatti *et al.* (1986) (Zabargad); Boudinier *et al.* (1988) (Pyrenees); Downes *et al.* (1992) (Hungary); Unpubl. data (Ojen); Stosch & Seck (1980) (Dreiser Weiher). RMM compositions are given for 5% (RMM5) to 25% (RMM25) melt extraction. Oxides are in wt%, elements in ppm

|  | PUM | FMM | RMM5 | RMM10 | RMM15 | RMM20 | RMM25 | EFM | ERM |
|---|---|---|---|---|---|---|---|---|---|
| Nb | 0.71 | 0.2 | 0.01 | 0.0005 | tr | tr | tr | 6 | 0.6 |
| Zr | 11.2 | 9.2 | 2.0 | 0.3 | 0.05 | 0.007 | 0.0013 | 95 | 26.8 |
| TiO$_2$ | 0.21 | 0.175 | 0.12 | 0.05 | 0.02 | 0.009 | 0.004 | 0.51 | 0.17 |
| Y | 4.55 | 3.9 | 2.2 | 1.2 | 0.6 | 0.3 | 0.15 | 8.1 | 2.85 |
| Yb | 0.49 | 0.42 | 0.32 | 0.19 | 0.1 | 0.055 | 0.03 | 0.56 | 0.16 |
| CaO | 3.6 | 3.25 | 2.6 | 2.0 | 1.35 | 0.7 | 0.25 | 4.35 | 1.2 |
| Al$_2$O$_3$ | 4.45 | 3.75 | 2.9 | 2.3 | 1.7 | 1.1 | 0.5 | 3.3 | 1.89 |
| Ga | 4.5 | 4.0 | 3.5 | 3.1 | 2.2 | 1.5 | 1.0 | 3.7 | 2.5 |
| V | 82 | 78 | 68 | 58 | 48 | 38 | 28 | 76 | 40 |
| Sc | 17.1 | 15.5 | 13.5 | 11.4 | 9.4 | 7.4 | 5.4 | 14.2 | 6.7 |
| MnO | 0.135 | 0.13 | 0.131 | 0.132 | 0.133 | 0.134 | 0.135 | 0.14 | 0.12 |
| FeO | 8.8 | 8.8 | 8.85 | 8.9 | 8.85 | 9.0 | 9.05 | 9.35 | 9.4 |
| Co | 102 | 106 | 110 | 114 | 118 | 122 | 126 | 105 | 116 |
| MgO | 37.8 | 38.4 | 40.0 | 41.6 | 43.4 | 45.2 | 47.0 | 37.04 | 42.16 |
| Cr | 2580 | 2500 | 2590 | 2680 | 2770 | 2860 | 2950 | 2500 | 2700 |
| Ni | 2190 | 2020 | 2140 | 2260 | 2380 | 2500 | 2620 | 2150 | 2060 |

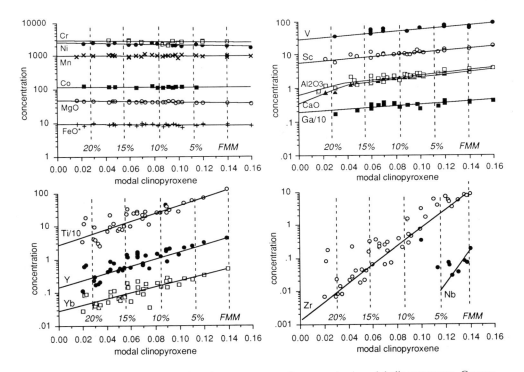

**Fig. 5.** Elements in peridotites plotted against percentage of non-exsolved modal clinopyroxene. Concentrations of elements are in ppm, oxides in wt%. The slope of each curve should match the theoretical residues to melting if the melting models are correct. The greater the positive slope the greater the incompatibility. For data sources see Table 2 and text. The dashed lines give the percentage of melt extracted from the fertile MORB mantle (FMM) source.

plot and should generally steepen with increasing depletion because the bulk partition coefficients decrease as clinopyroxene is used up. We use the logarithmic axis in part because the slope gives an indication of the relative compatibilities of the elements of interest. Thus, the most compatible elements have negative slopes and the most incompatible have steep positive slopes. It is apparent that the order of compatibility seen in these plots corresponds with that determined theoretically from the partition coefficients in Table 1.

Because they are depleted and enriched so readily, and because their compositions lie close to detection limits, fertile and residual MORB mantle concentrations of the HI and VHI elements are difficult to define, particularly Nb and Zr. To construct Fig. 5, we have calculated the mantle compositions for Zr, Ti, Y (based on Dy) and Yb from ion microprobe data on clinopyroxenes (Johnson *et al.* 1990; Johnson & Dick 1992) using the modal compositions and 1000°C mineral–clinopyroxene partition coefficients to carry out the convertion. We have not used their data from samples collected near plumes to construct the depletion trends.

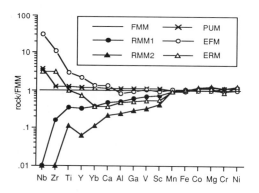

**Fig. 6.** Peridotite patterns normalized to fertile MORB mantle (FMM) (see Table 2 and text for data sources). RMM1 and RMM2 are the Residual MORB Mantle (RMM) compositions for 7.5% and 15% melt extraction respectively. Primitive Upper Mantle (PUM), Enriched Fertile Mantle (EFM) and Enriched Residual Mantle (ERM) compositions are discussed in the text. The patterns give the approximate spread of patterns for mantle wedge sources.

Enriched mantle compositions are potentially highly variable both because the composition of the metasomatizing fluid can vary and because the chemistry of wall–rock interaction is complex. We have selected two typical examples of Pyrenean mantle enriched by vein–wall inter-

action with silicate melt, one in which the wall–rock was close to FMM in composition and one in which the wall–rock had a RMM composition (Boudinier *et al.* 1988).

Figure 6 illustrates these compositions as patterns relative to the FMM composition. The RMM compositions emphasize the extremely rapid depletion of the VHI elements that can result from partial melting. As a number of authors have pointed out, even small differences in partition coefficients can cause large differences in the extent of mantle depletion. The enriched mantle compositions indicate that mantle enrichment by silicate melt interaction is dominated by Nb, Zr, Ti and, to a lesser extent, Y, with Yb and Ca showing very small enrichment and other elements having no discernible enrichment. For EFM, this enrichment is superimposed on a flat FMM pattern. In ERM, it is superimposed on RMM patterns. Enrichment by carbonatite fluids gives a very different pattern with strong enrichment in Y and Yb relative to Zr and Nb (Yaxley *et al.* 1991), but there is no evidence of such enrichment in the mantle wedge for any of the volcanoes studied. The patterns in Fig. 6 should thus bracket the compositional range of most mantle wedges for the elements not introduced by subduction.

## Theoretical behaviour of the mantle-derived elements during partial melting

Accurate modelling of mantle melting is restricted by our lack of knowledge of precisely how the mantle melts and the extent of equilibration between melt and residue. The nature of the melting event is probably constrained most effectively by the compositions of residual mantle. In particular, Frey *et al.* (1985) use bulk analyses of orogenic peridotites, and Johnson *et al.* (1990) use ion microprobe analyses of clinopyroxenes from abyssal peridotites, to demonstrate that batch melting cannot explain the observed incompatible element depletions in residual mantle and that melting must be near-fractional. Johnson & Dick (1992) obtain a better fit to abyssal peridotite data by considering open system fractional melting with continuous re-equilibration with a small volume of pooled melt percolating from lower in the melting column. Prinzhofer & Allègre (1985) further emphasize the importance of taking into account whether melting begins in the garnet or spinel lherzolite facies and the extent to which equilibration is achieved. O'Hara (1985) emphasizes the importance of considering the geometry of the melt zone.

Our first objective is to examine the effect of

these different melting models on the patterns generated by melting of fertile MORB mantle. We accept the evidence from peridotite compositions for near-fractional melting and for the need to incorporate trapped melt into the models. Thus, we believe that the right approach is that adopted by Johnson & Dick (1992). They use Shaw's (1970) equations for fractional melting, as adapted by McKenzie (1985) and Williams & Gill (1989) for dynamic melting, but modified to take into account the fact that melting is nonmodal. Our method, we believe, achieves a similar end but in a much simpler way. We use the fractional melting equation but with the trapped melt treated as a phase with a partition coefficient of 1. This phase is present in a volume proportion (the porosity) from which the mass proportion can be determined. This trapped melt then has the effect of increasing the bulk distribution coefficient for all incompatible elements, but has the greatest effect on the most incompatible (VHI) elements. We have chosen a mass fraction of trapped melt of 0.01 to simulate the peridotite depletion trends, as explained below. For simplicity, we do not allow re-equilibration with upward-advecting melts. Note that this makes little difference to the composition of aggregate melts if these melts are produced by a single melting column behaving as a closed system, but is important if the system is open.

Our starting point is the FMM lherzolite mineralogy in Table 1. For spinel lherzolite melting, we use rates of phase disappearance such that clinopyroxene disappears at 25% melting, orthopyroxene at 40% melting and chrome spinel (a product of incongruent melting of aluminous spinel) at 80% melting. For garnet lherzolite melting, we use rates of phase disappearance such that garnet disappears at 15% and clinopyroxene at 25% melting. For melting in garnet lherzolite facies before spinel lherzolite facies, we define the transformation by the expression: ol + gt = 2.5 opx + sp + 0.75 cpx (McKenzie & O'Nions 1991).

Figure 7 shows the result of modelling four different melting scenarios using the method outlined above.

(a) Fractional melting of a rectangular melting column that is in spinel lherzolite facies throughout its melting history.
(b) Fractional melting of a triangular melting column in spinel lherzolite facies. This scenario assumes an equilateral triangular cross-section to the melting column, two-phase flow only in the plane of this section, and degrees of melting that increase from zero at the edges of the section to a maximum at the centre.

(c) Fractional melting of a rectangular melting column in spinel lherzolite facies assuming 5% porosity.
(d) Fractional melting of a rectangular melting column which undergoes 5% melting in the garnet lherzolite facies before continuing to melt in the spinel lherzolite facies.

Each figure shows the element pattern relative to fertile MORB mantle for 5% melting steps up to 30% of pooled melt. These imply the following.

1. The general shape of the patterns predictably shows depletions (relative to the FMM source) of the compatible elements, little change in Fe or Mn, and enrichment in the incompatible elements. For low degrees of melting, the contrasts in abundance for differences in incompatibility are most evident, with the VHI elements Nb and Zr noticeably more enriched than the HI elements, Ti, Y and Yb, which are in turn noticeably more enriched than the MI elements. For high degrees of melting, this contrast is much less marked, the MI, HI and VHI elements forming a flat pattern.
2. The type of melting has some influence on the shapes of the patterns. Inclusion of porosity (Fig. 7c) has the effect of depressing the incompatible element content of low–moderate degree melts. However, bearing in mind that the value used (5%) is a maximum value for mantle porosity, the real effect may not be so great. Varying the shape of the melting column by allowing small-degree melts from the margins of a column of triangular cross-section to mix with large-degree melts from the centre of the column (Fig. 7b), increases incompatible element contents and enables the effect of differences in incompatibility to persist to high degrees of melting.
3. Initiation of melting in the garnet lherzolite facies (Fig. 7d) has the effect of suppressing Yb and Sc for low degrees of melting because of the presence of the garnet in the residue. Particularly distinctive is the fact that Sc behaves as a slightly incompatible element, similar to Mn and Fe, in such melts. With melting continuing into the spinel lherzolite facies, however, these anomalies are rapidly smoothed out.

It is for remelting of already-depleted mantle that melt retention becomes important. With no melt retention, Nb and Zr are very strongly depleted in the mantle residue and hence in any melt derived from it. Even changing the shape of the melting column and initiating melting in the garnet lherzolite facies cannot mask this depletion. By contrast, melt retention, or inter-

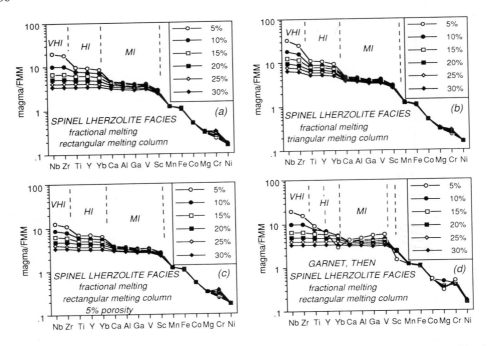

**Fig. 7.** Theoretical FMM-normalized patterns for different melting models. All assume fractional melting but with different assumptions for melt generation, namely (**a**) a rectangular melting column in spinel lherzolite facies, (**b**) a triangular melting column, (**c**) 5% porosity, and (**d**) a melting column in which melting starts in the garnet lherzolite facies. The values in the key give the percentage of pooled melt. VHI, HI and MI refer to very highly incompatible, highly incompatible and moderately incompatible elements respectively as defined in Fig. 4.

action of melt residue with more enriched melt from lower levels in the melting column, can have a marked effect in retaining the highly incompatible elements for the second stage of melting. To model remelting of depleted (RMM) sources, we therefore need to make some decision on how much melt to retain. The most incompatible elements, Zr and Nb, are also the most sensitive to melt retention. The curves in Fig. 8 show how different volume percentages retained (porosity) theoretically affect the Zr depletion. The data in Fig. 8 are the Zr contents of fertile and residual mantle also plotted in Fig. 5d. It is apparent that porosities between about 0.5 and 1% best fit most data. In Johnson & Dick's (1992) model, lower porosities are needed because the pores contain more enriched melt from deeper in the melt column, so that less trapped melt is required to achieve the same effect on Zr concentrations. For the purposes of this paper we assume that melt derived from deeper in the melt column escapes in channels before reacting with upper parts of the column. In practice, however, there are few constraints

on this part of the model and the actual process may lie somewhere between the two extremes.

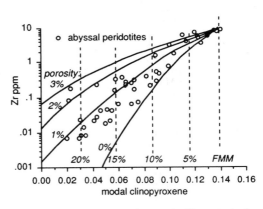

**Fig. 8.** Effect of melt retention on the Zr content of residual mantle. Construction of the theoretical curves is explained in the text. Fractional melting without melt retention fails to fit the residual peridotite data. A value of 0.5–1% porosity gives the best fit.

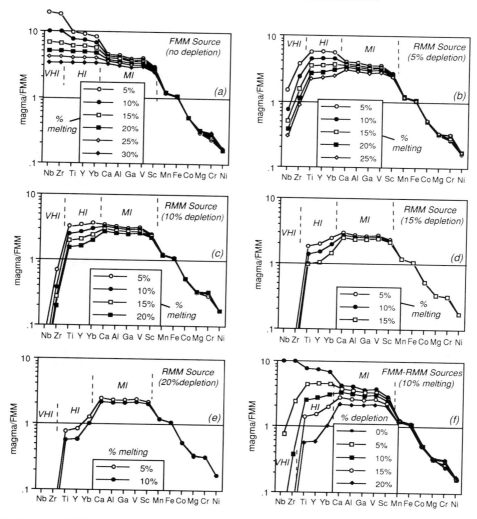

**Fig. 9.** Theoretical FMM-normalized patterns for sources of variable depletion (melt loss). Each diagram is modelled for up to 30% total melting (the sum of source depletion and % of melting), **(f)** summarizes the variations for a given degree of melting (10%) of variably depleted mantle. For key to element type (VHI, HI, MI), see Fig. 7. FMM: Fertile MORB Mantle; RMM: Residual MORB Mantle. The diagram demonstrates that source depletion is more effective than a high degree of melting at reducing the incompatible element content of a melt.

Patterns for varying amounts of partial melting of FMM and RMM (FMM depleted by 5%, 10%, 15% and 20% of previous melting) with the maximum likely value of 1% porosity are shown in Figs 9a–e. It is apparent from these figures that the pattern shapes are markedly changed by a previous episode of melt extraction. For melting of undepleted mantle, normalized abundances are in the order VHI > HI > MI for low degrees of melting with VHI = HI = MI at high degrees of melting (Fig. 9a). For 5% source depletion, (Fig. 9b) the order is now

VHI < HI > MI for low degrees of melting which becomes VHI < HI = MI at intermediate degrees of melting and VHI < HI < MI at high degrees of melting. For 10% depletion or more, (Figs 9c–e) the order is typically VHI < HI < MI for all but the lowest degrees of melting. Figure 9f summarizes the compositions of pooled melt for 10% pooled melting of variably depleted mantle columns. Comparing Figs 9a and 9f gives a measure for the relative importance of degree of partial melting and source depletion in accounting for pattern variations. From these, it

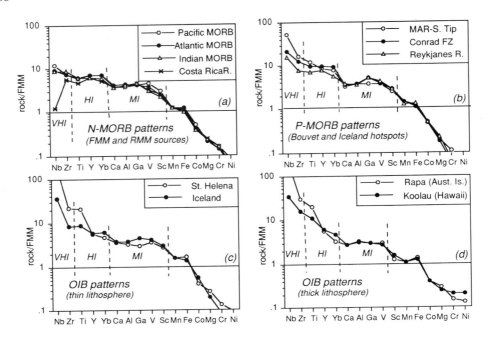

**Fig. 10.** FMM-normalized patterns for mid-ocean ridge (MORB) and ocean island basalts (OIB). **(a)** Typical N-MORB patterns from the Atlantic Ocean (ODP Site 418A: Joron *et al.* 1979), the Pacific Ocean (ODP Site 597C: Pearce *et al.* 1986) and the Indian Ocean (Triple junction: Price *et al.* 1986), and a highly incompatible element-depleted pattern (ODP Site 504B: Tual *et al.* 1985). **(b)** P-type MORB patterns influenced by the Bouvet plume (S. Tip of the Mid-Atlantic Ridge and the Conrad Fracture Zone: Le Roex *et al.* 1983) and the Iceland plume (DSDP Site 409: Tarney *et al.* 1978; Wood *et al.* 1978). **(c)** Patterns for OIB on thin lithosphere at St Helena (Chaffey *et al.* 1989) and Iceland (Wood *et al.* 1979). **(d)** Patterns for OIB on thick lithosphere at Oahu, Hawaii (Roden *et al.* 1984) and Rapa, Austral Is. (Dupuy *et al.* 1988).

is apparent that the effects of increasing partial melting and increasing source depletion are quite distinct.

## Basic pattern types in MORB and OIB

Before considering FMM-normalized patterns in subduction-related lavas, it is informative to examine patterns in mid-ocean ridge and ocean island basalts, for which melting processes are better understood. Figure 10a shows patterns for some typical N-MORB from the three major oceans. The patterns are those predicted for moderate degrees of pooled melt generated within the spinel lherzolite facies from FMM, in keeping with current ideas on mantle upwelling beneath mid-ocean ridges (e.g. Niu & Batiza 1991). Also included on this figure is one of the best examples of an N-MORB derived from a depleted source, a basalt dyke from the deep borehole at DSDP Site 504B on the Costa Rica Rift. The depletion in Nb and Zr compared with

the 'typical' N-MORB pattern fits the modelled patterns for remelting of slightly depleted mantle. This depletion could originate by selective tapping of the upper part of a single melting column or be a larger-scale phenomenon related to upper mantle convection patterns. Examples of typical P-type MORB from plume-influenced ridge segments are shown in Fig. 10b. These display the enrichment in highly incompatible elements expected for derivation from more enriched mantle sources.

Figure 10c presents patterns for OIB erupted onto thin oceanic lithosphere, in which the melting column extends to the base of the crust. The patterns resemble those from plume-influenced ridge segments but with greater enrichment of the more incompatible elements. In patterns for OIB erupted onto thick oceanic lithosphere, shown in Fig. 10d, the principal features are the depletions in Yb (relative to Y) and Sc (relative to V) that can be explained by a deep melting column located primarily within garnet lherzolite facies mantle (Watson & MacKenzie 1991).

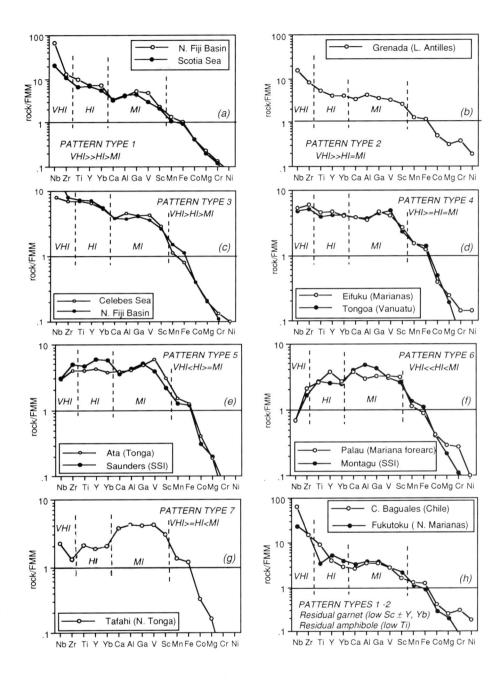

**Fig. 11.** FMM-normalized patterns for supra-subduction zone mantle showing a variety of pattern types that can be related to melting and depletion-enrichment events in the mantle. For key to element type, see Fig. 7. For details of pattern types, see text. Note that Figs a, b and h have scales appropriate for comparison with Fig. 7, whereas Figs c–g have scales appropriate for comparison with Fig. 9.

## Basic pattern types in SSZ lavas

Figure 11 presents patterns for a variety of marginal basin and island arc basalts organized according to pattern type as follows:

- Type 1: (VHI ≫ HI > MI). This pattern type matches the theoretical pattern for low to moderate melting of a FMM source (Fig. 7 and Fig. 9a). However, concentrations of VHI elements greater than those predicted from modelling indicate a source more enriched than FMM.
- Type 2: (VHI ≫ HI = MI). This pattern type matches the theoretical pattern for a high degree of melting of a FMM source (Fig. 7 and Fig. 9a), in which HI elements are no longer more enriched than MI elements. Again, however, the concentrations of VHI elements indicates a source more enriched than FMM.
- Type 3: (VHI > HI > MI). This pattern type matches the theoretical pattern for moderate melting of an unenriched FMM source (Fig. 7 and Fig. 9a).
- Type 4: (VHI > = HI = MI). This pattern type matches the theoretical pattern for high degrees of melting of an unenriched FMM source (Fig. 7 and Fig. 9a).
- Type 5: (VHI < HI > = MI). This pattern type, in which the VHI elements now have lower normalized abundances than the HI elements, matches the theoretical pattern for high degrees of melting of a very slightly depleted source (Fig. 9a–b).
- Type 6: (VHI ≪ HI < MI). This pattern type, which now shows the inverse order of that obtained for melting of an FMM source, matches the theoretical pattern for high degrees of melting of a moderately depleted source (Fig. 9b).
- Type 7: (VHI > = HI < MI). This pattern type matches the theoretical pattern for high degrees of melting of a depleted source (Fig. 9c–d) but with re-enrichment of the VHI elements

Figure 11h shows the effect of residual phases on the geochemical patterns. The Mariana arc pattern (Bloomer *et al.* 1989) has low Ti with respect to Zr and Y which can be explained by residual amphibole in the mantle source. The Andean backarc pattern (Stern *et al.* 1990) has low Y and Yb with respect to Ti, and Sc has an abundance level similar to Mn rather than between Mn and V, indicative of residual garnet (Fig. 7c). These pattern types are, however, rare in volcanic arcs.

From these patterns, we can conclude that a wide range of sources, from enriched to depleted, are available in the mantle wedge beneath island arcs. From data available at the time of writing, pattern types 1 and 3 are restricted to marginal basins and mid-ocean ridges. Island arc basalts rarely exhibit the characteristic of HI > MI which requires moderate–low degrees of melting of a fertile source. More typically, the pattern shapes for island arcs indicate high degrees of melting of fertile sources, or moderate amounts of melting of depleted sources. This result is at variance with that of Davies & Bickle (1991) who require only small amounts of melting. However, the latter consider only fluid-induced melting. The implication of this work is that it is the combination of decompression melting and fluid fluxing that produces a high degree of melting above subduction zones. This qualitative interpretation is now examined in more detail using bivariate plots.

## Bivariate plots for investigating mantle melting above subduction zones

### Databases

We use five databases to investigate melting behaviour above subduction zones: an oceanic arc database, the principal subject of this study; a boninite database, which extends the data set to the products of partial melting of very depleted mantle; a MORB database which provides a basis for comparing arc lavas with lavas of relatively well-known petrogenesis; a peridotite database which constrains the melting models; and a continental arc database which provides an insight into the effect of lithosphere thickness and composition on arc genesis. As with comparable studies on major elements in MORB (Klein & Langmuir 1987) or island arcs (Plank & Langmuir 1988), we constructed the volcanic data sets to minimize the effects of fractional crystallization and hence emphasize variations in primary magmas. To do this we selected only samples with high MgO contents (> 5% MgO). For incompatible elements, we then used element-MgO plots to extrapolate or interpolate trends to give a concentration for each volcano at MgO = 9 wt%. Although magmas at 9 wt% MgO are not primary, they lie on the olivine–chrome spinel cotectic and are close to primary compositions for incompatible trace elements. We did not make this correction for the compatible elements (Ni, Cr, Co) as these are very sensitive to the precise extent of olivine and chrome spinel crystallization. The databases are as follows:

(1) The *island arc database*. This comprises analyses of basalts from the South Sandwich, Tonga, Kermadec, Vanuatu, Mariana, Aleutian and Lesser Antilles arcs. With the exception of some samples from the Aleutian arc (Nye & Reid 1986, Gamble *et al.* 1993, Kay & Kay, in press), all samples are from published sources (Brown *et al.* 1977; Dupuy *et al.* 1982; Bloomer *et al.* 1989; Ewart *et al.* 1973; Ewart & Hawkesworth 1987), augmented by ICP-MS analyses at Durham for the trace elements used in this paper.

(2) The *boninite database*. This comprises a set of boninites from the Western Pacific, from the Bonin outer arc high (ODP Leg125), the Bonin islands, Guam, Palau, the Mariana inner trench wall, and the Mariana forearc basin (ODP Leg 60). All samples are primitive with MgO contents >8 wt% and phenocrysts are mafic. Although the aim of this paper is primarily to examine mantle melting beneath island arcs, the boninites provide an opportunity to examine compositions related to the most depleted sources. All samples in the database have been analysed by ICP-MS at Durham.

(3) A *MORB database*. This comprises values from the now extensive set of published MORB data from ODP volumes and elsewhere with MgO contents greater than 8 wt%. All oceans are represented, as are ridge segments adjacent to hot-spots.

(4) A *peridotite database*. This comprises the data from unenriched orogenic peridotites and abyssal peridotites used in Table 2 and in Fig. 5 (see text and table caption for references). Supra-subduction zone peridotites are represented by drilled samples from the Mariana and Izu-Bonin forearcs (Parkinson *et al.* 1992).

(5) A *continental arc database*. This comprises published data from the Philippines (Defant *et al.* 1990, 1991), Japan (Arculus *et al.* 1991), the Andes (Hickey *et al.* 1986; Hickey-Vargas *et al.* 1989) and Indonesia (Whitford 1975; Varne & Foden 1986)

Our aim here is to examine petrogenesis rather than discrimination between tectonic settings, which will be the subject of a separate publication. We have chosen five projections to illustrate some of the key features. The first three of these are plots of C–HI (Cr–Yb), MI–HI (Sc–Yb) and VHI–HI (Nb–Yb). The final two examine the effect of residual garnet (Ti–Yb) and oxygen fugacity (V–Yb). For reasons of space, we do not consider ratio-plots here: examples of these will be presented in subsequent publications.

## Cr–Yb

This projection represents the covariation between a compatible element (Cr) and an incompatible element (Yb). Its petrogenetic significance is that partial melting and mafic crystallization trends are almost orthogonal. Moreover, it is little affected by source enrichment. A similar projection (Cr–Y) has been used to investigate arc petrogenesis and to discriminate between MORB and SSZ-type ophiolites (Pearce 1982). This work re-examines the modelling in that publication in the light of recent advances in our knowledge of mantle melting.

Figure 12a shows the theoretical source depletion and partial melting trends for the Cr–Yb projection. In this and the diagrams that follow, we have (unless otherwise stated) modelled a melting column entirely within spinel lherzolite facies, assuming 1% porosity. We assume that chrome solubility is not exceeded during melting. We have drawn partial melting trends for variously depleted mantle sources and annotated them for disappearance of clinopyroxene (at 25% total melting, where total melting = source depletion + degree of partial melting), orthopyroxene (at 40% total melting) and spinel (at 80% total melting). Characteristically these trends exhibit little change in the compatible element (Cr) content for large variations in the incompatible element (Yb) content, up to high degrees of melting. The mantle depletion trend correspondingly also shows only a small enrichment in Cr for rapid depletion in Yb. The diagram thus demonstrates that Yb decreases in primary melts in response to both mantle depletion and increasing degree of melting, and that mantle depletion makes the greater contribution to the total variance (see also Fig. 9).

Figure 12b shows the distribution of the most mafic samples from the three oceanic lava databases plotted on an expanded part of Fig. 12a. The diagonal melting trends represent the liquids formed by variable (1–25%) degrees of partial melting of a constant mantle composition (trends shown depict fertile mantle and mantle already depleted by 5–25% of previous melting). Melts formed by a constant (15%) degree of partial melting of variable mantle compositions form a trend linking the open diamonds. The sub-horizontal trend is the locus of melt compositions for 25% total melting (% depletion + % melting).

Of the oceanic basalt data points plotted on the diagram, few plot within the predicted region of primary melts delineated by the partial melting trends. Fractional crystallization from the primary magmas should produce straight-line

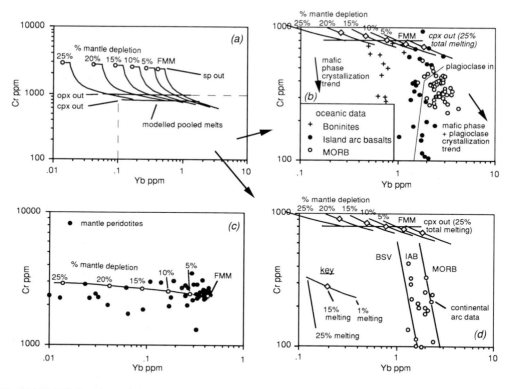

**Fig. 12.** Modelled and measured melt and residue compositions observed in a plot of a compatible element (Cr) against a highly incompatible element (Yb). **(a)** Theoretical melts and residues; **(b)** compositions of oceanic samples; **(c)** residual peridotite compositions; and **(d)** continental arc compositions. The key features are that melting trends and crystallization of mafic minerals give sub-orthogonal trends, and that variations observed in oceanic arcs must involve source depletion as well as high degrees of melting. Data points are the most basic mafic lavas from volcanoes used in this paper. The box bounded by dashed lines in (a) is expanded in (b) and (d). For details, see text.

vectors, first for mafic phases (olivine, spinel and pyroxene) and then for mafic phases plus plagioclase. Plagioclase becomes a crystallizing phase at higher Cr concentrations at mid-ocean ridges than in supra-subduction zone settings, and this is reflected by the shape of the empirically-drawn plagioclase-in line. We can extrapolate an evolved lava back to its primary magma composition, using the mafic–plagioclase crystallization vector (if necessary) as far as the plagioclase-in line, then the mafic crystallization vector. If this is done, it is apparent that the incompatible element, Yb, decreases from MORB through island arc basalts to boninites. MORB can be explained by up to 20% melting of a fertile MORB source which matches other estimates. Oceanic arcs mostly fall in the range that requires between 15 and 40% melting of a fertile MORB source or 1 and 10% melting of a

10% depleted MORB source or somewhere between these extremes. The principal exceptions are the alkaline arc volcanoes, which overlap the MORB range. Boninites require unrealistically high degrees of partial melting if their source is of FMM composition: thus, this diagram provides further evidence that source depletion must play a major role in boninite genesis.

Figure 12c shows the data points for mantle residues. The abyssal peridotites fall into the range 0–20% depletion, while samples from the Bonin–Mariana inner trench walls extend this range to about 25% melting. The spread of data exceeds that expected theoretically, perhaps because of sampling or analytical errors resulting from variable distribution of chromite.

Figure 12d shows the composition of continental arcs. The field boundaries separate most

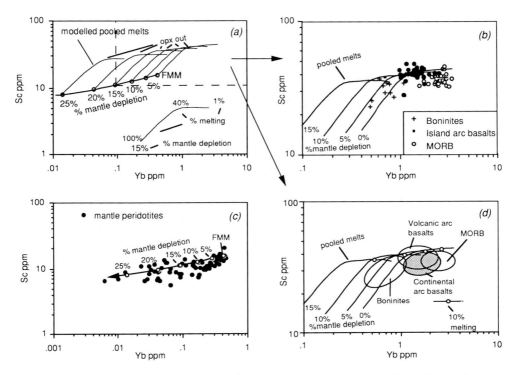

**Fig. 13.** Modelled and measured melt and residue compositions observed in a plot of a moderately incompatible element (Sc) against a highly incompatible element (Yb). **(a)** Theoretical melts and residues; **(b)** compositions of oceanic samples; **(c)** residual peridotite compositions; **(d)** the continental arc distribution. Data are adjusted for MgO = 9 wt%. The diagram further confirms the role of source depletion in explaining the compositions of supra-subduction zone magmas. For details, see text.

boninite series volcanics (BSV), island arc basalt (IAB) and MORB compositions as plotted in Fig. 12b. Continental arcs plot within and on the edge of the oceanic arc field on this plot, also indicating higher degrees of total melting than MORB. This is a somewhat surprising conclusion as we might expect low degrees of melting beneath continental lithosphere. Note that none of these samples have negative Yb or Sc anomalies on the geochemical patterns, so the low Yb cannot be explained by residual garnet.

## Sc–Yb

This diagram (Fig. 13) highlights the covariation between an MI element (Sc) and an HI element (Yb). Sc and Yb are again useful elements because neither appears greatly affected by source enrichment (see Fig. 3).

Figure 13a shows the modelled melting trends for melting within spinel lherzolite facies. For degrees of partial melting up to disappearance of orthopyroxene (40% total melting), liquid com-

positions follow trends of rapid depletion in Yb for very little change in Sc. These variations are similar to those seen in the Cr–Yb diagram (Fig. 12a), but the fractional crystallization trend in this projection is parallel, rather than orthogonal, to the melting trend. Mantle residue compositions follow a similar trend of strong depletion in Yb for a small depletion in Sc. For melting starting in garnet lherzolite facies (not shown here), both Sc and Yb are suppressed in the melt, but the compositions follow the same trend.

The boninite, island arc and MORB data plot around the modelled trend for partial melting with a pyroxene-bearing residue (Fig. 13b). For the more depleted sources, the compositions tend to fall off the modelled trends to lower Sc values for a given Yb concentration. This may be explained by the fact that bulk distribution coefficients decrease with melting as clinopyroxene is used up, an effect not modelled here. There is also a general displacement along the melting trend from MORB through island arc basalts to boninite compositions.

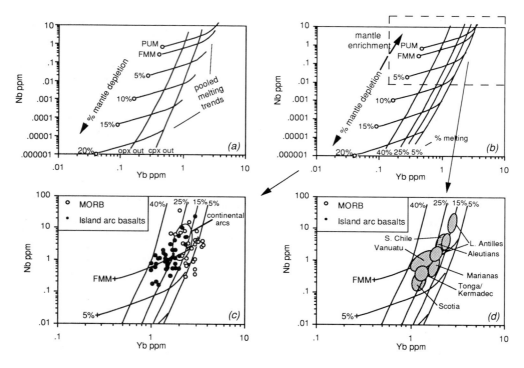

**Fig. 14.** Variations observed in a plot of a very highly incompatible element (Nb) against a highly incompatible element (Yb). **(a)** Theoretical melts and residues with contours for total melting (degree of melting + degree of mantle depletion); **(b)** theoretical melts and residues with contours for degree of melting; **(c)** compositions of oceanic samples and a field for continental arcs with contours for degree of melting; **(d)** the c. 90% probability contours for individual arcs with contours for degree of melting. Data are adjusted for MgO = 9 wt%. This projection is most effective at separating partial melting from source depletion trends, but is susceptible also to source enrichment processes. It shows that arcs with active backarc basins involve depleted sources (below FMM) whereas those without active backarc basins involve FMM or enriched sources. Arcs on the thinnest lithosphere plot on lines of greatest melting. For details, see text.

The peridotite data set is plotted in Fig. 13c. The data plot around the modelled values for 0–25% melting, indicating that the peridotite residues match the theoretical residues computed from the melting models.

Figure 13d examines further the relationship between mantle depletion and partial melting. As in the Cr–Yb projection, the difference between many island arc basalts and MORB can only be explained in terms of the same FMM source if at least some island arc tholeiites were derived from 40% or more of melting. However, a small amount of depletion of the source of some island arc basalts reduces the degree of melting needed to more realistic levels. Most boninites cannot be derived from any amount of melting of a FMM source, according to these models. The implication of this diagram is, therefore, that island arc basalts generally represent more melting and/or more depleted

sources than MORB. Continental arcs largely overlap the oceanic arc field, but with a slight displacement toward MORB indicating that they are derived from less depleted sources than oceanic arc basalts, less melting or both.

*Nb–Yb*

This diagram (Fig. 14) highlights the covariation between an HI element (Yb) and a VHI element (Nb). The use of a VHI element has the effect of producing a much greater separation between mantle depletion and partial melting trends than is possible using the previous diagrams. However, unlike the MI and C elements plotted in the previous diagrams, Nb is often added to the mantle source during mantle enrichment processes.

Figure 14a shows the melting trends for melting within spinel lherzolite facies. Unlike the previous diagram, the depletion of Nb in the mantle residue is so great for even small degrees of depletion that the depletion and partial melting trends are distinct. As Fig. 9 shows, source depletion for the most incompatible elements greatly exceeds the effect of variable partial melting. For more than 5% depletion, Nb falls below detection limit for all analytical methods. At these levels, the Nb concentration of the mantle is very sensitive to the composition and proportion of trapped melt and may not be as low as indicated here.

Figure 14b gives the same diagram with a grid that enables degree of melting and degree of source depletion to be determined, provided there is no contribution of Nb or Yb from the slab and provided the samples plotted have experienced little fractional crystallization. Residual garnet will cause the degree of melting to be overestimated.

Figure 14c gives the distribution of MORB and island arc data sets. Boninite sources may have experienced slab-related Nb enrichment (see Fig. 3) and are not considered here. The oceanic arc basalts form a trend sub-parallel to the trend of source depletion. There are no arc basalts that fall below the melting trend for 5% source depletion. We can, therefore, infer that the amount of melt removed from the mantle during the depletion process is below 5% (a maximum of about 3%) even in the most extremely depleted islands of the Tonga, Kermadec and South Sandwich arcs. The degree of melting is also high in most arcs. Some lavas plot above the FMM melting trend and can thus be inferred to involve melting of enriched sources. These also require moderate to high degrees of melting. Most of the enriched samples occupy anomalous settings, such as subduction–transform intersections (Grenada). If the diagram is correctly calibrated, oceanic arc basalts involve 15–35% melting. This result is consistent with those obtained from the MI–HI and C–HI plots where slab fluxes can be treated as negligible.

In contrast, MORB basalts are displaced to lower degrees of melting than arc basalts, although the range of enriched and depleted sources is similar. According to the model, the lowest degrees of melting are associated with the most depleted sources, and the highest with the enriched sources. This is a predictable result, given that most of the enriched samples come from plume-influenced ridge segments, at which more melting would be expected.

Figure 14d shows the same plot but annotated according to arc. It is noticeable that the arcs on thin lithosphere with associated active backarc basins (Scotia, Tonga, Kermadec, Mariana) require high degrees of melting of depleted sources to plot beneath the FMM melting trend and around the 25% melting contour. Those with thicker lithosphere (Lesser Antilles, Andes) require lower degrees of partial melting. Oceanic arcs without associated backarc basins, and continental arcs require FMM or enriched sources. In the case of the continental arcs, the subcontinental lithosphere may contribute to this enrichment.

## Ti–Yb

This projection is effective at indicating whether garnet is a residual phase during melting. For melting in spinel lherzolite facies, both elements behave as highly incompatible. For melting in garnet lherzolite facies, however, Ti continues to behave as an HI element while Yb behaves as a MI element. (see Fig. 4). While in garnet lherzolite facies, therefore, Yb is suppressed relative to Ti.

Figure 15a shows melting trends in spinel lherzolite facies. Because Ti and Yb have similar bulk distribution coefficients, the Ti/Yb ratio in the melts does not vary greatly and the result is a series of sub-parallel melting trends with slight inflections where clinopyroxene disappears.

Figure 15b shows the comparable diagram for melting that started in the garnet lherzolite facies. For undepleted mantle, we assume that the first 5% of melting takes place in garnet lherzolite facies. At this stage, Yb is suppressed in the melt relative to Ti. The remainder of the column lies in spinel lherzolite facies and the effect of continued melting is to dilute this melt until the suppression of Yb is no longer evident, giving a curved melt trajectory. Conversely, melt residues are enriched in Yb relative to Ti. Remelting of these thus gives melting curves that resemble those in Fig. 15a, but are displaced to higher Yb values relative to Ti.

Figure 15c gives the compositions of fertile and residual peridotites as a check on the model. The residues plot between the trends for mantle residues from a spinel lherzolite melting column and one initiated in garnet lherzolite facies. This may be a reasonable observation, as a number of the abyssal peridotites originate in hot-spot areas where melting may have initiated in garnet lherzolite facies.

Figure 15d gives the compositions of MORB, island arc basalts and boninites on this projection, together with a field for continental arcs. It is apparent, in particular, that the island arc basalts plot along the trend for spinel lherzolite melting. The inference is, therefore, that any depletion of the island arc mantle source takes

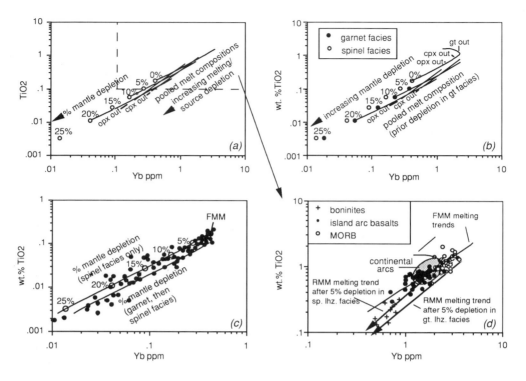

**Fig. 15.** Variations observed in a plot of a highly incompatible element (Ti) against a highly incompatible element that becomes moderately incompatible in garnet lherzolite facies (Yb). **(a)** Theoretical melts and residues for melting in spinel lherzolite facies; **(b)** theoretical melts and residues for melting in garnet lherzolite, followed by spinel lherzolite, facies; **(c)** compositions of fertile and residual peridotites; **(d)** the data points relative to the melting trends from (a)–(b). Data are adjusted for MgO = 9 wt%. The diagram separates depleted sources in which melt was lost in spinel lherzolite facies, from depleted sources in which melt was lost in garnet lherzolite facies. It shows that arc lavas from depleted sources lost their melt in spinel lherzolite facies. For details, see text.

place in spinel, not garnet, lherzolite facies. Continental arcs also plot along this trend. However, that is less significant because Fig. 14d indicated that they are derived from fertile sources. Melting may have started in garnet lherzolite facies, but any signature of residual garnet has been masked by the high degree of melting. The tectonic implications of these inferences are discussed in the next section.

Note that we have not reported the results of a parallel study on the effect of amphibole on this projection. Although amphibole does retain Ti with respect to Yb during melting, and thus has the opposite effect to garnet on these diagrams, the resultant trends do not differ from amphibole-free trends within experimental error. The only exception is for small amounts of melting with residual amphibole, which is better seen in the negative Ti anomaly in the geochemical pat-

terns of Fig. 11. As noted earlier, there is no evidence for residual amphibole in the great majority of island arc samples used in this paper.

## V–Yb

This projection superficially resembles Sc–Yb, in that it also utilizes a MI element (V) and a HI element (Yb). In this case, however, the compatibility of the MI element (V) is strongly influenced by oxygen fugacity, as explained in the section on partition coefficients: for low oxygen fugacities (as at mid-ocean ridges), V behaves as a MI element; for high oxygen fugacities (as in island arcs), V can behave as a HI element.

The partial melting variations for melting in the spinel lherzolite facies at QFM oxygen fugacity are shown in Fig. 16a. The trajectories

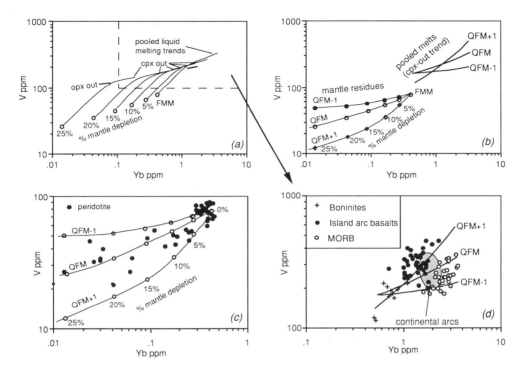

**Fig. 16.** Variations observed in a plot of a highly incompatible element at low oxygen fugacity that becomes moderately incompatible at moderate to high oxygen fugacity (V) against a highly incompatible element (Yb). **(a)** Theoretical melts and residues at QFM oxygen fugacity; **(b)** theoretical melts and residues for different oxygen fugacities; **(c)** residual peridotite compositions; and **(d)** the data distribution. Data are adjusted for MgO = 9 wt%. The diagram supports a higher oxygen fugacity in oceanic arcs compared with ocean ridges but suggests that continental arcs may be more variable. For details, see text.

resemble those of the Sc–Yb diagram in Fig. 13, but with V decreasing more rapidly than Sc during increased melting and increased source depletion.

The theoretical effect of oxygen fugacity is shown in Fig. 16b. With high oxygen fugacity in the order of QFM plus one log unit (QFM + 1), the lower bulk distribution coefficient produces steeper melting trends and mantle depletion trends. In contrast, lower oxygen fugacity at QFM minus one log unit (QFM − 1) gives higher distribution coefficients and shallower melting trends.

The peridotite data set is plotted in Fig. 16c. The data plot within the depletion trends of QFM + 1 and QFM − 1 but with a mean trend along QFM.

Figure 16d shows the MORB, island arc basalt and boninite compositions. The arc data set is marked by the distinctly higher V contents than MORB. This supports the concept of a

higher oxygen fugacity in arc genesis. Interestingly, many of the island arc basalts plot above even the estimated QFM + 1 trend. Although V analyses are not very accurate, this is significantly beyond experimental error. One possibility is that the oxygen fugacity in some arcs is even higher than QFM + 1. Another possibility is that the first depletion event took place at a ridge under low $fO_2$, thus depleting the residue in Yb with respect to V. Remelting then gives high V/Yb ratios. The field for continental arcs spans the arc and MORB fields, perhaps indicating a wide range of oxygen fugacities in this setting. Alternatively, temperature variations may be significant in causing variations in distribution coefficients.

## Conclusions

From the data presented here, we can infer the following:

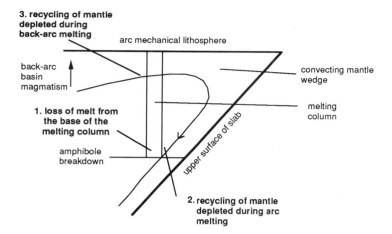

**Fig. 17.** Three possible causes of incompatible element depletion of the mantle wedge prior to, or during, supra-subduction zone melting.

(1) Arcs with active backarc basins (Scotia, Tonga, Kermadec, Mariana) have depleted mantle sources. Although the depletion rarely exceeds a few percent, the effect on the very highly incompatible elements is dramatic. There are at least three possible causes of mantle depletion: (a) loss of melt from the base of the melting column beneath the arc; (b) recycling of depleted mantle within the mantle wedge; (c) extraction of melt in the backarc basin prior to advection into the mantle wedge (Fig. 17).

Ti–Yb covariations suggest that this depletion takes place in spinel, rather than garnet, lherzolite facies. The first option is therefore unlikely. Recycling and mixing of depleted mantle within the wedge (option b) does not explain the Nb depletion, because mixing is linear whereas the Nb depletion is logarithmic: for example, well over 90% of mantle containing no Nb must be mixed with fertile MORB mantle to explain the low levels of Nb in the source of some of the Scotia arc volcanoes. The depletion can thus best be attributed to loss of melt in the back arc basin (Ewart & Hawkesworth 1987), which is consistent with the selective association between mantle wedge depletion and the presence of a backarc basin. An extreme case of this process is probably provided by boninites, which are widely believed to have formed by remelting of the mantle residues from mid-ocean ridge genesis.

(2) Oceanic arcs with no backarc basins typi-

cally have mantle sources close to fertile MORB mantle, although locally enriched sources are common in particular settings, notably at arc–transform intersections, above subducted transform faults, and in arcs undergoing rifting (De Long et al. 1975).

(3) Continental arcs have sources that vary from fertile MORB mantle to more enriched mantle. The latter reinforce the possibility that enriched sub-continental lithosphere may be involved in the genesis of some continental arcs (Pearce 1983).

(4) Although there is a clear theoretical basis for fractionating trace elements by chromatographic and other reactions during two-phase flow in the melting column (Navon & Stolper 1987; Keleman et al. 1990), it is difficult to envisage how these processes could explain the systematic intra-arc variations reported in this paper. We consider it likely, therefore, that the high degrees of melting largely smooth out such effects in volcanic arcs.

(5) Modelling suggests that the degree of melting in the arcs studied mostly falls within the range 15–30%. This is within error of the Plank & Langmuir (1988) estimate of 10–25% which was based on major element criteria. It is significantly greater than the Davies & Bickle (1991) estimate of 2–8%. However, the latter considered only the effect of fluid addition to static mantle. Our interpretation is that a maximum of 10% of the melting is caused by fluid addition, the

remaining 5–20% being caused by decompression.

(6) The decompression component of melting is clearly dependent on lithospheric thickness, the conclusion reached also by Plank & Langmuir (1988). The highest degrees of melting are found in young arcs built on oceanic lithosphere (Tonga, Kermadec, Scotia). Oceanic arcs with thicker lithosphere, such as the Lesser Antilles, and continental arcs such as the Andes have undergone considerably less melting.

(7) One surprising result is the lack of a clear residual garnet signature in the Andean lavas, where the thick lithospheric cap might be expected to restrict melting to the garnet lherzolite facies. One possibility is that the addition of subduction-derived fluid to the mantle is sufficient to melt out the garnet, even though there may be little decompression. Another surprising result is the absence of any clear amphibole signature in the arcs studied (the pattern in Fig. 10 is in a backarc, rather than arc, setting). A possible explanation is that fluids induce melting at temperatures above the temperature of amphibole stability so that amphibole never was part of the fertile mantle assemblage. Alternatively amphibole is completely melted out at the temperatures of arc genesis. Note also that the continental arc data set used in this paper is not comprehensive and that residual garnet and amphibole may characterise arcs not studied here.

JAP is particularly indebted to the late Ian Gass for his encouragement in applying trace element techniques to ophiolites and island arcs while they were colleagues at the Open University. Both authors are grateful to Peter Baker, Claude Dupuy, Bob Stern, David Peate, Richard Arculus, Grenville Holland, Tracy Vallier, Sorena Soresen and Chris Hawkesworth for their help, particularly in obtaining powders for ICP-MS analysis. We thank Robin Gill and Nick Rogers for their constructive reviews of the manuscript and Hazel Prichard for her editorial help.

# References

ARCULUS, R. J., GUST, D. A. & KUSHIRO, I. 1991. Fuji and Hakone. *National Geographic Research and Exploration*, **7**, 276–309.

BARTELS, K. S., KINZLER, R. J. & GROVE, T. L. 1991. High pressure phase relations of primitive high alumina basalts from Medicine Lake volcano, northern California. *Contributions to Mineralogy and Petrology*, **108**, 253–270.

BEATTIE, P. 1993. Uranium–thorium disequilibrium and partitioning on melting of garnet peridotite. *Nature*, **363**, 63–65.

——, FORD, C. & RUSSELL, D. 1991. Partition coefficients for olivine-melt and orthopyroxene-melt systems. *Contributions to Mineralogy and Petrology*, **109**, 212–224.

BLOOMER, S. H., STERN, R. J., FISK, E. & GESCHWIND, C. H. 1989. Shoshonitic volcanism in the Northern Mariana arc 1. Mineralogic and major and trace element characteristics. *Journal of Geophysical Research*, **94**, 4469–4496.

BONATTI, E., OTTONELLO, G. & HAMLYN, P. R. 1986. Peridotites from the island of Zabargad (St. John), Red Sea: petrology and geochemistry. *Journal of Geophysical Research*, **91**, 599–631.

BOUDINIER, J. L., DUPUY, C. & DOSTAL, J. 1988. Geochemistry and petrogenesis of Eastern Pyrenean peridotites. *Geochimica et Cosmochimica Acta*, **52**, 2893–2907.

BROWN, G. M., HOLLAND, J. G., SIGURDSSON, H., TOMBLIN, J. F. & ARCULUS, R. J. 1977. Geochemistry of the Lesser Antilles volcanic island arc. *Geochimica et Cosmochimica Acta*, **41**, 785–801.

CARMICHAEL, I. S. E. & GHIORSO, M. S. 1990. The effect of oxygen fugacity on the redox state of natural liquids and their crystallizing phases. *In*: NICHOLLS, J. & RUSSELL, J. K. (eds) *Reviews in Mineralogy*. Mineralogical Society of America, Washington D.C., **24**, 191–212.

CHAFFEY, D. J., CLIFF, R. A. & WILSON, B. M. 1989. Characterization of the St. Helena magma source. *In*: SAUNDERS, A. D. & NORRY, M. J. (eds) *Magmatism in the Ocean Basins*. Geological Society, London, Special Publication, **42**, 257–276.

COLSON, R. O. & GUST, D. 1989. Effects of pressure on partitioning of trace elements between low-Ca pyroxene and melt. *American Mineralogist*, **74**, 31–36.

——, McKAY, G. A. & TAYLOR, L. A. 1988. Temperature and composition dependencies of trace element partitioning: olivine/melt and low-Ca pyroxene/melt. *Geochimica et Cosmochimica Acta*, **52**, 539–553.

DAVIDSON, J. P. 1987. Crustal contamination versus subduction zone enrichment; examples from the Lesser Antilles and implications for the mantle source composition of island arc volcanic rocks. *Geochimica et Cosmochimica Acta*, **51**, 2185–2198.

DAVIES, J. H. & BICKLE, M. J. 1991. A physical model for the volume and composition of melt produced by hydrous fluxing above subduction zones. *Philosophical Transactions of the Royal Society of London*, **A335**, 355–364.

—— & STEVENSON, D. J. 1992. Physical model of source region of subduction zone volcanics. *Journal of Geophysical Research*, **97**, 2037–2070.

DEFANT, M. J., MAURY, R. C., JORON, J.-L., FEIGENSON, M. D., LETERRIER, J., BELLON, H., JACQUES, D. & RICHARD, M. 1990. The geochemistry and tectonic setting of the northern section of the Luzon arc (the Philippines and Taiwan). *Tectonophysics*, **183**, 187–205.

——, ——, RIPLEY, E. M., FEIGENSON, M. D. & JACQUES, D. 1991. An example of island-arc petrogenesis: geochemistry and petrology of the southern Luzon arc, Phillipines. *Journal of Petrology*, **32**, 455–500.

DE LONG, S. E., HODGES, F. N. & ARCULUS, R. J., 1975. Ultramafic and mafic inclusions, Kanaga Island, Alaska, and the occurrence of alkaline rocks in island arcs. *Journal of Geology*, **83**, 721–736.

DOSTAL, J., DUPUY, C., CARRON, J. P., LE GUEN DE KERNEIZON, M. & MAURY, R. C. 1983. Partition coefficients of trace elements: application to volcanic rocks of St. Vincent, West Indies. *Geochimica et Cosmochimica Acta*, **47**, 525–533.

DOWNES, H., EMBEY-ISZTIN, A. & THIRLWALL, M. F. 1992. Petrology and geochemistry of spinel peridotite xenoliths from the western Pannonian Basin (Hungary): evidence for an association between enrichment and texture in the upper mantle. *Contributions to Mineralogy and Petrology*, **109**, 340–354.

DUKE, J. M., 1976. Distribution of the period four transition elements among olivine, calcic clinopyroxene and mafic silicate liquid: experimental results. *Journal of Petrology*, **17**, 499–521.

DUNN, T. 1987. Partitioning of Hf, Lu, Ti and Mn between olivine, clinopyroxene and basaltic liquid. *Contributions to Mineralogy and Petrology*, **96**, 476–484.

—— & MCCALLUM, I. S. 1982. The partitioning of Zr and Nb between diopside and melts in the system diopside–albite–anorthite. *Geochimica et Cosmochimica Acta*, **46**, 623–629.

DUPUY, C., BARSCZUS, H. G., LIOTARD, J.-M. & DOSTAL, J. 1988. Trace element evidence for the origin of ocean island basalts: an example from the Austral Islands (French Polynesia). *Contributions to Mineralogy and Petrology*, **98**, 293–302.

——, DOSTAL, J., LIOTARD, J. M. & LEYRELOUP, A. 1980. Partitioning of transition elements between clinopyroxene and garnet. *Earth and Planetary Science Letters*, **48**, 303–310.

——, ——, MARCELOT, G., BOUGAULT, H., JORON, J. L. & TREUIL, M. 1982. Geochemistry of basalts from central and southern New Hebrides arc: implication for their source rock composition. *Earth and Planetary Science Letters*, **60**, 207–225.

EGGINS, S. M. 1992. Petrogenesis of Hawaiian tholeiites: 2, aspects of dynamic melt segregation. *Contributions to Mineralogy and Petrology* **110**, 398–410.

ELTHON, D. 1992. Chemical trends in abyssal peridotites: refertilization of depleted suboceanic mantle. *Journal of Geophysical Research*, **97**, 9015–9025.

EWART, A., BRYAN, W. B. & GILL, J. 1973. Mineralogy and geochemistry of the younger volcanic islands of Tonga, S.W. Pacific. *Journal of Petrology*, **14**, 429–465.

—— & HAWKESWORTH, C. J. 1987. The Pleistocene–Recent Tonga–Kermadec arc lavas: interpretation of new isotopic and rare earth data in terms of a depleted mantle source model. *Journal of Petrology*, **28**, 495–530.

FREY, F. A., SUEN, C. J. & STOCKMAN, H. W. 1985. The Ronda high temperature peridotite: geo-

chemistry and petrogenesis, *Geochimica et Cosmochimica Acta*, **49**, 2469–2491.

FUJIMAKI, H., TATSUMOTO, M. & AOKI, K. 1984. Partition coefficients of Hf, Zr, and REE between phenocrysts and groundmass. *Journal of Geophysical Research*, **89 suppl.**, B662–B672.

GAMBLE, J. A., SMITH, I. E. M., MCCULLOCH, M. T., GRAHAM, I. J. & KOKELAAR, B. P. 1993. The geochemistry and petrogenesis of basalts from the Taupo Volcanic Zone and Kermadec Island Arc, S.W. Pacific. *Journal of Volcanology and Geothermal Research*, **54**, 265–290.

GREEN, D. H. 1973. Contrasted melting relations in a pyrolite upper mantle under mid-ocean ridge, stable crust and island arc environments. *Tectonophysics*, **17**, 285–297.

—— 1976. Experimental testing of 'equilibrium' partial melting of peridotite under water-saturated, high pressure conditions. *Canadian Mineralogist*, **14**, 255–268.

GREEN, T. H., SIE, S. H., RYAN, C. G. & COUSENS, D. R. 1989. Proton microprobe-determined partitioning of Nb, Ta, Zr, Sr and Y between garnet, clinopyroxene and basaltic magma at high pressure and temperature. *Chemical Geology*, **74**, 201–216.

HERVIG, R. L., SMITH, J. V. & DAWSON, J. B. 1986. Lherzolite xenoliths in kimberlites and basalts: petrogenetic and crystallographic significance of some minor and trace elements in olivine, pyroxenes, garnet and spinel. *Transactions of the Royal Society of Edinburgh: Earth Sciences*, **77**, 181–201.

HICKEY, R. L., FREY, F. A., GERLACH, D. C. & LOPEZ-ESCOBAR, L. 1986. Multiple sources for basaltic arc rocks from the southern volcanic zone of the Andes (34°–41°S): trace element and isotopic evidence for contributions from subducted oceanic crust, mantle and continental crust. *Earth and Planetary Science Letters*, **91**, 5963–5983.

HICKEY-VARGAS, R. L., MORENO, H., LOPEZ-ESCOBAR, L. & FREY, F. A. 1989. Geochemical variations in Andean basaltic and silicic lavas from Villarica-Lanin volcanic chain (39.5°S); an evaluation of source heterogeneity, fractional crystallization and crustal assimilation. *Contributions to Mineralogy and Petrology*, **103**, 361–386.

IRVING, A. J., 1978. A review of experimental studies of crystal/liquid trace element partitioning. *Geochimica et Cosmochimica Acta*, **42**, 743–770.

—— & FREY, F. A. 1984. Trace element abundances in megacrysts and their host basalts: constraints on partition coefficients and megacryst genesis. *Geochimica et Cosmochimica Acta*, **48**, 1201–1221.

JAGOUTZ, E., PALME, H., BADDENHAUSEN, H., BLUM, K., CENDALES, M., DREIBUS, G., SPETTEL, B., LORENZ, V. & WANKE, H. 1979. The abundances of major, minor, and trace elements in the Earth's mantle as derived from primitive ultramafic nodules. *Proceedings of the 10th Lunar and Planetary Science Conference*, 2031–2050.

JOCHUM, K. P., MCDONOUGH, W. F., PALME, H. & SPETTEL, B. 1989. Compositional constraints on the continental lithospheric mantle from trace elements in spinel peridotite xenoliths. *Nature*,

340, 548–550.

JOHNSON, K. T. M. & DICK, H. J. B. 1992. Open system melting and temporal and spatial variation of peridotite and basalt at the Atlantis II fracture zone. *Earth and Planetary Science Letters*, 97, 9219–9241.

——, —— & SHIMIZU, N. 1990. Melting in the Oceanic upper mantle: an ion microprobe study of diopsides in abyssal peridotites. *Earth and Planetary Science Letters*, 95, 2661–2678.

—— & KINZLER, R. J. 1989. Partitioning of REE, Ti, Zr, Hf and Nb between clinopyroxene and basaltic liquid. *EOS Transactions of the American Geophysical Union*, 69, 1388.

JORON, J. L., BOLLINGER, C., QUISEFIT, J. P., BOUGAULT, H. & TREUIL, M. 1979. Trace elements in Cretaceous basalts at 25°N in the Atlantic Ocean: alteration, mantle compositions, and magmatic processes. *In*: DONNELLY, T. *et al.* (eds) *Initial Reports of the Deep Sea Drilling Project*, 51–53, 1087–1098.

KATO, T., RINGWOOD, A. E. & IRVINE, T. 1987. Experimental determination of element partitioning between silicate perovskites, garnets and liquids: constraints on early differentiation of the mantle. Geological Society, London, Special Publication, 89, 123–145.

KAY, S. M. & KAY R. W., in press. Aleutian magmas in space and time. *In*: PLAFKER, G. & BERGH, C. (eds) *The geology of Alaska*. Geological Society of America, Boulder, Co.

KELEMAN, P. B., DICK, H. J. B. & QUICK, J. E. 1992. Formation of harzburgite by pervasive melt/rock reaction in the upper mantle. *Nature*, 358, 635–641.

——, JOHNSON, K. J. M., KINZLER, R. J. & IRVING, A. J. 1990. High-field-strength element depletions in arc basalts due to mantle–magma interaction. *Nature*, 345, 521–524.

KINZLER, R. J. & GROVE, T. L. 1992. Primary magmas of mid-ocean ridge basalts 1. Experiments and methods. *Earth and Planetary Science Letters*, 97, 6885–6906.

KLEIN, E. M. & LANGMUIR, C. H. 1987. Global correlations of ocean ridge basalt chemistry with axial depth and crustal thickness. *Earth and Planetary Science Letters*, 92, 8089–8115.

LEEMAN, W. P. & SCHEIDEGGER, K. F. 1977. Olivine/liquid distribution coefficients and a test for crystal–liquid equilibrium. Geological Society, London, Special Publication, 35, 247–257.

LE ROEX, A. P., DICK, H. J. B., ERLANK, A. J., REID, A. M., FREY, F. A. & HART, S. R. 1983. Geochemistry, mineralogy and petrogenesis of lavas erupted along the Southwest Indian Ridge between the Bouvet triple junction and 11 degrees east. *Journal of Petrology*, 24, 267–318.

LINDSTROM, D. J. 1976. *Experimental study of the partitioning of the transition metals between clinopyroxene and coexisting silicate liquids*. PhD dissertation, University of Oregon.

—— & WEILL, D. F. 1978. Partitioning of transition metals between diopside and coexisting silicate liquids. I. Nickel, cobalt and manganese. *Geochi-*

*mica et Cosmochimica Acta*, 42, 817–831.

LIU, C.-Q., MASUDA, A. & XIE, G. H. 1992. Isotope and trace element geochemistry of alkali basalts and associated megacrysts from the Huangyishan volcano, Kuandian, Liaoning, NE China. *Chemical Geology*, 97, 219–231.

McCALLIUM, I. S. & CHARETTE, M. P. 1978. Zr and Nb partition coefficients: implications for the genesis of mare basalts, KREEP and sea floor basalts. *Geochimica et Cosmochimica Acta*, 42, 859–869.

McDONOUGH, W. F. & FREY, F. A. 1989. Rare earth elements in upper mantle rocks. *In*: LIPIN, B. R. & McKAY, G. A. (eds) *Geochemistry and mineralogy of rare earth elements*. Minerological Society of America, Washington D.C., 21, 99–145.

McKAY, D. B. & MITCHELL, R. H. 1988. Abundance and distribution of gallium in some spinel and garnet lherzolites. *Geochimica et Cosmochimica Acta*, 52, 2867–2870.

McKAY, G. A. 1986. Crystal/liquid partitioning of REE in basaltic systems: extreme fractionation of REE in olivine. *Geochimica et Cosmochimica Acta*, 50, 69–79.

McKENZIE, D. 1985. $^{230}$Th and $^{238}$U disequilibrium and the melting processes beneath ridge axes. *Earth and Planetary Science Letters*, 72, 149–157.

—— & BICKLE, M. J. 1988. The volume and composition of melt generated by extension of the lithosphere. *Journal of Petrology*, 29, 625–679.

—— & O'NIONS, R. K. 1991. Partial melt distributions from inversion of rare earth element inversions. *Journal of Petrology*, 32, 1021–1091.

NAVON, O. & STOLPER, E. 1987. Geochemical consequences of melt percolation: the upper mantle as a chromatographic column. *Journal of Geology*, 95, 285–307.

NIELSEN, R. L., GALLAHAN, W. E. & NEWBERGER, F. 1992. Experimentally-determined mineral-melt partition coefficients for Sc, Y and REE for olivine, orthopyroxene, pigeonite, magnetite and ilmenite. *Journal of Structural Geology*, 110, 488–499.

NIU, Y. & BATIZA, R. 1991. An empirical method for calculating melt compositions produced beneath mid-ocean ridges: application for axis and off-axis (seamounts) melting. *Journal of Geophysical Research*, 96, 21753–21777.

NYE, C. J. & REID, M. R. 1986. Geochemistry of primary and least fractionated lavas from Okmok volcano, Central Aleutians: implications for arc magmagenesis. *Journal of Geophysical Research*, 91, 10271–10287.

O'HARA, M. J. 1985. Importance of the 'shape' of the melting regime during partial melting of the mantle. *Nature*, 314, 58–62.

OHTANI, E., KAWABE, I., MORIYAMA, J. & NAGATA, Y. 1989. Partitioning of elements between majorite garnet and melt and implications for petrogenesis of komatiite. *Contributions to Mineralogy and Petrology*, 103, 263–269.

ONUMA, N., HIGUCHI, H., WAKIDA, H. & NAGASAWA, H. 1968. Trace element partition between two pyroxenes and the host lava. *Earth and Planetary Science Letters*, 5, 47–51.

OTTONELLO, G., JORON, J. L. & PICCARDO, G. B. 1984. Rare earth and 3d transition element geochemistry of peridotitic rocks: I Peridotites from the Western Alps. *Journal of Petrology*, **25**, 343–372.

PARKINSON, I. J., PEARCE, J. A., THIRLWALL, M. F., JOHNSON, K. T. M. & INGRAM, G. 1992. Trace element geochemistry of peridotites from the Izu–Bonin–Mariana forearc, Leg 125. *In:* FRYER, P. PEARCE, J. A. & STOKKING, L. B. *et al.* (eds) *Proceedings of the ODP Scientific Results*, **125**, 623–659.

PEARCE, J. A., 1982. Trace element characteristics of lavas from destructive plate boundaries. *In:* THORPE, R. S. (ed.) *Orogenic andesites and related rocks.* John Wiley and Sons, Chichester, 525–548.

—— 1983. Role of the sub-continental lithosphere in magma genesis at active continental margins. *In:* HAWKESWORTH, C. J. & NORRY (eds) *Continental basalts and mantle xenoliths.* Shiva Publishing, Nantwich, UK, 230–249.

—— & NORRY, M. J. 1979. Petrogenetic implications of Ti, Zr, Y and Nb variations in volcanic rocks. *Contributions to Mineralogy and Petrology*, **69**, 33–47.

—— ROGERS, N., TINDLE, A. J. & WATSON, J. S. 1986. Geochemistry and petrogenesis of basalts from Deep Sea Drilling Project Leg 92, Eastern Pacific. *In:* LEINEN, M., REA, D. K. *et al.* (eds) *Initial Reports of the Deep Sea Drilling Project*, **92**, 435–457.

——, VAN DER LAAN, S. R., ARCULUS, R. J. MURTON, B. J., ISHII, T., PEATE, D. W. & PARKINSON, I. J., 1992. Boninite and harzburgite from Leg 125 (Bonin–Mariana forearc): a case study of magma genesis during the initial stages of subduction. *In:* FRYER, P., PEARCE, J. A. & STOKKING, L. B. *et al.* *Proceedings of the ODP Scientific Results*, **125**, 623–659.

PLANK, T. & LANGMUIR, C. H. 1988. An evaluation of the global variations in the major element chemistry of arc basalts. *Earth and Planetary Science Letters*, **90**, 349–370.

PRICE, R. C., KENNEDY, A. K., RIGGS-SNEERINGER, M. & FREY, F. A. 1986. Geochemistry of basalts from the Indian Ocean triple junction: implications for the generation and evolution of Indian Ocean ridge basalts. *Earth and Planetary Science Letters*, **78**, 379–396.

PRINZHOFER, A. & ALLÈGRE, C. J. 1985. Residual peridotites and the mechanisms of partial melting. *Earth and Planetary Science Letters*, **74**, 251–265.

RAY, G. L., SHIMIZU, N. & HART, S. R. 1983. An ion microprobe study of the partitioning of trace elements between clinopyroxene and liquid in the system diopside–albite–anorthite. *Geochimica et Cosmochimica Acta*, **47**, 2131–2140.

RODEN, M. F., FREY, F. A. & CLAGUE, D. A. 1984. Geochemistry of tholeiitic and alkalic lavas from the Koolau Range, Oahu, Hawaii: implications for Hawaiian volcanism. *Earth and Planetary Science Letters*, **69**, 141–158.

ROEDER, P. L. & EMSLIE, R. F. 1970. Olivine–liquid equilibrium. *Contributions to Mineralogy and*

*Petrology*, **29**, 275–289.

—— & REYNOLDS, I. 1991. Crystallization of chromite and chromium solubility in basaltic melts. *Journal of Petrology*, **32**, 909–934.

SHAW, D. M. 1970. Trace element fractionation during anatexis. *Geochimica et Cosmochimica Acta*, **34**, 237–243.

SHERVAIS, J. W. 1982. Ti-V plots and the petrogenesis of modern and ophiolitic lavas. *Earth and Planetary Science Letters*, **59**, 101–118.

SHIMIZU, N. & ARCULUS, R. J. 1975. Rare earth element concentrations in a suite of basanitoids and alkali olivine basalts from Grenada, Lesser Antilles. *Contributions to Mineralogy and Petrology*, **50**, 231–240.

SPIEGELMAN, M. & McKENZIE, D. 1987. Simple 2D models for melt extraction at mid-ocean ridges and island arcs. *Earth and Planetary Science Letters*, **83**, 137–152.

STERN, C. R., FREY, F. A., FUTA, K., ZARTMAN, R. E., PENG, Z. & KYSER, T. K. 1990. Trace element and Sr, Nd, Pb, and O isotopic composition of Pliocene and Quaternary alkali basalts of the Patagonian Plateau lavas of southernmost South America. *Contributions to Mineralogy and Petrology*, **104**, 294–308.

STERN, R. J., MORRIS, J., BLOOMER, S. H. & HAWKINS, J. W. 1991. The source of the subduction component in convergent margin magmas: trace element and radiogenic isotope evidence from the Eocene boninites, Mariana forearc. *Geochimica et Cosmochimica Acta*, **55**, 1467–1481.

STOSCH, H.-G. 1981. Sc, Cr, Co and Ni partitioning between minerals from spinel peridotite xenoliths. *Contributions to Mineralogy and Petrology*, **78**, 166–174.

——, SECK, H. A. 1980. Geochemistry and mineralogy of two spinel peridotite suites from Dreiser Weiher, West Germany. *Geochimica et Cosmochimica Acta*, **44**, 457–470.

SUN, S.-S. & McDONOUGH, W. F. 1989. Chemical and isotopic systematics of oceanic basalts: implications for mantle composition and processes. *In:* SAUNDERS, A. D. & NORRY, M. J. (eds) *Magmatism in the Ocean Basins.* Geological Society, London, Special Publication, **42**, 313–345.

TAKAHASHI, E. 1978. Partitioning of $Ni^{2+}$, $Co^{2+}$, $Fe^{2+}$, $Mn^{2+}$ and $Mg^{2+}$ between olivine and silicate melts: compositional dependence of partition coefficient. *Geochimica et Cosmochimica Acta*, **42**, 1829–1844.

TARNEY, J., SAUNDERS, A. D., WEAVER, S. D., DONNELLAN, N. C. B. & HENDRY, G. L. 1978. Minorelement geochemistry of basalts from Leg 49, North Atlantic Ocean. *In:* LUYENKYK, B. P., CANN, J. R. *et al.* (eds) *Initial Reports of the Deep Sea Drilling Project*, **49**, 657–691.

TATSUMI, Y., SAKUYAMA, M., FUKUYAMA, H. & KUSHIRO, I. 1983. Generation of arc basalt magmas and thermal structure of the mantle wedge in subduction zones. *Journal of Geophysical Research*, **88**, 5815–5825.

TORMEY, D. R., GROVE, T. L. & BRYAN, W. B., 1987. Experimental petrology of normal MORB near the Kane Fracture Zone: 22°–25°N, mid-Atlantic ridge. *Contributions to Mineralogy and Petrology*, **96**, 121–139.

TUAL, E., JAHN, B. M., BOUGAULT, H. & JORON, J. L. 1985. Geochemistry of basalts from Hole 504B, Leg 83, Costa Rica Rift. *In*: ANDERSON, R. N., HONNOREZ, J., BECKER, K. *et al.* (eds) *Initial Reports of the Deep See Drilling Project*, **83**.

VALLIER, T. L., STEVENSON, A. J. & SCHOLL, D. W. 1985. Petrology of igneous rocks from Ata island, Kingdom of Tonga. *In*: SCHOLL, D. W. & VALLIER T. L. (eds) *Geology and Offshore Resources of Pacific Island Arcs – Tonga Region*. Circum-Pacific Council for Energy and Mineral Resources, Houston, 301–316.

VARNE, R. & FODEN, J. D. 1986. Geochemical and isotopic systematics of Eastern Sunda volcanics: implications for mantle sources and mantle mixing processes. *In*: WEZEL F. C. (ed.) *The origin of arcs*. Elsevier, Amsterdam, 159–189.

WATSON, E. B., BEN OTHMAN, D., LUCK, J.-M. & HOFFMANN, A. W. 1987. Partitioning of U, Pb, Cs, Yb, Hf, Re and Os between chromian diopsidic pyroxene and haplobasaltic liquid. *Chemical Geology*, **62**, 191–208.

WATSON, S. & MCKENZIE, D. 1991. Melt generation by plumes: a study of Hawaiian volcanism. *Journal of Petrology* **32**, 501–537.

WHITE, R. S. & MCKENZIE, D. P. 1989. Magmatism at rift zones: the generation of volcanic continental margins and flood basalts. *Journal of Geophysical Research*, **94**, 7685–7729.

WHITFORD, D. J. 1975. *Geochemistry and petrology of volcanic rocks from the Sunda arc, Indonesia*. PhD thesis, Australian National University.

WILLIAMS, R. W. & GILL, J. B. 1989. Effects of partial melting on the uranium decay series. *Geochimica et Cosmochimica Acta*, **53**, 1607–1619.

WOOD, D. A., JORON, J.-L., TREUIL, M., NORRY, M. & TARNEY, J. 1979. Elemental and Sr-isotope variations in basic lavas from Iceland and the surrounding ocean floor. *Contributions to Mineralogy and Petrology*, **70**, 319–339.

—— VARET, J., BOUGAULT, H., CORRE, O., JORON, J. L., TREUIL, M., BIZOURD, H., NORRY, M. J., HAWKESWORTH, C. J. & RODDICK, J. C. 1978. The petrology, geochemistry, and mineralogy of North Atlantic basalts: a discussion based on IPOD Leg 49. *In*: LUYENKYK, B. P., CANN, J. R. *et al.* (eds) *Initial Reports of the Deep Sea Drilling Project*, **49**, 597–655.

YAXLEY, G. M., CRAWFORD, A. J. & GREEN, D. H. 1991. Evidence for carbonatite metasomatism in spinel peridotite xenoliths from western Victoria, Australia. *Earth and Planetary Science Letters*, **107**, 305–317.

ZINDLER, A. & HART, S. 1986. Chemical geodynamics. *Annual Review of Earth and Planetary Science*, **14**, 493–571.

# Amphibolite dehydration-melting: sorting out the solidus

PETER J. WYLLIE[1] & MICHAEL B. WOLF[2]

[1] *Division of Geological and Planetary Sciences, California Institute of Technology, Pasadena, CA 91125, USA*
[2] *School of Geology and Geophysics, University of Oklahoma, Norman, OK 73019, USA*

**Abstract**: Amphibolite melts under vapour-absent conditions by dehydration-melting, during which $H_2O$ released from hornblende is transferred directly into $H_2O$-undersaturated silicate liquid. Five independent 1991 studies on amphibolite dehydration-melting differ from each other and from earlier conceptual treatments. Five solidi between 7 and 10 kb vary from 975°C to 740°C. Two solidi above 10 kb are near-vertical, near 975°C and 850°C. Some differences are due to different amphibolite compositions and mineralogy. We use the results of earlier experiments involving garnet, supported by our own new results, to construct a closed-system phase diagram for a simple, fully-hydrated amphibolite (hornblende + plagioclase) showing the solidus and the melting interval for (hornblende + garnet + other minerals + liquid). The amphibolite vapour-absent solidus is defined by the beginnings of two multivariant reactions: (1) a near-vertical curve (large positive $dP/dT$) where the formation of augite dominates; and (2) a near-horizontal curve at higher pressures where the formation of garnet dominates. The solidus curve bends back (estimated near 900°C, 9 kb) with slope changing to low positive $dP/dT$. The new phase diagram expands the field for liquid generation with garnet-amphibolite residues to much lower temperatures and pressures than the other recent experimental results, increasing the range from which small amounts of hydrous granitoid melts may be segregated by compaction. The reversed, near-horizontal slope of the solidus near 10 kb has interesting petrological consequences.

Partial melting of amphibolite is important for magma genesis in several tectonic environments. An understanding of the phase relationships of amphibolites is required for modelling the origin of Archean continental crust, anatexis of lower continental crust, of thickened oceanic plateaus, and of relatively hot, subducted oceanic crust. Amphibolite may melt in the presence of aqueous pore fluid, or under vapour-absent conditions by dehydration-melting, during which $H_2O$ released by the breakdown of amphibolite is transferred directly into a $H_2O$-undersaturated silicate liquid.

There have been several experimental studies with bearing on the melting of amphibolite in basalt–$H_2O$ and basalt–vapour systems (e.g. Yoder & Tilley 1962; Holloway & Burnham 1972; Lambert & Wyllie 1970, 1972; Helz 1973, 1976; Allen & Boettcher 1978, 1983; Spulber & Rutherford 1983; Foden & Green 1992). Until recently, only Brown & Fyfe (1970), Huang & Wyllie (1973, 1981), and Millhollen & Wyllie (1974) had reported solidus curves for the vapour-absent melting of rocks containing hydrous minerals. Holloway (1973) used $H_2O$–$CO_2$ mixtures to determine the effect of reduced water activity on the melting of synthetic pargasite. Lambert & Wyllie (1970, 1972) used the results of $H_2O$-saturated experiments to deduce the con-

ditions for dehydration-melting of amphibolite, and Burnham (1979) presented a detailed experimentally-based theoretical analysis of melting in vapour-absent biotite and hornblende gneisses. Helz (1982) presented a monumental review of amphibole phase relations in rock-melting experiments, with no dehydration-melting solidus curves recorded for amphibolite.

Ellis & Thompson (1986) studied $H_2O$-saturated and $H_2O$-undersaturated melting with amphibole in the synthetic CMASH system ($CaO$–$MgO$–$Al_2O_3$–$SiO_2$–$H_2O$). Experimental dehydration-melting of rocks containing biotite or biotite + hornblende has been reported by Le Breton & Thompson (1988), Vielzeuf & Holloway (1988), Rutter & Wyllie (1988), Patiño-Douce & Johnston (1991), and Skjerlie & Johnston (1992). Detailed experimental results for the dehydration-melting of amphibolites were not published until 1991, when five independent studies were presented: Beard & Lofgren; Rapp *et al.*; Rushmer; Winther & Newton; and Wolf & Wyllie. Hacker (1990) also determined some phase changes in connection with a deformation study of partly melted amphibolite. Foden & Green (1992) studied basalt glass with 2% $H_2O$, equivalent to amphibolite with about 1% $H_2O$; all runs were above the solidus, but applications to dehydration-melting were drawn.

*From* Prichard, H. M., Alabaster, T., Harris, N. B. W. & Neary, C. R. (eds), 1993,
*Magmatic Processes and Plate Tectonics*, Geological Society Special Publication No. 76, 405–416.

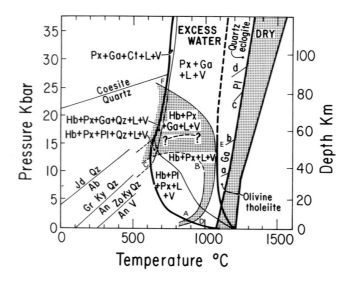

**Fig. 1.** Partial phase relationships for dry basalt, and basalt–H₂O (Lambert & Wyllie 1972). a–b–c–d represents the complex phase transition from gabbro to quartz eclogite; a–d according to Ito & Kennedy (1971); b–c according to Green & Ringwood (1967). Note that garnet may be formed at pressures below 10 kb, and that the last plagioclase may persist to high pressures approaching 28 kb. The phase boundaries for basalt–H₂O are based on results of Lambert & Wyllie (1972) to 800°C, connected to results of Yoder & Tilley (1962) at pressures below 10 kb. Heavy lines mark solidus and liquidus boundaries. The shaded area ABCDEF represents the reaction band for amphibole. Subsolidus reactions for anorthite and albite are given (see Lambert & Wyllie 1972, for detailed sources). Lambert & Wyllie (1972) identified the line ABC as the vapour-absent solidus for amphibolite. Abbreviations – Hb: amphibole; Pl: plagioclase; Px: pyroxene; Qz: quartz; Ct: coesite; Ga: garnet; An: anorthite; Ab: albite; Zo: zoisite; Ky: kyanite; Gr: grossularite; Jd: jadeite; L: silicate liquid; V: vapour.

The results published in these recent investigations are not in close agreement with each other, and some of them depart from earlier conceptual treatments. In this contribution, we review the earlier work, and then present the outline of a closed-system phase diagram for a simple, fully-hydrated amphibolite (hornblende + plagioclase) which we believe to be conceptually correct, and consistent with our own experiments (Wolf & Wyllie 1989, 1991, 1993*a,b*). This provides a firm, experimentally-based framework for comparison of the recent round of experimental results on varied rock compositions, and for petrological applications. In particular, attention is drawn to a wide range of pressures at moderate temperatures where amphibole and garnet coexist with siliceous liquid, which has implications for trace element partitioning during magmatic processes.

**Earlier studies on amphibolite phase relations**

Two experimental studies provide the frame-

work for comparison of the 1991 studies on dehydration-melting of amphibolites. Yoder & Tilley (1962) demonstrated that in H₂O-excess experiments to 10 kb, with a variety of basalts, amphibole coexists with liquid over a wide temperature interval above the solidus, breaking down near the liquidus with formation of clinopyroxene. Lambert & Wyllie (1972) followed the melting relationships in basalt–H₂O from 10 to 35 kb (with a temperature limit of 850°C), thus traversing the basalt–eclogite transition. This extension brings in the pressure-sensitive hornblende reactions involving the formation of garnet and jadeitic pyroxene. They combined their results with those of other related studies at higher temperatures to produce the phase diagram in Fig. 1, which also shows the melting interval and basalt–eclogite transition for dry basalt. Note that the shaded band for the reaction of amphibole consists of two parts, the low-pressure relatively narrow, near-vertical band (ABDE) where augite is the main mineral product from dehydration of the amphibole, and the broad, sub-horizontal band (BCEF) where garnet and jadei-

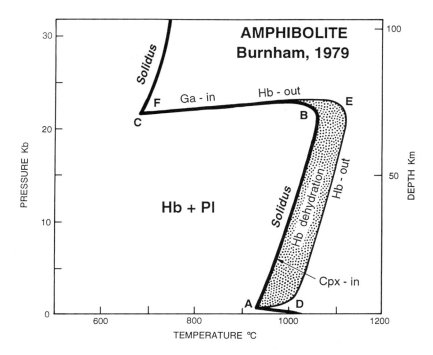

**Fig. 2.** Selected phase boundaries for the dehydration-melting of amphibolite, from Burnham (1979). The distinctive feature is that garnet is first generated just as the amphibole dissociates completely. Augite is produced in the shaded band ABDE. For abbreviations see Fig. 1.

tic pyroxene are the breakdown products. The position and width of the shaded band will vary as a function of rock composition and $H_2O$ content, as illustrated schematically by Wyllie (1971a, figs 8–18) and confirmed by Ellis & Thompson (1986) in a synthetic system. However, the topology remains as shown in Fig. 1.

Lambert & Wyllie (1970) and Wyllie (1971b, Fig. 5) used the Fig. 1 results to estimate a phase diagram for vapour-absent amphibolite, with the solidus corresponding closely to the amphibole-out curve (DEF). With subsequent publication of their experimental results, Lambert & Wyllie (1972) took into account the reaction interval of the amphibole, the shaded band in Fig. 1, concluding that the solidus would coincide with the boundary ABC. They wrote:

'. . . in earlier estimates . . . we took the hornblende-out curve . . . as our guide to the position of the vapour-absent solidus . . . We anticipate now that . . . partial melting would begin at depths corresponding closely to the beginning of amphibole reaction indicated tentatively by the dashed line.'
Lambert & Wyllie (1974 p. 704)

Burnham (1979, fig. 3.3) used experimentally based data to calculate the position of the 'fluid-absent' solidus for amphibolite of olivine–tholeiite composition. The relevant reaction intervals are reproduced in Fig. 2, and equivalent lines in Figs 1 and 2 are identified by the same letters, ABCDEF. Burnham's amphibole reaction interval is similar to the shaded band in Fig. 1 (ABDE) up to 10 kb, but he concluded that the formation of garnet would coincide with the completion of amphibole dehydration at considerably higher pressures than in Fig. 1, and ABDE therefore extends up to about 22 kb. Furthermore, because of the coincidence of the Ga-in and Hb-out curves, there is no area between BC and DE in Fig. 2 for the coexistence of garnet and amphibole with liquid, which is a distinctive feature of Fig. 1.

The position of the amphibole-out curve was reported by Yoder & Tilley (1962) for several basaltic compositions in the presence of excess water to 10 kb. The curve DE shifts to higher temperatures and then lower temperatures as water activity is reduced (Holloway 1973; Burnham 1979; Helz 1982). Helz (1982, fig. 56) and Merrill & Wyllie (1975) compared the published amphibole-out curves (DEF, Figs 1 and 2) for basaltic rocks with vapour present. Most of the results dominated by those of Allen & Boettcher (1978, 1983) on the effect of activity of water and oxygen fugacity on the position of the amphibole-out curve, conform approximately to DEB in Fig. 2, with an abrupt change in slope between 20 and 25 kb, and some indication of a pressure maximum near E along EF. Helz (1982, fig. 58) noted that the corresponding curves for more ultramafic compositions, excluding peridotites: '... do not exhibit the abrupt 'corners" usually seen in basalts: the change in slope is in all cases much more gradual ...', in the style of Fig. 1 (EF). The data are too few for definition of the curve EF, or of a pressure maximum. None of the experimental curves has been extended down to the solidus. The existence of the pressure-sensitive breakdown of amphibole near F (Fig. 1) was determined by Lambert & Wyllie (1968).

A related experimental study is that of Mill-hollen & Wyllie (1974, figs 2 and 4), in which phase boundaries corresponding to ABC and DEF in Fig. 1 were determined for the brown-hornblende mylonite from St Paul's Rocks (equivalent to hornblende–basanite). They reported in addition a trace of liquid below AB (clinopyroxene-in) due probably to traces of low-temperature hydrous minerals and some chlorine. The Ga-in curve was situated between 15 and 20 kb, but details of the results are unreliable because the runs were of relatively short duration to combat the problem of iron-loss to the capsules. Similar phase diagrams determined by Merrill & Wyllie (1975) for the Kakanui kaersutite–eclogite (equivalent to olivine–basanite) and for a kaersutite megacryst (equivalent to olivine–nephelinite) from New Zealand located the amphibole-out curves, but the reactions were too sluggish for the determination of dehydration-melting curves with the experimental capabilities then available.

Helz (1982) reported no solidus curves for the dehydration-melting of hydrated basaltic rocks, and we are aware of no definitive experimental results on the low P–T side of the shaded band, ABC (Figs 1–2) until the 1991 studies (Beard & Lofgren 1991; Rapp *et al.* 1991; Rushmer 1991; Winther & Newton 1991; Wolf & Wyllie 1991).

## Amphibole reaction and amphibolite solidus

The phase relationships may be considered in terms of a reaction occurring through a temperature interval where hornblende progressively breaks down, making available $H_2O$ (with no intervening vapour phase) for $H_2O$-undersaturated melting to occur. The 'dehydration-solidus'

is defined by the initial breakdown of hornblende. Consider a simple, fully hydrated amphibolite composed of hornblende plus plagioclase, without quartz, biotite or other hydrous minerals. There are two parts to the multivariant dehydration reaction:

(1) the low-pressure reaction (ABDE) where the distinctive product is clinopyroxene (augite):

$$\text{Hornblende} + \text{Plagioclase}$$
$$= \text{Liquid} + \text{Clinopyroxene} \, (+ \text{other minerals})$$
$$[1A]$$

(2) the high-pressure, pressure-sensitive reaction interval (BCEF) related to the gabbro-eclogite transition where garnet is the dominant product, followed by jadeitic pyroxene:

$$\text{Hornblende} + \text{Plagioclase}$$
$$= \text{Liquid} + \text{Garnet} \, (+ \text{other minerals}) \quad [1B]$$

The solidus curve for dehydration-melting is accordingly composed of two parts, a near-vertical curve (AB, large, probably positive dP/dT), and a near-horizontal curve (BC) at higher pressures where garnet is formed; the latter curve bends back with slope changing to low positive dP/dT. At pressures higher than C and lower than A, where the hornblende dissociates at temperatures lower than the $H_2O$-saturated solidus, the solidus in a closed system coincides with the $H_2O$-excess curve. This occurs because partial dissociation of hornblende associated with the formation of garnet releases $H_2O$, which forms a free vapour at temperatures below CF and the low-pressure solidus below AD.

Figures 1 and 2 show two very different locations for the solidus BC associated with reaction [1B]. Experimental studies summarized by Green (1982) on basalt–$H_2O$ indicate that garnet is produced below 10 kb up to about 1000°C, at even lower pressures than BC in Fig. 1. This is confirmed by the recent results of Winther & Newton (1991), Rapp *et al.* (1991) and Wolf & Wyllie (1989, 1993a). Both the garnet-producing reaction and the position of BC are sensitive to the bulk composition of the amphibolite. The low-pressure solidus AB will be situated at lower temperatures for amphibolites with quartz (e.g. Rushmer 1991), or with other hydrous minerals such as biotite and chlorite (e.g. Rutter & Wyllie 1988; Beard & Lofgren 1991; Patiño-Douce & Johnston 1991; Skjerlie & Johnston 1992). The dissociation of hydrous minerals will cause vapour-absent $H_2O$-undersaturated melting if it occurs within the area above the $H_2O$-saturated solidus curve, and will yield vapour if it occurs at lower temperatures.

Figures 3 and 4 show two possibilities for

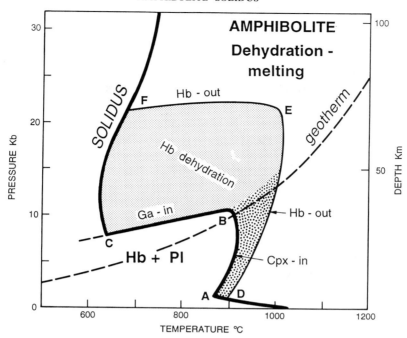

**Fig. 3.** Dehydration-melting of amphibolite, with the Hb-out curve in essentially the same position as in Fig. 2 (Burnham 1979), but with the garnet-in curve at much lower pressure (compare a–b in Fig. 1; see Green 1982, and other sources in the text). Augite is produced in the shaded band ABD (point halfway toward E), and garnet and jadeitic clinopyroxene are formed within the shaded band BCEF. The dehydration of hornblende produces no vapour, because H₂O is transferred directly into the liquid. The geotherm is from Fig. 5 (SE Australia, active tectonic environment). For abbreviations see Fig. 1.

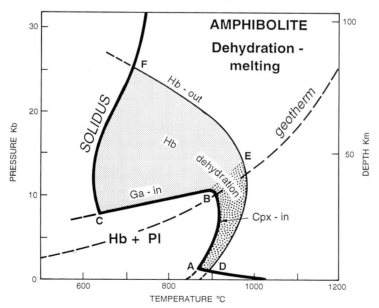

**Fig. 4.** Dehydration-melting of amphibolite, with the Hb-out curve in essentially the same position as in Fig. 1. All other features correspond to those in Fig. 3. The dehydration of hornblende produces no vapour, because H₂O is transferred directly into the liquid. The geotherm is from Fig. 5 (SE Australia, active tectonic environment). For abbreviations see Fig. 1. We consider this more likely than Fig. 4.

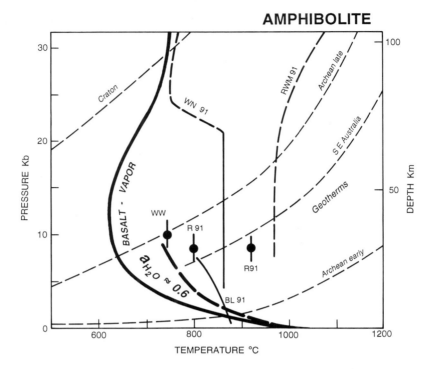

**Fig. 5.** Experimentally determined values of the solidus for dehydration-melting of amphibolites. BL91: Beard & Lofgren (1991); RWM91: Rapp *et al.* (1991); R91: Rushmer (1991); WN91: Winther & Newton (1991); WW: Wolf & Wyllie 1991, 1993*a,b*). The dashed line sections for WN91 and RWM91 were inferrred, not directly measured. The heavy lines are solidus curves for amphibolite with excess vapour (see text for sources). Dashed lines are various geotherms (see text for sources).

dehydration-melting of a fully hydrated amphibolite composed of only (hornblende + plagioclase). Both versions have the same solidus, ABC, corresponding to the formation of clinopyroxene (AB) and garnet (BC), and the vapour-present curves at pressures below A and above C. They differ in the position of the Hb-out curve. In Fig. 3, the curve backbends abruptly at E into a position subparallel to the Ga-in curve, following Fig. 2 in principle, with some experimental support for the abrupt 'corner' at E as outlined above. In Fig. 4, Hb-out follows the curve in Fig. 1, consistent with curves determined for somewhat more ultramafic compositions (Helz 1982). The reason for the backbend in slope from positive to negative at E in Fig. 4 is associated with the progressive formation of dense garnet (and jadeitic pyroxene). In Fig. 3, the backbend at E occurs at much higher pressures than the garnet-in reaction (contrast Fig. 2), and there is no obvious mineralogical reason for the abrupt backbend and slope reversal at this high pressure (A. B. Thompson, pers. comm.,

1992). Experimental resolution between these two versions is needed.

## Recent experimental results on dehydration-melting of amphibolites

The experimentally determined vapour-absent solidus results for the dehydration-melting of amphibolite published in 1991 by five groups of investigators are compared in Fig. 5 with the solidus curves for excess $H_2O$ and for excess vapour, but with the water activity reduced by $CO_2$ to $a_{H_2O} = 0.6$ (Yoder & Tilley 1962; Lambert & Wyllie 1972; Holloway & Burnham 1972). The five groups studied different amphibolites under different conditions, with emphasis on somewhat different petrological applications. There is a wide range of values reported, with differences caused, at least in part, by variation in the bulk compositions and mineralogies of the amphibolites used by different investigators. Only Rushmer (1991) among these publications mentions the possibility of a 'backbend' in the vapour-absent solidus associated with garnet formation (BC in Figs 1–4), citing the experiments of Millhollen & Wyllie (1974), Merrill & Wyllie (1975) and the calculations of Percival (1983).

Beard & Lofgren (1991) studied the $H_2O$-saturated melting and dehydration-melting relationships of five natural low-potassium greenstones and amphibolites (four of them containing quartz) at 1, 3 and 6.9 kb, 800–1000°C. In the dehydration-melting experiments, the breakdown of amphibole (with quartz) defines the solidus plotted in Fig. 5.

Rapp et al. (1991) used four natural olivine-normative amphibolites, and hydrous glasses formed from them, to study the compositions of melts produced under vapour-absent conditions from 900–1100°C, at 8 kb, and from 1000–1150°C at 16,22, and 32 kb. The position of the 'vapour-absent' solidus was inferred, and it is located at temperatures higher than in the other experiments outlined here.

Rushmer (1991) investigated the dehydration-melting of two coarsely ground amphibolites, and three mechanically mixed amphibolitic compositions at 8 kb. Four of the five materials contained 8–17% modal quartz. The solidi are located at 925°C for an alkali basalt and 800°C for a tholeiite. The low solidus temperature of the tholeiite is due mainly to the breakdown of biotite and cummingtonite in the sample, and the presence of quartz.

Winther & Newton (1991) studied the melting relationships of two low-potassium basalts, a high-alumina basalt and the average Archean tholeiite (AAT) composition with different amounts of added $H_2O$ (1–15 wt%), at 5–30 kb, and 750–1000°C. Quartz was present in all of the AAT runs with 2.68% or 0% added $H_2O$. For the AAT dehydration-melting experiments, the solidus was bracketed between 800 and 900°C from 5–20 kb.

Wolf & Wyllie (1991) melted a solid cylinder of lineated amphibolite at 10 kb, to explore the effect of texture and time on the melting relationships. At 850°C, liquid formed in layers between hornblende and plagioclase crystal faces. In a parallel set of experiments using a powdered sample of the same rock, Wolf & Wyllie (1989, 1993a, b) determined that the solidus was below 750°C at 10 kb. No garnet grew in the solid sample, whereas it grew abundantly in the powdered sample.

The experimental results for the low-pressure part of the amphibolite solidus (AB in Figs 1–4) are conveniently compared in Fig. 5 at 10 kb. Lambert & Wyllie (1972) and Burnham (1979) in Figs 1 and 2 both estimated a solidus temperature near 1000°C for garnet-free amphibolite of olivine–tholeiite composition (near B in Figs 3 and 4). All five experimental solidi at or near 10 kb in Fig. 5 are at lower temperatures, from about 975°C (Rapp et al. 1991) to 740°C (Wolf & Wyllie 1989, 1993b). Beard & Lofgren's (1991) solidus, extrapolated to 10 kb, gives a temperature near 800°C (Fig. 5). Rushmer's (1991) two garnet-free solidus determinations show the effect of quartz in lowering the solidus temperature, although $H_2O$ from biotite is also involved here.

The solidus curves WN91 and RWM91 involve assemblages with garnet, and they should, therefore, provide information about the position of BC (Figs 3 and 4). Winther & Newton (1991) gave 800–900°C brackets for the vapour-absent solidus curve for quartz–garnet–amphibolite between 6 and 20 kb. For their estimate of the solidus at pressures above 20 kb, they used the amphibole-out curve EF, following Lambert & Wyllie's (1970) earlier estimate of the solidus rather than their later estimate of ABC (Lambert & Wyllie 1972), as in Figs 1, 3 and 4. We suggest that the hornblende dehydration implied by the formation of garnet in their 800°C runs should generate small amounts of liquid below their reported solidus curve.

Rapp et al. (1991) reported no subsolidus runs, no garnet in runs at 8 kb, but garnet in runs at 16 kb and above. They showed garnet-in at about 11 kb. Their solidus curve was presented as an 'inferred vapour-absent solidus', but the basis for the inference was not given. The inferred solidus at 10 kb approximates the values estimated for dehydration-melting of garnet-free amphibolite by Lambert & Wyllie (1972) and Burnham (1979) (near B in Figs 3 and 4), but the slope and position of the high-pressure part of the solidus has not been related to either BC or EF in Figs 1 and 2. We suggest that vapour-absent runs in the garnet field below their inferred solidus should yield small amounts of liquid.

The results of Rapp et al. (1991) and Winther & Newton (1991) do not define the Hb-out curve well enough to permit selection between Figs 3 and 4.

Consider a partly melted specimen just above the solidus BC in Fig. 4. Upon heating at constant pressure, the specimen would cross the solidus BC and enter the field for Hb + Pl; i.e. the amount of liquid would decrease and disappear, as the sample dissolved garnet and precipitated amphibolite. An informative comparison in addition to the solidus boundaries would, therefore, be among the shapes of the melting profiles of percentage liquid as a function of

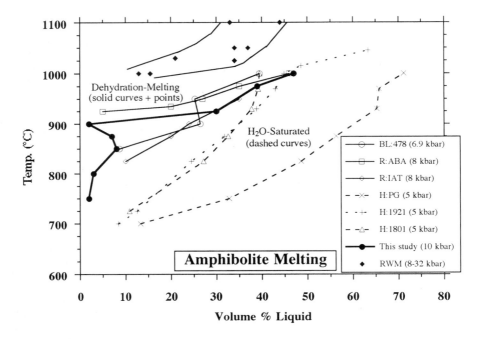

**Fig. 6.** Volume percents of liquids produced in various amphibolite melting experiments as a function of temperature (compare with solidus values in Fig. 5). Sources – BL: Beard & Lofgren (1991), 6.9 kb; R: Rushmer (1991), 8 kb; H: Helz (1976), 5 kb, $H_2O$-saturated; this study: Wolf & Wyllie (1993a), 8/9- and 4-day runs, 10 kb; RWM: Rapp *et al.* (1991), 8–32 kb. Data from the literature have been converted from wt% to vol. % liquid (except Rushmer 1991). This conversion increases the percent of liquid by *c.* 10% at the high end of the range. Dehydration-melting (solid curves) produces less liquid at a given temperature than $H_2O$-saturated melting (dashed curves). The dehydration-melting results are broadly similar, with a 'ledge' corresponding to the main breakdown (dehydration) reaction of the hornblende, but the results of Rapp *et al.* (1991) indicate higher temperatures required to produce a given amount of liquid. Note the steep low-temperature part of the melting profile from 'This work', which is explained in the text in terms of the hornblende–garnet relationships above the solidus line CB in Fig. 4.

temperature and pressure. Several sets of experimental data are available for melting profiles at constant pressure.

Figure 6 compares isobaric melting profiles of amphibolites, mostly within the range 5–10 kb. The dashed lines for $H_2O$-saturated melting differ from the dehydration-melting profiles. Excluding these saturated results, Fig. 6 shows a general pattern of rapid increase in melt fraction within the temperature interval 850/900–1000°C, the interval within which most of the hornblende reaction occurs. The results of Rapp *et al.* (1991) are displaced to somewhat higher temperatures (RWM), perhaps because they were from several different rocks involving higher pressures (8–32 kb). The heavy curve for Wolf & Wyllie (1989, 1993a) is similar to three others, except that it shows in addition a few percent liquid down to at least 750°C (compare Fig. 5), which explains its lower temperature in Fig. 5 (WW);

note also that with increase in temperature the percentage of liquid increases, but there is a sharp decrease between 875 and 925°C.

We interpret our 10 kb melting profile in Fig. 6 (this study; Wolf & Wyllie 1993a) as follows. Garnet nucleation and growth is sluggish at low temperatures. The recorded solidus WW in Fig. 5 is a kinetic boundary, and with even longer runs at lower temperatures garnet would form, yielding $H_2O$-undersaturated liquid all the way down to the solidus CF (Fig. 4), given equilibrium. The percentage of liquid present between 750°C and 975°C is the result of competition between the effect of increasing temperature in increasing reaction rates for the production of garnet and liquid at the expense of hornblende and plagioclase, and the effect of approaching the solidus BC in decreasing the amount of liquid. The latter effect becomes dominant between 850°C and 900°C, and the amount of liquid drops from 9–2%. Through the next 50°C, extensive breakdown of hornblende is associated with the generation of another 30% liquid (Fig. 6). The situation at 900°C corresponds to an isobaric section through the shaded interval in Fig. 4 passing just above point B. Therefore, we conclude from the Fig. 6 melting profile that for the amphibolite of Wolf & Wyllie (1993a), the abrupt backbend at B (Fig. 4) is situated near 900°C and 9 kb.

The new phase diagrams (Figs 3 and 4) show that progressive dissociation of hornblende to yield garnet (and pyroxene) produces small quantities of liquid through a substantial temperature and pressure interval. An informative comparison in addition to the solidus boundaries would be among the shapes of the melting profiles of percentage liquid as a function of temperature and pressure. Such data might permit selection between Figs 3 and 4, but for reasons given above, we conclude that the Hb-out curve is more likely to be as depicted in Fig. 4.

## Petrological applications

The experimentally determined phase equilibria and phase compositions are applicable to the vapour-absent anatexis of amphibolite. The potential of amphibolite for yielding tonalite and trondhjemite magmas and leaving a granulite restite has often been discussed (e.g. Barker 1979; Rapp et al., 1991; Winther & Newton 1991).

A word of caution is required in transferring the closed-system phase diagrams of Figs 3 and 4 to real processes in open systems. The solidus curve CF, for example, exists for a closed-system amphibolite with total $H_2O$ content defined by the fully hydrated assemblage (Hb + Pl) at pressures below BC. An equilibrium amphibolite at temperatures below CF would already be partially dehydrated compared with the low-pressure (Hb + Pl), because some garnet would have been generated at pressures above the Ga-in curve (BC extended). A garnet-amphibolite (without pore fluid) in the deep crust at 10 kb could thus be transported deeper with no further hornblende dissociation as it crossed the solidus CF, and therefore with no melting. Only if the PT trajectory is such that additional breakdown of hornblende occurs continuously will partial melting begin at CF; otherwise melting will be delayed until the next stage of hornblende reaction occurs within the shaded area CFBE, yielding $H_2O$ for vapour-absent melting.

## Materials and geotherms

The conditions for anatexis of amphibolites depend upon the tectonic setting and history. These affect both the type of amphibolite involved, and the changes of the geotherm position with time. Selected geotherms from various tectonic environments and stages of evolution are given in Fig. 5, with the SE Australia geotherm (O'Reilly & Griffin 1985) reproduced in Figs 3 and 4 to facilitate comparison of the phase diagrams. The range of Archean geotherms according to Martin (1986, 1987) sweeps across the experimentally measured solidus boundaries indicating early partial melting near 875°C at only 2 kb, to late partial melting which varies according to the solidus values of different experiments. In fact, for our preferred solidus (Fig. 4) the lowest-temperature Archean geotherm of Fig. 5 shows the possibility that dehydration-melting could begin in amphibolite at a temperature as low as 630°C at about 8 kb.

The cratonic geotherm from Boyd & Gurney (1986) is similar to the P–T trajectories estimated for the top of modern subducted oceanic crust according to Martin (1987). Considerable variation is possible depending on the age of the subducted oceanic lithosphere, the rate of subduction, and other factors (Peacock 1990). The P–T trajectories for the surface of a hot, young lithosphere slab might enter the vapour-absent melting field for garnet amphibolite (through F into the area BCEF in Figs 3 and 4) and experience dehydration-melting. Details of possible events depend on the extent of previous partial dehydration of the garnet-amphibolite, whether or not the depth-temperature trajectory is in the direction through the phase diagram causing additional hornblende breakdown and, of course, the availability of $H_2O$ from other sources.

The geotherm for SE Australia (O'Reilly & Griffin 1985), which is similar to that for the Rio Grande rift (Bussod & Williams 1991) illustrates relatively high temperatures in the deep crust in tectonically active environments. Sinking amphibolite would certainly experience dehydration-melting at temperatures depending not only on the geotherm, depth-T trajectory, and the amphibolite composition and mineralogy, but specifically on the depth of the garnet-in curve for the amphibolite.

## Magma generation

Rapp et al. (1991) and Winther & Newton (1991) provided detailed reviews on the generation of

Archean trondhjemites and tonalites (TTG rocks) based on their experimental results. These results confirm that liquids with compositions corresponding to TTG magmas (at least with respect to their feldspar components) can be produced during amphibolite dehydration-melting at temperatures ranging from 850–1100°C, through a wide range of pressures. Amphibolite dehydration-melting on a voluminous, crustal-addition scale appears to be largely confined to the Archean, based on the intersection of calculated Archean geotherms with amphibolite solidi (Fig. 5). Wyllie & Wolf (1993) have compared the residual mineral assemblages expected in amphibolite after removal of $H_2O$-undersaturated granitoid melts with the liquidus minerals on the $H_2O$-undersaturated liquidus surfaces of a series of natural tonalites, trondhjemites and granites. Matching the mineral assemblages in these two aproaches should help to place limits on the conditions of depth, temperature and $H_2O$ contents for the generation of these granitoid magmas.

Although the low-temperature solidus in the new phase diagram extends the tectonic range for amphibolite anatexis, temperatures in cratonic environments are still not high enough to induce vapour-absent anatexis (cratonic geotherm in Fig. 5). Localized amphibolite dehydration-melting can occur near intrusions within any geological environment (e.g. Beard 1990). Amphibolite dehydration-melting could also occur within hot, young oceanic crust subducted into a warm mantle wedge, but the release of water by dehydration of lower grade metabasalts and serpentine from deeper levels in the subducted lithosphere (Wyllie 1984) would also provide a hydrous flux to enhance melting at the vapour-saturated solidus CF (Figs 3–5).

Wolf & Wyllie (1991) described textures and calculated melt viscosities in experimentally melted solid amphibolite, and concluded that, within a limited temperature interval above the solidus, hydrous granitic melt may be segregated by compaction and percolation. With increasing temperature and percentage of liquid and concomitant decrease in dissolved $H_2O$, the melt viscosity becomes too high for segregation by this process. Sawyer (1991) presented geochemical data from migmatites in amphibolites, confirming that the granitoid melts are extracted from within their host rocks even during the early stages of partial melting, and that segregation may occur under disequilibrium conditions if non-hydrostatic stress conditions cause melt separation faster than equilibrium concentrations of Zr and REE are reached in the melt.

The position and slope of the solidus BC provides some unusual conditions, with the prospect for the occurrence of some unfamiliar processes. For example, in a situation with a geotherm crossing the solidus BC, heating of the crust from below by influx of basaltic magma into a layer of migmatite in the lower crust would cause the local geotherm to migrate up-temperature, causing the point of intersection with the solidus BC to move to higher pressures, which should have the effect of causing crystallization of the upper, shallower layer of the migmatite.

### Granulites

Granulites comprise a substantial portion of Archean (and younger) crust. Proposals that granulites can be produced by the separation of hydrous liquid from amphibolites and other partially fused crustal rocks (Fyfe 1973; White & Chappel 1977; Powell 1983; Wolf & Wyllie 1991) are consistent with the experimental results.

For a tectonic environment with the geotherm crossing the garnet-in curve from the lower-pressure amphibolite field (CB in Figs 3 and 4), partial melting will occur if the amphibolite is transported to deeper levels as garnet forms and $H_2O$ is made available (without forming a pore fluid). The partial melting of deep crustal amphibolite can leave a granulitic assemblage containing abundant garnet and only minor plagioclase (Wolf & Wyllie 1993a).

### Rare-earth element behaviour

Archean grey gneisses are characterized by highly fractionated rare-earth elements (REE) (Jahn et al. 1984; Martin 1987), and this appears to require that amphibole, or garnet or both were residual minerals during magma genesis (Barker 1979). Rapp et al. (1991) calculated the REE patterns in their experimental liquids using a simple batch-melting model, their determined phase proportions, the measured REE patterns of their starting rocks, and the partition coefficients used by Martin (1987). They obtained results, from partial melts at high pressures with an eclogitic residue, which were similar to the REE patterns typical of Archean granitoids (tonalites, trondhjemites, and granodiorites). For conditions with a residue of garnet-amphibolite, the REE pattern of liquids was less fractionated. The calculations were for liquids above the dashed line RWM91 in Fig. 5, at 1000°C and higher.

The new phase diagrams in Figs 3 and 4 have two features of significance for REE and other trace element concentrations in partial melts from amphibolite. First, the field for liquid generation with garnet-amphibolite residues has been expanded to much lower temperatures and pressures compared with the other recent experimental results (Fig. 5). Wolf & Wyllie (1991) suggested that small percentages of hydrous granitoid melt in this region could be segregated by compaction. Secondly, given the finding of Rapp et al. (1991) that REE patterns in liquids differ considerably depending on whether the residual mineral assemblage is eclogite or garnet-amphibolite, the position of the amphibolite-out curve in Figs 3 and 4 becomes significant for defining conditions of depth and temperature of magma generation.

This research was supported by the Earth Science section of the US National Science Foundation, grant EAR 89-04375.

## References

ALLEN, J. C. & BOETTCHER, A. L. 1978. Amphiboles in andesite and basalt: II. Stability as a function of P–T–$f(_{H_2O})f_{O_2}$. American Mineralogist, **63**, 1074–1087.

—— & —— 1983. The stability of amphibole in andesite and basalt at high pressures. American Mineralogist, **68**, 307–314.

BARKER, F. 1979. Trondhjemite: definition, environment and hypotheses of origin. In: BARKER, F. (ed.) Trondhjemites, Dacites and Related Rocks. Elsevier, Amsterdam, 1–12.

BEARD, J. S. 1990. Partial melting of metabasites in the contact aureoles of gabbroic plutons in the Smartville complex, Sierra Nevada, California. In: ANDERSON, J. L. (ed.) The Nature and Origin of Cordilleran Magmatism. Geological Society of America Memoir **174**, 303–313.

—— & LOFGREN, G. E. 1991. Dehydration melting and water-saturated melting of basaltic and andesitic greenstones and amphibolites at 1, 3 and 6.9 kb. Journal of Petrology, **32**, 365–401.

BOYD, F. R. & GURNEY, J. J. 1986. Diamonds and the African lithosphere. Science, **232**, 472–477.

BROWN, G. C. & FYFE, W. S. 1970. The production of granitic melts during ultrametamorphism. Contributions to Mineralogy and Petrology, **28**, 310–318.

BURNHAM, C. W. 1979. Magmas and Hydrothermal Fluids. In: BARNES, H. L. (ed.) Geochemistry of Hydrothermal Ore Deposits (2nd edn). Wiley Interscience, New York, 71–136.

BUSSOD, G. Y. A. & WILLIAMS, D. R. 1991. Thermal and kinematic model of the southern Rio Grande rift: inferences from crustal and mantle xenoliths from Kilbourne Hole, New Mexico. Tectonophysics, **197**, 373–389.

ELLIS, D. J. & THOMPSON, A. B. 1986. Subsolidus and partial melting reactions in the quartz-excess $CaO + MgO + Al_2O_3 + SiO_2 + H_2O$ system under water-excess and water-deficient conditions to

10 kb: some implications for the origin of peraluminous melts from mafic rocks. Journal of Petrology, **27**, 91–121.

FODEN, J. D. & GREEN, D. H. 1992. Possible role of amphibole in the origin of andesite: some experimental and natural evidence. Contributions of Mineralogy and Petrology, **109**, 479–493.

FYFE, W. S. 1973. The granulite facies, partial melting and the Archaean crust. Philosophical Transactions of the Royal Society of London, **A273**, 457–462.

GREEN, D. H. & RINGWOOD, A. E. 1967. An experimental investigation of the gabbro to eclogite transformation and its petrological applications: Geochimica et Cosmochimica Acta, **31**, 767–833.

GREEN, T. H. 1982. Anatexis of mafic crust and high pressure crystallization of andesite. In: THORPE, R. S. (ed.) Andesites: Orogenic Andesites and Related Rocks. Wiley, Chichester, 465–487.

HACKER, B. R. 1990. Amphibolite-facies-to-granulite-facies reactions in experimentally deformed, unpowdered amphibolite. American Mineralogist, **75**, 1349–1361.

HELZ, R. T. 1973. Phase relations of basalts in their melting range at $P_{H_2O} = 5$ kb as a function of oxygen fugacity: Part I. mafic phases. Journal of Petrology, **14**, 249–302.

—— 1976. Phase relations of basalts in their melting range at $P_{H_2O} = 5$ kb: Part II. melt compositions. Journal of Petrology, **17**, 139–193.

—— 1982. Phase relations and compositions of amphiboles produced in studies of the melting behavior of rocks. In: VERBLEN, D. R. RIBBE, P. H. (eds) Amphiboles: Petrology and Experimental Phase Relations. Mineralogical Society of America, Reviews in Mineralogy, **9B**, 279–347.

HOLLOWAY, J. R. 1973. Compositions of fluid phase solutes in a basalt–$H_2O$–$CO_2$ system. Geological Society of America Bulletin, **82**, 233–238.

—— & BURNHAM, C. W. 1972. Melting relations of basalt with equilibrium water pressure less than total pressure. Journal of Petrology, **13**, 1–29.

HUANG, W. L. & WYLLIE, P. J. 1973. Melting relations of muscovite-granite to 35 kbar as a model for fusion of metamorphosed subducted oceanic sediments. Contributions to Mineralogy and Petrology, **42**, 1–14.

—— & —— 1981. Phase relationships of S-type granite with $H_2O$ to 35 kb: muscovite granite from Harney Peak, South Dakota. Journal of Geophysical Research, **86**, 1015–1029.

ITO, K. & KENNEDY, G. C. 1971. An experimental study of the basalt–eclogite garnet–granulite transition. In: HEACOCK, J. G. (ed.) The Structure and Physical Properties of the Earth's Crust. American Geophysical Union Monograph, **14**, 303–314.

JAHN, B. M., VIDAL, P. & KRONER, A. 1984. Multichronometric ages and origin of Archaean tonalitic gneisses in Finnish Lapland: a case for long crustal residence time. Contributions to Mineralogy and Petrology, **86**, 398–408.

LAMBERT, I. B. & WYLLIE, P. J. 1968. Stability of hornblende and a model for the low velocity zone. Nature, **219**, 1240–1241.

—— & —— 1970. Low-velocity zone of the Earth's mantle; incipient melting caused by water. *Science*, **169**, 764–766.

—— & —— 1972. Melting of gabbro (quartz eclogite) with excess water to 35 kilobars, with geological applications. *Journal of Geology*, **80**, 693–708.

LE BRETON, N. & THOMPSON, A. B. 1988. Fluid-absent (dehydration) melting of biotite in metapelites in the early stages of crustal anatexis. *Contributions to Mineralogy and Petrology*, **99**, 226–237.

MARTIN, H. 1986. Effect of steeper Archean geothermal gradient on geochemistry of subduction-zone magmas. *Geology*, **14**, 753–756.

—— 1987. Petrogenesis of Archaean trondhjemites, tonalites, and granodiorites from eastern Finland: major and trace element geochemistry. *Journal of Petrology*, **28**, 921–953.

MERRILL, R. B. & WYLLIE, P. J. 1975. Kaersutite and kaersutite eclogite from Kakanui, New Zealand – Water-excess and water-deficient melting at 30 kilobars. *Geological Society of America Bulletin*, **86**, 555–570.

MILLHOLLEN, G. L. & WYLLIE, P. J. 1974. Melting relations of brown-hornblende mylonite from St. Paul's rocks under water-saturated and water-undersaturated conditions to 30 kilobars. *Journal of Geology*, **82**, 589–606.

O'REILLY, S. Y. & GRIFFIN, W. L. 1985. A xenolith-derived geotherm for southeastern Australia and its geophysical implications. *Tectonophysics*, **111**, 41–63.

PATIÑO-DOUCE, A. E. & JOHNSTON, A. D. 1991. Phase equilibria and melt productivity in the pelitic system: implications for the origin of peraluminous granitoids and aluminous granulites. *Contributions to Mineralogy and Petrology*, **107**, 202–218.

PEACOCK, S. M. 1990. Fluid processes in subduction zones. *Science*, **248**, 329–337.

PERCIVAL, J. A. 1983. High-grade metamorphism in the Chapleau-Foleyet, Ontario. *American Mineralogist*, **68**, 667–686.

POWELL, R., 1983. Processes in granulite-facies metamorphism. *In*: ATHERTON, M. P. & GRIBBLE, C. D. (eds) *Migmatites, Melting and Metamorphism*. Shiva, Cheshire, 127–139.

RAPP, R. P., WATSON, E. B. & MILLER, C. F. 1991. Partial melting of amphibolite/eclogite and the origin of Archean of trondhjemites and tonalites. *Precambrian Research*, **51**, 1–25.

RUSHMER, T. 1991. Partial melting of two amphibolites: contrasting experimental results under fluid-absent conditions. *Contributions to Mineralogy and Petrology*, **107**, 41–59.

RUTTER, M. J. & WYLLIE, P. J. 1988. Melting of vapour-absent tonalite at 10 kbar to simulate dehydration-melting in the deep crust. *Nature*, **331**, 159–160.

SAWYER, E. W. 1991. Disequilibrium melting and the rate of melt-residuum separation during migmatization of mafic rocks from the Grenville Front, Quebec. *Journal of Petrology*, **32**, 701–738.

SKJERLIE, K. P. & JOHNSTON, A. D. 1992. Vapor-absent melting at 10 kbar of a biotite- and amphibole-bearing tonalitic gneiss: implications for the generation of A-type granites. *Geology*, **20**, 263–266.

SPULBER, S. D. & RUTHERFORD, M. J. 1983. The origin of rhyolite and plagiogranite in oceanic crust: an experimental study. *Jounal of Petrology*, **24**, 1–25.

VIELZEUF, D. & HOLLOWAY, J. R. 1988. Experimental determination of the fluid-absent melting relations in the pelitic system. *Contributions to Mineralogy and Petrology*, **98**, 257–276.

WHITE, A. J. R. & CHAPPELL, B. W. 1977. Ultrametamorphism and granitoid genesis. *Tectonophysics*, **43**, 7–22.

WINTHER, K. T. & NEWTON, R. C. 1991. Experimental melting of hydrous low-K tholeiite: evidence on the origin of Archean cratons. *Bulletin of the Geological Society of Denmark*, **39**, 213–228.

WOLF, M. B. & WYLLIE, P. J. 1989. The formation of tonalitic liquids during the vapor-absent partial melting of amphibolite at 10 kb. *Transactions of the American Geophysical Union (EOS)*, **70**, 506.

—— & —— 1991. Dehydration-melting of solid amphibolite at 10 kbar: textural development, liquid interconnectivity and applications to the segregation of magmas. *Mineralogy and Petrology*, **44**, 151–179.

—— & —— 1993a. Dehydration-melting of amphibolite at 10 kb: effects of temperature, time and texture. *Contributions to Mineralogy and Petrology*, in revision.

—— & —— 1993b. Garnet growth during amphibolite anatexis: implications of a garnetiferous restite. *Journal of Geology*, **101**, 357–373.

WYLLIE, P. J. 1971a. *The Dynamic Earth*. Wiley, New York.

—— 1971b. The role of water in magma general and initiation of diapiric uprise in the mantle. *Journal of Geophysical Research*, **76**, 1328–1338.

—— 1984. Sources of granitoid magmas at convergent plate boundaries. *Physics of Earth and Planetary Interiors*, **35**, 12–18.

—— & WOLF, M. B. 1993. Conditions for formation of tonalites and trondhjemites: magmatic sources and products. *In*: DE WIT, M. J. & ASHWAL, L. D. (eds) *Tectonic Evolution of Greenstone Belts*. Oxford University Press, in press.

YODER, H. S. & TILLEY, C. E. 1962. Origin of basalt magmas: an experimental study of natural and synthetic rock systems. *Journal of Petrology*, **3**, 342–532.

# Evaluating Late Quaternary uplift in Greece and Cyprus

CLAUDIO VITA-FINZI

*Research School of Geological and Geophysical Sciences, University College,*
*Gower Street, London WC1E 6BT*

**Abstract**: Uplift data based on radiometric and archaeological dating are being used to trace the tectonic history of the eastern Mediterranean. In the Gulf of Corinth new new U-series and [14]C ages suggest that there is an upper limit to coseismic uplift on both main and antithetic normal faults and that distributed extension develops serially. U-series and [14]C dates from southwestern Cyprus support geomorphological and archaeological evidence for Late Quaternary southward tilting of the island.

Variations in the rate of crustal shortening and extension, which provide valuable clues to the nature of the driving forces and resistances, are often concealed by the long-term averages yielded by palaeomagnetic methods and evidently lie outside the scope of geodetic techniques. To obtain useful measurements away from strike-slip faults, where offsets may span the last few $10^3$ years, it is necessary to press vertical displacements into service. If uplift appears to be wholly the product of shortening, as on some coasts undergoing serial folding at a plate margin, an average convergence rate can be calculated mathematically for successive uplift episodes (Mann & Vita-Finzi 1988). In other tectonic environments, such as forearc accretionary prisms, imbricate faulting complicates the connection between vertical and horizontal displacement, but uplift data still allow some test of the proposed deformation mechanism (Vita-Finzi & Situmorang 1989).

The present paper considers two further tectonic settings where vertical displacements may usefully complement other sources of plate history: backarc extension, and subduction without benefit of a well-defined Benioff zone. The eastern Mediterranean (Fig. 1) supplies pertinent case studies, the Gulf of Corinth and southwestern Cyprus, the intention being to discover whether the data might reveal shared, as well as contrasting, tectonic features. The topic seems appropriate in a volume dedicated to Ian Gass, who was long interested in the tectonic implications of elevated land surfaces and drainage patterns in the Troodos Massif (see for instance Gass & Masson-Smith 1963).

## Extension

The rapid extension that characterizes the Aegean Sea and the land around it, though driven by the Hellenic subduction zone, is

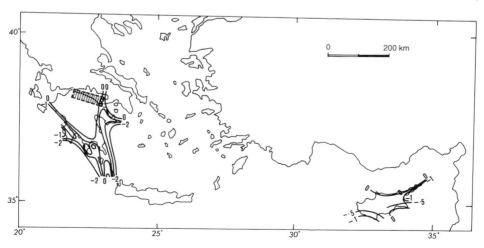

**Fig. 1.** The eastern Mediterranean. Contours of rate of vertical displacement in metres per millennium relative to present sea-level (after Flemming 1978). Box denotes area included in Fig. 2.

*From* Prichard, H. M., Alabaster, T., Harris, N. B. W. & Neary, C. R. (eds), 1993,
*Magmatic Processes and Plate Tectonics*, Geological Society Special Publication No. 76, 417–424.

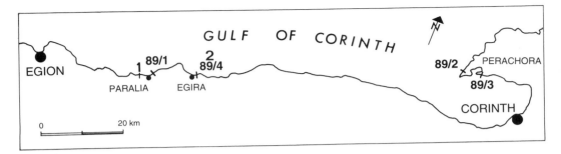

**Fig. 2.** Location of sample sites on Gulf of Corinth. Holocene sites are also shown.

strongly affected by the westward motion of Turkey and the resistance to deformation offered by the Apulia–Adriatic platform to the west (Taymaz *et al.* 1991). Much of the motion is taken up on large but segmented normal faults (Roberts & Jackson 1991). A group of these faults border the Gulf of Corinth, an asymmetric graben whose continuing development is attested by an obviously fault-controlled topography and a high level of seismic activity. The southern shore is steeper and deeper than the northern and it displays extensive lacustrine and shallow-water marine Quaternary deposits (Ori 1989). Moreover, there is structural evidence for progressive southward tilting of the sea floor (Brooks & Ferentinos 1984; Doutsos & Piper 1990).

In addition to abandoned wave undercuts and notches, especially on the peninsula of Perachora immediately to the north of Corinth (Fig. 2), there are numerous Quaternary faults. For instance, southeast of Egion a series of normal faults have dislocated Pleistocene cemented gravels. Though remarkably fresh, most of the faults do not cut surface colluvium. Two kilometres west of modern Corinth, the marls that compose the local bedrock are ruptured by a normal fault (280°/80° N) with a downdip throw of 115 cm, but a prominent fossil beach at a height of about 23 m, though disrupted by settlement along the underlying fault plane, shows no measurable disruption. A sequence of five normal faults and grabens in marls and gravels is exposed along the road to Mamousia, 10 km east of Egion. The structures strike 255–310°, with a net vertical displacement of 11 m over 80 m of vertical exposure, and increase in throw progressively updip from 0.5 m to over 5 m. A plausible explanation is that new faulting downdip is accompanied by reactivation of existing features. On the northern shore there are large alluvial fans which reflect continuing extensional

conditions into the late Pleistocene. North of Andirrhion, for example, a fan some 60 m above sea-level and composed of fine, calcareous sands containing subrounded gravels in channels and discrete beds displays numerous normal faults striking 215–235° and with downdip throws of up to 5.5 m. Kontopoulos & Doutsos (1985) show that normal faulting in this area was in response to continuing subsidence of the Gulf.

Despite many decades of field investigation the chronology of faulting remains obscure. In 1982 only two radiometric ages were available for the Quaternary record of the entire Gulf, both of them U/Th determinations considered to represent minimum ages (Sébrier 1977). Twenty $^{14}$C determinations were then made on molluscs from terraces at the eastern end of the Gulf but many of them were at the outer limits of the method and thus open to doubt (Vita-Finzi & King 1985). Collier (1990; see also Collier *et al.* 1992) later published U-series ages of >350 000; 205 200 +12 000/−11 700 and 311 800 +33 400/−22 500 years on three *Acropora* samples bearing on the development of the Isthmus of Corinth which, together with two non-finite $^{14}$C ages by accelerator mass spectrometry (AMS) on material associated with samples previously dated radiometrically (Vita-Finzi 1992), show that the $^{14}$C ages in excess of 25 000 years are to be treated as minima.

A search was accordingly made for coral within the critical palaeoshorelines in the hope that it would be suitable for U-series assay. The four samples discussed here consisted of *Cladocora caespitosa* composed of 95–100% aragonite as determined by X-ray diffractometry. Uranium and thorium concentrations and isotopic activity ratios were determined by isotope dilution alpha spectrometry. Samples were cleaned mechanically by scraping and ultrasonic washing in distilled water. They were then heated to 900°C for about 8 hours to destroy organic matter and

**Table 1.** *U-series ages for the Gulf of Corinth*

| Sample no. | Elevation (m) | U (ppm) | Th (ppm) | $^{234}U/^{238}U$ | $^{230}Th/^{232}Th$ | $^{230}Th/^{234}U$ | Uncorrected age (ka) |
|---|---|---|---|---|---|---|---|
| 89/1 | 30 | $2.80 \pm 0.03$ | $0.03 \pm 0.01$ | $1.064 \pm 0.009$ | $308 \pm 59$ | $0.99 \pm 0.01$ | $386 + 56/-38$ |
| 89/2 | 22 | $3.01 \pm 0.04$ | $0.03 \pm 0.01$ | $1.14 \pm 0.01$ | $284 \pm 49$ | $0.706 \pm 0.009$ | $128 \pm 3$ |
| 89/3 | 26 | $3.19 \pm 0.04$ | $0.01 \pm 0.01$ | $1.17 \pm 0.01$ | $> 400$ | $0.727 \pm 0.009$ | $134 \pm 3$ |
| 89/4 | 3.0 | $2.60 \pm 0.03$ | $0.04 \pm 0.01$ | $1.18 \pm 0.01$ | $13 \pm 1$ | $0.057 \pm 0.002$ | $6.4 \pm 0.2$ |

convert $CaCO_3$ to CaO, dissolved in 6 *N* HCl and equilibrated with a combined $^{229}Th-^{236}U$ spike. U was separated from Th using an anion exchange column in chloride form, and further purified by coprecipitation and ion exchange methods (Table 1).

Sample 89/1 was collected at 30 m from a sequence of alternating gravels and coralline sands from a Gilbert-type fan exposed by the coast road 2.6 km east of Paralia Platanou, about 20 km east of Egion. Some of the pebbles are bored and associated with fragments of *Ostrea* and other marine molluscs. To judge from the account by Ori (1989) the deposit forms part of the latter part of the second phase in the history of the Gulf during which the basin was connected to the Ionian Sea through the Gulf of Patras and deposition took place in deltas as well as in a deep-sea environment.

Sample 89/2 was from the surface of a prominent 22 m marine terrace 1 km east of the lighthouse on the northern shore of Perachora (Site 103 of Vita-Finzi & King 1985). Sample 89/3 was on a 26 m marine deposit 100 m east of the canal into the Vouliegmeni lagoon on the south side of Perachora where an AMS age of > 42 000 years had been obtained on *Lithophaga lithophaga* in their burrows at a height of 23.5 m (Site 502 of Vita-Finzi & King 1985). The agreement between the two U-series ages for Perachora at 1 $\sigma$ (Table 1) reinforces the evidence for unitary emergence of the western part of the peninsula. The last sample (89/4) is from the surface of a wave-cut terrace (Section 2), 1 km east of Egira and about 28 km SE of Egion, where the country rock (partly composed of cemented fault gouge) is covered by patches of calcareous, fossiliferous Quaternary marine deposits. The coral, on a

**Fig. 3.** *Cladocora caespitosa* at Section 2 (Sample 89/4).

**Table 2.** *Holocene* $^{14}C$ *ages for the Gulf of Corinth*

| Site | Height (m) | Species | $\delta^{13}C$ ‰ | $^{14}C$ age years BP (uncalib.) | Lab. no. |
|------|-----------|---------|------|------------|----------|
| **North Shore** | | | | | |
| Perachora | 1.7 | *Notirus irus* | $-1.3$ | $6890 \pm 90$ | SRR-2244 |
| | | *N. irus* | n.d. | $7100 \pm 1300$ | UCL-10 |
| | | *Mytilus galloprovincialis* | n.d. | $7200 \pm 350$ | UCL-230 |
| **South Shore** | | | | | |
| Section 2 | 6.5 | *Lithophaga lithophaga* | 3.43 | $4880 \pm 270$ | BETA-29306 |
| Section 1 | 4.0 | *L. lithophaga* | 3.6 | $8730 \pm 340$ | BETA-30231 |

n.d.: not determined.

**Fig. 4.** Undercut and *Lithophaga lithophaga* borings at Section 2.

6 m bench (Fig. 3), represents a pause in the emergence of the section, which also yielded a sequence of undercuts and borings (Fig. 4).

A section at the mouth of the lagoon on Perachora has now yielded three Holocene ages for a level 1.7 m above high water (Table 2) in the region of 7000 years BP. $^{14}C$ ages on *Litho-phaga lithophaga* from two coastal exposures on

the shore, east of Egion, also fall within the Holocene (Table 2; Fig. 4; Mouyaris *et al.* 1992). Several Classical sites have suffered submergence. At two of them, one at the mouth of the Corinth Canal and the other on Perachora, this was followed by 0.5–1 m of emergence (Vita-Finzi & King 1985).

The U-series age for Sample 89/1 shows that at least one of the Gilbert fan deltas on the northern shore of the Peloponnese (Ori 1989; Roberts & Jackson 1991) was accumulating 386 ka ago. Allowing for a eustatic sea-level 6 m above the present, the two U-series ages for Perachora indicate some 15 m of emergence in 125 ka or 0.14 mm a$^{-1}$. The corresponding correction for the Holocene dates on Perachora is in the order of $-11$ m, giving an average emergence rate of 1.7 mm a$^{-1}$. A similar discrepancy between Holocene and Pleistocene uplift rates is reported in many tectonically active regions.

In their account of the structural evolution of the Gulf of Corinth, Jackson *et al.* (1982) assumed that normal faulting was accompanied by footwall uplift amounting to about 10% of the throw. This value tallies with the ratio between the maximum height of unambiguous marine terraces on the southern shore of the Gulf and the maximum depth of the Gulf itself (Vita-Finzi & King 1985), suggesting that the gross morphology could be explained by coseismic deformation. The field evidence also showed that shifts in the locus of faulting could transform a hanging wall block into a footwall block and thus substitute subsidence for uplift.

In consequence, net uplift in such blocks is the algebraic sum of all the displacements and will not yield an informative average uplift rate. By the same token, comparisons between the rates of different periods need not have any significance. But it does not follow that the differences between localities or periods are fortuitous. Thus the coast near Egion has undergone almost 5 m more uplift during the last 7000 years than the coast of Perachora, presumably because the former is on the footwall of a major normal fault whereas Perachora is by turns affected by footwall and by hanging wall behaviour.

To judge from the 1980 Corinth earthquakes, events with $M_S > 6$ can produce vertical increments of movement of as much as 2 m (Jackson et al. 1982). The morphological evidence near Egion points to three episodes of stillstand during some 6 m of emergence (Mouyaris et al. 1992), equivalent to a repeat period of c. 2000 years for the operating earthquake. The interval between the two events known to have produced clear fault movement near the site of ancient Helice (373 BC and AD 1860) is 2234 years. Extrapolation of this rate yields some 200 m of relief at Section 89/1. In short, the morphology of the Gulf can be explained by the deformation on major normal faults that accompanies large ($M_S > 6.0$) events if they operate with a recurrence of about 2000 years and their effects are cumulative.

A well-developed Pleistocene terrace is found at about 23 m above sea-level on both shores of the eastern Gulf. The southern exposure has a minimum age of $> 48\,000$ years (OxA-1243) and thus could be contemporaneous with the 120 000 year (89/2 and 89/3) surface of Perachora, whereupon it might represent a single marine platform which was subsequently disrupted. The present data prompt an intriguing alternative explanation: that in an extensional setting there is a limit, probably isostatic, to the height which footwall uplift can attain. Jackson et al. (1982) have already noted that antithetic faulting on the northern shores of the Gulf will preclude net uplift there, and we have seen that Perachora experiences both uplift and subsidence by virtue of its intermediate position.

A plausible inference is that, as in the Basin and Range province of the USA, faulting is confined to a thin lithosphere and little extension can be accommodated by any fault however shallow its dip. Very limited uplift could result from rotation, even on low-angle faults. Any marine levels higher and older than those identified at 200 m (Vita-Finzi & King 1985) would then indicate earlier compressional conditions; conversely, prolonged extension can be accommodated only by distributed faults whose development would be serial in the sense that, by analogy with serial folds (Price 1975), they would develop sequentially once those already in existence were incapable of accommodating any further substantial strain.

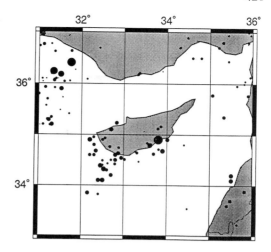

**Fig. 5.** Cyprus: earthquakes of $M \geqslant 4$ for 1960–1988, from USGS Global Hypocenter Data Base.

## Compression

Shorelines have also been studied in western Cyprus (Fig. 5) in the hope of illuminating uplift – and hence dynamic – history. Harrison (1955) remarked on the rejuvenated appearance of the streams within the Troodos Massif, a fragment of Late Cretaceous oceanic crust. Some of the rivers draining the area have stepped longitudinal profiles which are consistent with repeated uplift but, like the high erosion surfaces within the Troodos Massif described by de Vaumas (1961), the profiles have yet to be dated. The one fluvial unit for which radiometric ages are available is an alluvial fill of historical age (Gomez 1987) which is readily explained by a slight shift in the rainfall regime without invoking tectonic controls.

Recent uplift of the Troodos Range of western Cyprus has long been suspected: the rivers that drain from Mount Olympus are deeply incised, and Late Pliocene marine deposits are found up to 450 m above sea-level (Harrison 1955). An erosion level around Mt Olympus has been dated to the Upper Miocene by reference to similar levels in Lebanon and Turkey and used to infer over 2000 m of post-Cretaceous differential uplift of this area relative to the rest of Cyprus (de Vaumas 1961, 1962). The summit morphology of Mt Olympus has been explained by faulting of an erosion surface, perhaps as result of a rise in the underlying serpentine diapir, resulting in a southward tilt of 6° of the original bevel (Houghton et al. 1990).

Palaeontological evidence suggests that

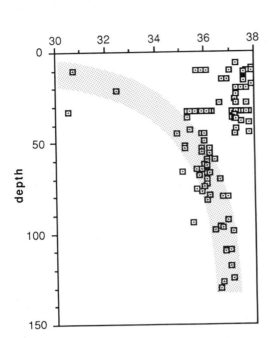

**Fig. 6.** Plot of earthquakes of M ≥ 4 for 1913–1988 between 30° and 32° E against depth, from USGS Global Hypocenter Data Base.

unroofing of the Troodos Massif began in the late Miocene and that uplift, which was at its fastest in Late Pliocene–Pleistocene times, has since taken place at an average rate of 1 mm a$^{-1}$ (Houghton *et al.* 1990). The depositional record of the Mesaoria basin north of the Troodos is thought to show that the process was pulsatory (McCallum & Robertson 1990). Although serpentinization of the plutonic core of the Troodos (Gass & Masson-Smith 1963) may have locally contributed to the process, especially in the Quaternary, rapid Pleistocene uplift is ascribed by McCallum & Robertson (1990) to subduction, albeit sluggish and interrupted by extensional phases.

De Vaumas (1962) applied the term 'rejuvenated' to the Troodos rivers and was struck by what he considered to be the recency of many coastal features and alluvial infills, but he claimed that, at least in the bays of Morphou and Famagusta, the final retreat of the sea was the product of aggradation rather than of orogenic movements.

A preliminary attempt to date some of the shorelines around the periphery of the Troodos Massif led to a set of ambiguous results. Ten shell samples from fossil beaches were checked for contamination by X-ray diffraction, scanning electron microscopy and stable isotope analysis. But the experience of Corinth had shown that it was wiser to view the results (Vita-Finzi 1990) as minima.

Poole *et al.* (1990) then secured a series of U-series ages on *Cladocora caespitosa* from terraces at 8–11 m and <3 m of 185–192 ka and 130–116 ka respectively. The results are not as tidy as this summary suggests: the ages for the higher group range from 141 ± 4 to >300 ka and for the lower group from 108 ± 6 to 138 ± 4 ka, that is to say the groups overlap at 1 σ. But if we grant as valid the correlation proposed by the authors with stages 7 and 5e of the isotopic eustatic curve, and deposition in a water depth not exceeding 10 m, the older level indicates 18 m of uplift and the younger 5–8 m, equivalent, after eustatic correction, to average rates of between 0.05 and 0.24 mm a$^{-1}$. Coral deposition in substantially less than 10 m of water would, of course, render these values even lower.

According to Poole *et al.* (1990) the main phase of uplift on the south coast of Cyprus must therefore have taken place earlier. Indeed, in some places there is geological and archaeological evidence for recent subsidence. Flemming (1978) reported submergence at 13 ancient harbour sites by totals ranging from 0.1–2.0 m, and he used evidence from 32 sites to compute contours for the rate of vertical displacement which showed zero movement along the north coast and subsidence with a maximum of 1 mm a$^{-1}$ over the last 2000 years in the southwest. In his view, the north of the island forms part of a stable block. Dreghorn (1981) reports about 1 m of post-Byzantine uplift on the north coast, where Pleistocene marine terraces have long been taken to indicate progressive emergence; Giangrande *et al.* (1987) found evidence for seaward tilting of the coastal plain on the southwestern coast of Cyprus. Figure 1, derived from the study by Flemming (1978), outlines his results for other parts of the northeastern Mediterranean, including the central Peloponnese where he suspects doming or folding may be taking place.

The cessation of uplift in southern Cyprus could stem from the close of subduction or a change to strike-slip movement. The lack of Holocene uplift is further attested by a series of first-order $^{14}$C ages on terraces 2–5 m above sea-level, all of which gave background readings and thus exceeded the 12 000 years maximum range of the method as then practised (Vita-Finzi 1991; Samples UCL 320–4).

The island is seismically not inert. Activity, historical (Ambraseys 1965) as well as instrumental, is concentrated at the latitude of the southern coast of Cyprus, where a 2 km scarp, normal to the direction of convergence, borders the shelf on which Cyprus sits (see fig. 11 of Jackson & McKenzie 1984), and corresponds to a structural discontinuity marked by faulting (Woodside 1977). During 1960–1988, for instance, this coast and the area immediately offshore experienced at least 6 events with $M \geqslant 5.0$, including one of $M_s = 5.9$ (Fig. 5). Ambraseys & Finkel (1987) show two earthquakes with $6.5 > M_s > 6.0$ within the same belt off Cyprus in 1918 and 1953.

Interpretation of the structure of the eastern Mediterranean is obscured by over 10 km of sediment overlying parts of the sea floor and by an earthquake record which is patchy (Woodside 1977) and probably unrepresentative of long-term trends (Ambraseys & Finkel 1987). In the classic formulation by McKenzie (1970), deformation between Africa and Turkey is taken up along the Cyprus arc, and regional kinematics indicate a rate of shortening of 30 mm $a^{-1}$. Granted that the seismicity around Cyprus is poorly constrained (Jackson & McKenzie 1984), the presence of a subduction zone between Egypt and Turkey is supported by a plot of seismicity based on events of $M \geqslant 4$ (Fig. 6).

Without necessarily implying that the island has moved throughout as a single unit, simple geometrical considerations show that southward tilting of Cyprus could account for the expected convergence of 30 mm $a^{-1}$ (Jackson & McKenzie 1988) by sub-horizontal underthrusting of the African margin beneath the Turkish Plate. In order to test this reconstruction and discover when emergence in the south gave way to submergence, the need is for numerical ages on the emerged features on the north coast of Cyprus. It should then be possible to integrate the result with the neotectonic record of other parts of the eastern Mediterranean, notably Crete, where general eastward tilting is now well documented (Thommeret et al. 1981), and ultimately to obtain a clear picture of crustal response to plate interaction (Woodside 1977) on a time scale measured in millennia.

I thank D. R. Muhs and P. B. Maat of the US Geological Survey for the U-series ages, P. Schooling and W. Murphy for help with computing, and M. Gray and C. Stuart for the illustrations. Fieldwork was funded by the Royal Society, the Central Research Fund of London University and the Natural Environment Research Council.

## References

AMBRASEYS, N. N. 1965. The seismic history of Cyprus. *Revue pour l'Etude des Calamités*, **5**, 1–26.
—— & FINKEL, C. F. 1987. Seismicity of Turkey and neighbouring regions, 1899–1915. *Annales Geophysicae*, **5B**, 701–726.
BROOKS, M. & FERENTINOS, G. 1984. Tectonics and sedimentation in the Gulf of Corinth and the Zakynthos and Kefalinia channels, western Greece. *Tectonophysics*, **110**, 25–54.
COLLIER, R. E. Ll. 1990. Eustatic and tectonic controls upon Quaternary coastal sedimentation in the Corinth Basin, Greece. *Journal of the Geological Society, London*, **147**, 301–314.
——, LEEDER, M. R., ROWE, P. J. & ATKINSON, T. C. 1992. Rates of Tectonic Uplift in the Corinth and Megara Basins, central Greece. *Tectonics*, **11**, 1159–1167.
DE VAUMAS, E. 1961. Further contributions to the geomorphology of Cyprus. *Annual Report of the Geological Survey Department, Cyprus, 1960*, 24–34.
—— 1962. Notes on the geomorphology of Cyprus. *Annual Report of the Geological Survey Department, Cyprus, 1961*, 29–43.
DOUTSOS, T. & PIPER, D. J. W. 1990. Listric faulting, sedimentation and morphological evolution of the Quaternary eastern Corinth rift, Greece: First stages of continental rifting. *Bulletin of the Geological Society of America*, **102**, 812–829.
DREGHORN, W. 1981. Recent uplift in northern Cyprus. *Geologie en Mijnbouw*, **60**, 281–284.
FLEMMING, N. C. 1978. Holocene eustatic changes and coastal tectonics in the northeast Mediterranean: implications for models of crustal consumption. *Philosophical Transactions of the Royal Society of London*, **A289**, 405–458.
GASS, I. G. & MASSON-SMITH, D. 1963. The geology and gravity anomalies of the Troodos Massif, Cyprus. *Philosophical Transactions of the Royal Society of London*, **A255**, 417–467.
GIANGRANDE, C., RICHARDS, G., KENNET, D. & ADAMS, J. 1987. *Cyprus Underwater Survey, 1983–1984, A Preliminary Report*. Report of the Department of Antiquities, Nicosia, Cyprus.
GOMEZ, B. 1987. The alluvial terraces and fills of the Lower Vasilikos valley, in the vicinity of Kalavasos, Cyprus. *Transactions of the Institute of British Geographers*, **12**, 345–359.
HARRISON, J. C. 1955. An interpretation of the gravity anomalies of the eastern Mediterranean. *Philosophical Transactions of the Royal Society of London*, **A289**, 405–458.
HOUGHTON, S. D., JENKINS, D. G., XENOPHONTOS, C. & GASS, I. G. 1990. Microfossil evidence for a latest Pliocene age for the Amathus and Khirokitia channel deposits, southern Cyprus and thereby the unroofing of the Troodos Massif. *In*: MALPAS, J., MOORES, E. M., PANAYIOTOU, A. & XENOPHONTOS, C. (eds) *Ophiolites*. Geological Survey Department, Nicosia, 231–234.
JACKSON, J. A., GAGNEPAIN, J., HOUSEMAN, G., KING, G. C. P., PAPADIMITRIOU, P., SOUFLERIS, C. & VIRIEUX, J. 1982. Seismicity, normal faulting, and

the geomorphological development of the Gulf of Corinth (Greece): the Corinth earthquakes of February and March 1981. *Earth and Planetary Science Letters*, **57**, 377–397.

—— & McKenzie, D. 1984. Active Tectonics of the Alpine–Himalayan Belt between western Turkey and Pakistan. *Geophysical Journal of the Royal Astronomical Society*, **77**, 185–264.

—— & —— 1988. Rates of active deformation in the Aegean Sea and surrounding areas. *Basin Research*, **1**, 121–128.

Kontopoulos, N. & Doutsos, T. 1985. Sedimentology and Tectonics of the Antirion Area (Western Greece). *Società Geologica Italiana*, **10**, 479–489.

McCallum, J. E. & Robertson, A. H. F. 1990. Pulsed uplift of the Troodos massif – evidence from the Plio-Pleistocene Mesaoria basin. *In*: Malpas, J., Moores, E. M., Panayiotou, A. & Xenophontos, C. (eds) *Ophiolites* Geological Survey Department, Nicosia, 217–229.

McKenzie, D. P. 1970. The plate tectonics of the Mediterranean region. *Nature*, **226**, 239–243.

Mann, C. D. & Vita-Finzi, C. 1988. Holocene serial folding in the Zagros. *In*: Audley-Charles, M. G. & Hallam, A. (eds) *Tethys and Gondwana.* Oxford University Press, Oxford, 51–59.

Mouyaris, N., Papastamatiou, D. & Vita-Finzi, C. 1992. The Helice Fault? *Terra Nova*, **4**, 124–129.

Ori, G. G. 1989. Geologic history of the extensional basin of the Gulf of Corinth (?Miocene–Pleistocene), Greece. *Geology*, **17**, 918–921.

Poole, N. J., Shimmield, G. B. & Robertson, A. H. F. 1990. Late Quaternary uplift of the Troodos ophiolite, Cyprus: Uranium-series dating of Pleistocene coral. *Geology*, **18**, 894–897.

Price, N. J. 1975. Rates of deformation. *Journal of the*

*Geological Society, London*, **131**, 553–575.

Roberts, S. & Jackson, J. 1991. Active normal faulting in central Greece: an overview. *In*: Roberts, A. M., Yielding, G. & Freeman, B. (eds) *The Geometry of Normal Faults.* Geological Society, London, Special Publication, **56**, 125–142.

Sébrier, M. 1977. *Tectonique recent d'une tranversale à l'Arc Egéen.* PhD thesis, Université de Paris XI, Paris.

Taymaz, T., Jackson, J. & McKenzie, D. 1991. Active tectonics of the north and central Aegean Sea. *Geophysical Journal International*, **106**, 433–490.

Thommeret, Y., Thommeret, J., Laborel, J., Montaggioni, L. F. & Pirazzoli, P. A. 1981. Late Holocene shoreline changes and seismo-tectonic displacements in western Crete (Greece). *Zeitschrift für Geomorphologie, Supplement-Band*, **40**, 127–149.

Vita-Finzi, C. 1990. $^{14}$C dating of Late Quaternary uplift in western Cyprus. *Tectonophysics*, **172**, 135–140.

—— 1991. First-order dating Mark II. *Quaternary Proceedings*, **1**, 11–17.

—— 1992. Radiocarbon dating of late Quaternary fault segments and systems. *Journal of the Geological Society, London*, **149**, 257–260.

—— & King, G. C. P. 1985. The seismicity, geomorphology and structural evolution of the Corinth area of Greece. *Philosophical Transactions of the Royal Society of London*, **A314**, 379–407.

—— & Situmorang, B. 1989. Holocene coastal deformation in Simeulue and Nias. *Marine Geology*, **89**, 153–161.

Woodside, J. M. 1977. Tectonic elements and crust of the eastern Mediterranean Sea. *Marine Geophysical Researches*, **3**, 317–354.

# Continental rifting

# The Proterozoic Gardar rift zone, south Greenland: comparisons with the East African Rift System

RAY MACDONALD[1] & BRIAN G. J. UPTON[2]

[1]*Environmental Science Division, Lancaster University, Lancaster LA1 4YQ, UK*
[2]*Department of Geology and Geophysics, University of Edinburgh, West Mains Road, Edinburgh EH9 3JW, UK*

**Abstract**: The late Tertiary to Recent Kenya rift valley and the deeply dissected, Proterozoic, Gardar province of south Greenland are both parts of continental rift systems thousands of kilometres long. Both were generated within stabilized orogenic belts skirting cratonic forelands, in regions in which repeated reactivation of earlier structures has occurred. Both may represent failed attempts at continental separation.

Mafic magmatism in Kenya has ranged from strongly silica-undersaturated, melanephelinitic types through basanites to mildly alkaline and transitional basalts. Gardar activity was dominated by mildly alkaline and transitional basalts; basanites and nephelinites are rare or absent, the most undersaturated representatives being ultramafic lamprophyres. Very primitive (possibly primary) magmas are scarce in both rifts. Trace element chemistry suggests that the majority of the mafic rocks have lithospheric signatures, and that asthenospheric magmas had no direct access to the crust. The primary magmas were generated as small-degree melts in mantle sources which had experienced earlier depletion events and which were subsequently metasomatized. An important, mantle-derived feature of the Gardar basalts is their strongly aluminous nature, which appears to have generated an abundance of anorthositic bodies in the crust; this feature is not shown in the Kenya rift. Considerable amounts of underplating are inferred to characterize both rifts, limiting crustal thinning in regions of lithospheric extension.

Both rift zones have extensive axial dyke swarms, which are particularly focused on central complexes/caldera volcanoes. Kenya apparently lacks, however, the massive dykes, up to several hundred metres wide, of the Gardar province.

During the 1970s, Ian Gass and his colleagues made important contributions to our understanding of how rift valleys can be produced by ascent of asthenospheric plumes under continental lithosphere. In this paper, we note geological similarities and differences between sectors of the classic active continental rift, the East African Rift System, and a Proterozoic system which must have been equally impressive in its scale and tectonic and magmatic development. We are delighted by this opportunity to acknowledge the major influence exerted by Professor Gass on research and teaching in the Earth Sciences for over 30 years. We also acknowledge a special indebtedness for his friendship and support over that time.

The youthfulness of the East African Rift System (EARS), and the consequent lack of deep dissection, means that we have little direct information on deeper structures. In this paper, we expand on suggestions by Upton & Blundell (1978) and Upton *et al.* (1990) that some features of the mid-Proterozoic Gardar rift zone of south Greenland may provide analogies with the EARS and thus permit insights into the possible sub-surface anatomy of the EARS. Concentrating, but not exclusively, on the Kenya sector with which we are most familiar, we describe common features of the evolution of the rifts and comment on how the intrusive phenomena of the Gardar may be related to those at deep level within the EARS deduced from geological and geophysical studies. We start by outlining briefly the geological evolution of both provinces.

## The East African Rift System

The eastern branch of the EARS extends more than 2000 km from the Afar triangle in Ethiopia through Kenya into northern Tanzania, where it splays out into a diffuse region of normal faults (Fig. 1). The rift is generally 40–80 km wide and traverses two broad areas of uplift, the Ethiopian and Kenya Domes, each about 750 km across. Major uplift of the domes occurred in late Eocene, mid-Miocene and Plio-Pleistocene times, with the total uplift being approximately 1.5–2 km (Baker *et al.* 1972; Karson & Curtis 1989).

*From* Prichard, H. M., Alabaster, T., Harris, N. B. W. & Neary, C. R. (eds), 1993, *Magmatic Processes and Plate Tectonics*, Geological Society Special Publication No. 76, 427–442.

427

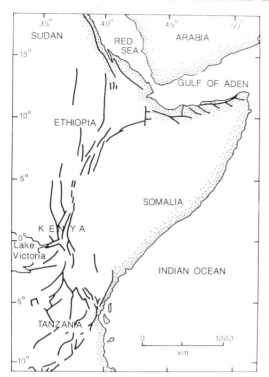

**Fig. 1.** Major faults of the eastern branch of the East African Rift System, simplified from Baker *et al.* (1972, fig. 18).

The EARS was initiated as a chain of basinal depressions which deepened as the domes grew. By early Pliocene times, faulting had produced four asymmetrical sub-basins, each 50–160 km long and 30–70 km wide. The sub-basins are half-grabens, bounded on one side by major, listric normal faults with vertical displacements of around 2 km, and on the other side by smaller, antithetic normal faults. The major faults alternate between east and west sides of adjacent sub-basins, and the areas between sub-basins have been interpreted as 'accomodation zones' of wrench and oblique-slip faulting (Bosworth *et al.* 1986; Bosworth 1987; Green & Meyer 1992). The sub-basins are partially filled with coarse clastic sediments, lake beds and minor hydrothermal deposits as well as volcanics. Pleistocene uplift was accompanied by major graben faulting. Most recent faulting has fractured the rift floor along an axial zone, which in the last 0.5 Ma has also been marked by the growth of caldera volcanoes (Williams *et al.* 1984; Baker 1987; Macdonald 1987).

Magmatism associated with the growth of the Kenya rift started in the Oligocene. Since that time, there has been a minimum of 109 400 km³ of extrusives in the sector of the rift between 4°N and 2°S (Williams 1972; Karson & Curtis 1989). Mafic rocks, ranging from nephelinites to hypersthene-normative transitional basalts, have been important at all stages of rift evolution. A notable feature, however, has been the eruption of enormous volumes of magma of felsic composition, e.g. the Miocene flood phonolites and Plio-Pleistocene flood trachytes. Although there has been a tendency for volcanism to become increasingly confined to the rift valley floor, eruptions have occurred on the flanks at all stages of rift development.

The EARS is underlain by a broad, negative Bouguer gravity anomaly of around 500 g.u. Under the rift valley proper, the upper mantle has anomalously low seismic velocity (P-wave velocity = 7.5 km s⁻¹; KRISP Working Party 1991), and high electrical conductivities (Banks & Beamish 1979). These have been interpreted to show that the Cenozoic history of rifting, uplift and magmatism has been related to a rise in the lithosphere – asthenosphere boundary.

Baker (1987; see also Kampunzu & Mohr 1991) divided the volcanic rocks of the Kenya rift into three associations, partly on the basis of degree of alkalinity and partly on association in space and time:

(1) a strongly undersaturated, primitive series, commonly in association with carbonatites, of melilitites and melanephelinites, evolving to nephelinites and phonolites rich in Ca, Ba and Sr. There tends to be a compositional break between these and the rocks of association 2;

(2) an association comprising limburgites, basanites, alkali olivine basalts, tephrites and low-Ca phonolites;

(3) transitional basalts, ferrobasalts, mugearites, benmoreites, trachytes, trachyphonolites and peralkaline rhyolites.

The **nephelinite–carbonatite association** in the EARS is represented by central volcanoes, such as Mt Elgon (Fig.2), composed mainly of pyroclastic rocks and debris flows, which tend to lie outside the main graben sector of the rift. The parental magmas are believed to be carbonated melanephelinites, generated by very small degrees of melting, at pressures >15 kb, of mantle with high $CO_2/(CO_2 + H_2O)$ ratios (Le Bas 1977, 1987). According to Le Bas, the carbonate fraction was formed by liquid immiscibility and the silicate component evolved through nephelinite to high-Ca phonolite by fractionation of olivine + clinopyroxene + sphene assemblages.

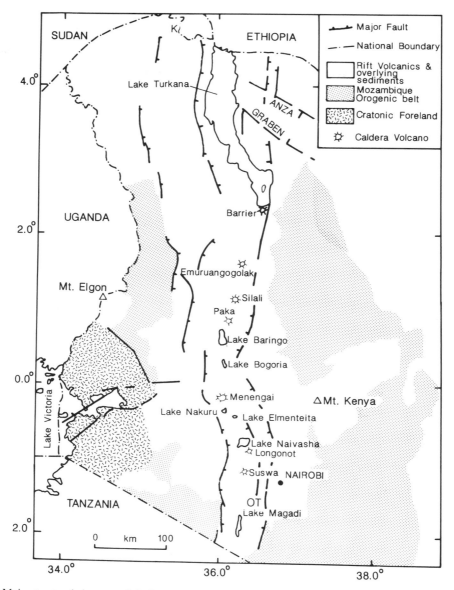

**Fig. 2.** Main structural elements of the Kenya rift valley, simplified from KRISP Working Party (1991, fig. 1). K: Korath Range; OT: Ol Tepesi basalts.

The volumetrically dominant mafic rocks in the Kenya rift are basanites and mildly undersaturated to transitional basalts of **associations 2** and **3**. Among these, there is a scarcity of any high-MgO, high-Ni rocks which could represent primary melts of fertile mantle, presumably as a result of extended fractionation histories (Macdonald 1993). Karson & Curtis (1989) and Macdonald (1993) invoke fractionation at or near the base of the crust to explain the scarcity of highly magnesian basalts in Kenya. The crust is inferred to have acted as a very efficient filter, discriminating against shallow ascent of dense, primitive magmas.

Chondrite-normalized incompatible trace element (ITE) plots of Kenyan mafic rocks typically show negative Zr anomalies and moderate positive P anomalies (Fig. 3). An important

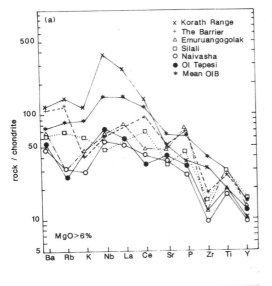

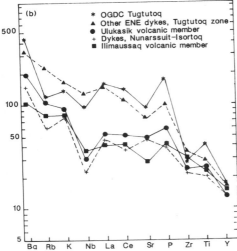

**Fig. 3.** Chondrite-normalized element abundance plots for selected mafic rocks from the Kenya rift (Macdonald 1993) and the Gardar province (Upton & Emeleus 1987). Mean oceanic island basalt given for comparison, from data in Fitton *et al.* (1991).

sphere or that any asthenospheric parents were modified during passage through the lithosphere (Macdonald 1993).

The low ITE abundances in many Kenyan volcanics relative to OIB tie in with (admittedly sparse) isotopic evidence that the mantle sources experienced melting events prior to metasomatism less than 100 Ma ago (Norry *et al.* 1980; Davies & Macdonald 1987; Kampunzu & Mohr 1991). The nature of these metasomatic events may have been recorded in mantle xenoliths from northern Tanzania. The xenoliths point to a heterogeneous lithospheric mantle, involving a compositional spectrum from depleted harzburgites, through garnet lherzolites (derived from mantle enriched 2.2 Ga ago), to modally metasomatized ultramafites related to the Cenozoic activity (Dawson & Smith 1988; Dawson 1992). A question not satisfactorily answered for the province is whether modally metasomatized mantle is ubiquitous or patchily distributed beneath the rift zone. The small volume, geographical restriction, and overlap in time with less undersaturated rocks might suggest uneven distribution of the lithospheric metasomites. Alternatively, the range in magma compositions may be related to degree of melting (Macdonald 1993); small melt fractions are strongly silica-undersaturated and show large ranges in trace element abundances and ratios as a result of the major influence of the metasomites. More advanced melting dilutes the influence of the metasomite component and generates more homogeneous, less alkaline melts.

## The Gardar province

The Gardar igneous province of southern Greenland (Fig. 4) comprises a suite of intrusions and lavas, ranging in age from approximately 1350–1150 Ma. General reviews have been provided by Emeleus & Upton (1974) and Upton & Emeleus (1987). Mafic rocks are predominantly represented among the dykes, although basaltic/hawaiitic lavas are preserved in down-faulted blocks and gabbros are a minor component of some of the plutons. It is probable that the province exposes erosion levels corresponding to Gardar crustal depths of $5\pm2$ km (Upton & Blundell 1978; Upton & Emeleus 1987).

The youngest phase of rifting (Upton & Blundell 1978) occurred in the interval 1200–1100 Ma and affected early Proterozoic (Ketilidian) lithosphere (Windley 1991). It involved a belt some 70 km broad, just south of the Archaean craton and lying approximately parallel to the WSW–ENE-trending Archaean–Proterozoic boundary.

feature of the patterns is that they distinguish Kenyan basalts from oceanic island basalts (OIB). On the assumptions (cf. Fitton & Dunlop 1985; Fitton *et al.* 1988, 1991; and Thompson *et al.* 1989) that OIB represent pristine asthenospheric melts, that the asthenosphere is well mixed by convection, and that it is similar under oceans and continents, we infer either that the Kenyan rocks were generated within the litho-

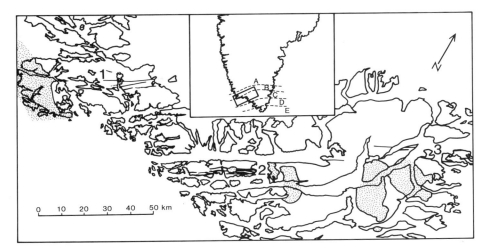

**Fig. 4.** Location map of the Tugtutoq–Ilimaussaq (2–3) and Nunarssuit–Isortoq (1) lineaments, Gardar province, south Greenland. Axial dyke swarm, including massive dykes, shown much simplified in black. Stippled areas are syenite intrusions. Note the en echelon displacement of the Tugtutoq dyke swarm by comparing its position at 2 and 3. In the inset, the zones A–E represent – A: Archaean craton; B–C: Julianehaab Granite; D: Sardloq Shear Zone; E: thrust stack.

The belt is divisible into a northwesterly zone (Nunarssuit–Isortoq; 1 in Fig. 4) and a south-easterly zone (Tugtutoq–Ilimaussaq; 2 in Fig. 4) (Upton & Blundell 1978; Upton & Emeleus 1987). The Nunartssuit–Isortoq zone (*c.* 30 km across) is inferred to represent a fault block abundantly penetrated by dykes of transitional basaltic parentage with widths of up to 500 m (Bridgwater & Coe 1970). The Nunarssuit–Isortoq dyke swarms are transected by syenite, quartz syenite and granite plutons which are the youngest manifestations of Gardar magmatism in the zone. The plutons contain metabasaltic and quartzitic xenoliths believed to have been derived from a cover of Gardar lavas and sediments that has otherwise been lost by erosion.

The Tugtutoq–Ilimaussaq lineament is regarded as representing a 15–20 km broad palaeorift. As with the Nunarssuit–Isortoq zone, the limits are defined by major fjords thought to overlie the outcrops of boundary faults and the zone is one of intense dyke intrusion. The lineament can be traced, with en echelon offsets, for *c.* 140 km, passing west-southwestwards into the sea and east-northeastwards beneath the inland ice. As in the Nunarssuit–Isortoq zone, some of the dykes attain plutonic proportions, with widths up to 800 m. Although the massive dykes may have generally terminated upwards at the unconformity between the granitoid basement and overlying supercrustal strata, some

surface eruption is regarded as likely and their emplacement is inferred to have been accompanied by some volcanic activity and graben formation. Fault-bounded basins containing up to 3 km sequences of subaerial lavas (basaltic to trachytic) and fluviatile, lacustrine and aeolian sediments (the Eriksfjord Formation) occur in association with the Tugtutoq–Ilimaussaq zone. Recent dating of the lavas ($1170 \pm 3$ and $1200 \pm 3$ Ma) raises the possibility that parts of these sequences are late Gardar in age and are related to the observed dyke swarms (Paslick *et al.* 1993).

An elongate, strong, positive gravity anomaly is coaxial with the dyke swarm in the Tugtutoq area (Blundell 1978). This, together with the alkaline nature of the magmatism, the presence of fault-bounded basins containing terrestrial lavas and sediments and off-sets of the dyke swarms indicating a segmentation of the rift (Fig. 4), is further evidence of a rift setting.

The massive dykes of the Tugtutoq–Ilimaussaq zone were emplaced at the start of the late Gardar magmatic cycle and involved a crustal dilatation of *c.* 1 km (Fig. 5). Crustal extension continued with injection of further dykes approximately coplanar with the initial massive dykes. There was a tendency for the widths of dykes in the swarm to decrease with time and for the dyke magmas to become increasingly differentiated, evolving with time from transitional

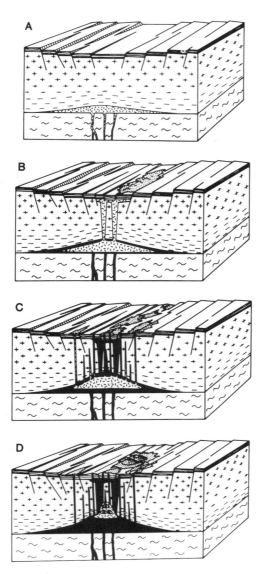

Fig. 5. Evolutionary model of the Tugtutoq–Ilimaus-saq rift, from Upton *et al.* (1990). (**A**) Lithospheric thinning with rift formation and emplacement of a mafic magma body at or near the Moho. (**B**) Partial crystallization of the magma body and intrusion of relatively fractionated melts as massive dykes. (**C**) Subsequent emplacement of more fractionated magmas as dykes, during progressive crystallization of the parental, deep crustal, magma body. (**D**) Ascent of residual liquids by ring faulting and stoping, during post-extensional phase. Growth of central volcanoes along rift axis.

basalt and hawaiite through trachytes to phono-lites or peralkaline rhyolites. As in the Nunars-suit–Isortoq zone, late Gardar magmatism in the Tugtutoq–Ilimaussaq zone was effectively termi-nated by formation of shallow-crustal, alkaline, salic plutons in a culminating, post-extensional phase. It is inferred that at least some of the plutons underlay caldera volcanoes comparable to the trachytic, phonolitic and rhyolitic volca-noes of the axial part of the EARS (Parsons & Butterfield 1981; Upton *et al.* 1990; Parsons *et al.* 1991).

The intensity of the dyke swarm in the Tugtutoq–Ilimaussaq lineament, taken in con-sideration with their large sizes and shallow crustal levels, is such as to make it probable that a proportion gave rise to fissure lavas, varying from abundant, early, mafic varieties to less voluminous, later, salic compositions. Fissure flood lavas of compositions as evolved as ben-moreitic to trachytic may have been erupted in much the same manner as has been proposed for the flood trachytes and phonolites of the Kenya rift.

Carbonatite bodies in the Gardar are associ-ated, not with nephelinites, but with foyaites and also with ultramafic lamprophyres (Upton & Emeleus 1987). Carbonatite intrusions are intimately associated with nepheline syenites at Grønnedal-Ika (Emeleus 1964; Bedford 1989) and in the Igaliko district (Emeleus & Harry 1970). However, siderite is also one of the major components of the Ivigtut cryolite deposit and carbonates (including cancrinite) are common components of the more differentiated facies of other Gardar plutons. The ultramafic lampro-phyres occur as lava flows, hypabyssal intrusions and blocks in diatremes. They represent cafemic, volatile-rich magmas with high contents of both compatible and incompatible elements. Like the melilitites and melanephelinites of the EARS, they are interpreted as primitive, small-degree melts from the mantle, that rose to shallow levels in an unfractionated condition. This inference is supported by the fact that mantle xenoliths oc-cur in both the EARS melilitite-melanephelinite and Gardar ultramafic lamprophyre suites.

Basanitic members of **association 2** are rare or absent in the Gardar, and the dominant mafic rocks range from mildly undersaturated alkali basalts to transitional basalts, mirroring the situ-ation in the EARS (Baker 1987). The bulk of the basaltic magmas (in contrast to the very subordi-nate ultramafic lamprophyre magmas) reaching shallow crustal levels in the Gardar had low Mg ♯ and low Ni and Cr contents (Upton & Emeleus 1987). It is concluded that, as with their counter-parts in the EARS, the Gardar basalts are resi-

**Table 1.** *Comparison of mafic rock compositions (MgO >4 wt%) from the Kenya rift and Gardar province*

| | Kenya rift | | | | Gardar | | |
|---|---|---|---|---|---|---|---|
| | 1 | 2 | 3 | 4 | 5 | 6 | 7 |
| **Major elements (wt%)** | | | | | | | |
| $SiO_2$ | 45.8 | 47.6 | 47.5 | 48.6 | 46.65 | 46.26 | 43.47 |
| $TiO_2$ | 2.5 | 2.0 | 2.6 | 3.4 | 2.40 | 2.52 | 4.40 |
| $Al_2O_3$ | 14.0 | 14.8 | 14.7 | 15.1 | 15.92 | 16.36 | 15.65 |
| $Fe_2O_3$* | 14.0 | 12.7 | 13.9 | 11.9 | 14.74 | 13.46 | 15.57 |
| MnO | 0.3 | 0.2 | 0.2 | 0.2 | 0.19 | 0.16 | 0.19 |
| MgO | 8.0 | 6.4 | 5.9 | 4.2 | 6.38 | 5.64 | 4.76 |
| CaO | 10.8 | 11.5 | 11.6 | 8.5 | 5.85 | 7.77 | 7.70 |
| $Na_2O$ | 2.9 | 2.7 | 2.9 | 4.1 | 3.22 | 3.59 | 3.45 |
| $K_2O$ | 1.2 | 0.8 | 1.0 | 2.4 | 1.15 | 0.93 | 1.81 |
| $P_2O_5$ | 0.5 | 0.3 | 0.5 | 0.8 | 0.39 | 0.49 | 1.95 |
| **Trace elements (ppm)** | | | | | | | |
| Ni | 135 | 86 | 69 | 44 | 78 | — | 22 |
| Sc | 23 | 37 | 33 | 14 | 25 | 22 | 16 |
| Sr | 735 | 453 | 447 | 1073 | 538 | 516 | 1039 |
| Rb | 33 | 14 | 20 | 52 | 31 | 31 | 39 |
| Zr | 291 | 116 | 140 | 396 | 225 | 102 | 162 |
| Ba | 440 | 390 | 472 | 882 | 663 | 387 | 1669 |
| La | 31 | 22 | 33 | 78 | 22 | 9 | 47 |
| Ce | 61 | 20 | 31 | — | 49 | 23 | 103 |
| Nd | 30 | 44 | 39 | 69 | 27 | 23 | 57 |
| Y | 26 | — | 32 | 38 | 30 | 16 | 35 |
| $Al_2O_3$/CaO | 1.3 | 1.3 | 1.3 | 1.8 | 2.7 | 25 | 2.0 |

*Kenya rift* 1: average olivine basalt from Kenya, eastern Uganda and northern Tanzania; 2: average of 31 transitional Quaternary basalts from the southern rift; 3: average of 10 Ol Tepesi basalts; 4: average Olokisalie basalt (all from Baker (1987), tables 2 and 4).
*Gardar province* 5: average of 24 NE and ENE dykes of the Ivigtut region; 6: average of 9, Ulukasik volcanic member, Eriksfjord Formation; 7: average of 3, older giant dyke, Tugtutoq (chilled facies). All from Upton & Emeleus (1987, table 1).
$Fe_2O_3$* = total Fe as $Fe_2O_3$

dues after extensive crystal fractionation of olivine ± clinopyroxene and spinel.

Table 1 presents averages of various alkali olivine and transitional basalt suites in the Kenyan and Gardar provinces. There are many overall similarities; for example, all are relatively rich in $TiO_2$ (>2%), $K_2O$ (>0.9%) and $P_2O_5$ (>0.39%). However, differences are brought out in chondrite-normalized ITE plots (Fig. 3); for example, the Kenyan rocks have larger negative Zr anomalies than the Gardar basalts and generally do not possess the pronounced positive Ba anomalies characteristic of the Gardar basalts. Most notably, the Gardar rocks typically have significant, negative Nb anomalies, and thus high La/Nb ratios. Mafic rocks from the two environments occupy different, though overlapping, fields on a La/Ba vs. La/Nb plot (Fig. 6). In terms of these elements, some Kenyan rocks fall

in the field of oceanic island basalts (OIB) but the Naivasha basalts extend to lower La/Ba values, which accords with strong isotopic evidence that these rocks have assimilated sialic crustal material (Davies & Macdonald 1987). All analysed Gardar basalts have $^{87}Sr/^{86}Sr$ comparable to Bulk Earth, precluding significant chemical modification by radiogenic granitic crust (although not by mafic granulites of the lower crust; Blaxland *et al.* 1978). The low-Nb character may reflect, therefore, a source feature, possibly inherited from an earlier Proterozoic subduction event.

Earlier, we assumed that OIB represent asthenospheric melts essentially unmodified chemically by interaction with the lithosphere. In the Gardar case, we must also assume that the Proterozoic asthenosphere was, with the possible exception of volatile components, compositio-

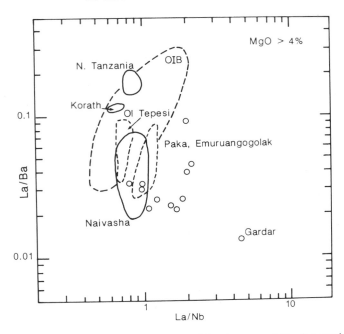

**Fig. 6.** La/Nb–La/Ba plot for mafic rocks (MgO > 4%) of the Kenyan and Gardar provinces. Kenyan data sources compiled by Macdonald (1993); Gardar data are means for various suites given by Upton & Emeleus (1987).

nally similar to the present one. From their compositional dissimilarity to OIB (Fig. 3), we must infer either that, as in Kenya, the Gardar rocks were generated within the lithosphere or that any asthenospheric parents were grossly modified during passage through the lithosphere. It seems that in neither rift was extension sufficiently strong to rupture the lithosphere and allow direct passage of asthenospheric melts into the crust. Given the completely different evolutionary histories of their respective lithospheres, it is hardly surprising that the Gardar and Kenyan rocks have different ITE characteristics (Figs 3 & 6).

One notable difference between the Gardar and Kenyan rifts, especially in more primitive basalts, is the higher $Al_2O_3/CaO$ ratios in the Gardar rocks, which confer on them high contents of relatively sodic plagioclase (modally and normatively) and low clinopyroxene contents (Table 1). It is possible that the aluminous character of the magmas reflects the mineralogy of the mantle sources, in particular a deficiency of diopside relative to garnet in the Gardar. The Gardar mantle sources may thus have been diopside-poor lherzolites or even harzburgitic as a result of earlier Precambrian melting events. The relative enrichment of the Gardar magmas

in K, Ba, Sr, REE, C and halogens was due, as in Kenya, to subsequent metasomatism of relatively depleted peridotites (Upton & Emeleus 1987). The difference between the Kenyan and Gardar situations may then simply be one of mantle mineralogy; clinopyroxene was a residual phase after pre-metasomatic melting events in the EARS but probably not in the Gardar. We return to the different Al/Ca ratios in the section 'Significance of cumulates'.

The scarcity or absence of nephelinitic rocks in the Gardar, and the presence in their place of ultramafic lamprophyres, may simply have been a function of mantle composition. The lamprophyres represent primitive magmas from melting of metasomites which may have been unusually rich in phlogopite and poor in jadeite component of pyroxene.

The Erta'Ale volcanic range of the Ethiopian sector of the EARS appears to offer a close analogue to the events represented in the late Gardar Tugtutoq rift (Upton et al. 1990). The range is c. 100 km long, 20–30 km broad and occurs in the rapidly extending axial zone of the Danakil Depression (Barberi et al. 1970). A phase of simple fissural eruptions was replaced by the development of central-type caldera volcanoes. The volcanism gave rise to a progression from abundant early transitional basalts through serially decreasing volumes of Fe-rich intermediate compositions to culminating eruptions of highly differentiated trachytic and peralkaline rhyolitic products. Comparable Recent volcanic lineaments occur north of the Ethiopian sector along the western side of Saudi Arabia. Thus, the 600 km long Makkah–Madinah–Nafud volcanic fields, developed over the past 10 Ma, commenced like Erta'Ale, with voluminous transitional basalt activity, with younger activity involving not only basalts but differentiates ranging to trachyte and with peralkaline rhyolite produced in the most recent central-vent eruptions. The Makkah–Madinah–Nafud lineament is divided into smaller, en echelon, linear vent segments. It is concluded that uplift and erosion of structures such as those exemplified by Erta'Ale and Makkah–Madinah–Nafud would reveal intrusive lithologies, structures and sequences comparable to (although possibly on a smaller scale than) those displayed in the Tugtutoq region of the Gardar rifts.

## Scale and geological setting of the rifts

The Gardar province is an integral part of a major tectonomagmatic feature which traversed the Proterozoic supercontinent (Piper 1982). In a reassembled Laurentia (Fig. 7), the massive late Gardar dykes of the Tugtutoq–Ilimaussaq lineament are roughly colinear with the Great Abitibi Dyke, which is traceable for more than 700 km across the Canadian Shield (Ernst & Bell 1992). The dyke is formed of olivine gabbro to monzonite, is mineralogically and structurally similar to the Tugtutoq massive dykes, but is less silica-undersaturated. It appears to be slightly younger, however, having a U–Pb age of 1140.6 ± 2 Ma (Krogh et al. 1987), as compared with c. 1150 Ma for the Gardar rocks. If the Gardar rift and the Great Abitibi Dyke belong to the same broad tectonomagmatic event, their combined length exceeds 2000 km.

The Great Abitibi Dyke is about 30 Ma older than mafic volcanic rocks and dykes of the Keweenawan rift system, located in the Lake Superior basin. Ernst & Bell (1992) have inferred that they are again part of the same magmatic event. A further extension may be the Mid-continental Rift System (MRS), which traverses some 2000 km across the North American craton and which developed in a geologically brief period (15 Ma) of lithospheric extension and mafic magmatism (Hutchinson et al. 1990). The MRS consists of shallowly inward-dipping strata on the flanks, around a central graben or half-graben. A 15–20 km thick succession of

dominantly tholeiitic lavas, totalling some 1.3 million km³, was erupted mainly between 1098 and 1091 Ma ago (Nicholson & Shirey 1990). The MRS is underlain by some of the largest positive Bouguer gravity anomalies on the craton. Its dimensions are comparable to those of the EARS. The central basin is, for example, 80–100 km wide around Lake Superior, 40 km in Kansas and about 60 km in southern Michigan. The MRS shows a large-scale segmentation similar to that of the EARS (Rosendahl 1987).

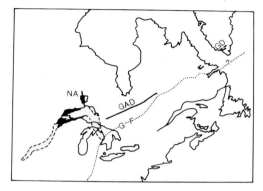

Fig. 7. The Gardar province as part of a major, mid-Proterozoic, tectonomagmatic province. GD: younger Gardar activity; GAD: Great Abitibi Dyke; black areas: Keweenawan volcanics; dotted area: mid-continent gravity high; G-F; Grenville Front. NA is the Nipigon arm of the speculative triple junction (Cannon & Hinze 1992).

It is possible to view the Gardar–Great Abitibi Dyke–Keweenawan–Mid-continental Rift sectors as being part of one, evolving rift system, >4000 km long, becoming progressively younger away from the Gardar. Furthermore, there is in detail a change from more silica-undersaturated, ITE-enriched varieties in the Gardar to tholeiitic types in the Keweenawan. It could be inferred that during the initial (Gardar province) stages of rift development, there was only small degree partial melting of the mantle sources, taking place incrementally over a long time period, and relatively little crustal separation. The Great Abitibi Dyke represents a more advanced stage, the more silica-saturated nature of the magmatism indicating higher degrees and/or levels of melting of the mantle sources. In both the Great Abitibi Dyke and Gardar, however, the mafic rocks show lithospheric signatures; any asthenospheric contribution to the melts was diluted. The generation in the MRS of an enormous volume of relatively homogeneous, tholeiitic magma in a restricted time interval suggests that the source was an adiabatically

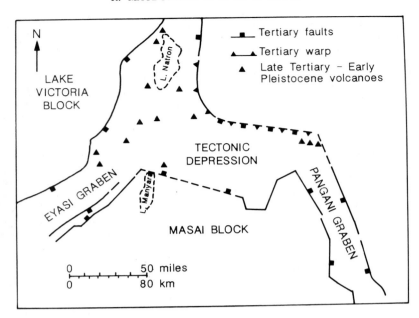

**Fig. 8.** Distribution of major mid-Tertiary faults, the late Tertiary tectonic depression, and Pliocene–Pleisto-cene volcanic centres, in northern Tanzania (adapted from Dawson 1992, figs 2 & 3).

decompressing, asthenospheric plume (Nichol-son & Shirey 1990; Hutchinson *et al.* 1990). Using the orientation of dyke swarms in the Lake Superior area as indicators of regional stress, Cannon & Hinze (1992) have suggested that the Great Abitibi Dyke system was gener-ated in response to farfield stresses related to the Grenville orogeny. This was replaced by a radial stress field during MRS times when the plume impinged on the base of the lithosphere. Full continental separation was, however, prevented because the craton was undergoing Grenville compression.

There are some similarities in this model to the development of the EARS. In Kenya, there is no unequivocal evidence from mafic magma chemistry of an asthenospheric component. Further north, in the Main Ethiopian Rift, basalt chemistry can be interpreted in terms of hybridization between asthenosphere- and litho-sphere-derived materials (Hart *et al.* 1989). Even further north, the system evolved to a stage beyond that of the MRS; it diverges into the oceanic spreading regions of the Red Sea and Gulf of Aden, where asthenosphere is palpably creating new lithosphere.

In both the EARS and Gardar, the rifts occupy long-lived zones of continental weak-ness. During the Proterozoic in eastern Africa, a collisional event resulted in the accretion of

a thick sequence of tectonized gneisses (the Mozambique Belt) onto the margin of the Nyanza craton (Fig.2). The Kenyan sector of the EARS straddles the margin of the craton, reflecting the larger-scale observation that African rifts are preferentially located around craton margins, following the trends of Protero-zoic orogenic belts (McConnell 1972; King 1978; Smith & Mosley 1993). Within the Mozambique Belt, a framework of crustal-scale ductile/brittle shear zones has controlled the location and geo-metry of graben structures and the pattern of magma emplacement (Smith & Mosley 1993). The latest rifting in northern Tanzania follows the grain of the Mozambique Belt, but fractures bounding the earlier, Tertiary, depression cut across the Belt (Fig.8). The Pangani graben is controlled by Proterozoic shear zones and the Eyasi graben cuts across the craton-mobile belt boundary, following the trend of a swarm of Proterozoic dykes (Dawson 1992). Also in Tan-zania, carbonatites are usually restricted to ex-tensive, linear, shear zones within the mobile belt close to the margin of the Tanzania craton. The mechanically weak zones have been repeatedly rejuvenated and probably extend deep into the crust (van Straaten 1989).

The position of the Gardar rift was also dic-tated by earlier tectonic episodes. The younger Gardar rifts developed within an area of plutonic rocks formed during the Ketilidian orogeny (1850–1600 Ma ago), but the province impinges on the marginal parts of the Archaean craton which composes much of southern Greenland. Windley (1991) recently proposed a model for the evolution of the early Proterozoic terrain of southern Greenland. A northern foreland (A, Fig. 4) is composed of Archaean (>2.6 Ga) gneisses unconformably overlain by supracrustal rocks of the Ketilidian Formation. The gneisses plus cover become increasingly deformed and metamorphosed southwards towards a major suture, the Kobberminebugt shear zone. South of the zone lies a complex granitoid batholith, the Julianehaab Granite (B-C, Fig. 4), regarded by Windley as being of Andean type. The Julianehaab Granite is bounded to the south by the Sardloq shear zone, which separates the batholith from a thrust stack of meta-supracrustals, paragneisses and rapakivi granites.

Gardar magmatism occurred on the craton, close to its southern margin (the Gronnedal-Ika intrusion, c. 1300 Ma ago, and the Kungnat and Ivigtut intrusions at c. 1219 Ma ago) but younger Gardar activity, including the Tugtutoq–Ilimaussaq lineament, lies within the Julianehaab Granite. Gardar rocks are absent in, and south of, the Sardloq shear zone.

The location of the rifts may be fundamentally related to the thermal and mechanical contrasts between the thicker, colder Archaean lithosphere and the thinner, hotter lithosphere of the orogenic belts. Gass et al. (1978) noted that orogenic regions, or mobile belts, of Africa tend to have higher elevation, higher heat flow, smaller lithospheric thicknesses and lower seismic velocities than the cratonic areas. It is possible that the thinner lithosphere has acted as a focus for upwelling asthenosphere, permitting local decompression melting (Thompson & Gibson 1991). The other physical properties of the mobile belts are then a result of the upwelling.

A further point of comparison between the EARS and Gardar phenomena is in the length of time between stabilization of the host craton and the initiation of rift activity. In Greenland, uplift, faulting and magmatism followed c. 400–600 Ma after Ketilidian plutonism, whilst in the MRS, the craton had been stable for at least 200 Ma before rifting. In East Africa, the Mesozoic rifting which acted as a precursor to the Cenozoic activity post-dated Pan-African events by c. 400 Ma. These delays between crustal stabilization and renewed rifting may be related to thermal blanketting by the lithosphere (Gass et al. 1978; Ashwal & Burke 1989). Large-scale development of lithospheric metasomes may well occur in the pre-rifting stage in response to

persistent small-degree melt infiltration from the asthenosphere. We envisage the rifts as providing linear foci for the repetitive, persistent genesis within the asthenosphere of small-scale, low viscosity, low density, asthenospheric melts rich in C, F, Cl, S and P that penetrated the overlying lithosphere, metasomatizing it and rendering it susceptible to further melting on development of a new thermal anomaly (Gass et al. 1978).

It is a common feature of continental rift systems that they show evidence of multiple episodes of magmatism and rifting, sometimes extending back into the Precambrian. In the Rungwa province of southern Tanzania, for example, a Tertiary–Recent alkaline province was preceded by alkali-carbonatite activity in the Mesozoic and by at least two earlier periods of similar magmatism in the late Precambrian–early Phanerozoic (Bailey 1977). In northern Kenya, the EARS was superimposed on an extensive Mesozoic rift system; recent geophysical surveys and hydrocarbon exploration have revealed a large, NW-trending trough in northern Kenya, the Anza graben (Fig.2), which was a Cretaceous–Tertiary rift itself possibly representing reactivation of a Triassic–Jurassic rift (Reeves et al. 1987).

In the Gardar, the Tugtutoq–Ilimaussaq rift represented reactivation of an early Gardar zone of faulting and magmatism, now preserved as a downfaulted supracrustal sequence of clastic sediments and alkaline lavas. The Motzfeldt intrusion, which lies within the lineament, has been dated at $1350 \pm 10$ Ma ago (Paslick et al. 1993). On a broader scale, Gardar activity persisted for c. 200 Ma, but was confined to a zone only 70 km wide. On the southern margin of the craton, rifting and alkaline magmatism (as exemplified by Kungnat and Ivigtut) at c. 1219 Ma ago occurred some 80 Ma after the emplacement of the Gronnedal-Ika foyaite-carbonatite centre at c. 1300 Ma ago.

The fact that rifting has been repeatedly controlled by pre-existing lithospheric structures raises the question of the role of mantle plumes; namely whether such plumes are responsible for rifting, taking advantage of relatively weak zones in the lithosphere, or whether the rifts are merely responses to dynamic stresses imposed from elsewhere. Although this question has not been satisfactorily resolved for the EARS, four lines of argument suggest a role for active rifting:

(1) The sub-vertical nature of the seismic and axial gravity anomalies and the fact that maximum lithospheric thinning appears to have taken place under the rift axis suggest that rift formation was controlled by pure

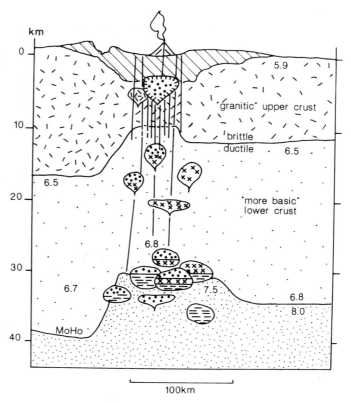

**Fig. 9.** Schematic representation of the structure of the crust and upper mantle beneath the axial part of the Kenya rift. The seismic structure and P-wave velocities are from KRISP Working Party (1991, fig. 3b). Igneous bodies – horizontal ruling: ultramafic cumulates; crosses: gabbros; random tics: syenites; dots: melt. Diagonal ruling represents rift infill.

shear deformation, with the asthenosphere playing an active role (Green *et al.* 1991; Smith & Mosley 1993).

(2) Despite the observation that extension across the rift has been small (?6–10 km; King 1978; Henry *et al.* 1990), great volumes of magma have been generated; Latin *et al.* (1993) estimate that 800 000 km³ of mafic magma have been formed over the last 30 Ma. Such a situation appears to require melting of a source substantially hotter than typical lithospheric mantle. It also requires involvement of sub-lithospheric mantle – the lithosphere beneath Kenya is simply not thick enough to be a reservoir for such melt volumes.

(3) The large volumes of magma are of alkaline compositions. If generation of these required small degrees of melting of large volumes of source peridotite, the segregation of such large volumes of melt may be impossible

from *asthenatic* (non-convecting) source. Incremental segregation from a large volume of convecting mantle along a developing zone of lithosphere attenuation may be a more likely explanation. We noted earlier, however, the constraint that the great heterogeneity of mafic magma compositions in both the Kenya and Gardar rifts is not likely to have been a result of the decompression melting of an upwelling, enriched, chemically homogeneous, mantle plume unless the melts have been severely modified by interaction with the lithosphere. It remains an open question as to how homogeneous the asthenosphere may be.

(4) In most sectors of the Kenya rift, volcanism normally preceded faulting and rifting. This would seem to preclude an origin for the magmas by decompressional melting in response to lithosphere extension.

# Deep crustal structure: significance of cumulates

Seismic evidence indicates that, on a regional basis, the crust is thinner under the axis of the Kenya rift than under the flanks (KRISP Working Party 1991). Nevertheless, under the central part of the Kenya Dome, the crust has not been significantly thinned, being >30 km thick even under the rift axis (Fig.9). Karson & Curtis (1989) have drawn attention to the requirement that emplacement of the huge volumes of volcanic rocks in the Kenya rift (109 400 km$^3$ between 4°N and 2°S) would have had to have been accompanied by the formation of even larger amounts of mafic and ultramafic cumulates (c. 373 000 km$^3$). Basaltic magma compositions indicate that a considerable proportion of the cumulates must have formed at or close to the crust–mantle boundary, maintaining crustal thickness by underplating, even where lithospheric extension may have been greatest.

From the evolved character of almost all Gardar igneous rocks at the present level of erosion, it can be inferred that Gardar magmatism also deposited great quantities of cumulates at all levels in the lithosphere wherever magma ascent was delayed or terminated. The levels at which the magmas may be expected to have undergone stagnation and extensive fractionation, namely those where significant density breaks occurred, include the crust-mantle boundary, boundaries between lower crustal mafic granulites and more silicic, upper crustal, amphibolitic gneisses (i.e. within the craton) or between deep crustal granulites and mid/upper crustal granitoids (e.g. within the Julienehaab Granite terrain), as well as at shallow levels where low-density supercrustal strata overlie gneisses and/or granitoids. At visible erosion levels such shallow-level cumulates are copiously represented. Xenoliths of coarse anorthositic cumulates are widespread throughout the Gardar intrusions. These anorthositic cumulates are nowhere seen in situ and are presumed to have been derived from large mid- or lower-crustal layered intrusions. It is likely that we observe only a highly biased sample of these deep-seated cumulates, the low-density, feldspar-rich facies being preferentially elutriated as xenoliths.

Assuming that Gardar basaltic magmas were derived from picritic primary melts, extensive fractionation of magnesian olivine must be postulated to have taken place at depth. The most magnesian olivine phenocrysts and cumulus olivine crystals observed in Gardar basaltic/gabbroic rocks have compositions of c. Fo$_{70}$ Conversely, olivine from peridotite xenoliths (representing refractory lithospheric mantle with which the primary magmas may have equilibrated?) entrained within Gardar ultramafic lamprophyres has a composition of Fo$_{91-92}$ (Upton 1990). Large volumes of ultramafic cumulates involving olivines with compositions Fo$_{91-70}$ (or less) may be hypothesized beneath the Gardar province. These are likely to be housed primarily (but not exclusively) within the upper parts of the lithospheric mantle.

The least-evolved Gardar basalt magmas reaching high levels commonly show indications that they have not experienced significant plagioclase fractionation (e.g. high Al/Ca and Sr values, lack of negative Eu anomalies, and textures signifying plagioclase supersaturation). Low Cr values suggest previous separation of garnet, spinel and/or pyroxene at depth. Pyroxene crystallization from the Gardar magmas at high crustal levels was characteristically late (i.e. relatively low temperature). However, pyroxene fractionation at higher pressures may have accompanied olivine in deep crustal or mantle level cumulate formation. A large positive gravity anomaly (up to 300 g.u.) reported by Blundell (1978) in association with the Tugtutoq lineament was interpreted by him as due to a major mafic intrusion some 80 km long by 25 km broad and which reaches close to surface level at one point but elsewhere lies at 3–5 km depth. Petrological indications are that this is almost certainly dominated by olivine-rich (dunitic), with subordinate olivine-plagioclase, cumulates.

Magma batches that were retained around the crust–mantle boundary may have evolved through relatively extended fractionation involving separation of olivine ± pyroxene and plagioclase, through hawaiitic to benmoreitic compositions before densities were lessened sufficiently for further ascent by diapiric and/or stoping mechanisms. In such a case the ultramafic and feldspathic cumulates may have respectively contributed to the uppermost mantle and lowermost crust in an overplating/underplating process as envisaged by Cox (1980).

Figure 9 may be considered to be a highly schematic cross-section through the uppermost mantle and lower crust underneath the axial sections of both rifts in their active stages. The lithospheric mantle contains pockets of ultramafic cumulates from the fractional crystallization of primitive basaltic magma and also crystallizing melt batches, the latter contributing to the low-density, low-velocity nature of the mantle under the rift axis. The crust has been thinned relative to the flanks by a combination of asthenospheric upwelling (perhaps in response to external, plate-driving stresses but more likely an expression of a deep thermal plume) and volume increase of the mantle on metasomatism. Underplating by basaltic magmas at or near to the crust–mantle boundary limits the amount of crustal extension, such that even under the rift axis the crust is locally >30 km thick. The Moho is at least partly determined by the transition from plagioclase-free to gabbroic cumulates in the EARS and from dunitic to anorthositic cumulates in the Gardar, and a lower crust containing bodies of basalt melt and gabbroic to ultramafic cumulates.

## The mid- and upper-crust gravity highs, dykes and central complexes

There is very little direct evidence for the nature of the mid-crustal regions beneath either rift. Seismic data for Kenya indicate a boundary between a granitic and a more mafic lower crust at about 15 km depth, whilst the brittle–ductile transition occurs at about 12 km (KRISP Working Party 1991). The form of mid-crustal intrusive bodies is unknown, though it is highly likely that in the Gardar province massive dykes pass through this zone.

At higher levels in both rifts, an estimated 5 km of volcanic and sedimentary fill overlies (EARS) or overlay (Gardar) a basement comprised of gneisses and granites. At this level, the rifts form a complementary pair, in that geophysical data for one can be interpreted using geological data for the other.

Superimposed on the −500 g.u. regional Bouguer anomaly over the EARS is a +200 g.u. gravity high centred on the rift axis. The maximum anomalies coincide with the young (<0.5 Ma) central volcanoes on the inner rift floor, and must represent, therefore, a high-density (2800 kg m$^{-3}$) body or bodies related in some way to the crustal structure under the centres. The most recent geological interpretation of the gravity anomaly is that by Swain (1992), who modelled it as resulting from pervasive dyke injection over the whole width of the inner graben (c. 40 km) and down to a depth of 22 km. The density increase of the dyke-injected crust (50–60 kg m$^{-3}$) implies that 22–26% of the crust is dykes. Superimposed on the axial high are gravity highs under the Suswa and Menengai caldera volcanoes, interpreted by Swain (1992) as basic intrusions.

The Tugtutoq–Ilimaussaq lineament provides clear evidence of the nature of the gravity high. A 30 km-wide gravity high of 300 g.u. amplitude is coincident with the axial zone of dykes and central complexes (Blundell 1978). It has been modelled as a mafic mass some 50 km long and 25 km wide, the top of which must have been <5 km from the Gardar land surface. From the petrology of the Tugtutoq massive dykes, it can be inferred that the high-density mass beneath is likely to be composed principally of olivine-rich (dunitic) and olivine-plagioclase (troctolitic) cumulates. Field evidence indicates that the anomaly is probably related to a combination of the regional dyke swarm (including the massive dykes), and high-level plutons, the interpretation used in Fig. 9. The plutons – the Central Tugtutoq, Narssaq and Ilimaussaq complexes – are composed almost exclusively of low-density felsic rocks, but they probably overlie higher density gabbroic roots. The plutons (central complexes) are composed of cumulates, often strikingly layered. They are thought to have formed from low viscosity, relatively anhydrous (but C- and halogen-rich) alkaline salic magmas (Upton & Emeleus 1987). Our unpublished observations are that syenitic xenoliths from Quaternary caldera volcanoes in Kenya, such as Kilombe, Longonot, Menengai and Suswa, are petrologically similar to Gardar syenites. We infer, therefore, that layered syenitic cumulates underlie the caldera volcanoes of the axial zone of the EARS.

There is no positive evidence of the existence of massive dykes beneath the EARS, although we note that geophysical studies cannot currently resolve such features from a dense swarm of thinner dykes. Dykes exceeding 100 m in width are rare in the Phanerozoic but relatively abundant in Precambrian swarms. One explanation for this is that asthenospheric convection was more vigorous in the Archaean and Proterozoic and shear rates on overlying lithospheric plates were greater. The greater stresses led to more dramatic lithospheric failure than in Phanerozoic rifts, and dyke formation tended to be longer-lived and more extensive. Huge volumes of relatively small-scale basaltic melts could have been concentrated and intruded as kilometre-scale mega-dykes.

We thank Dr D. Latin and an anonymous journal referee for very helpful reviews of the manuscript. RM's work in Kenya has been supported by the Natural Environment Research Council.

## References

ASHWAL, L. D. & BURKE, K. 1989. African lithospheric structure, volcanism, and topography. *Earth and Planetary Science Letters*, **96**, 8–14.

BAILEY, D. K. 1977. Lithosphere control of continental rift magmatism. *Journal of the Geological Society, London*, **133**, 103–106.

BAKER, B. H. 1987. Outline of the petrology of the Kenya rift alkaline province. *In*: FITTON, J. G. & UPTON, B. G. J. (eds) *Alkaline Igneous Rocks*. Geological Society, London, Special Publication, **30**, 293–311.

——, MOHR, P. A. & WILLIAMS, L. A. J. 1972. *Geology of the Eastern Rift System of Africa*. Geological Society of America Special Paper, **136**.

BANKS, R. J. & BEAMISH, D. 1979. Melting in the crust and upper mantle beneath the Kenya rift: evidence from geomagnetic deep sounding experiments. *Journal of the Geological Society, London*, **136**, 225–233.

BARBERI, F., BORSI, S., FERRARA, G., MARINELLI, G. & VARET, J. 1970. Relations between tectonics and magmatology in the northern Danakil Depression. *Philosophical Transactions of the Royal Society of London*, **A267**, 293–311.

BEDFORD, C. M. 1989. *The mineralogy, geochemistry, and petrogenesis of the Grønnedal-Ika alkaline igneous complex, south-west Greenland*. PhD thesis, University of Durham.

BLAXLAND, A. B., VAN BREEMEN, O., EMELEUS, C. H. & ANDERSON, J. G. 1978. Age and origin of the major syenite centers in the Gardar province of South Greenland: Rb–Sr studies. *Geological Society of America Bulletin*, **89**, 231–244.

BLUNDELL, D. J. 1978. A gravity survey across the Gardar igneous province, SW Greenland. *Journal of the Geological Society, London*, **135**, 545–554.

BOSWORTH, W. 1987. Off-axis volcanism in the Gregory rift, East Africa: Implications for models of continental rifting. *Geology*, **15**, 397–400.

——, LAMBAISE, J. & KEISLER, R. 1986. A new look at Gregory's rift: the structural style of continental rifting. *EOS*, **67**, 582–583.

BRIDGWATER, D. & COE, K. 1970. The role of stoping in the emplacement of the giant dykes of Isortoq, South Greenland. *In*: NEWALL, G. & RAST, N. (eds) *Mechanisms of Igneous Intrusion*. Geological Journal Special Issue, **2**, 67–78.

CANNON, W. F. & HINZE, W. J. 1992. Speculations on the origin of the North American Midcontinent rift. *Tectonophysics*, **213**, 49–55.

COX, K. G. 1980. A model for flood basalt volcanism. *Journal of Petrology*, **21**, 629–650.

DAVIES, G. R. & MACDONALD, R. 1987. Crustal influences in the petrogenesis of the Naivasha basalt-rhyolite complex: combined trace element and Sr–Nd–Pb isotope constraints. *Journal of Petrology*, **28**, 1009–1031.

DAWSON, J. B. 1992. Neogene tectonics and volcanicity in the North Tanzania sector of the Gregory Rift Valley: contrasts with the Kenya sector. *Tectonophysics*, **204**, 81–92.

—— & SMITH, J. V. 1988. Metasomatised and veined upper-mantle xenoliths from Pello Hill, Tanzania: evidence for anomalously-light mantle beneath the Tanzanian sector of the East African Rift Valley. *Contributions to Mineralogy and Petrology*, **100**, 510–527.

EMELEUS, C. H. 1964. The Grønnedal-Ika alkaline complex, South Greenland. The structure and geological history of the complex. *Bulletin*

*Grønlands Geologiske Undersøgelse*, **45** (also *Meddelelser om Grønland*, **172**, No. 3).

—— & HARRY, W. T. 1970. The Igaliko nepheline syenite complex. General description. *Bulletin Grønlands Geologiske Undersøgelse*, **85** (also *Meddelelser om Grønland*, **186**, No. 3).

—— & UPTON, B. G. J. 1974. The Gardar period in Southern Greenland. *In*: ESCHER, A. & WATT, W. S. (eds) *The Geology of Greenland*. The Geological Survey of Greenland, Copenhagen, 153–181.

ERNST, R. E. & BELL, K. 1992. Petrology of the Great Abitibi Dyke, Superior Province, Canada. *Journal of Petrology*, **33**, 423–469.

FAIRHEAD, J. D. 1976. The structure of the lithosphere beneath the Eastern Rift, East Africa, as deduced from gravity data. *Tectonophysics*, **30**, 269–298.

FITTON, J. G. & DUNLOP, H. M. 1985. The Cameroon Line, West Africa, and its bearing on the origin of oceanic and continental alkali basalt. *Earth and Planetary Science Letters*, **72**, 23–38.

——, JAMES, D., KEMPTON, P. D., ORMEROD, D. S. & LEEMAN, W. P. 1988. The role of lithospheric mantle in the generation of late Cenozoic basic magmas in the western United States. *Journal of Petrology* (Special Lithosphere Issue), 331–349.

——, —— & LEEMAN, W. P. 1991. Basic magmatism associated with late Cenozoic extension in the western United States: compositional variations in space and time. *Journal of Geophysical Research*, **96**, 13693–13711.

GASS, I. G., CHAPMAN, D. S., POLLACK, H. N. & THORPE, R. S. 1978. Geological and geophysical parameters of mid-plate volcanism. *Philosophical Transactions of the Royal Society of London*, **A288**, 581–597.

GREEN, W. V., ACHAUER, U. & MEYER R. P. 1991. A three-dimensional seismic image of the crust and upper mantle beneath the Kenya rift. *Nature*, **354**, 199–203.

—— & MEYER, R. P. 1992. Array observations of PKP phases across the Kenya Rift: Implications for structure and tectonics. *Tectonophysics*, **204**, 41–58.

HART, W. K., WOLDEGABRIEL, G., WALTER, R. C. & MERTZMAN, S. A. 1989. Basaltic volcanism in Ethiopia: constraints on continental rifting and mantle interactions. *Journal of Geophysical Research*, **94**, 7731–7748.

HENRY, W. J., MECHIE, J., MAGUIRE, P. K. H., KHAN, M. A., PRODEHL, C., KELLER, G. R. & PATEL, J. 1990. A seismic investigation of the Kenya Rift Valley. *Geophysical Journal International*, **100**, 107–130.

HUTCHINSON, D. R., WHITE, R. S., CANNON, W. F. & SCHULZ, K. J. 1990. Keweenaw hot spot: geophysical evidence for a 1.1 Ga mantle plume beneath the Midcontinent Rift System. *Journal of Geophysical Research*, **95**, 10869–10884.

KAMPUNZU, A. B. & MOHR, P. 1991. Magmatic evolution and petrogenesis in the East African Rift System. *In*: KAMPUNZU, A. B. & LUBALA, R. T. (eds) *Magmatism in Extensional Structural Settings*. Springer-Verlag, Berlin, 85–136.

KARSON, J. A. & CURTIS, P. C. 1989. Tectonic and

magmatic processes in the Eastern Branch of the East African Rift and implications for magmatically active continental rifts. *Journal of African Earth Sciences*, **8**, 431–453.

KING, B. C. 1978. Structural and volcanic evolution of the Gregory Rift Valley. *In*: BISHOP W. W. (ed.) *Geological Background to Fossil Man: Recent Research in the Gregory Rift Valley, East Africa*. Scottish Academic Press, Edinburgh, 29–54.

KRISP WORKING PARTY. 1991. Large-scale variation in lithospheric structure along and across the Kenya rift. *Nature*, **354**, 223–227.

KROGH, T. E., CORFU, F., DAVIS, D. W., DUNNING, G. R., HEAMAN, L. M., KAMO, S. L., MACHADO, N., GREENOUGH, J. D. & NAKAMURA, E. 1987. Precise U–Pb isotopic ages of diabase dykes and mafic to ultramafic rocks using trace amounts of baddeleyite and zircon. *In*: HALLS, H. C. & FAHRIG, W. F. (eds) *Mafic Dyke Swarms*. Geological Association of Canada Special Paper, **34**, 147–152.

LATIN, D., NORRY, M. J. & TARZEY, R. J. E. 1993. Magmatism in the Gregory rift, East Africa: evidence for melt generation by a plume. *Journal of Petrology*, in press.

LE BAS, M. J. 1977. *Carbonatite – Nephelinite Volcanism*. Wiley, New York.

—— 1987. Nephelinites and carbonatites. *In*: FITTON, J. G. & UPTON, B. G. J. (eds) *Alkaline Igneous Rocks*. Geological Society, London, Special Publication, **30**, 53–83.

MACDONALD, R. 1987. Quaternary peralkaline silicic rocks and caldera volcanoes of Kenya. *In*: FITTON, J. G. & UPTON, B. G. J. (eds) *Alkaline Igneous Rocks*. Geological Society, London, Special Publication, **30**, 313–333.

—— 1993. Petrological evidence regarding the evolution of the Kenya Rift Valley. *Tectonophysics*, in press.

MCCONNELL, R. B. 1972. Geological development of the rift system of eastern Africa. *Geological Society of America Bulletin*, **83**, 2549–2572.

NICHOLSON, S. W. & SHIREY, S. B. 1990. Midcontinent rift volcanism in the Lake Superior region: Sr, Nd, and Pb isotopic evidence for a mantle plume origin. *Journal of Geophysical Research*, **95**, 10851–10868.

NORRY, M. J., TRUCKLE, P. J., LIPPARD, S. J., HAWKESWORTH, C. J., WEAVER, S. D. & MARRINER, G. F. 1980. Isotopic and trace element evidence from lavas, bearing on mantle heterogeneity beneath Kenya. *Philosophical Transactions of the Royal Society of London*, **A297**, 259–271.

PARSONS, I. & BUTTERFIELD, A. W. 1981. Sedimentary features of the Nunarssuit and Klokken syenites, S. Greenland. *Journal of the Geological Society, London*, **138**, 289–306.

——, MASON, R. A., BECKER, S. M. & FINCH, A. A. 1991. Biotite equilibria and fluid circulation in the Klokken intrusion. *Journal of Petrology*, **32**, 1299–1333.

PASLICK, C. R., HALLIDAY, A. N., DAVIES, G. R., MEZGER, K. & UPTON, B. G. J. 1993. Timing of Proterozoic magmatism in the Gardar province,

Southern Greenland. *Geological Society of America Bulletin*, **105**, 272–278.

PIPER, J. D. A. 1982. The Precambrian palaeomagnetic record: the case for the Proterozoic Supercontinent. *Earth and Planetary Science Letters*, **59**, 61–89.

REEVES, C. V., KARANJA, F. M. & MACLEOD, I. N. 1987. Geophysical evidence for a failed Jurassic rift and triple junction in Kenya. *Earth and Planetary Science Letters*, **81**, 299–311.

ROSENDAHL, B. R. 1987. Architecture of continental rifts with special reference to East Africa. *Annual Review of Earth and Planetary Sciences*, **15**, 445–503.

SMITH, M. & MOSLEY, P. 1993. Crustal heterogeneity and basement influence on the development of the Kenya Rift, East Africa. *Tectonics*, **12**, 591–606.

SWAIN, C. J. 1992. The Kenya rift axial gravity high: a re-interpretation. *Tectonophysics*, **204**, 59–70.

THOMPSON, R. N. & GIBSON, S. A. 1991. Subcontinental mantle plumes, hotspots and pre-existing thinspots. *Journal of the Geological Society, London*, **148**, 973–977.

——, LEAT, P. T., DICKIN, A. P., MORRISON, M. A., HENDRY, G. L. & GIBSON, S. A. 1989. Strongly potassic mafic magmas from lithospheric mantle sources during continental extension and heating: evidence from Miocene minettes of northwest Colorado. *Earth and Planetary Science Letters*, **98**, 139–153.

UPTON, B. G. J. 1990. Gardar mantle xenoliths: Igdlutalik, South Greenland. *Rapport Grønlands Geologiske Undersøgelse*, **150**, 37–43.

—— & BLUNDELL, D. J. 1978. The Gardar igneous province: evidence for Proterozoic continental rifting. *In*: NEUMANN, E. R. & RAMBERG, I. B. (eds) *Petrology and Geochemistry of Continental Rifts*. Reidel, Dordrecht, 163–172.

—— & EMELEUS, C. H. 1987. Mid-Proterozoic alkaline magmatism in southern Greenland: the Gardar province. *In*: FITTON, J. G. & UPTON, B. G. J. (eds) *Alkaline Igneous Rocks*. Geological Society, London, Special Publication, **30**, 449–471.

——, MARTIN, A. R. & STEPHENSON, D. 1990. Evolution of the Tugtutoq Central Complex, South Greenland: a high-level, rift-axial, late-Gardar centre. *Journal of Volcanology and Geothermal Research*, **43**, 195–214.

VAN STRAATEN, P. 1989. Nature and structural relationships of carbonatites from Southwest and West Tanzania. *In*: BELL, K. (ed) *Carbonatites*. Unwin Hyman, London, 177–199.

WILLIAMS, L. A. J. 1972. The Kenya rift volcanics: a note on volumes and chemical composition. *Tectonophysics*, **15**, 83–96.

——, MACDONALD, R. & CHAPMAN, G. R. 1984. Late Quaternary volcanoes of the Kenya rift valley. *Journal of Geophysica Research*, **89**, 8553–8570.

WINDLEY, B. F. 1991. Early Proterozoic collision tectonics, and rapakivi granites as intrusions in an extensional thrust-thickened crust: the Ketilidian orogen, South Greenland. *Tectonophysics*, **195**, 1–10.

# Alkali basalts from Shuqra, Yemen: magmas generated in the crust-mantle transition zone?

K. G. COX, N. CHARNLEY, R. C. O. GILL[1] & K. A. PARISH

*Department of Earth Sciences, Parks Road, Oxford OX1 3PR, UK*
[1]*Present address: Department of Geology, Royal Holloway and Bedford New College, Egham Hill, Egham, Surrey, TW20 0EX, UK*

**Abstract**: The alkali basalts from Shuqra, Yemen, contain a megacryst suite consisting of olivine, aluminous diopside, kaersutite, pleonaste, plagioclase, and apatite. Deformational kink bands in the olivines, and the existence of multi-phase inclusions (e.g. olivine + pleonaste, aluminous diopside + pleonaste, kaersutite + pleonaste, aluminous diopside + plagioclase) suggest that the megacrysts are derived from disaggregated plutonic rocks. Whole-rock compositional variation cannot have been generated by the fractionation of the phenocrysts present (olivine, augite, labradorite), but is readily explicable as a mixing line between alkali basalt melt and restite, represented by the megacryst suite. It is suggested that the source rock was a deep-crustal, or uppermost mantle, hydrous, and very alkalic, picritic, gabbroic, or syenogabbroic intrusion, which was remelted, perhaps by the injection of further picritic magma. Although the Shuqra rocks themselves do not appear to contain mantle xenoliths, the proposed mechanism of magma generation, if operating on an interleaved crust/mantle transition zone, could provide a general explanation for the occurrence of occasional alkali basalt flows which are extremely rich in spinel lherzolite inclusions.

The recent alkali basaltic volcanics from Shuqra, Yemen, were first studied by a Royal Society expedition in 1964, led by the late I. G. Gass and including D. I. J. Mallick and the present senior author (Gass *et al.* 1965). An account of the general geology of the area was given by Cox *et al.* (1977), and on the basis of petrography and limited analytical work some speculative petrological suggestions were made. Until now, however, no detailed information has been published on the mineralogy and geochemistry of what has, indeed, proved to be an exceptionally interesting group of rocks. It is a pleasure to be able to produce this paper, albeit so belatedly, as a tribute to Ian Gass.

The town of Shuqra lies on the northern coast of the Gulf of Aden approximately 100 km ENE of Aden itself (see Fig. 1). The geologically-recent Shuqra volcanic field extends east of the town for 80 km, and inland for about 50 km. Only the western part has been studied in detail. The volcanic rocks consist of a series of prominent cinder cones, in some cases rising 300 m above the general surface, and an extensive coalescing apron of basaltic lava flows. These overlie a faulted monoclinal sequence of Jurassic limestones, dipping towards the Gulf of Aden, which themselves overlie Precambrian basement. The lava field represents the most recent volcanic activity on the north shore of the western part of the Gulf of Aden (the Aden volcanic line), which

included earlier the central volcanoes of Perim (Mallick *et al.* 1990), Jebel Khariz (Gass & Mallick 1968), Jebel Umm Birka, and Ras Imran, Little Aden, and Aden (Cox *et al.* 1970). Volcanism appears to have started in the west at Perim Island at *c.* 10 Ma and to have moved eastwards with time to the most recent site at Shuqra. The erupted rocks also show a progressive change of composition, from the relatively silica-rich basalts and basaltic andesites of Perim to the undersaturated Shuqra alkali basalts (see Mallick *et al.* 1990 for review). Although in some ways the Shuqra volcanism appears to extend the compositional and age-trend of the Aden line, it shows two important differences. The other volcanoes are all of the central type, whereas the Shuqra field consists of many relatively small separate eruptive centres. Secondly, the other volcanoes contain a full series of rock types between basaltic compositions and rhyolites or trachytes. There is every indication that the evolved rock types are the products of extensive fractional crystallization in high-level magma chambers. In contrast, the Shuqra rocks are relatively primitive, with MgO contents in the range 5–12 wt%. We shall argue that the Shuqra magmas have been erupted directly through the crust without the establishment of high-level chambers.

The previous study of Shuqra (Cox *et al.* 1977) showed that the lavas contain a wide-

*From* Prichard, H. M., Alabaster, T., Harris, N. B. W. & Neary, C. R. (eds), 1993,
*Magmatic Processes and Plate Tectonics*, Geological Society Special Publication No. 76, 443–453.

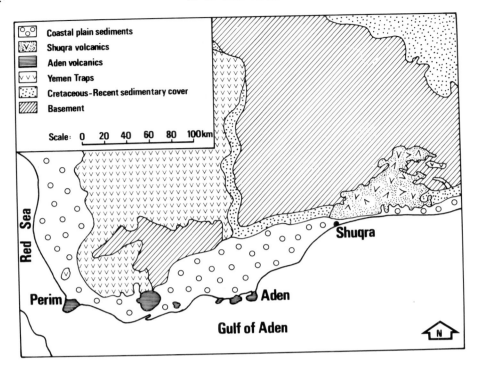

**Fig. 1.** Location map of the Shuqra volcanic field.

spread suite of **megacrysts** (large crystals showing evidence of being out of equilibrium with the
host liquids), consisting of olivine, kaersutite,
aluminous diopside, pleonaste, and basic plagioclase. To this list apatite can now be added.
The modal amount of megacryst material present in individual flows has not been determined,
but field observations suggest that it is unlikely
to exceed 10 volume percent, and is mainly
substantially less than that. The most evolved
rocks (lowest MgO) do not appear to contain
any.
   **Phenocrysts** (distinguished by smaller size
and lack of disequilibrium features) of olivine,
augite, and plagioclase were also identified. The
compositional trend of the whole-rock compositions was not investigated in detail, but it was
clear that it was unlikely to have been generated
by fractionation of the observed phenocrysts.
Hence it was suggested that the megacryst suite
might represent fragments of the source material
(i.e. restite), and that the compositional trend
might represent a mixing line between the original melt and the source composition. The present study has amply confirmed the feasibility of
this general model.

## The megacryst suite

The megacryst suite most closely corresponds
with the Group A megacrysts of Irving (1984)
i.e. an assemblage typified by Al-augite, Al-
bronzite, olivine, kaersutitic amphibole, pyropic
garnet, pleonaste and plagioclase, although
orthopyroxene and garnet have not been
observed from Shuqra.
   Plagioclase crystals up to 1 cm across and
somewhat smaller clinopyroxenes and olivines
are the most commonly observed megacrysts in
hand specimens, but occasional samples also
contain 1 cm kaersutites. In thin sections plagioclase, clinopyroxene, and olivine megacrysts,
though generally smaller than those described
above, are widely distributed. Kaersutite and
spinel are much less common and are seen in
only about 20% of thin sections. Relatively large
apatite crystals are enclosed in plagioclase and
clinopyroxene megacrysts.
   Many of the megacrysts seen in thin sections
appear as single crystals, but aggregates of two
or more phases have been observed in a number
of cases. For example, smaller grains of pleonaste have been observed embedded or partially

**Table 1.** *Mineral analyses*

| | Olivine megacrysts | | Pyroxene megacrysts | | Pyroxene phenocrysts | | Amphibole megacrysts | | Spinel megacrysts | | Plagioclase megacrysts | |
|---|---|---|---|---|---|---|---|---|---|---|---|---|
| | 1 | 2 | 3 | 4 | 5 | 6 | 7 | 8 | 9 | 10 | 11 | 12 |
| $SiO_2$ | 40.66 | 39.75 | 47.07 | 46.63 | 48.71 | 47.35 | 39.84 | 39.62 | — | — | 59.03 | 51.78 |
| $TiO_2$ | — | — | 2.19 | 2.00 | 1.51 | 1.91 | 5.54 | 5.58 | 0.57 | 0.70 | — | — |
| $Al_2O_3$ | 0.06 | — | 9.27 | 9.57 | 4.78 | 7.37 | 15.19 | 14.79 | 60.98 | 60.61 | 25.80 | 30.16 |
| $Fe_2O_3$ | — | — | — | — | — | — | — | — | 5.58 | 6.56 | — | — |
| $FeO$ | 12.38 | 17.10 | 5.78 | 5.39 | 9.16 | 7.74 | 7.93 | 9.43 | 13.89 | 13.71 | 0.1 | 0.43 |
| $MnO$ | 0.17 | 0.24 | 0.12 | 0.09 | 0.24 | 0.18 | 0.09 | 0.14 | 0.12 | 0.13 | — | — |
| $MgO$ | 46.80 | 43.46 | 13.32 | 13.51 | 13.53 | 13.17 | 14.02 | 13.27 | 18.27 | 18.28 | — | — |
| $CaO$ | 0.30 | 0.14 | 21.22 | 21.48 | 21.10 | 21.44 | 11.25 | 10.82 | — | — | 7.51 | 13.35 |
| $Na_2O$ | — | — | 0.73 | 0.72 | 0.68 | 0.56 | 2.86 | 2.88 | — | — | 6.95 | 3.88 |
| $K_2O$ | — | — | — | — | — | — | 0.72 | 0.72 | — | — | 0.52 | 0.27 |
| $Cr_2O_3$ | — | — | — | — | — | — | — | — | 0.21 | 0.44 | — | — |
| $NiO$ | 0.36 | 0.22 | — | — | 0.05 | 0.10 | — | — | — | — | n.d. | n.d. |

Total Fe as FeO except for spinels, where Fe-oxidation is calculted from stoichiometry.
n.d. = not detected.

embedded in olivines, aluminous diopsides, and kaersutites. Similarly, several examples of associated aluminous diopside and plagioclase have been found, and apatite is often included in these. Although the polymineralic grains could represent the partially dissolved remains of high-pressure glomeroporphyritic phenocryst aggregates, we consider it at least as likely that they represent the disaggregated remains of a former series of solid rocks composed of the mineral assemblage: olivine + aluminous diopside + kaersutite + pleonaste + plagioclase + apatite. The impression that the megacrysts were derived from a rock protolith is reinforced by the common occurrence of deformational kink bands in the olivines, which probably formed in a rock matrix rather than within a liquid, and by the comparative lack of zoning of individual grains (see below).

Because of the range of compositions in some of the megacrysts (see below), the proposed protolith was probably a somewhat variable suite of rocks rather than a specific composition. Clearly, though, it was a volatile-bearing and highly alkalic suite. As we shall show in a later section it is possible to estimate the relative proportions of the ferromagnesian minerals originally present but the amount of feldspar is not determinable.

With regard to mineral compositions, the **olivine** megacrysts show little zoning (typically less than 2% Fo) but a wide range of compositions between $Fo_{79}$ and $Fo_{88}$. **Plagioclase** megacrysts, are also very variable in composition, being andesines and labradorites in the range $An_{38}$–$An_{65}$. Zoning in individual megacrysts is not obvious, though a little reverse zoning is seen on the margins of some. Our microprobe studies have revealed less variation in the compositions of pyroxenes, spinels, and kaersutites, but this may be an effect of sampling. The pyroxenes have distinctive compositions, and are **aluminous diopsides** with $Al_2O_3$ in the range 8–10 wt%. The distinctive feature of the **kaersutites** is their very high $TiO_2$ (5–6 wt%) and very low $SiO_2$ (*c.* 40 wt%). Spinels are **pleonastes**, with very low Cr-contents.

Selected microprobe analyses of megacrysts are given in Table 1.

## Phenocrysts

The distinction between phenocrysts and megacrysts previously made on petrographic grounds has been confirmed by microprobe studies, at least in the case of the clinopyroxenes and plagioclases. **Olivine** phenocrysts are very variable in composition, most commonly approaching the same high-Mg values as the megacrysts (e.g. $Fo_{80}$–$Fo_{88}$). Nevertheless more Fe-rich examples do exist in the range $Fo_{68}$–$Fo_{80}$. **Augite** phenocrysts are easy to distinguish from diopside megacrysts because of their lower $Al_2O_3$ contents (4–7 wt%), and there appears to be no overlap with the $Al_2O_3$ contents of the megacrysts. **Plagioclase** phenocrysts are mostly calcic labradorites ($An_{60}$–$An_{70}$), occasionally extending into the bytownite range (as calcic as $An_{74}$. On average the phenocrystal plagioclases are clearly significantly more calcic than the megacrysts.

## Whole-rock compositional variation

In the course of the present study 20 whole-rocks have been analysed for major and selected trace elements by XRF, and for Cr by AA (Table 2). The rocks are mineralogically fresh but frequently contain oxidized and semi-opaque interstitial glasses. Inter-element relationships are somewhat scattered but approximate to linearity (see MgO variation diagrams in Fig. 2). The two most magnesian rocks (S.982 and S.983) are rich in olivine phenocrysts and appear in most elemental respects to be cumulus-enriched versions of more evolved magmas with *c.* 9% MgO. They are omitted from the following discussion.

As MgO falls we see increases in $SiO_2$, $Al_2O_3$, $Na_2O$, $K_2O$, Sr, Rb, Zr, and Nb. Slight decreases takes place in CaO and stronger decreases in Cu, Ni, and Cr. $Fe_2O_3$ (total) and $TiO_2$ remain almost constant. Silica-saturation correlates well with MgO, and the less-magnesian rocks are clearly the least silica-undersaturated (see Fig. 3). The decrease in silica-saturation with evolution to more evolved compositions rules out the possibility that the fractionation trend is generated mainly by removal or addition of the observed phenocryst assemblage (olivine + augite + plagioclase), though fractionation of this assemblage may have generated some of the scatter seen in the trend.

Obviously the role of the megacryst suite in the fractionation process now becomes of great interest, because it includes the two strongly silica-undersaturated phases, kaersutite and spinel. Removal of such an assemblage from the most basic magmas could clearly drive residual liquids towards the plane of critical silica saturation.

To investigate this question in more detail we have estimated the compositions of two end-member magmas with 5% and 11% MgO, respectively. Extrapolation of the trend between the two end-members into more magnesian compositions, using regression lines against MgO,

**Table 2.** *Whole-rock analyses*

| | S.953 | S.954 | S.957 | S.958 | S.959 | S.960 | S.961 | S.963 | S.964 | S.969 | S.982 | S.983 | S.984 | S.985A | S.986A | S.986C | S.987 | S.991 | S.1000 | S.1002 |
|---|---|---|---|---|---|---|---|---|---|---|---|---|---|---|---|---|---|---|---|---|
| $SiO_2$ | 45.68 | 45.19 | 46.24 | 47.39 | 48.86 | 46.55 | 46.75 | 47.16 | 45.26 | 45.54 | 44.02 | 44.35 | 44.85 | 45.13 | 45.09 | 45.63 | 45.97 | 45.38 | 44.84 | 44.42 |
| $TiO_2$ | 2.03 | 2.18 | 2.10 | 2.03 | 1.97 | 2.21 | 2.16 | 2.11 | 2.30 | 1.90 | 2.04 | 2.07 | 2.34 | 2.38 | 2.30 | 2.32 | 2.18 | 1.71 | 2.31 | 2.31 |
| $Al_2O_3$ | 16.03 | 15.55 | 16.61 | 16.80 | 17.30 | 16.09 | 17.66 | 17.94 | 15.35 | 16.21 | 15.00 | 15.07 | 15.89 | 16.52 | 17.24 | 17.58 | 15.93 | 15.48 | 16.06 | 16.15 |
| $Fe_2O_3$ | 1.95 | 1.29 | 5.18 | 1.09 | 3.89 | 3.52 | 5.25 | 9.54 | 0.91 | 3.83 | 3.85 | 2.52 | 1.96 | 2.36 | 4.24 | 4.64 | 8.11 | 3.58 | 2.27 | 1.99 |
| $FeO$ | 7.26 | 8.87 | 5.46 | 8.52 | 6.00 | 7.05 | 4.41 | 0.64 | 8.85 | 6.01 | 6.88 | 8.25 | 7.59 | 7.40 | 5.69 | 5.37 | 2.03 | 5.67 | 7.42 | 7.63 |
| $MnO$ | 0.15 | 0.18 | 0.17 | 0.18 | 0.18 | 0.17 | 0.16 | 0.16 | 0.16 | 0.16 | 0.17 | 0.18 | 0.16 | 0.16 | 0.17 | 0.17 | 0.15 | 0.16 | 0.17 | 0.16 |
| $MgO$ | 10.35 | 8.52 | 8.70 | 6.72 | 5.03 | 9.50 | 6.47 | 5.94 | 10.87 | 9.62 | 11.36 | 11.71 | 10.65 | 9.87 | 7.43 | 7.17 | 9.85 | 9.30 | 10.22 | 9.79 |
| $CaO$ | 11.46 | 10.61 | 9.58 | 9.10 | 10.07 | 10.43 | 8.66 | 9.10 | 10.65 | 11.20 | 10.15 | 10.19 | 11.56 | 10.54 | 10.08 | 9.50 | 10.37 | 13.08 | 11.48 | 11.08 |
| $Na_2O$ | 2.89 | 3.18 | 3.53 | 3.97 | 3.92 | 3.60 | 4.18 | 4.56 | 3.33 | 2.53 | 2.76 | 3.01 | 3.52 | 3.44 | 2.95 | 4.04 | 3.59 | 3.10 | 3.14 | 3.28 |
| $K_2O$ | 0.89 | 1.40 | 1.13 | 1.15 | 1.70 | 1.10 | 1.55 | 1.59 | 1.11 | 0.90 | 0.88 | 1.02 | 1.17 | 1.19 | 1.47 | 1.46 | 1.19 | 0.69 | 1.13 | 1.10 |
| $P_2O_5$ | 0.43 | 0.57 | 0.54 | 0.57 | 0.54 | 0.52 | 0.67 | 0.63 | 0.50 | 0.42 | 0.57 | 0.57 | 0.38 | 0.41 | 0.68 | 0.66 | 0.46 | 0.36 | 0.41 | 0.40 |
| L.O.I. | 1.69 | 2.05 | 0.61 | 2.76 | 2.01 | 0.57 | 2.03 | 1.55 | 1.20 | 2.09 | 1.77 | 1.12 | 0.78 | 0.69 | 3.15 | 1.37 | 1.41 | 3.10 | 1.26 | 0.78 |
| Total | 100.81 | 99.59 | 99.85 | 100.28 | 101.47 | 101.22 | 99.93 | 100.83 | 100.49 | 100.42 | 99.45 | 100.06 | 100.85 | 100.09 | 100.48 | 99.91 | 101.24 | 101.61 | 100.71 | 99.09 |
| Sr (ppm) | 612 | 676 | 566 | 649 | 651 | 542 | 630 | 677 | 573 | 499 | 613 | 569 | 526 | 529 | 787 | 665 | 580 | 532 | 580 | 597 |
| Rb | 20 | 34 | 27 | 67 | 38 | 25 | 42 | 40 | 26 | 35 | 21 | 22 | 27 | 28 | 34 | 37 | 30 | 11 | 28 | 28 |
| Zr | 157 | 201 | 175 | 230 | 241 | 168 | 240 | 234 | 171 | 127 | 162 | 160 | 160 | 168 | 221 | 218 | 174 | 149 | 176 | 171 |
| Nb | 48 | 60 | 51 | 65 | 66 | 48 | 64 | 61 | 50 | 38 | 44 | 44 | 49 | 51 | 66 | 66 | 52 | 44 | 54 | 53 |
| Y | 23 | 25 | 25 | 26 | 26 | 25 | 29 | 28 | 25 | 23 | 25 | 25 | 24 | 25 | 28 | 27 | 26 | 22 | 27 | 25 |
| Zn | 60 | 73 | 71 | 71 | 68 | 68 | 70 | 69 | 65 | 61 | 70 | 70 | 61 | 59 | 66 | 67 | 63 | 57 | 68 | 64 |
| Cu | 66 | 65 | 64 | 60 | 55 | 61 | 51 | 49 | 70 | 82 | 73 | 76 | 66 | 64 | 50 | 47 | 61 | 66 | 64 | 67 |
| Ni | 186 | 168 | 152 | 99 | 69 | 160 | 85 | 82 | 205 | 167 | 255 | 256 | 139 | 139 | 96 | 99 | 169 | 170 | 155 | 159 |
| Cr | — | — | 399 | — | — | 258 | 66 | 91 | 301 | — | — | — | 183 | — | 122 | — | — | — | 244 | 239 |

Major element and trace elements by X-ray fluorescence except for $Fe_2O_3$ (Wilson titration) and Cr (atomic absorption).

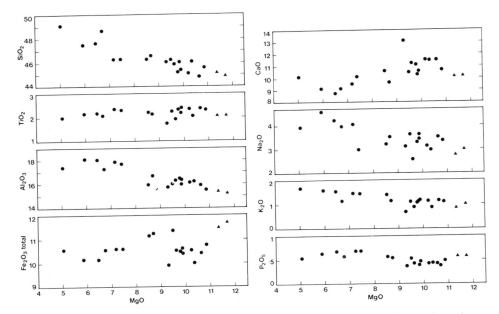

**Fig. 2.** Major and trace elements plotted against MgO. The two olivine-enriched samples are shown by triangles.

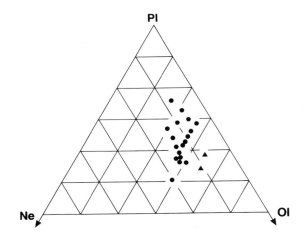

**Fig. 3.** Normative whole-rock compositions projected into the Ol–Pl–Ne triangle (grid lines at 10% intervals). Norms were calculated assuming $Fe^{3+}/(Fe^{3+} + Fe^{2+}) = 0.1$. Note the displacement of the olivine-enriched samples towards the olivine apex.

shows that several elements (notably K, Rb, and Zr) fall to near-zero concentrations at about 18–19% MgO (see Table 3). Hence, any solid material (the 'extract' in the sense of Cox *et al.* 1979) which is removed from the more basic liquid to generate the more evolved, cannot contain more MgO than this.

Next we have employed mixing calculations based on Wright & Doherty (1970) to see whether mixtures of the megacryst suite minerals can be extracted from the 11% MgO liquid to generate the bulk composition of the 5% MgO liquid. The results of six calculations are given in Table 4, the first two using no plagioclase in the

**Table 3.** *Elemental regression lines*

|  | Evolved liquid | Basic liquid | 18% MgO extract | 19% MgO extract |
|---|---|---|---|---|
| SiO$_2$ | 48.56 | 45.01 | 40.88 | 40.29 |
| TiO$_2$ | 2.07 | 2.22 | 2.39 | 2.41 |
| Al$_2$O$_3$ | 18.18 | 15.66 | 12.73 | 12.31 |
| FeO(T) | 10.49 | 10.59 | 10.70 | 10.72 |
| MnO | 0.18 | 0.16 | 0.13 | 0.13 |
| MgO | 5.00 | 11.00 | 18.00 | 19.00 |
| CaO | 8.93 | 11.46 | 14.41 | 14.83 |
| Na$_2$O | 4.18 | 3.04 | 1.72 | 1.53 |
| K$_2$O | 1.63 | 0.95 | 0.16 | 0.05 |
| P$_2$O$_5$ | 0.67 | 0.40 | 0.09 | 0.04 |
| Sr | 701 | 542 | 357 | 329 |
| Rb | 42 | 24 | 3 | 0 |
| Zr | 252 | 147 | 24 | 6 |
| Nb | 69 | 46 | 20 | 16 |
| Y | 28 | 24 | 20 | 19 |
| Zn | 71 | 62 | 52 | 50 |
| Cu | 49 | 70 | 96 | 98 |
| Ni | 64 | 186 | 330 | 350 |
| Cr | 64 | 294 | 564 | 602 |

Columns 1 and 2 are estimated end-member liquid compositions. Columns 3 and 4 show estimated elemental concentrations at 18 and 19% MgO when trends in Fig. 1 are regressed into Mg-rich composition.

**Table 4.** *Mineral percentages in calculated extracts*

| OL 1 | 15.46 | — | 15.27 | 15.71 | — | — |
|---|---|---|---|---|---|---|
| OL 2 | — | 16.19 | — | — | 16.08 | 15.96 |
| AMPH 1 | 19.94 | — | 20.68 | 20.55 | — | — |
| AMPH 2 | — | 20.33 | — | — | 21.85 | 22.03 |
| CPX | 57.32 | 57.04 | 53.16 | 55.12 | 49.47 | 51.77 |
| SP | 7.28 | 6.50 | 6.51 | 6.74 | 5.02 | 5.83 |
| PL 1 | — | — | 4.46 | — | 7.58 | — |
| PL 2 | — | — | — | 1.87 | — | 4.41 |
| Total % | 43.14 | 43.72 | 45.32 | 43.74 | 47.77 | 44.93 |
| MgO% | 19.25 | 18.52 | 18.31 | 19.19 | 17.39 | 18.35 |
| Fit | 0.75 | 0.31 | 1.34 | 0.94 | 1.08 | 0.97 |

Each vertical column represents one calculation, showing minerals used and amount required in the extract. Mineral compositions used are from the following columns in Table 1: OL1–1, OL2–2, AMPH1–7, AMPH2–8, CPX–3, SP–9, PL1–11, PL2–12. MgO% indicates bulk MgO of the assemblages given. 'Fit' signifies Sigma $r^2$, where $r$ is the difference between the concentration of an element in the calculated evolved liquid and the concentration actually present in column 1.

input, and the remaining four using all five minerals. The degree of fit is quite reasonable in all cases, but no particular emphasis should be attached to the second calculation where the fit is best. The general features of all the calculations are however:

1. the bulk compositions of the extracted assem-blages are all very close to the value of 18–19% MgO predicted from the regression line analysis above;

2. mineral proportions for olivine, amphibole, clinopyroxene, and spinel remain consistent throughout, at *c.* 16:20:53:6, and the total amount of extract is *c.* 44 wt%;

3. the fits without plagioclase (columns 1 and 2)

are certainly no worse than the others, and when plagioclase is included the amount required is always rather small;

4. although not included in the table, calculations excluding amphibole are always unsatisfactory because they fail to explain the behaviour of $TiO_2$.

From the major element considerations we cannot be certain whether plagioclase is a necessary part of the extracted assemblage or not. However, it is clearly not a voluminous constituent. Otherwise, the extraction of the ferromagnesian phases in the megacryst suite appears to account very satisfactorily for the major element composition of the 5% MgO liquid. The amphibole ought to contribute about 0.3% $K_2O$ to the extract, which is a little higher than the estimates in Table 3, though given the scattered nature of the data, clearly within error.

Amongst the trace elements, Zn, Cu, Ni, and Cr (see Table 3) are evidently present in significant amounts within the extracted assemblage, while Rb, Zr, and Nb are low, clearly in accord with the dominantly ferromagnesian mineralogy. Sr provides the interesting exception, since it appears to have a concentration of > 300 ppm in the extract. During the study this presented a real problem for a time, because it was not clear how so much Sr could be accommodated in the extracted minerals. However, it transpired that there was so much Sr in the amphibole and the plagioclase that it could be analytically determined, at least semi-quantitatively, on the electron microprobe. Analysed amphibole contains $475 \pm 50$ ppm, and plagioclases from 1740–2500 ppm. An extract containing 20% amphibole and 9% plagioclase (of the high-Sr type) would provide the necessary Sr-content of the total extract, i.e. *c.* 320 ppm. This seems to suggest that at least some plagioclase was included in the extracted assemblage, although the possibility of Sr in apatite has not been investigated.

## Petrogenetic model

Group A megacrysts have generally been regarded as having a genetic relationship with their host liquids (e.g. Irving & Frey 1984, Menzies *et al.* 1987, Schulze 1987), most often being interpreted as products of high-pressure crystallization. The calculations above certainly provide an excellent demonstration of the genetic link between a megacryst suite and its host magma, and show that the Shuqra basalts could have originated by the fractional crystallization of such a suite. However, impressed by the

petrographic evidence that the megacrysts are at least as likely to have been derived from a solid protolith as to have been phenocrysts, in the following section we explore the alternative possibility, that is that the megacrysts are restite material derived from the source.

The possibility that crystalline materials brought to the surface during basic magmatism represent restites has to our knowledge only been postulated once before, i.e. for the Nuanetsi picrite basalts from the Karoo province (Cox 1987). The cases share the common feature that the crystals of interest are usually present in very small amounts, yet were widely distributed in substantial quantities of erupted magma, suggesting that they were not accidental inclusions but bore some more-fundamental relationships to the magmas in which they were enclosed. In the Karoo case the distinctive feature is the unique deformational fabric which the entrained aggregates of orthopyroxene show, suggesting that these do not represent high-pressure phenocrysts.

Although in the present case the postulated protolith for the megacryst suite was evidently somewhat variable, we assume for simplicity in this section that it had a fixed composition, which we will refer to as the source composition because we suggest that the alkali basaltic magmas were generated directly from it by partial melting. As an initial model, we assume that at the time of mobilization of the partially melted source, an interstitial melt was present, with composition similar to that of the 5% MgO liquid (because that is the most fractionated liquid erupted). Then, as a first approximation (the behaviour of plagioclase to be discussed later) we visualize mobilization as consisting of the disaggregation of the whole source-rock, followed by its upward injection as a crystal (restite)-rich mush. During upward movement, restite material was lost gravitationally, by different amounts in different magma-batches. In the ideal case, bulk compositions eventually would then lie on a mixing line defined by two end-members, the 5% MgO liquid and the bulk composition of the source, respectively. A magma reaching the surface with *c.* 11% MgO had according to our calculations lost the least amount, of restite, and the 5% MgO liquid had lost virtually all of it. The low concentration of restite fragments reaching the surface was partly a consequence of restite-loss, but the dissolution of non-segregated fragments during magmatic ascent must also have been important.

However, the behaviour of plagioclase, i.e. the fact that although it is a prominent phase amongst the megacrysts but does not appear to have contributed much to the extract, complicates this picture. One possibility is that it actually was a relatively minor constituent of the source, and it separated during ascent with the same efficiency as the ferromagnesian minerals. If this were the case the mixing line would still pass through the bulk composition of the source. However, the gravitational separation of plagioclase is likely to have been much less effective than for the ferromagnesian minerals. The selective gravitational separation of olivine and pyroxene relative to plagioclase has been well-documented elsewhere (Cox & Mitchell 1988; Harris *et al.* 1990). Unfortunately, this consideration makes it impossible to estimate the amount of plagioclase in the presumed source relative to the ferromagnesian minerals, and as a consequence the extrapolated mixing line cannot be guarantied to pass through the source composition.

Hence, although we know something about the mineralogy of the source, probably including a reliable estimate of the relative proportions of the ferromagnesian minerals, and that it was plagioclase-bearing, the amounts of feldspathic (and possible feldspathoidal) constituents remain unknown, as does the bulk chemical composition.

The initial model discussed here is internally consistent with regard to the mass-balance of the various elements, in initial liquid, erupted magma compositions, and source composition. As formulated, however, it takes no account of the energetics of restite dissolution. For example, we calculated above that the most basic magmas erupted contained c. 40% of source material, and the least basic, virtually none. If the megacryst suite were actually present in negligible quantities even in the most basic magmas, this would carry the implication of an effectively complete dissolution of the transported source material. The latest experimental evidence for peridotite melting (e.g. Takahashi *et al.* 1993) suggests, however, that the figure of 40% is unrealistically high, by a factor of about 2. For example, because plagioclase is part of the source mineralogy it is unreasonable to suppose that segregation took place at pressures greater than c. 15 kb. Using a solid/liquid adiabatic gradient of $3.5°$ km$^{-1}$ (cf. McKenzie & Bickle 1988) the diagram of melt fraction vs. P and T of Takahashi *et al.* (1993) suggests that the melt fraction in peridotite ascending adiabatically would increase from, for example, nil at 15 kb to c. 20% at the surface. Even though the phase assemblage dissolving in the present case is somewhat different (amphibole is included) this is a good indication of the amount of solid we could expect an ascending magma to dissolve

during ascent through this pressure interval.

To reduce the requirement from 40% dissolution to 20% we can modify the model in two respects. Firstly, probably c. 10% of restite material remains in the more basic erupted magmas, so the requirement is reduced to 30%. Secondly, the assumption that the interstitial liquid at the time of mobilization was to be equated with the most evolved erupted magma (5% MgO) can readily be modified slightly. Restite appears to be absent from the low MgO samples, and it is possible that the more evolved magmas have undergone some degree of crystal fractionation involving the phenocryst suite. Although this would obviously be on a different compositional trend to that discussed so far, because of the compositional scatter it would be difficult to detect. If we thus postulate that the liquid at the time of mobilization contained c. 7% MgO rather than 5%, the total requirement for restite dissolution is reduced to 20%.

## Discussion

As observed earlier, the absence of evolved rocks, and the volcanic field eruptive-style, contrasts strongly with the central volcanoes of the Aden line. When combined with the evidence of the preservation of a high-pressure fractionation trend, however generated, this argues strongly for the direct eruption of magma from depth, without the establishment of high-level crustal chambers, though why this difference should exist is not known. The Shuqra region clearly lies within the influence of the Afar plume (Gass 1970; White & McKenzie 1989), though in a marginal position. Low degrees of melting are likely to characterize such a location, and we suggest that the protolith for the Shuqra magmas was emplaced as a volatile-bearing, alkali-rich, underplate, probably sub-crustally or along the Moho, at some earlier stage of the development of the Gulf of Aden rift. For comparison, in eastern Australia a rich variety of megacryst suites, and peridotite and basic granulite inclusions in alkalic host-magmas has led to the postulation of a complex crust/mantle transition zone by O'Reilly & Griffin (1987). This originates from repeated emplacement of magma (e.g. see also O'Reilly *et al.* 1988), and in such an environment the re-melting of the more fusible parts of earlier intrusions (e.g. low-temperature cumulate suites) is not only possible, it indeed seems highly likely if some of the emplaced magmas are picritic. This is the sort of environment we visualize for the source of the Shuqra magmas. If the process postulated is of general importance it provides a possible explanation for the occasional world-wide eruption of alkali basalts (and basanites and nephelinites) which are very densely charged with spinel peridotite inclusions. Mantle lenses interleaved with intrusions in the transition zone might suddenly find themselves without visible means of support as the surrounding matrix became mobilized.

The interpretation given in the present work is consistent with the observed facts, though it involves high degrees of speculation. It is in the nature of our hypothesis that it is difficult to distinguish the proposed mechanism from one in which the megacryst suite is interpreted as of phenocrystal origin, and the bulk compositional range as generated by fractional crystallization of the megacrysts. Clearly, liquids capable of precipitating the megacryst suite as a series of cumulates could be very similar to the partial melting products of the same cumulates. In view of our studies however, the one thing that seems quite unlikely is that the liquids and the megacrysts are only accidentally associated.

The mechanism we have proposed may, however, eventually be seen to be important – it hints at the possibility that not all basaltic rocks are generated by the melting of four-phase mantle lherzolites, but may be the products of reworking in the crust-mantle transition zone. Nevertheless, our argument hangs on some slender threads – kink bands in olivines, very little zoning in individual minerals, and the association of different phases, usually only pairs, leading to the possible identification of the mineralogy of a source rock. It is to be hoped that future research can improve on the argument.

Grateful acknowledgement is made to the Royal Society for their support of the 1964 expedition, and to D. I. J. Mallick for his major contribution to the field-work.

# References

Cox, K. G. 1987. Postulated restite fragments from Karoo picrite basalts: their bearing on magma segregation and mantle deformation. *Journal of the Geological Society, London*, **144**, 275–280.

——, Bell, J. D. & Pankhurst, R. J. 1979. *The Interpretation of Igneous Rocks*. George Allen & Unwin, London.

——, Gass, I. G. & Mallick, D. I. J. 1969. The evolution of the volcanoes of Aden and Little Aden, South Arabia. *Quarterly Journal of the Geological Society of London*, **124**, 283–308.

——, —— & ——. 1970. The peralkaline volcanic suite of Aden and Little Aden, South Arabia. *Journal of Petrology*, **11**, 433–461.

——, —— & ——. 1977. The western part of the Shuqra volcanic field, South Yemen. *Lithos*, **10**, 185–191.

—— & Mitchell, C. 1988. Importance of crystal settling in the differentiation of Deccan Trap basaltic magmas. *Nature*, **333**, 447–449.

Gass, I. G. 1970. The evolution of vulcanism in the junction area of the Red Sea, Gulf of Aden and Ethiopian rifts. *Philosophical Transactions of the Royal Society of London*, **A267**, 369–381.

—— & Mallick, D. I. J. 1968. Jebel Khariz: an Upper Miocene strato-volcano of comenditic affinity on the South Arabian coast. *Bulletin Volcanologique*, **32-1**, 33–88.

——, —— & Cox, K. G. 1965. Royal Society volcanological expedition to the South Arabian Federation and the Red Sea. *Nature*, **205**, 952–955.

Harris C., Marsh, J. S., Duncan, A. R. & Erlank, A. J. 1990. The petrogenesis of the Kirwan basalts of Dronning Maud Land. *Journal of Petrology*, **31**, 341–369.

Irving, A. J. 1984. Polybaric mixing and fractionation of alkalic magmas: evidence from megacryst suites. *EOS*, **65**, 1153

—— & Frey, F. A. 1984. Trace element abundances in megacrysts and their host basalts: constraints on partition coefficients and megacryst genesis. *Geochimica et Cosmochimica Acta*, **48**, 1201–1221.

Mallick, D. I. J., Gass, I. G., Cox, K. G., De Vries, B. v. W. & Tindle, A. G. 1990. Perim Island, a volcanic remnant in the southern entrance to the Red Sea. *Geological Magazine*, **127**, 309–318.

Menzies, M. A., Arculus, R. J., Best, M. G., Bergman, S. C., Ehrenberg, S. N., Irving, A. J., Roden, M. F. & Schulze, D. J. 1987. A record of subduction process and within-plate volcanism in lithospheric xenoliths of the southwestern USA. *In*: Nixon P. H. (ed.) *Mantle Xenoliths*. John Wiley & Sons, Chichester, 59–74.

McKenzie, D. P. & Bickle, M. J. 1988. The volume and composition of melt generated by extension of the lithosphere. *Journal of Petrology*, **29**, 625–679.

O'Reilly, S. Y. & Griffin, W. L. 1987. Eastern Australia – 4000 kilometres of mantle samples. *In*: Nixon, P. H. (ed.) *Mantle Xenoliths*. John Wiley & Sons, Chichester, 267–280.

——, —— & Stabel, A. 1988. Evolution of phanerozoic eastern Australian lithosphere: isotopic evidence for magmatic and tectonic underplating. *In*: Cox, K. G. & Menzies, M. A. (eds) Oceanic and continental lithosphere: similarities and differences. *Journal of Petrology*, Special Lithosphere Issue, 98–108.

Schulze, D. J. 1987. Megacrysts from alkalic volcanic rocks. *In*: Cox, K. G. & Menzies, M. A. (eds) Oceanic and continental lithosphere: similarities and differences. *Journal of Petrology*, Special Lithosphere Issue, 433–451.

Takahashi, E., Shimazaki T., Tsuzaki, Y. & Yoshida, H. 1993. Melting study of a peridotite KLB-1 to 6.5 GPa and the origin of basaltic magmas. *In*: Cox, K. G., McKenzie, D. P. & White, R. S. (eds) *Philosophical Transactions of the Royal Society of London*, **342**, 105–120.

WHITE, R. S. & MCKENZIE, D. P. 1989. Magmatism at rift zones: the generation of volcanic continental margins and flood basalts. *Journal of Geophysical Research*, **94**, 7685–7729.

WRIGHT, T. L & DOHERTY, P. C. 1970. A linear programming and least squares computer method for solving petrologic mixing problems. *Geological Society of America Bulletin*, **81**, 1995–2008.

# The isotope and trace element geochemistry of basalts from the volcanic islands of the southern Red Sea

## N. W. ROGERS

*Department of Earth Sciences, The Open University, Milton Keynes MK7 6AA, UK*

**Abstract:** Alkali basalts from the Hanish-Zukur and Zubair island groups in the southern Red Sea have been analysed for major, trace elements and Sr, Nd and Pb isotopes. They have close to primary compositions with high Mg$\sharp$ (60–70) and Ni and Cr concentrations up to 298 ppm and 597 ppm respectively. Many have only experienced olivine fractionation and this can be readily corrected. Compositional variations in the corrected analyses are interpreted to result from variations in the degree of melting, and a simple inversion of the corrected incompatible element abundances reveals a source composition intermediate between that of N-MORB and primitive mantle. This is suggested to result from the interaction of depleted asthenospheric mantle with less depleted material derived from the nearby Afar plume.

The overall geochemical characteristics of the basalts are comparable with ocean island basalts erupted through thin (young) lithosphere. $SiO_2$ varies from 44.0–47.9%, Nb/Y from 0.8–1.4 and Ce/Y averages 1.64, close to values from Ascension Island. $^{143}Nd/^{144}Nd$ ratios show minimal variation between 0.51301–0.51309 whereas $^{87}Sr/^{86}Sr$ ranges between 0.70323–0.70396, and the analyses define a horizontal trend extending to the right of the mantle array. Pb isotopes also show marked variation, $^{206}Pb/^{204}Pb$ values varying from 18.675–19.077, but the analyses remain within the ranges defined by MORB and are generally comparable with samples from the Red Sea axial trough and the Gulf of Aden.

Comparison with basalts from Afar and the Main Ethiopian Rift (MER), together with those from other parts of the Red Sea and Gulf of Aden reveal systematic shifts in isotope ratios with degree of extension. Along the constructive plate margins and including the island basalts, isotope results are dominantly asthenospheric, showing variations from N-MORB towards a possible plume end-member. In Afar, where β factors are lower (<2.5), isotope ratios show a greater deviation from oceanic basalts and this is most marked in the MER basalts where β factors are lowest (<1.2).

These data are tentatively related to a model of passive extension over a mantle plume, driven by plate motions, with the possibility of active, plume-driven extension being restricted to the early stages of Ethiopian flood basalt volcanism and the subsequent development of the MER during the Miocene.

The association of mantle plumes and flood basalts with continental breakup is now well established and has fuelled old debates concerning the importance of active and passive rifting in areas of continental extension. (e.g. White & McKenzie 1989; Coffin & Eldholm 1992). The arguments centre on whether the driving forces for continental separation are derived from a mantle plume or whether they are applied tectonically as two plates are pulled apart. The Red Sea and Gulf of Aden is arguably the clearest and most recently active example of continental breakup and the generation of new ocean crust, subsequent to the separation of Arabia and Africa, and the proximity of the Afar plume has produced a natural laboratory for investigating the role of mantle plumes in continental fragmentation.

Basaltic volcanism in Ethiopia and Yemen has been active for at least 40 Ma and there is clear evidence for extensional tectonic activity since the early Miocene. The earliest expressions of magmatic activity >40 Ma ago were outpourings of transitional tholeiitic magma in the region of the present Ethiopian Plateau. Extension followed but was diachronous, initiating earlier in the North in the Red Sea and Gulf of Aden at *c.* 25 Ma ago, and later in the South where the Main Ethiopian Rift formed between 20–15 Ma ago. Both areas have been the site of alkali basaltic activity and recent activity is confined to areas of active extension, largely within the tectonically complex Afar Depression, along the two constructive plate margins in the Red Sea and Gulf of Aden and associated with minor movements along the Main Ethiopian Rift.

The only surface manifestations of recently active volcanism in the axial parts of the southern Red Sea are the Zubair and Hanish-Zukur island groups and the island of Jebel-at-Tair (Fig. 1). Apart from two descriptive notes in the 1930s, these islands were first described in detail

*From* Prichard, H. M., Alabaster, T., Harris, N. B. W. & Neary, C. R. (eds), 1993,
*Magmatic Processes and Plate Tectonics,* Geological Society Special Publication No. 76, 455–467.

by Gass *et al.* (1973) after the Royal Society Expedition to the Red Sea in 1964. Although only Jebel-at-Tair is currently active, all the islands are morphologically young and probably of Holocene age. They are therefore critical in understanding the recent tectonomagmatic evolution of the southern Red Sea and hence the development of young ocean basins after continental breakup. In this paper new major, trace element and radiogenic isotope data are presented on samples collected by Ian Gass and co-workers from the Zubair and Hanish-Zukur island groups. The aim is to investigate the nature of the mantle sources supplying material to recent volcanism in the Southern Red Sea region and nearby rifts and to assess the controls on magmatism in this key example of continental breakup.

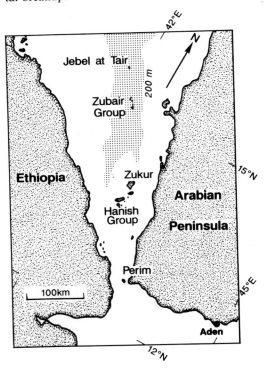

**Fig. 1.** Sketch map of the southern Red Sea showing the locations of the Hanish-Zukur and Zubair island groups and the island of Jebel-at-Tair. Shaded region denotes bathymetric depths of 200 m, the limits of the Red Sea median trough.

## Geology and previous research

The islands of the Zubair and Hanish-Zukur groups, together with the island of Jebel-at-Tair,

are located along the central depression of the Red Sea, or an extension of it, south of latitude 15°20'N (Fig. 1). Sea-floor spreading is active north of 15°30'N in the Red Sea (Cochran 1983) and oceanic crust is now confirmed east of 45°E in the Gulf of Aden (Schilling *et al.* 1992). The region in between, including the southernmost Red Sea, is considered to be characterized by continental lithosphere undergoing diffuse extension involving listric faulting and dyke injection (Cochran, 1983). The basement upon which these islands are constructed is therefore unlikely to be truly oceanic in character but highly attenuated continental crust.

The most northerly of the islands, Jebel-at-Tair rises from the centre of the Red Sea axial trough, from a depth of 1200 m to its summit 244 m above sea-level. All of the lavas are tholeiitic with plagioclase phenocrysts and microphenocrysts of clinopyroxene, olivine and ore. The Zubair group, 50–75 km south of Jebel-at-Tair, comprises ten islands that are the surface expression of a ridge that rises from the axial trough from a depth of *c.* 900 m. By contrast to Jebel-at-Tair, all the islands are characterized by mildly alkaline basalts, varying in composition from picrites to trachy-basalts, with plagioclase and olivine the most abundant phenocrysts. Some 150–200 km south of the Zubair group, the Hanish-Zukur group comprises the largest of the volcanic islands. These rise from relatively shallow water, well to the south of, but in line with, the Red Sea axial trough. Lavas range in composition from mildly alkaline through to strongly alkaline basalts that are almost basanitic, and a few evolved hawaiites and trachytes. Thus there is a general trend of increasing alkalinity from N to S, away from the locus of contemporary sea-floor spreading (Gass *et al.* 1973).

The islands show clear evidence of the influence of extensional tectonics on volcanic morphology. Both Jebel-at-Tair and the Zubair group have fissures, often with associated lava flows, orientated along NNW–SSE trends, parallel to that of the extensional Red Sea axis. The dominant trend in the Hanish-Zukur group is NE–SW, sub-parallel to the strike of transform faults within the Red Sea basin and similar to trends seen in the alignment of volcanic cones in the so-called transverse ranges in Afar. These, Barberi *et al.* (1980) also interpret as the trace of major transform features. Thus in all three cases local extensional features can be related to regional tectonics, but the amount of extension associated with volcanism in any one example is poorly defined.

**Table 1.** *Major and trace element analyses of alkali basalts from Hanish-Zukur (H) and Zubair (Z and JZ) Island groups in the southern Red Sea*

| Sample | H18 | H24 | H25 | H30 | H4 | H42 | Z2 | Z3 | Z12 | Z13 | Z27 | Z39 | Z63 | Z70 | Z71 | JZ9A | JZ11 |
|---|---|---|---|---|---|---|---|---|---|---|---|---|---|---|---|---|---|
| $SiO_2$ | 47.48 | 46.29 | 47.13 | 46.89 | 45.75 | 44.00 | 47.90 | 47.80 | 47.87 | 45.85 | 47.54 | 47.34 | 45.36 | 45.92 | 46.58 | 47.84 | 47.50 |
| $TiO_2$ | 2.16 | 2.08 | 2.23 | 2.11 | 2.87 | 2.82 | 2.06 | 2.05 | 2.08 | 1.94 | 1.93 | 2.47 | 2.24 | 2.35 | 2.33 | 1.82 | 1.81 |
| $Al_2O_3$ | 15.56 | 14.94 | 15.00 | 15.10 | 19.28 | 18.36 | 15.34 | 14.79 | 15.30 | 14.50 | 17.95 | 15.27 | 15.66 | 15.86 | 16.29 | 16.85 | 16.39 |
| $Fe_2O_3$ | 11.05 | 10.60 | 11.11 | 10.75 | 11.08 | 10.91 | 10.08 | 10.36 | 10.34 | 9.37 | 9.37 | 11.21 | 10.38 | 10.40 | 10.38 | 9.70 | 9.76 |
| $MnO$ | 0.17 | 0.14 | 0.15 | 0.14 | 0.16 | 0.16 | 0.15 | 0.15 | 0.15 | 0.14 | 0.12 | 0.17 | 0.14 | 0.15 | 0.15 | 0.15 | 0.15 |
| $MgO$ | 9.30 | 9.72 | 9.45 | 10.19 | 4.64 | 4.54 | 10.28 | 11.30 | 10.27 | 9.50 | 5.86 | 8.77 | 8.72 | 7.44 | 7.51 | 7.52 | 7.79 |
| $CaO$ | 10.00 | 9.29 | 10.21 | 9.43 | 11.69 | 11.39 | 9.94 | 9.61 | 9.93 | 10.55 | 12.10 | 10.61 | 12.45 | 10.50 | 10.90 | 11.80 | 11.99 |
| $Na_2O$ | 3.05 | 2.69 | 2.87 | 2.67 | 3.06 | 3.95 | 3.17 | 3.03 | 3.03 | 3.68 | 2.92 | 3.09 | 2.33 | 3.88 | 3.46 | 2.66 | 2.70 |
| $K_2O$ | 0.60 | 0.56 | 0.59 | 0.56 | 0.89 | 0.62 | 0.71 | 0.70 | 0.62 | 0.47 | 0.53 | 0.72 | 0.65 | 0.47 | 0.56 | 0.48 | 0.48 |
| $P_2O_5$ | 0.32 | 0.30 | 0.32 | 0.30 | 0.43 | 0.43 | 0.40 | 0.41 | 0.39 | 0.58 | 0.29 | 0.41 | 0.32 | 0.37 | 0.35 | 0.27 | 0.27 |
| Loss | 0.15 | 1.62 | 1.52 | 1.92 | 0.32 | 3.36 | 0.30 | 0.12 | 0.32 | 3.07 | 1.27 | 0.10 | 1.92 | 2.96 | 1.45 | 1.37 | 1.00 |
| Total | 99.84 | 98.23 | 100.6 | 100.1 | 100.2 | 100.5 | 100.3 | 100.3 | 100.3 | 99.65 | 99.88 | 100.2 | 100.2 | 100.3 | 99.96 | 100.5 | 99.84 |
| Mg# | 0.676 | 0.694 | 0.678 | 0.701 | 0.509 | 0.507 | 0.716 | 0.730 | 0.711 | 0.715 | 0.608 | 0.659 | 0.675 | 0.639 | 0.642 | 0.657 | 0.644 |
| Rb | 13 | 13 | 14 | 11 | 20 | 18 | 18 | 16 | 13 | 12 | 12 | 16 | 15 | 14 | 15 | 8 | 10 |
| Sr | 379 | 337 | 355 | 336 | 625 | 610 | 424 | 409 | 423 | 406 | 454 | 407 | 526 | 411 | 454 | 376 | 361 |
| Y | 26 | 26 | 26 | 26 | 26 | 24 | 27 | 27 | 27 | 24 | 24 | 30 | 22 | 24 | 25 | 22 | 27 |
| Zr | 153 | 158 | 154 | 155 | 185 | 171 | 181 | 182 | 179 | 165 | 142 | 183 | 147 | 154 | 162 | 138 | 147 |
| Nb | 21 | 23 | 22 | 21 | 36 | 34 | 32 | 32 | 32 | 28 | 23 | 30 | 27 | 26 | 28 | 21 | 22 |
| Ni | 231 | 227 | 219 | 227 | 20 | 20 | 244 | 298 | 256 | 223 | 87 | 154 | 157 | 106 | 121 | 117 | 134 |
| V | 555 | 434 | 478 | 531 | 344 | 272 | 592 | 677 | 690 | 434 | 307 | 463 | 430 | 130 | 345 | 430 | 442 |
| Cr | 449 | 443 | 418 | 436 | 54 | 55 | 523 | 597 | 568 | 485 | 199 | 370 | 340 | 222 | 224 | 285 | 292 |
| Co | 48.4 | 48.3 | 44.9 | 47.7 | 34.2 | 34.9 | 44.9 | 47.5 | 44.7 | 41.8 | 34.5 | 43.0 | 43.3 | 38.5 | 38.7 | 38.9 | 40 |
| Sc | 29.4 | 30.1 | 29.3 | 29.4 | 24.9 | 25.2 | 28.3 | 28.3 | 28.9 | 28.3 | 29.1 | 31.5 | 34.4 | 29.8 | 29.7 | 34.1 | 33.7 |
| La | 17.1 | 16.9 | 16.8 | 16.3 | 25.4 | 25.7 | 27.7 | 24.3 | 24.1 | 22.1 | 18.5 | 23.9 | 19.8 | 22.2 | 21.8 | 15.3 | 17.2 |
| Ce | 35.0 | 36.5 | 36.1 | 34.8 | 53.8 | 53.2 | 49.8 | 47.8 | 49.4 | 48.5 | 38.0 | 49.9 | 42.1 | 44.6 | 44.0 | 31.0 | 39.4 |
| Nd | 21.6 | 22.5 | 23.0 | 20.7 | 28.7 | 30.5 |  | 26.3 | 26.5 | 23.5 | 21.7 | 27.8 | 23.7 | 25.6 | 24.5 | 17.7 | 21.5 |
| Sm | 4.81 | 5.17 | 4.99 | 4.93 | 6.42 | 6.35 | 5.50 | 5.25 | 5.36 | 5.17 | 4.55 | 5.93 | 4.80 | 5.20 | 5.16 | 3.97 | 4.89 |
| Eu | 1.78 | 1.86 | 1.91 | 1.81 | 2.21 | 2.20 | 1.86 | 1.87 | 1.95 | 1.82 | 1.75 | 2.16 | 1.78 | 1.88 | 1.92 | 1.50 | 1.71 |
| Tb | 0.85 | 0.93 | 0.89 | 0.84 | 1.09 | 1.17 | 0.84 | 0.82 | 0.87 | 0.92 | 0.80 | 1.07 | 0.82 | 0.86 | 0.86 | 0.71 | 0.91 |
| Yb | 2.04 | 2.06 | 2.12 | 2.00 | 2.12 | 2.14 | 2.16 | 2.22 | 2.26 | 2.04 | 1.95 | 2.38 | 1.74 | 2.11 | 2.09 | 1.83 | 2.25 |
| Lu | 0.32 | 0.33 | 0.32 | 0.31 | 0.31 | 0.33 | 0.32 | 0.32 | 0.34 | 0.30 | 0.31 | 0.40 | 0.28 | 0.33 | 0.32 | 0.29 | 0.35 |
| Th | 1.98 | 1.98 | 2.04 | 1.78 | 2.94 | 3.02 | 2.89 | 3.10 | 3.14 | 2.76 | 2.11 | 2.98 | 2.41 | 2.61 | 2.56 | 1.79 | 1.94 |
| Ta | 1.34 | 1.40 | 1.43 | 1.36 | 2.48 | 2.47 | 2.07 | 2.06 | 2.14 | 1.97 | 1.56 | 2.04 | 1.78 | 1.89 | 1.89 | 1.30 | 1.45 |
| Hf | 3.55 | 3.62 | 3.86 | 3.61 | 4.18 | 4.18 | 3.93 | 4.02 | 4.07 | 3.71 | 3.44 | 4.49 | 3.46 | 3.99 | 4.00 | 3.05 | 3.36 |

## Results

### Major and compatible trace elements

Major and trace element analyses of selected basalts from the Hanish-Zukur and Zubair Island groups are summarized in Table 1. Major element analyses of other samples from these islands have been presented in Gass *et al.* (1973) and the data presented here are very similar. Lavas are alkali basalts and their evolved derivatives, mainly hawaiites and trachybasalts. The more evolved samples define an excellent positive correlation between MgO and CaO (Fig. 2), consistent with separation of clinopyroxene, plagioclase and minor olivine. All of the latter are represented in the phenocryst phases in these samples (Gass *et al.* 1973) and the data suggest that evolved lava compositions are controlled by low pressure fractional crystallization. In contrast, there is a broad, but less well-defined negative trend between MgO and CaO in the alkali basalts. To a first approximation, this trend could be the result of olivine fractionation with the scatter resulting from the separation and/or accumulation of clinopyroxene. However, such an interprteation is not consistent with variations in trace element abundances.

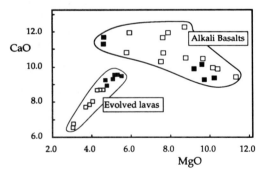

**Fig. 2.** A plot of MgO against CaO for basalts and more evolved lavas from Hanish-Zukur and Zubair Island groups. Filled squares: Hanish-Zukur; open squares: Zubair.

Compatible trace elements such as Ni and Cr, show wide variations in concentration. Both are high in the basalts, up to 300 ppm and 500 ppm respectively, within which group they show a strong correlation with MgO (Fig. 3) and Mg$\sharp$, decreasing to values below 20 ppm in the evolved trachytes and hawaiites. The most magnesian of the basalts have Mg$\sharp$ of *c.* 70, suggesting that they are primary melts derived directly from their mantle source region (Frey *et al.* 1978).

They lie close to the model melting curves in Fig. 3, calculated for low degrees of melting according to the model proposed by Hart & Davis (1978). They therefore appear to have experienced little if any olivine fractionation prior to eruption. By contrast, basalts with MgO less than 10% have Ni concentrations below 200 ppm and lower Mg$\sharp$ and they also lie below the model melting curves in Fig. 3. These characteristics are more consistent with significant olivine separation, as shown by the model fractionation trend calculated for the removal of olivine from the most MgO-rich composition and these calculations suggest that even the least magnesian basalts have experienced only 17% olivine fractionation and the rest > 10%. In addition, as the samples lie close to the fractionation curve and well below the melting curve, it is apparent that olivine accumulation has not occurred to a significant extent. Thus the alkali basalts from both island groups can be considered to represent the compositions of primary or near-primary melts derived directly from their mantle source regions.

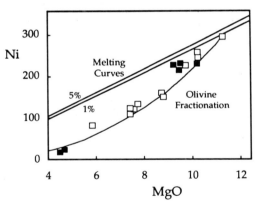

**Fig. 3.** Variation of Ni with MgO in basalts from Hanish-Zukur and Zubair Island groups (data from Table 1). Melting curves are for 1 and 5% melting of spinel lherzolite, calculated according to the method of Hart & Davis (1978). Olivine fractionation calculated assuming variation of $D_{Ni}$ with MgO given by Hart & Davis. Key as in Fig. 2.

### Incompatible trace elements

The incompatible trace elements show typical within-plate patterns on mantle-normalized diagrams (Fig. 4), with maxima in the region of Nb and Ta, light rare earth element enrichment and depletion of the highly incompatible elements, K, Th and Rb relative to Nb. Overall incompatible element abundances are intermediate between typical OIB (e.g. St Helena and Ascension) and E-MORB (Fig. 4) and can be regarded as indicating a distinctly asthenospheric source region.

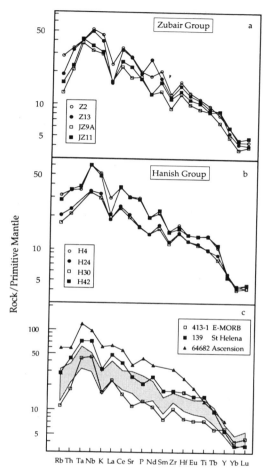

**Fig. 4. (a, b).** Mantle-normalized incompatible element abundances in selected basalts from the two island groups, normalized to primitive mantle concentrations from Sun & McDonough (1989). **(c)** Comparison of the range of incompatible element abundances in the Red Sea Island basalts with E-MORB (Wood *et al.* 1979), and basalts from St Helena (Chaffey *et al.* 1989) and Ascension Island (Weaver *et al.* 1987).

In detail there is significant incompatible element fractionation both within and between the islands, even when only the basaltic samples are considered. The Hanish-Zukur samples fall into two groups, those with Nb/Y ratios >1 (e.g. H24 and H30) and those with values <1 (e.g. H4 and H42). The lavas from Zubair show a more continuous range of trace element compositions, but Nb/Y ratios still vary significantly from 0.8 to 1.2. In addition all of the Hanish-Zukur samples have similar HREE abundances, indicating that these elements at least were not behaving incompatibly during trace element fractionation. Clearly these variations cannot be the result of olivine separation, as all of the elements discussed are equally incompatible with olivine. Thus, while some aspects of the variations in the basalts are without doubt the result of magma chamber processes, their near-primary compositions suggest that the most significant compositional variations, notably the fractionation of the incompatible elements, were established within the mantle melt regime. Furthermore, the buffering of the HREE implies that this regime extended to pressures high enough to stabilize garnet in the source peridotite.

## Radiogenic isotopes

The radiogenic isotope results are listed in Table 2 and illustrated on conventional isotope diagrams in Fig. 5 and 6. $^{143}Nd/^{144}Nd$ varies within the narrow range of 0.51301–0.51309, comparable with many MORB and similar to basalts from ocean islands, such as Iceland (Zindler *et al.* 1979) and Ascension (O'Nions *et al.* 1977). The $^{143}Nd/^{144}Nd$ ratios are also similar to those of MORB samples from the axial trough of the Red Sea and Gulf of Aden (Eissen *et al.* 1990; Schilling *et al.* 1992). $^{87}Sr/^{86}Sr$ shows greater variation from 0.7032–0.7040 and as a consequence the data define a flat-lying trend that extends to the right of the global MORB field on the Nd–Sr isotope diagram. In detail, most of the Hanish-Zukur group lie within the MORB field while all four of the analysed Zubair samples are displaced to the right. Although the causes of this displacement away from the MORB field to high $^{87}Sr/^{86}Sr$ are unclear, similar variations occur in the basalts from the main Ethiopian Rift and Afar (Hart *et al.* 1989; Vidal *et al.* 1991) and are also observed in basaltic dykes from Zagarabad Island further north (Brueckner *et al.* 1988). This encourages speculation that the trend to high $^{87}Sr/^{86}Sr$ may be of primary origin.

Pb isotope ratios are also very similar to those from MORB and Iceland, (Fig. 6) with the Zubair group having the most radiogenic ratios ($^{206}Pb/^{204}Pb = 18.9$–19.1) and the Hanish-Zukur samples extending to slightly lower values ($^{206}Pb/^{204}Pb = 18.7$–19.0). The ranges of $^{207}Pb/^{204}Pb$ and $^{208}Pb/^{204}Pb$ are also similar to those in the

**Table 2.** *Radiogenic isotope ratios for selected basalts from the Red Sea Islands, including data (\*) from Altherr et al. (1990). Sample G27(Gm) is from Great Hanish*

| Sample | $^{87}Sr/^{86}Sr$ | $^{143}Nd/^{144}Nd$ | $^{206}Pb/^{204}Pb$ | $^{207}Pb/^{204}Pb$ | $^{208}Pb/^{204}Pb$ |
|---|---|---|---|---|---|
| H4 | 0.70331 | 0.513060 | | | 38.460 |
| H24 | 0.70323 | 0.513035 | 18.675 | 15.505 | 38.582 |
| H30 | 0.70324 | 0.513055 | 18.788 | 15.512 | 38.762 |
| H42 | 0.70396 | 0.513077 | 19.002 | 15.539 | |
| H18* | 0.70336 | | | | |
| G27 (Gm) | 0.70331 | 0.513032 | 19.050 | 15.552 | 38.887 |
| Z2 | 0.70343 | 0.513075 | 19.041 | 15.547 | 38.855 |
| Z13 | 0.70380 | 0.513013 | 19.022 | 15.567 | 38.841 |
| Z4* | 0.70327 | | | | |
| Z10* | 0.70332 | | 18.857 | 15.562 | 38.721 |
| Z48* | 0.70331 | | | | |
| JZ9A | 0.70369 | 0.513026 | | | |
| JZ11 | 0.70359 | 0.513092 | 19.077 | 15.694 | 39.124 |

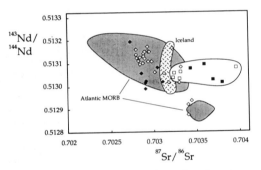

**Fig. 5.** Conventional Nd–Sr isotope plot of analyses from Hanish-Zukur (open squares) and Zubair (filled squares) island groups compared with the range of analyses from Atlantic MORB and Iceland (Zindler *et al.* 1979). Also shown are analyses of MORB from the Red Sea (filled diamonds) (Eissen *et al.* 1989 and Altherr *et al.* 1990) and Gulf of Aden MORB (open diamonds) (Schilling *et al.* 1992)

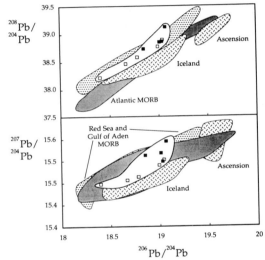

**Fig. 6.** Pb isotope plots of analyses of the Red Sea Island basalts compared with Atlantic MORB, Red Sea and Gulf of Aden MORB, Ascension Island and Iceland. Zubair and Hanish-Zukur islands coincide with the range seen in local MORB and are displaced to slightly higher $^{208}Pb/^{204}Pb$ ratios compared with Atlantic MORB. Red Sea and Gulf of Aden data from Dupré *et al.* (1988) and Schilling *et al.* (1992).

Gulf of Aden and Red Sea axial trough basalts. Thus as with Nd, Pb isotope ratios show a profound influence from a MORB source and confirm conclusions made from the incompatible elements that the mantle source region of the Red Sea Island basalts is distinctly asthenospheric in its geochemical characteristics, with only Sr isotope ratios indicating possible minor additions of geochemically more enriched material.

## Discussion

### Mantle melting and source composition

The importance of the melting regime in controlling the compositions of the basalts is emphasized by variations in major and trace element abundances that remain after analysed compositions have been corrected for the effects of olivine fractionation. Basalts with Mg$\sharp$ >70 that lie on the olivine fractionation trend in Fig. 3 can be easily corrected back to their primary compositions by adding olivine of an appropriate forsterite content until the Mg$\sharp$ of the basalt reaches 70 (cf. Hoffman & Feigenson 1983). The composition of the added olivine is calculated according to the Mg/Fe exchange partition coefficient (Roeder & Emslie 1970) and readjusted with each 1% incremental addition. These corrected compositions reflect those of the parental primary basalts and show a well-defined negative correlation between $SiO_2$ and Nb/Y (Fig. 7). Nb is more incompatible during mantle melting than Y; hence this variation implies that the basalts derived by lower degrees of melting have the lowest $SiO_2$ contents. Furthermore, within the Zubair group there is a tendency for $Na_2O$ to increase with Nb/Y, reflecting the incompatible behaviour of $Na_2O$ during mantle melting. Both of these conclusions are consistent with experimental results that indicate that $SiO_2$ decreases and $Na_2O$ increases at low melt fractions (e.g. Thompson 1987), confirming the importance of the melting regime in controlling both the major and incompatible element composition of the erupted basalts. Note that despite the regional change in alkalinity suggested by Gass et al. (1973), the primitive basalts from both island groups cover a similar range of $SiO_2$ and Nb/Y values.

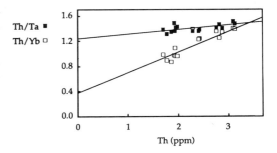

**Fig. 8.** Variation of Th/Ta and Th/Yb with Th abundance in fractionation-corrected basalts from Hanish-Zukur and Zubair. Basalts from both island groups lie on the same regression lines indicating derivation from a common source region.

Further constraints on basalt source regions can be derived from diagrams such as Fig. 8. Minster & Allègre (1978) and subsequently Hoffman & Feigenson (1983) have shown that on diagrams of this type, variable degrees of melting of a homogeneous mantle source generate straight lines, the slopes and intercepts of which are related to various source parameters. The slopes of the lines, for example, reflect the relative incompatibilities of the elements under investigation and allow the different elements to be placed in an order of incompatibility. The value of the intercept is a function of both the incompatible element ratio of the source and P, the bulk distribution coefficient based on the melt norm (see Hoffman & Feigenson (1983) for more details). For incompatible elements with low values of P and hence D, the intercept approximates the element ratio of the source region. In this case Th has been selected as the reference element because it shows the greatest relative variation, being highly incompatible, and its abundance is considered to be inversely related to the degree of melting.

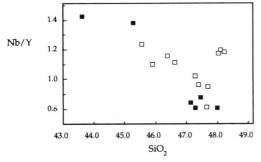

**Fig. 7.** Variation of Nb/Y with $SiO_2$ corrected for olivine fractionation. Key as in Fig. 2.

**Table 3.** *Comparison of source characteristics calculated for the Red Sea Island compared with the source of N-MORB (Wood 1979) and Primitive Mantle (Sun & McDonough 1989). Ratios for the Red Sea Islands below the line are calculated from the ratios above the line*

| Ratio | Red Sea Islands | N-MORB | Primitive Mantle |
|---|---|---|---|
| Th/Ta | $1.24 \pm 0.09$ | 0.91 | 2.07 |
| Th/Nb | $0.074 \pm 0.006$ | 0.065 | 0.119 |
| Th/La | $0.103 \pm 0.008$ | 0.065 | 0.124 |
| Th/Sm | $0.152 \pm 0.033$ | 0.063 | 0.191 |
| Th/Hf | $> .232$ | 0.059 | 0.275 |
| Th/Zr | $> .006$ | 0.002 | 0.0076 |
| La/Nb | 0.72 | 1.00 | 0.96 |
| La/Sm | 1.48 | 0.97 | 1.54 |
| Nb/Zr | $< 0.081$ | 0.031 | 0.064 |
| Nb/Hf | $< 3.13$ | 0.91 | 2.31 |

The first and probably most significant observation from these diagrams is that the corrected analyses from both Hanish-Zukur and Zubair groups lie on the same regression lines for those elements that define good correlations. This implies a marked degree of homogeneity in the source region for both island groups for these incompatible element ratios. Source element ratios calculated using simple regression analysis of the linear arrays shown by the most incompatible elements are listed in Table 3 and compared with values of these ratios in MORB mantle and model primitive mantle. They show that the source of the Red Sea Island basalts is characterized by element ratios intermediate between model primitive mantle and depleted mantle compositions. However, Nb/Zr and Nb/Hf ratios, calculated from the Th/Zr, Th/Nb and Th/Hf ratios, are close to primitive mantle values, within the error of the regression analysis, whereas Nb is enriched relative to Th, Rb, K and the LREE compared with primitive mantle. This feature is clearly reflected in the mantle-normalized diagrams of the basalts themselves (Fig. 4) which show distinct Nb–Ta peaks relative to the neighbouring elements. Thus whereas the REE and LIL elements indicate a slightly depleted source, the HFSE indicate a composition closer to primitive mantle.

The regression lines for other incompatible elements, especially P, Sr and Ti were too poorly defined for any conclusions to be drawn regarding the value of the intercept and hence the source composition. Interestingly, the less well-defined correlation for Sr contrasts with that shown by the LREE, including Nd, and may reflect the greater variation in $^{87}Sr/^{86}Sr$ values in the basalts compared with $^{143}Nd/^{144}Nd$. This may indicate that whereas the source was homogeneous with respect to the REE and REE fractionation was controlled by the mineralogy of the melting regime, Sr abundances and isotope ratios result from a more complex process, possibly involving the incorporation of more incompatible element-enriched material into the source region.

The slopes for the HREE correlations are strongly positive (Yb is illustrated in Fig. 8), reflecting the greater compatibility of these elements during melting. However, despite this greater degree of compatibility and the restricted Yb concentration range in the basalts (1.65–2.26 ppm), the intercept for Yb is positive. This suggests that, although present as a liquidus phase, garnet did not contribute significantly to the melt (cf. Ormerod et al. 1991). Thus whereas the melting regime extended to depths where garnet is stable, as implied above, it probably did not extend deeper than the region in the mantle which marks the transition of spinel to garnet lherzolite. McKenzie & O'Nions (1991) have calculated that the depth of the garnet-in reaction will occur at c. 60 km depth in areas with a normal geothermal gradient but closer to 80–100 km as mantle temperatures approach those appropriate for a mantle plume and the latter is probably appropriate for these samples located close to the Afar plume.

As Gass et al. (1973) emphasized and reiterated above, the Red Sea Island basalts are more akin to those from ocean islands (OIB). Models of OIB generation have demonstrated the controlling effects of the overlying lithosphere (e.g. Watson & McKenzie 1991) which can be regarded as a rigid, thermally conducting lid over the adiabatic, convecting asthenosphere. The lithosphere is too cool and chemically infertile to melt and therefore places minimum depth limits on any melting regime in the underlying mantle by restricting the continued upward movement of the rising plume. The effects of this physical limitation on incompatible element abundances and fractionation in OIB have been discussed by Ellam (1992) who showed that within the Atlantic Ocean there is a regular increase in these two factors as the age, and hence thickness, of the underlying lithosphere increases away from the ridge. Ellam used the average Ce/Y ratio of the various ocean islands as a measure of the degree of incompatible element fractionation in the basalts and it is instructive to compare his results with those reported here.

The Ce/Y ratios of the Red Sea Island basalts range from 1.34–2.02 with an average of 1.64. Compared with many OIB, these values are low but within the lower bounds of the OIB range, most closely comparable with the Ascension Island average cited by Ellam (1992). They are much higher than N-MORB and exceed values in all but the most incompatible element-enriched E-MORB (Wood et al. 1979). According to Ellam's model, this range of Ce/Y ratios suggests a thin (c. 30 km) lithosphere, which, if generated at a normal spreading centre, would be ⩾ 10 Ma old. Such an age interpretation is unlikely, largly because sea-floor spreading in the Red Sea only began c. 3–5 Ma ago, but the thickness is consistent with a basement of highly attenuated continental lithosphere as suggested by Cochran (1983) and others. An alternative is that the basement may be oceanic but, by analogy with Iceland and the Reykjanes ridge, the elevated mantle temperatures caused by the proximity of the Afar plume have allowed the generation of a much greater volume of melt for a given amount of extension and hence led to a substantially thicker crust. However, this is regarded as being unlikely. Regardless of the correct geological interpretation, the incompatible element fractionation in the Red Sea Island basalts is consistent with a thin lithosphere.

It must be emphasized that this conclusion is dependent on a number of assumptions including source composition and the thermal state of the mantle. The incompatible element ratios deduced above imply a source composition slightly depleted in the LREE compared with primitive mantle although not as depleted as the mantle source of MORBs. In this case, to explain the degree of LREE enrichment in the basalts requires a lower degree of melting and hence a thicker lithosphere. By contrast, a cooler geotherm would reduce the depth of melting and imply a thinner lithosphere. Despite these reservations, however, the isotope and incompatible element evidence points to a mantle source comparable with that beneath ocean islands without significant additions from enriched material and so the conclusions regarding lithospheric thickness are regarded as being robust. By analogy with isotope variations seen in Afar and the Main Ethiopian Rift (see below), the displacement to high $^{87}Sr/^{86}Sr$ may be due to a small contribution from the continental mantle lithosphere but this contribution is of minor significance. These results, therefore, imply that even though sea-floor spreading is not yet active in this region of the Red Sea, the underlying mantle is largely asthenospheric and that any pre-existing continental mantle lithosphere has either been completely removed or the more easily fusible components have been extracted during the earlier phases of extension (see Gallagher & Hawkesworth 1992).

## Comparison with basalts from Ethiopia, the Gulf of Aden and the Red Sea axial trough

The three tectonic regimes of the Red Sea/Gulf of Aden, Afar and the Ethiopian Rift exemplify three major stages in continental extension. In the Main Ethiopian Rift (MER) cutting through the Ethiopian Plateau, extension is limited to low β factors of 1.1–1.3 (Ebinger et al. 1993) and was probably restricted to movements in the Miocene (15–20 Ma ago). In Afar, the effective elastic plate thickness determined from gravity and topography is less than that of the plateau (Ebinger et al. 1989) and suggests a degree of lithospheric thinning intermediate between that of the MER and the Red Sea/Gulf of Aden. This region, including the southern Red Sea, is

regarded as one of diffuse extension where plate motions are accommodated by extensional faulting, block movements and magma injection. Joffe & Garfunkel (1987) limit extension to a maximum of 250% (β = 2.5) before true sea-floor spreading is initiated. Finally the Red Sea axial trough and the Gulf of Aden are regions of true ocean crust, the final result of continental extension, and are the main loci of contemporary extension and volcanism.

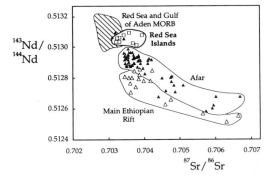

**Fig. 9.** Nd–Sr isotope diagram comparing analyses of basalts from the Red Sea Islands with Red Sea and Gulf of Aden MORB, basalts from Afar and the Main Ethiopian Rift. Note the trend to lower $^{143}Nd/^{144}Nd$ ratios in regions that have experienced less extension and are therefore more continental. Data sources: Schilling et al. (1992), Eissen et al. (1989), Hart et al. (1989) and Vidal et al. (1991).

Comparison of radiogenic isotope analyses of basalts from these three tectonic regimes reveals systematic variations which reflect variations in the mantle sources being tapped during magmatism. These variations are well illustrated in Fig. 9, which shows a distinct hiatus between the analyses of basalts from the Red Sea/Gulf of Aden and those from Afar and the MER. Those from the Red Sea, including the volcanic islands, and the Gulf of Aden, are restricted to high values of $^{143}Nd/^{144}Nd$ above 0.5130, with the exception of a few anomalous samples from the Gulf of Aden. By contrast, basalts from Afar and the main Ethiopian Rift plot, with one or two exceptions, below 0.5130. The exceptions are samples from the Tadjoura Trough, in an analogous tectonic setting to the Red Sea islands. The basalts from Afar and the MER are also distinct from each other, with the MER basalts plotting at lower $^{143}Nd/^{144}Nd$ ratios than those from Afar. Both regions also have some samples which define a trend to much higher $^{87}Sr/^{86}Sr$ and lower $^{143}Nd/^{144}Nd$ values than are seen in oceanic basalts generally, suggesting contributions from an old, incompatible element-enriched source. Thus as β factors increase, the isotopic characteristics of the basalts increasingly converge towards typical asthenospheric MORB values from both lower $^{143}Nd/^{144}Nd$ and higher $^{87}Sr/^{86}Sr$ values.

The distinction between basalts from the different tectonic regimes is reinforced by Pb isotope variations (Fig. 10) which define two contrasting trends. Basalts from the Red Sea/Gulf of Aden follow a trend similar to that seen in the oceans generally, parallel with the NHRL of Hart (1984) and typical of oceanic basalts outside the area of the so-called Dupal anomaly. The Afar and the MER basalts, by contrast, define a cloud of data points towards low $^{206}Pb/^{204}Pb$, but $^{207}Pb/^{204}Pb$ and $^{208}Pb/^{204}Pb$ ratios above the NHRL. This latter tendency has been recognized previously (Hart et al. 1989) and in Afar has been shown to correlate with both the age of eruption and incompatible element ratios (Vidal et al. 1991). Critically, $^{206}Pb/^{204}Pb$ ratios tend to increase with time, such that the most recent basalts plot closest to oceanic values (Vidal et al. 1991).

again coinciding with trends shown by oceanic basalts in general, reinforcing earlier interpretations. The trend is anchored at high $^{143}Nd/^{144}Nd$ and low $^{206}Pb/^{204}Pb$ by world-wide MORB which can be identified with depleted asthenospheric mantle. By contrast, the basalts from Afar and the MER are displaced to lower $^{143}Nd/^{144}Nd$ ratios at a given $^{206}Pb/^{204}Pb$ value and this is most marked in samples from the MER. Similarly low $^{143}Nd/^{144}Nd$ and $^{206}Pb/^{204}Pb$ are characteristic of other continental mafic rocks thought to have been derived from the continental mantle lithosphere, (e.g. lamproites and group II kimberlites (Fraser et al. 1985), and some Gondwana continental flood basalts (Carlson & Hart 1988)) and so these variations in the Afar and Ethiopian basalts, together with their continental location further encourage the link between the low $^{143}Nd/^{144}Nd$ and $^{206}Pb/^{204}Pb$ end-member with the continental mantle lithosphere. Significantly, both oceanic and continental trends converge on a common region of the diagram, corresponding to $^{143}Nd/^{144}Nd$ of 0.5129–0.5130 and $^{206}Pb/^{204}Pb$ of 19.0–19.2. These values are common in OIB and have been suggested to represent the isotopic composition of the Afar mantle plume (cf. Hart et al. 1989; Vidal et al. 1991 and Schilling et al. 1992)

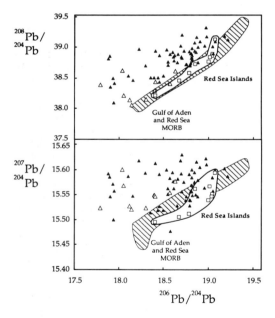

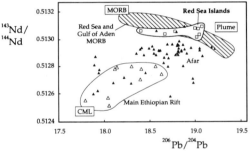

**Fig. 11.** $^{206}Pb/^{204}Pb$ vs. $^{143}Nd/^{144}Nd$ for basalts from the Red Sea, Gulf of Aden, Afar and the MER. Note the negative trend for those samples from the Gulf of Aden and the Red Sea, including the Red Sea Islands, and the positive trend for samples from Afar and the MER. The low $^{206}Pb/^{204}Pb$, $^{143}Nd/^{144}Nd$ end-member is considered to be derived from the continental mantle lithosphere. The oceanic trend is anchored at low $^{206}Pb/^{204}Pb$ and high $^{143}Nd/^{144}Nd$ by global MORB. The region of the diagram where the two trends converge may represent the isotopic composition of the Afar plume.

**Fig. 10.** Comparison of Pb isotope results from the Red Sea, Gulf of Aden, Afar and the MER. Data sources as in Fig. 9

The three groups can also be distinguished on a plot of $^{143}Nd/^{144}Nd$ vs. $^{206}Pb/^{204}Pb$ (Fig. 11) with the Red Sea/Gulf of Aden samples once

Thus the isotopic variations in the basalts of the region as a whole can be interpreted within the framework of the interaction of a mantle plume with either the continental mantle lithosphere or depleted MORB-source asthenosphere. In areas of limited crustal extension the plume interacts with the continental mantle lithosphere and this effect decreases as β increases. In areas with high β factors where ocean crust formation is underway, as in the Red Sea and Gulf of Aden axial troughs, or where the lithosphere is particularly thin, as beneath the Red Sea Islands and the Gulf of Tadjoura, the plume interacts with local asthenosphere. The effects of the continental mantle lithosphere are also most marked in the oldest basalts from both Afar and the MER, which were probably erupted at a time when the lithosphere in both areas was much thicker.

### Extension-driven versus plume-driven magmatism

A major debate in the development of continental basalt provinces involves the relative roles of mantle plumes and extensional tectonics as major triggers of melting. The presence of a mantle plume beneath the Ethiopian province has led to suggestions that extension in this region may be an example of active continental rifting. The common involvement of a plume-related end-member in both the continental and oceanic sectors of the Red Sea and Ethiopian Rift, as discussed above, might be interpreted to support this contention. However, it is quite clear that contemporary magmatism throughout the whole region is extension-related; lithospheric thinning giving rise to melting in the underlying mantle, parts of which are unusually hot due to the proximity of the Afar plume.

The Red Sea Island basalts are clearly distinct from those generated by active sea-floor spreading in the axial trough of the Red Sea, despite their location along the natural extension of the latter. It is therefore unlikely that sea-floor spreading has extended as far south as the islands, consistent with recent models of the evolution and present tectonic state of the Red Sea as a whole (Cochran 1983). Extension is currently driven by plate motions as Arabia drifts slowly to the NE and this appears to have been the dominant driving force behind extension since the initial development of the proto-Red Sea depression during the early Miocene, c. 25 Ma ago. Sea-floor spreading has only been active for c. 10 Ma in the Gulf of Aden and for a maximum of 5 Ma in the Red Sea. Prior to these times, plate motions were accommodated by diffuse extension as described by Cochran (1983). Initial magmatism was either synchronous with, or post-dated, extension and so all of the stretching in the Red Sea and Gulf of Aden can be related to plate tectonic movements (Joffe & Garfunkel 1987) and is thus entirely passive. The lack of magmatism prior to extension indicates that this too is a passive phenomenon.

By contrast, within the Main Ethiopian Rift, there is increasing evidence that magmatism pre-dated crustal extension by up to 25 Ma. The volcanism that produced the basalts now preserved in the Ethiopian plateau started much earlier than that associated with the Red Sea/Gulf of Aden rifts. Basalts as old as 40 Ma are widespread in S Ethiopia where thicknesses of up to 1 km were erupted prior to the onset of Tertiary extension (Davidson & Rex 1980; Berhe et al. 1987). The main phase of extension occurred between 20–15 Ma ago, but was of limited duration and extent with maximum β factors of c. 1.2 (Ebinger et al. 1993).

Joffe & Garfunkel (1987) have shown that this small amount of extension can be accommodated within a plate tectonic model but the estimates of extension they used were poorly constrained. An alternative interpretation is that extension across the MER was a direct response to plume activity as Africa came to rest over the site of the already active Afar plume c. 40 Ma ago (Briden & Gass 1974). Basaltic melts were generated both within the plume and in the lithosphere as a result of conductive heating, perhaps because it was hydrated (Gallagher & Hawkesworth 1992). Hence the mantle lithosphere was substantially thinned by a combination of melting and thermal re-equilibration, and at the same time the crust was thickened by the upward migration of basaltic magma. The combination of these two processes, lithospheric thinning and crustal thickening, enhanced initial uplift produced by the plume, thus generating extensional buoyancy forces within the crust (Sandiford & Powell 1990). Limited extension followed and this triggered further melting in the underlying mantle but this second phase of magmatism was derived almost completely from plume material that had replaced those parts of the original mantle lithosphere previously removed or melted. The implication of this model is that the pre-extension basalts contain a significant component derived from the lithosphere and that this component is most pronounced in the earliest manifestations of magmatic activity. Subsequently, magmatism became increasingly dominated by melts derived directly from the mantle plume such that basalts erupted during extension were almost entirely plume-derived. This appears to be the case in the Afar region (Vidal et al. 1991) but there are few samples available that pre-date extension to place more rigorous constraints on this model.

Thus the Afar plume has played a minor role in generating extension and magmatism in the Red Sea and Gulf of Aden but it may have been dominant in the early phases of the development of the Ethiopian flood basalts and the MER. The current position of the plume is probably best defined geophysically and this would place it beneath the Ethiopian plateau (Ebinger *et al.* 1989). Recent magmatism is confined to those areas where extension is active, i.e. Afar and the constructive plate margins, and so the location of magmatism may not be a reliable indicator of the location of the plume (cf. Thompson & Gibson 1991). The plume may have played a role in determining the location of initial extension during continental fragmentation but the main fractures (i.e. Gulf of Aden and Red Sea) were more probably located along older zones of lithospheric weakness (e.g. Berhe 1986; Wilson & Guiraud 1992).

Thanks are due to all those who helped in the analysis of the samples, especially Mabs Johnston for help in the isotope laboratory and John Watson for XRF analyses. I should also like to thank Ray MacDonald and Godfrey Fitton for reviews and Rob Ellam for some incisive comments on an earlier draft. This work has benefited from discussions with Kathy Stewart, Simon Turner, Seife Berhe and Cindy Ebinger. We are all indebted to Ian Gass for his contributions to the Earth Sciences in general and I should like to express my thanks to him not only for supplying the samples that are the subject of this paper, but also for stimulating my broader interest in the geology of the Red Sea and the Ethiopian Rift.

# References

ALTHERR, R., HENJES-KUNST, F., PUCHELT, H. & BAUMANN, A. 1990. Asthenosphere versus lithosphere as possible source for basaltic magmas erupted during formation of the Red Sea: constraints from Sr, Pb and Nd isotopes. *Earth and Planetary Science Letters*, **96**, 269–286.

BARBERI, F., CIVETTA, L. & VARET, J. 1980. Sr isotopic composition of Afar volcanics and its implication for mantle evolution. *Earth and Planetary Science Letters*, **50**, 347–359.

BERHE, S. M. 1986. Geologic and geochronologic constraints on the evolution of the Red Sea-Gulf of Aden and Afar Depression. *Journal of African Earth Sciences*, **5**, 101–117.

——, DESTA, B., NICOLETTI, M. & TEFERRA, M. 1987. Geology, geochronology and geodynamic implications of the Cenozoic magmatic province in W and SE Ethiopia. *Journal of the Geological Society, London*, **144**, 213–226.

BRIDEN, J. C. & GASS, I. G. 1974. Plate movement and continental magmatism. *Nature*, **248**, 650–653.

BRUECKNER, H. K., ZINDLER, A., SEYLER, M. &

BONATTI, E. 1988. Zabargad and the isotopic evolution of the sub-Red Sea mantle and crust. *Tectonophysics*, **150**, 163–176.

CARLSON, R. W. & HART, W. K. 1988. Flood basalts volcanism in the northwestern United States. *In*: MACDOUGALL, J. D. (ed.) *Continental Flood Basalts*. Kluwer Academic Publishers, Dordrecht, 35–62.

CHAFFEY, D. J., CLIFF, R. A. & WILSON, B. M. 1989. Characterisation of the St. Helena magma source. *In*: SAUNDERS, A. D. & NORRY, M. J. (eds) *Magmatism in the Ocean Basins*. Geological Society, London, Special Publication, **42**, 257–276.

COCHRAN, J. R. 1983. A model for the development of the Red Sea. *American Association of Petroleum Geologists Bulletin*, **67**, 41–69.

COFFIN, M. F. & ELDHOLM, O. 1992. Volcanism and continental break-up: a global compilation of large igneous provinces. *In*: STOREY, B. C., ALABASTER, T. & PANKHURST, R. J. (eds) *Magmatism and the Causes of Continental Break-up*. Geological Society, *London, Special Publication*, **68**, 17–30.

DAVIDSON, A. & REX, D. C. 1980. Age of volcanism and rifting in southwestern Ethiopia. *Nature*, **283**, 654–658.

DUPRÉ, B., BLANC, G., BOULÈGUE, J. & ALLÈGRE, C. J. 1988. Metal remobilisation at a spreading centre studied using lead isotopes. *Nature*, **333**, 165–167.

EBINGER, C. J., BECHTEL T. D., FORSYTH, D. W. & BOWIN, C. O. 1989. Effective elastic plate thickness beneath the East African and Afar Plateaus and dynamic compensation of the uplifts. *Journal of Geophysical Research*, **94**, 2883–2901.

——, YEMANE T., WOLDEGABRIEL, G., ARONSON, J. L. & WALTER, R. C. 1993. Late Eocene–Recent volcanism and faulting in the southern main Ethiopian rift. *Journal of the Geological Society, London*, **150**, 99–108.

EISSEN, J-P., JUTEAU, T., JORON, J-L., DUPRÉ, B., HUMLER, E. & AL'MUKHAMEDOV, A. 1989. Petrology and geochemistry of basalts from the Red Sea Axial Rift at 18°N. *Journal of Petrology*, **30**, 791–839.

ELLAM, R. M. 1992. Lithosphere thickness as a control on basalt geochemistry. *Geology*, **20**, 153–156.

FRASER, K. J, HAWKESWORTH, C. J, ERLANK A. J., MITCHELL, R. H. & SCOTT-SMITH, B. H. 1985. Sr, Nd and Pb isotope and minor element geochemistry of lamproites and kimberlites. *Earth and Planetary Science Letters*, **76**, 57–70.

FREY F. A., GREEN, D. H. & ROY, S. D. 1978. Integrated models of basalt petrogenesis: A study of quartz tholeiites to olivine melilitites from south eastern Australia utilising geochemical and experimental petrological data. *Journal of Petrology*, **19**, 463–513.

GALLAGHER, K. & HAWKESWORTH, C. J. 1992. Dehydration melting and the generation of continental flood basalts. *Nature*, **358**, 57–59.

GASS, I. G., MALLICK, D. I. J. & COX, K. G. 1973. Volcanic islands of the Red Sea. *Journal of the Geological Society, London*, **129**, 275–310.

HART, S. R. 1984. A large scale isotope anomaly in the southern hemisphere mantle. *Nature*, **309**, 753–757.

—— & DAVIS, K. E. 1978. Nickel partitioning between olivine and silicate melt. *Earth and Planetary Science Letters*, **40**, 203–219.

HART, W. K., WOLDEGABRIEL, G., WALTER, R. C. & MERTZMANN, S. A. 1989. Basaltic volcanism in Ethiopia: constraints on continental rifting and mantle interactions. *Journal of Geophysical Research*, **94**, 7731–7748.

HOFFMAN, A. W. & FEIGENSON, M. D. 1983. Case studies on the origin of basalt, 1. Theory and reassessment of Grenada basalts. *Contributions to Mineralogy and Petrology*, **84**, 382–389.

JOFFÉ, S. & GARFUNKEL, Z. 1987. Plate kinematics of the circum Red Sea – a re-evaluation. *Tectonophysics*, **141**, 5–22.

MCKENZIE, D. P. & O'NIONS, R. K. 1991. Partial melt distributions from inversion of rare earth element concentrations. *Journal of Petrology*, **32**, 1021–1091.

MINSTER, J-F & ALLÈGRE, C. J. 1978. Systematic use of trace elements in igneous processes. Part III; Inverse problem of batch partial melting in volcanic suites. *Contributions to Mineralogy and Petrology*, **68**, 37–52.

O'NIONS, R. K., HAMILTON, P. J. & EVENSON, N. M. 1977. Variations in $^{143}Nd/^{144}Nd$ and $^{87}Sr/^{86}Sr$ in oceanic basalts. *Earth and Planetary Science Letters*, **34**, 13–23.

ORMEROD, D. S., ROGERS, N. W. & HAWKESWORTH, C. J. 1991. Melting in the lithosphere mantle: Inverse modelling of alkali-olivine basalts from the Big Pine Volcanic Field, California. *Contributions to Mineralogy and Petrology*, **108**, 305–317.

ROEDER, P. L. & EMSLIE, R. F. 1970. Olivine-liquid equilibrium. *Contributions to Mineralogy and Petrology*, **29**, 275–289.

SANDIFORD, M. & POWELL, R. 1990. Some isostatic and thermal consequences of the vertical strain geometry in convergent orogens. *Earth and Planetary Science Letters*, **98**, 154–165.

SCHILLING, J-G., KINGSLEY, R. H., HANAN, B. B. & MCCULLY, B. L. 1992. Nd–Sr–Pb isotopic variations along the Gulf of Aden: evidence for Afar mantle plume-continental lithosphere interaction. *Journal of Geophysical Research*, **97**, 10927–10966.

SUN, S-S. & MCDONOUGH, W. F. 1989. Chemical and isotopic systematics of oceanic basalts: implications for mantle composition and processes. *In*: SAUNDERS, A. D. & NORRY, M. J. (ed.) *Magmatism in the Ocean Basins*. Geological Society, London, Special Publication, **42**, 313–345.

THOMPSON R. N. 1987. Phase equilibria constraints on the genesis and magmatic evolution of oceanic basalts. *Earth Science Reviews*, **24**, 161–210.

—— & GIBSON S. A. 1991. Subcontinental mantle plumes, hotspots and pre-existing thinspots. *Journal of the Geological Society London*, **147**, 973–977.

VIDAL, Ph., DENIEL, C., VELLUTINI, P. J., PIGUET, P., COULON C., VINCENT, J. & AUDIN, J. 1991. Changes of mantle sources in the course of a rift evolution: the Afar case. *Geophysical Research Letters*, **18**, 1913–1916.

WATSON, S. & MCKENZIE, D. P. 1991. Melt generation by plumes: a study of Hawaiian volcanism. *Journal of Petrology*, **32**, 501–537.

WEAVER, B. L., WOOD, D. A., TARNEY, J. & JORON, J. L. 1987. Geochemistry of ocean island basalts from the South Atlantic: Ascension, Bouvet, St. Helena, Gough and Tristan da Cunha. *In*: FITTON, J. G. & UPTON, B. G. J. (eds) *Alkaline Igneous Rocks*. Geological Society, London, Special Publication, **30**, 253–268.

WHITE, R. S. & MCKENZIE, D. P. 1989. Magmatism at rift zones: the generation of volcanic continental margins and flood basalts. *Journal of Geophysical Research*, **94**, 7685–7729.

WILSON M. & GUIRAUD, R. 1992. Magmatism and rifting in Western and Central Africa from late Jurassic to Recent times. *Tectonophysics*, **213**, 1–23.

WOOD, D. A. 1979. A variably veined suboceanic upper mantle – Genetic significance for mid-ocean ridge basalts from geochemical evidence. *Geology*, 7, 499–503.

——, TARNEY, J., VARET, J., SAUNDERS, A. D., BOUGAULT, H., JORON, J-L., TREUIL, M. & CANN, J. R. 1979. Geochemistry of basalts drilled from the north Atlantic by IPOD leg 49: implications for mantle heterogeneity. *Earth and Planetary Science Letters*, **42**, 77–97.

ZINDLER, A., HART, S. R., FREY, F. A. & JAKOBSSON, S. P. 1979. Nd and Sr isotope ratios and rare earth element abundances in Reykjanes Peninsula basalts: evidence for mantle heterogeneity beneath Iceland. *Earth and Planetary Science Letters*, **45**, 249–262.

# Basic and intermediate volcanism of the Mogollon-Datil volcanic field: implications for mid-Tertiary tectonic transitions in southwestern New Mexico, USA

JON M. DAVIS,[1] WOLFGANG E. ELSTON[2] & CHRIS J. HAWKESWORTH[1]

[1]*Department of Earth Sciences, The Open University, Milton Keynes MK7 6AA, UK*
[2]*Department of Geology, University of New Mexico, Albuquerque, New Mexico 87131, USA*

**Abstract**: Basic to intermediate volcanism of the Tertiary Mogollon-Datil volcanic field can be divided petrologically and geochemically into three temporal groups; Pre-30 Ma, 30–20, Ma and Post-20 Ma. The Pre-30 Ma and 30–20 Ma groups are dominated by high-K calc-alkaline andesites and mildly alkaline basaltic andesites respectively. These both have major and trace element characteristics typical of an orogenic origin. In contrast, the late Tertiary, Post-20 Ma lavas are typically alkaline basalts and have geochemical characteristics more consistent with a within-plate setting. The 30–20 Ma basic lavas have high Ba and Sr, and low Nb contents, resulting in high LIL/HFS element ratios (Ba/Nb c. 80). $^{87}Sr/$ $^{86}Sr$ ratios are $>0.7065$. These features are inferred to have been derived from continental mantle lithosphere modified by subduction-related processes in the Proterozoic. The Pre-30 Ma lavas have many similar characteristics but with Rb and Th enriched relative to Ba and Sr, lower $^{87}Sr/^{86}Sr$, and more subalkalic parental magmas. In contrast, the Post-20 Ma lavas show a tendency to higher Nb contents (low LIL/HFS ratios), and lower $^{87}Sr/^{86}Sr$ ratios similar to OIB-like magmas derived from partial melting of the convecting asthenospheric mantle. The overall shift from predominantly lithosphere to asthenosphere-derived magmas with time in the evolution of the Mogollon-Datil volcanic field is consistent with models in which magmatism was triggered by lithosphere extension. It is concluded that calc-alkaline magmas with minor and trace element features similar to those from destructive plate margins were generated in an extensional tectonic setting. In detail, the marked change to within-plate style magmatism took place c. 10 Ma after the period of maximum extension.

Detailed field-based studies on the relationship between changes in magmatism and regional tectonics provide important constraints on the causes of melt generation, and the composition of the resultant magmas. In the last 40 Ma, the tectonics of the southwestern United States and western Mexico have changed dramatically from the remnants of the Laramide orogeny compression, and the subduction of the Farallon Plate, to a within-plate extensional regime evident today in the horst-and-graben topography of the Basin and Range province. In the mid-Tertiary (approximately 40 to 20 Ma ago) voluminous broadly calc-alkaline intermediate to silicic volcanic rocks were erupted over an area of c. $1 \times 10^6 \, km^2$ (Fig. 1), and this was followed in the late Tertiary by an abundance of basalt, mainly alkalic, and a growing tendency toward a bimodal, basalt-rhyolite association. A surprising feature is that such large volumes of calc-alkaline magma were generated up to 900 km from the contemporaneous destructive plate margin, and in some cases several millions of years after subduction ceased.

Early papers by Lipman *et al.* (1972) and Christiansen & Lipman (1972) proposed a model in which the andesitic–rhyolitic association was part of a broad continental arc, related to subduction of the Farallon Plate under the western margin of the North American Plate. Initial ridge–trench collision, then dated at around 30 Ma ago (Atwater 1970), resulted in a transform margin with subsequent northwest–southeast expansion, and the transition from the andesite–rhyolite 'subduction-related' to the basaltic–rhyolitic, or 'fundamentally basaltic', magmatism of the Basin and Range provinces was attributed to the northwestward migration of the Mendocino triple junction. This model was accepted by many authors, and subsequent papers sought to relate changes in the spatial and temporal composition of magmatism to different interactions between the subducted and overlying plates, arising from variations in the angle of subduction and from changes in the rate of plate convergence (Coney & Reynolds 1977; Snyder *et al.* 1976).

In detail, however, it now appears that aspects of the mid-Tertiary magmatism are not adequately explained by such simple tectonic models (Elston 1984a; Gans *et al.* 1989). Recent work (Engebretson *et al.* 1985) has dated the initial

*From* Prichard, H. M., Alabaster, T., Harris, N. B. W. & Neary, C. R. (eds), 1993, *Magmatic Processes and Plate Tectonics*, Geological Society Special Publication No. 76, 469–488.

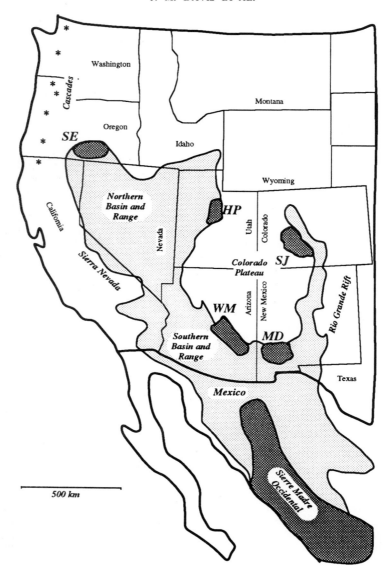

**Fig. 1.** Map of the Western US and Mexico showing the distribution of mid-Tertiary volcanism (light stipple), a province that extended from SE Oregon to central Mexico. The darker stipple refers to specific mid-Tertiary volcanic fields – MD: the Mogollon-Datil, New Mexico; SJ: the San Juans Mountains, Colorado; HP: the High Plateau, Utah; WM; the White Mountains, Arizona; SE; southeast Oregon; and the Sierre Madre Occidental in central Mexico. All these fields are relatively undeformed compared to the southern and northern Basin and Range provinces, and all, except the Sierre Madre Occidental and southeast Oregon, lie in the transition zone between the Colorado Plateau and the Basin and Range provinces.

ridge–trench collision at around 37 Ma ago, near the beginning of mid-Tertiary magmatism. Throughout the mid-Tertiary, volcanism was an andesite–rhyolite association and basalt only became abundant after about 15 Ma ago. According to some authors, pre-20 Ma ago andesitic–rhyolitic magmatism was not contemporaneous throughout the province. Rather, a southward sweep from SE Oregon in the Eocene to Nevada in the early Miocene (Armstrong 1970) was mirrored by a northward sweep from northern Mexico in the Oligocene through to

Nevada in the Miocene (Glazner & Bartly 1984). In this interpretation, magmatism was migratory and occurred in bands that moved at a high angle to the plate margin. Whereas magmatism in recent arcs is restricted to narrow zones less than 300 km wide, late Oligocene to early Miocene magmatism was continuous from western Nevada and eastern California to Trans-Pecos Texas, a present-day distance of some 1200 km and at least 900 km at the beginning of the mid-Tertiary, allowing for subsequent extension. The tendency to bimodal basalt–rhyolite suites after about 15 Ma ago began more than twenty million years after the end of subduction and was not simply related to the onset of extension. It was not, therefore, simply related to the position of the Mendocino triple junction. Furthermore, magmas of intermediate composition continued to erupt after 15 Ma ago in many localities, such as the Rio Grande rift–Jemez Mountains region of northern and central New Mexico (Baldridge et al. 1989; Gardner et al. 1986; McMillan & Dungan 1988).

One of the major successes of plate tectonic theory has been its ability to explain the occurrence of different styles of magmatic activity, and their associated compositions, in terms of different interactions between lithospheric plates. Studies of late Tertiary ($< 15$ Ma ago) basaltic magmatism in the western USA have used isotope and trace element geochemistry to identify interactions between distinctive mantle source regions, which are then modelled in terms of tectonic transitions (Ormerod et al. 1988; Perry et al. 1988; Fitton et al. 1988, 1991). The aim of this study is to use a similar approach in the mid-Tertiary Mogollon-Datil volcanic field (MDVF) and to relate magmatism in this area to the tectonic evolution of southwestern New Mexico over the same period. The MDVF was chosen because:

(i) it was active from the end of the Eocene through to the late Miocene, beginning near the end of subduction at about 38 Ma ago and continuing for some 18 Ma after its cessation;

(ii) it was contemporaneous with extension, which reached a peak in the middle Oligocene in southwestern New Mexico, (Gans et al. 1989);

(iii) the MDVF has a greater proportion of mafic material than the surrounding Basin and Range provinces, minimizing the amount of differentiation which has to be evaluated before any discussion of the compositions of the likely parental magmas.

The petrography and chemistry (major, trace and isotopic) of rocks from the MDVF are described relative to their stratigraphic positions, to assess whether chemically distinct groups can be identified, and to document mineralogical and chemical changes with time, and changing tectonic environment.

## The stratigraphy of the Mogollon-Datil volcanic field

The MDVF of southwestern New Mexico covers an area of some 40 000 $km^2$ and thus forms only a small part of the $1 \times 10^6$ $km^2$ mid- to late Tertiary province shown in Fig. 1. Within this province the Sierra Madre Occidental is the largest single plateau and the MDVF is often regarded as an outlier, separated from the main mass by a prong of the Mexican Highlands section of the southern Basin and Range (Cameron et al. 1988). Alternatively, the field may be associated with a number of other fields, such as the San Juan in Colorado, High Plateau in Utah, and the White Mountains, Arizona, in that these were all active in the mid-Tertiary, and they lie in the present-day transition zone between the highly extended terrains of the northern and southern Basin and Range and the relatively undeformed Colorado Plateau (Fig. 1).

The geology of southwestern New Mexico is summarized in Fig. 2, which highlights the surficial predominance of the mid-Tertiary volcanics and subsequent clastic continental detritus. However, older rocks are exposed on the peripheries of the volcanic field, in fault-bounded uplifted blocks and sometimes in the resurgent domes of exhumed calderas, for example, the Emory cauldron of the southern Black Range. The basement is believed to be c. 1.7 Ga old (Condie 1986) and it comprises an intercalation of metabasic volcanics, metaquartzites and pelitic schists. It is overlain by an essentially conformable sequence of late Cambrian to Permian limestones, sandstones and shales deposited in a shallow-marine shelf environment, with a resumption in sedimentary deposition occurring during the Cretaceous. Pre-Tertiary granodiorite to quartz monzonite calc-alkaline plutons, including such well known copper-bearing porphyries as Santa Rita and Tyrone, were intruded between 75–56 Ma ago (Elston 1984a) and comprise the eastern fringe of a broad Laramide orogenic belt. Where it is exposed, the base of the mid-Tertiary volcanic sequence is unconformable on pre-Tertiary rocks or quasi-conformable on the Eocene Baca Formation, a sequence of continental clastic sediments.

Detailed mapping of the MDVF began in the 1950s with the work of Kuellmer (1954), Jicha

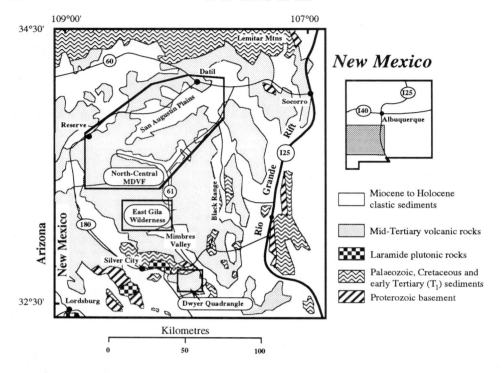

**Fig. 2.** The geology of southwestern New Mexico, showing the present distribution of the pre-Tertiary lithologies and highlighting the voluminous nature of the mid-Tertiary volcanism that forms the Mogollon-Datil volcanic field. The majority of samples for this study were collected from the East Gila Wilderness, the Dwyer Quadrangle and north-central MDVF regions.

(1954), Elston (1957) and Tonking (1957), and since then over 150 units have been identified (Elston 1976). Given the enormous number of named volcanic units and the size of the field, it has been necessary to combine the localized stratigraphy into a regional stratigraphic column, applicable for the MDVF as a whole. Similar units have been grouped on the basis of petrography and stratigraphic position, initially using K–Ar techniques to date or to bracket the ages of undated units. These data have been compiled by Marvin *et al.* (1987), Osburn & Chapin (1983) and Elston (1976). Recent work includes Ar–Ar ages on the more regionally extensive ignimbrite sheets (McIntosh 1989), and aspects of the regional stratigraphy are outlined in Elston (1989). The division of the Tertiary of New Mexico into six major units (T1 through to T6) was adopted by the New Mexico Geological Society (Clemons 1983).

Table 1 summarizes the regional stratigraphy and demonstrates that the mid-Tertiary succession is represented by three 'broadly andesitic' lava sequences, T2 (38–34 Ma ago),

T3a (31–29 Ma ago) and T4a (25–20 Ma ago), separated by two highly voluminous but short-lived periods of ignimbrite activity, T3r (35–31 Ma ago) and T4r (29–27 Ma ago). The andesitic lavas appear to have been erupted from small shield/stratovolcanoes (Elston *et al.* 1976), and many T4a volcanoes are preserved today; there are a few eroded remnants of earlier T3a eruptive centres, but little is known about the sources of T2. In contrast the T3r and T4r groups have been interpreted as the products of multiple, massive caldera collapse events (Elston 1984*b*; Ratté *et al.* 1984). The mid-Tertiary succession is capped by volumetrically minor rhyolites and basalts of the late Tertiary T5r and T6b groups respectively ( < 15 Ma ago).

Detailed field work and sampling were undertaken in the north–central MDVF, East Gila Wilderness and Dwyer Quadrangle (Fig. 2). Initial observations regarding temporal variations in petrology and mineralogy may be summarized as follows (Davis 1991).

(i) The earliest lavas, group T2 and the lower

members of T3a, show a wide range in composition from basaltic andesite through to rhyodacite, with andesite dominant. These are strongly porphyritic, and they have a mineral assemblage of plagioclase, augite with or without enstatite, and the hydrous ferromagnesian minerals oxy-hornblende, and biotite, in a trachytic groundmass. The statistical mode is c. 58% $SiO_2$ (Bornhorst 1980).

(ii) In contrast, the upper T3a and T4a lavas have a more restricted and slightly more mafic compositional range. The mode remains at 58% $SiO_2$ but the distribution is skewed towards basaltic andesite. The rocks tend to be aphyric and are more vesicular, with an anhydrous mafic minera-logy of olivine (invariably altered to 'idd-ingsite'), augite and plagioclase, with ensta-tite common in andesites. The groundmass is intergranular. Basaltic andesite and ande-site tend to have a basaltic aspect and have frequently and mistakenly been depicted as basalt on maps.

(iii) The late Tertiary group T6b is volumetri-cally minor, and consists only of olivine alkali basalt in the MDVF. Basalt is rich in fresh olivine and augite, with plagioclase confined to the groundmass except for sparse coarse phenocrysts and/or xeno-crysts. The mesa-capping flows contain xeno-liths of spinel peridotite, a feature not seen in rocks from the mid-Tertiary succession. T5r is confined to a few small occurrences of rhyodacite, mostly on both sides of the San Augustin Plains.

## Chemical stratigraphy

Over 150 samples were collected from the MDVF; the majority are from the late Eocene to early Miocene 'andesitic' groups (T2, T3a, T4a) but there are also a small number of late Tertiary (T6b) rocks. Analyses of representative rocks from these groups are presented in Table 2. Major and trace element analyses were carried out at the Grant Institute, Edinburgh University using Philips PW1450 and PW1480 automatic XRF spectrometers, according to the technique described by Fitton & Dunlop (1985). Rare earth and a number of other elements (Cs, Hf, Ta, Th, U, Sc, Co) were determined by Instrumental Neutron Activation Analysis, at the Open University, following the techniques described by Potts et al. (1981, 1985).

Sr was separated using standard ion exchange techniques and the isotopic ratios determined at the Open University using VG-Isomass 54E and Finnigan MAT261 thermal ionization mass spectrometers. All $^{87}Sr/^{86}Sr$ ratios were norma-lized to $^{88}Sr/^{86}Sr = 0.1194$. Over the period of the study, replicate standard runs gave $^{87}Sr/^{86}Sr = 0.71017$ for NBS987, at a reproducibility of 0.0074% (2 s on 25 runs) on the VG 54E, and $^{87}Sr/^{86}Sr = 0.71022$, at a reproducibility of 0.0055% (2 s on 35 runs) on the MAT261. In view of these results, the VG54E data were normalized to NBS987 = 0.71022. Blanks for Sr were less than 2 ng.

## Major and minor elements

Despite their 'broadly andesitic' description, the late Eocene to early Miocene groups (T2, T3a and T4a) display a wide variation in silica (50–69% $SiO_2$, Fig. 3). Most samples have >52% $SiO_2$, low MgO (<7%), low CaO (<8%) and high $Al_2O_3$ (16–18%), which emphasizes the evolved quartz – normative nature of the se-quence. Their alkali-lime indices are in the range 55–59, and so they are near the boundary of the alkali-calcic and calc-alkalic fields in the defi-nition of Peacock (1931). In terms of the IUGS classification, the T2, T3a and T4a rocks form a narrow band that borders the basalt–dacite and trachybasalt–trachydacite series on the Total Alkali–Silica (TAS) variation diagram (Fig. 3) of Le Bas et al. (1986), although a number of samples are shifted towards the centres of the shoshonite and latite fields as a result of higher $K_2O$ contents. Figure 3 also shows that the T2, T3a and T4a basalts and basaltic andesites are both alkalic and subalkalic, whereas the ande-sites and dacites are predominantly subalkalic. When the subalkalic rocks are plotted on a diagram of FeO (as total Fe)/MgO versus $SiO_2$ they fall into the calc-alkaline field of Miyashiro (1974), reflecting their lack of iron enrichment with increasing silica content. In summary, the late Eocene to early Miocene lavas of the MDVF form an 'alkalic-high K calc-alkaline' association.

The late Tertiary (T6b) lavas are, in contrast, all basalts (<52% $SiO_2$) with relatively high MgO contents (5–9%) albeit with low Mg# (<60). They plot in the basalt and basanite fields on Fig. 3 and on the basis of their more nepheline normative character they would be classified as alkali basalts (Le Bas et al. 1986).

Figure 4 illustrates the major element vari-ations with stratigraphic position for the rocks of the Dwyer Quadrangle, East Gila Wilderness area and the north–central MDVF sections. The thicknesses of the different units are not well constrained, but Bornhorst (1980) estimated them to be; 300–700 m (1500 m max.) for T2,

**Table 1.** *Simplified regional stratigraphy of the Mogollon-Datil volcanic field, based on Clemons (1983) Osburn & Chapin (1983) and Elston (1976, 1989)*

| Group | Age | Lithology | Petrography | Major units within group | Notes |
|---|---|---|---|---|---|
| T6b | Mid- to late Miocene and Pliocene | Basalt (*Alkali/tholeiitic*) | Ol+Aug+Plag (*Spinel peridotite xenoliths*) | Mimbres Valley, Hillsboro, Winston, Apache Creek. | Minor flows interbedded with, or capping mesas of, late Tertiary clastic sediments; Gila or Santa Fe Conglomerate. |
| T5r | Mid-Miocene | Dacite–high silica rhyolite | | Eagle Peak Dacite, Magdalena Quartz Latite, John Kerr Peak Quartz Latite, Horse Mtn. Rhyodacite. | Minor domes and flows; often forming late plugs to the stratocones of T4a. |
| T4a | Early to mid-Miocene | Basalt–dacite (*Basaltic andesite is the most common rock type, the dacites are very minor*) | Basalts: Ol (idd.) +Aug+Plag. Basaltic andesites: Plag+Aug+Ol+Opx. Andesites: Plag+Aug+Opx. (*Minor Ol & Plag phenocrysts, but usually aphyric. Black and often vesicular*) | Bearwallow Mtn Formation (Elston 1976), includes Black Mtn, Bearwallow Mtn, John Kerr Peak, Mangas Mtn, Luera Peak, Pelona Mtn, O-Bar-O Mtn, Eagle Peak, Negrito Mtn, Mogollon Mtn, West Elk, Elk Peak centres. Double Springs Andesite. Last Chance Andesite. | Shield/stratocone volcanoes still recognizable today. Also minor basaltic flows not obviously derived from the cones. Distributed throughout the field, Mangas Mtns, Tularosa Mtns, Mogollon Mtns. |
| T4r | Late Oligocene 29–27 Ma ago (*Ar–Ar dating, McIntosh 1989*) | High silica rhyolite | Qtz+Sand+Biot±Plag. (*Plag (albite) is minor or absent, with Hbl & Aug rare. Sanadine tends to be cryptoperthite*) | Apache Springs Tuff & Bloodgood Canyon Tuff & Davis Canyon Tuff (Bursum-Gila caldera, Ratté et al. 1984). Lemitar Tuff & Vicks Peak Tuff (Socorro area, Osburn & Chapin 1983). | Related to massive caldera collapse of the Bursum and Gila Cliff Dwellings calderas (Ratté et al. 1984) for the central area of the field and similar calderas in the Socorro area for the north, followed by post-caldera fill and ring fracture domes. |
| T3a | Mid-Oligocene | Basalt–andesite (*Upper*) | Basalts: Ol(idd)+Plag+Aug. Andesites: Plag+Aug+Opx. (*Aphyric/slightly porphyritic*) | Bears Springs Formation. (Elston et al. 1981), Middle Mtn Member (Krier 1980), Poverty Creek basaltic andesite (Abitz 1989). | Localized sequences, centres largely unknown, but similar distribution to T2. The complete sequence consists of andesite–rhyolite–basalt (±andesite). |
| | | Andesite–rhyodacite (*Lower*) | Andesites: Plag+Aug±Ol. Dacites: Plag+Aug+Opx+Hbl. Rhyolites: Plag+Hbl+Biot. (*Slightly to coarsely porphyritic*) | Razorback Formation (Elston 1957), Salt Creek M. and Gila Flat M. (Krier 1980), Alum Mtn. Complex, Gila Flat latite & Murtocks' Hole Andesite (Ratté & Gaskill 1975). | The lower andesite–rhyolite part is similar in appearance and petrology to T2, whilst the upper basalt–andesite is similar to the T4a group. A period of erosion locally separates the upper from the lower sequences. This is locally represented by sedimentary rocks of the Pilscillo Fm (Dwyer Quad.) or a 1 m thick red soil. |

| Unit | Age | Rock type | Mineralogy | Formation / references | Description |
|---|---|---|---|---|---|
| T3r | Early Oligocene 35–31 Ma ago (Ar–Ar dating, McIntosh 1989) | Dacite–rhyolite | Plag + Sand + Biot ± Qtz. (*Qtz abundant–absent, with Hbl and Aug rare*) | Sugarlump Tuff & Kneeling Nun Tuff (Emory caldera, Abitz 1989; Elston 1989) Caballo Blanco, Coney and Whitewater Tuffs (Mogollon caldera) Datil Well Tuff & Hells Mesa Tuff (Socorro area). | Extensive ash flow tuffs associated with caldera collapse of the Emory and Mogollon calderas in the southern part of the field, and calderas in the Socorro region for the north. Collapse was followed by caldera fill deposits and ring fracture domes. |
| T2 | Late Eocene to early Oligocene | Basaltic andesite–rhyodacite (*Andesite is the most common rock type*) | Basaltic andesites: Plag + Aug + Ol. Andesites: Plag + Aug + Hbl. Dacite: Plag + Hbl ± Biot. (*Strongly porphyritic*) | Rubio Peak Formation (south, Elston 1957) and the Spears Formation (north, Tonking 1957; Lopez & Bornhorst 1979), the latter is included in the Datil Group by Osburn & Chapin (1983). | Distributed as thick sequences around the periphery of the field, and assumed to be buried by younger volcanics in the centre. In the south, flows and volcanic breccias are interbedded in near equal proportions. However, in the north and west, thick sequences of andesitic/dacitic breccia and conglomerate dominate with localized basaltic andesite flows. |
| T1 | Mid- to late Eocene | Siliclastic detrital sediments. | Fragments of Upper Palaeozoic limestones, sandstones, siltstones, with subordinate amounts of Precambrian lithologies. | Baca Formation (Cather & Chapin 1989). | Found only in the north around Datil and west of Socorro. Formed in Laramide basins known as Baca Basin and the Carthage-La Joya Basin. |

Ol: olivine; Aug: augite; Plag: plagioclase feldspar; Sand: sanidine; Biot: biotite; Opx: orthopyroxene; Qtz: quartz; Hbl: hornblende. The Eocene–Oligocene and Oligocene–Miocene boundaries have been placed at 36 Ma ago and 23 Ma ago respectively from data in Faure (1986).

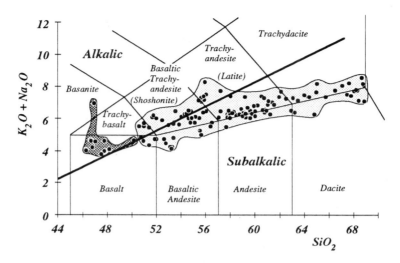

**Fig. 3.** Total alkali vs. silica (wt%) for all samples from the MDVF, using the IUGS classification defined by Le Bas *et al.* (1986). The light shading refers to mid-Tertiary rocks and the darker shading to the late Tertiary rocks. Also shown is the alkalic/subalkalic division of MacDonald & Katsura (1964).

about 500 m (700 m max.) for T3a and 150–350 m (1000 m max.) for T4a. The excellence of the exposure in the T2 group (Rubio Peak Formation) allowed samples to be collected up-section and so the order of relative stratigraphic position is well established, although inevitably Fig. 4 does not take into account the horizontal distances between sample localities. In contrast, the T3a and T4a groups have a more complex internal stratigraphy, in particular for the north–central section where samples from the T4a group were collected from individual volcanic centres and not from continuous field sections. Thus the relative stratigraphic positions of these samples had to be inferred from the K–Ar dates of Marvin *et al.* (1987) and from field relation-ships (Davis 1991). Further complications arose within the T3a group in that samples from strati-graphically correlated units were collected from different areas. In such cases the different sets of samples have been plotted at the same relative stratigraphic positions. For example, within the T3a group, the andesite member of the Razor-back Formation and Bear Springs Basalt of the Dwyer Quadrangle were correlated with the upper member of the Salt Creek Formation and the basaltic andesite of Middle Mountain of the East Gila Wilderness, respectively (Elston 1981). The shaded portions correspond to the periods of dominantly silicic volcanism. The broad bands of the T3r and T4r groups represent periods of extensive ignimbrite eruption of roughly equal volume, and Elston (1984*b*) gives

estimates of 1500–2500 km$^3$ for the Emory and Bursum calderas. The narrow band represents the early Miocene volumetrically minor rhyolite flows and domes of the T5r group.

From Fig. 4, it is clear that the silica variation within the groups is consistent with the petro-logical observations concerning the varying de-grees of differentiation in the different groups. The T2 and lower T3a groups have much wider ranges in silica content, from basaltic andesite through to rhyodacite, and andesite is the dominant rock type. In contrast, the upper T3a and T4a groups have a more restricted range of basalt to andesite; samples with >62% SiO$_2$ are rare and they are usually younger plug domes in the T4a centres that might reasonably be con-sidered to be part of the T5r group. Signifi-cantly, within the T2 and T3a groups there appear to be a number of sequences within which SiO$_2$ increases with time, and yet in the T4a group there is a marked decrease in SiO$_2$ with time. Some caution is necessary because the relative stratigraphic positions of many of the samples in T4a are not well known. Nonetheless, the oldest T4a rocks in this study (Black Moun-tain and Bearwallow Mountain) are predomi-nantly andesites, and the youngest T4a rocks (Lake Roberts and Black Canyon) are basalts, so that overall there is a general tendency for silica to decrease with time within the T4a Group.

Different information is available from the variations of minor elements with stratigraphic

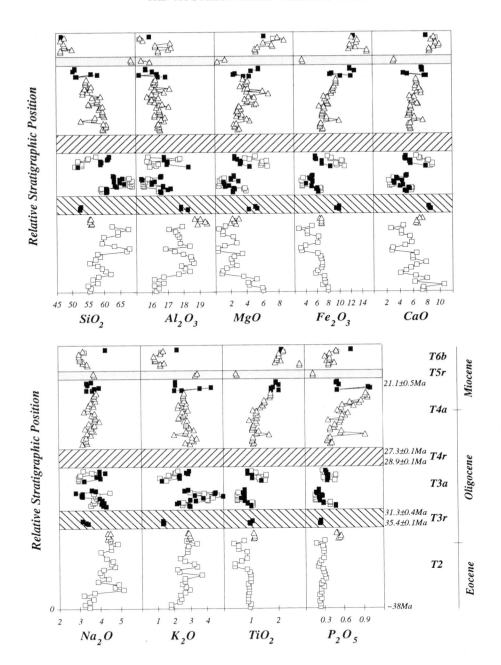

**Fig. 4.** Abundances of major and minor element oxides (wt%) plotted against relative stratigraphic position. The shaded portions represent dominantly silicic volcanism, the broad bands refer to the two periods of extensive ignimbrite eruption, T3r and T4r, with the narrow band representing the volumetrically minor early Miocene T5r group. The Ar–Ar dates are taken from McIntosh (1989). The symbols refer to the different sampling areas – open square: Dwyer Quadrangle; filled square: East Gila Wilderness area; open triangle: north-central MDVF. The open triangles in T2 are from the Spears Formation at *c.* 34° N.

**Table 2.** *Chemical and isotopic analysis of representative mid- and late Tertiary rocks from the Mogollon-Datil volcanic field*

| Sample | Rp88-8 | Rp87-7 | Rp87-6 | Ss89-3 | Ra87-11 | Ra87-18 | A188-10 | A188-6 | Bs87-3 | A188-13 | Jk88-7 | Bw88-10 | Bw88-8 | Bm88-3 | Bm88-12 | Jk89-9 | Ab88-1 | Mimbres |
|---|---|---|---|---|---|---|---|---|---|---|---|---|---|---|---|---|---|---|
| Formation | Rubio Peak | Rubio Peak | Rubio Peak | Spears | Razorback | Razorback | Salt Creek | Salt Creek | Bear Springs | Middle Mtn | John Kerr Peak | John Kerr Peak | Bearwallow Mtn | Bearwallow Mtn | Bearwallow Mtn | Bearwallow Mtn | John Kerr Peak | Mimbres |
| Group | T2 | T2 | T2 | T2 | Lower T3a | Lower T3a | Lower T3a | Lower T3a | Upper T3a | Upper T3a | T4a | T4a | T4a | T4a | T4a | Upper T4a | T5r | T6b |
| Latitude | 32°45'00" | 32°39'15" | 32°39'15" | 34°10'30" | 32°45'30" | 32°44'00" | 33°4'00" | 33°3'00" | 32°43'00" | 33°05'30" | 33°45'00" | 33°45'45" | 33°24'15" | 33°27'15" | 33°24'30" | 33°11'15" | 33°48'45" | 32°52'00" |
| Longitude | 107°55'15" | 107°50'15" | 107°50'15" | 107°54'00" | 107°54'30" | 107°52'30" | 108°00'30" | 108°9'45" | 107°52'30" | 108°08'00" | 108°31'30" | 108°32'15" | 108°34'30" | 108°37'00" | 108°13'00" | 108°01'45" | 108°28'30" | 107°58'30" |
| $SiO_2$ | 55.47 | 59.38 | 63.08 | 55.57 | 59.22 | 67.73 | 61.21 | 66.46 | 51.98 | 59.17 | 53.33 | 54.02 | 52.94 | 57.02 | 60.76 | 50.96 | 47.71 | 47.74 |
| $TiO_2$ | 1.00 | 0.86 | 0.67 | 1.16 | 1.12 | 0.58 | 0.90 | 0.67 | 1.61 | 1.40 | 1.40 | 1.56 | 1.70 | 1.24 | 1.09 | 1.97 | 2.01 | 2.26 |
| $Al_2O_3$ | 16.30 | 17.77 | 18.00 | 19.36 | 16.46 | 15.79 | 17.02 | 16.03 | 15.86 | 17.05 | 16.04 | 17.14 | 16.78 | 16.61 | 16.52 | 15.68 | 16.28 | 15.33 |
| $Fe_2O_3$ | 8.03 | 6.24 | 4.68 | 6.90 | 6.85 | 3.75 | 6.10 | 4.24 | 10.71 | 7.05 | 8.67 | 9.08 | 9.94 | 7.88 | 6.66 | 11.96 | 12.06 | 12.25 |
| $MnO$ | 0.12 | 0.12 | 0.05 | 0.09 | 0.10 | 0.06 | 0.08 | 0.06 | 0.14 | 0.09 | 0.13 | 0.13 | 0.14 | 0.12 | 0.09 | 0.17 | 0.18 | 0.18 |
| $MgO$ | 6.11 | 2.76 | 1.20 | 2.41 | 3.90 | 1.26 | 2.51 | 1.24 | 6.11 | 3.35 | 6.84 | 4.19 | 4.42 | 4.10 | 2.53 | 5.63 | 7.27 | 7.91 |
| $CaO$ | 7.44 | 5.86 | 4.50 | 6.60 | 5.83 | 3.14 | 5.58 | 3.26 | 8.33 | 5.66 | 7.31 | 7.06 | 7.53 | 6.33 | 5.57 | 7.59 | 10.08 | 9.21 |
| $Na_2O$ | 3.50 | 4.31 | 4.57 | 4.42 | 3.58 | 4.49 | 4.10 | 4.00 | 3.05 | 3.84 | 3.43 | 3.58 | 3.58 | 3.39 | 3.33 | 3.42 | 3.10 | 3.23 |
| $K_2O$ | 1.80 | 2.40 | 2.81 | 2.95 | 2.56 | 3.00 | 2.20 | 3.81 | 1.72 | 2.34 | 2.29 | 2.56 | 2.04 | 2.74 | 3.10 | 2.13 | 0.91 | 1.42 |
| $P_2O_5$ | 0.24 | 0.29 | 0.30 | 0.55 | 0.39 | 0.20 | 0.29 | 0.22 | 0.49 | 0.35 | 0.56 | 0.69 | 0.94 | 0.56 | 0.36 | 0.50 | 0.40 | 0.49 |
| Orig. Total | 98.37 | 99.44 | 98.98 | 99.23 | 98.56 | 97.37 | 98.39 | 98.36 | 98.10 | 98.90 | 99.81 | 97.92 | 98.59 | 98.81 | 98.07 | 98.53 | 99.97 | 98.81 |
| Mg.No. | 63 | 50 | 40 | 44 | 56 | 43 | 48 | 40 | 56 | 52 | 64 | 51 | 50 | 54 | 46 | 51 | 58 | 59 |
| U | 0.83 | 1.14 | 1.48 | 3.80 | 2.24 | — | 1.20 | — | 0.81 | 1.27 | 1.09 | 1.49 | 0.94 | 1.65 | 2.10 | 1.20 | — | 1.52 |
| Cs | 1.07 | 1.22 | 0.88 | 2.27 | 1.37 | — | 1.40 | — | 2.37 | 0.57 | 0.90 | 0.93 | 0.31 | 1.06 | 1.01 | 0.66 | 0.34 | — |
| Rb | 36 | 52 | 63 | 90 | 66 | 127 | 52 | 106 | 31 | 47 | 38 | 56 | 39 | 73 | 101 | 55 | 15 | 26 |
| Ba | 749 | 1010 | 1200 | 990 | 1088 | 1071 | 941 | 1142 | 884 | 1194 | 980 | 1266 | 1189 | 1168 | 1006 | 843 | 408 | 585 |
| Th | 3.81 | 5.22 | 6.19 | 15.5 | 8.69 | 10 | 4.22 | 10 | 3.96 | 4.21 | 4.67 | 5.99 | 4.35 | 7.62 | 11.30 | 3.94 | 2.83 | 3.34 |
| Nb | 6 | 8 | 10 | 23 | 10 | 11 | 8 | 12 | 10 | 10 | 13 | 16 | 15 | 14 | 14 | 17 | 28 | 40 |
| Ta | 0.40 | 0.58 | 0.59 | 1.55 | 0.79 | — | 0.52 | — | 0.57 | 0.56 | 0.91 | 1.02 | 0.84 | 0.89 | 0.78 | 1.15 | 1.98 | 2.75 |
| Sr | 576 | 734 | 720 | 1058 | 789 | 410 | 799 | 512 | 814 | 623 | 715 | 775 | 834 | 689 | 508 | 677 | 519 | 630 |
| Hf | 3.79 | 4.93 | 5.62 | 8.93 | 4.98 | — | 4.89 | — | 5.70 | 6.62 | 5.54 | 6.55 | 7.06 | 7.10 | 7.61 | 5.30 | 3.81 | 3.93 |
| Zr | 181 | 205 | 238 | 408 | 216 | 323 | 231 | 245 | 255 | 276 | 233 | 294 | 337 | 313 | 342 | 229 | 160 | 179 |
| Y | 20 | 24 | 23 | 43 | 22 | 28 | 21 | 19 | 32 | 23 | 26 | 32 | 39 | 34 | 39 | 33 | 23 | 28 |
| Ni | 95 | 10 | 5 | 32 | 39 | 10 | 92 | 19 | 150 | 39 | 188 | 64 | 39 | 66 | 25 | 151 | 73 | 165 |
| Cr | 244 | 4 | 2 | 17 | 44 | 7 | 127 | 27 | 228 | 65 | 260 | 87 | 84 | 78 | 16 | 198 | 104 | 219 |
| Sc | 20 | 13 | 8 | 15 | 13 | 5 | 15 | 8 | 26 | 12 | 20 | 18 | 21 | 18 | 14 | 20 | 31 | 22 |
| V | 163 | 118 | 73 | 152 | 128 | 43 | 116 | 72 | 205 | 121 | 157 | 164 | 184 | 146 | 123 | 185 | 270 | 181 |
| Co | 32 | 17 | 9 | 20 | 21 | 43 | 20 | 72 | 37 | 22 | 35 | 29.7 | 31 | 35 | 19 | 44.7 | 47 | 47 |
| La | 22.6 | 31.7 | 34.3 | 61.1 | 37.2 | 58 | 33.7 | 56 | 36.8 | 39.3 | 37.9 | 50.2 | 63.3 | 52.2 | 53.9 | 31.5 | 25.7 | 26.9 |
| Ce | 47.3 | 63.1 | 65.2 | 106 | 73.8 | 113 | 64.3 | 97 | 79.1 | 76.6 | 76.3 | 102 | 122.9 | 105.6 | 112 | 70.6 | 54.5 | 52.4 |
| Nd | 25.4 | 31.5 | 30.9 | 54.5 | 34.0 | 49 | 33.2 | 41 | 42.8 | 40.8 | 42.2 | 51.2 | 59.4 | 53.9 | 51.2 | 38.7 | 30.1 | 24.9 |
| Sm | 4.85 | 5.54 | 5.53 | 9.49 | 6.32 | — | 6.12 | — | 8.11 | 7.65 | 7.24 | 9.10 | 11.30 | 9.50 | 9.76 | 8.20 | 5.79 | 5.70 |
| Eu | 1.48 | 1.69 | 1.62 | 2.27 | 1.74 | — | 1.63 | — | 2.30 | 2.05 | 2.11 | 2.62 | 2.18 | 2.41 | 1.93 | 2.46 | 1.94 | 2.02 |
| Gd | | | | | | | | | | | | | | | | | | |
| Tb | 0.72 | 0.79 | 0.77 | 1.21 | 0.82 | — | 0.76 | — | 1.15 | 0.92 | 1.01 | 1.21 | 1.40 | 1.27 | 1.23 | 1.19 | 0.95 | 0.92 |
| Dy | | | | | | | | | | | | | | | | | | |
| Yb | 1.70 | 2.05 | 2.13 | 3.35 | 1.80 | — | 1.75 | — | 2.72 | 1.69 | 2.25 | 2.68 | 3.12 | 2.95 | 3.19 | 2.86 | 2.43 | 2.22 |
| Lu | 0.27 | 0.34 | 0.34 | 0.55 | 0.28 | — | 0.26 | — | 0.44 | 0.26 | 0.36 | 0.45 | 0.48 | 0.47 | 0.52 | 0.46 | 0.38 | 0.36 |
| $^{87}Sr/^{86}Sr_i$ | 0.70629 | 0.70649 | 0.70650 | 0.70539 | 0.70581 | 0.70863 | 0.70569 | 0.70692 | 0.70715 | 0.70834 | 0.70707 | 0.70734 | 0.70712 | 0.70819 | 0.70811 | 0.70648 | 0.70416 | 0.70353 |

position. $TiO_2$ discriminates the late Eocene to early Miocene (T2, T3a and T4a) from the late Tertiary (T6b) lavas, although it is of interest that the increase in $TiO_2$ appears to start in the middle of the T4a group. Also within the late Eocene to early Miocene sequence there is a tendency for $TiO_2$ contents to increase up-section, in that $TiO_2$ is <1% in most of the T2 and lower T3a groups and it is >1% in most of the upper T3a and T4a samples. $Fe_2O_3$ displays a similar pattern but it is less pronounced. $P_2O_5$ is also a good discriminant within the late Eocene to early Miocene sequence, where the T2 and lower T3a groups have similar low $P_2O_5$ contents (<0.3%), and the upper T3a and T4a have $P_2O_5$ contents in the range 0.3–1.0%. However, $P_2O_5$ is less effective at distinguishing the late Tertiary rocks, since they have an average $P_2O_5$ content of c. 0.4%. In contrast, $K_2O$ varies in much the same way as silica, and so rocks with similar $SiO_2$ contents have broadly similar $K_2O$, irrespective of their stratigraphic positions (Fig. 4).

### Trace elements

The following trace elements have been selected as representative of different chemical groups – Ba (Large Ion Lithophile, LILE), Nb, Zr, Y (High Field Strength, HFSE), La (Light Rare Earths, LREE), and Ni (Transition Metals), and these have been plotted against stratigraphic position in Fig. 5. Ba, Nb, Zr, La and Y are all incompatible, to varying degrees, in the mineral assemblages that normally fractionate in the differentiation from basalt and basaltic andesite, and Ni was chosen because it is more compatible, particularly into olivine.

The low Ni contents (<200 ppm), and the low concentrations of other compatible elements (Cr, Sc, Table 2) confirm the evolved nature of the MDVF rocks. In contrast, the concentrations of incompatible elements are high and variable, Ba = 500–1750 ppm, La = 20–80 ppm, Zr = 150–400 ppm and Y = 20–50 ppm. Moreover, despite being of similar incompatibility to Ba and La, Nb has comparatively low concentrations, 5–20 ppm (Fig. 6). Thus LILE/HFSE (Ba/Nb and K/Ti) and LREE/HFS (La/Nb) ratios are high, with Ba/Nb = 50–120 for the T2 to T4a succession, consistent with the lavas being classified as 'orogenic', from the definition of Gill (1981) (i.e. Ba/Nb >30, which is equivalent to Ba/Ta >450). The late Tertiary (T6b group) typically has lower Ba, La, Zr, and Y and higher Nb abundances (up to 50–60 ppm in the early Pliocene alkali basalts), which reduce Ba/Nb ratios to 10–30. Such values are too low to be defined as 'orogenic' and are closer to the range of Ba/Nb ratios associated with MORB and OIB type lavas.

In terms of temporal evolution within the T2 to T4a rocks it appears that Nb behaves similarly to $TiO_2$, generally increasing with time

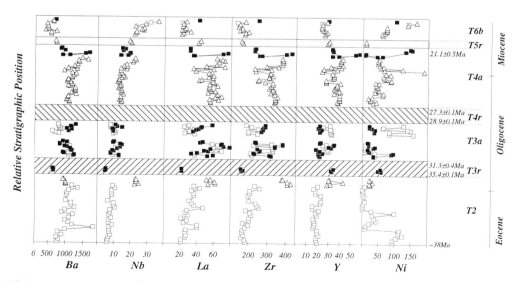

**Fig. 5.** Abundances of selected trace elements (ppm), arranged in order of increasing compatibility, plotted against relative stratigraphic position (symbols as in Fig. 4.).

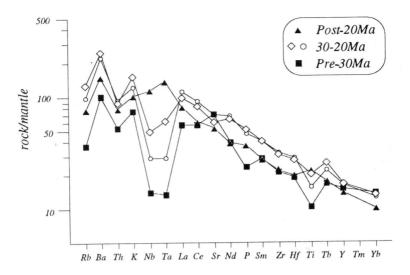

**Fig. 6.** A mantle-normalized trace element diagram illustrating the changes in minor and trace element abundances in selected Pre-30 Ma, 30–20 Ma and Post-20 Ma volcanic rocks. Samples: Pre-30 Ma, olivine tholeiite Tc 88-1; 30–20 Ma, potassic trachybasalts Bs 87-3 and BL 88-12; Post-20 Ma, olivine alkali basalt A688–1. Data from Davis (1991).

from the early Oligocene T2 basaltic andesites (5–7 ppm) to the basaltic andesites from group T4a (13–20 ppm; Fig. 5). Similar trends are observed for the other HFSE (Zr and Y) and the LREE (La), so that when comparing rocks with similar $SiO_2$ contents, those from the upper T3a and T4a have higher HFSE and LREE contents than those from the lower T3a and T2 groups. However, this is not true for Ba which behaves like $K_2O$, in that Ba contents remain similar throughout the section for rocks with broadly similar $SiO_2$. Thus Ba/Nb largely depends on the variation in Nb content, with Ba/Nb being highest in the T2 and lower T3a groups and then decreasing up-section (Figs 5 and 6).

An exception to such general trends are the basaltic andesites from the early Oligocene Spears Formation (T2), from the northern MDVF, which have extreme concentrations of Zr *c.* 400 ppm and high Ba, Nb, La and Y. They are broadly contemporaneous with the Rubio Peak Formation, the other sampled member of the T2 group, which confirms that some of the observed geochemical variations are spatial as well as temporal. The Spears Formation samples were collected in the part of the MDVF which overlaps the Colorado Plateau, north of lat. 34°N.

*Sr isotopes*

Initial Sr isotope ratios range from 0.703–0.709,

and the variations in Sr isotopes with stratigraphic position are illustrated in Fig. 7. The late Eocene to early Miocene T2, T3a and T4a rocks all have relatively high $^{87}Sr/^{86}Sr$ ratios, 0.7055–0.7090, whereas the late Tertiary rocks (T6b) have lower values of 0.7030–0.7055. Within the older sequence the late Eocene and early Oligocene (T2 and lower T3a) rocks tend to display a wider range, 0.7055–0.7090, but the majority of samples have $^{87}Sr/^{86}Sr = 0.7055$–0.7065. The few with $^{87}Sr/^{86}Sr > 0.7065$ are strongly differentiated dacites and rhyolites, mostly from the localized units of the lower T3a (rhyolite member of the Razorback Formation and equivalent dacite members of the Gila Flat Formation). The younger, late Oligocene to early Miocene (upper T3a and T4a) rocks, despite their tendency towards more mafic compositions, have slightly higher $^{87}Sr/^{86}Sr$ in the range 0.7065–0.7085. However, the highest $^{87}Sr/^{86}Sr$ ratios are again associated with the more differentiated, andesitic, rock types.

In the same way that the T6b rocks are distinguished by their high $TiO_2$ (>2%), high Nb (>25 ppm) and low Ba (<600 ppm), they also have markedly lower $^{87}Sr/^{86}Sr$ (>0.7055). Within the T2 to T4a suite the Sr isotope variations are more subtle, but there is some suggestion that in the lower silica rocks ($SiO_2$ <60%), the older groups (T2 and lower T3a) have lower $^{87}Sr/^{86}Sr$ (<0.7065) than the younger, upper T3a and T4a rocks which have $^{87}Sr/^{86}Sr$ >0.7065. If so, this isotope shift accompanies the previously established subtle variations in major and trace elements, in that the older rocks have low $TiO_2$ ($<1\%$) and higher LILE contents relative to the HFSE and the REE.

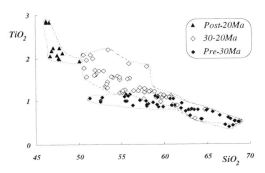

**Fig. 8.** $TiO_2$ vs. $SiO_2$ (wt%) with the MDVF samples divided into three temporally defined groups; Pre-30 Ma, 30–20 Ma and Post-20 Ma.

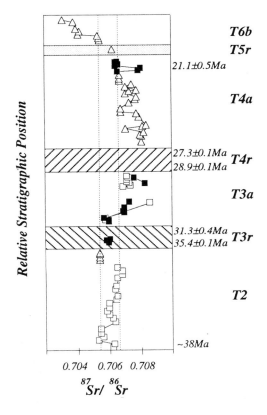

**Fig. 7.** $^{87}Sr/^{86}Sr$ plotted against relative stratigraphic position (symbols as in Fig. 4).

### Temporal variations in chemistry

As indicated above, there is a major chemical change between the more evolved late Eocene to early Miocene and essentially basaltic late Tertiary sequences, and a further significant change probably occurs within the T3a group, in the middle Oligocene. The transitional nature of T3a had previously been documented by Krier (1980) on the basis of petrography and major-element chemistry. In petrological terms the lower T3a rocks are more closely associated with the older T2 group, in that they tend to contain amphibole and/or minor biotite, whereas the upper T3a samples are better associated with the T4a group (see also Fig. 9). Thus, it is argued that the major

change within the late Eocene to early Miocene sequence occurs between the lower and upper T3a, and that the rocks of the MDVF may usefully be considered in three chemically and stratigraphically distinct units. The late Tertiary rocks (T6b) are now described as the 'Post-20 Ma' group, since they post-date the youngest Bearwallow Mountain Formation members which are thought to be *c*. 20 Ma old. No members of this group are known to be older than *c*. 15 Ma old. The age of the transition between the lower and upper T3a, was taken to be at 30 Ma ago and although fairly arbitrary it is probably accurate to $\pm1.2$ Ma since the T3a group is bracketed by ash flow tuffs dated at $31.3\pm0.4$ Ma ago and $28.9\pm0.1$ Ma ago (McIntosh 1989). Moreover, in the East Gila area the division is just above the lower T3a Gila Flat member which has been dated at $30.4\pm1.0$ Ma ago (K–Ar, Ratté & Gaskill 1975). The lower T3a and T2 are therefore termed the 'Pre-30 Ma' group, and the upper T3a and T4a are the '30–20 Ma' group.

$TiO_2$ is one element that varies systematically with stratigraphic position (Fig. 4). Figure 8 is a plot of $TiO_2$ vs. $SiO_2$, which illustrates that the three groups are readily distinguished at lower $SiO_2$ values ($SiO_2 <56\%$), but less so at higher values. The 30–20 Ma group andesites appear to have slightly higher $TiO_2$, but this plot does not provide sufficient information to say with any certainty that the groups may be distinguished at higher $SiO_2$, or that andesites from one group cannot be related to the more mafic members of the other group. For that, it is necessary to use incompatible trace element ratios, which are not changed significantly during differentiation to more silicic, andesitic, magmas. Figure 9, therefore, shows the variation of a number of frac-

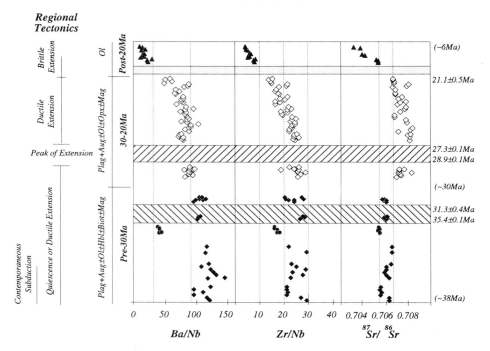

**Fig. 9.** Ba/Nb, Zr/Nb and $^{87}Sr/^{86}Sr$ plotted against relative stratigraphic position, for samples with 62% $SiO_2$. The MDVF samples are divided into three temporally defined groups; Pre-30 Ma, 30–20 Ma and Post-20 Ma (symbols as in Fig. 8, plus filled circles for the Pre-30 Ma Spears Formation rocks). The petrology of each group is from Table 1, with the regional tectonic information taken from Elston (1984a) and Gans *et al.* (1989). Ar–Ar dates for the silicic units are from McIntosh (1989). Mineral abbreviations as for Table 3.

tionation-independent parameters, Ba/Nb, Zr/Nb and $^{87}Sr/^{86}Sr$, with stratigraphic height, for rocks with <62% $SiO_2$, to ensure that Ba, Zr and Nb were reasonably incompatible. Also included in Fig. 9 is the petrology of the different groups and the timing of significant tectonic events: namely, the cessation of subduction at this latitude (*c*. 33° N), and the peak of extension in southwestern New Mexico.

In Fig. 9 the two mid-Tertiary groups both have high Ba/Nb (>30) and high Zr/Nb (>10) ratios, and although they have similar Zr/Nb ratios, the Pre-30 Ma rocks are distinguished by having higher Ba/Nb (>90). The different behaviour for Ba–Nb and Zr–Nb holds for other LILE, REE and HFSE, and reflects the relatively high LILE (Ba, Rb, Th and K) contents of the Pre–30 Ma rocks compared with the REE and HFSE (Fig. 6). In contrast, the lower Ba/Nb and Zr/Nb of the 30–20 Ma group are largely due to their higher HFSE (Nb, Ta and Ti) contents. It is also interesting to note that the younger members of the 30–20 Ma group show some chemical affinity with the Post-20 Ma group.

In summary, the LILE/HFSE and LILE/REE ratios for the Pre-30 Ma rocks >30–20 Ma ≫ Post-20 Ma. Furthermore, in rocks with <62 wt% $SiO_2$, $^{87}Sr/^{86}Sr$ is noticeably higher (>0.7055) in the Pre-30 Ma and 30–20 Ma groups than in the Post-20 Ma, whilst the 30–20 Ma group displays consistently higher values (>0.7065) than the Pre-30 Ma group, despite the apparently more evolved nature of the latter (higher $SiO_2$, Fig. 4).

The above trace element and isotopic distinctions are summarized in Fig. 10, a plot of Ba/Nb vs $^{87}Sr/^{86}Sr$. This diagram highlights the regional differences between T2 rocks of the stable Colorado Plateau north of lat. 34° N, which have more within plate affinities, and the higher Ba/Nb rocks of the transition to the Basin and Range zone of extension to the south. For the three main groups of the MDVF, this diagram is a powerful discriminant, since not only do the samples fall into distinct fields, but samples in any field cannot be related to those in other fields by simple crystal fractionation processes, since in low silica magmas ($SiO_2$ <62%) with the observed mineral assemblages (see Table 1), Ba/Nb and $^{87}Sr/^{86}Sr$ ratios are unaffected by

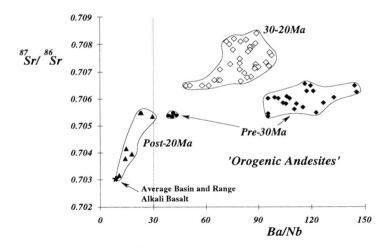

**Fig. 10.** $^{87}Sr/^{86}Sr$ vs Ba/Nb for samples with <62% $SiO_2$, with symbols as in Fig. 9. Those with Ba/Nb >30 fall into the 'Orogenic Andesite' field as defined by Gill (1981; equivalent to Ba/Ta >450, using Nb ≈ Ta × 15). Also shown is average Basin and Range alkali basalt, taken from Ormerod *et al.* (1988).

such processes. However, both Ba/Nb and $^{87}Sr/$ $^{86}Sr$ can be changed by magma mixing and crustal assimilation, or by changes in parental magma composition due to differences in source composition. These clearly need to be evaluated before confirming the independence and significance of each group.

The Post-20 Ma group has low Ba/Nb and $^{87}Sr/^{86}Sr$, similar to MORB and OIB, and the Pre-30 Ma and 30–20 Ma rocks have higher LIL/HFSE and Sr isotope ratios, which are features more typically associated with crustal rocks than mantle-derived material. Thus it might be argued that the Pre-30 Ma and 30–20 Ma rocks were derived by variable degrees of crustal contamination of basaltic magmas similar to those in the Post-20 Ma group. However, the amounts of contamination required are too great to be consistent with the presence of basalts and basaltic andesites with $SiO_2$ <55%, MgO >6% and Ni >150 ppm in each group. In addition the Pre-30 Ma and 30–20 Ma rocks have low concentrations of Nb = 5–15 ppm, in contrast to the OIB-like alkali basalts from the Post-20 Ma group which have Nb = 50–60 ppm. Thus, in order to reduce the concentration of Nb to the level observed in the mid-Tertiary rocks, even with a contaminant containing no Nb, at least 70% contamination is required (Ormerod *et al.* 1988; Fitton *et al.* 1991). It is argued, therefore, that crustal contamination provides an inadequate explanation for the major chemical differences between the Pre- and Post-20 Ma

rocks in the MDVF, and instead this marks a significant change in the source regions tapped by the MDVF. Within the late Eocene to early Miocene succession the Pre-30 Ma samples typically have lower $^{87}Sr/^{86}Sr$ and, with the exception of the Spears Formation samples from lat. 34° N, higher Ba/Nb (and other LILE/HFSE ratios) than the 30–20 Ma rocks (Fig. 9). However, the rocks with the higher Sr isotope ratios also tend to have lower silica contents (Fig. 4), and assuming that most crustal materials have relatively high silica contents, the differences between the Pre-30 Ma and the Pre-30 Ma rocks are also not easily explained by crustal contamination processes.

In summary, the lower silica rocks of the MDVF (basalts, basaltic andesites and andesites) can be usefully subdivided into three groups with distinctive geochemical characteristics; these are presented in Table 3 along with the petrological characteristics discussed earlier. These distinctions justify the choice of groups, and indicate the close correlation between the observed chemical and petrological changes. The late Eocene to early Miocene sequence comprises the broadly andesitic, hydrous Pre-30 Ma and anhydrous 30–20 Ma groups, which both have major and trace element compositions consistent with Gill's (1981) definition of 'orogenic andesite'. The younger, late Tertiary, Post-20 Ma group consists predominantly of alkali basalts, which have geochemical characteristics more in common with OIB type magmas.

**Table 3.** *Summary of the chemical, isotopic and petrological characteristics of the Pre-30 Ma, 30–20 Ma and Post-20 Ma groups*

| Properties | Pre-30 Ma* | 30–20 Ma | Post-20 Ma |
|---|---|---|---|
| Major and minor elements | Broad range in $SiO_2$ 55–69 wt%. Low $TiO_2$ ($<1$ wt%) and $P_2O_5$ ($<0.3$ wt%) | Restricted range in $SiO_2$ 50–62 wt%, higher $TiO_2$ (1–2 wt%) and $P_2O_5$ (0.3–1.0 wt%) | Basalts and basanites with $SiO_2$, 46–49 wt%. High $TiO_2$ ($>2$ wt%) and medium $P_2O_5$ (c.0.4 wt%) |
| Trace elements | High incompatible element contents, except Nb, Ta. Ba = 750–1250 ppm Zr = 150–250 ppm Nb = 5–12 ppm | High incompatible element contents, except Nb, Ta. HFS and REE contents higher than Pre-30 Ma but at similar LIL. (Zr = 180–350 ppm, Nb = 10–20 ppm) | Lower LILE, REE and HFS than mid-Tertiary groups except for high Nb and Ta. Ba = 450–650 ppm Zr = 150–200 ppm Nb = 25–60 ppm |
| Ba/Nb ratio | Highest, Ba/Nb = 95–125 | High, Ba/Nb = 45–100 | Low, Ba/Nb = 10–25 |
| Sr-isotopes | $^{87}Sr/^{86}Sr$ = 0.7055–0.7065 (some rhyolites with $^{87}Sr/^{86}Sr$ $>0.7065$) | $^{87}Sr/^{86}Sr$ = 0.7065–0.7085 (andesites have higher $^{87}Sr/^{86}Sr$ $>0.7075$) | $^{87}Sr/^{86}Sr$ = 0.7030–0.7055 |
| Phenocryst mineralogy | Plag+Aug $\pm$ Ol $\pm$ Hbl $\pm$ Oxides Hydrous (strongly porphyritic with trachytic groundmass) | Plag+Aug $\pm$ Ol $\pm$ Opx $\pm$ Oxides Anhydrous (Aphyric, dark and vesicular with intergranular/subophitic groundmass) | Ol Anhydrous ($\pm$ coarse Plag xeno/phenocrysts in an ophitic to intergranular groundmass) |

*This column refers to T2 rocks collected in the zone of extension south of lat. 34° N, Pre-30 Ma rocks from north of lat. 34° N (Spears Formation on the southern margin of the Colorado Plateau) have $TiO_2 > 1\%$, $P_2O_5 > 0.5\%$, Zr $>350$ ppm, Nb $>20$ ppm, Ba/Nb $<50$, $^{87}Sr/^{86}Sr$ $<0.7055$.
Plag: plagioclase; Aug: augite, Ol: olivine; Hbl: hornblende; Opx: orthopyroxene.

## Discussion: the relationship between magmatism and tectonics in southwestern New Mexico

One of the stated aims of this study was to relate changing styles of magmatism to changing tectonic environments. During the Tertiary, tectonism changed from compressional regimes carried over from the Laramide orogeny to an extensional regime associated with the late Tertiary block faulting, so characteristic of the Basin and Range provinces. Although most workers agree that the Laramide compression in New Mexico and Arizona had finished at around 40 Ma ago and before the onset of volcanism (Elston 1984a; Morgan *et al.* 1986; Cather 1990), the exact timing, and duration of the transition from a compressional stress regime to one of extension is a matter of debate. Elston (1984a) suggested that the period 40–20 Ma was one of 'massive ductile extension'. In its earliest stages, extension provided room for plutons that fed T3a calderas, $\sigma_1$ was vertical and in the horizontal $\sigma_2$ and $\sigma_3$ were very similar. Other authors see the period 40–30 Ma ago as one of transition with no strong regional stress field (Aldrich *et al.* 1986; Morgan *et al.* 1986). In the

Lemitar Mountains, north of Socorro and on the western margin of the Rio Grande rift (Fig. 2) detailed structural mapping and palinspastic reconstructions of listric ('domino-style') faults by Chamberlin (1978, 1983), and Ar–Ar dating of tuff sheets by McIntosh (1989), have shown that the Lemitar Tuff (28.0 Ma old) is some 20–25° less rotated than the underlying La Jenica Tuff (28.8 Ma old) and the Vicks Peak Tuff (28.5 Ma old), which have the same dip as the underlying Oligocene volcanic and Palaeozoic sediment rocks. These observations, together with the voluminous nature of the syn-extensional volcanism, encouraged Gans *et al.* (1989) to argue that extension began at 28.5 Ma ago and was rapid and covariant with the local peak in volcanism. Significantly the onset of extension in the Socorro area was also approximately contemporaneous with a peak in T4r silicic volcanism in the central MDVF, with the eruption of the regional Bloodgood Canyon Tuff, at 28.0 $\pm 0.03$ Ma ago (McIntosh 1989), related to the collapse of the Bursum caldera. It seems reasonable, therefore, to infer that the major phase of ductile extension was nearly contemporaneous throughout the field at around 28.5 Ma ago.

Also, in the Socorro area the extensional data seem to be consistent with the view that the pre-28.5 Ma period was one of tectonic quiescence, as suggested by Aldrich *et al.* (1986) and Morgan *et al.* (1986). However, Cather (1990) suggested that in the northern MDVF, extension had already commenced by 36 Ma ago. Similarly, in the Mimbres Valley area of the southern MDVF, angular unconformities between the oldest Pre-30 Ma group lavas and overlying tuff sheets of the T3r group, dated at 35.4 ± 0.1 Ma to 31.3 ± 0.4 Ma old (McIntosh 1989), indicate this region also experienced earlier phases of extension.

In the context of this tectonic framework it is striking that magmas which on the basis of major elements (calc-alkaline) and minor and trace elements (relatively low HFSE abundances, Fig. 6), have often been regarded as typical of destructive plate margins, were here generated in a period of extensional tectonics. In detail, the 30 Ma age used to subdivide the late Eocene to early Miocene rocks into the Pre-30 Ma and 30–20 Ma groups, is close to that for the local peak in extension (Fig. 9). Moreover, the oldest members of the 30–20 Ma group are the first major units of basaltic lavas to be erupted, and the Pre-30 Ma group has a higher proportion of more differentiated, dacites and rhyodacites, than the 30–20 Ma group (Fig. 4). These observations suggest a first-order model for the pre-30 Ma period in which the majority of mafic magmas were trapped on their passage through the crust, whereupon they differentiated to the higher silica contents of the observed eruptive products, predominantly andesites and dacites. A rapid increase in extension rate at around 30 Ma, then allowed less differentiated magmas to be erupted, as observed in the basalts and basaltic andesites of the Post-30 Ma period. Furthermore, the distinct trace element and Sr isotope compositions of the Pre-30 Ma ago and 30–20 Ma groups (Fig. 10) suggest that the onset of rapid extension at around 30 Ma ago also resulted in a shift in the composition, and hence the position, of the magma source regions. This chemical transition is quite subtle, and in general high-K calc-alkaline magmas were continuous throughout the mid-Tertiary period, contemporaneous with both late Eocene subduction and Oligocene extension.

With regard to the Post-20 Ma group lavas, extensional strain rates in the Socorro area slowed considerably after 27 Ma, and then a further period of extension occurred between 12–7 Ma (Chamberlin 1978), with the present block faulting initiated some 7–4 Ma ago. Thus, the minor basaltic volcanism of the late Tertiary

appears to have been related to these more recent, but less dramatic periods of extension. More significant, however, is the dramatic change in magma compositions during this period, away from the calc-alkaline, high LIL/HFSE character of the mid-Tertiary lavas towards a progressively more OIB-like, within-plate character. Furthermore, it is suggested that this period, Post-20 Ma, represents the true transition to bimodal magmatism and, therefore, postdates the local peak in extension by some ten million years. This conclusion differs from that of Cather (1990), who suggested a transition age of 36 Ma for the northern MDVF, coincident with the onset of extension. However, it is suggested that the transition noted by Cather (1990), to more basaltic andesite compositions, has greater similarity to that observed in this study between the Pre-30 Ma and 30–20 Ma groups, rather than the transition to the more within-plate-like late Tertiary basalts. The area studied by Cather (1990) lies within the Rio Grande rift, the deep fracture system that marks the boundary between the relatively stable mid-continent region and the zone of Basin and Range extension. Possibly the transition to basaltic andesite occurred earlier in the area of deeper fractures.

In the preferred model the Pre-30 Ma and the 30–20 Ma rocks with relatively low HFSE, high Ba/Nb and La/Nb, and high Sr isotope ratios were derived from the continental mantle lithosphere. As discussed by Gallagher & Hawkesworth (1992) and Bradshaw *et al.* (1993) such melts may be generated within the mantle lithosphere in the presence of small amounts of $CO_2$ and $H_2O$, in response to lithospheric extension. The relatively low HFSE and enriched radiogenic isotope signatures have been attributed to element fractionation processes associated with subduction in the Proterozoic (Davis 1991). In contrast, the lower Ba/Nb, La/Nb and $^{87}Sr/^{86}Sr$ ratios in the T6b alkali basalts indicate that they were largely derived from source regions similar to those sampled by oceanic basalts. This shift from predominantly lithosphere- to asthenosphere-' derived magmas with time in the evolution of a magmatic province is consistent with models in which magmatism is triggered by lithospheric extension, rather than by, for example, the emplacement of a mantle plume (Bradshaw *et al.* 1993, Hawkesworth *et al.* 1993). In detail, the changes in the style and chemistry of volcanism in the MDVF can be successfully related to a transition in the local stress regime from Pre-30 Ma quiescence/slightly extensional to a period of rapid ductile extension at 30–27 Ma, and subsequent Post-20 Ma relatively minor brittle extension. Specifically the more marked change to within-plate OIB-like, magmatism occurred *c.* 10 Ma after the local peak extension. Further work is required before these observations can be extended to a more regional framework of plate interactions.

None of this work would have been possible without the vision and encouragement of Ian Gass. He made the decision that a new radiogenic isotope group should be set up at the Open University in the late 1970s, he was always present to remind us that we were studying rocks and their origins (rather than anything more fanciful), and he co-supervised Jon Davis' PhD project. He continues to be very sadly missed as a colleague and a friend. Elston's research was supported by the US National Science Foundation grant EAR83-0639 and by a Royal Society Guest Research Fellowship at the Open University. Jon Davis gratefully acknowledges a NERC research studentship. We thank Peter Hooper and Ray MacDonald for their constructive and helpful reviews, and the manuscript was prepared by Janet Dryden.

# References

ABITZ, R. F. 1989. *Geology and Petrogenesis of the northern Emory Caldera, Sierra County, New Mexico.* PhD dissertation, University of New Mexico, Albuquerque.

ALDRICH, M. J. Jnr, CHAPIN, C. E. & LAUGHLIN, A. W. 1986. Stress history and tectonic development of the Rio Grande Rift, New Mexico. *Journal of Geophysical Research,* **91**, 6199–6212.

ARMSTRONG, R. L. 1970. Geochronology of Tertiary igneous rocks, Eastern Basin and Range province, western Utah, eastern Nevada, and vicinity, USA. *Geochimica et Cosmochima Acta,* **34**, 203–232.

ATWATER, T. 1970. Implications of plate tectonics for the Cenozoic tectonic evolution of western North America. *Geological Society of America Bulletin,* **81**, 3513–3536.

BALDRIDGE, W. S., PERRY, F. V., VANIMAN, D. T., NEALEY, L. D., LEAVY, B. D., LAUGHLAN, A. W., KYLE, P., BARTOV, Y, STEINITZ, G. & GLADNEY, E. S. 1989. Magmatism associated with lithospheric extension: Middle to late Cenozoic magmatism of the southeastern Colorado Plateau and central Rio Grande rift, New Mexico and Arizona. *New Mexico Bureau of Mines and Mineral Resources Memoir,* **46**, 187–230.

BORNHORST, T. J. 1980. *Major- and trace-element geochemistry and mineralogy of Upper Eocene to Quaternary volcanic rocks from the Mogollon-Datil Volcanic Field, southwestern New Mexico.* Dissertation, University of New Mexico, Albuquerque.

BRADSHAW, T. K., HAWKESWORTH, C. J. & GALLAGHER, K. 1993. Basaltic volcanism in the Southern Basin and Range: No role for a mantle plume. *Earth and Planetary Science Letters,* **116**, 45–62.

CAMERON, K. L., NIMZ, G. J., KOENEZ, D., NIEMAYER, S. & GUNN, S. 1988. The southern Cordilleran basaltic andesite suite, southern Chihuahua Mexico: a link between Tertiary continental arc and flood basalt magmatism in North America. *Journal of Geophysical Research,* **94**, 7817–7840.

CATHER, S. M. 1990. Stress and volcanism in the northern Mogollon-Datil volcanic field, New Mexico: effects of the post-Laramide tectonic transition, *Geolocical Society of America Bulletin,* **102**, 1447–1458.

—— & CHAPIN, C. E. 1989. *Field Guide to the upper Eocene and lower Oligocene volcaniclastic rocks of the northern Mogollon-Datil volcanic field.* New Mexico Bureau of Mines and Resources, Memoir **46**, 60–68.

CHAMBERLIN, R. M. 1978. Structural development of the Lemitar Mountains, an intrarift tilted fault block uplift, central New Mexico (abs), *In: Proceedings of an International Symposium on the Rio Grande Rift, Sante Fe, New Mexico, October 1978.* Los Alamos Laboratory Conference Proceedings LA-7487-C 22–24.

—— 1983. Cenozoic domino-style crustal extension in the Lemitar Mountains, New Mexico. *A summary, New Mexico Geological Society, Guidebook,* **34**, 111–118.

CHRISTIANSEN, R. L. & LIPMAN, P. W. 1972. Cenozoic volcanism and plate-tectonic evolution of the Western United States. II Late Cenozoic. *Philosophical Transactions of the Royal Society of London,* **A271**, 249–284.

CLEMONS, R. E. (ed.) 1983. *New Mexico highway geologic map.* New Mexico Geological Society, 1: 1,000,000.

CONDIE, K. C. 1986. Geochemistry and tectonic setting of early Proterozoic supra-crustal rocks in the Southwestern United States. *Journal of Geology,* **94**, 845–864.

CONEY, P. J. & REYNOLDS, S. J. 1977. Cordilleran Benioff zones. *Nature,* **270**, 403–406.

DAVIS, J. 1991. *The geochemical evolution of basic and intermediate mid to late Tertiary volcanism from the Mogollon-Datil Volcanic field, southwestern New Mexico, USA.* PhD Thesis, Open University, Milton Keynes.

ELSTON, W. E. 1957. Geology and mineral resources of Dwyer Quadrangle, Grant, Luna and Sierra Counties, New Mexico. *New Mexico Bureau of Mines and Mineral Resources Bulletin,* **33**.

—— 1976. Glossary of stratigraphic terms of the Mogollon-Datil volcanic province. *In:* ELSTON, W. E. & NORTHROP, S. A. (eds) *Cenozoic volcanism in southwestern New Mexico.* New Mexico Geological Society, Special Publication, **5**, 131–151.

—— 1981. *Assessment of geothermal potential of southwestern New Mexico.* New Mexico Energy and Minerals Department Report, EMD2-67–2123.

—— 1984*a.* Subduction of young oceanic lithosphere and extensional orogeny in southwestern North America during mid-Tertiary time. *Tectonics,* **3**, 229–250.

—— 1984*b.* Mid-Tertiary ash flow tuff cauldrons, southwestern New Mexico. *Journal of Geophysical Research,* **89**, 8733–8757.

—— 1989. Overview of the Mogollon-Datil volcanic

field. *New Mexico Bureau of Mines and Mineral Resources Memoir*, **46**, 43–46.

—— DAMON, P. E., CONEY, P. J., RHODES, R. C., SMITH, E. I. & BIKERMAN, M. 1973. Tertiary volcanic rocks, Mogollon-Datil province, New Mexico, and surrounding region; K–Ar dates, patterns of eruption and periods of mineralisation. *Geological Society of America Bulletin*, **81**, 3393–3406.

——, RHODES, R. C., CONEY, P. J. & DEAL, E. G. 1976. Progress report on the Mogollon Plateau volcanic field, southwestern New Mexico, No. 3 – Surface expression of a pluton. *In*: ELSTON, W. E. & NORTHROP, S. A. (eds) *Cenozoic volcanism in southwestern New Mexico*. New Mexico Geological Society, Special Publication, **5**, 3–28.

ENGEBRETSON, D. C., COX, A. & GORDON, R. G. 1985. *Relative motions between oceanic and continental plates in the Pacific basin*. Geological Society of America Special Paper, **206**.

FAURE, G. 1986. *Principles of Isotope Geology*. John Wiley & Sons, Chichester.

FITTON, J. G. & DUNLOP, H. M. 1985. The Cameroon line, West Africa, and its bearing on the origin of oceanic and continental alkali basalt. *Earth and Planetary Science Letters*, **72**, 23–38.

——, JAMES, D., KEMPTON, P. D., ORMEROD, D. S. & LEEMAN, W. P. 1988. The role of lithospheric mantle in the generation of late Cenozoic basic magmas in the S.W. United States. *In*: MENZIES, M. A. & COX, K. G. (eds) Oceanic and Continental Lithosphere: Similarities and Differences. *Journal of Petrology Special Lithosphere Issue*, **29**, 331–350.

——, —— & LEEMAN, W. P. 1991. Basic Magmatism associated with Late Cenozoic Extension in the Western United States: Compositional variations in space and time. *Journal of Geophysical Research*, **96**, 13693–13711.

GALLAGHER, K. & HAWKESWORTH, C. J. 1992. Dehydration melting and the generation of continental flood basalts. *Nature*, **358**, 57–59.

GANS, P. B., MAHOOD, G. A. & SCHERMER, E. 1989. *Synextensional magmatism in the Basin and Range Province; a case study from the eastern Great Basin*. Geological Society of America Special Paper, **233**.

GARDNER, J. N., GOFF, F., GARCIA, S. & HAGAN, R. C. 1986. Stratigraphic relations and lithologic variations in the Jemez volcanic field, New Mexico. *Journal of Geophysical Research*, **91**, 1763–1778.

GILL, J. B. 1981. *Orogenic andesites and plate tectonics*. Springer-Verlag, Berlin.

GLAZNER, A. F. & BARTLEY, J. M. 1984. Timing and tectonic setting of Tertiary low-angle normal faulting and associated magmatism in the southwestern United States. *Tectonics*, **3**, 385–396.

HAWKESWORTH, C. J., GALLAGHER, K., BRADSHAW, T. K. & HOOPER, P. 1993. Causes of continental magmatism: Plumes vs regional tectonics in the Western USA. Abs. *EUG, Strasbourg, April 1993*.

JICHA, H. L., Jnr. 1954. Geology and mineral deposits of Lake Valley quadrangle, Catron, Luna and Sierra Counties, New Mexico. *New Mexico Bureau of Mines and Mineral Resources Bulletin*, **37**.

KRIER, D. J. 1980. *Geology of the southern part of the Gila Primitive Area, Grant County, New Mexico*. MSc thesis, University of New Mexico, Albuquerque.

KUELLMER, F. J. 1954. Geologic section of the Black Range at Kingston, New Mexico. *New Mexico Bureau of Mines and Mineral Resources Bulletin*, **33**.

LE BAS, M. J., LE MAITRE, R. W., STRECKEISEN, A. & ZANETTIN, B. 1986. A chemical classification of volcanic rocks based on the total alkali-silica diagram. *Journal of Petrology*, **27**, 745–750.

LIPMAN, P. W., PROSTKA, H. J. & CHRISTIANSEN, R. L. 1972. Cenozoic volcanism and plate-tectonic evolution of the western United States. I. Early and Middle Cenozoic. *Philosophical Transactions of the Royal Society of London*, **A271**, 217–248.

LOPEZ, D. A. & BORNHORST, T. J. 1979. *Geologic Map of the Datil area, Catron County, New Mexico*. US Geological Survey, Miscellaneous Geologic Investigations Map 1–1098, scale 1:50 000, 1 sheet.

MACDONALD, G. A. & KATSURA, T. 1964. Chemical composition of Hawaiian lavas. *Journal of Petrology*, **5**, 82–133.

MARVIN, R. F., NAESER, C. W., BIKERMAN, M., MEHNERT, H. H. & RATTÉ, J. C. 1987. Isotopic ages of post-Paleocene igneous rocks within and bordering the Clifton 1° × 2° quadrangle, Arizona–New Mexico. *New Mexico Bureau of Mines and Mineral Resources Bulletin*, **118**.

MCINTOSH, W. C. 1989. Timing and distribution of ignimbrite volcanism in the Eocene–Miocene, Mogollon-Datil volcanic field. *New Mexico Bureau of Mines and Mineral Resource Memoir*, **46**, 58–59.

MCMILLAN, N. J. & DUNGAN, M. A. 1988. Open system magmatic evolution of the Taos Plateau volcanic field, New Mexico. *Journal of Petrology*, **29**, 527–557.

MIYASHIRO, A. 1974. Volcanic rock series in island arcs and active continental margins. *American Journal of Science*, **274**, 321–355.

MORGAN, P., SEAGER, W. R. & GOLOMBEK, M. P. 1986. Cenozoic thermal, mechanical, and tectonic evolution of the Rio Grande rift. *Journal of Geophysical Research*, **91**, 6263–6276.

ORMEROD, D. S., HAWKESWORTH, C. J., ROGERS, N. W., LEEMAN, W. P. & MENZIES, M. A 1988. Tectonic and magmatic transitions in the Western Great Basin. *Nature*, **333**, 349–353.

OSBURN, G. R. & CHAPIN, C. E. 1983. Ash-flow tuffs and cauldrons in the northeast Mogollon-Datil volcanic field: a summary. *New Mexico Society Guidebook*, **34**, 197–204.

PEACOCK, M. A. 1931. Classification of Igneous Rock Series. *Journal of Geology*, **39**, 54–67.

PERRY, F. V., BALDRIDGE, W. S. & DEPAOLO, D. J. 1988. Lithospheric thinning beneath the Rio Grande rift. *Nature*, **332**, 432–434.

POTTS, P. J., THORPE, O. W., ISSACS, M. C. & WRIGHT, D. W. 1985. High-precision instrumental neutron-activation analysis of geological samples employing simultaneous counting with both planar and coaxial detectors. *Chemical Geology*, **48**, 145–155.

——, —— & WATSON J. S. 1981. Determination of the rare-earth element abundances in 24 international rock standards by instrumental neutron activation analysis: A critical appraisal of calibration errors. *Chemical Geology*, **34**, 331–352.

RATTÉ, J. C. & GASKILL, D. L. 1975. *Reconnaissance geologic map of the Gila Wilderness study area, southwestern New Mexico*. U.S. Geological Miscellaneous Geologic Investigations Map 1-886, scale 1:62,500.

——, MARVIN, R. F., NEASER, C. W. & BIKERMAN, M. 1984. Calderas and ash flow tuffs of the Mogollon Mountains, southwestern New Mexico. *Journal of Geophysical Research*, **89**, 8713–8732.

SNYDER, W. S., DICKINSON, W. R. & SILBERMAN, M. L. 1976. Tectonic implications of space–time patterns of Cenozoic magmatism in the western US. *Earth and Planetary Science Letters*, **32**, 91–106.

TONKING, W. H. 1957. Geology of the Puertecito quadrangle, Socorro County, New Mexico. *New Mexico Bureau of Mines and Mineral Resources Bulletin*, **41**.

# Re-evaluation of inclined intrusive sheets and dykes in the Cuillins volcano, Isle of Skye

GEORGE P. L. WALKER

*Hawaii Center for Volcanology, Department of Geology and Geophysics, School of Ocean and Earth Science and Technology, University of Hawaii, Honolulu, Hawaii 96822, USA*

**Abstract**: This paper presents new quantitative data on the mafic dykes and classic centrally inclined sheets (cone-sheets) of the Cuillin Hills. Most dykes were intruded into the NW and SE rift zones of the Cuillins volcano. The dyke-widths, and the downrift rate of increase of widths, are almost identical with those of Koolau dykes in Oahu (Hawaii). The dilation vector (direction of opening) is roughly normal to the plane of the inclined sheets, showing that the sheets are simple extensional intrusions like the dykes. Sheet thicknesses are nearly identical with dyke-widths, reinforcing this conclusion. Sheets cut dykes, and dykes cut sheets, showing that dyke or sheet injections alternated. Sheets are concentrated in the NW and SE sectors of the Cuillins where they comprise a coherent complex having intrusion-intensities of 40–80% preferentially injected into the rift zones. A mechanism is proposed in which magma batches were injected as bladed dykes or bladed sheets as the $\sigma_3$ stress direction oscillated between vertical and horizontal; this was in a tectonic setting where, because of slow extension, magma excursions could not all be accommodated as dykes. Injection of sheets resulted in a vertical thickening of the volcanic edifice by *c.* 1.5 km about the same as the amount of widening by dykes.

The rugged mountains of the Cuillin Hills and Blaven on the Isle of Skye are composed of a great number of mafic intrusions. The intrusive complex was mapped in the classic study by Harker (1904) following the realization by Judd (1889), questioned by Geikie (1897), that the rocks constitute the erosion-bared core of a large central volcano of early Tertiary age. Subsequent work has broadly supported this concept.

In the 1950s to 1970s much attention was directed at the details of the gabbroic intrusions that make up most of the inner part of the Cuillin Hills, as summarized by Wager & Brown (1967) and Emeleus (1982). Little attention was focused on the small intrusions, but Speight *et al.* (1982) made a quantitative study of dyke swarms in the whole Scottish part of the Hebridean Province, including those of Skye.

One of Harker's major discoveries was that a complex of inclined intrusive sheets cuts the gabbros of the Cuillins. He showed that the layering in the gabbros exhibits a funnel-like attitude and dips toward a central focus (on the whole more steeply as the focus is approached), and that the inclined sheets dip toward the same focus (on the whole a little more steeply than the gabbro layering). This complex is re-examined herein.

Bailey *et al.* (1924) demonstrated that great numbers of intrusive sheets similar to those in the Cuillins occur in the intrusive core of the Mull volcanic centre, and named them cone-sheets. Cone-sheet complexes have since been identified in many deeply-eroded volcanoes. A particular origin unfortunately tends to be implicit in the name cone-sheet; Anderson (1936, 1951) and Robson & Barr (1964) attributed cone-sheets to roof failure of a pressurized magma chamber on curved inverted-conical shear fractures, accompanied by injection of magma along these fractures. In the following, centrally inclined sheet (CIS) is employed instead of cone-sheet as a descriptive term devoid of any genetic connotation.

## Procedure

This paper records a quantitative reconnaissance study of small intrusions in the outer parts of the Cuillin Hills. About 80 measurement sites were selected for study (Fig. 1), and all of the exposed small intrusions were measured at each site. The average cross-swarm length of each site was 75 m. Intrusion width, strike, dip direction, dip angle, and dilation-vector plunge were routinely measured and recorded. In all, some 1100 small intrusions, roughly half of them dykes and half of them sheets (CIS), were documented. At each site the total outcrop width normal to the predominant dyke trend was also measured from which the intensity of the dyke swarm, expressed as the volume percentage of rock composed of dykes, was determined. A similar procedure was employed to determine the intensity of the CIS complex.

*From* Prichard, H. M., Alabaster, T., Harris, N. B. W. & Neary, C. R. (eds), 1993,
*Magmatic Processes and Plate Tectonics,* Geological Society Special Publication No. 76, 489–497.

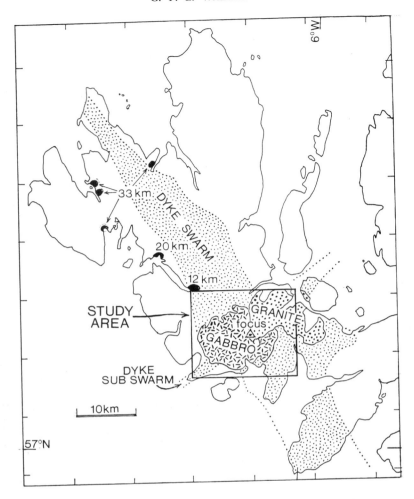

**Fig. 1.** Index map of the Isle of Skye showing location of the Cuillin Hills, and the most intense parts of the regional and local dyke swarms (Speight *et al.* 1982). Black areas are places where dyke-width populations were measured for Fig. 5.

## Small intrusions in the Cuillins

Several more or less distinct groups of small intrusions occur in the Cuillins and Blaven area:

(1) a regional dyke swarm having a generally NW–SE trend, well developed in the Cuillins and Blaven but extending well outside this area and distributed along the whole length of Skye and beyond;

(2) a minor local dyke sub-swarm, much less well defined than the regional swarm, and commonly having a more or less NE–SW trend or a radial distribution;

(3) a centrally-inclined sheet complex (CIS);

(4) a regional sill swarm. Many thin sills cut Jurassic sedimentary rocks and Tertiary lava flows just outside the Cuillin Hills. They are very probably the outward extension of CIS. Much larger sills that occur further afield in northern Skye and on many small islands such as the Shiants (Anderson & Dunham 1966; Gibson & Jones 1991) may be unrelated to the CIS.

### The regional dyke swarm

The regional dyke swarm is actually part of a much wider system of dyke swarms that extends throughout the Hebridean Province (Richey

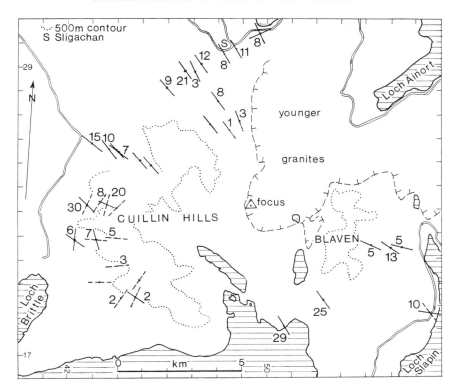

**Fig. 2.** Sketch map of the Cuillin Hills and Blaven showing predominant strikes of the main NW–SE regional dyke swarm (solid lines) and the localized, roughly NE–SW, sub-swarm (dotted lines). Figures record the approximate dyke intensity expressed as the percentage of rock composed of dykes. Triangle is the focus toward which gabbro layering and intrusive sheets dip, after Harker (1904). Marks and numbers around the margin are the National Grid map coordinates.

1932; Speight *et al.* 1982). Here, attention is directed at the swarm that occurs in the Cuillin Hills and extends outward along strike from the Cuillins (Fig. 1). A comparison is made with the dyke complex in the Koolau volcano (Oahu, Hawaii) for which good quantitative data are available (Walker 1987).

## Dyke strikes

The dykes in the regional swarm show a fairly high degree of parallelism. At any given locality individual strike values typically range over about 60° and arithmetic average directions are plotted in Fig. 2. One main reason for the range in values appears to be the propensity for dykes to follow earlier structures. Many examples were observed where a dyke changes course abruptly and follows the margin of an earlier dyke for a short distance, or, after following one joint,

changes course to follow another joint having a different strike.

From one site to another the average strike direction varies over about 40°. This is mainly because of the somewhat radiating fanning of dykes out from the Cuillins into northern and southern Skye. The term fascicular (from the Latin *fascia*, meaning bundle or sheaf, as of sticks or corn) is proposed for this arrangement of dykes between radiating and parallel.

## Dyke dips

As observed in the Koolau dyke complex the Cuillins dykes systematically depart from the vertical. Figure 3 summarizes the dip variation. The range is from 20–90°, the median is 78°, and the arithmetic average is 75°. These figures are almost identical to those of the Koolau complex.

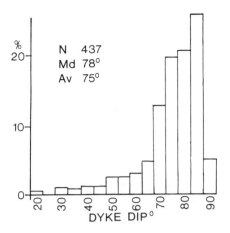

**Fig. 3.** Dyke-dip histogram for the dykes of the Cuillin Hills and Blaven area. N: number of intrusions; Md: median dip; Av: average dip.

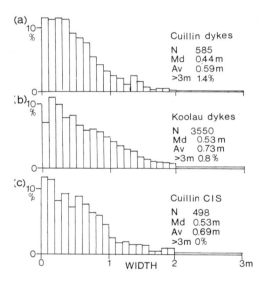

**Fig. 4.** Intrusion-width histograms for all the dykes and intrusive sheets measured in the Cuillin Hills area. Dykes of the Koolau complex, Oahu (Hawaii) plotted for comparison. Note the very close similarity between the three histograms. N: number of intrusions; Md: median width; Av: average width.

### Dyke widths

Figure 4a is a histogram of dyke widths based on all the measured dykes in the Cuillins and Blaven area. The median width is 0.44 m, and the average width is 0.59 m. Only 1.4% of the dykes exceed 3 m wide. The dyke population conforms fairly well to a log-normal distribution. The dyke width histograms for the Cuillins dykes and the Koolau dyke complex in Oahu (Walker 1987; Fig. 4b) are strikingly similar.

### Dyke-width variation with distance from centre

A reconnaissance of the Cuillins dyke swarm from 12–33 km northwest of Harker's focus (Fig. 1) shows that, although the number of dykes measured (total 93) was small, a very clear trend exists toward increasing width as distance from focus increases (Fig. 5). This broad relationship has long been known but has never been well-documented quantitatively. The Koolau dyke complex (Walker 1987) shows similar trends and when Koolau data are plotted (Fig. 5) they show a remarkably good agreement in median dyke-width with the Cuillins dykes, although the standard deviation of Koolau dykes is slightly larger. Bearing in mind the different tectonic settings of the two volcanoes, this close similarity is either a coincidence or, more likely, the expression of common underlying physical controls. Median thickness and standard deviation for the CIS are also plotted in Fig. 5 and show good agreement with the dykes except in having a slightly larger median width and standard deviation. The conclusion is that the dykes and CIS intrusions constitute nearly identical width populations at any given distance from focus, and there is thus a very close similarity between them. The 'conventional' formation mechanism for cone-sheets (Anderson 1936, 1951; Robson & Barr 1964) is, however, quite different from that for dykes.

At many sites in and close to the Cuillin Hills, some dykes were found having strikes considerably different from the regional trend. These aberrant dykes appear to belong to a lesser sub-swarm striking very roughly NE–SW. In detail, their strike is highly variable, both at the same location and from one location to another. Speight et al. (1982) interpreted these dykes to constitute a low-intensity sub-swarm spanning the whole width of the Cuillins and Red Hills. Dykes of the regional swarm and sub-swarm appear to cut one another indiscriminately, indicating that they were emplaced over the same time period. Generally, the localized sub-swarm is much less intense than the regional swarm, but this is not true of locations east of the head of Loch Brittle where all the dykes appear to belong to the sub-swarm.

### Centrally inclined sheets

The great complex of centrally inclined intrusive

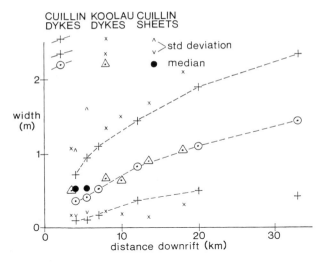

**Fig. 5.** Median intrusion-width and standard deviation at varying distances downrift for dykes of the Cuillin swarm, Cuillin inclined sheets, and dykes of the Koolau complex, Oahu. Note the close similarities between all three. Distances measured from Harker's focus, or from the centre of Kailua caldera, Oahu.

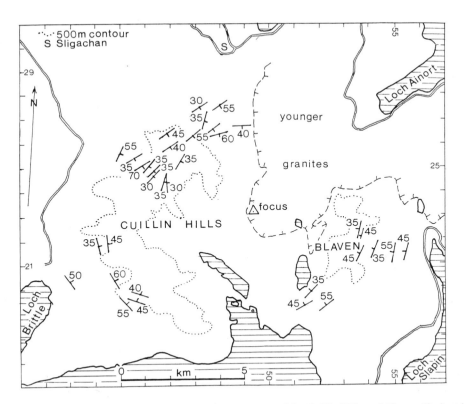

**Fig. 6.** Strike and dip of inclined intrusive sheets in the outer part of the Cuillin Hills and Blaven. Each strike and dip value is an average of several sheets. Triangle is the focus toward which the sheets dip, after Harker (1904).

sheets comprises one of the most striking features of the Cuillin Hills and, in the outer Cuillins, rivals or exceeds in outcrop area the exposed gabbro. The present quantitative study qualifies the geographic distribution and dip pattern, better characterizes the sheets, and considerably changes the perception of the CIS complex: over an area of $> 16 \, km^2$ this complex, together with minor contained screens of country rock, is a major mountain-building unit in its own right, and the sheets do not merely 'dilute' a mountain-building unit of gabbro.

## Sheet widths

The widths of some 500 sheets were measured, and range from 0.03–2.8 m, with a median of 0.53 m and an arithmetic average of 0.69 m (Fig. 4c). These figures are very close to the median of 0.44 m and arithmetic average of 0.59 m given by the dyke swarms.

## Attitude of dilation vector

When a small intrusion is irregular or cuts across earlier rock boundaries, it is possible to draw a straight line joining irregularities or boundaries of earlier rocks from one wall to the opposite wall of the intrusion. This line records the direction that the two walls moved apart and was referred to by Walker (1987) as the dilation vector. Kuenen (1937) recognized its significance and recorded its orientation on two cone-sheets in Mull. Strictly, the vector is a line in three-dimensional space, but on most rock outcrops is seen only as a line on a two-dimensional surface. Examples seen in vertical cross-sections are illustrated in Fig. 8.

In the Koolau dyke complex, Walker (1987) found that the angle between the dilation vector and a line normal to the local plane of a dyke varies commonly by as much as several tens of degrees. He found that many dykes are highly irregular in shape, depended heavily on these irregular dykes to yield the dilation vector, and showed that the vector is randomly disposed with respect to the local dyke-normal. He proposed that the vector is normal to the overall-average plane of the intrusion (not determinable in small outcrops).

The CIS in the Cuillins display closely similar relationships summarized in Fig. 8, consistent with their displacement vector being normal to their overall-averaged plane of intrusion. On previous interpretations of cone-sheet genesis (Anderson 1936, 1951; Robson & Barr 1964), cone-sheets are injected into shear fractures inclined at about 45° to the direction of maxi-

mum principal compressive stress operating vertically above the magma chamber. An implication is that the dilation vector should be vertical, or at the least systematically displaced toward the vertical from the sheet-normal. Such verticality or systematic displacement toward the vertical has never been demonstrated, and is not found by the present study. This study thus fails to support previously proposed cone-sheet mechanisms. Gautneb et al. (1989) studied a sheet swarm in Iceland and likewise found no evidence that the sheets occupy shear fractures.

## Distribution of inclined sheets

In previous studies, cone-sheet swarms have been observed or inferred to have a roughly uniform intensity in all directions about the focus, but the present study reveals that in the Cuillins the distribution is not uniform: the intensity is high in the northwest and southeast sectors, and low in the other two sectors (Fig. 7). The sectors of highest CIS intensity coincide with the direction of the regional dyke swarm: the dykes delineate rift zones of the Cuillins centre, and the CIS are predominantly concentrated in these same rift zones. Bearing in mind the nearly identical thickness populations of dykes and CIS, the fact that the dilation vectors for dykes and CIS are approximately normal to the intrusion-plane, and the cross-cutting relationships (dykes cut CIS, and CIS cut dykes, in roughly equal proportions), the conclusion is that dykes and CIS are closely similar in origin and are alternative intrusion-forms resulting when magma excursions occurred into the rift zones. Many narrow intrusive sills occur outside the limit of the CIS but within about 10 km of the focus. They average 0.75 m thick and are thought to be the outward extension of CIS.

## Mechanisms

Dykes and centrally inclined sheets form two alternative intrusion-geometries that were injected into the rift zones of the Cuillins volcano during magma excursions from the central magma chamber. Some magma excursions generated one type, and some generated the other type. A proposed mechanism invokes frequent excursions from the Cuillins centre but slow extension such that not all magma excursions could be accommodated as dykes. It is supposed that the direction of maximum deviatoric stress operated in the NW–SE direction. It is postulated that the minimum and intermediate deviatoric stress axes oscillated in orientation from horizontal to vertical (Fig. 9) as slow exten-

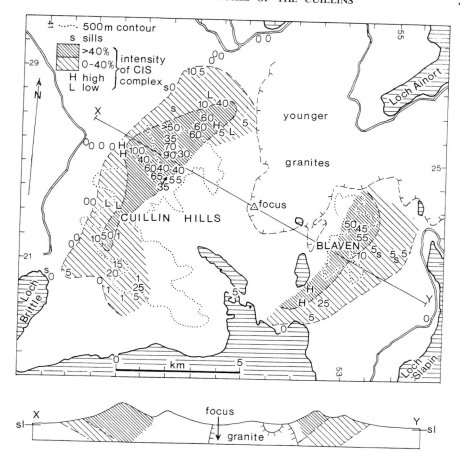

**Fig. 7.** Intensity of the inclined-sheet complex in the outer part of the Cuillin Hills and Blaven, expressed as the volume percentage of whole rock made from sheets. Close-shaded areas: intensity exceeding 40%; H: high intensity; open-shaded areas: intensity 0–40%; L: low intensity. Note that high intensities characterize the NW and SE sectors, attributed to preferential injection of sheets into the NW or SE rift zones of the Cuillins volcano. Section X–Y: no vertical exaggeration.

sion occurred. When the minimum was horizontal, dykes were injected and were accommodated by lateral crustal extension. When the minimum was vertical, dykes could not be accommodated and intrusive sheets were injected instead.

The aggregate thickness of intrusive sheets in the northwest sector is estimated to be 1.5 km. The sheets comprise a coherent complex here and on Blaven, and the early formation of a coherent complex here with neutral buoyancy positions at its margins was an important factor in channelling lateral magma excursions and building up of the complex by the addition of further sheets as envisaged by Walker (1992). The dyke swarm in this same sector is about 15 km wide (Fig. 2) and has an average intensity

of about 9%, giving a total dyke width approaching 1.5 km.

Some intrusive sheets occur in the southwest sector of the Cuillin Hills. It is proposed that they are related to the southwest-trending dyke sub-swarm that occurs in this sector, that some magma excursions took place into this poorly developed southwest rift zone of the Cuillins volcano and formed either dykes or intrusive sheets as the state of extensional deviatoric stress varied.

## Summary and conclusions

Small intrusions are extraordinarily abundant in the core of the Cuillins volcano. They are prob-

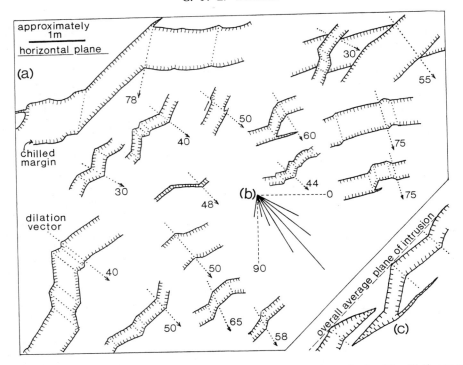

**Fig. 8(a).** Field sketches of vertical cross-sections of irregular sheets showing attitude of the dilation vector (dotted lines). The vector records the direction of opening of the sheet and is roughly normal to the plane of the sheet. Some drawings reversed so that all sheets dip in the same direction. **(b)** Rose diagram showing the plunge angle of the 16 sheets illustrated. **(c)** Schematic view of an irregular sheet showing how local dyke-normals deviate from the dilation vector; the dilation vector is, however, normal to the average plane of the sheet.

ably more favourable for study than those in the Mull and Ardnamurchan centres because the complications caused by silicic intrusions are minimal in the Cuillins. Drawing on experience from Hawaii, each intrusion records a magma excursion from the central magma chamber of the volcano. Some magma excursions no doubt resulted in volcanic eruptions.

One motivation for making this study of the Cuillins was the desire to examine the deep core of a large basaltic volcano. This is not feasible on young oceanic volcanoes, as in Hawaii, where downcutting by erosion is in competition with the rapid bodily subsidence of the volcano (Moore 1987), in consequence of which sections seldom reach much more than 1 km deep, whereas the Cuillins volcano is rafted on continental crust. It might be objected that the Cuillins and Hawaiian volcanoes are in such contrasted tectonic settings that one is not a good analogue for the other, but the remarkably close similarity of Cuillins and Hawaiian dyke populations tends to negate that objection.

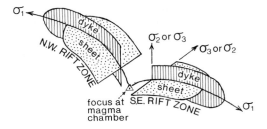

**Fig. 9.** Schematic view showing postulated attitude of bladed dykes and bladed inclined sheets resulting from magma excursions into the rift zones of the Cuillins volcano. Dykes are injected when the principal deviatoric stress axis $\sigma_3$ is horizontal, and sheets are injected when $\sigma_3$ is vertical.

One main finding of this study is that the inclined sheets and dykes are very similar in characteristics, have a similar distribution pattern being preferentially injected into the rift zones, and may be explained as alternative intrusion types. In a slow-extension setting where not all magma excursions can be accommodated as dykes, the $\sigma_3$ and $\sigma_2$ stress axes repeatedly switch position, to generate alternately dykes or sheets.

This study leaves unanswered the questions of the extent to which the inward dip of the sheets is due to post-emplacement tilting, and whether some of the gabbros are confluent intrusions built of sheets injected into one another at short time intervals.

This paper acknowledges many years of friendship with the late Ian Gass, dating from the time that we were contemporary students at the University of Leeds. Travel to Skye in 1992 and field expenses for the study recorded herein from the Jaggar Bequest Fund administered by the University of Hawaii. I am grateful to R. S. J. Sparks for useful comments on the manuscript. This is SOEST contribution number 3282.

# References

ANDERSON, E. M. 1936. Dynamics of formation of cone-sheets, ring-dykes and cauldron-subsidences. *Proceedings of the Royal Society of Edinburgh*, **61**, 128–157.

—— 1951. *The Dynamics of Faulting and Dyke Formation with Applications to Britain* (2nd edn). Oliver & Boyd, Edinburgh.

ANDERSON, F. W. & DUNHAM, K. C. 1966. *The geology of northern Skye*. Memoir of the Geological Survey of Scotland.

BAILEY, E. B., CLOUGH, C. T., WRIGHT, W. B., RICHEY, J. E. & WILSON, G. V. 1924. *Tertiary and post-Tertiary geology of Mull, Loch Aline, and Oban*. Memoir of the Geological Survey of Scotland.

EMELEUS, C. H. 1982. The central complexes. *In*: SUTHERLAND, D. S. (ed.) *Igneous Rocks of the British Isles*. Oliver & Boyd, Edinburgh, 369–414.

GAUTNEB, H., GUDMUNDSSON, A. & OSKARSSON, N. 1989. Structure, petrochemistry and evolution of a sheet swarm in an Icelandic central volcano. *Geological Magazine*, **126**, 659–673.

GEIKIE, A. 1897. *The ancient volcanoes of Great Britain*. Vol. 2. Macmillan, London.

GIBSON, S. A. & JONES, A. P. 1991. Igneous stratigraphy and internal structure of the Little-Minch sill complex, Trotternish Peninsula, Isle of Skye, Scotland. *Geological Magazine*, **128**, 51–66.

HARKER, A. 1904. *The Tertiary igneous rocks of Skye*. Memoir of the Geological Survey of the United Kingdom.

JUDD, J. W. 1889. The Tertiary volcanoes of the Western Isles of Scotland. *Quarterly Journal of the Geological Society of London*, **45**, 187–219.

KUENEN, P. H. 1937. Intrusion of cone sheets. *Geological Magazine*, **74**, 177–183.

MOORE, J. G. 1987. Subsidence of the Hawaiian Ridge. *In*: DECKER, R. W., WRIGHT, T. L. & STAUFFER, P. H. (eds) *Volcanism in Hawaii*. US Geological Survey Professional Paper 1350, 85–107.

RICHEY, J. E. 1932. Tertiary ring structures in Britain. *Transactions of the Geological Society of Glasgow*, **19**, 42–140.

ROBSON, G. R. & BARR, K. G. 1964. The effect of stress on faulting and minor intrusions in the vicinity of a magma body. *Bulletin Volcanologique*, **27**, 315–330.

SPEIGHT, J. M., SKELHORN, R. R., SLOAN, T. & KNAPP, R. J. 1982. The dyke swarms of Scotland. *In*: SUTHERLAND, D. S. (ed.) *Igneous Rocks of the British Isles*. Oliver & Boyd, Edinburgh, 449–459.

WAGER, L. R. & BROWN, G. M. 1967. *Layered Igneous Rocks*. W. H. Freeman & Co, San Francisco.

WALKER, G. P. L. 1987. The dike complex of Koolau volcano, Oahu: internal structure of a Hawaiian rift zone. *In*: DECKER, R. W., WRIGHT, T. L. & STAUFFER, P. H. (eds) *Volcanism in Hawaii*. Geological Survey Professional Paper 1350, 961–993.

—— 1992. 'Coherent intrusion complexes' in large basaltic volcanoes – a new structural model. *Journal of Volcanology and Geothermal Research*, **50**, 41–54.

# Analytical techniques

# Advances in analytical technology and its influence on the development of modern inorganic geochemistry: a historical perspective

PHILIP J. POTTS, CHRIS J. HAWKESWORTH, PETER van CALSTEREN
& IAN P. WRIGHT

*Department of Earth Sciences, The Open University, Walton Hall,
Milton Keynes MK7 6AA, UK*

**Abstract**: Since the 1960s, a range of new instrumental analytical techniques have become widely available in geochemical laboratories, replacing traditional wet chemical procedures that were in common use throughout the first half of the twentieth century. These new techniques have resulted not only in an enormous advance in analytical productivity, but also in the sensitivity with which a wide range of trace elements and isotope ratios may now be determined on a routine basis. It is argued that there is a symbiosis between analytical technology and geochemical application which has resulted in geochemistry currently being regarded as one of the dominant strands of modern geological sciences. The present paper reviews the development of this analytical revolution, evaluates the impact that successive techniques have had on geochemical thinking and looks to the future to suggest areas that may result in advances over the next decade.

The development of ideas and advances in analytical techniques in geochemistry are intimately interconnected, and together they have revolutionized many subject areas within the Earth Sciences. In the first half of the twentieth century, most bulk analyses were performed by gravimetric techniques, and resultant data were primarily used to build up a descriptive framework for the composition of common rock types. During the second half of this century, the advent of new instrumental techniques, both for determining the major and trace compositions of bulk samples and for the analysis of individual minerals in situ in thin section, propelled a largely descriptive subject into the dynamic science now concerned with unravelling details of natural processes. The influence of this revolution can clearly be seen by the change of emphasis in the geological sciences from an often largely static description of igneous and metamorphic rocks, to studies of petrogenesis, within the full meaning of the word. As part of this analytical revolution, the development of mass spectrometric techniques resulted in the first radiometric estimate of the age of the Earth (Patterson 1956) and an unambiguous documentation of the vastness of geological time. The success of these early isotopic measurements stimulated further analytical developments, such that isotopic data are now widely used as highly sensitive tracers for the full range of geological processes. Indeed, isotopic measurements remain the key to any study of how planets, or segments of planets, have evolved through their history.

The continuing rapid growth in geochemistry owes much to symbiotic developments in analytical technology. Indeed, Ian Gass was one of the first to recognize that high quality analytical geochemistry was a necessary prerequisite for a successful modern Earth Science Department. In this contribution, we review the interrelationship between the development of new analytical techniques and the post-plate tectonic revolution in the Earth Sciences. On the basis of a historical perspective, future trends in the further development of these sciences are predicted.

## Before 1950: the early days

Before the 1950s, analytical technology was based mainly on classical schemes of analysis, typified by the procedures published in the classical texts of Washington (1919, 1932) and Hillebrand (1919). These techniques were based on wet chemical separations and were largely dependent on gravimetric methods of quantification. From a modern perspective, analytical productivity was low, a skilled operator being able to analyse perhaps a dozen samples per week. Although excellent accuracy and precision could be obtained in the determination of a limited range of major elements, sensitivity was restricted, routine determination being made down to the fractions of a weight percent level, rather than fractions of a $\mu g\ g^{-1}$, which is the expectation of modern techniques. Thus, when applied to silicate rocks, classical schemes were capable of determining the major elements, and with less confidence, a limited number of minor elements.

*From* Prichard, H. M., Alabaster, T., Harris, N. B. W. & Neary, C. R. (eds), 1993,
*Magmatic Processes and Plate Tectonics,* Geological Society Special Publication No. 76, 501–520.

Little standardization existed in the precise details of schemes of analysis, variations being developed in particular laboratories, based on the judgement and perception of the analyst. Furthermore, no independent means existed of demonstrating the accuracy of silicate data until the first rock reference materials, G-1 and W-1 were distributed for analysis in about 1948 in a programme organized for the USGS by Fairbairn *et al.* (1951). Although quantitative trace element determinations were largely unavailable throughout this period, qualitative results could be obtained by arc/spark source optical emission spectrography. Furthermore the analytical capabilities of x-ray fluorescence had been demonstrated during the second decade of the twentieth century and the potential of this technique recognized for trace determinations in rock samples by Goldschmidt, one of the pioneers of modern geochemistry (Mason 1992). Of greater significance than the untapped potential for trace element analysis, was the discovery by von Laue in 1912 that the regular arrangement of atoms in crystals acts as a diffraction grating for x-rays, so revealing information about the atomic structure of solid substances. This discovery clearly marks a critical step in the development of the geochemistry, since early results demonstrated that minerals could be distinguished on structural as well as chemical characteristics. Goldschmidt was almost certainly the first to appreciate fully the significance of crystal structure determinations for geochemistry, and it was largely through his stimulus that geochemistry developed from 'a somewhat incoherent collection of factual data to a philosophical science based on the concept of the geochemical cycle in which the individual elements play their part according to established principles' (Mason 1966, p. 5).

However, the techniques of analytical geochemistry then available were slow and labour intensive. In contrast to later years, much of the quantitative study of rocks depended on the microscopic examination of samples prepared as thin sections. On the basis of such a preliminary examination, a more limited selection of samples was then submitted for chemical analysis, in most cases for the major elements, only. Geochemical interpretation of results largely involved calculation of the normative variation in a series of rocks as a basis for rock classification and of niggli values to provided further petrological characterization (Burri 1959). Nonetheless, as well as providing the basis for some rock classification schemes, these results were used to develop early models to explain variations in major elements abundances in terms of the fraction-

ation of minerals of different composition (Harker 1909; Bowen 1928).

## Developments post-1950

In the decades following 1950, rapid developments occurred in analytical technology, which revolutionized the capabilities of laboratories both in terms of analytical productivity and the range of elements that could be determined routinely. These analytical developments led directly to a corresponding revolution in geochemistry, advancing this topic so that it is now regarded as one of the dominant branches of the geological sciences. To set these advances into a simplified framework, each decade has been categorized to identify the developments that had the greatest impact on progress in geochemical research. This categorization is to some extent both arbitrary and subjective. Before a technique can offer accurate and useful geochemical data on a routine basis, considerable effort must be expended, both in developing the analytical technology (i.e., instrumentation and methodology) and in establishing the best methods of applying results in geochemical applications. In some cases, this learning curve may span one or more decades before the technique emerges as a clear priority within the scientific community. Moreover, once this happens, interest in other well-established techniques may wane, such that they become perceived as routine 'work-horse' methods, despite continuing to contribute important geochemical data. The ebb and flow of techniques that have had an important impact on the development of geochemical studies are plotted schematically in Fig. 1, and some of the more significant dates in the evolution of analytical geochemistry are summarized in Table 1. The following commentary outlines these developments and evaluates their impact on geochemical research.

### 1950–1960: dawn of instrumental techniques

Trends plotted in Fig. 1 suggest that the period from 1950 to 1960 can be regarded as a transition period. During much of the decade, wet chemical techniques still dominated in the routine production of geochemical data. However, considerable analytical effort was expended in the development of rapid schemes of analysis, which progressively replaced classical gravimetric techniques. Rapid schemes incorporated techniques based on colorimetric analysis (see for example, Sandell 1959 and Jeffery 1975), complexiometric titrations (based on ethylenediaminetetraacetic acid: EDTA, Schwarzenbach

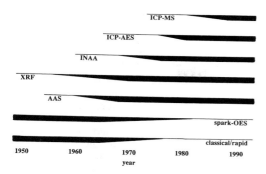

**Fig. 1.** Schematic diagram showing the contribution selected techniques have made to geochemical research over the last five decades. The width of the line of progression reflects the perceived contribution made by the technique, but does not allow for the enormous increase in productivity available from modern techniques. Microbeam and mass spectrometry techniques (other than ICP–MS) are not included in this diagram.

1957) and flame photometry, all methods which offer the advantages of high element specificity. Wet chemical manipulations were still required for the group separation of elements. However, some improvement in analytical productivity arose from the fact that in many cases, it was no longer necessary to isolate individual elements. Some standardization occurred in the methods used between laboratories with the publication of several comprehensive schemes of analysis, notably those developed by Shapiro & Brannock (1956) and (1962) for use at the US Geological Survey and Riley (1958).

During this period, several developments occurred which had an important impact on geochemical studies in subsequent decades. In 1951, Fairbairn *et al.* published the results for reference materials G-1 and W-1 which had been distributed to a total of 34 laboratories for analysis. Although Ahrens (1977) indicates that the main motivation for this study was to provide better standards for accurate major element calibration of arc/spark optical emission instrumentation for modal analysis, the principal achievement was to demonstrate the substantial influence of unsuspected inter-laboratory bias in major element data originating from different laboratories. Many would argue that inter-laboratory bias still represents the largest source of inaccuracy in data from modern geochemical laboratories, though hopefully not on the scale described in the 1951 report.

In the quest for routine trace element analysis of silicate rocks, spark source optical emission

was seen as one of the leading contenders in the early 1950s. In retrospect, the precision of results by this technique has never matched geochemical expectations and its main application has been in the semi-quantitative analysis of trace elements (with results often reported to the nearest half order of magnitude) for geochemical survey work. In this field, the high analytical productivity in the semi-quantitative determination of large suites of elements could be used to advantage.

The main strands of geoanalytical development lay elsewhere. One was in the development of x-ray fluorescence analysis, and one of the first instruments capable of commercial exploitation was described in 1948 by Friedman & Birks. Throughout the 1950s, considerable development work was undertaken on various aspects of XRF, not the least being the publication of the theoretical expressions for the excitation and attenuation of fluorescence x-rays (Sherman 1955). A second geoanalytical strand stemmed from the publication by Walsh (1955), and independently by Alkemade & Milatz (1955), of practical laboratory instrumentation that was capable of performing atomic absorption measurements. Although both these instrumental developments offered considerable potential, neither reached the stage of contributing significant geoanalytical data during the 1950s, one reason being that early instrumentation tended to be bulky, temperamental and prone to electrical drift. Furthermore, the small number of geological reference materials then available had poorly characterized trace element contents, and so precluded independent validation of accuracy.

In retrospect, the 1950s can be regarded as a period of analytical development; the potential of trace elements had been identified by some geochemical research groups, but the full significance of good quality data was only demonstrated in subsequent decades.

## 1960–1970: start of the geoanalytical revolution

At the beginning of the 1960s two forms of analytical instrumentation had been developed commercially to the point where they became much more widely available in analytical laboratories: flame atomic absorption spectrophotometry and x-ray fluorescence spectrometry.

*Atomic absorption spectrophotometry (AAS)*

With suitable developments in sample prep-

**Table 1.** *Selected developments in geochemical techniques and applications listed in chronological sequence*

## Classical and rapid schemes of analysis

*Classical techniques:*
| | |
|---|---|
| 1919, 1932 | Washington |
| 1919 | Hillebrand |

*Comprehensive schemes of analysis incorporating 'rapid' techniques:*
| | |
|---|---|
| 1956, 1962 | Shapiro & Brannock |
| 1958 | Riley |
| 1959 | Sandell |
| 1964 | Peck[1] |
| 1965 | Langmyhr & Graf[1] |

## AAS

*Basis for practical AAS analysis published:*
| | |
|---|---|
| 1955 | Walsh |
| 1955 | Alkemade & Milatz |
| 1960 | Commercial AAS instrumentation becomes generally available. |

*Early applications of AAS in analysis of selected major elements:*
| | |
|---|---|
| 1964 | Trent & Slavin[1] |
| 1964 | Billings & Adams[1] |
| 1966 | Ingamells[1] |
| 1966 | Suhr & Ingamells[1] |
| 1967 | Shapiro[1] |

*Comprehensive schemes of analysis for the major elements:*
| | |
|---|---|
| 1968 | Langmyhr & Paus[1] |
| 1969 | Van Loon & Parissis[1] |
| 1969 | Omang[1] |
| 1969 | Yule & Swanson[1] |
| 1969 | Medlin *et al.*[1] |
| 1970 | Boar & Ingram[1] |

*Schemes of analysis for the determination of trace elements:*
| | |
|---|---|
| 1971 | Buckley & Cranston |
| 1975 | Rantala & Loring[1] |
| 1975 | Warren & Carter[1] |

## Graphite furnace AAS

*Proposal for use of graphite furnace as atom cell in english language publication:*
| | |
|---|---|
| 1961 | L'Vov[1] |

*Proposal of a modified design used as the basis for commercial instrumentation:*
| | |
|---|---|
| 1968 | Massman[1] |

*Specialized geological applications:*
| | |
|---|---|
| 1973 | Sighinolfi[1] |
| 1978 | Barredo *et al.*[1] |
| 1978 | Elson *et al.*[1] |
| 1979 | Schnepfe[1] |
| 1981 | Sen Gupta[1] |
| 1983 | Bettinelli[1] |

*Proposal for use of graphite platform for isothermal atomization:*
| | |
|---|---|
| 1977, 1978 | L'Vov *et al.*[1] |

*Studies of atomization mechanisms using isothermal atomization:*
| | |
|---|---|
| 1980 | Slavin & Manning[1] |
| 1981 | Kaiser *et al.*[1] |
| 1982 | Slavin[1] |
| 1983 | Chakrabarti *et al.*[1] |

## XRF

*Law relating wavelength of fluorescence line to atomic number is formulated:*
| | |
|---|---|
| 1913, 1914 | Moseley[1] |

*X-ray method described for the analysis of minerals:*
| | |
|---|---|
| 1922 | Hadding |

*Moseley's law used to confirm the identity of a new element, hafnium:*
| | |
|---|---|
| 1923 | Coster & von Hevesy |

*Prototype of first commercial XRF:*
| | |
|---|---|
| 1948 | Friedman & Birks |
| 1955 | First commercial XRF systems become available. |

*Equations to model fluorescence intensity:*
| | |
|---|---|
| 1955 | Sherman |

*Fusion of samples with borax to form glass discs:*
| | |
|---|---|
| 1957 | Claisse[1] |

*Comprehensive analysis of powder pellets:*
| | |
|---|---|
| 1969 | Leake *et al.* |

*Major elements on glass discs:*
| | |
|---|---|
| 1969 | Norrish & Hutton |
| 1973 | Harvey *et al.* |

## INAA

*Proposals for neutron activation (REE):*
| | |
|---|---|
| 1936 | von Hevesy & Levi |
| 1960+ | High resolution Ge(Li) detectors become available. |

*REE/trace elements using coaxial detector:*
| | |
|---|---|
| 1968 | Gordon *et al.* |

*REE/trace elements using planar detectors:*
| | |
|---|---|
| 1971 | Hertogen & Gijbels |

*Routine schemes of analysis:*
| | |
|---|---|
| 1977 | Baedecker *et al.*[1] |
| 1977 | Schock[1] |
| 1979 | Borley & Rogers[1] |
| 1981 | Henderson & Williams[1] |
| 1981 | Hoede and Das[1] |
| 1981 | Potts *et al.*[1] |

## ICP-AES

*Analytical potential of the ICP as an atomic emission source demonstrated:*
| | |
|---|---|
| 1964 | Greenfield *et al.* |
| 1965 | Wendt & Fassel[1] |
| 1975 | First commercial ICP-AES instrumentation introduced. |

*Schemes of analysis for major and trace elements:*
| | |
|---|---|
| 1979 | McQuaker *et al.*[1] |
| 1980 | Walsh[1] |
| 1980 | Walsh & Howie[1] |
| 1981 | Church[1] |
| 1981 | McLaren *et al.*[1] |

*Schemes of analysis for the determination of the rare earth elements:*
| | |
|---|---|
| 1981 | Brenner *et al.*[1] |
| 1981 | Broekaert & Hormann[1] |
| 1981 | Walsh *et al.*[1] |
| 1982 | Crock & Lichte[1] |
| 1983 | Bolton *et al.*[1] |
| 1984 | Crock *et al.*[1] |
| 1985 | Jarvis & Jarvis[2] |

## ICP-MS

*Potential of plasma source MS demonstrated using a dc plasma:*
1974, 1975    Gray[2]

*Ions extracted from ICP:*
1980    Houk et al.[2]

*Other instrumental developments:*
1981, 1983    Date & Gray[2]
1981, 1986    Douglas & French[2]
1982    Houk & Thompson[1]
1983    First commercial instruments launched.

*Determination of trace elements:*
1985    Date & Gray (1985)[2]
1987    McLaren et al. (1987)[2]
1987    Hall et al. (1987)[2]

*Determination of the REE:*
1985    Doherty & Van der Voet[2]
1987    Date & Hutchison[2]
1987    Longerich et al.[2]
1988    Jarvis[2]

*Os/Re applications:*
1986    Lichte et al.[2]
1986    Masuda et al.[2]
1987    Bazan[2]
1987    Russ et al.[2]
1988    Dickin et al.[2]
1989    Richardson et al.[2]
1990    Gregoire
1990    Richardson et al.[2]

*PGE determination:*
1987    Date et al.[2]
1990    Jackson et al.[2]

*Isotopic analysis (lead):*
1983    Date & Gray[2]
1987    Longerich et al.[2]
1987    Russ & Bazan[2]

## TIMS

*Developments in instrumentation:*
1951    Cross[1] (extended geometry)
1960    Dall[1] (detector).
1982    Brunnée (new developments)

*Strontium applications:*
1962    Gast[1]
1965    Compston et al.
1965    Engel et al.
1967    Bofinger & Compston
1968    Boelrijk[1]
1969    Hart
1969    Papanastassiou & Wasserburg
1969    Sanz & Wasserburg[1]
1973    Pankhurst & O'Nions[1]
1973    Birck & Allegre[1]
1975    Moorbath et al.
1975    Gale et al.[1]

*REE by isotope dilution:*
1967    Schnetzler et al.[1]
1968    Masuda[1]
1973    Masuda et al.[1]
1973    Nakamura & Masuda[1]
1974    Nakamura
1975    Hooker et al.[1]
1979    Schuhmann and Philpotts[1]
1982    Thirlwall et al.[1]

*Lead applications:*
1956    Wetherhill
1969    Cameron et al.
1969    Compston & Oversby
1973, 1982    Krogh[1]
1972, 1975    Tera & Wasserburg[1]
1973    Tilton
1974    Allegre & Albarede[1]
1974    Arden & Gale[1]
1975    Krogh & Davis[1]
1975    Oversby[1]
1984    Manhes et al.[1]

*Neodymium applications:*
1974    Lugmair
1976    Richard et al.[1]
1976    DePaolo & Wasserburg
1977    O'Nions et al.[1]
1978    Lugmair & Marti[1]
1979    Jacobsen & Wasserburg
1979    Hawkesworth et al.[1]
1981    DePaolo
1981    Wasserburg et al.[1]

*Disequilibrium studies:*
1982    Ivanovich & Harmon
        Negative ion mass spectrometry (Os/Re):
1991    Volkening et al.
1991    Creaser et al.

## Gas source mass spectrometry

*Developments in instrumentation and conventions:*
1947    Urey (theoretical framework)
1947    Nier (mass spectrometer)
1947    Murphey (change-over valve)
1948    Urey
1950    McKinney et al. (delta function)
1956    Reynolds (static mass spectrometer)
1975    Schoeller & Hayes[3] (ion counting device)
1978    Des Marais[3] (stepped combustion)
1979    Gardiner & Pillinger[3]
1990    Prosser et al. (static mass spectrometry for carbon)

*H/D applications:*
1952    Bigeleison et al.[1]
1961    Craig
1976    Craig & Lupton[1]
1984    Kyser & O'Neil[1]

*Carbon isotope applications:*
1950    Trofimov[3]
1960    Park & Epstein
1967    Hoefs & Schidlowski
1980    Fallick et al.[3]
1983    Wright et al.[3]
1983    McNaughton et al.[1]
1984    Des Marais & Moore[1]
1984    Mattey et al.[3]

*Nitrogen isotope applications:*
1981    Frick & Pepin[3]
1983    Des Marais[1]
1984    Sakai et al.[1]

*Oxygen isotope applications:*
1950    McCrea[1]

**Table 1** *cont.*

| | |
|---|---|
| 1952 | Baertschi & Schwander |
| 1953 | Epstein *et al.* |
| 1962 | Taylor & Epstein[3] (silicates, $F_2$ attack) |
| 1963 | Clayton & Mayeda (silicates, $BrF_3$ or $BrF_5$ attack) |
| 1965 | Craig |
| 1965 | Sharma & Clayton[1] |
| 1977 | Freidman & O'Neil[1] (carbonate materials, phosphoric acid attack) |
| 1977 | Deinnes (*review*) |
| 1983 | Haimson & Knauth[1] (stepwise fluorination) |

*Ar/Ar dating:*

| | |
|---|---|
| 1959 | Wanke & Konig[1] |
| 1962 | Sigurgeirsson[1] |
| 1965 | Merrihue[1] |
| 1966 | Merrihue & Turner |
| 1971 | Turner[1] |
| 1971, 1974 | Dalrymple & Lanphere[1] |
| 1978 | Roddick[1] |
| 1979 | Ozima *et al.*[1] |
| 1980 | Roddick *et al.*[1] |
| 1980 | Tetley *et al.*[1] |
| 1983 | Roddick[1] |
| 1990 | Scaillet *et al.* |
| 1991 | Kelley & Turner |
| 1992 | Kelley & Bluck |

*Sulphur isotope applications:*

| | |
|---|---|
| 1965 | Hulston & Thode[3] |
| 1983 | Ueda & Sakai[1] |
| 1984 | Sakai *et al.*[1] |

*Noble gas isotope applications:*

| | |
|---|---|
| 1956 | Gerling & Levskii |
| 1963 | Signer & Suess |
| 1965 | Pepin & Signer |
| 1971 | Podosek *et al.*[1] |
| 1975 | Lupton & Craig[1] |
| 1976 | Craig & Lupton[1] |
| 1978 | Voshage & Feldman[1] |
| 1981 | Frick & Pepin[3] |
| 1983 | Rison & Craig[1] |
| 1984 | Bottomley *et al.*[1] |

---

[1] Reference quoted in Potts (1987)
[2] Reference quoted in Jarvis *et al.* (1992)
[3] Reference quoted in Pillinger (1984)

aration, flame atomic absorption spectrometry proved capable of replacing most aspects of rapid schemes of analysis in the determination of the major elements. By the end of this decade, a series of papers had been published which described techniques for the comprehensive analysis of major elements in silicate rocks (Table 1). Although offering very high elemental specificity, the technique was found to suffer several interference effects, including ionization interferences (affecting the alkali metals) and interferences caused by the difficulty in breaking down refractory element–oxide bonds at the relatively low temperatures achieved in the flame. Silicon was difficult to determine because of its noisy atomic absorption signal, the magnitude of which was sensitive to flame stoichiometry, and so some laboratories retained traditional wet chemical methods for the determination of silicon, as well as other major components that could not be determined by AAS (including ferrous iron, phosphorus, carbon dioxide and structural water). By the end of this decade, AAS techniques had been extended to the determination of a number of geochemically important trace elements down to $\mu g\,g^{-1}$ detection limits (including Ba, Be, Co, Cr, Cu, Li, Ni, Pb, Rb, Sr, V, Zn). As listed in Table 1, several notable schemes of analysis were published (e.g. Buckley & Cranston 1971). The adoption of AAS techniques represented a natural line of progression for laboratories with a strong tradition in wet chemical methods. However, the geochemical impact of AAS in the determination of trace elements was somewhat over-shadowed by contemporary developments in x-ray fluorescence which offered a similar elemental coverage (except in the determination of the low atomic number elements), but with superior analytical productivity.

## X-ray fluorescence spectrometry

Developments in electronic technology by the 1960s were sufficiently well advanced to permit routine operation of commercial XRF instrumentation in geochemical laboratories. Indeed, by the end of this decade, XRF was widely regarded as the central analytical technique for the routine determination of good quality major and trace element analyses. This accolade arose not only from the capability of the technique to determine the major elements (Na–Fe) to high sensitivity, but also from the comprehensive range of trace elements that could be determined down to low $\mu g\,g^{-1}$ detection limits (including Ba, Co, Cr, Cu, Ga, La, Nb, Ni, Pb, Rb, Sc, Sr, Th, U, V, Y, Zn and Zr). By the end of this decade, several land-mark schemes of XRF analysis had been published. Leake *et al.* (1969) described the comprehensive determination of major and trace elements in silicate rocks prepared as compressed powder pellets. Matrix and mineralogical effects, which influenced the accuracy of determinations of the lightest elements (particularly Na, Mg, Al and Si), were minimized by calibrating instrumentation over several restricted ranges of silicate rock types. Matrix corrections, although theoretically understood from work published in the previous decade (e.g. Sherman 1955), were still regarded as troublesome, the development of practical correction procedures being restricted by the lack dedicated mini-computer technology. In geochemical applications, the routine determination of major elements on powder pellets did not withstand the test of time, proving to lack accuracy owing to mineralogical effects. Instead, schemes were developed for the analysis of samples prepared as glass discs by fusing rock powder with a lithium borate-based flux, as described by Norrish & Hutton (1969) and subsequently, Harvey *et al.* (1973). Norrish & Hutton proposed the use of heavy-absorber fluxes, the lanthanum content of which minimized differences in the mass attenuation properties between samples and standards, so reducing the magnitude of correction factors for matrix effects. Partly as a result of the use of heavy absorber fluxes and partly owing to the relatively thick beryllium windows fitted to contemporary x-ray tubes, excitation of the lightest elements which could be determined by XRF, particularly sodium, was not always adequate. To compensate for this deficiency, some laboratories continued to determine this element on powder pellets to enhance sensitivities. Over subsequent decades, advances in both instrumental technology and the accuracy of matrix correction procedures (facilitated by the availability of microcomputer instrumentation) have largely overcome these difficulties so that sodium would now be determined together with the other major elements on glass discs and heavier absorber fluxes are no longer necessary to minimize uncertainties in matrix correction procedures.

In many ways a surprising aspect of the development of the AA and the XRF techniques is that they did not have a more immediate impact on geochemical research. More major element data became available, but many of the models for magmatic differentiation were primarily refinements of the general models articulated by Bowen (1928) and others earlier this century. Trace elements provide a more sensitive index of both partial melting and fractional crystallization, particularly for magmas which evolved at a cotectic, and they also better constrain the residual or fractionating phases responsible for the chemical variations in related igneous rocks. However, much of the pioneering work on the distribution of trace elements between phases had been undertaken on the the basis of data available from wet chemical techniques (Goldschmidt 1937; Neumann *et al.* 1954; Shaw 1961), and the development of more sophisticated treatments was to be closely linked to the analysis of coherent element groups, such as the

rare earth elements, by other techniques. The principal advantage of XRF, in particular, was in the generation of large amounts of high quality data, and its most direct impact has, therefore, been in the formulation of minor and trace element discriminant diagrams, and in geochemical mapping.

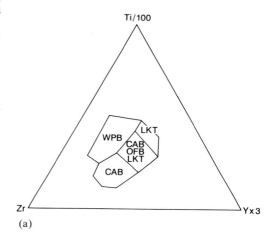

(a)

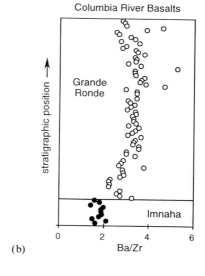

(b)

**Fig. 2(a)** Diagram after Pearce & Cann (1973) showing the discrimination that can be afforded between with-plate basalt (WPB), low-potassium tholeiite (LKT), calc-alkaline basalt (CAB) and ocean floor basalt (OFB) on the basis of the Zr, Ti and Y contents. **(b)** Diagram of the stratigraphic position of the Grande Ronde and Imnaha units of the Columbia River continental flood basalt showing that these two components can be discriminated into mappable units by the Ba/Zr ratio (after Hooper 1988).

As an example, a discriminant diagram published by Pearce & Cann (1973) is illustrated in Fig. 2a. This demonstrates that basalts generated in different tectonic regimes are characterized by significant chemical differences, an approach that has been of great value in the development of models for magma genesis in different tectonic settings. However, these developments only became feasible once an analytical technique like XRF had been developed to a point where the necessary database could be established. A second area where ease of analysis, and good quality data, have been invaluable is in geochemical mapping. Detailed studies, particularly in continental flood basalt provinces, have demonstrated that these provinces may be subdivided into groups of rocks which have very similar minor and trace element compositions, and that these groups often occur in mappable units (Swanson *et al.* 1979; Cox & Hawkesworth 1985; Hooper 1988) (Fig. 2b). For the first time, it was possible to distinguish an internal stucture in what appeared at first sight to be a large volume of homogenous basalt, an aspect that has been critical in the development and testing of models of magma generation. Specifically it has been shown that lavas step up, and hence get younger, in certain directions in continental flood basalt provinces such as the Deccan and the Parana (Cox & Hawkesworth 1985; Beane *et al.* 1986; Peate *et al.* 1990), and this has been used to distinguish models in which magmatism is triggered by the emplacement of a mantle plume (Richards *et al.* 1989; Watts & Cox 1989), from those in which magmatism is triggered by lithospheric extension (White & McKenzie 1989; Peate *et al.* 1990).

## 1970–present

The late 1960s was a time of great change in geochemistry, in that radiogenic isotopes, which had long been used for the dating of rocks and minerals, began to be used as tracers in petrogenetic processes. This development reflected dramatic improvements in the analytical precision of thermal ionization mass spectrometers, and it fostered an emphasis on research into processes, rather than the description of natural phenomena. The first lunar samples were returned to Earth in July 1969, and the Lunar Landing Programme stimulated considerable technique development in the laboratories of participating research groups, leading to a focus in many high profile debates in both analytical and theoretical geochemistry. The commonly used radioactive decay schemes involve trace elements, and this encouraged improvements in both the measurement of trace element abundances, and in the handling of resultant data. The early 1970s were also a time of enormous advances in semi-conductor technology which benefited all instrumental analytical techniques. One of the first to have a substantial impact on geochemical studies was instrumental neutron activation analysis, based on high resolution gamma ray spectrometry, using high purity, lithium-drifted, germanium crystals.

### Instrumental neutron activation analysis

Although the principles of neutron activation analysis had been understood since the publication of von Hevesy & Levi's work in 1936, routine application of the technique to geological samples had not previously been possible using the sodium iodide scintillation detectors then available. These devices had adequate resolution for the analysis of the relatively simple gamma spectra derived, for example, from the natural activity of K, U and Th and indeed could be used successfully for the analysis of rock samples both in the laboratory and the field. However, the resolution characteristics were quite inadequate for the complex multi-peak spectra encountered in neutron activation analysis. In a pioneering paper, Gordon *et al.* (1968) demonstrated the feasibility of rare earth element determination of geological samples using a large volume coaxial lithium-drifted germanium detector. In a complementary paper, Hertogen & Gijbels (1971) demonstrated that smaller volume 'planar' germanium detectors gave superior detection characteristics in the determination of REE from the lower gamma spectral range (eg. 60–200 keV). The elements that could be determined by these techniques included a range of rare earth elements [La, Ce, Nd, Sm, Eu, (Gd), Tb, (Tm), Yb and Lu], together with other trace elements including Ta, Hf, Th, (U), Co, Sc, Cr, (Ba), Cs, Rb (the elements in parentheses can cause problems in some schemes of analysis due to spectrum overlap interference or low sensitivity). One difficulty that affected both the selection of gamma lines for analysis and the evaluation of spectrum overlap interferences was that gamma ray decay schemes for all the elements of geological interest took some time to characterize fully, not least because the new germanium detectors were capable of measuring the energy of gamma emissions to an order of magnitude greater precision than with earlier generations of NaI detectors. Although the INAA technique proved to be relatively insensitive to matrix effects, calibration procedures relied, in general, on the single comparator method. One calibration standard is irradiated with each batch of samples analysed and the activity induced in this sample of known composition used to quantify results from other samples in the batch. Taking into account the less than perfect characterization of REE concentrations in reference materials then available and the influence, in some schemes of analysis, of unsuspected spectral overlap interferences, comparison of REE data from different INAA laboratories sometimes demonstrated significant analytical bias. In consequence, effort continued to be expended during the 1970s in the determination of REE by isotope dilution thermal ionization mass spectrometry. Although this technique is both labour intensive (detailed chemical separations are required before analysis) and suffers from a relatively low sample throughput rate (caused by both the chemistry and the relatively large amount of machine time required to achieve adequate precision), results are much less prone to analytical bias.

As a result of these developments, measurements of rare earth and other trace element abundances (some down to sub-$\mu$g g$^{-1}$ detection limits) became available on a range of geological materials. The rare earth elements were the subject of particular attention because the small but systematic decrease in ionic radius with increase in atomic number for a given co-ordination number (the lanthanide contaction effect) causes a small but systematic fractionation during petrological and mineralogical processes. Most of the REEs are stable in the 3+ oxidation state but two, Ce and Eu, can occur as 4+ and 2+ respectively. Thus, the REEs may be used both for modelling petrogenetic processes, and as an indication of the prevailing redox conditions.

It was some time before a satisfactory scheme was developed for the presentation of REE data. Early results were plotted on a concentration versus atomic number axis, but the resultant 'saw-tooth' pattern expected from the Oddo-Harkins rule (elements of even atomic number are more abundant than adjacent elements of odd atomic number) made it very difficult to interpret trends when comparing data between suites of rocks. To overcome this problem, early workers in the field found that it was useful to normalize REE concentration data to the corresponding elemental concentration in some reference sample, usually representing the average composition of sedimentary rocks, such as North American Composite Shale (Haskin et al. 1968). Alternatively, the composition of the bulk Earth, as represented by the average composition of C1 chondritic meteorites was proposed as the normalizing factor by Masuda (1962) and

Coryell et al. (1963) (Fig. 3). As the popularity of the latter convention grew, it became important to characterize accurately the average composition of C1 chondrites and the values of Nakamura (1974) and subsequently Evensen et al. (1978) have been widely used. The REE concentrations of magmatic rocks can also be plotted by normalization to a hypothetical source composition and REE patterns evolved by various melting and crystal fractionation processes can easily be calculated (Gast 1968). Similar diagrams constructed by extending the REE plot with additional data for other major and trace elements with the elements ordered according to partition coefficient can be used with even greater effect (Pearce 1983; Hofmann 1988).

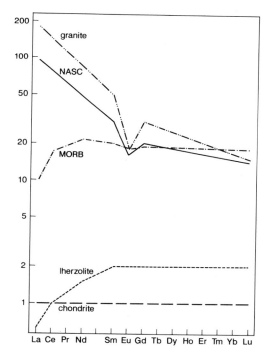

**Fig. 3.** Chondrite normalized REE plot for average granite, North American composite shale (NACS), average mid-ocean ridge basalt (MORB) and average lherzolite using data from Henderson (1984). These data demonstrate that MORB can be derived from a lherzolite source by about 10% partial melting and that granite and its erosion product, shale (which together represent most of the continental crust) show similar patterns. The negative europium anomaly is caused by fractionation of plagioclase during magma generation in the lower crust.

## Inductively coupled plasma–atomic emission spectrometry

In the mid-1970s, commercial instrumentation for inductively coupled plasma–atomic emission spectrometry was introduced. This technique is designed for the analysis of samples in solution, which are atomized and excited in a high temperature argon plasma. Instrumentation, therefore, comprises a solution nebulizer, coupled to a torch assembly at the end of which is propagated an inductively coupled argon plasma. Optical emission lines are then measured using an optical spectrometer focused on the plasma tail-flame. Development of practical analytical instrumentation depended on a number of technical innovations in the previous decade, notably by Greenfield *et al.* (1964), which resulted in the successful propagation of a plasma at atmospheric pressure and a torch assembly designed for effective sample introduction. In view of the very much higher atomization temperature in the plasma (8000°C as opposed to 2500–3000°C in flame AAS), atomization interferences in ICP–AES (e.g. the incomplete breakdown of refractory oxides) are much less significant. Furthermore, ionization interferences (i.e. matrix-influenced variations in the ionization of alkali metals) are essentially suppressed by the buffering effect of the argon ionization process in the plasma, argon having a first ionization energy of about 15 eV. Introduction of ICP–AES offered, therefore, the potential for much greater analytical sensitivity and productivity than established AAS techniques, whist avoiding the semi-quantitative nature of results by arc-source optical emission spectrography.

For these reasons, the ICP–AES technique saw a rapid introduction, laboratories involved in geochemical applications being particularly enthusiastic. However, the initial expectations that the argon plasma represented a near-ideal excitation source were to be tempered by practical experience. It was soon discovered that careful attention had to be expended in matching solution compositions, in terms of both the acid strength and total dissolved salt content of sample and standard solutions, to avoid solution-dependent discrepancies in the emission signal strength. Furthermore, in comparison with AAS where spectral overlap interferences are extremely rare, emission spectra from ICP sources are much more complex. In the early days of the technique, tables of optical emission lines were inadequate, particularly as the relative intensity of existing data derived from traditional arc/spark source optical emission spectrometry proved not to be directly applicable to emission lines observed in the ICP source. Unsuspected spectral overlap effects were not always easy to avoid in the analysis of complex samples. Despite these difficulties, early schemes of analysis (see Table 1) clearly demonstrated the advantages of this technique in the analysis of geological materials. Routine determinations could be made of the major elements and a wide range of trace elements (eg. B, Ba, Be, (Ce), Co, Cr, Cu, Ga, La, Li, Mo, Nb, Ni, Pb, (Sb), Sc, (Sn), Sr, Th, U, V, Y, Zn, Zr). Although detection limits are inadequate for the direct determination of the rare earth elements, by employing a relatively simple ion exchange separation, all the naturally-occurring rare earth elements can be determined to high sensitivity (see references in Table 1).

The overall geochemical impact of ICP–AES was to enhance the capabilities of laboratories with a tradition of wet chemistry up to (and perhaps beyond) the level of analytical productivity associated with XRF laboratories. Furthermore, ICP–AES offered an alternative route to both XRF and INAA in the routine determination of the major elements and selected trace elements (XRF) and the REE (INAA). Routine determinations of low atomic number trace elements (notably Be, Li and B) were also possible (cf. AAS). The introduction of ICP–AES did not substantially facilitate routine determination of new categories of elements in silicate rocks compared with contemporary analytical technology. However, the technique did have an important impact on progress in geochemistry not only because of its high analytical productivity (limited mainly by sample preparation procedures). In particular, ICP–AES represented an independent analytical method for the determination of a range of trace and REEs with the option that calibrations could be achieved by absolute techniques (i.e. relative to standard solutions prepared from high purity chemical reagents), rather than by using previously characterized rock samples, as is common practice in XRF and INAA. In this way, ICP–AES made a significant improvement to the overall accuracy of geochemical results.

## Inductively coupled plasma–mass spectrometry

The extraction of ions from an argon plasma, propagated at atmospheric pressure, into a mass spectrometer held under ultra-high vacuum is not technically simple. However, following pioneering development work notably by Gray (see Table 1), commercial instrumentation was launched in 1983. Although the plasma excitation source is similar to that used on the ICP–AES, ions are extracted into a quadrupole mass spectrometer for analysis. As a detection device, the mass analyser offers a very low background signal which, coupled with the high elemental sensitivity resulting from the high degree of ionization of analytes in the plasma, gives the technique very low detection limits. As well as a capability for determining isotopic ratios, a further advantage of ICP–MS is the relatively uniform sensitivity response over the entire Periodic Table. Detection limits of elements are mainly influenced by the relative abundance of the isotope selected for analysis. The particular analytical capabilities of ICP–MS that have relevance to geochemical studies include:

(i) direct determination of the REE in sample solutions without further sample preconcentration;

(ii) effective determination of the platinum-group elements to ng $g^{-1}$ detection limits, although preliminary preconcentration is necessary;

(iii) specific application in the determination of osmium isotope ratios, an application in which conventional thermal ionization mass spectrometry does not offer adequate precision. However, it should be noted that in this application, ICP–MS is progressively being overtaken by negative ion thermal ionization mass spectrometry;

(iv) the potential of undertaking radiogenic isotope ratio measurements, although precision is not sufficient for most geochemical applications unless sophisticated multiple collector instrumentation, such as that described by Walder & Freedman (1992), is used.

One limitation of the ICP–MS technique is that the low atomic number mass spectrum suffers from some isobaric interferences from solvent and plasma gas species. ICP–MS is not, therefore, a technique that would be considered for routine major element determinations in silicate rocks. Furthermore, ICP–MS is relatively intolerant to sample solutions containing significantly greater than 0.1% total dissolved solids or 1% acid so that it is sometimes necessary to dilute sample solutions prior to analysis so compromising some of the detection limit capability of the technique. It is ironic, therefore, that the introduction of this instrumentation of the highest sophistication has led to considerable interest in evaluating basic sample preparation techniques. These studies are necessary to ensure that the above restrictions are complied with and

to confirm the quantitative dissolution of refractory minerals containing trace elements that could not previously be determined directly by alternative solution techniques. Considerable interest also continues in the development of novel forms of sample preparation (including microwave digestions, selective extractions and on-line chemical separation using ion chromatography), and of new sample introduction procedures (including flow injection, slurry nebulization and electrothermal vaporization).

ICP–MS has the facility to determine a wide range of trace elements, including several 'difficult' elements that cannot readily be measured directly by competitive techniques. However, it could be argued that it is too early to judge the geochemical impact of conventional solution-nebulization ICP–MS because the geochemical 'rules' by which ultra-trace element data may be interpreted, have not yet been fully formulated. In this sense, it is easier to argue that alternative forms of sample introduction, especially laser abaltion may have a greater geochemical impact in future years because it has the capability of acquiring new types of geochemical data in the sphere of microprobe analysis.

*Reference materials*

In the decade following the publication of the report on reference materials W-1 and G-1 (Fairbairn *et al.* 1952), significant improvements occurred in the accuracy of major element results for silicate rocks. However, the situation for trace elements was still not entirely satisfactory. The substantial increase in sensitivity offered by techniques such as XRF and then ICP–AES, which enabled routine determinations to be made for a range of trace elements down to the $\mu g\,g^{-1}$ level, was not immediately matched by the availability of a range of silicate rock reference materials with accurately characterized trace element compositions. In these circumstances, it is not surprising that discrepancies could be detected when comparing results from different laboratories, often caused by unsuspected inter-laboratory bias related to the difficulty in validating, independently, the calibration procedure.

These difficulties more than justified the increasing number of geological reference materials that became available during the 1970s, distributed by organizations such as the US Geological Survey, Centre de Recherche Petrographique et Géochimique and the Association Nationale de la Recherche Technique (France), Geological Survey of Japan and the National Institute for Metallurgy (South Africa).

Although considerable efforts were undertaken by distributing organizations to characterize these materials, data compilations were not always widely available and so users often had insufficient data with which to assess the accuracy of reference material values. An important focus for such studies arose, therefore, with the publication from 1977 of a new journal, Geostandards Newsletter, with the aim of fostering cooperation and further understanding between users and producers of geochemical reference samples (Govindaraju 1977).

## Isotope geochemistry

### Thermal ionization mass spectrometry

Practical mass spectrometry can be dated back to the work of J.J. Thompson in the years before the First World War. Furthermore, the first use of mass spectrometers in the Earth Sciences can be traced back to the early years of the twentieth century (Boltwood 1907) and the principles of modern mass spectrometry have been understood since the 1950s (Brunnée 1982), including electrostatic analysers, extended geometry mass analysers, quadrupole mass analyser technology, retarding potential lenses and ion multiplier detectors.

Nevertheless, there have been a number of more recent technical advances which have had a significant impact on extending geochemical applications.

(1) Improvements in the efficiency of thermal ionization sources, especially the introduction of appropriate chemical modifiers to promote efficient thermal ionization characteristics, exemplified by the use of phosphoric acid and silica gel in the determination of lead (Cameron *et al.* 1969) and the development of multiple filament ion sources.

(2) Improvements in the ion transmission characteristics of mass spectrometer instrumentation, in particular, improvements in peak-to-background performance as measured in terms of abundance sensitivity (i.e. the ability to resolve effectively adjacent mass peaks).

(3) The introduction of the Daly detector with its high internal gain, and subsequently, electron multiplier detectors, so offering high sensitivity in the measurement of very low intensity ion beams.

(4) Advances in preparative chemistry to minimize the reagent blank, including the development of miniaturized ion exchange procedures (e.g. Tera & Wasserburg 1975), subboiling distillation to produce high purity reagents, and adequate laboratory facilities, including laminar-flow cabinets and filtered air supplies. These advances contributed to a reduction in reagent blanks by a factor of over 100 or so (Tilton 1973).

(5) The preparation and distribution of isotope ratio reference materials, particularly by the National Bureau of Standards (now NIST), permitting the measurement of accurate isotope ratios (Shields 1966–1970) and the availability of isotopically enriched spikes, first from the Oak Ridge National Laboratory, facilitating accurate analysis by isotope dilution. The establishment of geological reference materials having 'standardized' isotope ratio compositions so permitting accurate intercomparison and geochemical interpretation of data from different laboratories (e.g. Wasserburg *et al.* 1981).

(6) The introduction of multiple collector instruments capable of detecting simultaneously the ion beams of interest so enhancing the precision in isotope ratio measurements compared with traditional single collector / beam switching mass spectrometers and extending geochemical applications.

Contemporaneous with this background of continuous technical development, modern geochronological applications originated in the 1950s when the formalism for calculating isochron diagrams was developed by Nicolaysen (1957) and the concordia treatment, relevant to zircon dating was proposed by Wetherhill (1956). Both calculation methods produced results with statistically valid errors. Early geochemical applications, such as the analysis of Sr isotope ratios by TIMS (Bofinger & Compston 1967) were mainly restricted to igneous rocks from sequences that had been well characterized using palaeontological data, to establish 'absolute' age marker points in the stratigraphic column. A notable achievement from this era was the unambiguous dating of the age of the Earth from Pb–Pb measurements of recent deep-sea sediments and of uranium-free sulphides in meteorites like Canyon Diablo (Patterson 1956). These early results were subsequently confirmed by Rb/Sr age determinations of basaltic achondrite meteorites (Papanastassiou & Wasserburg 1969) (Fig. 4).

Following early geochronological studies, thermal ionization mass spectrometry was to have substantial influence on the more general development of geochemistry over the last

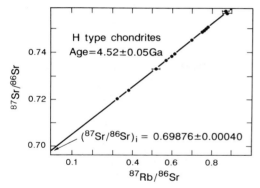

**Fig. 4.** Rb/Sr isochron diagram for H-type chondrites taken from Papanastassiou & Wasserburg (1969). This work was the first evidence to confirm the Pb–Pb model age of the Earth. The calculated initial $^{87}Sr/^{86}Sr$ ratio (0.69876) can be considered as the initial ratio of the chondrite reservoir, which is used for the calculation of model ages.

decades of the twentieth century. One important concept to emerge as a result of TIMS studies was that of different closure temperatures for different minerals and whole rock samples for various decay schemes. This concept was placed on a firm theoretical basis by Dobson (1973) and was used to good effect to constrain the uplift and cooling history of the Alps (Jäger 1973). Another major landmark was the realization that ocean floor basalts were young ($< 150$ Ma), and that rocks with old ages of up to 3.7 Ga in Greenland (Moorbath *et al.* 1975) were restricted to continental areas. From the dating of oceanic rocks, it was found that their initial Sr isotopic ratios were nearly always $< 0.703$ (Engel *et al.* 1965), whereas continental rocks were nearly always above 0.705 (Moorbath 1965). In contrast, it was concluded from meteoritic studies that the silicate component of the Earth was likely to have a $^{87}Sr/^{86}Sr$ ratio of 0.7045 (Hart 1969). These observations lead to the concept of various long-lived reservoirs in the Earth having characteristic Rb/Sr, $^{87}Sr/^{86}Sr$ and average age, which became of crucial importance to petrogenetic interpretations (Faure & Hurley 1963), and to models for the evolution of the Earth's crust and upper mantle.

Refinements in analytical techniques were given a great impetus by the analytical requirements specified by NASA for the returned Lunar samples following the successful Apollo 11 mission in July 1969. As a result of improvements in both precision and sensitivity, together with developments in sample preparation procedures, the routine analysis of neodymium isotope ratios became practicable (Lugmair 1974). Because

both parent (Sm) and daughter (Nd) isotopes are rare earth elements, they behave during petrogenetic processes in a much more predictable way than Rb/Sr or U/Pb, and hence they are much better indicators of such processes. Fractionation of Sm from Nd is substantial during mantle melting processes, but much less pronounced during intracrustal melting and usually negligible during weathering. Consequently, Nd model ages can be interpreted as the age of mantle fractionation. Initially, such ages were calculated with respect to a whole Earth or chondrite reservoir CHUR (DePaolo & Wasserburg 1976). Subsequently, it was argued that model ages were more geologically relevant if calculated relative to depleted mantle reservoir DM, which was assumed to be the source of ocean ridge basalts (DePaolo 1981).

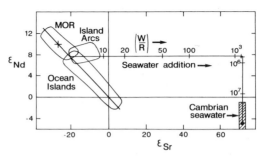

**Fig. 5.** $\varepsilon_{Nd}$ versus $\varepsilon_{Sr}$ diagram taken from Jacobsen & Wasserburg (1979). Data are plotted on this diagram relative to the CHUR reservoir and are, therefore, independent of the age of the rock. The diagram shows that island arc rocks may be derived from either mid-ocean ridge or ocean island rocks by interaction with sea water.

Sr and Nd isotope ratios considered together and relative to a common reservoir such as CHUR can be represented on an $\varepsilon$–$\varepsilon$ diagram (Jacobsen & Wasserburg 1979), independent of the age of the rocks. On this diagram, various rock types plot in reasonably defined fields (Fig. 5) and this approach was extended by Zindler & Hart (1986) to include Pb isotope ratios, which led to the idea that the radiogenic isotope ratios of most mantle-derived rocks can be explained by mixing material from 5 or 6 components or reservoirs.

A number of other radiogenic isotope decay schemes have been shown to be amenable to TIMS analysis, including Lu/Hf and La/Ce. However, because of their geochemical characteristics, neither of these has had a comparable influence on petrogenetic modelling as Sr, Nd and Pb. Given the advances in analytical methodology and instrumentation during the 1960s, and the pioneering geochemical studies during the 1970s, isotope geochemistry studies based on TIMS became one of the dominant techniques contributing to advances in geochemistry during the 1980s. Now, current interest centres on two further applications of the technique. The Re/Os decay scheme is potentially of great significance in mantle melting studies because Os is highly chalcophyle, in contrast to other geochronometers. However, analysis is hampered by the very low abundances of both Re and Os in silicate rocks and the high ionization potential of Os, which makes conventional analysis by TIMS impractical. One possibility was, therefore, to use ICP–MS as an alternative technique (see earlier). However, the development of negative ion TIMS (Völkening *et al.* 1991), which exploits the low ionization potential of $OsO_3^-$, makes possible the high precision Os isotopic analysis by TIMS and is currently attracting considerable geochemical interest.

For a number of years, alpha spectrometry has been used to analyse selected short-lived isotopes in the uranium and thorium decay series. Such techniques can, for example, elucidate processes in magma chambers and date young carbonate deposits (e.g. Ivanovich & Harmon 1982). The recent introduction of secondary electron multiplier detectors for use with TIMS instrumentation (capable of operating in pulse counting mode), as well as improved ion focusing elements (offering enhanced abundance sensitivity performance) provides an alternative means of undertaking such analyses, but with enhanced sensitivity and precision compared with alpha spectrometry (e.g. McDermott *et al.* 1993). These developments facilitate the analysis of samples with high Th/U ratio, so contributing data to Th/U series disequilibrium studies of carbonate deposits which, combined with stable isotope analysis of the same samples, is likely to be of great relevance to studies of changes in palaeoclimate over the last 300 000 years and in applications to archaeologically significant deposits.

## Gas source mass spectrometry

The dominance of isotopic studies in geochemistry during the 1980s was not confined to the radiogenic isotopes. Similar advances were being made in applications of stable isotope geochemistry, based on the isotopic analysis of elements which exist as, or can be converted into, simple gaseous forms. There are two main fields of research which use gas source mass spectrometry: stable isotope geochemistry

(where interest centres on physical fractionation processes that influence the stable isotopic composition of H, C, N, O and S); and noble gas geochemistry.

Conventionally, determinations are made either by acid attack to release carbon dioxide fron carbonate phases or by igniting a sample under appropriate conditions to release the element of interest in gaseous form. Vacuum line technology is then used to isolate and purify this gas sample, prior to isotopic analysis using a gas source mass spectrometer. Of all analytical techniques of contemporary importance in geochemistry, stable isotope analysis is perhaps the one that benefited most from the very early standardization in: (i) the development of a theoretical framework for the interpretation of stable isotope data (Urey 1947); (ii) the establishment of the 'delta' convention by which stable isotope data from different laboratories may be compared reliably (Urey 1948; McKinney *et al.* 1950) through the use of internationally accepted reference materials (e.g. Craig 1957), so avoiding the need for absolute measurement of isotopic composition; (iii) the design and construction of enduring forms of instumentation for 'dynamic' measurements (e.g. Nier 1947; McKinney *et al.* 1950); (iv) the design of a change-over valve to facilitate accurate isotope ratio measurements on a sample relative to those from a standard sample (Murphey 1947); and (v) the development of the noble gas mass spectometer capable of making measurements in 'static' mode (Reynolds 1956).

Some of the more recent advances in analytical technology that have influenced analytical capabilities in this area include the following.

(1) The development of gas source mass spectrometers of very high sensitivity, required for the characterization of extraterrestrial samples where only very small sample masses are available (see for example Gardiner *et al.* 1978 and Prosser *et al.* 1990).

(2) Stepped combustion techniques in which the sample is heated in steps through a sequence of increasing temperatures, isotopic measurements being made at each step. By evaluating trends in the resultant isotopic data, it is possible to distinguish the effect of atmospheric contamination (which mainly effects lower temperature measurements) from the geochemically significant signal, mainly associated with the higher temperature fractions.

*Stable isotope geochemistry* originated in the late 1940s in the laboratory of H. C. Urey (University of Chicago). It was Urey (1947) who constructed the theoretical framework with which to interpret the results of stable isotopic investigations of a group of low atomic number elements (H, C, N, O, S). The first implementation of stable isotope geochemistry was conducted with the analysis of the carbon and oxygen isotopic composition of marine carbonates. Early work also resulted in the temperature dependence of the oxygen isotopic composition of calcite, precipitated in equilibrium with water, being derived from the work of Epstein *et al.* (1953) and later modified by Craig (1965). As a result of this work, the determination of palaeotemperatures has become one of the more important applications of stable isotope geochemistry to terrestrial samples. The oxygen isotopic composition of carbonates can also yield information about palaeosalinities. Furthermore, benthic species recovered from the ocean depths can record variations in the oxygen isotopic composition of sea water (e.g. Shackleton 1968), which in turn can be related to the effects of continental glaciation and thus global climate. These are areas of research that are likely to play a pivotal role in future studies, providing information regarding the recent evolution of environmental conditions on Earth.

Another area that has been the subject of intensive investigation is the isotopic composition of hydrogen and oxygen in natural waters. The original work of Epstein & Mayeda (1953) was further developed by the seminal studies of Craig (1961) and Taylor (1974) as a result of which it became apparent that the hydrogen and oxygen isotopic composition of meteoritic water samples are linearly related. This phenomenon is a consequence of isotopic fractionation, which accompanies evaporation and condensation, waters from different latitudes having vastly different isotopic compositions. This observation is invaluable in assessing the origin of fluids, for example the source of water responsible for the formation of low-temperature secondary mineralization. In the same way, oxygen isotope measurements can also be used in the study of ore deposits (Taylor 1974), as a means of assessing the origin of hydrothermal fluids. In this area of study, sulphur isotope measurements are also of value in evaluating the temperature of formation of an ore body, the source of sulphur (e.g. mantle or sea water), and the pH of the ore-forming fluids.

Although the studies summarized above have involved measurements of the composition of the hydrosphere and of sedimentary rocks, extensive investigations have also been carried out on complementary lithospheric materials. The technique for extracting oxygen from silicate materials using the reagent $BrF_5$ was developed by Clayton & Mayeda (1963) and has been used in experimental studies of oxygen isotopic fractionation between co-existing mineral–mineral or mineral-water pairs to elucidate formation temperatures of natural rock samples (see for example the review by Deines 1977). Because samples of mantle origin have distinctly different oxygen isotopic compositions from crustal rocks, it is possible to use this parameter as a means of assessing likely levels of crustal contamination in igneous rocks.

The stable isotopic compositions of carbon, nitrogen and hydrogen have also contributed to certain investigations in the field of organic geochemistry. It has long been recognized that carbon becomes isotopically fractionated when it is incorporated into plant materials by photosynthesis (e.g. Park & Epstein 1960). Furthermore, plants undergoing different forms of photosynthesis, fractionate the isotopes to different degrees. On this basis, it is possible to use the carbon isotopic composition of sedimentary organic carbon to assess the source of its constituents. This approach can be extended to fossil fuels, and is used, in particular, in attempts to relate oil reservoirs to their source rocks. In this field of study, Hoefs & Schidlowski (1967) made the important observation that reduced carbon in Precambrian rocks of sedimentary origin has a similar isotopic composition to that of modern sediments. The conclusion derived from this work is that the carbon in the Precambrian samples was involved in the process of photosynthesis, one of the lines of evidence used to prove the existence of life at this time.

In addition to studies of terrestrial geochemistry, stable isotope investigations have also had an important impact on the characterization of extra-terrestrial materials (see the review by Pillinger 1984). In this area of research, oxygen isotope studies have been used to demonstrate that the solar nebula was heterogeneous and not well mixed as was once thought (Clayton *et al.* 1973; Clayton 1993). Furthermore, analysis of organic material in primitive chondrites has shown that some of the hydrogen associated with these compounds is vastly enriched in deuterium (Kolodny *et al.* 1980), which is considered to represent a signature of processing by ion-molecular reactions in the interstellar medium. The origins of further pre-solar components have been constrained by the application of carbon and nitrogen stable isotope studies to diamond, graphite and silicon carbide, phases that were formed as stellar condensates, but which have survived intact the process of solar system formation (e.g. Lewis *et al.* 1983; Swart *et al.* 1983).

*Noble gas geochemistry* was first applied in the area of age-dating, with the implementation of techniques such as U–He, K–Ar (Wasserburg & Hayden 1955) and $^{40}$Ar–$^{39}$Ar (Merrihue & Turner 1966). Of these, the $^{40}$Ar–$^{39}$Ar technique has withstood the test of time and is considered further below. Other geochemical investigations of the noble gases have been led largely by the application of this technique to studies of extra-terrestrial samples. Gerling & Levskii (1956) first observed that meteorites contain trapped noble gases. Two different forms of noble gases were present, displaying so-called 'solar' and 'plane-tary' isotopic and abundance signatures (Signer & Suess 1963; Pepin & Signer 1965). The solar gases were derived from solar wind and match very well with gases implanted into lunar soils. Primitive meteorites contain gases which are predominantly of the planetary-type: these are presumably incorporated directly from the solar nebula. Meteorites also contain several other minor noble gas components, which are often described as isotopically anomalous. These com-ponents are thought to be of nucleo-synthetic origin, formed in various astronomical environ-ments, such as novae, supernovae and stars undergoing the slow process of neutron capture. Noble gases in meteorites also record the history of cosmic ray bombardment.

In recent times, some of the instrumentation developed for the analysis of extraterrestrial materials has been applied to the study of noble gases in samples of terrestrial origin. In particu-lar, a number of investigations have been made into the helium content of sea water and mantle rocks. These studies have shown that helium in sea water can be used as a tracer for the move-ment of water masses and that the helium and argon isotopic content of mantle rocks serve as an important parameter in models of mantle evolution and atmospheric degassing. More recently, it has been discovered that rocks out-cropping at the Earth's surface can have their helium isotopic composition changed by inter-action with cosmic rays. There is now increasing interest in the analysis of the other noble gases (Ne, Kr and Xe) in attempts to study geochemi-cal processes (Ozima & Podosek 1983).

$^{40}$Ar–$^{39}$Ar *studies* A geologically important chronometer arises from the radioactive decay of naturally occurring $^{40}$K to $^{40}$Ar. Originally, measurement of $^{40}$Ar was made by gas source mass spectrometry, using isotope dilution tech-niques, and of K on an independent sample by XRF. However, a considerable advance was made in the 1970s by the development of the $^{40}$Ar/$^{39}$Ar method involving irradiation of the sample in a nuclear reactor. $^{39}$Ar, formed by neutron activation of $^{39}$K, is then the measure of the potassium content and can be ratioed directly to radiogenic $^{40}$Ar by gas source mass spectrometry. These advances have been exploited during the decade 1980–1990 by the further development of laser extraction tech-niques that permit the *in situ* extraction of argon from individual minerals. Indeed, after earlier successes in providing precise temporal con-straints to the magnetic reversals found at ocean floor spreading centres, technical innovations, in particular laser extraction, have made the $^{40}$Ar–$^{39}$Ar method the most commonly used technique for high precision dating. Recent applications include dating detrital grains in sedimentary en-vironments (Kelley & Bluck 1992), the precise dating of continental flood basalt terrains (Hawkesworth *et al.* 1992; Renne & Basu 1991) and studying complex cooling histories in oro-genic rocks (Scaillet *et al.* 1990; Kelley & Turner 1991).

## In search of the novel: 1990–2000

In evaluating the development of geochemistry over the past four decades, it is hard to escape the conclusion that the greatest influence has arisen from the introduction of analytical tech-niques that offer new capabilities in the determi-nation of new categories of elements, com-pounds or isotope ratios. However, novel analytical techniques can have little geochemical impact until an adequate geochemical frame-work has been developed, within which analyti-cal results can be interpreted. Thus, REE data were of limited interest in terms of their import-ance in petrogenesis until models for partial melting and fractional crystallization had been refined. Furthermore, the capability of deter-mining isotope ratios by TIMS did not have a substantial geochemical impact until models for converting these data into reliable ages were fully developed. Thus, new analytical techniques undergo a further gestation period during which a geochemical framework for the interpretation of results is established, before their application becomes widespread within the geochemical community.

It seems probable, therefore, that techniques offering new categories of analytical data will be seen, in retrospect, to have had the most impact on geochemical research during the 1990s. This is not to decry the importance of developments in existing techniques that result in improvements in accuracy, precision and detection limits. However, whereas these developments are essential in sustaining the geochemical science, they are not in themselves likely to open up new areas of research.

As both analytical developments and scientific output continue to grow exponentially, it is rash to place too much faith in speculations on the future. None-the-less, a personal list of those areas that appear to offer the greatest potential for influencing progress in geochemical studies during the 1990s would include:

(1) Os/Re geochronometry using negative ion mass spectrometry (and possibly resonance ionization mass spectrometry);
(2) U/Th disequilibrium studies by thermal ionization mass spectrometry at enhanced sensitivity and precision;
(3) More specialized trace element and isotopic analysis: Li by ICP–MS, $^{10}$Be, $^{26}$Al, $^{36}$Cl by accelerator mass spectrometry, ion probe in mineralogical studies;
(4) platinum-group element studies in mantle rocks, subject to the development of a relevant geochemical framework;
(5) compound specific stable isotope analysis by applying gas chromatograph separation techniques to gas source mass spectrometry;
(6) micro-beam analysis of individual mineral phases for (i) the trace elements to $\mu$g g$^{-1}$ detection limits by techniques such as laser ablation ICP–MS, synchrotron x-ray microprobe, PIXE, ion probe; (ii) stable isotopes by micro laser ablation gas source mass spectrometry; (iii) laser Ar/Ar studies;
(7) extending routine trace element determinations to the ng g$^{-1}$ or even pg g$^{-1}$ range (ICP–MS, isotope dilution techniques, accelerator mass spectrometry);
(8) locating and analysing small rare mineral phases;
(9) fluid inclusion analysis by laser Raman spectroscopy.

The authors are very grateful to colleagues who have offered assistance in compiling this paper including Doug Miles (British Geological Survey), Simon Kelley and John Taylor (diagrams) and for the valued comments of Nick Walsh.

## References

AHRENS, L. H. 1977. A story of two rocks. *Geostandards Newsletter*, **1**, 157–161.
ALKEMADE, C. J. T. & MILATZ, J. M. W. 1955. A double beam method of spectral selection with flames. *Applied Science Research*, **B4**, 289–299.
BAERTSCHI, P. & SCHWANDER, H. 1952. Ein neues Verfahren zur Messung der Unterschiede im $^{18}$O gehalt von Silikatgesteinen. *Helvitica Chimica Acta*, **35**, 393–417.
BEANE, J. E., TURNER, C. A., HOOPER, P. R., SUBBARAO, K. V. & WALSH, J. N. 1986. Stratigraphy, composition and form of the Deccan basalts, Western Ghats, India. *Bulletin of Volcanology*, **48**, 61–83.
BOFINGER, V. M. & COMPSTON, W. 1967. A reassessment of the age of the Hamilton Group, New York and Pennsylvania, and the role of inherited radiogenic Sr$^{87}$. *Geochimica et Cosmochimica Acta*, **31**, 2353–2359.
BOLTWOOD, B. B. 1907. On the ultimate disintegration products of the radioactive elements. *American Journal of Science*, **4**, 77–88.
BOWEN, N. L. 1928. *The evolution of igneous rocks*. Princeton University Press.
BRUNÉE, C. 1982. New instrumentation in mass spectrometry. *International Journal of Mass Spectrometry and Ion Physics*, **45**, 51–86.
BUCKLEY, D. E. & CRANSTON, R. E. 1971. Atomic absorption analysis of 18 elements from a single decomposition of aluminosilicate. *Chemical Geology*, **7**, 273–284.
BURRI, C. 1959. *Petrochemische Berechnungsmethoden auf equivalenter Grundlage*. Birkhäuser Verlag, Berlin.
CAMERON, A. E., SMITH, D. H. & WALKER, R. L. 1969. Mass spectrometry of nanogram-size samples of lead. *Analytical Chemistry*, **41**, 525–526.
CLAYTON, R. N. 1993. Oxygen isotopes in meteorites. *Annual Reviews of Earth and Planetary Science*, **21**, 115–149.
——, GROSSMAN, L. & MAYEDA, T. K. 1973. A component of primitive nuclear composition in carbonaceous meteorites. *Science*, **182**, 485–488.
—— & MAYEDA, T. K. 1963. The use of bromine penta-fluoride in the extraction of oxygen from oxides and silicates for isotopic analysis. *Geochimica et Cosmochimica Acta*, **27**, 43–52.
COMPSTON, W., LOVERING, J. F. & VERNON, M. J. 1965. The Rb/Sr age of the Bishopville aubrite and its component enstatite and feldspar. *Geochimica et Cosmochimica Acta*, **29**, 1085–1099.
—— & OVERSBY, V. M. 1969. Lead isotopic analysis using a double spike. *Journal of Geophysical Research*, **74**, 4338–4348.
CORYELL, G. G., CHASE, J. W. & WINCHESTER, J. W. 1963. A procedure for geochemical interpretation of terrestrial rare-earth abundance patterns. *Journal of Geophysical Research*, **68**, 559–566.
COSTER, D. & VON HEVESY, G. 1923. Missing element of atomic number 72. *Nature*, **111**, 79.
COX, K. G. & HAWKESWORTH, C. J. 1985. Geochemical stratigraphy of the Deccan Traps, at Mahabaleshwar, Western Ghats, India with implications for open system magmatic processes. *Journal of Petrology*, **26**, 355–377.
CRAIG, H. 1957. Isotopic standards for carbon and oxygen and correction factors for mass spectrometric analysis of carbon dioxide. *Geochimica et Cosmochimica Acta*, **12**, 133–149.
—— 1961. Isotopic variations in meteoric waters. *Science*, **133**, 1702–1703.

—— 1965. The measurement of oxygen isotope paleo-temperatures. *In*: *Stable isotopes in oceanographic studies and paleotemperatures*. Spoleto, July 26–27, 1965, Consiglio Nazionale delle Richerche, Laboratorio di Geologia Nucleare, Pisa, 1–24.

CREASER, R. A., PAPANASTASSIOU, D. A., WASSERBURG, G. J. 1991. Negative thermal ion mass spectrometry of osmium, rhenium and iridium. *Geochimica et Cosmochimica Acta*, **55**, 397–401.

DEINES, P. 1977. On the oxygen isotope distribution among minerals and triplets in igneous and metamorphic rocks. *Geochimica et Cosmochimica Acta*, **41**, 1709–1730.

DEPAOLO, D. J. 1981. Neodymium isotopes in the Colorado Front range and crust-mantle evolution in the Proterozoic. *Nature*, **291**, 193–196.

—— & WASSERBURG, G. J. 1976. Nd isotopic variations and petrogenetic models. *Geophysical Research Letters*, **3**, 249–252.

DOBSON, M. H. 1973. Closure temperature in cooling geochronology and petrological systems. *Contributions to Mineralogy and Petrology*, **40**, 259–274.

ENGEL, A. E., ENGEL, C. G. & HAVENS, R. G. 1965. Chemical characterisation of oceanic basalts and the upper mantle. *Geological Society of America Bulletin*, **76**, 719–734.

EPSTEIN, S., BUCHSBAUM, R., LOWENSTAM, H. A. & UREY, H. C. 1953. Revised carbonate–water isotopic temperature scale. *Geological Society of America Bulletin*, **64**, 1315–1326.

—— & MAYEDA, T. K. 1953. Variation of $^{18}O$ content of waters from natural sources. *Geochimica et Cosmochimica Acta*, **4**, 213–224.

EVENSEN, N. H., HAMILTON, P. J. & O'NIONS, R. K. 1978. Rare-earth abundances in chondritic meteorites. *Geochimica et Cosmochimica Acta*, **42**, 1199–1212.

FAIRBAIRN, H. W., SCHLECH, W. G., STEVENS, R. E., DENNEN, W. H., AHRENS, L. H. & CHAYES, F. 1951. A cooperative investigation of precision and accuracy in chemical, spectrochemical and modal analysis of silicate rocks. *US Geological Survey Bulletin*, **980**.

FAURE, G. & HURLEY, P. M. 1963. The isotopic composition of strontium in oceanic and continental basalts: Applications to the origin of igneous rocks. *Journal of Petrology*, **4**, 31–50.

FREIDMAN, H. & BIRKS, L. S. 1948. Geiger-counter spectrometer for x-ray fluorescence analysis. *Review of Scientific Instruments*, **19**, 323–330.

GARDINER, L. R., JULL, A. J. T. & PILLINGER, C. T. 1978. Progress towards a direct measurement of $^{13}C/^{12}C$ ratios for hydrolysable carbon in lunar soil by static mass spectrometry. Proceedings of the 9th Lunar and Planetary Science Conference, 2167–2193.

GAST, P. W. 1968. Trace element fractionation and the origin of tholeiitic and alkaline magma types. *Geochimica et Cosmochimica Acta*, **32**, 1057–1086.

GERLING, E. K. & LEVSKII, L. K. 1956. On the origin of the rare gases in stony meteorites. *Doklady Akademiya Nauk SSSR*, **10**, 750.

GOLDSCHMIDT, V. M. 1937. Geochemische Verteilungsgesetze der Elemente. *Skrifte Norske Videns-kops Ackad., Oslo, Mat.-Naturv.* **Kl. IV**, 4.

GORDON, G. E., RANDLE, K., GOLES, G. G., CORLISS, J. B., BEESON, M. H. & OXLEY, S. S. 1968. Instrumental activation analysis of standard rocks with high-resolution gamma-ray detectors. *Geochimica et Cosmochimica Acta*, **32**, 369–396.

GOVINDARAJU, K. 1977. Numero un. *Geostandards Newsletter*, **1**, 3.

GREENFIELD, S., JONES, I. Ll. & BERRY, C. T. 1964. High pressure plasmas as spectroscopic emission sources. *Analyst*, **89**, 713–720.

GREGOIRE, D. C. 1990. Sample introduction techniques for the determination of osmium isotope ratios by inductively coupled plasma mass spectrometry. *Analytical Chemistry*, **62**, 141–146.

HADDING, A. 1922. Mineral analysis by x-ray spectroscopic methods. *Zeitschrift anorganische algemeine Chemische*, **122**, 195–200.

HARKER, A. 1909. On the similar granite of Eskdale see Dwerryhouse. *Quarterly Journal of the Geological Society*, **LXV**, 61–63.

HARVEY, P. K., TAYLOR, D. M., HENDRY, R. D. & BANCROFT, F. 1973. An accurate fusion method for the analysis of rocks and chemically related materials by x-ray fluorescence spectrometry. *X-ray Spectrometry*, **2**, 33–44.

HART, S. R. 1969. Isotope geochemistry of crust-mantle processes. *In*: HART, P. J. (ed.) The Earth's crust and upper mantle. *American Geophysical Union Monograph*, **13**, 58–62.

HASKIN, L. A., HASKIN, M. A., FREY, F. A. & WILDEMAN, T. R. 1968. Relative and absolute abundances of rare earths. *In*: AHRENS, L. H. (ed.) *Origin and Distribution of Elements*. Pergamon, Oxford, 889–911.

HAWKESWORTH, C. J., GALLAGHER, K., KELLEY, S. P., MANTOVANI, M., PEATE, D. W., REGELOUS, M. & ROGERS, N. W. 1992. Parana magmatism and the opening of the South Atlantic. *In*: STOREY, B. C., ALABASTER, T. & PANKHURST, R. J. (eds) *Magmatism and the Causes of Continental Break-up*. Geological Society, London, Special Publication, **68**, 221–240.

HENDERSON, P. (ed.) 1984. *Rare Earth Element Geochemistry*. Elsevier, Amsterdam.

HERTOGEN, J. & GIJBELS, R. 1971. Instrumental neutron activation analysis of rocks with a low-energy photon detector. *Analytica Chimica Acta*, **56**, 61–82.

HEVESY, G. VON & LEVI, H. 1936. Action of slow neutrons on the rare earth elements. *Nature*, **137**, 185.

HILLEBRAND, W. F. 1919. The analysis of silicate and carbonate rocks. *US Geological Survey Bulletin*, **700**.

HOEFS, J. & SCHIDLOWSKI, M. 1967. Carbon isotope composition of carbonaceous matter from the Precambrian of the Witwatersrand System. *Science*, **155**, 1096–1097.

HOFMANN, A. W. 1988. Chemical differentiation of the Earth: Relationship between mantle, continental crust and oceanic crust. *Earth and Planetary Science Letters*, **90**, 297–314.

HOOPER, P. R. 1988. The Columbia River basalt. *In*:

MACDOUGALL, J. D. (ed.) *Continental Flood Basalts*. Kluwer Academic Publishers, Dordrecht, 1–33.

IVANOVICH, M. R. & HARMON, R. S. 1982. *Uranium series disequilibrium: Applications to environmental problems*. Oxford University Press.

JACOBSEN, S. B. & WASSERBURG, G. J. 1979. Nd and Sr isotopic study of the Bay of Islands ophiolite complex and the evolution of the source of mid-ocean ridge basalts. *Journal of Geophysical Research*, **84**, 7429–7445.

JÄGER, E. 1973. Die alpine Orogenese im Lichte der radiometrischen Altersbestimmung. *Eclogae Geologae Helvetica*, **66**, 11–21.

JARVIS, K. E., GRAY, A. L. & HOUK, R. S. 1992. *Handbook of Inductively Coupled Plasma Mass Spectrometry*. Blackie, Glasgow.

JEFFERY, P. G. 1975. *Chemical Methods of Rock Analysis*. Pergamon Press, Oxford.

KELLEY, S. P. & BLUCK, B. J. 1992. Laser $^{40}Ar$–$^{39}Ar$ ages for individual detrital muscovites in the Southern Uplands of Scotland, UK. *Chemical Geology*, **101**, 143–156.

—— & TURNER, G. 1991. Laser probe $^{40}Ar$–$^{39}Ar$ measurement of loss profiles within individual hornblende grains from Giants Range granite, northern Minnesota, USA. *Earth and Planetary Science Letters*, **107**, 634–648.

KOLODNY, Y., KERRIDGE, J. F. & KAPLAN, I. R. 1980. Deuterium in carbonaceous chondrites. *Earth and Planetary Science Letters*, **46**, 149–158.

LEAKE, B. E., HENDRY, G. L., KEMP, A., PLANT, A. G., HARVEY, P. K., WILSON, J. R., COATS, J. S., AUCOTT, J. W., LUNEL, T. & HOWARTH, R. J. 1969. The chemical analysis of rock powders by automatic x-ray fluorescence. *Chemical Geology*, **5**, 7–86.

LEWIS, R. S., ANDERS, E., WRIGHT, I. P., NORRIS, S. J. & PILLINGER, C. T. 1983. Isotopically anomalous nitrogen in primitive meteorites. *Nature*, **305**, 767–771.

LUGMAIR, G. W. 1974. Sm–Nd ages: A new dating method. *Meteoritics*, **9**, 369.

McDERMOTT, F., ELLIOTT, T. R., VAN CALSTEREN, P. & HAWKESWORTH, C. J. 1993. Measurement of $^{230}Th/^{232}Th$ ratios in young volcanic rocks by single-sector thermal ionisation mass spectrometry. *Chemical Geology*, **103**, 283–292.

McKINNEY, C. R., McCREA, J. M., EPSTEIN, S., ALLEN. H. A. & UREY, H. C. 1950. Improvements in mass spectrometers for the measurement of small differences in isotope abundance ratios. *Review of Scientific Instruments*, **21**, 724–730.

MASON, B. 1966. *Principles of Geochemistry (3rd edn)*. Wiley, New York.

—— 1992. *Victor Moritz Goldschmidt: Father of modern geochemistry*. The Geochemical Society, Special Publication, **4**.

MASUDA, A. 1962. Regularities in variation of relative abundances of lanthanide elements and an attempt to analyse separation-index patterns of some minerals. *Earth Science Nagoya University*, **10**, 173–187.

MERRIHUE, C. & TURNER, G. 1966. Potassium–argon dating by activation with fast neutrons. *Journal of Geophysical Research*, **71**, 2852–2857.

MOORBATH, S. 1965. Evolution of Precambrian crust from strontium isotopic evidence. *Nature*, **254**, 395–398.

——, O'NIONS, R. K. & PANKHURST, R. J. 1975. The evolution of Early Precambrian crustal rocks at Isua, West Greenland – geochemical and isotopic evidence. *Earth and Planetary Science Letters*, **27**, 229–239.

MURPHEY, B. F. 1947. The temperature variation of the thermal diffusion factors for binary mixtures of hydrogen, deuterium, and helium. *Physics Reviews*, **72**, 834–837.

NAKAMURA, N. 1974. Determination of REE, Ba, Fe, Mg, Na and K in carbonaceous and ordinary chondrites. *Geochimica et Cosmochimica Acta*, **38**, 757–775.

NEUMANN, H., MEAD, J. & VITALIANO, C. J. 1954. Trace element variation during fractional crystallisation as calculated from the distribution law. *Geochimica et Cosmochimica Acta*, **6**, 90–99.

NICOLAYSEN, L. O. 1957. Solid diffusion in radioactive minerals and the measurement of absolute age. *Geochimica et Cosmochimica Acta*, **11**, 41–59.

NIER, A. O. 1947. A mass spectrometer for isotope and gas analysis. *Review of Scientific Instruments*, **18**, 398–411.

NORRISH, K. & HUTTON, J. T. 1969. An accurate x-ray spectrographic method for the analysis of a wide range of geological samples. *Geochimica et Cosmochimica Acta*, **33**, 431–453.

OZIMA, M. & PODOSEK, F. A. 1983. *Noble Gas Geochemistry*. Cambridge University Press.

PAPANASTASSIOU, D. A. & WASSERBURG, G. J. 1969. Initial strontium isotopic abundances and the resolution of small time differences in the formation of planetary objects. *Earth and Planetary Science Letters*, **5**, 361–376.

PARK, R. & EPSTEIN, S. 1960. Carbon isotope fractionation during photosynthesis. *Geochimica et Cosmochimica Acta*, **21**, 110–126.

PATTERSON, C. C. 1956. Age of meteorites and the Earth. *Geochimica et Cosmochimica Acta*, **10**, 230–237.

PEARCE, J. A. 1983. Role of the sub-continental lithosphere in magmagenesis at active continental margins. *In*: HAWKESWORTH, C. J. & NORRY, M. J. (eds). *Continental Basalts and Mantle Xenoliths*. Shiva, Nantwich, UK, 230–244.

—— & CANN, J. R. 1973. Tectonic setting of basic volcanic rocks determined using trace element analysis. *Earth and Planetary Science Letters*, **19**, 290–300.

PEATE, D. W., HAWKESWORTH, C. J., MANTOVANI, M. S. M. & SHUKOWSKY, W. 1990. Mantle plumes and flood-basalt stratigraphy in the Parana, South America. *Geology*, **10**, 1223–1226.

PEPIN, R. O. & SIGNER, P. 1965. Primordial rare gases in meteorites. *Science*, **149**, 253–265.

PILLINGER, C. T. 1984. Light element stable isotopes in meteorites – from grams to picograms. *Geochimica et Cosmochimica Acta*, **48**, 2739–2766.

POTTS, P. J. 1987. *A Handbook of Silicate Rock Analy-*

*sis.* Blackie, Glasgow.

PROSSER, S. J., WRIGHT, I. P. & PILLINGER, C. T. 1990. A preliminary investigation into isotopic measurement of carbon at the picomole level using static vacuum mass spectrometry. *Chemical Geology*, **83**, 71–88.

RENNE, P. R. & BASU, A. R. 1991. Rapid eruption of the Siberian Traps flood basalts at the Permo-Triassic boundary. *Science*, **253**, 176–179.

REYNOLDS, J. H. 1956. High sensitivity mass spectrometer for noble gas analysis. *Reviews of Scientific Instruments*, **27**, 928–934.

RICHARDS, M. A., DUNCAN, R. A. & COURTILLOT, V. E. 1989. Flood basalts and hot-spot tracks: Plume heads and tails. *Science*, **246**, 103–107.

RILEY, J. P. 1958. The rapid analysis of silicate rocks and minerals. *Analytica Chimica Acta*, **19**, 413–428.

SANDELL, E. B. 1959. *Colorimetric Determination of Trace Metals* (3rd edn). Interscience, New York.

SCAILLET, S., FERAUD, G., LAGABRIELLE, Y., BALLEVRE, M. & RUFFET, G. 1990. $^{40}$Ar/$^{39}$Ar laser probe dating by step heating and spot fusion of phengites from the Dora Mara nappe of the western Alps, Italy. *Geology*, **18**, 741–744.

SCHWARZENBACH, G. 1957. *Complexiometric Titrations* (translated by Harry Irving). Chapman & Hall, London.

SHACKLETON, N. J. 1968. Depth of pelagic foraminifera and isotopic changes in Pleistocene oceans. *Nature*, **218**, 79–80.

SHAPIRO, L. & BRANNOCK, W. W. 1956. Rapid analysis of silicate rocks. *US Geological Survey Bulletin*, **1036-C**.

—— & —— 1962. Rapid analysis of silicate, carbonate and phosphate rocks. *US Geological Survey Bulletin*, **1144-A**.

SHAW, D. M. 1961. The camouflage principle and trace element distribution in magmatic minerals. *Geochimica et Cosmochimica Acta*, **23**, 142–152.

SHERMAN, J. 1955. The theoretical derivation of fluorescent x-ray intensities from mixtures. *Spectrochimica Acta*, **7**, 283–306.

SHIELDS, W. R. 1966–1970. Editor, *NBS technical notes*.

SIGNER, P. & SUESS, H. A. 1963. Rare gases in the Sun, in the atmosphere and in meteorites. Chapter 13. *In*: GEISS, J. (ed.) *Earth Science and Meteorites*. North Holland, 241–272.

SWANSON, D. A., WRIGHT, T. L., HOOPER, P. R. & BENTLEY, R. D. 1979. Revisions in stratigraphic nomencalture of the Columbia River basalt group. *US Geological Survey Bulletin*, **1957-G**, 1–59.

SWART, P. K., GRADY, M. M., PILLINGER, C. T., LEWIS, R. S. & ANDERS, E. 1983. Interstellar carbon in meteorites. *Science*, **220**, 406–410.

TAYLOR, H. P. 1974. The application of oxygen and hydrogen isotope studies to problems of hydrothermal alteration and ore deposition. *Economic Geology*, **69**, 843–883.

TERA, F. & WASSERBURG, G. J. 1975. Precise isotopic analysis of lead in picomole and sub-picomole quantities. *Analytical Chemistry*, **47**, 2214–2220.

TILTON, G. R. 1973. Isotopic lead ages of chondritic meteorites. *Earth and Planetary Science Letters*, **19**, 321–329.

UREY, H. C. 1947. The thermodynamic properties of isotopic substances. *Journal of the Chemical Society*, **1947**, 562–581.

——. 1948. Oxygen isotopes in nature and the laboratory. *Science*, **108**, 489–497.

VOLKENING, J., WALCZYK, T. & HEUMANN, G. 1991. Osmium isotope ratio determinations by negative thermal ionisation mass spectrometry. *International Journal of Mass Spectrometry and Ion Processes*, **105**, 147.

WALDER, A. J. & FREEDMAN, P. A. 1992. Isotope ratio measurement using a double focusing magnetic sector mass analyser with an inductively coupled plasma as an ion source. *Journal of Analytical Atomic Spectrometry*, **7**, 571–575.

WALSH, A. 1955. The application of atomic absorption spectra to chemical analysis. *Spectrochimica Acta*, **7**, 108–117.

WASHINGTON, H. S. 1919. *Manual of the Chemical Analysis of Rocks* (3rd edn). Wiley, New York.

—— 1932. *The Chemical Analysis of Rocks*. Wiley, New York.

WASSERBURG, G. J. & HAYDEN, R. J. 1955. K$^{40}$–Ar$^{40}$ dating. *Geochimica et Cosmochimica Acta*, **7**, 51–60.

——, JACOBSEN, S. B., DEPAOLO, D. J., MCCULLOCH, M. T. & WEN, T. 1981. Precise determination of Sm/Nd ratios, Sm and Nd isotopic abundances in standard solutions. *Geochimica et Cosmochimica Acta*, **45**, 2311–2323.

WATTS, A. W. & COX, K. G. 1989. The Deccan Traps: An interpretation in terms of progressive lithospheric flexure in response to migrating loads. *Earth and Planetary Science Letters*, **93**, 85–97.

WETHERHILL, G. W. 1956. Discordant uranium–lead ages. *Transactions of the American Geophysical Union*, **37**, 320–326.

WHITE, R. S. & MCKENZIE, D. P. 1989. Magmatism at rift zones: The generation of volcanic continental margins and flood basalts. *Geophysical Research*, **94**, 7685–7702.

ZINDLER, A. & HART, S. R. 1986. Chemical geodynamics. *Annual Reviews of Earth and Planetary Sciences*, **14**, 493–571.

# Index